Third Edition

Peters'

MUSIC THERAPY

An Introduction

By

WANDA LATHOM-RADOCY, Ph.D., RMT

CHARLES C THOMAS • PUBLISHER, LTD.
Springfield • Illinois • U.S.A.

Published and Distributed Throughout the World by

CHARLES C THOMAS • PUBLISHER, LTD.
2600 South First Street
Springfield, Illinois 62704

ISBN 978-0-398-09109-5 (hard)
ISBN 978-0-398-09110-1 (ebook)

First Edition, 1987
Second Edition, 2000
Third Edition, 2016

Library of Congress Catalog Card Number: 2016008831

Printed in the United States of America
UBC-R-3

Library of Congress Cataloging-in-Publication Data

Names: Lathom, Wanda, 1936- | Peters, Jacqueline Schmidt. Music therapy.
Title: Peters' Music Therapy : an introduction / by Wanda B. Lathom-Radocy.
Other titles: Music therapy
Description: Third edition. | Springfield, Illinois : Charles C Thomas, 2016.
 | Includes bibliographical references and index.
Identifiers: LCCN 2016008831 (print) | LCCN 2016009112 (ebook) | ISBN
 9780398091095 (hard) | ISBN 9780398091101 (ebook)
Subjects: LCSH: Music therapy.
Classification: LCC ML3920 .P383 2016 (print) | LCC ML3920 (ebook) | DDC
 615.8/5154--dc23
LC record available at http://lccn.loc.gov/2016008831

For previous editions, Jacqueline Schmidt Peters
dedicated this book:

To the glory of God,
who gave us music and the ability to use it to help others,
and to the memory of Leo C. Muskatevc (1917–1998),
who, by his instruction and mentorship,
profoundly influenced my life as a music therapist.

I would like to add:

To the memory of Dr. E. Thayer Gaston,
who started the music therapy association on a research base
which continues to this day.

WANDA LATHOM-RADOCY

PREFACE

Between publication of the first edition of *Music Therapy: An Introduction* in 1987 and the second edition in 2002, the field of music therapy continued to develop, and a wealth of new research and clinical literature was published. For the second edition (2002), Jacqueline Schmidt Peters reviewed the music therapy literature since 1985 extensively to update and expand the information contained in the first edition, especially regarding clinical practices. The chapters dealing with definitions of and guiding principles for music therapy also reflected developments in her own thinking and perspectives, based on reading, research, and clinical work.

Like the first edition, the second revision aimed to provide an overview of basic information regarding (1) a definition of music therapy; (2) the skills, knowledge, and attitudes that one needs to become a competent professional music therapist; (3) the historical development of the music therapy profession; (4) general principles and procedures that guide music therapy practice; and (5) major areas of clinical practice. Owing to many new developments in music therapy practice during the period between the first and second editions, the clinical practice section (Part III) was extensively revised and greatly expanded, with each population or area of clinical practice receiving its own chapter. The second edition also included more information on potential adult clients. Readers could elect to read the entire text to get an idea of the broad scope of music therapy and its history, processes, and practices, or they could choose to focus on topics of particular interest. Thus, this book became useful both to those who want to know about the field of music therapy as a whole and those who are interested only in an overview of particular topics.

When the publisher asked me to write a third edition of this book, I was pleased to do so. Mrs. Peters has produced thoroughly researched and well-written books. My job for a third edition was to include literature appearing since the second edition and to make changes in terminology that reflect the vocabulary used in the *Diagnostic and Statistical Manual of Mental Disorders, 5th edition* (DSM-5), which was published in 2013 by the American Psychiatric Association. For the literature search, I conducted a "hand-search" of the *Journal of Music Therapy* and *Music Therapy Perspectives* from 2000–2015. Since this volume is an introduction to music therapy, one which was quite long even before I started the third edition, I decided not to conduct an electronic search for further literature. If a fourth edition is written, that search should occur because music therapists continue to serve increasingly diverse populations and are producing more robust research. As an electronic search would probably double the number of references, the book then should be published in two volumes.

The book is divided into three major sections. Part I defines music therapy (Chapter One) and discusses the music therapist's education and training (Chapter Two). Part II gives the historical background for music therapy, both from the perspective of the use of music in healing practices from ancient times to the present (Chapter Three) and the development of the modern music therapy profession (Chapter Four). The concepts and historical overview presented in these sections provide a foundation that will enhance the reader's understanding of the clinical examples and applications presented in the final and most extensive section of the book. Part III begins with a discussion of general guidelines for using music in therapy (Chapters Five and Six), followed by specific examples of music therapy clinical practices with various client populations (Chapters Seven through Twenty-one). The final section concludes with an overview of several approaches to music therapy practice and a discussion of the importance of research for the practicing clinician. Some of the specific information to gain from this text is enumerated in the introduction to each section. Each chapter concludes with a summary, questions to help the reader reflect upon or apply the information, and suggestions for further reading. All references appear in a separate section at the end.

Since this book is an *introduction* to music therapy, it is directed primarily toward an audience that has little or no knowledge of the field: students in introductory music therapy courses; professionals in related disciplines who desire a basic knowledge of the scope of music therapy, including some of the research on which music therapy is based, but who have neither the time nor the inclination to search through many sources; individuals who are contemplating a career in music therapy; and those in the general public who want to learn more about the field. However, because of its copious references and wealth of suggestions for clinical work with various populations, this book may also be useful for some practicing music therapists: those who are (1) looking for a summary of research related to music therapy and a certain population; (2) searching for additional clinical techniques they might use in their practice; (3) seeking a current overview of music therapy practice and research; or (4) contemplating working with a different client population.

Because the text's purpose is to give the reader an idea of the entire scope of music therapy in the United States, it presents an overview of several basic topics and key concepts rather than treating any one area in great depth. In keeping with the project's survey nature, only brief examples of music therapy treatment procedures, rather than complete case histories, are presented. Therefore, when this text is used in an introductory music therapy course, the instructor may wish to use journal articles, case studies, and experiential activities to supplement and exemplify the material included in this book. In addition, those who use this text should be aware that its construction was guided by the philosophy that introductory courses in music therapy should primarily emphasize the *use of music* as an integral part of the treatment process, since using music and music-based experiences as their primary treatment modality is what sets music therapists apart from other therapists. An understanding of client problems and needs and an awareness of the dynamics of the client–therapist relationship are also important to the successful practice of music therapy, and these topics are mentioned briefly in this text.

This book also tries to provide the reader with a beginning list of sources for additional information. Therefore, all information presented is well referenced, and suggestions for further reading appear at the end of each chapter. These sources (as well as the references they cite) should provide the reader with a good starting point for finding more detailed information on a particular topic of interest. Instructors may wish to use these lists to check availability in their academic library and order books or journals that need to be added. Owing to the project's survey nature, many listed references refer to reviews or compilations of literature related to a particular topic rather than to numerous individual studies (although many individual studies are also referenced). As Clair (2007) states, "And, so, the beat goes on and on and on! Though we have been working diligently for a very long time, the journey has just begun (p. 79)."

My sincere thanks to my husband, Rudolf E. Radocy, for his patience and support throughout this revision. He has also read the manuscript and offered many suggestions for ways it could be improved. His editorial expertise is greatly appreciated.

WLR

CONTENTS

Peters'
MUSIC THERAPY

PART I

MUSIC THERAPY AND THE MUSIC THERAPIST

This section of this book provides the reader some initial answers to some basic questions: What is music therapy? What does the music therapist do? What kinds of training and education does the music therapist receive? What kinds of skills and knowledges does the music therapist possess?

The information presented in Part I helps to establish a frame of reference for the material in subsequent sections. Chapter One defines music therapy and discusses its aims and practice. Chapter Two focuses attention on the process of becoming a music therapist. After discussing the knowledge, skills, and attitudes that are important to the professional music therapist, the chapter gives a general overview of music therapy education and training programs in the United States and describes the professional credentials that music therapists commonly hold in the United States.

After completing Part I, the reader should have gained the knowledge and information needed to perform the following tasks:

1. Give a brief description or definition of music therapy.
2. List the key elements that must be present for an activity or experience to be music therapy.
3. List the knowledge, skills, and attitudes that are important to the professional music therapist.
4. List major areas of study and experience included in a music therapy curriculum.
5. List and briefly explain the professional credentials that are commonly held by music therapists in the United States.

Chapter One

A DEFINITION OF MUSIC THERAPY

Music Therapy has been a recognized professional discipline in the United States since 1950. Recognized by the Joint Commission on Accreditation of Health Care Organizations as one of the creative arts therapies, music therapy is listed as a related service in The Education for All Handicapped Children Act (Public Law 94-142), and it received special recognition at a hearing before the U.S. Senate Special Committee on Aging on August 1, 1991 (Special Committee on Aging 1992). Nevertheless, although public awareness of music therapy had increased to the point that two thirds of respondents in a 1991 survey had at least *heard* of music therapy (Furman, Adamek, and Furman 1991), even today many people are still not sure exactly what music therapy is. Even if they may have some vague idea that music therapy uses music to help people in some way, members of the general public often do not realize that music therapy is a distinct professional discipline that has a large body of research and stringent educational and training requirements.

While many definitions of music therapy exist, most definitions recognize "the significance of music and sound in achieving a broad variety of nonmusical goals in the areas of mental and physical health" (Moreno et al. 1990, 43). The American Music Therapy Association (AMTA) broadly defines music therapy as "the clinical and evidence-based use of music interventions to accomplish individualized goals within a therapeutic relationship by a credentialed professional who has completed an approved music therapy program" (Website, June 2014). Within this book, **music therapy is defined as a planned, goal-directed process of interaction and intervention based on assessment and evaluation of each individual client's specific needs, strengths, and weaknesses, in which music or music-based experiences** (e.g., singing, playing musical instruments, moving or listening to music, creating or discussing songs and music) **are specifically prescribed to be used by specially trained personnel** (i.e., music therapists or those they train and supervise) **to influence positive changes in an individual's condition, skills, thoughts, feelings, or behaviors**. This definition contains several key elements that help differentiate music therapy – a scientifically based, allied health profession – from new age music healers and mass-marketed music healing solutions (Summer 1995; Summer and Summer 1996) or from the general beneficial effects some individuals may experience when they participate in certain types of music experiences. For music-based experience to be true music therapy, all of the following basic components must be present.

MUSIC THERAPY IS A PROCESS

Music therapy is a *process* that occurs over time and involves growth, change, and development. According to Sears (1963, 1968/2007), the processes in music therapy "take place *by uniquely involving* the individual in experience within structure, experience in self-organization, and experience in relating to others" (2007, 15). Music therapy demands a commitment of time and energy from both the client and the therapist; it is not a simple, instant cure or a magical panacea. Thaut (2008, 183) mentions a "process-specific approach, which focuses on individual areas of mental ability (such as attention, memory, executive function, etc.)." This approach has been supported by research by Schulberg and Mateer (1987), as well. Gardstrom and Jackson (2011) define music therapy as

> a systematic process of intervention wherein a credentialed music therapist helps a client to access, work through, and resolve personal/interpersonal issues primarily through music interventions. Music therapy may occur individually or in a group setting. (233)

The clinical process of music therapy gradually produces an unfolding of growth toward desired outcomes (Aigen 1995a):

> Music therapy . . . is not an isolated therapeutic intervention or a single musical experience leading to a spontaneous or sudden cure. For the client, therapy is a gradual change process leading to a desired state; for the therapist, it is a systematic sequence of interventions leading to specific changes in the client. (Bruscia 1989a, 48)

The process of music therapy may include various musical, creative, artistic, therapeutic, developmental, educational, interpersonal, behavioral, and scientific components as music therapist and client interact over time in both musical and nonmusical areas. More specific information on these components is covered in Part III of this book.

MUSIC THERAPY IS PLANNED AND GOAL-DIRECTED, BASED ON INDIVIDUAL ASSESSMENT

Music therapy is not just any process involving musical experiences. A series of random experiences involving music that somehow help a person feel better is *not* music therapy. Rather, music therapy is a planned process that involves a carefully thought-out sequence of steps and procedures. First, the music therapist observes and assesses the client to determine problems and areas of need, as well as his or her strengths and responses to or preferences for various musical stimuli or musical experience (Lathom-Radocy 2014, 3). Based on the information from this assessment, the music therapist sets specific goals and objectives in one or more of the client's areas of need (with the input from the client when possible). These goals and objectives give direction to the therapeutic process (Hanser, 1987). They specify what changes must occur in the client's condition, thoughts, feelings, or behaviors to indicate improvement in the targeted physical, mental, social, or emotional functioning areas. The music therapist has goals for clients similar to those of other members of the treatment team (e.g., improving motor, social, cognitive, communication, behavioral, or emotional skills/functioning). The difference lies in the treatment modality: The music therapist uses music and music-based experiences to help clients reach their therapeutic goals. "Regardless of the theoretical model used, music is the primary tool of every music therapist" (Summer and Nolan 2001, 5).

After assessing and evaluating the client and specifying individual therapeutic goals, the music therapist designs a series of specific experiences that will help the client reach the goals. This music therapy treatment plan then is implemented over a designated period of time. After this period, the music therapist evaluates client progress to see if goals and objectives have been met or if revisions in treatment approaches are necessary.

MUSIC THERAPY INVOLVES INTERACTION AND INTERVENTION

Music therapy is not a solitary pursuit; it involves interaction between and among three main entities: the music therapist, the client, and the music. In music therapy, as in any therapeutic or helping encounter, a supportive, success-oriented atmosphere and a caring, trusting relationship are of vital importance. According to Hanser (1987, 46), "One of the most significant ingredients in any successful therapeutic program is the establishment of a caring relationship between therapist and client. Without it, even the most effective techniques may be utterly useless."

While the music therapist and client undoubtedly will interact through words and actions apart from music at times, the primary interactions in music therapy occur through and within music activities and experiences. Cross (2009) observes that music facilitates group relationships and contributes positively to members of the group in ways that may not be possible through words. In the musical relationship that develops within music therapy sessions, client and therapist meet on the common ground of expression in sound. Through their listening, singing, playing, creating, moving, discussing, and responding emotionally to music, they interact in unique ways that go beyond the constraints and limits of verbal expression.

The interaction of the music therapy process occurs because of a need for some kind of intervention: the client desires to change some area of his or her life and seeks the assistance of the music therapist in making this change. Therefore, the music therapist must introduce some elements into the relationship or process that will move the client toward positive change and growth in his or her current area of need. "The effectiveness of music as a therapeutic tool applied for particular use depends on the skill and knowledge of the therapist" (Davis, Gfeller, and Thaut 2008, 6). In order to find appropriate intervention strategies, the music therapist must assess the client in both musical and nonmusical areas to determine the client's particular strengths, weaknesses, interests, and areas of need because "individuals bring their prior experiences to the performance and listening situations, where such experiences interact with all the dynamic aspects of human intercourse" (Radocy and Boyle 2012, 7). Using both the special knowledge gained from the individual assessment of the client and the more general knowledge of various music experiences and their effects on human beings gained from his or her training and experience, the music therapist then plans a specific series of steps to interact purposefully with the client in and through various carefully chosen music experiences (i.e., music therapy interventions) to facilitate improvement in the client's particular condition, skills, thoughts, feelings, or behaviors. In the relational, goal-directed process of music therapy interactions, "music is used intentionally to bring about a positive change, and the choice of music and activities is governed by this intent" (Birkenshaw-Fleming 1993, vi). Much music therapy takes place in groups, as well as in sessions with individuals. Thus, information about and concern for all group members are necessary in designing music therapy for groups. The interaction among group members is an important component, as well as the interaction of the therapist and each client.

MUSIC THERAPY USES MUSIC OR MUSIC-BASED EXPERIENCES

Obviously, the music therapist's primary tool is music, the vehicle through which he or she establishes contact with the client and the structure or modality through which the client develops skills to reach therapeutic goals. In other words, "what makes music therapy different from every other form of therapy is its reliance on music" and the fact "at the core of every session is a musical experience of some kind" (Bruscia 1991a, 5). Goodman (2007) discusses the importance of the tool of music and is a good source for useful music resources.

Although musical involvement is a necessary component of music therapy, clients need not be accomplished musicians to partake in or benefit from music therapy experiences. Music is a pervasive phenomenon in cultures and societies throughout the world (see Chapter Five), and most human beings are capable of experiencing music in basic ways by listening to music, feeling its vibrations, singing, moving to music, playing simple instruments, or responding emotionally to music. As Radocy and Boyle (2012) explain,

> The ever-presence of music today, whether in the concert hall, supermarket, home, house of worship, school, commercial and electronic media, or elsewhere, provides evidence that music is as important today as it has been throughout humankind's history. (9)

Music therapists are trained to design music experiences in which people with little or no musical training can participate with some degree of success.

As music therapists formulate activities for therapeutic use, they employ their knowledge of the basic capabilities that every human being possesses to make or respond to music, as well as information they have gained about the client's musical preferences and capabilities from their assessment. The music used in music therapy may be composed (either selected from works of other composers or specially written by the music therapist) or improvised by the therapist and/or client. It may be in any style or form and may be conveyed or may elicit a response through singing, listening, playing instruments, moving to music, or using any combination of musical media, depending on the client's needs and capabilities. Musical experiences used for therapy may be active, requiring the client or clients to sing, play, move to, improvise, create, or make music in some way, or they may be receptive, achieving their effect by the client or clients listening to, taking in, or receiving the music (Bruscia, 1989a).

Music therapy interventions may utilize many different kinds of music (e.g., popular, classical, country, rock, vocal, instrumental) and music-based experiences (e.g., singing, playing musical instruments, moving or listening to music, creating or discussing songs and music). No one type of music or music experience is inherently more useful than another for therapeutic purposes. In choosing appropriate music experiences and activities for use in therapy, music therapists consider all possible modes of musical experience and expression and all possible styles or genres of music. As Thaut (2008, vii) clarifies, "Music's effects on the human experience have always been difficult to explain in their totality, as if always keeping a shroud of mystery, never entirely opening the curtain to the stage play of the forces on the human mind." Client needs, capabilities, responses, and preferences (as indicated by the assessment) help the therapist to determine the most appropriate selection of music experiences and materials for use in therapy with an individual client or group of clients. (For more information on planning music therapy intervention strategies, see Chapter Six.)

Since clients are directly involved with music and music materials during music therapy sessions, many of them develop certain musical skills as they move through the music therapy process. However, it is important to realize that the music therapist is not concerned with the development of these musical skills and behaviors for their own sake, as the music educator might be (Adamek and Darrow 2010, 105). Rather, the music therapist is concerned with how these musical skills and behaviors can be used to help the clients improve their level of physical, mental, social, or emotional functioning and to facilitate the development of nonmusical skills (e.g., motor control and coordination, physical comfort, perceptual skills, cognitive or academic skills, behavior patterns, appropriate emotional expression, communication skills, problem-solving skills, interpersonal skills). In other words, "music therapy contains many elements of recreational music and music education, but healing is its primary aim" (Birkenshaw-Fleming 1993, vi). Therefore, even when music therapy interventions involve teaching and learning musical skills, their primary focus remains on using these musical skills to improve client functioning in nonmusical areas. In this way, clients develop skills through music activity that help them reach their therapeutic goals.

MUSIC THERAPY IS SPECIFICALLY PRESCRIBED

Music therapists often work directly with other professionals (e.g., physicians, psychiatrists, social workers, physical therapists, special educators) on medical or educational treatment teams. In fact, in 1964, Dr. E. Thayer Gaston emphasized the importance of professional collaboration by opening the first volume and number of the *Journal of Music Therapy* with the following sentence: "One of the most important developments of modern science has been the interdisciplinary approach to problems" (1). When they work in teams, specialists meet together and decide how to coordinate their services in a way that will best help the client meet certain therapeutic goals. Music therapy services, just like the services of other professionals, are prescribed as a specific part of the client's treatment plan. In medical settings, the prescriptive order for music therapy is signed by the physician in charge, just as an order for medication or physical therapy would be. In nonmedical settings, music therapy services may be requested formally by such people as the client's caseworker, psychologist, teacher, or parents, or music therapy services may be written into the client's treatment plan by the general consensus of the professional team. When music therapists work in private practice, the music therapist and the individual client (and/or the client's family members) work together in determining therapeutic goals and establish some sort of contract stipulating the objectives, methods to be used, duration of treatment, and responsibilities of each party. In all settings, one must remember that music therapy is not an all-encompassing, "hit-or-miss" diversion, but a specific corrective agent prescribed to help influence positive changes in a client's targeted condition, skill, thought, feeling, or behavior.

MUSIC THERAPY IS IMPLEMENTED BY SPECIALLY TRAINED PERSONNEL

People certainly may experience some benefits by listening to relaxing music on their own or by banging on a drum or playing a piano to let off steam, but this is not music therapy. It also takes a music therapist – a person who is specially trained to select music and structure music experiences for maximum therapeutic benefit and who knows how to use music to establish and guide a dynamic, therapeutic relationship – to transform music activity into music *therapy*. Music activities can at times have therapeutic benefits without the direction of a music therapist, but these at best occur only haphazardly or accidentally. Under the direction of a trained music therapist, however, music and music-based experiences become potent therapeutic tools that can predictably and efficiently influence positive changes in an individual's condition, skills, thoughts, feelings, or behaviors. Music therapists are highly trained professionals who have skills and knowledge in various areas, including music, human behavior, human abilities and disabilities, and the influence of music on human beings. Those who pass an examination given by the Certification Board for Music Therapists receive the credential "music therapist-board certified" (MT-BC).

In planning music therapy intervention strategies, the music therapist selects the music or music activity to be used with a particular client carefully, based on the therapist's knowledge of music's effects on human behavior and the particular client's strengths, weaknesses, and therapeutic goals. Careful selection is important: "Music is used as a therapeutic tool, but its optimal benefit in therapy depends on the appropriate use by the therapist" (Davis, Gfeller, and Thaut 2008, 5–6). Although the outward appearance of music experiences may change only slightly from client to client, the way these experiences are used and the purposes they serve may vary considerably (Barnard 1953; Farnan and Johnson 1988b). It takes the skills of a trained music therapist to adapt and structure music experiences to fit the unique needs, personality, preferences, and response patterns of each individual client so that each may achieve the maximum possible therapeutic benefit. The music therapist also knows how to use the context of music experiences to establish a nurturing, growth-promoting relationship with the clients that will facilitate the achievement of therapeutic goals. The music therapist always keeps the client's goals in mind, structuring music therapy interventions and guiding interactions within music experiences to help the client gain skills that will help him or her reach those goals. Thus, the skills and guidance of the music therapist play a vital role in transforming music activity into music therapy.

Sometimes, music therapists may assess clients, establish goals, and plan music therapy treatment programs for clients and then train others (e.g., family members, teachers, other professionals, or paraprofessionals) to apply these programs on a daily basis. In these instances, the music therapist must meet regularly with the person implementing the program to evaluate client progress, make any necessary changes or revisions to the treatment program, and offer suggestions for more effective implementation.

MUSIC THERAPY IS DIRECTED TOWARD MEETING THE SPECIFIC NEEDS OF INDIVIDUAL CLIENTS

Mass-marketed music healing cures or music self-help programs are not music therapy. Music therapy interventions are directed to meet the specific needs of individual clients and are specially formulated to correspond to each client's unique preferences, personality, capabilities, and response patterns. Music therapy services exist to serve individual clients who need to improve some aspect of their physical, mental, social, and/or emotional functioning. Without clients who can benefit from what it has to offer, there would be no reason for music therapy, for as Sears (1968, 31) maintains, "of most importance in any therapeutic situation is the person receiving the therapy. Only through the individual's behavior, and changes therein, can the success of the therapeutic endeavor be seen."

Music therapy techniques have been used effectively in both group and individual settings with clients of all ages who have a wide variety of needs or disabilities. In the United States, music therapy services first became widely available in adult psychiatric settings and in mental retardation centers. Now, music therapists use their special skills to help clients in a greater number of treatment settings. The American Music Therapy Association (AMTA) states that

> Music therapists work in psychiatric hospitals, rehabilitative facilities, medical hospitals, outpatient clinics, day care treatment centers, agencies serving persons with developmental disabilities, community mental health centers, drug and alcohol programs, senior centers, nursing homes, hospice programs, correctional facilities, halfway houses, schools, and private practice." (AMTA website, 5 June 2014)

In addition to being used in a remedial, rehabilitative, habilitative, medical, psychological, or educational way to help clients who have various physical, mental, emotional, social, learning, or behavioral problems, music therapy also may be used as preventive medicine to help reduce stress, increase coping skills, and promote or maintain physical, mental, and emotional health in the general population or certain "at risk" groups (Beckett 1990; Bonny 1986; Gfeller 1988; Giles, Cogan, and Cox 1991; Goldman 1988; Hanser and Mandel 2010; Itoh and Lee 1989; Luetje 1989; McDonald, Kreutz, and Mitchell 2012; Ruud 2010; Staum 1993).

QUESTIONS FOR THOUGHT AND DISCUSSION

Determine whether or not each of the following examples represents a music therapy situation. If an example does represent a music therapy situation, identify the elements that make it music therapy. If it does not, identify the missing element(s).

1. Tina has low self-esteem and very little self-confidence. One day she told her social worker that she would like to be able to play the piano. The social worker talked to a music therapist who worked at a local recreation center. The music therapist, the social worker, and Tina met together and decided that learning to play the piano and preparing a song to perform at one of the recreation center's programs might be a good way to help Tina develop more confidence in herself and increase her self-esteem. The music therapist plans to give Tina piano lessons two times a week so that Tina will be able to play a simple duet with the therapist for the center's winter program and a simple piano solo for the center's spring program.

2. Ken is a client at a residential facility for multiply disabled children. Because he seems to enjoy listening to popular songs, his parents bought him a radio to keep in his room at the center. Ken often listens to the radio when he is in his room, and the music usually seems to make him calm and happy.

3. John has trouble relaxing after driving home in rush-hour traffic following a hard day at work. His friend Bill mentioned that he used to have the same problem, but he had found something that helped. Bill now plays relaxing music on the tape player in his car while he drives home and then listens to slow, quiet, soothing music on his stereo when he gets home. Bill suggests that John try this, too. John does, and he begins to feel much better and more relaxed.

4. A special education teacher has been working with her class of children

with intellectual disabilities on learning colors and numbers. Since her students enjoy music, the teacher asked the music therapist who worked for the school district to show her some music activities that would help the students learn and practice their colors and numbers. The music therapist loaned the teacher some educational records and a xylophone with colored bars and told her how to use these materials to teach and reinforce color and number concepts. (HINT: Remember, the music therapist is directing the teacher as to how to use the materials and activities.)

5. David had been attending a special school for orthopedically handicapped children until he was "mainstreamed" in junior high. David signed up for beginning band at the junior high school and is now learning to play the euphonium. He has band four times a week and private lessons with the band director once a week. David hopes to learn to play well enough to be able to play a solo for the spring contest.

SUGGESTIONS FOR FURTHER READING

Bruscia, K. E. (1989). *Defining music therapy*. Spring City, PA: Spring House Books.

Bruscia, K. E. (Ed.) (1991). *Case studies in music therapy*. Phoenixville, PA: Barcelona Publishers.

Dolan, M. C. (1973). Music therapy: An explanation. *Journal of Music Therapy, 10*(4), 172–176.

Gaston, E. T. (1954). Functions of the music therapist. In M. Bing (Ed.), *Music therapy 1953* (28–29). Lawrence, KS: Allen Press.

Gaston, E. T. (1968). Foreword. In E. T. Gaston (Ed.), *Music in therapy* (v–vii). New York: Macmillan.

Glassman, L. R. (2004). *Here comes the music lady: Memoirs of music therapist*. Bloomington, IN: AuthorHouse.

Hanser, S. B. (1987). *Music therapist's handbook*. St. Louis: Warren H. Green.

Lathom, W. (1981). *The role of the music therapist in the education of severely and profoundly handicapped children and youth*. Lawrence, KS: National Association for Music Therapy.

Muskatevc, L. C. (1961). The role of music therapy in the clinical setting. In E. H. Schneider (Ed.), *Music therapy 1960* (41–43). Lawrence, KS: Allen Press.

Pellitteri, J. (2009). *Emotional processes in music therapy*. Gilsum, NH: Barcelona.

Solli, H. P., Rolvsjord, R., & Borg, M. (2013). Toward understanding music therapy as a recovery-oriented practice within mental health care: A meta-synthesis of service users' experiences. *Journal of Music Therapy, 50*(4), 244–273.

Wigram, T., Pedersen, I. N., & Bonde, L. (2002). *A comprehensive guide to music therapy: Theory, clinical practice, research and training*. London: Jessica Kingsley.

Chapter Two

THE EDUCATION AND TRAINING OF
THE MUSIC THERAPIST

PERSONAL QUALITIES OF VALUE TO THE ASPIRING
MUSIC THERAPIST

Several personal qualities or characteristics will be beneficial to an individual who desires to become a professional music therapist (Gibbons 1989; Sandbank 1989b; Steele and Young 2009, 2011). The Career Handbook of American Music Therapy Association (AMTA, 2011) lists the following personal qualifications of a music therapist:

> a genuine interest in people and a desire to help others empower themselves. The essence of music therapy practice involves establishing caring and professional relationships with people of all ages and abilities. Empathy, patience, creativity, imagination, openness to new ideas, and understanding of oneself are also important attributes.

There have been many observations and studies of personality traits and attributes of music therapists. These date from the early years of the Association (Gilliland 1952; Eustis 1953; Ruppental 1957) to more recent reports (Lunt 2002; Sutton 2002; Borczon 2004). Some, such as Vega (2010) and Fowler (2006), are based on actual data, using established personality inventories and profiles.

Steele and Young (2008) used the Myers-Briggs Type Indicator and Demographic Profile (Myers-Briggs, McCaulley, Quenk, and Hammer 2003) to study personality characteristics of undergraduate music therapy and music education majors. Their findings are consistent with the characteristics listed by AMTA. In 2011, they compared the data from the undergraduate majors with data from professional music therapists and music educators. They found that "characteristics such as an interest in helping others, working with and supporting a variety of individuals, helping others to grow and understanding themselves better, seen in undergraduates may persist into professional life" (72).

The practice of music therapy is very demanding, both physically and mentally. Therefore, good physical health, energy, and stamina, as well as good mental health and emotional stability, are very important to the aspiring music therapist. Gardstrom and Jackson (2011) stress the need for self-awareness with a high degree of personal insight and development. They encourage music therapy students to participate in personal therapy to gain self-understanding. In the early curricula of the 1950s and 1960s, many schools required an interview at the campus counseling center. If the counselor felt therapy was advised, students were encouraged to participate in further counseling. This is not required by AMTA at this time. Other valuable skills and attributes include creativity, good coping skills, a high level of frustration tolerance, self-confidence, intelligence, good judgment, common sense, the ability to think clearly and quickly, imagination, flexibility, and an openness to new and innovative ideas and/or solutions.

Since the practice of music therapy involves establishing caring and helping professional relationships with people of many ages and ability levels, the aspiring music therapist should have a genuine interest in and desire to help people and work on developing good personal interaction skills. Qualities such as empathy and sincerity, patience, tact, and understanding, as well as the ability to relate to people of various abilities on their level, are also very valuable. In addition, music therapists need good observation and problem-solving skills and proficiency in both written and oral communication.

Music therapists are musicians as well as therapists. Music is their primary mode of therapeutic interaction – the medium through which they reach and relate to their clients. Therefore, the aspiring music therapist should have a strong interest and general background in music as well as the interest, commitment, and ability to develop strong musical skills. In addition, he or she should possess a genuine love for music, feel that music is an essential part of his or her being, and believe that music can be used to reach and help people.

Since music therapists often find themselves working in situations in which there are no other professional music therapists readily available for feedback and consultation, the aspiring music therapist would do well to develop an intrinsic sense of self-worth and motivation, a high level of self-confidence, an ability to evaluate his or her own work objectively and fairly, and an ability to work competently and efficiently without a high degree of supervision or praise from others. In addition, the ability to be a self-starter and to have the perseverance to carry tasks through to completion independently will be of great value in future music therapy work, both in researching problems and in developing and implementing treatment plans. The individual will also benefit from developing the ability to make connections and apply previous learning and experience intelligently in new situations and from learning how to integrate multidisciplinary knowledge and apply creativity in a given situation. These basic personal qualities, attributes, attitudes, and characteristics all help to provide a solid foundation on which to build the unique professional knowledge, skills, and attitudes that the aspiring music therapist will acquire during his or her formal professional education and training.

THE COMPONENTS OF PROFESSIONAL PREPARATION

The process of preparing to be a professional music therapist involves more than the acquisition of theoretical concepts in the classroom. Music therapy training also includes the practical aspects of learning to apply these concepts in clinical fieldwork and research. Both the classroom and practical learning experiences involved in music therapy training help the music therapy student develop certain professional attitudes. Thus, the training that a music therapist receives is "a unique type of preparation taking place in the classroom, laboratory and clinic that integrates several kinds of learning experiences, all directed toward producing a professional person" (Purtilo 1978, 3). During the course of their formal education and training, then, music therapy students acquire knowledge, as well as a number of special skills and attitudes that combine to help them become competent professional music therapists. They usually obtain much of this information through coursework in classroom situations.

Knowledge (Basic Theoretical Concepts)

What does a person need to *know* to become a competent professional music therapist? To help answer this question, it may be useful to remember that a music therapist is a person who uses music to help clients of many ages and with many different types of disabilities reach therapeutic goals. Thus, music therapists might be thought of as generalists who work with and through a special medium (i.e., music) (Goodman 2007; Michel 1985). In order to use music to help people, then, music therapy students must first acquire general and specific background knowledge and information (1) about music and all of its various aspects, (2) about both normal and abnormal functioning in people, and (3) about how music influences people.

Skills

What does a person need to be able to *do* to be a competent professional music therapist? In answering this question, one must take into account the therapist's "dual nature." Music therapists are both musicians and therapists; therefore, they must acquire technical skills in both music and therapy, as well as skills in using music in therapy. Skill learning, a process that involves the practical application of theoretical concepts, most often takes place in performance situations and in laboratory and clinical settings. Experiences may include instruction in and rehearsal of specific techniques or skills, role-play simulations, and supervised clinical field work or practicum experiences. These experiential learning activities are a very important part of the music therapist's education and training, for an individual must be able to apply theoretical concepts in practical ways and must develop skills in working effectively with people in order to be an effective music therapy clinician (Bruscia 1989b; Tims 1989).

Since music is what distinguishes music therapists from all other therapists, music therapists require highly developed technical and interpretive skills in at least one musical performance medium. Because music is the "language" music therapists use to establish contact and communicate with their clients, music therapists must learn to be fluent and expressive in this language. In addition to being a fluent and competent performer on his or her major instrument or voice, it is important that the aspiring music therapist develop functional skills on a number of instruments, be able to perform artistically and sensitively in a variety of musical styles and genres, and "be able to project himself or herself musically" (Boxill 1985, 89). As music therapy students gain technical musical performance skills in applied music studies, they are also developing important secondary skills (e.g., leadership, nonverbal interaction, musicianship, confidence) which can be transferred to and used in clinical settings (Cohen, Hadsell, and Williams 1997).

During the course of their music therapy training, individuals develop a number of specific musical skills, including keyboard, guitar, and vocal skills; the ability to arrange, compose, and improvise simple songs and accompaniments; proficiency in playing a variety of melodic and percussive nonsymphonic instruments; and conducting skills. They also learn to select music materials that are appropriate to an individual's background, age level, and skill level, and they gain skills in adapting materials as necessary to meet the special needs and capabilities of individual clients. In addition, aspiring music therapists learn to communicate musically in many different idioms and styles of music with freedom and confidence, and to improvise, compose, or arrange music for clinical and therapeutic purposes. They will begin to develop a repertoire of specific music materials, activities, and strategies that can be useful in various clinical situations and with different client populations.

To become effective *therapists*, music therapy students must learn to relate effectively to and communicate effectively with both other professionals and various clients who have wide ranges of functioning levels. To become effective *music therapists*, they must also learn how to use and structure music experiences to develop therapeutic relationships, promote growth, enhance communication, and facilitate desired changes in behavior. Much of music therapy students' practical training involves their learning how to assess clients, design treatment plans, and implement and evaluate music therapy sessions. Layman, Hussey, and Reed (2013, 155) note that "assessment is a critical component of therapeutic intervention as it serves as the basis from which clinical goals and objectives are derived." In conjunction with this, students develop skills in written and oral communication as they learn how to communicate information about client progress and music therapy treatment strategies to clients, other treatment team members, and/or the client's family. As they work with groups and individuals, music therapy students also learn group management skills and behavior control strategies that employ both musical and nonmusical elements.

Finally, music therapy students develop research skills. Through actual participation in research projects and activities, they learn how to formulate hypotheses, to collect and analyze data in a way that will help determine whether or not their hypotheses are acceptable, and to report research findings promptly and accurately. They also learn how to read, interpret, and critique research reports and how to apply research findings to clinical practice. The importance of research skills to professional music therapy clinicians is discussed in detail in Chapter Twenty-three.

Attitudes

Attitudes are the beliefs or dispositions one holds. They help determine how a person responds or reacts to various people, situations, or events. They "form a kind of 'bent,' an inclination to react in a certain, predictable way when certain stimuli are presented" (Michel 1985, 85). Attitudes may be fostered and developed through experience, discussion, exposure to certain standards or ideas, and observation of competent role models. Some attitudes may be rooted in deeply held personal convictions and may be very resistant to change. What particular *beliefs* or *attitudes*, then, does music therapy education and training try to instill, and how do these help one function optimally as a professional music therapist?

According to Michel (1985, 100), "a primary attitude would be one of willingness, or even of eagerness, to learn and accept the responsibilities of one's profession." Coupled with this attitude would be the development of a belief in the importance and efficacy of one's chosen profession. Music therapy students will develop an attitude of respect for and confidence in the profession of music therapy as they see the therapeutic power of music demonstrated in clinical situations, in controlled research studies, and in their own lives. They will learn professional responsibilities as music therapy ethics and standards of practice are discussed and analyzed in the classroom and observed and experienced in the clinic. In addition, both the American Music Therapy Association (AMTA 1998) and Certification Board for Music Therapists (CBMT 1998a) have established standards of professional practice and ethical conduct by which their members and certificants are to abide. The AMTA Code of Ethics, and the codes of five other worldwide music therapy associations are provided in *Ethical Thinking in Music Therapy* (Dileo 2000). The AMTA website also provides the code of ethics.

Since music therapy is an allied health field, music therapists also adhere to a general code of ethics followed by all health professionals (Michel 1976; 1985). Basic to this code is an attitude of concern for all human beings and a willingness to assist anyone in distress. Professional ethics also mandate certain standards of behavior for relationships with clients, other professionals, and the community. For example, professional music therapists should respect a client's right to privacy and exercise care in maintaining confidentiality. Knight (2008, 75) compared "perceptions of professional competency between preinternship music therapy students and internship supervisors." One area in which there was a discrepancy was in "maintaining client confidence." The need for a high regard for maintaining confidentiality is related to the Health Insurance Portability and Accountability Act of 1996, but it always has been important as general respect for each client served. Music therapists see their clients as people first, not as objects or diseases or conditions, and treat them as individual human beings with potential for wellness and growth: "Every action of a music therapist must demonstrate respect for the client and accord the client every dignity due to a fellow human being, no matter what the client's presenting problem or situation" (Prickett 1989, 100). Music therapists also act with integrity toward their colleagues in music therapy and other professions and should strive to maintain harmonious relationships. Moreover, professional music therapists should make every effort to ensure that public information materials give an accurate and complete picture of professional services and facilities. Professional music therapists should also respect the community's social and moral expectations at all times.

Two additional important attitudes for professional music therapists relate to the areas of continuing education and research. First, it is vital that music therapists be willing to take responsibility for continual self-assessment and be committed to seeking ongoing opportunities for continuing their own learning and professional growth (Gibbons 1989; Michel 1985). This may involve continually availing themselves of opportunities to grow and develop musically as well as in other professional areas. Second, it is important for music therapists to develop an open-minded, "scientific attitude" (Michel, 1985, p. 100) toward the world and themselves. This scientific or research attitude involves a willingness to question and rigorously test new evidence and a willingness to accept change and to change one's concepts in the face of new evidence. (The importance of the research attitude to music therapy pro-fessionals is discussed further in Chapter Twenty-three.) Shoemark (2013, 152) observes that music therapists "have the capacity to use theory and models of practice to scaffold between research and practice." While this statement is true, it assumes that music therapists are competent in both clinical practice and research. Much of the research training in music therapy is at the graduate level.

Finally, aspiring music therapists will benefit from developing the attitude of looking at everything with a therapist's eye (Muskatevc 1967). This process involves being open to learning from every encounter, perpetually asking, "What does this mean to me as a Music Therapist?" (Muskatevc 1967, 139). As they approach all people and situations with attitudes of humility and respect, as they continually search to make connections and take time to stop and listen, as they are open to learning from everything and everyone, aspiring music therapists will gain many valuable insights that will help them be better persons as well as better professional music therapists.

MUSIC THERAPY DEGREE PROGRAMS

In a historical review of the music therapy curriculum, de l'Etoile (2000, 53) explains that the first course in music therapy was offered at Columbia University in 1919, taught by Margaret Anderton and later by Isa Maud Ilsen. In the United States, the American Music Therapy Association (AMTA) has established standards for music therapy degree programs, as well as for equivalency programs and alternate route certifications. Basic music therapy degree programs approved by AMTA provide standards for completion of entry-level music therapy training at the bachelor's level that include at least four years of academic coursework, preinternship field experience, and an extended clinical internship (AMTA 2014; Maranto and Bruscia 1987). The American Music Therapy Association is the sole body for setting standards for music therapy degree programs in the United States. As of 2011, 72 colleges and universities offered degree programs approved by the AMTA, with 30 of these offering graduate as well as undergraduate programs (AMTA, 2011). For the most current information on AMTA-approved schools and internship sites, the reader should consult the AMTA website (www.musictherapy.org).

AMTA formed a Commission on Education and Clinical Training (ECTC) to recommend future paradigms for music therapy education and training. Their primary recommendation was to establish education and training standards based on competencies, rather than simply passing courses in an approved curriculum. Of course, the competencies required course work, so most of the course work was still required by the degree-granting college or university. According to these standards, "clinical training was defined as the entire experience from practicum to internship" (Groene and Pembrook 2000, 92–93). In its draft report, the Commission made recommendations for association standards to cover three levels of education (bachelor's, master's, and doctoral study), with each level reflecting "different levels of competence and professional designation" (Crowe and Bruscia 1999, 8). The Commission sees AMTA's role as ensuring the quality of music therapy education and training by establishing outcome-specific (i.e., competency-based), flexible standards that will be continually responsive to new developments in the field (Bruscia et al. 1998; Crowe and Bruscia 1999).

Groene and Pembrook (2000) surveyed music therapy educators to study curricular issues and attitudes about a competency-based curriculum. They found that educators favor a competency-based approach as compared with a curriculum that requires particular courses. Their survey includes a timeline of "Curriculum Revision and Competency Formulation in Music Therapy" (94).

Since using music as the primary therapeutic modality is what sets music therapists apart from other therapists, individuals who wish to become music therapists must have an in-depth knowledge of music and all of its many aspects. In the United States, most music therapy educational programs are currently part of university schools of music, and aspiring music therapists must be accepted as music majors by the university. Music history and music theory courses that are part of university music curricula give music therapy students more knowledge and understanding of their special tool, music. In music theory classes, they learn more about the elements of music and how those elements can be manipulated and arranged to create different effects, knowledge that will be useful as they later learn to select and create music for therapeutic purposes. In music history courses, they learn about many of the various forms, styles, and genres of music. Since music therapists will need to establish contact with clients from varying cultural backgrounds in their clinical work, it is important for their coursework to include basic information on various world music genres and ethnic and popular music in addition to Western art music (Moreno 1988; Prickett 1989).

Because they will be working with people in a helping profession, music therapy students must acquire a basic understanding of standard treatment methods for human problems as well as general knowledge of human beings and the way they communicate and interact with one another. Courses in the biological and natural sciences furnish a foundation for understanding the human body and the forces that act upon it, while behavioral science courses (e.g., psychology, sociology, anthropology) provide a basis for understanding the behaviors, needs, and interactions of people. Courses in abnormal psychology and exceptionalities provide background knowledge for understanding the unique needs of individuals who have various disabilities or handicapping conditions.

Since music therapists work with people and music not as isolated entities but as interacting entities, they also must know how people acquire musical skills (music learning and musical development) and how people perceive, respond to, and are influenced by various musical phenomena. Knowledge in these areas is often obtained through studies in music psychology and the influence of music on human behavior. In professional courses on music therapy principles and practices, students are exposed to readings, resource materials, case studies, and research that illustrate the breadth and depth of the field of music therapy and the many ways that music may help people reach therapeutic goals. In this way, music therapy educators strive to provide the background knowledge necessary "to help *every* student meet the *widest* possible range of client needs which he or she may encounter in a variety of clinical settings" (Bruscia 1989b, 84–85).

Undergraduate Degree Programs

In the United States, entry-level skills and competencies for music therapy practice are gained at the bachelor's level. Baccalaureate programs in music therapy include at least four years of academic coursework in music therapy; music; psychology; behavioral, biological, and social sciences; abnormal conditions or disabilities; and general studies. Concurrently with their academic coursework, students are involved in various supervised clinical field experiences, culminating with an in-depth internship. Through the internship, students experience the practical application of knowledge learned in the classroom as they observe and assist music therapy professionals and then learn to assess clients' needs and independently design, implement, document, and evaluate music therapy treatment plans. Thus, "education and clinical training are not separate processes, but rather reflect a continuum of learning experiences at the undergraduate level" (Crowe and Bruscia 1999, 9). In 2011, AMTA reported 187 internship programs. The AMTA argues that "the internship is a milestone and the capstone component of the students' practical training" (AMTA website 2011). Upon completion of a bachelor's degree in music therapy, individuals are eligible to take a standardized national examination offered by the independent Certification Board for Music Therapists (CBMT), which leads to the professional credential "Music Therapist-Board Certified" (MT-BC).

Master's Degree Programs

As the field of music therapy continually expands, "the need for graduate degrees becomes more pronounced, not only to train higher level clinicians but also to prepare them for jobs as educators, supervisors, and administrators" (Bruscia 1986, 58). According to a survey of music therapy educators by Maranto and Bruscia (1988), the attainment of advanced competencies in clinical skills, assessment skills, research skills, and supervisory skills is of primary importance in a master's degree program. The 2013 AMTA Membership Profile reports that 37 percent of survey respondents held a master's degree and eight percent held a doctoral degree. These statistics are from a survey of the AMTA membership, but many music therapists have chosen to be certified and not belong to the association. Therefore, the numbers they report are very conservative. Wyatt and Furioso (2000) surveyed music therapists who hold the Master of Music in Music Therapy or the Master of Music Therapy degree (note: this eliminated other degree designations, e.g., Master of Science in Music Therapy, Master of Arts in Music Therapy, Master of Music Education with an emphasis in Music Therapy, etc.). They found that 45 percent believed that their undergraduate curriculum or equivalency prepared them for a job in music therapy. Persons who have completed a bachelor's degree or equivalency program in music therapy and an approved internship or who have received alternate certification/registration are eligible to apply for admission to graduate programs in music therapy. Coursework at the master's degree level may include music therapy seminar, practicum, and research courses as well as work in supportive areas. Since graduate programs focus on more specific and in-depth learning, the content and orientation of master's degree programs in music therapy may vary greatly from school to school. The opportunity to pursue advanced clinical skills should be a major part of graduate study. This is then augmented with continuing education courses offered before the annual AMTA conference.

In its draft report of recommendations, the AMTA Commission on Education and Clinical Training viewed master's degree programs in music therapy as being designed to meet two educational objectives:

> 1) to provide advanced competence in entry level areas (i.e., breadth and depth of knowledge and skill in music foundations, clinical foundations, and music therapy); 2) to provide basic competence in any advanced topic or specialization in music therapy. (Crowe and Bruscia 1999, 8)

Advanced topics or specializations studied in master's degrees programs might include theory development, research, supervision, college teaching, clinical administration, or in-depth study of and training in particular areas of practice, client populations, or clinical approaches.

Doctoral Studies

Academic programs leading to doctoral degrees in music therapy or related disciplines are offered in some universities. Historically, "the University of Kansas was the first school to offer a doctoral program in music therapy, and Florida State University and New York University soon followed" (Pasiali, Lin, and Noh 2009, 282). Doctoral study may concentrate on research skills (experimental, historical, philosophical, and/or descriptive research), university teaching skills, advanced music therapy theory, and/or clinical specialization and advanced clinical skills (Maranto and Bruscia 1988). Doctoral programs often are tailored to individual interests (Gibbons 1989), and usually include a research component and require completion of a dissertation.

The AMTA Commission on Education and Clinical Training has made initial recommendations for specific doctoral degree programs in music therapy (Bruscia et al. 1998; Crowe and Bruscia 1999). According to these recommendations, doctoral degree programs in music therapy have two educational objectives:

> 1) to provide advanced competence in research (or theory development) along with college teaching and supervision; and 2) to provide advanced competence in any specialization area in music therapy. (Crowe and Bruscia 1999, 9)

As the field of music therapy continues to develop, specific doctoral programs in music therapy are likely to increase. The interested reader is urged to contact AMTA for current information on doctoral degree programs.

PROFESSIONAL CREDENTIALS FOR MUSIC THERAPISTS

When individuals have completed their bachelor's level training in music therapy, they are eligible to apply for a professional credential in music therapy. Credentials help assure the public and the employer that the individual holding the credential has received certain training and is capable of performing at a specified level of quality and competence. Professional credentialing for music therapists in the United States takes place at the national level under the direction of the Certification Board for Music Therapists (CBMT). CBMT is an independent certifying agency, fully accredited by the National Commission for Certifying Agencies (NCHCA) (CBMT 1991, 1992, 1997, 1998b). It was incorporated in 1983 as an autonomous certifying body for music therapists, independent from the professional membership association. Its function is to set rules and regulations for obtaining and maintaining a specific, voluntary credential; the music therapists certified by the CBMT may or may not be members of a professional music therapy membership association (CBMT 1992).

Since 1985, CBMT has granted the credential "Music Therapist-Board Certified" (MT-BC) to any music therapist who "has met specific educational and clinical training requirements for eligibility and has passed the Board Certification Exam" (CBMT 1998b, 4). This exam provides a national objective standard to demonstrate competence in the knowledge, skills, and abilities needed for current entry-level music therapy practice. It consists of multiple-choice questions covering the broad areas of music therapy foundations and principles, related clinical theories and techniques, music, and professional roles and responsibilities (CBMT 1991). To maintain board-certified status, MT-BCs must demonstrate continuing competence in music therapy practice by participating in the CBMT's recertification program, which involves ongoing continuing education or additional examinations related to current music therapy practice. MT-BCs must apply for recertification every five years (CBMT 1991, 1997, 1998b). As of September 16, 2013, the AMTA Membership Profile indicated that there were 5,775 board certified music therapists. On the national level, CBMT is currently the only credentialling agency for music therapists in the United States, and the MT-BC is the only music therapy credential now awarded. The MT-BC is recognized by American Music Therapy Association (AMTA) as *the* entry-level credential required to practice music therapy. (AMTA, 1998)

Prior to their unification on January 1, 1998, the National Association for Music Therapy (NAMT) and the American Association for Music Therapy (AAMT) both awarded various music therapy credentials to individuals they considered to be qualified music therapists. "Registered Music Therapist" (RMT), the oldest music therapy credential in the United States, is a title that the NAMT granted from 1956–1997 to persons who had successfully completed both an NAMT-approved academic program and an NAMT-approved clinical training program. Once the individual's records had been reviewed and approved by the NAMT Registration Committee, that individual's name was added to the National Registry list maintained by the NAMT. Individuals could also apply for registration through alternate routes under special circumstances (NAMT 1994b). The advent of the AAMT in 1971 spawned the creation of other music therapy credentials. Through 1997, the AAMT granted the title "Certified Music Therapist" (CMT) to persons who had successfully completed AAMT-approved baccalaureate degree or equivalency programs and internships in music therapy (AAMT 1993). Alternate route certification mechanisms also were available from the AAMT. From 1989–1997, the AAMT offered an additional credential, the title of "Advanced Certified Music Therapist" (ACMT), to music therapists who had advanced experience and training. Advanced certification required a master's degree in music therapy or a closely related field, at least 100 contact hours in continuing education, and extensive experience in music therapy (AAMT 1993).

So that qualified music therapists were not left without credentials when all credentialling responsibilities were yielded to the CBMT with the unification of AAMT and NAMT, the National Music Therapy Registry (NMTR) was formed in 1998 to serve the needs of those music therapists who held a valid credential from the former AAMT or NAMT but who were not board certified (i.e., not MT-BCs). The NMTR is "a separate and distinct organization with its own Board of Directors and staff" (AMTA 1998, xviii). For a yearly maintenance fee, those music therapists who held the professional designation of RMT, CMT, or ACMT prior to January 1, 1998, can be listed on a professional registry maintained by the NMTR. According to the Unification Agreement, the NMTR will continue to maintain a listing of those with current RMT, CMT, or ACMT credentials until the year 2020. Music therapists who become board certified (i.e., receive the MT-BC credential from CBMT by passing the national board certification exam) cease to use their RMT, CMT, or ACMT title and are no longer listed on the Registry (AMTA 1998).

QUESTIONS FOR THOUGHT AND DISCUSSION

1. What are some personal qualities or characteristics that will benefit the aspiring music therapist? Why or how will these be important in his or her professional work?
2. What knowledge, skills, and attitudes are important to professional music therapists?
3. How do "musician" skills and knowledge and "therapist" skills and knowledge interact in the delivery of music therapy services?
4. Why are standards for music therapy education and training and professional credentials for music therapists important? What organizations are currently responsible for these functions in the United States? How do they carry out their tasks?

SUGGESTIONS FOR FURTHER READING

American Music Therapy Association (AMTA). (n.d.). *Music therapy as a career* (brochure). Silver Spring, MD: Author.

Borczon, R. M. (2004). *Music therapy: A fieldwork primer.* Gilsum, NH: Barcelona.

Bruscia, K. E. (1986). Advanced competencies in music therapy. *Music Therapy, 6A(1),* 57–67.

Bruscia, K. E. (1989). The content of music therapy education at undergraduate and graduate levels. *Music Therapy Perspectives, 7,* 83–87.

Bruscia, K. E., Hesser, B., & Boxill, E. H. (1981). Essential competencies for the practice of music therapy. *Music Therapy, 1(1),* 43–49.

Certification Board for Music Therapists (CBMT). (1991). Recertification manual. Tucson, AZ: Author.

Certification Board for Music Therapists (CBMT). (2014). *CBMT: The certification board for music therapists* (brochure). Richmond, VA: Author.

Certification Board for Music Therapists (CBMT). (1998). *Your music therapist is certified by the certification board for music therapists* (brochure). Richmond, VA: Author.

Dileo, C. (2000). *Ethical thinking in music therapy.* Cherry Hill, NJ: Jeffrey Books.

Goodman, K. D. (2011). *Music therapy education and training: From theory to practice.* Springfield, IL: Charles C Thomas.

Grocke, D. & Wigram, T. (2007). *Receptive methods in music therapy: Techniques and clinical applications for music therapy clinicians, educators and students.* London: Jessica Kingsley.

Maranto, C. D. & Bruscia, K. E. (Eds.) (1987). *Perspectives on music therapy education and training.* Philadelphia: Temple University.

Maranto, C. D. & Bruscia, K. E. (1988). *Methods of teaching and training the music therapist.* Philadelphia: Temple University, Esther Boyer College of Music.

Michel, D. E. (1985). The professional music therapist: Responsibilities and attitudes. In D. E. Michel (Ed.), *Music therapy: An introduction, including music in special education* (2nd ed.) (98–111). Springfield, IL: Charles C Thomas.

Sandbank, G. (1989). The right personality for the music therapist. In R. R. Pratt (Ed.), *Music therapy and music in special education: The international state of the art II* (ISME Edition Number Four) (87–93). St. Louis: MMB Music.

Tims, F. (1989). Experiential learning in the music therapy curriculum. *Music Therapy Perspectives, 7,* 91–92.

Wheeler, B. L., Shultis, C. L., & Polen, D. W. (2005). *Clinical training guide for the student music therapist.* Gilsum, NH: Barcelona.

Wigram, T., Pedersen, I. N., & Bonde, L. O. (2012). *A comprehensive guide to music therapy: Theory, clinical practice, research, and training.* London: Jessica Kingsley.

SOURCES FOR ADDITIONAL INFORMATION*

American Music Therapy Association (AMTA), 8455 Colesville Rd., Suite 1000, Silver Spring, MD 20910, (301) 589-3300, FAX (301) 589-5175, email: info@ musictherapy.org, Web: http://www.musictherapy.org

Certification Board for Music Therapists (CBMT), 589 Southlake Blvd., Richmond, VA 23236, 1-800-765CBMT, FAX (804-379-9354), email: info@cbmt.com, Web: http://www.cbmt.com

National Music Therapy Registry (NMTR), P.O. Box 13623, Silver Spring, MD 20910-3623, (301) 562-9330

*Contact information current as of June, 2014.

PART II

MUSIC THERAPY THROUGH
THE AGES

What are the roots of music therapy? Is the idea of using music for healing purposes something new, or has music been used in connection with healing for a long time? Where can foreshadowings of modern music therapy practice be seen throughout history? How did the modern, scientific profession of music therapy develop in the United States? In Part II, these questions are answered as historical summaries of the uses of music in healing and the development of the modern music therapy profession are presented.

Although music therapy has become an organized, scientific discipline only in relatively recent times, music has been used to promote health and combat disease almost since the dawn of civilization. Chapter Three presents a general overview of the use of music in connection with healing practices, beginning with the rituals of primitive tribes and continuing through the centuries to current uses of music with the general public for stress reduction, general wellness, and enhanced creativity and cooperation. Chapter Four summarizes the development of music therapy as an organized, scientifically based professional discipline in the twentieth century. Much of the chapter focuses on the people and events that led to the eventual formation of the first professional music therapy organization in the United States, the National Association for Music Therapy, in 1950. Organizational developments since that time – such as the formation of the American Association for Music Therapy in 1971, the incorporation of the Certification Board for Music Therapists in 1983, the recent unification of professional music therapy associations in the United States that resulted in the formation of the American Music Therapy Association in 1998, and the increasing international scope of music therapy – are also briefly discussed. In addition, summaries of current treatment settings, job satisfaction and employment trends, and the changing roles of professional music therapists are presented.

After completing Part II, the reader should have gained the knowledge and information needed to complete the following tasks:

1. List several examples of ways music has been used to promote health at various times in history.
2. Trace the steps that led to the formation of a national professional music therapy organization in the United States.
3. Describe the function of the Certification Board for Music Therapists.
4. Name the only professional membership organization for music therapists that currently exists in the United States. Briefly describe how it came into being and summarize its mission.
5. List several types of treatment settings and populations in which and with whom music therapy is currently used.
6. Identify some employment trends and discuss the changing roles of a music therapy professional.
7. Name several other countries that have professional music therapy organizations.

Chapter Three

A HISTORICAL OVERVIEW OF THE USE OF MUSIC TO PROMOTE HEALTH

The connection between music and healing dates almost to the dawn of time and continues to spiral throughout history to the present day. To be sure, attitudes and practices regarding music and healing throughout history were always closely connected to the prevailing beliefs and practices of that time and culture. Nevertheless, echoes of various aspects of contemporary music therapy principles and practices are evident in some of the approaches and techniques of music healers throughout history. An essay published in 1899 by James Leonard Corning (1855–1923), a prominent American neurologist, "represented one of the earliest controlled attempts to treat disease with music" (Davis 2012, 103). Thus, music therapists draw on a long tradition of music healing practices as they use music or music-based experiences in a planned, prescribed, goal-directed process of interaction and intervention, based on assessment and evaluation of individual clients' specific needs, strengths, and weaknesses, to influence positive changes in an individual's condition, skills, thoughts, feelings, or behaviors.

PRIMITIVE AND ANCIENT CULTURES

Scholl and White (1970, 1) state that "sources do agree that man's earliest awareness of music may have been born of his associating an emotional satisfaction with the phenomenal sound that accompanied his need for self-expression through body motion." Association of music with and attraction to rhythm and movement have allowed music to encourage people to participate in music therapy.

In most primitive and ancient civilizations, the promotion of physical and psychological health and well-being were functions of religion, and medicine was closely tied to religious rituals. Music was also an important part of both medical and religious practices. According to Boxberger (1962, 138), "the close relationship of music to temple rituals indicates why it was so intimately bound up with medical practices in the cultures of ancient people." Anthropologists and ethnomusicologists have found that music and religion are still integrally tied to the healing practices of many of cultures (Nettl 1956).

African and American Indian Tribes

Connections among music, religion, and healing were very evident in many primitive tribal civilizations in Africa, where the *shaman* (i.e., witch doctor or medicine man) functioned as the tribe's chief musician, medicine man, and priest. The shaman used special songs, rhythms, musical instruments (especially drums, bells, and rattles), dances, and dramas in conjunction with magic or religious rituals to draw out or drive away illness and disease. Musical instruments served magical rather than musical aims because primitive instruments "act as the strongest charms at man's disposal when he performs the vital rites of magic to protect his health and existence" (Sachs 1955, 3). Music was used for functional purposes, not aesthetic. Singing was often an indispensable part of the healing process. For example, the Kung Bushman shaman used song both to awaken his healing powers and to focus that power on treating the patient's disease (Weldin and Eagle 1991). In other African tribes, shamans or medicine men would play special instruments believed to have healing powers (e.g., a magic drum or harp) over the afflicted part of a patient (e.g., his or her stomach) to effect a cure (Feder and Feder 1981).

American Indian medicine men also used songs and music as specific healing tools, even having specific songs to treat specific ailments (Apel 1972; Winn, Crowe, and Moreno 1989). Many medicine men or shamans of the American Southwest, Mexico, and Central America believed the power for healing a particular illness or disease resided in a particular song. Their belief in the healing power of specific songs was so great that "without the knowledge of the proper song, a shaman would not attempt a treatment" (Winn, Crowe, and Moreno 1989, 68). The Navaho Indians, for example, used "sings" as their healing ceremonies, employing special combinations of song, dance, and sand paintings in particular patterns to cure specific illnesses (Feder and Feder 1981; Kenny 1982; Weldin and Eagle 1991). For the Navaho, an important part of medicine was a belief that "the magic of the music will bring healing" (Kenny 1982, 77). Among the Walla Walla Indians, patients as well as medicine men used healing songs, as the sick were directed to play an active role in seeking their cure by singing for several hours a day (Weldin and Eagle 1991).

In addition to songs, drums and rhythms played an important part in the healing practices of many shamans and medicine men from primitive tribes and cultures of the Americas, Africa, and Asia (Hamel 1976/1979; Winn,

Crowe, and Moreno 1989). Shamans often used specific drum signals to contact the gods or spirits and establish communication between beings on earth and those in the sky and/or the underworld. Shamans also used drum rhythms, bells, chants, and special costumes and dances in healing rituals to help the patient reach a trance-like altered state of consciousness that facilitated crisis resolution and healing (Hamel 1976/1979; Kovach 1985):

> To the shaman, then, the act of therapy involves going beyond the seen reality of consciousness and into another level of awareness. . . . It is in this process of traveling to another dimension that one finds the earliest examples of music therapy as shamans enlisted the drumbeat for thousands of years in order to elicit the altered or shamanic state of consciousness. (Winn, Crowe, and Moreno 1989, 67)

Ancient Hebrews

Evidence recorded in the Bible indicates that music also played an important part in the life of the ancient Hebrews. When the Lord wanted the Hebrew people to be sure to remember special events, He instructed Moses to teach the people a song that told of those events to serve as a memory aid for them (Deuteronomy 31:19). Much music was included in the religious rites of the Hebrews; in fact, the temple establishment included 288 full-time musicians whose job it was to prophesy and help people reach their God, their source of strength and healing, through music (I Chronicles 25:1–8). The Hebrews also recognized that music could have calming effects on people in daily life: When an evil spirit troubled King Saul, his servants sent for a man, David, who was a skillful harp player, to calm and refresh Saul and make him well through playing harp music (I Samuel 16:14–23). Furthermore, "King David owed the possession of his beloved harp to the Egyptian exile or to his Mesopotamian ancestors for their adoption of India's *Kinnor-lyre*" (Scholl and White 1970, 22).

Egypt and Babylonia

Remains found in Sumeria and Egypt indicate musical practice dating back to 3000 B.C.:

> One of the most ancient musical relics is a Sumerian eleven-stringed harp from 2600 B.C. The earliest known example of musical notation (800 B.C.) is a Sumerian hymn on the creation of man written in the familiar cuneiform symbols. (Scholl and White 1970, 4)

These cultures ascribed power to the gods Rammen (thunder-god) and Ea (sea-god). The affective power of music was recorded in words: "A hymn ascribed to the great Sumerian king, King Gudea, attributed to music the power to fill the temple court with joy, to calm a troubled heart, and to chase away gloom" (Scholl and White 1970, 5).

Music, religious rituals, and healing practices also were intertwined in the cultures of ancient Egypt and Babylonia. The Babylonian priest-physicians used clappers and rattles to exorcise evil spirits, and chanting was an important part of temple healing practices (Apel 1972; Weldin and Eagle 1991). In Egypt, the connection among music, religion, and healing was so great that their priests also were required to become both musicians and physicians (Weldin and Eagle 1991). Egyptian priest-physicians considered music to be "the physic of the soul" (Feder and Feder, 1981, 3) and used hymns and incantations to cure sickness and suffering. The earliest medical papyri record special chant therapies used for these purposes (Davis, Gfeller, and Thaut 2008, 19). Egyptians also believed that music cast spells, that sounds symbolized other entities, and that each note had a particular magical force to summon the gods (Boxberger 1962). In addition, the Egyptians used songs for functional purposes: They had special work songs composed and organized for the particular tasks associated with sowing seed, harvesting, weaving, carrying stones from quarries, etc.: "The Egyptians realized that concerted singing facilitated labour, just as martial music encouraged the soldier as he set forth to war" (Scott 1958).

China and India

Ancient Asian cultures, too, believed in the healing powers of music and used it as an integral part of religious and health-promoting rituals. In China, as early as the second century B.C., "there were elaborate discourses on music in relation to the human spirit and on the use of music to inculcate moderation" (Apel 1972, 156). Cosmological connotations of pitches became an important part of Chinese musical thought and practice, and the emotions associated with various modes (i.e., systems of organizing pitches, comparable to our scales) regulated their use in musical drama.

The priests of ancient India valued music for its mantra-mystic qualities (Scott 1958). They discovered that certain tonal sequences produced meditative states, and they experimented and subtly refined these to achieve *Samadhi*, a superconscious trance. The Hindus believed that this music-induced, mystical, metaphysical state of consciousness helped them achieve oneness with the universe and promoted healthiness of body, mind, and spirit and a purer state of inner awareness. Already before the second century B.C., the *Samaveda* told of links among man, music, and the cosmos (Apel 1972; Hamel 1979). Strict adherence to correct performance of the *Veda* chant was essential, for the ancient Hindus believed that any mistake in intonation or enunciation would upset the balance of the universe (Apel 1972). Beginning with the second century A.D., intricate systems of pitch organization known as *ragas* were developed. Each *raga* was believed to promote distinct moods or psychological temperaments (rasas), ranging from erotic longing to humorous, sad, furious, brave or fearful states, or from disgust to amazement to peace, tranquility, and relaxation (Hamel 1979). Hindu thinkers prescribed ways in which the ragas should be used in drama, music instruction, and performance for maximal spiritual psychological benefit (Apel 1972; Hamel 1979).

Greek and Roman Cultures

The close association between music and healing that existed in ancient Greece is personified in the Greek god, Apollo, who was both the god of music and the god of medicine. The Greeks believed that disease was the result of disharmony in a person's being. Music, with its ethical and moral power, could be used to bring a person back into a state of harmony and order and thus promote health. According to the Greek doctrine of ethos, music was a potent force interlocked with the system of nature that could affect an individual's will, character, and conduct (Grout 1973). Different types of music affected human thought and conduct in different ways: Some types of music, such as those played on the lyre and related to the poetic forms of the ode and the epic, had calming and uplifting effects, while other types of music, such as those played on the aulos and related to the poetic forms of the dithyramb and the drama, "tended to produce excitement and enthusiasm" (Grout 1973, 9).

Since the Greeks found that different types of music and different modes had fairly predictable effects on human conduct and emotions, they began to apply music systematically as both curative and preventive medicine. Even the sixth century philosopher-mathematician, Pythagoras, who computed the mathematical ratios of musical intervals, "urged his followers to sing a hymn before retiring in order to compose their spirits and prepare them for rest" (Gillespie 1968, 84). This advice shows a functional use of music, rather than an aesthetic or a religious one. Pythagoras' belief that specially prescribed music could benefit one's health led him to investigate the physical qualities of sound and develop the foundation for today's tonal system (Munro and Mount 1978). (For an explanation of the Pythagorean scale and the ratios from which it was derived, see Radocy and Boyle 2012, 251–252). In addition, Pythagoras explored clinical applications of music, using dance and music to treat patients who were mentally ill and introducing treatments in which "musical medicine" was central in promoting order and proportions necessary for health (Feder and Feder 1981). The Greeks also used musical and dramatic performances to effect a cathartic purge of the emotions, something they felt was essential to mental health (Alvin 1975). Gilliland gave prominence to the emotional and spiritual importance of music in Greek civilization by opening the first volume and number of the *Bulletin of the National Association for Music Therapy* (January 1952, 1) with the sentence: "In his book 'Music in Western Civilization,' Paul Henry Lang has stated rather categorically that it isn't likely that any nation will ever again give as important a place to music in its mental and spiritual life as the Greeks did."

Much of the therapy using music in ancient Greece focused on listening to music to restore lost balance and promote health. In fact, "the use of music for curing mental disorders reflected the belief that it could directly influence emotion and develop character" (Davis, Gfeller, and Thaut 2008, 20). However, Greek physicians cautioned against the indiscriminate use of music in treating madness or mental illness, noting that music could cause harm instead of good if it was not applied correctly (Feder and Feder 1981). The Greek philosophers Plato and Aristotle, speaking often of the beneficial effects of music and its importance to health, advocated the carefully controlled use of music and rhythm to restore persons to health and to promote the development of healthy and ethical citizens (Alvin 1975; Boxberger 1962; Grout 1973; Pratt 1989; Schullian and Schoen 1948). Aristotle, in his essay called *Politics*, said, "The musical modes differ from one another, and those who hear them are differently affected by each" (Sachs 1955, 25). Echoing a tenet stated by Confucius a hundred years before, Plato suggested that music should be the foundation of the ideal state (Sachs 1955, 24). In conclusion, "If Hippocrates is called the father of medicine, we may recognize Plato and Aristotle as the forerunners of music therapy, which is the controlled use of music" (Alvin 1975, 38).

The Romans adopted the Greek philosophy regarding the beneficial moral, ethical, medicinal, and healing influences of music. For example, they believed that music could cure snakebites, combat pestilence, and aid in curing insomnia. The physician Aesclepiades treated insanity with harmonious sounds and calmed recalcitrant mobs by a change in music or by playing a certain kind of music (Boxberger 1962). Lucretius recommended that flute music be played after meals to aid digestion and also noted the influence music could have on a person's mind, emotions, and behavior. Theophrastus, a disciple of Aristotle, noted the somatic effects of flute music (Pratt 1989). Celsus, known as a master artist in medicine, recommended that music, cymbals, and sounds be used to dispel the melancholy thoughts associated with certain types of mental illness. Insanity was also treated with organ music by Zenocrates and with flute music and vocal exercises by Caelius Aurelianus. Aristedes Quintilianus wrote that music could apply the proper therapeutics to the abnormal emotions of psychotic states and gradually, by means of an unconscious purging, restore those emotions to a more normal state (Schullian and Schoen 1948). For Aristedes, the controlled use of music was essentially a form of psychotherapy. Consequently, he maintained that music, like medicine, had preventive as well as curative powers.

THE MIDDLE AGES

Boethius, an influential authority on music in the early Middle Ages, strongly emphasized the influence of music on a person's character and moral and ethical behavior (Davis, Gfeller, and Thaut 2008). Like the Greeks, Boethius regarded music as "a corollary of arithmetic, thus exemplifying in sounds the fundamental principles of order and harmony that prevail throughout the universe" (Grout 1973, 23). *Musica humana*, one of the three-fold divisions of music proposed by Boethius, showed how this order and harmony were exemplified in the human body and soul. Boethius believed music could influence human character and morals and have either beneficial or detrimental effects on the health and harmony of body and soul. Because of this, music became an important element in educating the young during the Middle Ages, holding a place in the four higher subjects in the medieval educational system (Grout 1973).

The Christian Church was the predominant influence on life in the Western world during the Middle Ages. Musical practices, like all other areas of life, were regulated by the church. The church regarded certain forms of music as unsuitable because they had pagan associations and would be detrimental to moral and ethical behavior (Grout 1973). Gregorian chant and the mass were the foundation of western musical cultural life of the Middle Ages (Scholl and White 1970, 47).

Music was to serve religion by opening the mind to Christian teachings and disposing it to holy thoughts. According to the prevalent theology of the day, disease was a punishment for sin. Consequently, religion and religious music played an important part in the medical practices of the Middle Ages: Special hymns were used as remedies for colds and other maladies; music was composed to honor saints who supposedly protected people from illness; and court composers wrote special music to help and cheer people of high rank who became ill (Boxberger 1962).

During the Middles Ages, a peculiar malady known as *tarantism* arose and was particularly prevalent in Italy (Alvin 1975; Boxberger 1962; Feder and Feder 1981; Schullian and Schoen 1948). This disease, believed to be caused by the sting of the tarantula, was characterized by alternating fits of frenzy and complete inertia. Whether this was a nervous disorder or, as some suspect, a persistence of pagan orgies and ecstatic dances which were now at odds with the prevailing Christian society, the fact remains that treatment and catharsis were achieved only through music and dancing. In order to effect a cure, musicians had to match their music to the patient's symptoms (dancing, violent behavior, sleeping, or melancholy). The curative *tarantellas* would mirror the tempi and movements appropriate to the particular type of spider that had bitten and taken possession of the afflicted individual and then change to show the return of the patient's identity and the fight against the spider's possession. Thus, through a treatment process based on specially organized music and dance that was specific to the patient and his or her individual manifestation of symptoms, the tarantism eventually would be cured (Alvin 1975; Feder and Feder 1981).

During the Middle Ages, the Greek and Roman traditions of philosophy, music, and medicine were preserved in the Arab culture, which was at its height in the eighth and ninth centuries (Feder and Feder 1981; Pratt 1989). Works of Greek physicians and philosophers were translated into Arabic, and the idea that musical regularity was related to universal order and relations was an integral part of Arab thought. In hospitals in Cairo, music was played on the wards, with human voices or stringed instruments being selected with regard to the proper proportion of the universal order (Feder and Feder 1981). Ibn Hindu, an eleventh century physician and theorist, discussed the psychic effects and therapeutic applications of the Arabian musical modes and felt that doctors should study music in order to be well rounded (Pratt 1989). The Sufi masters, the mystics of Islamic society, also advocated music's healing powers, speaking of music as being "life and health, a reflection of the grand scheme, divine itself" (Kenny 1982, 76). With the Crusades, Islamic and Arabic influences began to impact Europe, and Europeans began to rediscover Greek ideas, largely as they had been preserved and interpreted by Arabic scholars (Feder and Feder 1981; Pratt 1989).

THE RENAISSANCE

In the late middle ages, nation-states were assuming power in Europe. Control was now divided between two powers: "According to the medieval ideal of a universal society, God has assigned the care of the human race to two powers, church and state. One is in charge of divine concerns, the other human" (de Bary 2001, 321). The church's role diminished; the powers of individual states and their monarchs increased. By the time of the high Renaissance, corruption was notable in the papacy, as exemplified by Pope Paul II, who reigned from 1464 to 1471 (de Bary, 326).

During the Renaissance, which is associated with the fifteenth century, both musicians and physicians looked back to the classical Greek period for inspiration. Music was essential in the education of the Renaissance man:

"The ideal of the time was . . . the universally educated man who . . . was a perfect physical specimen as well. To rear such a man a well-rounded musical education was considered indispensable" (Lang 1941, 298). This was a time when music was greatly valued in the royal courts and when many monarchs were talented and well-trained musicians. The Renaissance also marked the advent of a music-loving public (Lang, 300), as well as the development of amateur music.

The prevailing view of health as a state of harmony and disease as a state of disharmony replaced the medieval view that disease was a punishment for sin. The Greek theory of the four humors, or elements, which must be in balance for a state of health, became "a point of contact for music and medicine, functioning in both medical and musical theory" (Boxberger 1962, 152). Just as medical theorists had derived the four humors of the human body (black bile, phlegm, blood, and yellow bile) and their corresponding temperaments (melancholic, phlegmatic, sanguine, and choleric) from the four elements that constituted the world according to Empedoclean theory (earth, water, air, and fire), so now did music theorists pair four musical vocal ranges (bass, tenor, alto, and soprano) with the Empedoclean cosmic elements. The four music modes commonly used at this time (Mixolydian, Dorian, Lydian, and Phrygian) were also related to the four musical elements and their corresponding temperaments (see Table 3-1). For people living during the Renaissance, harmony or health in music, in the body, and in the cosmos was required for a proper balance of the four elements (Boxberger 1962; Schullian and Schoen 1948). Application of the proper type of music could help restore balance and health in body and spirit.

The close connection between music and medicine during the Renaissance is also illustrated by the writings of Gioseffo Zarlino (1517–1590), a sixteenth-century music theorist and composer. Zarlino felt that music was indispensable to the practice of medicine, for a knowledge of music enabled a physician both to prescribe the proper proportion of the elements needed to restore health and to have the skill necessary to judge the rhythm of the human pulse correctly

Table 3-1
RELATIONSHIPS BETWEEN THE COSMIC, HUMAN, AND
MUSICAL SPHERES DURING THE RENAISSANCE

Cosmic	*Human*			*Musical*	
Element	*"Humor"*	*Source*	*Temperament*	*Element*	*Mode*
fire	yellow bile	liver	choleric	soprano	Phrygian
air	blood	heart	sanguine	alto	Lydian
water	phlegm	brain	phlegmatic	tenor	Dorian
earth	black bile	spleen	melancholic	bass	Mixolydian

(Schullian and Schoen 1948). Zarlino credited music with many beneficial effects, including those of mitigating pain, restoring hearing to the deaf, healing vermin bites, curing insanity and the habit of drunkenness, and banishing pestilence. In addition, Zarlino strongly believed that each of the different modes used in music could serve to arouse or abate particular passions and affections (i.e., moods, emotions, or feelings). Music was a source of both curative and preventive powers:

> Music in the Renaissance was not only used as a remedy for melancholy, despair, and madness, but also prescribed by physicians as preventive medicine. Properly dispensed music was recognized then, as it is today, as a powerful tool to enhance emotional health. (Davis, Gfeller, and Thaut 2008, 21)

During the Renaissance, music also became more unified with medicine "as Renaissance man attempted to integrate all areas of knowledge" (Weldin and Eagle 1991, 14). Renaissance physicians believed that music could have powerful effects on human psychological states, and it was common and accepted medical practice at this time to use music as preventive medicine. For example, Tommaso del Garbo, in giving medical advice on how to avoid the plague, stressed the importance of a happy state of mind and the desirability of listening to music (Schullian and Schoen 1948). Music was believed to have beneficial emotional effects that would help people resist disease, something that was of vital importance during this era of widespread plagues. Ambroise Pare, a surgeon of the time, also used music to ease pain and relieve symptoms of gout and sciatica (Feder and Feder 1981; Weldin and Eagle 1991).

THE BAROQUE ERA

The Baroque, or Age of Reason, brought new means of inquiry. Navigation and trade with eastern nations brought greater prosperity and new ideas. The desire for goods and the manufacturing process to produce them led to a mass market for the arts. This was also a period of growth in science, with the invention of the microscope and telescope and new mathematical systems that allowed observations to be codified: "Among its original members, the French Academy of Sciences included Descartes, Pascal, Fermat, Galileo, Newton, Leibniz, Robert Boyle, and William Harvey" (Scholl and White 1970, 116). These important figures helped shape man's view of the world and universe. This was followed by the "Age of Enlightenment."

During the Baroque Era, roughly, 1600–1750, a general philosophical orientation in medicine toward the theory of the four humors and an emphasis in musical composition on the ability of music to arouse affections and passions continued to provide a common meeting ground for music and medicine.

The belief in music's power to affect the character, affections, passions, mind, and body of human beings became codified by German music theorists in the *Figurenlehre,* or doctrine of figures (Grout 1973). In fact, "if there is any common thread that unites the great variety of music that we call baroque, then, it is an underlying faith in music's power, indeed its obligation, to move the affections" (Palisca 1968, 4–5). Numerous references to music's therapeutic effects made by the writers of this time, such as Shakespeare and Spencer, are further evidence of a strong popular belief in music's curative powers (Boxberger 1962).

For royalty, music retained its importance as a medical cure during this period. For example, in 1737, the Queen of Spain engaged the services of the famous Italian singer Farinelli to rouse King Philip V from his acute melancholia. Farinelli's efforts had such a beneficial effect that he was subsequently employed as a personal singer to the king, and he sang every night to keep King Philip in good spirits (Alvin 1975).

Physicians continued to write about purported curative effects of music for various physical maladies and diseases during the Baroque Era. However, from the seventeenth century onward, they also began to write more specifically about music's psychological effects. For example, Burton, in his 1621 classic, *The Anatomy of Melancholy,* devoted an entire chapter to using music as a remedy (Rogers 1918). Louis Roger, an eighteenth century French physician, wrote a serious treatise based on carefully observed case histories, and he advocated music as therapy to give order to minds craving structure and to stimulate the nervous system through sympathetic vibration, thereby helping them "throw off the thickened and foreign humors" (Feder and Feder 1981, 11). Roger also discussed music's effects on the human body and emphasized the need for careful scientific observation and experimentation to substantiate the salutary effects of music. In his review of seventeenth- and eighteenth-century treatises on music and medicine, Carapetyan noted that music received much serious consideration from the physicians of the time: "A number of these writers reject the well-known legends and strive to establish a more plausible and scientific place for music in the cure of psychopathic cases and of nervous disorders" (Schullian and Schoen 1948, 146).

THE MID-EIGHTEENTH CENTURY THROUGH
THE NINETEENTH CENTURY

Although the broad claims made for music's therapeutic power were beginning to be examined more critically during the last half of the eighteenth century and the early nineteenth century, some affinity remained between music and medicine. Davis, Gfeller, and Thaut (2008) report that the earliest known reference to music therapy in the United States was an unsigned article in *Columbian Magazine* in 1789. The article, entitled "Music Physically Considered," presented basic principles of music therapy that are still in use today and provided evidence of music therapy practice in Europe. (22)

Heller (1987, 361) noted that this article linked "European antecedents and consequent American developments in the field." Throughout the nineteenth century, many physicians remained convinced that music could play an important role in treating mental and emotional illnesses (Pratt 1989). Since many of the more traditional forms of medical treatment available in the nineteenth century were often life threatening, the therapeutic use of music offered an attractive, more humane, alternative approach to treatment (Davis 1987). As knowledge and understanding of human physiology increased during the nineteenth century, several physicians also began to investigate music's effects on physical parameters such as blood pressure, pulse rate, respiration, and digestion, and they circulated specialized scientific reports on music's physiological influences (Weldin and Eagle 1991). In addition, some musician-scientists of the time, such as Hermann von Helmholtz and Hector Berlioz, investigated and wrote of the effects of music and sound on human behavior and the power of music to relieve stress and cure illness (Weldin and Eagle 1991).

Late in the eighteenth century, the therapeutic effects of music received public attention as the press in the United States began to publish stories dealing with music as an adjunct to medical practice, especially to influence mental and emotional conditions (Heller 1987). Even as late as the 1960s, music therapy was often found in the Department of Adjunctive Therapy. In 1776, an article in the *New York Weekly Magazine* reported curing a fever with music (Heller 1987, 37).

Early in the nineteenth century, medical and psychiatric journals in the United States began to include reports advocating music as a viable alternative treatment for various mental and physical disorders (Davis 1987; Heller 1987). The physician/psychiatrist Benjamin Rush, a professor at the University of Pennsylvania, was a strong advocate for using music in treating mental disease. He included the therapeutic use of music in one of his sophisticated courses in psychiatry (Davis 1987) and likely encouraged his students to research the topic (Davis and Gfeller 1992). In 1804, Edwin Atlee wrote his dissertation on the topic, called *An Inaugural Essay on the Influence of Music in the Cure of Diseases* (Davis 1987, 77), which proposed that music was especially useful in *treating* mental disorders because of its unique capacity "to focus one's attention on healthy thoughts" (Heller 1987, 39). Two years later, Samuel Matthews' dissertation, *On the Effects of Music in Curing and Palliating Diseases*, outlined the therapeutic uses of music in the treatment of both mental and physical illnesses (Davis 1987, 78). Matthews noted music's ability to counteract pain as well as to influence moods and emotional states. He anticipated later principles of music therapy practice by recognizing the importance of the client's musical background, training, and preferences in selecting music for therapeutic purposes and by recommending that, in treating mental disorders, therapists first use music that matches the patient's mood and then gradually change the music to move the patient to the desired mood. This latter recommendation is now generally known as the *iso principle*. Heller (1987) noted that Matthews was also the first to advocate *in print* that music therapy be used in existing institutions.

Around the beginning of the nineteenth century, Pinel and other French physicians were using music to treat mental and nervous diseases such as hysteria (Rogers 1918). In 1846, Chomet presented his treatise, *The Influence of Music on Health and Life*, to the Paris Academy of Sciences, "a fact which shows the interest of a learned body in the subject" (Alvin 1975, 48). In an 1874 article entitled "Music as Medicine," Whittaker brought Chomet's ideas to the attention of physicians in the United States (Davis 1987; Davis, Gfeller, and Thaut 2008). This transfer of ideas led to an increased interest in the therapeutic use of music, especially as a viable treatment for psychiatric disorders. In 1878, a New York newspaper and the *Virginia Medical Monthly* reported a series of experiments testing the reactions of mentally ill patients at Blackwell's Island to live vocal and instrumental music. The patients responded so favorably to experimental music treatment of live concerts and individual sessions that the New York City Charities Commissioner and the hospital's medical director supported additional experimentation on the use of music to alleviate suffering among the destitute mentally ill (Davis 1987). George Adler Blumer, a leading reformer in the treatment of the mentally ill, advocated music therapy to treat the mentally ill in his article "Music in its Relation to the Mind" that appeared in the *American Journal of Insanity* (Davis, Gfeller, and Thaut 2008). Blumer recognized music's therapeutic value without making extravagant claims for its power, basing his argument on European, British, and American scientific publications and his own observations. As chief executive officer of Utica State Hospital, Blumer also hired musicians to perform for the patients and "may have been the first person to establish an ongoing music therapy program in an American hospital" (Davis 1987, 84). The neurologist James Leonard Corning, another physician of this time who was interested in music's psychological effects, used music extensively in private practice as a contribution to emotional therapy for his patients. In 1899, he published *The Use of Musical Vibrations Before and During Sleep − Supplementary Employment of Chromatoscopic Figures − A Contribution to the Therapeutics of Emotion* (Davis, Gfeller, and Thaut 2008, 26). This paper discussed the physiological and psychological constructs that provided a rationale for treating mental illness with aural and visual stimuli and described his controlled experiments to treat mental and nervous diseases and positively influence his patients' feelings.

Corning's premise was that music could be used to suppress the bad dreams of his patients, thus cleansing the mind and enabling patients to function more effectively during their waking hours (Davis 1987).

The therapeutic use of music was introduced in London hospitals in the late nineteenth century (Davis 1989). In 1891, the Reverend Frederick Kill Harford founded the Guild of St. Cecilia, an organization that provided on-call musicians to London hospitals to perform live sedative music to help dispel anxiety, reduce pain, and induce sleep in hospitalized patients. Harford emphasized that the Guild would work closely with the medical profession, dispensing its musical tranquilizer only upon the request of a physician, and also stressed that the musicians should be remunerated for their services. The use of music boxes and phonographs was recommended to help continue treatments between the musicians' visits. Guild members also conducted experiments to determine which mental and physical ailments were treated most effectively by music. They achieved some success in soothing patients, eliciting speech in some depressed patients, reducing fevers, calming delirium associated with high fever, and sedating patients with certain nervous disorders. Experiments with both stimulative and sedative music showed that while most patients felt they benefitted more from sedative music, some were interested in stimulative music. Davis (1989, 20) noted that Harford was "astute in his observation that differences in personality, age, and sex were important variables to consider when choosing appropriate music for patients." The Guild of St. Cecilia enjoyed the endorsement of Florence Nightingale and Queen Victoria's physician, Sir Richard Quain, and also was the first British organization dedicated to providing quality music therapy services to a significant number of hospitalized people and to scientifically testing the influence of music on people with physical and mental illnesses (Davis 1989). At the close of the nineteenth century, in 1899, the British physician Davison reported the beneficial effects of music on hospital wards, citing cases in which music reduced or eliminated pain and fever and cured insomnia. Davison also noted the importance of matching the patient's mood when first applying the music treatment, and he theorized that music achieved its effects by influencing the body directly, replacing the painful vibrations of disease and causing the body to vibrate synchronously with the pleasant vibrations of the music (Pratt 1989).

During the nineteenth century, institutions and schools for individuals who were blind, deaf, or physically handicapped also began to use music as an important part of their therapeutic activity programs (Darrow and Heller 1985; Heller 1987; Solomon 1980). One of the first uses of music as adaptive therapy came in 1832 when Lowell Mason organized a music program at the Perkins School for the Blind. In the 1840s, music and rhythm programs were instituted at schools and asylums for the deaf and included in model curricula for deaf education. Music therapy programs appeared in schools for physically disabled children. In addition, a series of articles in a popular magazine of the time helped inform the general public of music's health benefits, especially noting the benefits of music and singing instruction as vehicles for molding character, promoting the internalization of good moral values, motivating the better feelings of one's nature, soothing discordant persons, guarding against consumption, strengthening the lungs, and curing indigestion (Koza 1990).

The preceding examples are evidence that several physicians, psychiatrists, social reformers, and educators advocated and sought to demonstrate music's therapeutic value during the late eighteenth and nineteenth centuries. However, as Boxberger (1962) noted, the use of music as therapy at this time seemed restricted to specific cases rather than incorporated in a general theory and philosophy of medical treatment. During this time period, the fields of music and medicine also began to diverge somewhat, as technology increased and music developed into a performing art while medicine developed into a specialized science. Nevertheless, those isolated instances of therapeutic applications of music in specific clinical cases and the beginning of more scientific research into the influence of music on human physiology and various mental and physical ailments kept interest in the potential palliative, salutary, and adaptive applications of music alive (Heller 1987) and provided "the necessary link for a continuation of the use of music in medicine into the Twentieth Century" (Weldin and Eagle 1991, 17).

THE TWENTIETH CENTURY

Although "the traditional close association between music and medical practice was largely forgotten in the technological explosion of the twentieth century" (Munro and Mount 1978, 1029), some scientific investigations into music's therapeutic benefits continued around the turn of the century. For example, laboratory experiments with both human and animal subjects demonstrated that changes in various physical functions were related to different types of music (Taylor 1981). Several musicians in the New York area (e.g., Eva Vescilius, Margaret Anderton, Isa Maud Ilsen, and Harriet Ayer Seymour) also promoted the therapeutic use of music throughout the early to middle part of the twentieth century by conducting experiments, providing music in hospitals, giving lectures and teaching courses on music therapy, and forming organizations advocating the use of music therapy. In the 1920s and 1930s, scientific studies into the psychological effects of and psychological responses to music increased, as the field of music psychology developed through the pioneering efforts of psychologists James Mursell, Max Schoen, and Carl Seashore (Weldin and Eagle 1991). During the 1940s and 1950s, researchers also investigated effects on physiological responses, while continuing to research the influence of music on mood changes and general mental health. According to Feder and Feder (1981, 116), "such studies persuaded the Veterans Administration to develop comprehensive music therapy programs at all VA hospitals" during this period. Edwina Eustis, who was the director of Special Projects, Hospitalized Veterans Music Service, Musicians Emergency Fund, reported that "in 1945, St. Albans Hospital appealed to M. E. F. to supply teachers for their patents [sic], and this was the beginning of our Hospitalized Veterans Music Service which has grown quickly under Gladys Douglas' direction" (Eustis 1952, 5).

Many soldiers who were wounded in World Wars I and II returned to the United States on special ships. If they arrived at a port that had one of the women's military bands, "the band . . . performed until all injured men disembarked and were loaded onto ambulences taking them to the nearby military hospital" (Sullivan 2007, 290).

According to Robb (1999, 314), 671,801 military personnel needed treatment after World War II. Pioneers, such as Margaret Anderton, Isa Maud Ilson, and Harriet Aver Seymour had used music in hospitals in World War I, setting a precedent that led to further incorporation of music in VA hospitals in World War II. In addition, "musicians and hospital workers were the predominant providers of music in hospitals during and after World War II" (Robb 1999, 316). The American Red Cross hired and trained recreational workers to provide entertainment and diversion in hospitals. Robb (1999) wrote of one musician hired in this type of position. Some of their work was on neuropsychiatric wards: "The men on the neuropsychiatric ward sang and danced in response to music, where no other stimuli seemed to reach them" (Robb 1999, 325). They also discussed the lyrics to some of the sentimental songs that were their favorites.

In World War II, women were allowed to enlist in the armed services, which led to the Women's Army Corps (WAC), Women Accepted for Volunteer Emergency Services (WAVES), the Coast Guard SPARS (from the motto *Semper Paratus*–Always Ready), and the Marine Corps Women's Reserve (MCWR). Music was prominent in these women's units:

> Each women's military division had women's military bands and drum and bugle corps. There were three full military bands, one on the United States west coast, and two on the east coast. The bands worked for the ASF [Army Service Forces] Medical Department entertaining the injured soldiers. (Sullivan 2007, 287)

Medical personnel who observed the soldiers' response to music were convinced of music's value in hospital settings. Their observations led to the creation of courses in music therapy and the formation of a national organization.

The advent of the phonograph also led to a renewed interest in the use of music in hospital settings around the turn of the century (Boxberger 1963).

Recorded music was used as a diversion, as an aid to inducing sleep, to calm fears associated with medical operations, and as an aid to anesthesia and analgesia (Taylor 1981). Although the medical community did not widely accept music therapy early in the twentieth century, some physicians did continue to promote and endorse the therapeutic use of music in the operating room, recovery areas, on adult and children's wards, and with orthopedic patients (Davis and Gfeller 1992). During World War I, music activities were prescribed as exercises for joints and muscles to aid military patients in recovering the use of wounded limbs (Tyson 1981). During the inter-war period and World War II, music received increasing use both as a general psychological stimulus in the total hospital environment and as an adjunct to psychiatric treatment (Tyson 1981).

The musician Willem Van de Wall, who worked in hospitals in New York and Pennsylvania, and the psychiatrist and composer Ira Altshuler, who worked at Wayne County General Hospital in Michigan, developed significant music therapy programs in mental hospitals and prisons during this period (Boxberger 1963; Collins 1982; Davis and Gfeller 1992). Van de Wall also published important books on music therapy with grants from the Russell Sage Foundation, including the comprehensive *Music in Institutions* (1936). He also lectured on music and health at Columbia University (Davis, Gfeller, and Thaut 2008, 31).

Music therapy expanded greatly in the 1940s due to its use in hospitals serving war veterans. Several courses were offered, both in hospitals and colleges, to prepare musicians to meet this need. Seymour and Garrett (1944) wrote a clinical training book, *An Instruction Course in the Use and Practice of Musical Therapy.*

Some special education settings also continued to show an interest in adaptive uses of music throughout the twentieth century. For example, schools and institutions for hearing impaired individuals used music to improve residual hearing function and facilitate speech development (Solomon 1980).

As music therapy developed into an organized professional discipline in the years following World War II, the therapeutic use of music came to be applied to clients with widely varying disorders and conditions. In recent years, the use of music as preventive medicine and as a strengthener of health and relaxation seems to be making a resurgence in the United States. Corporations such as MUZAK have made a business out of supplying background music to influence and regulate people's moods and behaviors in offices, businesses, industries, and many other commercial and public environments (Radocy and Boyle 2012). The therapeutic use of music is finding its way into the board rooms and wellness programs of businesses, hospitals, and major corporations as employers recognize the need to reduce stress, alleviate staff burnout, and promote wellness, and seek innovative and effective ways to encourage teamwork and enhance creativity (Clark and Ficken 1988; McCarthy 1992; Weitz 1993). In addition, as the holistic health movement focuses public attention on the interconnection of body, mind, and spirit, chants and "sound healing" practices that have their roots in Eastern countries and philosophies are being used as tools for healing, wholeness, relaxation, and consciousness expansion in the Western world as well (Bonny and Savary 1973, 1990; Crowe and Scovel 1996; Halpern 1978; Hamel 1979; Trevisan 1978).

Since the late 1970s, leading medical doctors have exhibited renewed interest in music's role in medical treatment, and scientific studies in the field of music and medicine have increased steadily (Bartlett, Kaufman, and Smeltekopp 1993; Harvey 1991; Maranto 1991; Pratt 1989; Taylor 1988, 1997). The early 1980s saw the development of several professional organizations related to the use of music in medicine and healing, among them the International Society for Music in Medicine, Biology of Music Making, Inc., and the International Association of Music for the Handicapped (Taylor 1988). In a related development connecting music and medicine, "a substantial number of physicians have begun to specialize in the treatment of 'musiogenic' physical disorders, or therapy for musicians" (Taylor 1988, 91).

Recent years have seen an increased interest in using music for the health and good of society in general. For example, the organization Music Therapists for Peace was founded in 1988. The members of this worldwide movement sponsor various projects and activities, with the aim of "making more conscious use of the possibilities of music to promote healing and unite people" (Moreno 1992, 87). During the 1991 Persian Gulf War, the Israeli government also used music's power to help its citizens cope with the crisis (Brodsky 1991). The Israeli Broadcasting Authority specifically structured its programming in the days before the crisis by playing songs stressing strength and national unity and giving specific instructions for safety and defense preparations in parodies of popular tunes. Then, on the first night of the attack, as people waited in their sealed-off, gas-proof rooms, soothing, nostalgic music was broadcast to help reduce fear and anxiety. During the war, only Hebrew songs were broadcast, and special children's music was played in the evening to help the children cope with the stress and trauma of the situation. In these ways, "through mass communication, the power of music was used to assist the entire population in developing more adaptive coping methods, which included instilling feelings of national unity and establishing support systems" (Brodsky 1991, 99).

Recently, interest in achieving healing through the application of music vibrations directly to the body has increased. Several experiments have shown that the process of applying carefully selected music and vibrational frequencies to the body through special speakers in tables or chairs or through music-electro-acupuncture techniques has reduced arthritic pain, decreased muscle rigidity, lessened insomnia, and facilitated the recovery of muscle function in stroke victims (Chesky and Michel 1991; Shi-jing, Hui-ju, Guo, and Maranto 1991; Skille 1989). Noting the medical profession's renewed interest in researching music's effects in healing and the worldwide concern with increased quality of life for individuals with various handicaps or disabilities, Pratt (1989) summarized developments in music and healing in the latter part of the twentieth century:

> There are signs that physicians and musicians are seeking out each other. . . . Throughout the world, there is an awakening, a renaissance of dialogue between the arts of medicine and music. . . . The conversation they began so long ago has been renewed, this time with new vigor, more information, and the camaraderie of old friends. (10)

QUESTIONS FOR THOUGHT AND DISCUSSION

1. How did the effectiveness of music as a cure at various times in history relate to the prevailing philosophy of the time?
2. What does faith or trust in a cure or method of treatment have to do with the effectiveness or power of that cure? Must one believe a healing power is present in a particular music experience in order to receive therapeutic benefits from that music experience?
3. Are there any theories, philosophies, or techniques that seem to be prevalent throughout the history of the use of music to promote health? If so, what are they, and why do you think they keep resurfacing?
4. What connections can you see between some of the ideas contained in the contemporary definition of music therapy presented in Chapter One of this book and the ways music has been used to promote health throughout history? In what practices and philosophies throughout history do you see echoes of the ideas that using music for therapeutic or healing purposes (1) involves a process, (2) is planned and goal-directed, based on individual assessment, (3) involves interaction and intervention, (4) relies primarily on music or music-based experiences, (5) is specifically prescribed, (6) is implemented by specially trained personnel, or (7) is directed toward meeting the specific needs of individual clients?

SUGGESTIONS FOR FURTHER READING

Boxberger, R. (1962). Historical bases for the use of music in therapy. In E. H. Schneider (Ed.), *Music therapy 1961*. (125–166). Lawrence, KS: Allen Press.

Davis, W. B. (1987). Music therapy in 19th century America. *Journal of Music Therapy*, *24*(2), 76–87.

Davis, W. B. (1989). Music therapy in Victorian England: Frederick Kill Harford and the Guild of St. Cecilia. *Music Therapy Perspectives, 7*, 17–22.

Davis, W. B., & Gfeller, K. E. (2008). Music therapy: Historical perspective. In W. B. Davis, K. E. Gfeller, & M. H. Thaut, *An introduction to music therapy: Theory and practice* (3rd ed.) (17–39). Silver Spring, MD: American Music Therapy Association.

Hamel, P. M. (1979). *Through music to the self.* Trans. by P. Lemesurier. Boulder, CO: Shambala. (Original work published 1976.)

Heller, G. N. (1987). Ideas, initiatives, and implementations: Music therapy in America, 1789–1848. *Journal of Music Therapy, 24(1)*, 35–46.

Pratt, R. R. (1989). A brief history of music and medicine. In M. H. M. Lee (Ed.), *Rehabilitation, music and human well-being* (1–12). St. Louis: MMB Music.

Solomon, A. L. (1980). Music in special education before 1930: Hearing and speech development. *Journal of Research in Music Education, 28(4)*, 236–242.

Taylor, D. C. (1981). Music in general hospital treatment from 1900–1950. *Journal of Music Therapy, 18(2)*, 62–73.

Taylor, D. B. (1988). Therapeutic musicians or musical physicians: The future is at stake. *Music Therapy Perspectives, 5*, 86–93.

Weldin, C., & Eagle, C. T. (1991). An historical overview of music medicine. In C. D. Maranto (Ed.), *Applications of music in medicine* (7–27). Washington, D.C.: National Association for Music Therapy.

Chapter Four

THE DEVELOPMENT OF MUSIC THERAPY
AS AN ORGANIZED PROFESSION

Although people have recognized music's therapeutic benefits since primitive times, music therapy did not emerge as an organized discipline until the mid-twentieth century. As Unkefer (1961) noted, the professional development of music therapy relates more closely to the development of activity therapy than to historical support for music's therapeutic effects. Boxberger (1963, 133) concluded that, although historical precedents for using music in healing may have influenced musicians to experiment with the use of music activities in treatment, "it was the need to make music applicable to the scientific aspects of medicine in the twentieth century that initiated the drive toward an organization based on common goals and purposes."

EARLY TWENTIETH-CENTURY ATTEMPTS
AT ORGANIZATION

Heller (2000, 248) observed that "people, places, organizations, and events of times gone by helped form the present and thus laid the ground work for the future." In the early twentieth century, a renewed interest in the use of music in hospitals led to a more vigorous promotion of the clinical practice of music therapy and the development of specific courses for training music therapists (Boxberger 1963; Taylor 1981). During this time, three women – Eva Augusta Vescelius, who was active between 1900 and 1917 (de l'Etoile 2000); Isa Maud Ilsen, who was active between 1905 and 1930 (Davis, Gfeller, and Thaut 2008, 28); and Harriet Ayer Seymour (lived 1867–1944), who was active between 1915 and 1944 (Davis 1997, 74) – founded organizations designed to promote the practice of music therapy and help train music therapy practitioners (Davis 1993). (For important writings of these three pioneers, see the reading list at the end of the chapter.) Although none of the efforts by these women resulted in a sustained national music therapy movement in the first half of the twentieth century, their pioneering work led to the recognition of music therapy as a viable form of treatment by organizations such as the American Red Cross and the United States Army (Davis and Gfeller 1992; Davis, Gfeller, and Thaut 2008) and "provided the impetus for the continued growth and development of music therapy during the second half of the twentieth century" (Davis 1993, 43).

Eva Vescelius and the National Therapeutic Society of New York

Early in the twentieth century, Eva Augusta Vescelius, a trained professional singer who sometimes performed concerts in hospitals and asylums, became interested in "mental therapy" and the use of music in healing. She developed a personal theory of music therapy, first conducting experiments at home to perfect her theories and then applying the therapeutic use of music to patients in hospitals or mental institutions (Davis 1993). She also actively promoted music therapy through various lectures, writings, and demonstrations (Davis 1993; Davis and Gfeller 1992; Davis, Gfeller, and Thaut 2008). Vescelius (1918, 379) asserted that the cures affected by music were "based on the law of harmonious rhythmic vibration." Thus, it was essential to use appropriate musical selections in therapeutic work and to have harmony between the musician-therapist who transmitted the music and the patient receiving the music. To that end, Vescelius developed a system for classifying musical selections as to types and uses, suggested specific music prescriptions for various ailments, and offered a course in "musico-therapy" to train musicians as therapists before they worked with patients (Davis 1993; Davis and Gfeller 1992; Vescelius 1918). Those who worked for and with her also had to be very competent musicians, as individual artistry would be reflected in and affect the healing potential of the music. Thus, Vescelius recognized the importance of both musical and therapeutic skills for those who would use music in healing.

In an attempt to organize the work of music therapists and promote the use of music therapy, Vescelius founded the National Therapeutic Society of New York City in 1903 and served as its president until her death in 1917. She also published the first American music therapy journal, *Music and Health*, in 1913; however, the periodical lasted for only three issues. Nevertheless, Vescelius strongly influenced many individuals who continued to pursue and promote the use of music therapy in the early twentieth century (Boxberger 1963) and espoused some ideas that are still used in music therapy training and practice today.

Early University Courses in Music Therapy

In 1919, Margaret Anderton, a pianist who provided music therapy to Canadian soldiers during World War I, offered the first university courses in music therapy at Columbia University in New York (Davis, Gfeller, and Thaut 2008, 28). Anderton's courses aimed to prepare musicians to work in hospitals, provide information on psychological and physical reactions to music, and demonstrate practical ways of using music to help patients with neuropsychiatric problems or orthopedic injuries (Davis and Gfeller 1992; Taylor 1981; Weldin and Eagle 1991). Isa Maud Ilsen and Willem Van de Wall, two other early music therapy pioneers, also taught courses on music and health at Columbia University in the early decades of the twentieth century (Davis and Gfeller 1992).

Isa Maud Ilsen and the National Association for Music in Hospitals

Isa Maud Ilsen became interested in music's therapeutic use while attending nursing school in 1905 (Davis 1993). Ilsen used music therapy to treat people with mental illnesses, mental retardation, and terminal illnesses and advocated using music in factories to help humanize working conditions. Working with injured soldiers in Canada and the United States during World War I, she used music to alleviate pain and help in the rehabilitation of those with corrective or reconstructive needs (Davis 1993; Davis and Gfeller 1992). Ilsen briefly served as a lecturer in "musico-therapy" with Margaret Anderton at Columbia University in 1919. She also had extensive experience as an administrator, working for the American Red Cross as director of Hospital Music in Reconstruction Hospitals in 1918 and later serving as associate secretary for the Department of Hospital Services, New York Tuberculosis and Health Association. In both these positions, Ilsen advocated the therapeutic use of music for her patients and worked as a clinician to provide these services. Seeing the need for an organization that would train people to use music in hospitals and bring properly prepared music programs into hospitals as a supplement to medical treatment, Ilsen founded the National Association for Music in Hospitals in 1926 (Davis 1993; Davis and Gfeller 1992; Davis, Gfeller, and Thaut 2008; Graham 1974). This organization solicited medical professionals' support for the therapeutic use of music in hospitals and encouraged philanthropists to raise funds that were used to train music therapists and transport them to local hospitals and institutions.

Ilsen established several specific rules of conduct for using music in hospitals and emphasized that people using music in hospitals should ensure that the music is appropriate to the needs of the situation as well as to the patient's needs. According to Ilsen, music was to serve as an adjunct to treatment; therefore, it should never interfere with hospital routines and procedures (Boxberger 1963). Ilsen insisted on using qualified, trained professionals to provide music therapy services to patients and believed that a variety of music was necessary. She also believed it was important that the musicians be able to relate to clients and staff. As Davis (1993) noted, several of Ilsen's rules and ideas remain relevant to contemporary music therapy practice.

Harriet Ayer Seymour and the National Foundation for Music Therapy

Another active advocate of music therapy in the first half of the twentieth century, Harriet Ayer Seymour, was acquainted with the writings of Eva Vescelius and had direct experience working with hospitalized veterans during World War I. In 1920, she "taught classes at Steinway Hall in New York City, that housed the National Foundation of Music Therapy, of which she was president" (de l'Etoile 2000, 57). Seymour published a guide to the therapeutic use of music, entitled *What Music Can Do for You*, and she later taught courses and workshops in the New York City area on the therapeutic use of music (Boxberger 1963; Davis 1993, 1996; Davis and Gfeller 1992; Davis, Gfeller, and Thaut 2008). During the 1930s, Seymour became active in bringing live music to New York hospitals and prisons in connection with the Federal Music Project of the Works Project Administration (WPA). In connection with this work, she became involved with experiments striving to classify songs on the basis of their psychological and physiological effects. In the early 1940s, she worked with sick children and adults in New York City, becoming an especially strong advocate for using music in caring for sick children (Davis 1996).

Seymour founded the National Foundation for Music Therapy in 1941. As president of this organization until her death in 1944, she presented lectures and classes to train music therapists, emphasizing the use of music therapy with sick or injured World War II veterans. Seymour reportedly trained over 500 "musical doctors" to work in New York City hospitals during the short existence of her organization (Davis 1993; Davis, Gfeller, and Thaut 2008). Seymour's treatment philosophy incorporated the use of music and constructive thought (i.e., positive thinking) and prescribed the use of particular styles of music, or certain musical styles coupled with mental imagery, for various disorders, including heart ailments, paralysis, and depression. She included the use of folk music and marches in her treatments. In training music therapists, Seymour looked for people who could play music with good tone and rhythm, were sensitive to the patient's reactions, and "had a desire to become a 'channel' for the healing properties of music" (Davis 1993, 43). Some of these same qualities remain important to people who desire to become music therapists today. Just prior to her death, Seymour published *An Instruction Course in the Use and Practice of Music Therapy*, which provided information on appropriate ways to use music as therapy for various client populations. This was the first published practical handbook for the clinical practice of music therapy (Davis 1996).

THE DEVELOPMENT OF MUSIC THERAPY PROGRAMS IN INSTITUTIONS

While the activities and organizations of Vescelius, Ilsen, and Seymour were concentrated in the New York City area, interest in music therapy was present elsewhere in the United States during the first half of the twentieth century. Even though music therapy received only limited support and acceptance from the medical community, reports of music therapy activity in institutions continued to increase (Davis and Gfeller 1992; Taylor 1981). For example, some physicians and researchers promoted using music in operating rooms, and, by 1929, Duke University was using music extensively, giving every patient access to radio reception by way of speakers or earphones located throughout the hospital. During this period, the musician/therapist Willen van de Wall and the psychiatrist/musician/composer Ira Altshuler also developed significant music therapy programs at various institutions in New York, Pennsylvania, and Michigan.

Willem van de Wall

Willem van de Wall (1887–1953), who was considered by many to be one of the key early organizers and innovators in music therapy in the United States, contributed much to the development of music therapy programs in mental hospitals and prisons in the years between World War I and World War II (Boxberger 1963; Clair and Heller 1989; Davis 1997; Davis and Gfeller 1992). Several of his writings offer many ideas for using music with patients who have mental disorders, with prisoners, and with children with varying degrees of mentally deficiencies. They also describe ways to use music for pain relief, to promote aesthetic satisfaction, relaxation, emotional expression, and stress reduction in adults, and to increase efficient production in industrial settings (Clair and Heller 1989). Van de Wall had a career as a professional harpist with the Metropolitan Opera House, the New York Symphony, and the Marine Band. He also lectured at Columbia University between 1925 and 1932 (Davis, Gfeller, and Thaut 2008). After World War I, he began to work with music in the treatment of mental illness. His program at Central Islip State Hospital in New York attracted the attention of the Russell Sage Foundation, which subsequently supported his work. In 1923, Van de Wall began his tenure at Pennsylvania's Allentown State Hospital for Mental Diseases, where he established the first comprehensive institutional music therapy program in the United States (Boxberger 1963; Davis and Gfeller 1992; Graham 1974; Wheeler and Golden 1987). This hospital maintained an internship program and trained many music therapists. The components of this program became a prototype for music therapy programs across the United States. Van de Wall's monumental work *Music in Institutions*, written in 1936, summarizes this program.

Van de Wall believed that the most therapeutic music was that which the patient preferred, with the patient's particular racial, cultural, and social history also being important variables. In 1923, he advocated using music in the general hospital to "overcome apathy, provide moments of emotional unity, and promote the healing process" (Clair and Heller 1989, 169), and he argued that music was cost-effective medicine because it could serve many patients simultaneously and make the hospital environment more appealing to patients and their families. Van de Wall theorized that music was an effective therapy for patients suffering from mental illnesses because of its structure and organization, its power as a sensory stimulant, its ability to awaken emotions and provide a means of appropriate emotional expression, its ability to elicit memories, and, most importantly, because it provided a way for patients to actively participate in their treatment. As Part III of this text clarifies, some of these ideas still form the basis for much of music therapy practice today. Van de Wall's 1946 book, *Music in Hospitals*, summarizes his ideas, which were formed from his research and experience, and contains sections on the functions of music and the organization of hospitals, as well as practical suggestions for implementing hospital music programs and for educating and training hospital musicians. Clair and Heller (1989, 176) call this work van de Wall's legacy and a fitting culmination to his career, noting that "it contains a concise summary of the best information on music therapy available at that time, as well as the seeds of present and future ideas on those topics."

Ira Altshuler

In 1938, Dr. Ira M. Altshuler founded another significant institutional music therapy program at Detroit's Eloise Hospital (later called Wayne County General Hospital) in Michigan (Collins 1982; Davis 2003). Altshuler received his medical training in Switzerland and completed his training in neuropsychiatry at Harvard Medical School in 1927 and 1928. He was also a musician and composer who had specific theories about the way music acted upon psychiatric patients, and he wrote musical compositions for his clinical work and research in music therapy at Eloise. Altshuler's (1948) essay, "A Psychiatrist's Experience with Music as a Therapeutic Agent," summarized his work and theories. He advocated a strong relationship between psychiatry and music and stressed the importance of research on music and the relationship between man and music (Pratt 1989).

Altshuler noted the relationship between music and emotional expression. One of his most significant contributions to music therapy was his development of the "iso" principle in 1948, something that still plays a major role in music therapy clinical practice today. According to Altshuler's "iso" principle, music therapists must first use music that matches the patient's mood, activity level, or condition before gradually changing the music by altering the rhythm, tempo, dynamics, and melody (Davis 2003, 251) to effect a change in these areas. Altshuler also theorized that music was effective in helping patients with severe mental disturbances because music bypassed cerebral interpretive relays and appealed directly to the seat of aesthetic reactions, which he believed was located in the thalamus.

THE SUSTAINED MOVE TOWARD PROFESSIONAL ORGANIZATION FOLLOWING WORLD WAR II

During the course of their efforts to care for large numbers of soldiers wounded in World War II, physicians discovered that music could not only boost morale but also facilitate recovery. The physician George Ainlay supported using music in military hospitals and was largely responsible for having the U.S. Army and War Department develop and publish various music materials (Pratt 1989; Weldin and Eagle 1991). In 1943, music became part of the Army's Reconditioning Program, which was designed to help the wounded return to active duty or civilian life (Rorke 1996; Tyson 1981). In this model program, goal-directed, specifically prescribed music activities involving active participation (e.g., singing, playing instruments, making instruments, writing song parodies, doing calisthenics to music), passive participation (e.g., listening to music and discussing music applications) or audioreception (listening only to live or recorded music) were used (a) to facilitate exercise, (b) as postoperative exercises for patients with orthopedic or lung impairments, (c) as educational activities, (d) for resocialization, or (e) to assist in neuropsychiatric treatment (Rorke 1996). Music continued as part of the treatment program in 122 Veterans Administration Hospitals during the post-war years (1946–1950). Using music to help hospitalized veterans greatly stimulated the general use of music in hospitals and state institutions, which led to a marked increase in the employment of hospital musicians during the mid to late 1940s (Schneider, Unkefer, and Gaston 1968).

Most of the musicians who worked in Veterans Administration Hospitals and state institutions during the 1940s were volunteers or part-time staff members, with little professional training or status (Davis and Gfeller 1992).

The experiences of hospital musicians in both World War I and World War II led to many musicians joining this effort. This was recreational music, not music therapy. However, as the patient's responses to the music were noticed, the foundation for music therapy was laid. The service of musicians working in recreational therapy was noticed by Willem van de Wall and influenced his later writings (van de Wall 1948).

One example of a hospital musician working in the recreation department was Marian Erdman, who worked for the American Red Cross from 1945 to 1948 (Robb 1999). Because Erdman had experience as a pianist, she helped organize various music activities:

> Marian used her musical talents to provide a variety of activities in the recreation hall. Organizing dances, leading sing-alongs, leading parties with musical themes, and writing variety shows were among the many activities Marian provided in the recreation hall. (Robb 1999, 321)

Requests from hospitals to train these musicians in basic clinical techniques precipitated the development of college-degree programs in music therapy.

Roy Underwood developed the first curriculum leading to a bachelor's degree in music therapy in 1944 (Gilliland 1952) at what is now Michigan State University. At the University of Kansas, the first didactic and laboratory course was taught in 1946 (Schneider, Unkefer, and Gaston 1968), and the first music therapy degree was offered in 1948. This led to the first graduate music therapy program, under the direction of Dr. E. Thayer Gaston, then chairman of the Music Education Department (Davis, Gfeller, and Thaut 2008). He was "perhaps the most influential figure in American music therapy during this time and for the next 20 years" (Maranto 1993b, 608). In addition to initiating music therapy training programs at the undergraduate and graduate levels at the University of Kansas, Gaston also encouraged much research in the field, wrote and lectured extensively in support of using music in therapy, and established the first music therapy internship training site in collaboration with the renowned Menninger Clinic in Topeka, Kansas (Davis and Gfeller 1992; R. Johnson 1981). Internship programs soon followed in Topeka, Kansas, at Winter Veterans Administration Hospital, directed by Richard Gray, and at Topeka State Hospital, directed by Wayne Ruppenthal. Osawatomie State Hospital in Kansas soon followed, with a program directed by Lee Garton. Because of his leadership in scientific thought, research, and training in music therapy and education in the United States, many music therapists label E. Thayer Gaston as the "father of music therapy" (R. Johnson 1981, 279).

During the late 1940s, music therapy training programs were also initiated at institutions such as Chicago Musical College; the College of the Pacific in Stockton, California (1947), by Wilhemina Harbert; and Alverno College in Milwaukee, Wisconsin (1948), by Sister Xaveria, in cooperation with the

Sacred Heart School of Nursing (de l'Etoile 2000, 60). Some music therapy courses were taught at the Boston School of Occupational Therapy (Boxberger 1963; Davis and Gfeller 1992). This trend toward providing increased training for music therapists (or hospital musicians) did much to promote the growth of music therapy as a recognized professional discipline and helped provide the impetus for the formation of a national organization specific to the field of music therapy (Davis and Gfeller 1992; Lathom 1980).

In the 1940s, three professional music associations – the Music Teachers National Association (MTNA), the National Music Council (NMC), and the Music Educators National Conference (MENC) – were particularly influential in establishing communication among people working with therapeutic or functional music (Boxberger 1963). During the early years of the decade, MTNA heard special reports on music therapy projects (Altshuler 1940) and established special committees on Music in Psychotherapy, Music in Industry, and Music Therapy. Persons who were instrumental in establishing some of the first music therapy college programs were among the members of these committees. In 1945, based on the results of a 1944 survey that showed the need for medical testing of the effects of music and for standard curricular programs to train qualified personnel (van de Wall 1944), NMC formed the Committee on the Use of Music in Hospitals to work with musicians and psychiatrists in exploring the possibilities for adequately training workers to use music in therapy. Also in 1945, the councils of MENC recommended that the use of music in hospitals (i.e., any music performance presented at a hospital) be differentiated from the use of music in therapy and that definite steps be taken toward licensing people who practiced and taught music therapy. In addition, MENC formed the Special Committee on Functional Music, whose members began to emphasize the need for controlled research in music therapy and for some kind of publication for the field (Gaston 1947).

During 1948 and 1949, regional meetings of music therapists, hospital musicians, and others active in the field were held in Massachusetts, Kansas, and Illinois. At some of these meetings, plans for forming a national organization specifically for music therapy were discussed, but no definite progress was made. Meanwhile, MTNA's Committee on Music Therapy continued to present informational sessions on music therapy at various meetings. At MTNA's annual meeting in Cleveland, Ohio, February 28 to March 2, 1950, a special sectional meeting for the purpose of developing a national organization for music therapy was held. At this time, Ray Green was elected chairman of the organizational committee. On June 1, 1950, when reporting to an annual meeting of NMC in his capacity as chairman of NMC's Committee on the Use of Music in Hospitals, Green announced that a meeting would be held the following day to form an organization in the field of hospital music (Boxberger 1963).

The National Association for Music Therapy

The organizational meeting that marked the beginning of the National Association for Music Therapy (NAMT), the first enduring professional music therapy organization in the United States, was held on June 2, 1950, in New York City. Ray Green was elected as the first president, and one standing committee, the Research Committee, was established (Boxberger 1963). According to its constitution, the Association's purpose was "the progressive development of the use of music to accomplish therapeutic aims and the advancement of training, education, and research in the music therapy profession" (NAMT 1994a, xix).

From its inception in 1950 to its unification with the American Association for Music Therapy in 1998, NAMT continued to serve this purpose by developing and periodically reviewing standards for college course requirements, establishing criteria for the certification and registration of music therapists, establishing standards for clinical practice and ethical conduct, and encouraging research and publication among members of the profession. In 1956, NAMT established the first professional music therapy credential in the United States, the title of Registered Music Therapist (RMT), in conjunction with the accrediting agency, the National Association for Schools of Music (NASM) (Boxberger 1963; Davis and Gfeller 1992). This title signified that the individual had met all music therapy educational and clinical training standards established by NAMT and NASM. NAMT has also published a number of professional materials. From 1951–1962, NAMT published annual books of proceedings (e.g., *Music Therapy 1*) and a *Bulletin* that appeared three times a year. In 1964, NAMT began to publish a quarterly research journal, the *Journal of Music Therapy*, with William W. Sears as editor, as well as a bimonthly member newsletter. Since 1982, NAMT has also published *Music Therapy Perspectives*, a more clinically and practically oriented journal. Michael G. McGuire was the first editor of *Music Therapy Perspectives*. In 1961, NAMT established a central office in Lawrence, Kansas, and announced it to its membership at the Twelfth Annual Conference in Milwaukee. Ruth Boxberger was the first coordinator, with E. Thayer Gaston as consultant *(Bulletin of NAMT* 1961: *10*, 26). Both served on a nonpay basis, with the budget going to operational cash and secretarial assistance. Other coordinators included Helen Bonny and Margaret Sears, who served for many years.

For many years, NAMT's national office was located in Lawrence, Kansas. In 1982, it relocated to Washington, D.C., and later moved to Silver Spring, Maryland, a Washington suburb. On January 1, 1998, NAMT joined with the American Association for Music Therapy to form the American Music Therapy Association (AMTA). NAMT's governance structure was carried over into what is currently the only professional music therapy association in the United States. AMTA maintains an office in Silver Spring (AMTA 1998).

The American Association for Music Therapy

In 1971, a group of music therapists in the New York City area who had philosophical differences with the NAMT over the structure of clinical and educational training programs and a desire for more flexible internship sites in the area met at New York University and established a second professional organization for music therapists in the United States (Maranto 1993b; Tyson 1981; Wheeler and Golden 1987). Initially called the Urban Federation for Music Therapists, this group changed its name to the American Association for Music Therapy (AAMT) in 1975 to reflect the organization's broadening scope beyond the New York area and the urban northeast (Wheeler and Golden 1987).

Although AAMT offered more flexibility in its educational and clinical training programs by following a competency-based rather than a course-based approach, AAMT's purposes remained very similar to those of NAMT. The AAMT dedicated itself to

- improving the quality of life through the use of music in therapy
- establishing standards of professional competence
- implementing these standards through certification of individuals and approval of university curricula
- promoting and disseminating research through professional publications
- fostering community awareness and public education in regard to the goals and applications of music therapy
- developing employment opportunities
- developing continuing education curricula reflective of new trends in the field. (AAMT 1993, 1)

From 1981–1997, the AAMT published an annual professional journal, *Music Therapy*, which included clinical as well as research reports. It also published a quarterly member newsletter and the *Music Therapy International Report* (formerly *The International Newsletter of Music Therapy*). On January 1, 1998, AAMT joined with NAMT to form the American Music Therapy Association (AMTA).

The American Music Therapy Association

In 1994, the leadership and governing bodies of the AAMT and the NAMT began discussing possible unification of the two groups to form one professional association for music therapists in the United States (Aigen 1994;

Hunter 1994). During 1996, the members of the AAMT and the NAMT voted overwhelmingly in favor of unification, and the new, unified American Music Therapy Association (AMTA) came into being on January 1, 1998 ("Introducing the American Music Therapy Association" 1998). With unification, AMTA became the only music therapy professional membership association in the United States. In its first year of existence, AMTA had 3,611 members as of May 15, 1998 (AMTA 1998).

The mission of AMTA, according to its Member Survey, is "to increase public awareness of the benefits of music therapy and to increase access to quality music therapy services in a rapidly changing world" (AMTA 2013). AMTA publishes a quarterly research-oriented journal, *The Journal of Music Therapy*; a semiannual, practice-oriented journal, *Music Therapy Perspectives*; a quarterly newsletter, *Music Therapy Matters*; and numerous brochures, monographs, and informational publications. AMTA also maintains the *Journal of Music Therapy* website (www.musictherapy.org) that provides information for music therapists and the general public.

AMTA's governance structure, like that of the former NAMT, is modeled after the structure of the U.S. government and includes an Executive Board, an Assembly of Delegates (the legislative and policy-making body) that has proportionate representation from each region, an Appeals and Judicial Review Board, an Ethics Board, and various standing councils and committees related to (a) training and development and (b) professional practices and services (AMTA, 1998). The National Office is headed by the executive director, an association employee.

Annual national conferences are held in the fall, and regional conferences are held in the spring of each year. AMTA is now the United States' "primary organizational agency for the advancement of education, clinical practice, research, and ethical standards for the music therapy professional" (AMTA, 1998, xxxi). While AMTA continues to establish training and competency standards for music therapists, as did the former AAMT and NAMT, credentialling responsibilities are now yielded to the independent Certification Board for Music Therapists (CBMT).

The Certification Board for Music Therapists

In the early 1980s, professional music therapists began to feel a need for a process that would give more objectivity and credibility to certification procedures for music therapists and hopefully "have a positive effect on employment practices and reimbursement possibilities" (Certification Board for Music Therapists 1983, 6). The Certification Board for Music Therapists (CBMT), an independent certifying agency for music therapists established with the support of music therapists from NAMT and AAMT under the guidelines of the Institute for Credentialing Excellence, National Commission for Certifying Agencies (ICE/NCCA), was incorporated in 1983. CBMT received full accreditation in 1986. In contrast to NAMT, AAMT, or AMTA, which were or are professional membership associations, CBMT is a certifying agency. Its function is to set rules and regulations for obtaining and maintaining a specific, voluntary credential (CBMT 1992). Simply stated, "The mission of the Certification Board for Music Therapists is to ensure a standard of excellence in the development, implementation, and promotion of an accredited program for safe and competent music therapy practice" (CBMT 2014). CBMT's structure includes a Board of Directors that establishes policy for certification and recertification in accordance with the National Commission for Certifying Agencies.

CBMT has administered a standardized national certification exam for music therapists since 1985. Upon passing this exam, individuals receive the professional credential Music Therapist-Board Certified (MT-BC). The credential MT-BC provides public consumer protection, by indicating that the music therapist is a graduate of an AMTA-approved curriculum and has demonstrated competence on an exam given by an independent agency, CBMT: "As of 2014, 6000 board certified music therapists were reported by the Certification Board for Music Therapists" (AMTA 2014, 24). It is not necessary to belong to AMTA to be certified because the two organizations are separate. However, the applicant must have completed both the educational and clinical AMTA program requirements.

In 1988, CBMT implemented a recertification program (CBMT 1992). To maintain their board-certified status, MT-BCs must apply for recertification every five years. Recertification requires the demonstration of continuing competence in music therapy practice through participation in ongoing continuing education or taking additional examinations (CBMT 1991, 1997, 1998b, 2014).

CURRENT TREATMENT SETTINGS AND ROLES OF PROFESSIONAL MUSIC THERAPISTS

Where Music Therapy Is Used

When music therapy first became an organized profession in 1950, most music therapists worked in adult psychiatric settings. As people recognized music's value in treating children with various handicaps, music therapists also began to find increasing employment opportunities in institutions serving individuals with mental retardation (Lathom 1980). Surveys conducted in 1978 (Braswell, Maranto, and Decuir 1979a) and 1980 (Lathom 1982) found that psychiatric facilities continued to employ most music therapists, while mental retardation facilities employed the second greatest number. More recent surveys (AMTA 1998; Braswell, Decuir, and Jacobs 1989; NAMT 1994a; Taylor 1987a) indicated that, while psychiatric and mental health settings continued to be the most common work settings, the types of treatment settings in which music therapists work expanded greatly as new applications of music therapy services continually developed. Music therapists currently work in almost 80 different types of settings (AMTA 2013), including adult day care centers, community mental health centers, special education programs, hospice care, substance abuse programs, oncology treatment centers, correctional institutions, nursing homes, physical rehabilitation centers, psychiatric hospitals, medical hospitals, retirement facilities, day care programs, community centers and recreational programs, senior centers, programs for the developmentally disabled, group homes and halfway houses, outpatient clinics, schools, and private studios or clinics. The Profile of the 2013 AMTA Membership provides the following statistics on treatment settings:

> The largest categories of settings reported are Geriatric Facilities, which account for 15% of survey responses, followed by Mental Health Settings, 14% and Children's Facilites/Schools, 13%. The next largest categories reported are Medical Settings, 11%, and finally, Self Employed & Private Practice, 8%. All other settings account for 39% of the total listed. (AMTA 2013, 15)

In the 1970s, some music therapists began to work independently and contract their services to individuals or agencies (Henry, Knoll, and Anderson 1982; Michel 1981). Lathom (1982) reported that 4.1 percent of the 466 music therapists responding to her 1980 survey worked in private practice. Recent surveys demonstrate how the trend toward self-employment and private practice in music therapy continues to rise. As health care paradigms change and the trends in the workplace as a whole move more toward self-employment and contract work, nontraditional job opportunities, such as private practice, contractual arrangements, and independent consultant services, also continue to offer expanding, viable employment opportunities for music therapists (O'Brien and Goldstein 1985; Oliver 1989; Reuer 1996).

In recent years, as the fields of music and medicine once again converge, music therapists are finding more employment opportunities in medical, physical rehabilitation, and general hospital settings (AMTA 1998; Crowe 1985; Maranto 1991; Michel 1981; Standley 1996b). With attention focused on music therapy and the elderly in a hearing by the U.S. Senate Special Committee on Aging in August of 1991 and the passage of the Older Americans Act of 1992, elderly populations, too, are now emerging as a major recipient of music therapy services (NAMT 1994a; AMTA 1998). In addition, music therapists are beginning to explore job opportunities in wellness programs, expanding beyond traditional healing and educational institutional roles to helping people in everyday circumstances deal more effectively with life and live lives of "richer quality and deeper meaning" (Broucek 1987, 58).

Job Satisfaction and Employment Trends

A survey by Braswell, Decuir, and Jacobs (1989) found that most music therapists report being very satisfied to fairly satisfied with their jobs. The most positively rated aspects included "independence in work, importance of the job, challenge of the job, opportunity to learn, immediate supervisor, job security, staff relations, and professional respect" (16). The outlook for continued job development in music therapy also appears positive. For example, in 1997, "in most work settings, there were nearly twice as many new jobs as jobs lost" (AMTA 1998, 200). The Profile of the 2013 AMTA Membership reported that the "retention rate for professional members was 61% in 2011. Industry standards point out that a rate of > 60% is well above average" (AMTA Member Survey and Workforce Analysis 2013). Geographically, the most new music therapy jobs were developed in the Great Lakes and Mid-Atlantic regions. These areas currently also have the greatest number of music therapists.

Salaries for music therapists vary greatly, depending on population served, work setting, region of the country, job title, and years of experience. According to the Profile of the 2013 Membership, "the average salary reported for all music therapists was $51,899" (AMTA 2013, 4). In 2013, the 3,667 music therapists working outside the United States had the highest average salaries ($63,833). Within the United States, salaries were highest in the Western and Southwestern regions (AMTA 2013). Salaries also varied by work setting, with the highest average salaries found in universities and colleges (i.e., music therapy professors); population served; age range served; years in the profession; administrative responsibility; and educational level. Even in 1998, an analysis of salary trends by AMTA staff members was optimistic about improvement, for they concluded that despite the lowest salaries for music therapists remaining very low, "both the low and high range of salaries appear to be rising" (AMTA 1998, 202).

Changing Roles of Music Therapy Professionals

When music therapy first acquired recognition as a professional discipline in the late 1940s and early 1950s, music therapists generally were considered technicians, adjunct to other therapy specialists. They usually worked under many layers of supervision (Michel 1981, 1985). Since that time, however, music therapists have attained increasing recognition as independent, responsible allied health professionals. In the 1960s and 1970s, that recognition was facilitated by an increased research base in music therapy and an increased orientation to measurable data in music therapy practice facilitated recognition (Michel 1981, 1985). The passage of Public Law 94-142, the Education for All Handicapped Children Act, in 1975 also led to increased recognition of music therapists as independent, competent professionals and to expanded employment opportunities in special education and public school settings (Gfeller 1992e; Michel 1985; Lathom-Radocy 2014). By the late 1970s, many music therapists were serving as supervisors or primary therapists. McGinty (1980) found that over 61 percent of the music therapists surveyed had responsibility for supervising other personnel and that 46.5 percent were regarded as the primary therapist for some clients. Ninety-four percent of the respondents were responsible, either solely or in conjunction with a team, for setting up and evaluating client treatment plans. In addition, 89 percent had free access to confidential data on their clients, while another 3.9 percent had access with some limitations. According to McGinty, this access to confidential information indicated that music therapists were viewed as responsible people with integrity.

As the general trend in health care has moved away from large institutional settings, so music therapists, too, have begun to work more and more in community and special education settings. Michel (1976, 117) predicted that "the future of music therapy definitely lies in the mainstream of health-related services rather than in traditional institutions." A few years later, Henry, Knoll, and Anderson (1982, 2) observed that "non-traditional job opportunities such as self-employment, contractual arrangements, and consultant services" were definitely increasing in popularity as employment alternatives for music therapists. A recent survey by the American Music Therapy Association (2013) found that private practice by music therapists is a continuing source of employment. Music therapists currently use their professional skills to serve clients with a wide range of disabilities in various traditional and nontraditional treatment settings.

As our society begins to focus more and more on preventive medicine and health maintenance, music therapists may find a place for their skills in holistic health centers, adult education settings, and stress-reduction clinics. As people become more aware of the dangers of noise pollution, music therapists might also take on the role of designing healthy sonic environments for the home and other settings. The planners of space stations recognize the benefits music can have for promising a healthy stimulus environment (Clearwater 1985); perhaps music therapists will someday hold important positions in the National Aeronautics and Space Administration! In moving into the mainstream of health-related services, music therapists may well expand their role to help "normal" individuals as well as those with disabilities improve their condition, skills, thoughts, feelings, or behaviors through the use of specifically prescribed, goal-directed music and music-based experiences.

MUSIC THERAPY IN OTHER COUNTRIES

Probably the most widespread use of music therapy outside the United States developed in England, where the British Society for Music Therapy (first called the Society for Music Therapy and Remedial Music) was established in 1958 under the leadership of Juliette Alvin. During the 1960s and 1970s, music therapy developed in an organized way in several other European countries, including the Netherlands, the Scandinavian countries, East and West Germany, Austria, France, Switzerland, Yugoslavia, and Belgium (Michel 1985). In North America, a strong interest in music therapy also developed in Canada, and the Canadian Association of Music Therapy was established in 1974. Elsewhere, Australia has been reporting developments in music therapy since the 1960s (Michel 1985). The Australian Music Therapy Association was founded in 1975, with Ruth Bright as president. In the Far East, Japan was one of the first countries to embrace modern music therapy practices, with the first developments occurring after World War II (Maranto 1993a). Several professional organizations developed during the 1970s and 1980s, and a formal music therapy training program, the Nippon Institute of Music Therapy, was established in 1988. Modern music therapy practices also developed in China during the 1980s and 1990s (Maranto 1993a). There is a very active Music Therapy Association in Korea, with Dr. Choi Byung-Chul heading the effort. He also started a very successful graduate degree program at Sookmyung Women's University in Seoul. In addition, students in Far Eastern countries have been coming to the United States to receive music therapy training (Michel 1985). Writing about the reentry process of foreign music therapy students upon return to their home country and beginning work, Hsiao (2011, 437) recommended: "passion, devotion, commitment, determination, and entrepreneurship."

The Profile of the 2013 AMTA Membership stated that "in 2013, AMTA members live in 32 countries outside the United States and in 6 continents around the globe. International members comprise 4% of the AMTA membership" (AMTA 2013, 7). Of course not all international music therapists belong to AMTA. Maranto (1993a) and Moreno et al. (1990) reported that music therapy is practiced in almost 40 countries across the globe. (For a list of the countries with members belonging to AMTA, see the web site www.musictherapy.org.)

The first World Congress of Music Therapy was held in France in 1974. Subsequent world congresses have occurred in several cities around the world, approximately every two to three years (Maranto 1993a). The growing need for international communication and cooperation led to the formation of the World Federation of Music Therapy (WFMT) in 1985. The WFMT's stated mission is to develop and promote "music therapy throughout the world as an art and science. The Federation supports the global development of educational programs, clinical practice and research, to demonstrate the contributions of music therapy to humanity" (Fachner 2010). To help promote international communication within the profession, The World Federation of Music Therapy publishes a biannual online journal titled *Music Therapy Today* (Music Therapy Today.wfmt.info). Kaplan (2011) stated that the world-wide community of music therapists includes almost 1400 professionals and students. Members from 45 countries came together in Seoul, South Korea "to experience music and explore music therapy in eastern and western philosophy" (Kaplan 2011).

This brief history of the important founders of music therapy in the United States, now including a brief discussion of international music therapy practice, provides a foundation for the future of music therapy. As Heller (2000, 246) once stated, "History (knowledge of what has gone before) can help diagnose problems and point the way toward (but not predict) the future. History can inspire people and connect generations."

QUESTIONS FOR THOUGHT AND DISCUSSION

1. How and where was music therapy promoted and practiced in the United States in the first half of the twentieth century? What impact did these early promoters and practitioners have on the development and growth of music therapy in the United States?
2. How did musicians and professional music associations interact with medical and hospital personnel in the early to mid-1940s? How did these interactions pave the way for a closer association between the fields of music and medicine?
3. What factors precipitated the development of an organization to regulate practice and training in music therapy?
4. What are the current certifying and professional associations for music therapists in the United States? What are the functions of each, and how do these serve music therapists, employers, and consumers/clients?
5. How has the role of the professional music therapist changed since music therapy first emerged as an organized professional discipline in the 1950s?
6. What are some current employment trends in the field of music therapy? How do you think these will change in the future? What clinical and employment opportunities do you see developing for music therapists?
7. In what other parts of the world is music therapy practiced? How do you think the continued expansion of the global awareness and practice of music therapy will influence the development and practice of the field in the United States?

SUGGESTIONS FOR FURTHER READING

American Association for Music Therapy (AAMT). (1993). *Introducing the American Association for Music Therapy* [brochure]. Valley Forge, PA: Author.

American Music Therapy Association (AMTA). 2013 AMTA Member Survey Workforce Analysis. http://www.musictherapy.org

Boxberger, R. (1963). A historical study of the National Association for Music Therapy. In E. H. Schneider (Ed.) *Music therapy 1962* (133–197). Lawrence, KS: Allen Press.

Certification Board for Music Therapists (CBMT). (1997). *CBMT: The certification board for music therapists* (brochure). Richmond, VA: Author.

Certification Board for Music Therapists (CBMT). (1998). *Your music therapist is certified by the certification board for music therapists* (brochure). Richmond, VA: Author.

Clair, A. A., & Heller, G. N. (1989). Willem Van de Wall (1887–1953): Organizer and innovator in music education and music therapy. *Journal of Research in Music Education, 37*(3), 165–178.

Davis, W. B. (1993). Keeping the dream alive: Profiles of three early twentieth century music therapists. *Journal of Music Therapy, 30*(1), 34–45.

Davis, W. B. (1996). An instruction course in the use and practice of musical therapy: The first handbook of music therapy clinical practice. *Journal of Music Therapy, 33*(1), 34–49.

Davis, W. B., & Gfeller, K. E. (2008). Music therapy: Historical perspective. In W. B. Davis, K. E. Gfeller, & M. H. Thaut (Eds.), A*n introduction to music therapy: Theory and practice* (3rd ed.) (17–39). Silver Spring, MD: American Music Therapy Association.

Maranto, C. D. (Ed.) (1993). *Music therapy: International perspectives.* Pipersville, PA: Jeffrey Books.

Maranto, C. D. (1993). Music therapy in the United States of America. In C. D. Maranto (Ed.). *Music therapy: international perspectives* (605–662). Pipersville, PA: Jeffrey Books.

Michel, D. E. (1985). Developments in other countries. In D. Michel, *An introduction, including music in special education* (2nd ed.) (103–110). Springfield, IL: Charles C Thomas.

Michel, D. E. (1985). Recent historical perspectives. In D. Michel, *Music therapy: An introduction, including music in special education* (8–14). Springfield, IL: Charles C Thomas.

Moreno, J., Brotons, M., Hairston, M., Hawley, T., Kiel, H., Michel, D., & Rohrbacher, M. (1990). International music therapy: A global perspective. *Music Therapy Perspectives, 8,* 41–46.

Reuer, B. (1996). Posturing for a changing world: Consulting as a career option. *Music Therapy Perspectives, 14*(1), 16–20.

Rorke, M. A. (1996). Music and the wounded of World War II. *Journal of Music Therapy, 33*(3), 189–207.

Schneider, E. H., Unkefer, R. F., & Gaston, E. T. (1968). Introduction. In E. T. Gaston (Ed.), *Music in therapy* (1–4). New York: Macmillan.

Tyson, F. (1981). Music therapy in hospitals. In F. Tyson, *Psychiatric music therapy:*

Origins and development (7–12). New York: Fred Weidner & Sons Printers.

van de Wall, W. (1936). *Music in institutions.* New York: Russell Sage Foundation.

Wheeler, B. L., & Golden, S. (1987). NAMT and its Mid-Atlantic region: Changing together. *Music Therapy Perspectives, 4,* 56–63.

SOURCES FOR ADDITIONAL INFORMATION*

American Music Therapy Association (AMTA), 8455 Colesville Rd., Suite 1000, Silver Spring, MD 20910, (301) 589-3300, FAX (301) 589-5175, email: info@ music therapy.org, Web: http://www.music therapy.org

Certification Board for Music Therapists (CBMT), 506 E. Lancaster Ave., Suite 102, Downington, PA 19335, 1-800-765-CBMT, email: info@cbmt.com, Web: http://www.cbmt.com

*Contact information current as of July, 2014.

PART III

CURRENT CLINICAL PRACTICES
IN MUSIC THERAPY

How does one do music therapy? Are there any general guiding principles for theory and practice? What is involved in planning, implementing, and evaluating music therapy intervention strategies? In what specific ways can music and music-based experiences be used to benefit clients who have various disabilities? Are there different "schools" of music therapy techniques or approaches? Is research important to the practicing music therapy clinician? In Part III, these questions and others are discussed as more detailed information on the clinical practice of music therapy is presented.

The first two chapters in this section provide some general guidelines for the use of music in therapy. Chapter Five provides a theoretical foundation, discussing some reasons why music is useful as a treatment modality and presenting three basic principles that often guide the use of music and music-based experiences. Chapter Six gives more practical information, discussing the basic stages in the delivery of music therapy services and providing examples of music therapy experiences that may be used to address general goal areas. Chapters Seven through Twenty-one, then, give detailed information on music therapy interventions and practices with specific client populations. Each of these chapters contains (a) a definition of the particular population or disability, (b) descriptions of common characteristics, problems, and needs of individuals in that particular client group, (c) a listing of settings for service delivery, (d) examples of how music is used in therapy to benefit individuals in that client population, including common music therapy goals and approaches, and (e) special considerations and tips for success applicable to the particular client population. Short case study problems are included in the "Questions for Thought and Discussion" sections of each chapter to help the reader begin applying the information to specific clinical situations. Copious references and extensive suggestions for further reading are provided for readers who might desire more detailed information on music therapy practices and approaches with specific types of clientele. In addition, these readers may wish to consult bibliographic sources (e.g., Eagle 1976, 1978, 1982; Eagle and Miniter 1984) or music therapy web sites (e.g., www.musictherapy.org) and databases (e.g., CAIRSS for Music [http://galaxy.einet.net/ hytelnet/FUL064.html] or MuSICA [http://www. musica.uci.edu]) available through the Internet.

The use of music in therapy involves a wide range of procedures and techniques. Chapter Twenty-two overviews several approaches to music therapy practice to give the reader a basic understanding of some of the more common approaches to music therapy treatment that are currently used in the United States. Some of these approaches center on particular music techniques, while others adapt music education approaches and methodologies to clinical use. Still others are based on specific educational, psychotherapeutic, or medical models and theories. The pros and cons of choosing to adhere to one particular system or approach are also discussed.

Although a "research attitude" may sound like something that belongs in the laboratory rather that in the clinic, it is, in fact, an attitude that is of vital importance to effective clinical practice. Chapter Twenty-three focuses on the value of research to music therapy clinicians, both as they use the research of others and do research for themselves. Parallels are drawn between the approach the clinician takes in developing, implementing, and evaluating the effectiveness of a treatment plan and the steps the researcher follows in devising, conducting, and evaluating experiments. The importance of reporting clinical findings is also emphasized.

After completing Part III, the reader should have gained the knowledge and information needed to perform the following tasks:

1. Give several reasons why music is useful as a treatment modality.
2. Use Gaston's three guiding principles and/or Sear's three basic classifications to explain general ways music is used in therapy.
3. List and briefly describe the basic stages in the delivery of music therapy services.
4. Give examples of music experiences that might be used to help improve (a) behavioral skills (e.g., attending skills, compliance), (b) sensory skills, (c) motor skills, (d) language and communication skills, (e) emotional learning and emotional expression, (f) interpersonal (social) skills, (g) self-help/survival skills, and (h) academic/cognitive skills.
5. Describe music therapy goals and treatment procedures applicable to clients who have (a) intellectual disabilities, (b) specific learning disabilities, hearing impairments, (c) visual impairments, (d) orthopedic impairments, (e) communication disorders, (f) autism, (g) mental or behavioral disorders or severe emotional disturbances, or (h) severe and profound multiple disabilities.
6. Describe music therapy goals and treatment procedures used (a) in medical treatment settings,(b) in physical rehabilitation programs, (c)

with individuals who are elderly, (d) with individuals who are terminally ill, and (e) to promote health and well-being in the general population.

7. Describe several different approaches to music therapy.
8. Explain why research is important to the field of music therapy and to the music therapy clinician.
9. Describe methods and benefits of using and doing research in the clinical setting.

Chapter Five

GENERAL GUIDELINES FOR THE THERAPEUTIC USE OF MUSIC, PART I: THEORETICAL PRINCIPLES

WHY MUSIC IS USEFUL AS A TREATMENT MODALITY

As is evident from the information presented in Chapter Three, music has been connected with healing practices for many centuries. Contrary to ancient myths, music has no magical qualities that give it a special healing power. However, certain aspects of music's physical components and of the human uses of and reactions to music make music particularly useful as a therapeutic treatment modality. These various aspects and effects of music, together with its cultural meanings and uses, help one understand some of the processes that underlie both the use of music in therapy and the influences of music on human behavior (Abeles and Chung 1996; Bartlett 1996; Gaston 1968a; Gfeller 1992a; Hodges 1996; Hodges and Haack 1996; Merriam 1964; Radocy and Boyle 2012).

Music Is a Universal, Essential Part of Human Behavior

Anthropologists and ethnomusicologists tell us that music can be found in all cultures, both primitive and civilized (Blacking 1973; Dowling and Harwood 1986; Hodges and Haack 1996; Merriam 1964; Nettl 1956). As Spintge (1991, 59) noted, "there is no human civilization that has not experienced and produced music." Scientific anthropological and ethnomusicological studies of cultures throughout the world continue to show that "musical behavior is a human invariant" (Hodges and Haack 1996, 495) and that "music, like love, is one of the most universal of human experiences" (Whitwell 1993, 46). Sociological, psychological, and biological evidence, too, points to the prominent, all-inclusive place and influence music has in and on human behavior and experience (Hodges and Haack 1996). And, as Hesser (2001, 53) observes, "It is the experience of music in our lives and the lives of the people with whom we work that is the essence and heart of music therapy."

Even in today's complex societies, people are avid music consumers, spending considerable time and money on concert tickets, electronic music systems, recorded music, and music videos, etc. One hears some kind of music almost every day: as part of a commercial; during a television program or movie; from a radio, smartphone, or compact disc player; from a computer; while on hold on the telephone; as a background in stores or restaurants; from children singing at play; from cars passing by with their radios playing loudly, etc. Music is also associated with government and civic ceremonies, sporting events, and religious services, as well as with many formal and informal gatherings. In addition, it frequently is used as background sound to break monotony, mask unwanted sounds, establish certain moods, stimulate conversations during parties, alleviate a feeling of aloneness, or to help "humanize" impersonal environments (Hodges and Haack 1996; Radocy and Boyle 2012). Bruscia (2001, 20) notes that "music is a complex art form, and in a therapeutic context, it is even more complex."

Music has been a part of most people's lives from birth, when their mothers sang them to sleep with a lullaby or engaged them in play with sing-song speech and musical rhymes. Usually, music remains a prevalent art form for the rest of their lives (Gfeller 1992a), whether they participate mainly as listeners and consumers or actively engage in making music at a professional or an amateur level. Although they may not always agree on the particular forms it should take, music is something that is used and valued by people of all walks of life. As Hesser (1995, 45) observed, "We all recognize the power of music in our lives. . . . We may not understand intellectually exactly what it is about music that moves us so deeply, but we still spend a great deal of time listening to and making music." Research and clinical experience demonstrate that even individuals with severe physical, mental, or emotional disabilities can respond to and participate successfully in musical experiences (see Chapters Seven to Twenty).

Gaston (1968a) considered music to be a defining behavior of human beings, something that is vital to their nature and its expression:

> Music is the essence of humanness, not only because man creates it, but because he creates his relationship to it . . . Music is an essential and necessary function of man. It influences his behavior and condition and has done so for thousands of years. (15)

A lifetime of ethnomusicological research led Blacking (1973, 7) to concur: "Music, like language and possibly religion, is a species-specific trait of man." The physician and medical researcher Lewis Thomas (1974, 23) also found that "the need to make music, and to listen to it, is universally expressed by human beings. . . . It is, like speech, a dominant aspect of human biology."

Psychologists have proposed several theories of multiple intelligences (Hodges and Haack 1996). Howard Gardner (1993, 1999) proposed a theory that includes musical intelligence as one of the basic types of human intellectual competence. Thus, Gardner considers musical intelligence to be one of the important and valuable ways of human knowing. Current research on music and the brain is also demonstrating that music is an essential, biologically based aspect of human behavior. For examples, studies indicate that music has definite effects on neural processes, that human beings have a biological affinity for melodic patterns, that even infants recognize and respond to music, and that human beings are born with certain brain cells that respond to musical sounds (Hodges 1996; Taylor 1997; Whitwell 1993). After reviewing recent neuromusical research, Hodges (1996) concluded:

> All human beings are born with a musical brain. . . . We all have neurological and bodily mechanisms that allow us to be aware of and responsive to the music of the surrounding culture. . . . Given proper instruction and reinforcement, nearly everyone can improve musical skills. (258)

Trehub (2009, 5) discussed studies related to infant's perception of frequency, timing, timbre, and perceptual grouping that provide evidence of a neurological network that can respond to music in infancy.

Because it is such a pervasive, essential aspect of human behavior, music is something that is universally accessible to people of all cultures and age groups. Thus, it has great potential for use as a medium to facilitate growth and healing with individuals of many varying abilities and age levels.

Music Is Composed of Real Physical Structures, Ordered in Time

According to Hedden (1980a, 37), "All music has its basis in the physical world. . . . All involve the same starting point – vibrations have been initiated in some object(s)." Music consists of real physical structures, vibrations which can be felt, heard, measured, and graphed. Different frequencies, different wave forms, different intensities, and different durations of these vibrations produce various pitches, tone qualities, loudness levels, and rhythms (Hedden 1980b). In every culture "music involves an organization of sounds and silences, encompassing various pitches, loudness levels and timbres, all of which occur within a rhythmic framework" (Radocy and Boyle 2012, 24–25). Music, like other aspects of the physical world, is something we perceive through our senses: "All the senses bring to us aspects of reality. To hear a chord of music is no less real than to smell a rose, to see a sunset, to taste an apple, or to feel the impact of striking a wall" (Gaston 1968a, 24).

In recent years, findings and theories from modern physics and quantum mechanics which suggest that the basic substance of the universe is patterned vibration have led some music therapy philosophers and theorists to suggest that some of the power of music in therapy lies in the fact that music, which can be thought of as special patterns of vibrations moving through time, is congruent with the basic stuff of the universe (Eagle 1991). Truly, "the elements of music are in all of life" (Priestley 1985, 245).

Another special aspect of music's structure is that it is ordered in time and exists only through experiencing it in time:

> Except for relatively minute deviations, music (whether an entire piece or merely a measure or phrase in repeated practice) cannot be interrupted without losing its intent. . . . The music must be carried through in its time order. (Sears 1968, 35)

Music's rhythm, form, and structure relate to its time-ordered nature. Music unfolds in and through time even as life and individuals develop in and through time. The first step in organizational behavior is to gain a sense of "me" and "not me." "This basic aspect of self-orientation is needed long before the infant is able to separate from primary caregivers and begin to form a sense of autonomy" (Lathom-Radocy 2014, 4). Bunt and Hoskins (2002, 34) note that "musical frames and the whole fabric of co-created music within a relationship can be used to help establish these boundaries between 'me' and 'not me' and self and other." The rhythms, forms, and structures in music can be used to mirror, stimulate, enhance, or help sustain rhythmic and organizational processes within individuals and among group members. In its time order, too, music has connections to basic aspects of life and human development.

Music Affects the Whole Person

Music is a multisensory and multidimensional experience that affects people physically, cognitively, and emotionally. Music often is perceived and experienced consciously, but it also can be perceived and experienced on levels that do not involve conscious mental processes. Davis, Gfeller, and Thaut (2008, 168) explain *Musical Sensory Orientation Training (MSOT)*, which is used "to stimulate arousal and recovery of wakefulness" in patients who are in a coma. As Spintge (1991, 61) pointed out, music works on myriad levels: "Music is a very complex stimulus, influencing *conscious* brain functions as well as autonomic and unconscious cerebral processes effectively and in different ways." Music impacts the whole person in all of his or her functioning domains. Boxill (1985, 18) noted that "music contacts the human being on primordial to intricate physiological levels, on basic to dynamic psychological levels, and on simple to complicated cerebral levels." For purposes of research and for ease of discussion, the effects of music on each of these domains or levels is often treated separately; however, it is important to remember that music affects people in all these ways simultaneously, even though one aspect may be more dominant at a given time.

Music Affects Physical Responses

Although responses will vary somewhat from individual to individual based on each individual's preferences and previous musical experiences, research clearly shows that music does have definite effects on a person's physiological responses (Bartlett 1996, 348; Radocy and Boyle 1988; Taylor 1997). After examining many studies, Radocy and Boyle (2012, 49) conclude that "characteristically stimulative music tended to increase physiological rates (e.g., heart rate), whereas characteristically sedative music tended to have soothing or relaxing effects (e.g., decreasing muscle tension)."

Individual musical elements (e.g., rhythm, timbre) as well as distinctive combinations of musical elements in particular musical compositions may influence and affect physical responses. For example, rhythmic stimuli can enhance timing and readiness in gait training and physical fitness activities, help sustain muscular effort, and affect respiration and relaxation responses (Gfeller 1992a; Miller 1979). Thaut (2008, 89) reported that the Center for Biomedical Research in Music has produced over thirty publications "regarding the use of a rhythmic stimulus as a central nervous system driver to aid in the remediation of movement deficits typically resulting from stroke or Parkinson's disease." Research has also shown that music with different amounts of rhythmic activity and different degrees of percussive or sustained sounds (stimulative vs. sedative music) has different effects on several physiological responses, including heart and pulse rates, blood pressure, respiration, skin conductivity, muscular tension and motor activity, motor/postural responses, finger or peripheral skin temperature, stomach contractions, brain waves, and biochemical responses (e.g., changes in levels of various hormones related to stress or immune system function) (Bartlett 1996; Edwards et al. 1991; Radocy and Boyle 2012, 359–366). Bartlett (1996) provided several tables summarizing studies conducted in these areas over the prior 120 years. While the exact nature and extent of music's influence varied from study to study, at least partially because of various definition and measurement difficulties and uncontrollable confounding variables, the majority of the studies reviewed by Bartlett did show that music and sound stimuli do influence bodily systems and physiological responses. However, the listener's experience with music and cultural background require consideration.

In recent years, there has been a resurgence of interest in the way music and specific tones and frequencies affect various organs, tissues, and bones, all the way down to the cellular level, and the implications this might have for the use of music in healing (Crowe and Scovel 1996; Goldman 1988; Halpern 1978; Marcus 1995). Several experiments suggest that the application of carefully selected music and vibration frequencies to the body through special speakers in tables or chairs or through music-electro-acupuncture techniques may reduce arthritic pain, decrease muscle rigidity, alleviate insomnia, and aid in recovery of muscle function in stroke victims (Chesky and Michel 1991; Shi-jing, Hui-ju, Guo, and Maranto 1991; Skille 1989; Wigram 1995).

Music Affects Cognitive and Emotional Responses

Research has demonstrated that music can have definite effects on a person's brain function and cognitive processes (Hodges and Haack 1996; Radocy and Boyle 2012, 354–355; Taylor 1997). For example, music can assist a person in organizing and remembering information. As advertisers well know, product names and information are recalled more readily when they are presented as part of a catchy tune. A market has also developed in the educational field for songs that help students learn and retain information such as math and geography facts, spelling words, health and safety rules, and the like (Kimbo Educational 1995). Through music, information can be presented in a unique and appealing manner. As the composer Franz Liszt observed,

> Music is the intermediary which places emotion in harmony with intelligence; enabling us to enjoy and love that which intelligence enables us to become acquainted with. The Greeks . . . well understood the subtle connecting link provided by music between the perceptible and the impalpable – between that which is understood and that which is felt. (cited in Whitwell 1993, 30)

Zatorre (2009, 243) reported cortical differences in processing of auditory information. Our ability to produce and respond to speech and tonal sounds is "at the core of our uniquely human abilities to communicate. . . . It is perhaps also not irrelevant that both speech communication and tonal patterns appear to be ubiquitous across all human cultures."

When examining reports of research on the cortical function of music processing, one must consider the task. Zatorre (2009, 231) finds that "tonal processing recruits mechanisms in areas of the right auditory cortex." However, Griffiths (2009, 169) points out that "the ascending auditory pathway affords an extensive mechanism for the processing of complex signals before the cortex is reached." He also argues that temporal patterns, as compared with tonal patterns, require "bilateral temporo-frontal networks" 176). Thus, to assign musical processing to one hemisphere or location is too simple.

At an even more basic level, music can influence the very structure and organization of brain function. From studies in many fields, (e.g., psychophysics, neuroanatomy, and neurophysiology), a new way of looking at musical aesthetics is unfolding. Thaut (2008, 33) notes that "the research is showing that music has clear neurobiological substrates, organized in complex and distributed neuronal networks in the brain." Music influences both conscious and unconscious mental processes (Spintge 1991) and can affect different areas of the brain, "stimulating a variety of responses from the release of endorphins to the synchronization of the left and right hemispheres" (Goldman 1988, 29). Music can also induce different states of consciousness (Bonny and Savary 1973, 1990) and lead listeners to new levels of awareness. Music integrates diverse psychic processes and may serve to unite an individual's inner and outer worlds (Aigen 1991).

Different types of music also have varying effects on listeners' moods and emotional (affective) responses (Abeles 1980; Abeles and Chung 1996; Radocy and Boyle 2012, 350). For example, certain music may be relaxing to an individual, while other music may make a person feel happy or sad, and still other music evokes feelings of anger or frustration. While some general effects of music with certain characteristics that will be true for many people may be predicted, one must remember that an individual's previous experience with music largely will determine how he or she will react to a particular piece. If our experience of music "were specifically mechanical, we would all experience identical sensations while listening to a specific musical work, which is definitely not the case" (Deschenes 1990, 87). In an examination of Meyer (1956, 13–32) and his theory of how music arouses emotion, Radocy and Boyle (2012) explain,

> Central to Meyer's theory is the view that arrest or inhibition of a tendency to respond arouses emotion. An individual's tendencies to respond to music result from previous experiences with music of the style to which he or she is listening. (350–352)

Both Blacking (1995, 224) and Merriam (1964, 227) discuss musical phenomena as present in all human societies. How our biological system reacts to musical stimuli (pitch, loudness, timbre, pattern grouping, such as in rhythmic or melodic segments, etc.), however, relates to the surrounding cultural environment. Cross (2009, 54) says that "if music is in our birthright, its inheritance appears to be a fragile gift that rests on the humaneness [sic] and sympathy of the culture that surrounds us."

Music can both excite or arouse emotions in a listener and represent or mimic various emotional responses (Dowling and Harwood 1986). Associations that a listener makes with a certain piece of music, any imagery evoked by the music, reactions to lyrics and word meaning, reactions to various instruments or combinations of instruments, individual interests and values, attitudes, cultural or stylistic preferences, and environmental factors all may influence a person's affective responses to any given piece of music at any given time.

Music Facilitates Mind-Body Connections

In recent years, the Western world has taken a renewed interest in holistic healing processes in which music and psychobiology are connected and influence each other in achieving and maintaining health. This is sometimes called the *mind-body connection.* With the current emphasis on neurological functions in musical behavior, the term "mind" is used less frequently, but as Radocy and Boyle (2012, 455) explain, "The mind is what the brain does," and "the brain is an anatomical structure." (When the author took a graduate class in neurology, the professor used to pass a brain around the class so we could observe various anatomical structures. This is not possible with the "mind.") Restak (1984, 281) defined mind as a collection of thought processes and mental products. He described it as a metaphysical system related to the brain, but not within the brain (Radocy and Boyle 2012, 455). The Greeks used the term *psychosomatic,* with "psyche" meaning "breath or spirit" and "soma" meaning "body." The emphasis on treatment of stress-related conditions has led to increasing awareness of emotional and *psychological* states that relate to physiological distress (Pelletier 1980, 107).

The Diagnostic and Statistical Manual of Mental Disorders, Fifth Edition (2013) (DSM-5) includes criteria for Posttraumatic Stress Disorders (PTSD), a condition in which an individual has had exposure to or direct experience of a serious traumatic event. One symptom listed is "marked physiological reactions to internal or external cues that symbolize or resemble an aspect of the traumatic event(s)" (DSM-5, 271). This is only one symptom, but it indicates the connection between a psychological stressor and physiological response, thus the "mind-body" connection. Most of the time, the stressor is not as traumatic as that in PTSD, but there may still be adverse effects from living with high stress for long periods of time. Music therapy is one way to teach relaxation methods that may relieve stress.

Much of the therapeutic power and potential of music may lie in the fact that music directly influences the entire person, "entraining autonomic functions, stimulating the senses, probing the emotions, presenting ideas, and inspiring the spirit" (Bruscia 1995c, 182).

Music Affects Interpersonal Interactions

Just as music affects various processes and domains within an individual, so music also affects interactions between and among individuals. Gaston

(1968a, 27) noted that "music, by its very nature, draws people together for intimate, yet ordered, function." Moreover, once music has stimulated interaction among people, it also acts as a powerful reinforcer, encouraging people to maintain enjoyable and productive interactions (Maultsby 1977).

Gromko and Cohen (2011) described a choir program in prison as a way of establishing successful communities among offenders. They discuss the social reinforcement provided by group participation with music:

> Many students are drawn to music for its social value; they want to belong and fit in. When a musical ensemble is a community that is characterized by reciprocity and genuine sharing, participants in that community will come to know one another in ways that lessen their vulnerability and deepen their humanity. (114)

Music accompanies social, civic, and ceremonial occasions, for music often serves to put people at ease, encourages them to participate in the group activity, or helps them invest in common group goals or beliefs (Gaston 1968a; Merriam 1964; Radocy and Boyle 2012, 37–38; Sears 1968). In addition, communal music-making can be an expression of social solidarity and a symbol of cultural identity (Dowling and Harwood 1986). As Radocy and Boyle (2012, 38) suggest, "Culture clearly affects musical behavior. Conversely, music may influence the culture." It is a shared activity that brings people together:

> Since the dawn of time, one of the primary functions of music has been as communal activity. People have always gathered together to make music as a group experience, sharing the joyous spirit and life energy inherent in the creation of music. (Goldman 1988, 31)

Music's unifying and communal aspect remains evident today: People from all walks of life come together to listen to concerts, to listen or dance to live or recorded music at parties and other social gatherings, to sing or play instruments together in formally organized choirs and instrumental groups, to sing or play instruments informally with friends, to sing patriotic or religious songs, or to participate in songs or dances or music that are in some way special to their group or heritage. Music still functions as a signal for people to gather together, as a rallying point to draw individuals together in support of a common cause, and as a means of unifying group members' individual efforts, as everyone moves to the same beat and their actions become synchronized and coordinated (Merriam 1964; Radocy and Boyle 1988). This is possible only through the organizing element of rhythm (Gaston 1968; Radocy and Boyle 2012, 165; Thaut 2008).

Music affects people and relatationships by adding emotional impact, rhythmic energy and organization, and a subtle yet compelling motivation and encouragement to join in the group activity. Music and rhythm provide common bonds that organize and energize interactions, making it easier for people to work together and somehow encouraging them to interact more freely with one another (Gaston 1968a). As they participate in music experiences together, individuals form a special type of society. Through music activity, they find new ways to explore and understand relationships and to express themselves to and with the group:

> Playing music in a group provides an opportunity to explore and more deeply understand relationships in the community, and the changing dynamics of groups as they grow and develop. It is also a chance for each individual to explore his uniqueness in relations to the community. At times, we can feel the oneness of all group members when we make music and dance together. This consonance can be supportive and healing. (Hesser 1995, 49)

Music's ability to affect and facilitate group interactions has important implications for the use of music in therapy, for "the chief aim of therapy is to enable the individual to function at his best in society" (Gaston 1968a, 27; Lathom-Radocy 2014, xi; Maslow 1971, 168–169). And "if we always deal with the difficulties of life in isolation, and never relate ourselves to the whole, any solution or cure is likely to be merely an illusion, and short-lived" (Kenny 1982, 36).

Music also may enhance both the quantity and emotional depth of verbal interactions and facilitate the expression of highly emotional material between individuals and within groups (Gaston 1968a; Merriam 1964; Prueter and Mezzano 1973; Radocy and Boyle 2012, 350–352; Sears 1968/2007, 9). In addition, music can serve as an acceptable outlet for expressing displeasure and frustration with various situations (e.g., protest songs), or it can serve to convey or express group feelings in a powerful way. Musical vehicles such as theme songs may also affect group relationships by helping to give a group a particular identity, thereby increasing the cohesiveness of individual group members.

So, then, just as music affects the whole individual – physically, psychologically, emotionally, and spiritually – it also affects all these aspects of group interactions. Music and rhythm can provide the physical structure to coordinate and sustain group activity. Music can motivate people to participate or join with a group, and music can provide a vehicle for expressing common ideas, feelings, and philosophies. Music also can set a tone or mood that will affect group moods or activity levels even as it affects the individuals within the group. Through its ability to structure and organize and its ability to convey and influence ideas and feelings, music can have powerful effects on interpersonal interactions. Since all persons, even those with severe disabilities, respond to music, music's positive effects on interpersonal interactions can be important tools for establishing or reestablishing contact and positive interactions with individuals who are withdrawn from society and/or reality (Gaston 1968a; Sears 1968).

Music Is a Unique Form of Communication

Music's specially patterned sounds, which are derived from tender emotions and given meaning by the culture in which they are found (Gaston 1968a), serve as a very unique form of communication. Of course, the words of songs usually express some idea, feeling, story, or message. However, as Gaston (1968a, 23) noted, music's ability to communicate *nonverbally* is far more significant: "It is the *wordless* meaning of music that provides its potency and value."

This nonverbal communicative aspect of music, which adds emotional depth to human expression and provides a vehicle to speak for the experiential, feeling side of us (Whitwell 1993), can be of vital importance to therapy, for music may be able to communicate and help establish a relationship where words alone have failed. Even before we talk about it or in any way analyze it, "music speaks directly to us" and allows us to "gaze into the inmost Essence of ourselves" (Whitwell 1993, 65). For people who are unable to use words or those who hide behind words, musical experiences may provide a way to reach issues and achieve insight and growth through nonverbal processes (e.g., by playing or improvising with simple rhythm instruments in a therapy group, or by using a recorded song to express feelings they are unable to express verbally). Because music speaks directly to the emotions, it can be very useful in breaking through intellectual defenses and facilitating the expression of emotionally charged or fearful issues. Music is difficult to ignore, for it is a powerful form of multisensory stimulation that touches the depths of our being and experience. Therefore, music used in therapy often may elicit responses that are more honest and personally revealing than those elicited by purely verbal means.

Music, then, assists us in expressing those parts of ourselves and our experiences that cannot be touched or fully expressed by words alone. Lathom-Radocy (2014, 24–25) provides examples of communication goals in music therapy with children, beginning with imitation of sound to learn to talk and eventually using expressive communication to join in group discussion. Both receptive and expressive skills must be noted, within both verbal and nonverbal communication (4–6).

Music also is a powerful communication tool because it can convey symbolic meaning (Gfeller 1992a; Kenny 1982). Through the music they make and its symbolic representations, people may communicate uniquely some aspects of their experience that they cannot put into words. For example, in relating the story of a patient's inability to explain verbally the feelings or meanings that his chant and drumbeat expressed, Kenny (1982) observed:

He has already told me what it meant by singing and drumming. His music was a symbolic representation of some aspect of his experience – pure and simple. It was also self-contained and complete. It had already gone beyond words. It was an expression of clarity and communication. Everyone in the group had been moved. (58)

Music may express both specific cultural values and universal, archetypal ideas and myths (Gaston 1968a; Gfeller 1992a; Kenny 1982; Merriam 1964). Through music and the ceremonies associated with it, societies pass on various aspects of their culture (Gaston 1968a; Hodges and Haack 1996; Kenny 1982; Merriam 1964; Nettl 1956; Radocy and Boyle 2012, 15). Music also connects individuals with basic human emotions and archetypal patterns and themes that have been present throughout history (Gaston 1968a; Kenny 1982; Whitwell, 1993). While allowing people to express their most individual and intimate feelings and longings, music at the same time connects these with the universal feelings and longings of human beings of other times and places.

Music may stimulate various types of imagery and fantasy and be useful in retrieving old memories or revealing new perceptions, helping people to communicate with prior events or communicate with previously untouched aspects of themselves (Bonny and Savary 1973, 1990; Kenny 1982). When utilizing music's communicative properties, however, one must remember that musical meaning and expression usually connect with the traditions and practices of the culture in which they are found (Gaston 1968a; Gfeller 1992a; Hodges and Haack 1996; Merriam 1964): "Music is human behavior that occurs within a cultural context" (Radocy and Boyle 2012, 37). Even as different cultures have different languages and speech patterns, so different cultures use different scale patterns and instruments in their music. In addition, "musical symbols differ from culture to culture" (Gfeller 1992a, 50). Therefore, a person from one culture may find it extremely difficult to organize, interpret, understand, or communicate with the music of another culture. The degree to which a particular piece of music or type of musical expression communicates to or for a person is dependent somewhat on the degree to which that person understands or is familiar with that particular type or style of musical expression. This cultural distinction has important implications as one considers what music may be effective for therapy: "If patients are to be reached, the music employed must be that which they understand, at least to some extent" (Gaston 1968a, 22).

Music Is Integrally Connected to the Emotions

Much of the communicative power of music relates to the fact that music is integrally connected to the emotions, both through cultural convention and practice (Merriam 1964) and through common biological and neurological arousal and processing sites (e.g., limbic system, hemispheric specialization, brain stem activity) (Hodges 1980, 1996; Taylor,1997; Thaut 1989a; Whitwell 1993). Thaut (2008) refers to the unique input and organization of artistic expression as a need for brain development:

> Artistic expression may exercise fundamental brain functions and may create unique patterns of perceptual input that the brain needs and cannot generate through other means in order to keep its sensory, motor, and cognitive operations at optimal levels of functioning. (25)

Music can both excite or arouse a listener's emotions and symbolically represent his or her various emotional responses (Dowling and Harwood 1986). As Langer (1966) observed, while people express ideas primarily through language, they express emotions primarily through music.

Throughout history, people often have demonstrated and experienced the connection between music and emotion; they have used music to express strong feelings, such as joy or sorrow, patriotism or discontent; and they have become calmed, agitated, or otherwise moved by different types of music. In fact, using music for emotional expression heads Merriam's (1964) list of ten major functions of music that are common to most cultures. Many theories for this propensity of human beings to use music to express emotions have been proposed. Gfeller (1992a, 46–49) provides an excellent summary of various referentialist and expressionalist viewpoints. Whatever the explanation – whether emotional expression and perception in music are the result of external associations (referentialist view), are inherent in the structure of the music itself (expressionalist view), are the result of biological and neurological mechanisms, or are perhaps due to some combination of all of these – music obviously influences a person's emotions and provides an important vehicle for human emotional expression and understanding.

Music has the ability not only to move or express an individual's specific emotions but also to convey basic human feelings in a manner that is perceived similarly by most human beings (Clynes 1977, 1982, 1991; Whitwell 1993). This connection between music and the expression of the essence of universal emotions is basic to understanding how music can be used as a language of emotions among human beings in general, while still having its own unique meaning to a specific individual. Thus, music connects us with the basic emotions of all humankind, while at the same time giving us a unique way of accessing *and* expressing our own personal emotional experiences and identities.

The integral link between emotions and music offers many possibilities for the therapeutic use of music. For clients who are struggling to cope with overwhelming emotions or for those who have difficulty expressing emotions verbally, music may offer "a less threatening or alternative way to share emotions" (Gfeller 1992a, 50) and may provide a way to help express those feelings that are too deep for words alone (Gaston 1968a). Seeing and experiencing universal emotions through music also may help individuals feel less alone and more connected to the rest of society and humanity as they realize that others have shared the same fears and feelings (Kenny 1982). In this way, sounds and music that complement or mirror a client's feelings can provide some degree of comfort and reassurance. Conversely, music experiences that portray feelings or attitudes foreign to the client may give the client a vehicle for experiencing new feelings or for experiencing feelings and attitudes in new or alternative ways. Because of its link to the emotions, music also can provide a stimulus that taps into those emotional and affective components of a person that may motivate, facilitate, support, and sustain positive growth and change:

> The underlying purpose of music is in its attributes as a specific language of perception that engages brain and behavior. This engagement has a neurological basis and serves neurological purposes, stimulating cognitive, affective, and sensorimotor behavior in a way unique to aesthetic perception. (Thaut 2008, 36–37)

The integral connection between music and the emotions, therefore, may be considered to be a primary factor underlying the usefulness of music as a therapeutic treatment modality.

Music Is an Aesthetic and Creative Experience

Music is an *aesthetic* experience, one that both evokes aesthetic responses and provides a vehicle for creative expression of beauty, meaning, and order (Gaston 1968a; Radocy and Boyle 2012, 352). Aesthetic qualities of music play a major role in transforming sound into music; these qualities also help establish affinity for various sounds and are instrumental in determining the music's power and effects (Aigen 1995a; Summer 1995). When individuals become involved in aesthetic experiences, every aspect of their being – physical, mental, and emotional processes – are stimulated and integrated (Nagler 1995). Music is an aesthetic experience that can reach an individual's "inner core of humanness" (Nagler 1995, 79), regardless of that person's age, life experience, or functioning level (Boxill 1985; Nordoff and Robbins 1977), and give insight into and influence his or her lifeworld.

Many musical experiences also involve *creative* processes. People can create music as they sing, play instruments, write songs, orchestrate, or improvise. In addition, people create their relationship to music as they find personal meaning in listening, performance, or creative experience. Through these creative processes and experiences, music allows people to participate with their whole being – intellect, imagination, and emotions – in creating order out of disorder and form out of chaos as they "struggle to bring into existence new kinds of being that give harmony and integration" (May 1975, 169).

The need for aesthetic experiences and expression is fundamental to human existence; human beings in all cultures search for and try to express beauty and meaning in life (Gaston 1968a; Gfeller 1992a; Kenny 1982; Merriam 1964; Radocy and Boyle 2012, 37; Spencer 1978). Creativity, a process by which something new is brought into being and given form and expression, is also a basic human drive or instinct (Jung 1956; May 1975). As all cultures have recognized, music offers one vehicle through which desires for beauty, order, and meaning can be satisfied and through which creative instincts can be channeled towards constructive ends (Gaston 1968a; Hodges and Haack 1996; Merriam 1964; Radocy and Boyle 2012, 353). Researchers have found that most people, regardless of their degree of musical sophistication or training, respond aesthetically to music in fairly similar ways (Abeles 1980; Abeles and Chung 1996; Madsen et al. 1993; Radocy and Boyle 1988). As an aesthetic and creative art form, music contributes to the quality of life for *all* individuals in a society, whatever their age or degree of health, and helps them to experience, explore, express, and celebrate the nobler aspects of life (Boxill 1985; Gaston 1968a; Gfeller 1992a; Nordoff and Robbins 1977).

Aesthetic and creative experiences in music have the potential to be both curative and preventative, both enjoyable and rehabilitative, both artistic and therapeutic (Edelman 1978; Kenny 1982; Spencer 1978). Through aesthetic and creative experiences, emotional energy not only is released but also channeled productively and used for growth, nondestructive self-expression, and increased self-awareness (Aigen 1995a; Kenny 1982). Creative and aesthetic involvement, realized through some form of experience with music or the other arts, can give joy, relieve feelings of disappointment and failure, offer new ideas and new ways of experiencing, provide a safe structure within which to explore new possibilities, give order and meaning to life, provide forms to express intimate feelings, and help people find ways to adapt to their environment and relate constructively to their internal and external worlds (Edelman 1978; *The Healing Role of the Arts* 1978; Kenny 1982; Salas 1990; Spencer 1978).

The aesthetic qualities and creative processes involved in a music experience add much to music's usefulness and uniqueness as a therapeutic tool (Aigen 1995a; Gaston 1968a; Kenny 1992; Nagler 1995; Summer 1995). Because of human beings' basic need for aesthetic experience, their innate capacity to respond aesthetically, and their drive to be creative, even people who are not musically trained or sophisticated can experience therapeutic benefits from music that provides quality aesthetic experiences. A music therapist must observe each client carefully and be ready to modify the musical experience, as needed: "Creativity and flexibility must be the hallmark of the therapy approach in using music" (Goodman 2007, p. 175).

Aesthetically pleasing and stimulating music experiences and materials are vital aspects of music therapy processes, for the aesthetic experience helps provide integration, meaning, and connections to the basic processes of life and nature, and, in some cases, it may even serve as a direct vehicle for healing (Aigen 1995a; *The Healing Role of the Arts* 1978; Nordoff and Robbins 1971a, 1971b, 1977; Salas 1990). Moreover, many components of aesthetic experience, such as high levels of integration and meaning, enhanced personality development, increased cognitive functioning, and improved social interaction, relate strongly to many clinical goals (Aigen 1995a).

Kenny (1982, 79–80) observed that "even though music may not be the natural vehicle for everyone's creativity, it can be an experimental ground in which to try out creative processes and apply them through a powerful medium." Involvement in creative music experiences helps provide individuals with links to order and purpose, to form and organization. These experiences can be vital to clients who are striving to make sense of a chaotic and disordered life, trying to find meaning in their lives, or searching for better ways to function in and relate to the world (May 1975). Creative experiences in the arts may also open the door to other people and other treatments by giving clients successful, positive, hope-filled experiences (*The Healing Role of the Arts* 1978). In addition, successful participation in meaningful creative and aesthetic experiences also promotes increased feelings of self-worth and facilitates self-actualization (Gaston 1968a; Maslow 1968; May 1975; Nordoff and Robbins 1977). Music's aesthetic and creative aspects, therefore, have great potential for facilitating growth and healing, enhancing integration and insight, bringing meaning and order, increasing self-esteem, and generally contributing to a better quality of life for many clients in music therapy.

In both music education and music therapy, there has been an awareness of the need for opportunities to develop composition and improvisation skills. This has been especially true in the 1990–2005 time period, during which the music education profession adopted National Standards recommending content and skills for students at all levels (Rutkowki, Thompson, and Huang 2011). This seems to be a world-wide awareness. For example, McPherson and Dunbar-Hall (2001, 19) wrote about composition requirements for Australian music students: "The underlying premise is that composition is a process of continual rethinking and reworking, rather than the instantaneous writing of a finished product."

In music therapy, AMTA recognizes this premise in its statement of competencies required for entry-level music therapists. Goodman (2011) decribes the music foundation competencies (1–11) that are used as criteria for entry-level music therapists. Within the Music Foundations are Composition and

Arranging Skills, (2.1 and 2.2) (35), as well as Improvisation Skills (9.1, 9.2, and 9.3) (44). These skills require the music therapist to demonstrate creativity in both composition and improvisation to develop or adapt music materials for clients.

Music Provides a Source of Enjoyment and Gratification

Music is a fun, normal experience, part of everyday life. Throughout history, societies of all types have used music for enjoyment and entertainment (Blacking 1973; Hodges and Haack 1996; Merriam 1964; Radocy and Boyle 2012). Considering its potential for therapeutic effectiveness, one should not ignore music's positive affective qualities, which may motivate clients to engage in processes that will facilitate therapeutic change (*The Healing Role of the Arts* 1978; Thaut 1989a). In speaking of the unique factors that music therapy brings to treatment, Lathom (1981b) noted:

> There is no pain with music, as there may be with other aspects of rehabilitation, and the child can feel successful and capable if appropriate activities are selected. Music activities are fun and the person associated with them is greeted with pleasure. (22)

Radocy and Boyle (2012, 12) discuss both aesthetic enjoyment and the entertainment value of music: "Music may be chosen for its beauty and ability to arouse aesthetic pleasure. However, much popular music is chosen primarily for its entertainment value. Both are used in music therapy to attract and interact with the client." Thus, the sense of fun and enjoyment that are inherent in many music experiences can help clients begin to relate to others in positive ways. In addition, as clients participate successfully in fun, nonthreatening music experiences, they begin to gain a sense of gratification and pride in their accomplishments, which increases their feelings of self-worth and competence (Gaston 1968a; Lathom 1981b; Lathom-Radocy 2014, 35–36; Sears 1968).

Since music is highly valued by and pervasive in society in general, it also can help "normalize" the environment of hospital, special education, or other treatment settings. The situation in which music is encountered requires consideration (Hargreaves and North 1999, 74; Lamont 2009, 241). In music therapy, the therapist, other clients, and the room setting and organization are all important. Through music, people may be able to relate to some aspects of their lives outside the treatment setting or find new ways of relating to others who do not share their disabilities. Music may also provide a necessary diversion from the more stressful or painful aspects of treatment or therapy. As Gfeller (1992a, 54) noted, although using music for entertainment, diversional, or recreational purposes may somehow seem less noble or important, these types of music experiences, too, have their place, both in society and in various treatment settings and "can even contribute to emotional and physical well-being." Thus, the fact that music is a source of entertainment and pleasure highly valued by society in general also contributes to its potential usefulness as a treatment modality.

HOW MUSIC IS USED IN THERAPY

According to Gaston (1968b, v), the father of modern music therapy, three basic principles "form much of the foundation of music therapy . . . [and] are a primary source of direction in music therapy." These principles are

1. the use of music and music experiences to establish or reestablish inter-personal relationships,
2. the use of music and music experiences to bring about self-esteem through self-actualization, and
3. the use of the unique potential of rhythm to energize and bring order.

Although Sears (1968, 34) used a different sequence, his explanation of music therapy processes included that same triad of social relations, self-relations, and general order or structure: "The three classifications that underlie the constructs and processes of music therapy are (1) experience with structure, (2) experience in self-organization, and (3) experience in relating to others." The ideas embodied in Gaston's (1968b) guiding principles for using music in therapy and Sear's (1968) classifications of music therapy processes have much to say about the general ways music is used to accomplish therapeutic purposes. In fact, many of current clinical practices in music therapy stem from these basic concepts (Feder and Feder 1981; Gfeller 1987a). This will become increasingly evident in the discussions of music therapy practices with specific client populations found in later chapters.

Music Experiences Attract Attention and Provide Order and Structure

Some models of healing and human development view persons as moving on a continuum, from chaos and disorder to an eventual state of wholeness and health (Crowe 1991). Some music therapy clients have various severe physical, mental, or emotional impairments that cause them to function at the low end of this continuum. They may have difficulty perceiving or compre-hending their internal and external worlds and may be unable to control and organize their behavior or respond to stimuli in appropriate or meaningful ways. At times they may seem totally unaware of their surroundings. These clients often benefit greatly from music therapy interventions that "emphasize awareness of and response to the order and structure of music" (Crowe 1991, 114). Music can help attract and sustain attention, elicit and organize response, and exemplify ways to make beauty and order out of chaos. Lathom-Radocy (2014, 34) states, "Helping a child to function within structure is one of music therapy's most important contributions." The music therapist carefully selects, structures, and manipulates various musical elements and personal and environmental factors in ways that will assist the client in moving closer to a state of health (Bruscia 1989a; Gfeller 1987a). Particularly useful at this level are music's qualities that evoke basic sensory, rhythmic, and affective responses.

Music is a powerful form of sensory stimulation, a multisensory experience. Music contains sounds which can be heard (auditory stimulation) and vibrations which can be felt (tactile stimulation). Live performances may add visual stimulation; moving to music can add kinesthetic and proprioceptive stimulation. Therefore, music often can attract and hold a person's attention by providing stimulation that is almost impossible to ignore.

In addition, music experiences offer the individual a chance to respond through auditory, visual, tactile, and kinesthetic channels: by looking to the music source, by turning toward or reaching out to the music source, by moving to the music, by vocalizing with the music, by manipulating musical instruments to make sounds, etc. As a stimulus, music can provide multisensory input; as a response, music offers opportunities for multisensory output. A client who has difficulty perceiving, organizing, or responding through one sensory mode may be able to be stimulated by or respond through another sensory mode.

"Music is structured reality" (Gaston 1968a, 24), a real event that occurs in time and demands a moment-by-moment commitment from the individual (Sears 1968/2007). There are certain qualities inherent in music that demand, permit, evoke, and provoke specific physical, psychological, and affective behaviors (Abeles 1980; Abeles and Chung 1996; Bartlett 1996; Hodges 1980, 1996; Hodges and Haack 1996; Radocy and Boyle 2012; Sears 1968). Music's ability to touch an individual on all of these levels increases the likelihood that music will break into the individual's world or awareness in at least one of these areas. Furthermore, after the rhythms, sounds, and melodies attract an individual's attention, music's time-ordered structure and experience help hold that attention, providing an environment or structure in which growth and learning can occur. The order and structure of music, especially as contained in its rhythm and form, also may assist an individual in organizing his or her perceptions and responses (Lathom-Radocy 2014, 35).

For the individual whose world is often a confusing chaos, music's order is a welcome structured experience in which the child [or adult] may feel free from confusion and safe in the ability to predict the activity and the person associated with the music (Lathom 1981b, 23).

Music Experiences Provide Self-Knowledge, Self-Expression, and Self-Gratification

Before people can relate successfully and appropriately to those around them, they must be comfortable with themselves as individuals. Music can provide a means of self-expression and opportunities for enhancing feelings of self-worth (Sears 1968). As an avenue of both verbal and nonverbal communication, music can function as a vehicle for expressing moods, attitudes, and feelings. Music activities are also very adaptable and can allow for success at many different achievement levels. Achieving success and competency in music activities can enhance an individual's sense of self-esteem (Gaston 1968a; Lathom 1981b; Lathom-Radocy 2014; Sears 1968), especially since society mostly values music. Music experiences that involve song lyric analysis, song writing, improvisation, or guided imagery also can help individuals explore alternative viewpoints or possibilities for action in relatively safe and nonthreatening ways. In addition, music experiences can assist individuals in achieving new perspectives on the ways they view themselves and can help them see new possibilities for response, growth, and development (Bonny and Savary 1990; Crowe 1991).

Music Experiences Promote Positive Relationships with Others

For individuals to function in society, they must be able to relate successfully and appropriately to those around them. Music activities often occur as group activities: "Music, by its very nature, draws people together for intimate, yet ordered, function" (Gaston 1968a, 27). Music activities involving two or more people provide individuals with a nonthreatening atmosphere in which to learn to relate to others: "It is through loving relationships, sustained over a long period of time, that individuals learn to become social beings" (Lathom-Radocy 2014, 36). Because it is a positive, enjoyable activity and because of its inherent persuasive and communicative powers, music often may provide the motivation that individuals need to join in the group and interact with others (Gaston 1968a; Lathom 1981b; Sears 1968). As they participate in group vocal, instrumental, movement-to-music, improvisation, composition, and music-based discussion experiences, group members can see what types of actions lead to success or failure and can learn to relate to others in productive ways while participating in fun and enjoyable activities. Music experiences also may make destructive or ineffective patterns of relating to others apparent in ways that are much more potent than verbal, intellectual analysis. As Crowe (1991, 115) explains, "The sounds produced mirror the group dynamics and issues and concerns of the individuals involved. The musical event makes these processes overt and obvious so that they can be explored and discussed."

Group music experiences, then, can help individuals see the necessity for change in the ways they relate to others while simultaneously providing a vehicle through which to explore and practice more productive and effective methods of interaction. Music can both support clients while they question their current behavior patterns and belief systems and assist them in adopting and owning more effective and productive behavior and beliefs. Thus, through participation in carefully structured therapeutic group music activities, individuals can gain insights and skills that will help them relate more successfully, appropriately, and responsibly toward others.

QUESTIONS FOR THOUGHT AND DISCUSSION

1. What are some aspects of music that make it useful as a treatment modality? How or why do these impact its therapeutic effectiveness?
2. Describe three general ways music may be used in therapy. How do Gaston's guiding principles and Sears's classifications of processes relate to these?
3. How do music experiences attract attention and provide order and structure? What types of clients might benefit from this type of music therapy experience?
4. How do music experiences help individuals increase self-knowledge, self-expression, or self-gratification? What types of clients might benefit from this type of music therapy experience?
5. How do music experiences help individuals increase their skills and abilities to relate more successfully, appropriately, and responsibly toward those around them? What types of clients might benefit from this type of music therapy experience?

FURTHER READING

Blacking, J. (1973). *How musical is man?* Seattle: University of Washington Press.
Campbell, D. (Ed.) (1991). *Music: Physician for times to come.* Wheaton, IL: Quest Books.

Dowling, W. J., & Harwood, D. L. (1986). *Music cognition.* Orlando, FL: Academic Press.

Gaston, E. T. (1968). Foreword. In E. T. Gaston (Ed.), *Music in therapy* (v–vii). New York: Macmillan.

Gaston, E. T. (1968). Man and music. In E. T. Gaston (Ed.), *Music in therapy* (7–29). New York: Macmillan.

Gfeller, K. (1987). Music therapy theory and practice as reflected in research literature. *Journal of Music Therapy, 25*(1), 28–43.

Gfeller, K. (2008). Music: A human phenomenon and therapeutic tool. In W. B. Davis, K. E. Gfeller, & M. H. Thaut, *An introduction to music therapy: Theory and practice* (3rd ed.), (41–75). Silver Spring, MD: American Music Therapy Association.

Kenny, C. B. (Ed.) (1995). *Listening, playing, creating: Essays on the power of sound.* Albany, NY: State University of New York Press.

Lathom, W. (1981). Aspects of music therapy that are unique on the treatment and education team. In W. Lathom, *The role of the music therapist in the education of severely and profoundly handicapped children and youth.* Lawrence, KS: National Association for Music Therapy.

Lathom-Radocy, W. (2014). *Goals and objectives for children in music therapy* (22–38). Springfield, IL: Charles C Thomas Publisher, Ltd.

Nagler, J. C. (1995). *Toward the aesthetic life world. Music Therapy, 13*(1), 75–91.

Radocy, R. E., & Boyle, J. D. (2012). *Psychological foundations of musical behavior* (5th ed.). Springfield, IL: Charles C Thomas Publisher, Ltd.

Sears, W. W. (1968). Processes in music therapy. In E. T. Gaston (Ed.), *Music in therapy* (30–44). New York: Macmillan.

Sears, M. S. (Ed.). (2007) *Music: The therapeutic edge: Readings from William W. Sears.* Gilsum, NH: Barcelona Publishers.

Thaut, M. H. (1989). Music therapy, affect modulation, and therapeutic change: Toward an integrative model. *Music Therapy Perspectives, 7,* 55–62.

Thaut, M. H. (2008). *Rhythm, Music, and the Brain* (1–38). New York: Routledge.

Chapter Six

GENERAL GUIDELINES FOR THE THERAPEUTIC USE OF MUSIC, PART II: PRACTICAL PLANNING

Chapter five discussed some aspects of music that make it useful as a therapeutic treatment modality and described three general ways music is used in therapy. Chapter Six now focuses on the actual process a music therapist goes through in determining what a client needs and in planning, implementing, and evaluating music therapy intervention strategies. In addition, examples of various types of music experiences that may be useful in helping clients gain skills in several general areas are presented. Taken together, Chapters Five and Six provide fundamental background knowledge for the more specific information on music therapy practices with various client populations that appears in the next several chapters.

BASIC STAGES IN THE DELIVERY OF MUSIC THERAPY SERVICES

As Chapter One explained, music therapy is not a haphazard process where some kind of music is played in the hope that it will help people feel better. Music therapy is a planned, goal-directed process of interaction and intervention, based on assessment and evaluation of individual clients' specific needs, strengths, and weaknesses, in which music or music-based experiences are prescribed specifically for use by specially trained personnel (i.e., music therapists or those they train and supervise) to influence positive changes in an individual's condition, skills, thoughts, feelings, or behaviors. Music therapists, therefore, must engage in specific procedures that will help them (1) determine the client's strengths, weaknesses, and area(s) of need; (2) decide what types of music experiences will be most beneficial; and (3) find ways of evaluating whether or not the client is making progress as a result of the music therapy treatment.

The music therapy treatment process begins when a music therapist accepts a client for music therapy services based on some kind of referral (Davis 1992c;

Maranto 1993b). According to Gfeller and Davis (2008, 431), "The first step in the treatment process is referral, which facilitates access to health care providers." AMTA (2014) also includes referral in the first "Standard of Clinical Practice" (1.2). Referrals may come from many sources, including members of the interdisciplinary treatment team, other professionals, other music therapists, the client's family, parents, guardians, or advocates. Requests for treatment may be initiated by potential clients. After deciding to accept a client for treatment, the music therapist then must plan, implement, and evaluate a music therapy treatment program for that client. This process usually includes several general stages (AMTA 2014; Davis 1992c; Gfeller and Davis 2008, 432–443; Hanser 1987; Maranto 1993b): (1) assessing the client to determine strengths, weaknesses, problems, and areas of need; (2) setting goals and objectives; (3) planning music-based intervention strategies to help the client reach these goals and objectives; (4) implementing treatment procedures; (5) documenting progress and responses; and (6) termination, with a summary of progress and level of functioning at the time of termination. Recommendations for further treatment, placement, or periodic review may follow. All of these steps are integral to helping a music therapist carry out successful music therapy treatment interventions.

Assessment

Before music therapists can plan appropriate music therapy intervention strategies to help a client, they must know in what area(s) that client needs help. Therefore, the first step in planning effective music therapy intervention strategies involves the process of determining the client's individual strengths and weaknesses, including the client's particular problems or area(s) of need. This process generally is known as assessment. Completed prior to treatment, an assessment gives a broad overview and analysis of the client's functioning level in many areas. This information helps provide a direction for treatment and recommended services or treatment modalities (AMTA 2014; Davis 1992c; Hanser 1987; Lathom 1981b; Lathom-Radocy 2014; Maranto 1993b). Adamek and Darrow (2010, 31–32) explain the need for assessment for a child to have music therapy included in his/her Individualized Education Program (IEP), which is required under legislation known as the Individuals with Disabilities Act (IDEA). Crowe (2007, 15) specifies areas of assessment for adults in mental health treatment. This was also addressed by Gfeller and Davis (2008, 432–437).

During the assessment process, the music therapist seeks to gather as much background information about the client as possible. Knowledge about the client's strengths, weaknesses, skills, and abilities can be obtained in several ways: (1) by reviewing the client's developmental, personal, social, and medical history; (2) by interviewing the client or the client's family members, caregivers, or guardians; (3) by observing the client in various situations; (4) by discussing the client's needs with other members of the treatment team; and (5) by engaging or observing the client participating in music experiences that give some indication of the client's responses to and preferences for various types of music experiences and music materials as well as the client's level of motor, social, auditory, communication, and musical skills (AMTA 1998; Bruscia 1991a; Davis 1992c; Hanser 1987; Lathom 1981b; Lathom-Radocy 2014; Maranto 1993b). The music therapist needs background information in *both* musical and nonmusical areas to design a music therapy treatment program that will be meaningful to the client; appropriate to the client's chronological age, functioning level, and cultural background; and relevant to the client's needs.

Assessment tools and activities will vary with the orientation and training of the person doing the assessment; the particular disability, needs, or functioning level of the client being assessed; and the type of information being sought. Music therapists often gain much useful nonmusical information about a client from the assessments given by other professionals. In addition, however, music therapists will want to assess a client's specific responses, interactions, skills, and preferences regarding music and the many different types of modalities, media, activities, instruments, idioms, styles, moods, and qualities available in music experiences. Clients may respond differently in music settings than they do in other treatment settings; and different skills, responses, and aspects of their personality may become apparent through their interaction with music materials (Boxill 1985; Bruscia 1987, 1991a; Davis 1992c; Hanser 1987; Isenberg-Grzeda 1988; Lathom-Radocy 2014). Since music reaches the brain in diverse ways and has many inherent motivating and gratifying aspects, music also may be useful in assessing clients who are considered "untestable" with other assessment tools or methods (Isenberg-Grzeda 1988). However, it is important that the music therapist assess and be aware of the client's level of musical development, especially when working with children, for different phases of musical development have specific associated auditory, vocal/tonal, and rhythmic behaviors; what is appropriate for one stage of development may not necessarily be appropriate for another (Briggs 1991).

Often, music therapists develop clinical assessment tools specifically for their population or setting to help them gain the type of information they need in an efficient manner. Several sources, including Boxill (1985), Chase (2002), Davis (1992c), Davis and Farnan (2004, 99–101), Hanser (1987), Isenberg-Grzeda (1988), and Lathom-Radocy (2014), as well as general references on assessment development or samples of various assessments, may be helpful to the reader desiring more information in this area. Later chapters of this book cover some music therapy assessment tools that have been developed for various client populations and for various music therapy techniques, but reliability and validity have not been established for most of these (Davis 1992c; Maranto 1993b).

Setting Goals and Objectives

After obtaining a clear picture of the client's strengths, needs, preferences, and overall level of functioning, the music therapist has the necessary information to set appropriate and realistic therapeutic goals and objectives. Therapeutic goals and objectives state what the client is to accomplish or what changes in behavior the client will show if the therapeutic intervention strategies are successful. Goals and objectives give direction, purpose, and focus to music therapy treatment procedures. The specific expectations set forth in the goals and objectives also help the music therapist know whether or not the client is receiving any benefit from music therapy treatment.

Usually, goals are broad statements of desired outcomes in a certain area, whereas objectives are more specific and involve operationally defined steps and definite time frames for achievement (AMTA 1998; Davis 1992c; Hanser 1987). Consider the analogy of standing on a river bank and trying to reach the other side. The river bank on which you are currently standing represents the client's current level of functioning, as determined from the assessment. The opposite river bank represents the goal, the final state of improved functioning you hope the client will reach. The objectives, then, might be thought of as the stepping stones that will help the client reach the goal – the specific behaviors or skills the client needs to develop in order to achieve the goal. Lathom-Radocy (2014) explains the procedure followed when working with children:

> The procedure the therapist follows is to (1) make an assessment, (2) pinpoint specific behavioral changes necessary for the child to benefit from school and live in the community, (3) develop a statement of goals and objectives (for inclusion on the child's IEP), (4) design a plan to achieve the goals and objectives, (5) implement the plan, and (6) reevaluate the IEP with a statement of progress and suggestions for new goals and objectives. (23)

Goals usually indicate the desire for improvement or maintenance of skills in a broad division of a general skill area in which the client has a problem or weakness. Goals sometimes are expressed as infinitive phrases rather than as complete statements:

"To increase positive interactions with other group members."
"To improve receptive language skills."
"To increase reality orientation."
"To maintain range of motion in upper extremities."

"To increase ability to express feelings accurately and appropriately."
"To increase functional motor skills."

Hanson-Abromeit and Colwell (2008, 247–260) provide "Sample Music Therapy Intervention Plans" that exemplify goals, objective, procedures, and measurement tools.

After defining this broad treatment focus, the music therapist breaks it down into a series of short-term objectives, each of which relate to the goal and define a specific step, skill, or behavior needed to achieve the goal. By clearly defining expectations in terms of observable outcomes, objectives help the therapist measure and evaluate the changes that occur (or fail to occur) throughout the course of therapy. Each objective delineates (1) a specific *behavior* the client must show (what the client will do to demonstrate competency in the defined area; e.g., "look at speaker," "wait to be called upon before speaking," "address group members by name," "grasp and hold a maraca," "sing at same tempo and volume as rest of group"); (2) the *criterion* for successful performance (the level of proficiency the client must demonstrate to indicate mastery, usually expressed quantitatively as number of times, length of time, or percent; e.g., "4 out of 5 times," "each time," "for two minutes," "within 3 seconds," "at least three times each session," "for four consecutive sessions"); (3) any important *conditions* or *qualifiers* for performance of the task (prompts or restrictions which will be part of the setting or procedure; e.g., "with one physical prompt," "independently," "given a list of five song titles," "without gestural cues"); and (4) a *time frame* or termination date (the targeted date for achieving the objective; e.g., "within six months," "during the next two weeks," "by the end of ten sessions"). [Note: Often, more cues or prompts are given in the initial stages of treatment, while a client's skills are just emerging. The degree of independence required for performance increases throughout the course of therapy as the client gains skills; this is reflected in the conditions or qualifiers.] Including all these elements (behavior, criterion, qualifiers or conditions, and time frame) in the objective may make the process of constructing objectives difficult and time-consuming (Davis 1992c), but a well-written, operationally defined objective is essential to providing a direction for therapeutic treatment and a means of measuring and evaluating client progress.

Planning Music-Based Intervention Strategies

Music, the music therapist's main tool, differentiates music therapy from other therapies. Therefore, in planning treatment interventions, the music therapist must develop specific procedures that use music and music materials to help the client reach the therapeutic goals and objectives. Doing this requires consideration of several factors, including (a) how music will function to help the client meet the goals and objectives; (b) what types of music experiences and musical materials will be used; (c) if the intervention procedures will incorporate any specific therapeutic or educational strategies; and (d) any environmental or structural factors that may affect the activity or the client's response. Above all, however, the music therapist must always keep in mind how these factors relate both to the individual client's needs, strengths, preferences, age, cultural background, skills, and capabilities and to the desired objective. In planning music-based intervention strategies, one must never forget the purpose for which they are intended (goal/objective) or the client's unique individual qualities: "The initial selection of music for therapy must reflect the clients' interests, preferences, and background as well as the nonmusical therapeutic objectives" (Prickett 1989, 98).

Determining the Function of Music

Music experiences selected for use in music therapy treatment programs are designed so that something in their content or process stimulates or provides a means of reward for the client to progress toward the established therapeutic goal (Prickett 1989). Duerksen (1978) has identified five general ways in which music activities can help clients gain the nonmusical skills they need to reach therapeutic goals:

1. Music as a carrier of information.
2. Music as a reinforcer.
3. Music as a background for learning.
4. Music as a physical structure for the learning activity.
5. Music as a reflection of skills or processes to be learned. (cited in Lathom 1981a, 160)

All the various learning and expressive experiences of music – singing, playing musical instruments, creating or composing music, moving to music, discussing music – can be used therapeutically in one or more of these ways. For example, special songs may be written to include information (e.g., facts, sequences of events in a task) that relate to skills a client is trying to master (Kramer 1978; Wolfe and Hom 1993; Wolfe and Stambaugh 1993; Wolfe and Waldon 2009, 48). Songs and musical games also can help teach various academic and social skills. In addition, song lyrics, instrumental improvisations, and movement-to-music experiences can provide safe, nonthreatening frameworks in which to express and discuss emotionally laden material.

Since music is something that is pleasurable to most people, various music activities and experiences, such as listening to preferred music, singing, dancing, or playing musical instruments, also can serve as powerful reinforcers of skills and behaviors (Bellamy and Sontag 1973; Dorow 1976; Jorgenson 1974; Metzler 1974; Michel 1971; Reid et al. 1975; Saperston 1989; Saperston, Chan, Morphew, and Carsrud 1980; Underhill and Harris 1974; Wilson 1976; Wolfe 1980). Maultsby (1977) suggested that music is such a powerful reinforcer of new learning because of its connection to meeting basic survival needs, for parents throughout the world often sing as they give their babies food, water, and shelter. According to Lathom (1981b, 21), music is especially effective as a reinforcer "because it can be started immediately after the desired response and it does not produce satiation, as does food or other reinforcers." In conjunction with praise, music can be a powerful social reinforcer: "Reinforcement techniques are of value in working with . . . children. Often the music may be the reinforcement, but by pairing it with praise, a social consequence of participation may occur" (Lathom-Radocy 2014, 67–68).

Music also can be used therapeutically as a background for learning. By masking unwanted sounds, helping break monotony, or helping to establish a specific mood, carefully selected background music can facilitate learning, improve task performance, increase verbal interaction, enhance performance on some spatial and numerical processing tasks, and provide a pleasant environment for other activities (Miller and Schyb 1989; Radocy and Boyle 2012; Wolfe and Stambaugh 1993). In addition, music can structure the time frame of an activity, as in "choreographing" a specific motor action to particular music. Music's rhythmic structure can facilitate improvement in physical rhythmic activities, such as respiration, gait training, range of motion, and relaxation (Miller 1979; Thaut 2008). Finally, the way in which the client interacts with the music materials, the music therapist, and other individuals in the music therapy session often serves as a reflection of how well the client is progressing toward the therapeutic goal or of the level at which the client is functioning. For example, Rider (1978, 1981) has shown that musical perception tasks may be used to assess levels of cognitive functioning.

Selecting Musical Materials and Types of Music Experiences

In designing intervention strategies and selecting appropriate types of music and music experiences to accomplish certain goals and objectives, music therapists employ their knowledge of the general functions and effects of various types of music and music experiences. General knowledge, however, must be tempered by specific knowledge of the individual client's actual reactions to and preferences for various musical stimuli, which the music therapist gained in the client's assessment. Just as physicians consider individual variables and reactions and do not prescribe uniform courses of treatment or dosages of medication for all patients with the same condition, music therapists take into account individual variables when determining what music or types of music experiences will be used for treatment interventions with a particular client (Summer 1995). While generalizations and precategorized music or music activities certainly can serve as starting points in seeking suitable music experiences to reach certain objectives or achieve certain effects, appropriateness for an individual client must be verified by checking that individual's responses or reactions (Hadsell 1989). On the other hand, while the client's preferences and requests do influence the selection and design of musical materials used in music therapy interventions, "it is also important to realize that the client's preferences may be a manifestation of his/her problem, and therefore in need of modification or expansion" (Bruscia 1991a, 10).

As music therapists determine which music experiences to use with individual clients to achieve specific purposes, they have many aspects to consider. For example, there are many modes of music activity or ways of interacting with music, including listening, moving, singing/chanting/humming, playing musical instruments, creating music (improvising or composing), discussing music, and notating music (Boxill 1985; Bruscia 1987; Crowe 2007, 17–18; Standley 1991a). These activities may be used alone or in combination with one another (e.g., sing and move, sing and play instruments, listen and notate, etc.), and experiences may include both passive and active participation. Radocy and Lathom-Radocy (1999, 47) spoke of "music's potential to stimulate and soothe, to provide a time-based sequential order for cooperative activities, and to provide a means of expression, in short, to serve some of humanity's functional needs." The therapist and/or clients may use many musical media, including voice, guitar, piano or keyboard, autoharp, rhythm instruments, band or orchestral instruments, electronic instruments, records, audio or video tapes, compact discs, and computer programs. These various media, too, may be used alone or in combination with others. In addition, the therapist might present music in one mode or medium (e.g., sing), while the client may respond in another mode or with another medium (e.g., by moving or playing instruments). Some intervention strategies also might have the therapist and client interacting or performing together while using various activities.

At a more basic level, the music therapist must consider the effect of various musical elements (e.g., rhythm, tempo, pitch, melody, harmony, texture, timbre, dynamics, song text [if applicable], and different ways of manipulating them [amount of novelty, redundancy, complexity, etc.]). Obviously, myriad possible combinations exist, making a wide range of idioms, styles, and moods of music available for use in therapy. Again, the therapist's knowledge of music's general effects, coupled with knowledge and observation of the individual client's specific preferences, interests, needs, and capabilities, will be primary factors in selecting the specific type, style, mood, or aspect of music used for therapeutic intervention. In addition, if the music is to be paired with a learning task, the music therapist will want to carefully monitor the complexity of the rhythms, melody, lyrics, and/or accompaniment. Generally, the more repetitive the words, rhythms, notes, and chords, the simpler the learning (Standley 1991a); or, in other words, "the greater the music's perceptual redundancy, the more predictable the musical response" (Radocy and Boyle 2012, 391). Finally, the music therapist should always monitor the age appropriateness of musical selections, materials, and activities being considered for use with clients. Activities, experiences, and materials should be appropriate to the individual's chronological age.

Music therapists often must be very creative to fit the demands and focus of music activities to a client's individual needs, abilities, and interests. Lathom-Radocy (2014, 48) stated that when working with children with profound intellectual disabilities, "The therapist must have great patience, the ability to be thrilled with small improvements over a long time, and much ingenuity to devise tasks that are possible for children with such limited ability." Not every client is interested in the same type of music, the same instrument, or the same song; nor does every client possess the same degree of motor coordination, communication and social skills, or intellectual ability. Therefore, in planning music therapy intervention strategies, music therapists must consider each client individually and strive to design activities that will engage the client's interest and utilize the client's strengths as well as ameliorate the client's weaknesses. For example, a client who does not have the psychomotor coordination needed to finger chords on a guitar might still be able to play simple guitar accompaniments if the open strings were tuned to a major chord (Cassity 1977). According to Tyson (1959), the ability to adapt musical concepts and materials to each client's level of understanding and capacity to respond is a crucial factor in developing effective therapeutic relationships with clients. And, as Bruscia (1991, 9) observed, "the subtle and wonderful thing about music therapy is that, in actuality, every musical experience can be adapted to meet a broad spectrum of client needs."

Incorporating Specific Therapeutic or Educational Strategies

In order to develop a coordinated treatment approach with other members of the professional team, music therapists often incorporate specific therapeutic, educational, or psychological theories or approaches into their music therapy intervention strategies. For example, music therapists working in settings that emphasize cognitive approaches will structure their presentation strategies differently than music therapists who work in settings emphasizing a strong behavior modification approach. It is important for the client and consistency of treatment that the music therapist's approach be congruent with that of the rest of the treatment team and with the general therapeutic milieu of the institution or facility (AMTA 1998; Isenberg-Grzeda 1988; F. Johnson 1981).

Therefore, music therapists must be knowledgeable of the techniques, philosophies, and approaches used by the other professionals with whom they work and find ways of incorporating or complementing those strategies and approaches in any music therapy treatment interventions they design.

Considering Environmental and Structural Factors

As music therapists plan music-based intervention strategies, they want to create activities and experiences that are appropriately challenging to the client (Aigen 1995a; James 1987). Within a success-oriented environment, music therapists strive to provide therapeutic music experiences in which the demands do not exceed the client's capabilities, yet which do provide enough challenge to be engaging and move the client toward productive growth. It is most important to consider the client's developmental level. This is often identified in reports and observations of others on the team (psychiatrist, psychologist, special educator, physical therapist, or others). However, Goodman (2007, 93) notes that "there may be cases where the child's behavior is developmentally higher or even lower in the music therapy session." While clients may need immediate success experiences in the initial stages of therapy, gratification can become more delayed and activities may become more challenging as the clients gain competence in performance and develop increased confidence in themselves and their abilities. As clients occasionally fail and learn to try again, they begin to develop coping skills needed to face the realities and challenges of daily life. However, "while some failure indicates that a client is being challenged, constant and repeated failure indicates poor assessment on the part of the therapist" (James 1987, 33).

Including an appropriate amount of structure in activities is essential to help clients attain therapeutic goals and objectives (Hadsell 1993; Lathom-Radocy 2014, 14). References to the amount of structure needed for a client to successfully perform a task may be included as a condition or qualifier portion of the objective (see above). In addition to the music variables considered above, several other environmental aspects may be controlled to help eliminate behavior problems and provide clear expectations and necessary cues for desired responses. These include (1) *time* (general organization of session, length of activities, time between activities, organization of transitions, time spent waiting for turns); (2) *physical space* and *equipment* (room arrangement, number of visual or auditory distractions, type and placement of equipment used in session, storage or placement of equipment not being used); (3) *choices* (number and complexity of options); (4) *materials* (color, spacing, texture, amount of information, number of materials used in the session, therapist- or client-selected or -provided placement and manner of presentation, appropriateness for age and developmental level and physical capabilities); (5) *instructions* (appropriateness of language, speed, form, and complexity to client's function-ing level); and (6) *presentation of activities* (sequencing and pacing, number and timing of cues, complexity and amount of information, age appropriateness, adequate task analysis, variations) (Hadsell 1993; Lathom-Radocy 2014, 3–21).

Often, clients develop new skills and behaviors through successive steps of approximation. Thus, more structure, assistance, cues, and prompts may be needed in the initial stages of therapy or in the client's first encounters with a certain type of music experience or medium. Structure can be reduced and cues or assistance faded as the client's skills emerge and develop (Hadsell 1993; Hanser 1987). The type and amount of structure needed vary from client to client, from environment to environment, from task to task, and from one stage of therapy to another; thus, the therapist must carefully monitor the client's responses and adjust accordingly (Hadsell 1993). Carefully analyzing the various aspects of external structure can both facilitate the performance of an individual client and make the same activity "appropriate for many clients if its structure is varied to meet their individual needs" (Hadsell 1993, 64).

Implementing Treatment Procedures

After devising strategies for music therapy intervention and treatment, the therapist must implement them to see whether they will, in fact, help the client progress toward the established therapeutic goal. Continuous observation and evaluation of the client's responses, both to the music therapy activities themselves and to the music therapist's methods of implementing these activities, are very important factors in developing effective music therapy intervention strategies. No matter how wonderful a procedure or activity may look on paper, if the client cannot or will not respond to it, some modification is necessary. Therefore, while the music therapist strives to deliver services according to the written program plan (AMTA 1998), the implementation phase of treatment also allows for adjustments in procedures, materials, and approaches as necessary to help the client achieve the highest possible level of functioning and the maximum therapeutic benefit. As Hesser (2001, 54) maintains, "We need to develop skills on our major instrument and expand our repertoire, allowing us to more freely respond to our clients musically." Thus, the implementation phase of therapy involves both science and art, both convention and spontaneity (Bruscia 1989a; Kenny 1982). In conclusion, "It is the rare case that proceeds according to plan without any deviation whatsoever" (Hanser 1987, 141).

Therefore, while attending to the predetermined treatment plan, the music therapist must also observe continuously. Bruscia (2001, 7) explains the impor-tance of carefully *listening* to each client and the music they produce: "In fact, of the many and diverse competencies required of a music therapist, listening is the most fundamental and unique to the discipline." Paying close attention to the client's smallest responses, the music therapist continuously shapes and molds the therapeutic encounter, using his or her best clinical judgment to adjust components as necessary to meet the client's immediate needs. Even in this process of spontaneous adaptation – the "art" of doing music therapy – the music therapist always is mindful of the client's goals and objectives, the reason and purpose behind the therapeutic encounter (Hanser 1987). According to Boxill (1985, 179), "Virtually everything the skilled therapist does is therapeutically purposeful, engaging clients in active participation in their own growth."

Documentation and Data Collection

In order to maintain a record of client progress and response to treatment, music therapists need some format for collecting data on the client's responses and for documenting the client's progress. These procedures help provide a chronological account of the client's treatment, help monitor effectiveness and efficiency of treatment, provide for quality assurance and accountability, and provide communication links to all involved with the client's care (Davis 1992c; Hanser 1987). Usually, music therapists are required to document a client's referral to music therapy, assessment, placement, program plan, and ongoing progress in music therapy (AMTA 2014). Reporting formats may vary greatly from one setting to another, dependent in part upon state, federal, and facility regulations. Generally, however, music therapists have some method of collecting data on the targeted client behaviors and some manner of periodically reporting client progress. All documentation is "written in an objective, professional style based on observable client responses" (AMTA 1998, xliii).

In collecting data to see if a client is making progress, the therapist focuses on changes in the specific behavior outlined in the client's therapeutic objective. A baseline measurement indicates the client's level of behavior before treatment and serves as a reference point by which to gauge progress (Gfeller and Davis 2008, 442; Goodman 2007, 244–267). Even if clients do not reach the established criterion level for successful completion of the objective within the projected time frame, they still may be making some progress toward the objective as compared with their initial level of performance.

A summary of a client's initial proficiency level is usually given in the music therapy assessment. During the implementation phase of treatment, the music therapist regularly collects data on the frequency or duration of the targeted behaviors specified in the objective. Data may be charted in many ways, using formats such as tables, graphs, or written progress notes. Video and audio recordings also may be useful tools for tracking and recording data and progress in music therapy; however, the music therapist must be sure to obtain client (or guardian) consent for recording. The objective's behavior and criterion sections will help the therapist determine what sort of data collection strategies to employ. In order to be useful in evaluating the effectiveness of music therapy treatment, the data must relate to the treatment's objective or purpose. Analysis of the data collected on the client's observed responses during the implementation of music therapy treatment intervention helps the music therapist determine the relative success or failure of that course of treatment. This, along with recommendations for future treatment, is duly documented in periodic progress reports.

All music therapy documentation becomes part of the client's file, which, like any professional documentation, is to remain confidential unless proper authorization is given for release (AMTA 2014; Gfeller and Davis 2008, 444–445). In accordance with the standards of professional ethics, the music therapist also keeps *all* client information – written, pictorial, audio, or verbal – confidential and does not share it outside the treatment team without proper release from the client or his/her responsible party. This principle of confidentiality helps protect the client's right to privacy.

Evaluation and Termination

As noted above, the music therapist continually observes and evaluates the client's responses during the course of treatment and adapts or revises the details of procedure accordingly. However, more formal evaluation of the entire program occurs at scheduled intervals to determine how successful the treatment interventions are in helping the client reach the specified goals and objectives. In this overall evaluation, the music therapist also may report secondary outcomes of therapy and make recommendations for future action. The evaluation process helps the music therapist, client (if applicable), and treatment team (if applicable) decide whether the treatment program should be continued in a similar fashion, revised in some way, or terminated.

Sometimes the evaluation schedule is specified in the time frame section of the objective or the targeted completion date for the objective listed in the client's treatment plan. Schedules for periodic evaluation and review of client treatment plans also may be specified by facility procedures or by state or federal regulations. Whatever the case, it is important that the music therapy treatment program be evaluated regularly to determine whether, in fact, the client is benefitting from services. Analysis of the data collected in therapy sessions and comparison of the client's current level of functioning with his or her initial level of functioning will help the therapist, client, and treatment team make this determination.

Music therapy services may be discontinued for several reasons (Gfeller and Davis 2008, 450). Music therapy treatment is terminated when the client has met the stated goals and objectives for treatment, when the client fails to benefit from services, or when the treatment team feels the client has received the maximum possible benefit from the services. Music therapy services also may be terminated if the client no longer can be scheduled or is discharged from the facility. Termination of services may be initiated by either client or therapist, by mutual consent, or by external factors related to personal, time, financial, or agency-related considerations (McGuire and Smeltekop 1994a, 1994b).

At the time of termination, the music therapist prepares a discharge report, which usually summarizes and evaluates the entire music therapy treatment process, including goals and objectives set, any progress made, and the client's level of functioning at the time of termination. Often, recommendations and suggestions for follow-up treatment or integration of community services may be given. Whenever possible, a discharge or termination plan should be developed in sufficient time to allow for coordination of services and ensure a smooth transition for the client.

The process of terminating a significant therapeutic relationship also may arouse strong feelings and personal issues for both client and therapist. It is important that adequate notice of the impending termination be given whenever possible and that the persons involved be allowed time to review and evaluate the course of treatment, express feelings, project into the future, and say good-bye (McGuire and Smeltekop 1994b). Activities involving these processes can be incorporated into the final music therapy sessions to facilitate successful termination for both client and therapist (McGuire and Smeltekop 1994a, 1994b).

INDIVIDUAL VS. GROUP TREATMENT

When devising a music therapy treatment plan for a particular client, a music therapist must consider whether that client's needs can be met best in an individual setting, a group setting, or some combination of group and individual treatment (Hanser 1987). Sometimes, the setting or facility will dictate the treatment option; at other times, the amount of time or space the therapist has available for group or individual sessions will be limited or fixed in some way. Music therapists must at times make difficult decisions about how a limited number of resources can be distributed most effectively to meet the needs of a large number of potential clients. Considerations such as what other types of services the client is receiving, how favorably the client responds to various treatment modalities, the client's long-term prognosis or placement options, the client's ability to function in a group setting, etc., all may affect the treatment team's and/or music therapist's decision to recommend group or individual treatment in music therapy. Each type of treatment has certain advantages, and either one or some combination of both may be appropriate at various times for clients served in music therapy.

Individual music therapy treatment is a one-to-one relationship between therapist and client. This provides unique opportunities for initial explorations of a client's individual skills, preferences, and problems, and allows for a concentrated focus on the client's needs and development at all times during the course of treatment (Boxill 1985; Hanser 1987; Nordoff and Robbins 1971b). Individual treatment affords a more intensive and in-depth experience to both client and therapist. Although most clients probably could benefit from this type of concentrated treatment effort, the reality of staffing situations in most facilities usually precludes this possibility. Therefore, "referrals for one-to-one therapy depend on the needs of each client relative to those of others" (Boxill 1985, 92).

For clients who lack the impulse control necessary for appropriate group behavior, or who require isolation for certain medical conditions, or who cannot or will not come to a group setting for any reason, one-to-one treatment may be the only viable alternative, at least for the initial course of therapy. Also, individual treatment may be the usual setting of choice for therapists of a particular theoretical orientation (e.g., psychoanalytic, guided imagery and music, some types of improvisational music therapy).

Group music therapy obviously allows more clients to receive services at one time; thus, if it is successful, group treatment is more cost-effective than individual treatment (Hanser 1987). In addition, group settings have several therapeutic advantages (Boxill 1985; Gaston 1968a; Hanser 1987). For example, clients in music therapy groups with peers can learn and practice appropriate ways of relating to and interacting with others, developing skills that they will need to function effectively and successfully in the real world. Moreover, group treatment provides the benefits of support, insights, and encouragement from other group members. In some groups, members also may model appropriate behaviors or responses for one another and, in so doing, learn from one another (Gfeller and Davis 2008, 441). Furthermore, as Lathom-Radocy (2014, 35–36) explains, "Because most music is a group function, music therapists can reinforce positive interpersonal behavior by arranging experiences in which the child will feel that he or she is a needed, contributing, and accepted group member."

Music usually is perceived as an enjoyable experience with inherent motivating and socializing qualities, and music experiences can be structured to meet a wide variety of needs simultaneously (Boxill 1985; Bruscia 1991a; Gaston 1968a; Hanser 1987; Nordoff and Robbins 1971b; Sears 1968). Given such conditions, as well as consideration of budgetary or time constraints, music therapists frequently provide group treatment. In some settings, music therapy often is used as the first group experience for many clients. As music therapists work in group treatment, they must be aware of the basic principles of group development and note how these apply to their work in music therapy groups (Sandness 1991). In addition, music therapists working in group settings must become adept at individualizing approaches, taking into account a particular group member's capabilities and needs and encouraging his or her active participation, while simultaneously attending to all group members and keeping in mind the needs, goals, and objectives of the group as a whole (Boxill 1985; Farnan and Johnson 1988b; Hanser 1987; Krout 1987). Hannan (2008) described music therapy in general pediatric medical/surgical areas of a hospital, where patients have diverse needs, backgrounds, and even ages, but must be seen within one music therapy group:

> Patients with chronic illnesses walk the halls with patients who are recovering from an acute condition requiring simple pharmacological intervention. Surgical patients attend activities and group sessions with patients whose set of symptoms eludes a diagnosis from the medical team. Teenaged patients, whose hospital admissions number in the hundreds, share rooms with young or newly diagnosed patients experiencing their first admission. These diverse patient experiences create a rich and challenging environment for the pediatric music therapist. (130)

Hanser (1987, 90–93) provides several excellent suggestions for individualizing treatment within music therapy groups.

EXAMPLES OF MUSIC EXPERIENCES USEFUL IN ADDRESSING GENERAL GOAL AREAS

As Chapter One noted, the therapeutic goals that music therapists have for clients are the same kinds of goals other members of the treatment team have for those clients: improving motor skills, communication skills, academic or cognitive skills, social skills, etc. The difference lies in the treatment modality. Music therapists use music and music-based experiences to help their clients reach these goals. The final section of this chapter gives general examples of music experiences that music therapists might use to help clients improve their skills in several general goal areas, such as behavioral, sensory, motor, communication, emotional (affective), interpersonal (social), self-help/survival, and academic or cognitive skills. Descriptions and examples of various music activities and experiences that are useful in addressing these areas are drawn from sources such as Cassity and Cassity (1991, 1994a), Eagle (1982), Lathom (1981a, 1981b), Lathom-Radocy (2014), Nocera (1979), Schulberg (1981), and Standley (1991a), as well as from the author's own experience. The discussion in this section is purposely kept on a very broad and general level; specific examples and applications of music therapy experiences to the unique needs, capabilities, goals, and characteristics of client groups with various disabilities are presented in Chapters Seven through Twenty-two.

Individual Behavioral Skills
(Attending and Compliance)

Since music provides a powerful form of multisensory stimulation that is almost impossible to ignore, music experiences can be very useful in attracting the attention of clients who seem oblivious to most of the surrounding world. Improvisatory exploration of various music media is often useful in finding sounds, styles, or idioms that will attract the attention and interest of these clients (Alvin 1978; Nordoff and Robbins 1977). Music's time-ordered structure also helps clients attend to tasks presented in a musical format for longer periods of time. At first, the client may only be able to attend for a few seconds. Through the course of therapy, the music therapist gradually may increase the length of songs and music experiences, with the rhythm and form of the music assisting the client to attend and participate for longer and longer periods of time. Lathom-Radocy (2014, 116) discusses using music to increase the attention span of clients diagnosed with Attention Deficit Hyperactivity Disorder (ADHD). Seven areas usually need special focus when working with clients with short attention span:

1. When giving directions, be sure the child has focused attention and is listening.
2. Avoid complex instructions. Clearly asking for *one* response may be all the child can process.
3. Encourage task completion. Music therapy may include many very short tasks, thereby providing many opportunities for reinforcing task completion.
4. Provide order in the environment, materials, and task design. The child is easily overwhelmed by disorder because it is difficult to organize. Providing consistency within the session and over the day helps the child to feel in better control.
5. Be aware of what the client brings to the session (coat, toy, school supplies, etc.) and help him or her leave with all possessions.
6. Help control impulsive behavior by stating clear expectations: "Stay in this room"; "Wait for your turn – you will get one"; "Sit on this carpet square or chair"; "Only take one instrument and place it on the floor until it is your turn to play."
7. Help with tasks of grooming (e.g., buttons in the right order, pants zipped, arms in *both* sleeves of the coat) and hygiene (e.g., wash hands after using the toilet *and* dry them, blow your nose on a tissue and place it in the waste basket rather than on the floor). (Lathom-Radocy 2014, 118)

Action songs, singing activities, and individual or group instrumental performance activities all can be increased in length and difficulty, gradually requiring clients to attend and remain on task for more extended periods of time. Music activities that require clients to wait to sing or play an instrument or move until a specific point in the music also can help clients develop the impulse control necessary to achieve that desired result. The musical structure provides a stimulus that attracts and holds their attention and orders and cues their responses.

In some situations, structured relaxation exercises to music may help clients develop skills necessary to control impulsive, violent, or destructive behavior, while various vocal, instrumental, or movement-to-music improvisation exercises may be useful in channeling restless or agitated behavior into more structured and productive forms. In more formal music situations, such as individual lessons or group ensembles, clients also may learn to increase their frustration tolerance and develop skills necessary to see tasks through to completion as they practice and rehearse to develop the required proficiency. Moreover, the rewards of music performance provide increased self-esteem and positive recognition by others.

Sensory Skills

Music is a multisensory experience that may include auditory, visual, tactile, and kinesthetic components. Therefore, music experiences can be structured to help clients increase their perception and discrimination skills in many sensory areas. Music experiences related to increasing auditory perception skills may include activities such as (1) indicating by word or gesture when sounds start and stop; (2) identifying the location of hidden sound sources; (3) using words or gestures to indicate contrasts of loud-soft or fast-slow; (4) singing or playing instruments loud or soft or fast or slow, as directed; (5) moving, playing, or clapping with the beat; (6) imitating rhythm patterns; (7) using words or gestures to indicate whether pitches are the same, higher, or lower; (8) identifying instruments by their sound; and (9) playing instruments in the sequence played by the leader. Activities used to develop the visual perception skills of clients include (1) playing musical instruments on a visual cue from a conductor; (2) locating specific notes or symbols in musical scores; (3) imitating, during musical games, movements demonstrated by another person; (4) playing color-coded instruments; (5) identifying colors, shapes, or objects as requested by song lyrics; (6) sorting individual resonator bells from biggest to smallest to arrange them in scale order; and (7) creating and playing from musical scores that use colors, pictures, shapes, or letters to represent certain instruments, sounds, pitches, chords, or rhythm patterns. Music therapists may help clients increase their tolerance for tactile stimulation by involving them in touching, holding, and manipulating musical instruments made of various materials, by having clients touch or feel different textured objects during relaxing background music; or by having clients activate switches covered with different textures to turn on recordings of preferred music. The prospect of producing a musical sound may do much to motivate a very tactilely defensive client to reach out and touch and explore objects in the environment.

Motor Skills

Many music experiences, such as those that involve playing instruments or moving to music, require some degree of motor skill for their performance. For clients who lack motor control and coordination, music may provide the motivation they need to engage in or sustain various movement or exercise activities, or it may give the structure needed to help clients coordinate movement patterns. Music carefully selected for relaxing or stimulating qualities or for a rhythmic and melodic structure that mirrors the patterns of the required movement can facilitate a range of motion exercises, gait training, and the performance of other exercise routines. Thaut (2008, 88–89) discusses using music and a steady rhythm provided by a metronome to facilitate movement in patients who have movement deficits resulting from stroke or Parkinson's disease. Music also may help lessen pain perception so that clients with painful conditions such as arthritis will engage in prescribed movement activities. Other music experiences and activities that may help clients improve their motor control and coordination skills include (1) performing locomotor movements (walking, running, jumping, etc.) to a steady or rhythmic beat; (2) performing nonlocomotor movements (bending, swaying, rocking, etc.) to the beat of the music; (3) performing actions described by song lyrics; (4) learning and performing dances and movement games; (5) playing musical instruments that require different kinds of arm, hand, and finger movements; (6) conducting music in various beat patterns; (7) grasping, holding, and releasing musical instruments or various objects or props as required by musical songs or games; and (8) participating in marching bands, drum corps, or drill teams. Goodman (2007, 159–160, 163–164) provides guidelines and considerations in using movement activities with special needs children.

Language and Communication Skills

Language and communication skills include both receptive (processing and responding to language) and expressive (speaking or signing) components, as well as prespeech skills (Lathom-Radocy 2014, 153–188). Music experiences that are useful in helping clients to develop receptive language skills include (1) picking up or pointing to objects or pictures as requested by song lyrics; (2) responding to commands to stop, start, look, touch, etc., contained in songs or musical games; (3) performing actions or playing instruments as directed by song lyrics; and (4) following directions to play instruments or perform dance movements in a certain sequence. Activities such as (1) playing simple wind instruments like kazoos, whistles, and recorders to help develop the breath and muscle control needed for speech (Thaut 2008) or (2) singing vowel sounds or simple syllables in imitation of the therapist may be useful in helping clients develop prespeech skills. Higher level expressive language skills may be developed through experiences that include (1) singing or signing or using a communication board to provide specific words in a song; (2) singing or signing phrases, choruses, verses, or entire songs; (3) singing or chanting original answers in questions and answer or fill-in-the-blank songs; (4) adding new words or verses to existing songs; and (5) writing original song lyrics.

Emotional Learning and Emotional Expression

In praise of music, Borczon (1997, 21) says, "Music is a gift. It can be entertaining, relaxing, energizing, sad, soulful, contemplative, and creative." Since music is a language of the emotions, music experiences can facilitate emotional learning and provide appropriate, socially acceptable means of emotional expression. As they participate in structured music experiences, individuals can be guided to experience, identify and express various emotions and moods. In addition, they can learn to perceive the emotional communications of others and increase their ability to control, adjust, and adapt their own emotional behaviors and responses (Thaut 2008).

Interpersonal (Social) Skills

When they participate in small or large group music experiences, clients have many opportunities to develop and practice various interpersonal or social interaction skills, such as establishing and maintaining eye contact, being aware of other group members, interacting appropriately with others, working cooperatively with others, complying with stated rules and limits, taking turns, sharing, exchanging roles of leader and follower, showing respect for others and their property, giving and accepting constructive feedback, and listening attentively to others. Activities and experiences that may be useful in helping clients gain skills in these areas include (1) songs or chants that require clients to name themselves or other group members; (2) group songs, dances, or instrumental activities that require clients to play, sing, or move together with one or more other group members; (3) rondo form chants and songs that alternate group and individual responses; (4) songs and games that require clients to take turns suggesting movements or rhythms and imitating the movements or rhythms suggested by other group members; (5) writing group songs or developing group improvisations according to specified guidelines; (6) taking turns playing solos on instruments; (7) taking turns conducting group vocal or instrumental performances; (8) discussing song lyrics with others; (9) choosing songs for the group to listen to and listening quietly and attentively to everyone's selection; (10) working together on group shows, music videos, or other performance projects; (11) evaluating performances and giving constructive suggestions for improvement; and (12) incorporating the constructive suggestions of others in revising composition projects or refining performance techniques.

Self-Help/Survival Skills

Some clients may need help in learning basic self-help or survival skills. The American Association on Intellectual and Developmental Disabilities (AAIDD) published a new manual for the Diagnostic Adaptive Behavior Scales (DABS). One of the defined domains is practical skills: "activities of daily living (personal care), occupational skills, use of money, safety, health care, travel/transportation, schedules, routines, and use of the telephone" (AAIDD 2011).

Special songs that teach the sequence of steps needed to perform various tasks like dressing or washing hands may be useful in this area (Kramer 1978). Specially designed song lyrics and musical games help clients practice identifying things like items of clothing or safety and survival signs or learn and rehearse safety rules. In addition, participation in performance groups or in special musical shows or productions may give some clients the incentive they need to take pride in their appearance and practice good grooming and personal hygiene skills.

Academic or Cognitive Skills

Academic concepts, such as letters, colors, numbers, spatial direction and position, and time, can be learned and reinforced in music activities that require clients to read graphics, letters, or color-coded musical scores, participate in special musical games or dances, or learn songs explaining the concepts in their lyrics (Lathom-Radocy 2014, 26–28). Cognitive skills, such as reality orientation, long- and short-term memory, sequencing skills, problem-solving skills, organizational skills, and the like, also can be learned, practiced, or reinforced through participation in various types of music experiences. Music activities useful in these areas include (1) experiential, structured instrumental activities, such as playing instruments in rhythm or with the proper chords and at the proper time; (2) singing, playing, or listening to and discussing songs that refer to some aspects of person, place, or time; (3) recalling song titles or lyrics; (4) learning songs or accompaniments by rote and then performing them from memory; (5) composition or music analysis activities or lyric substitution song writing activities; (6) directed listening activities; (7) discussion of lyrics dealing with problem solving methods; (8) following along on a song sheet, chord chart, song map, or musical score; (9) playing, singing, or chanting ostinato accompaniment patterns; (10) recalling items mentioned by song lyrics in the proper sequence; (11) learning and performing specific dance or movement-to-music routines or relaxation metnods in music exercises; (12) learning and recalling fingering patterns or positions needed to play notes or chords on various instruments; and (13) learning and remembering the sequence of steps needed to operate tape players, compact disc players, etc., or learning and remembering how to find one's preferred music on the radio or in a tape library.

QUESTIONS FOR THOUGHT AND DISCUSSION

1. What are the basic stages in the delivery of music therapy services? How is each stage important to successful music therapy treatment?

2. What is involved in the assessment process? What type of information is gathered and in what ways? How does this information impact other stages of the music therapy treatment process?

3. What is the difference between a goal and an objective? Why do music therapists establish therapeutic goals and objectives for their clients? How do goals and objectives impact other stages of the music therapy treatment process?

4. What four factors do music therapists consider as they design music-based intervention strategies? How/why are these important? In considering these factors, what must the music therapist always keep in mind? Why?

5. How does treatment implementation involve both science and art, both convention and spontaneity?

6. Why is it important for music therapists to collect data and document client progress?

7. What is involved in the evaluation of music therapy services? Why is evaluation important?

8. What factors may be involved in deciding whether to treat a client in a group or individual setting? What are some advantages/disadvantages of each type of treatment? What are some examples of times when one may be more appropriate than the other?

9. How do the general goal areas and related music experiences listed in the last section of this chapter relate to Gaston's (1968a) three guiding principles and Sears's (1968) three classifications discussed in Chapter Five?

10. Review the general examples of music activities and experiences which

may be useful in helping clients develop various behavioral, sensory, motor, communication, emotional (affective), interpersonal (social), self-help/survival, and academic or cognitive skills. For each goal area, describe some ways the process or content of the sample music experiences relate to the therapeutic goal area or desired behavioral response. What are some other music experiences that might be used to help clients develop skills in these areas?

SUGGESTIONS FOR FURTHER READING

American Music Therapy Association [AMTA]. (1998). Standards of clinical practice. In *AMTA Member Sourcebook 1998* (xli–1). Silver Spring, MD: Author.

Cassity, M. D., & Cassity, J. E. (1994). *Multimodal psychiatric music therapy for adults, adolescents, and children.* St. Louis: MMB Music.

Davis, W. B. (1992). The music therapy treatment process. In W. B. Davis, K. E. Gfeller, & M. H. Thaut, *An introduction to music therapy: Theory and practice* (287–301). Dubuque, IA: Wm. C. Brown.

Eagle, C. T., Jr. (Ed.). (1982). *Music therapy for handicapped individuals: An annotated and indexed bibliography.* Washington, D.C.: National Association for Music Therapy.

Farnan, L., & Johnson, F. (1988). *Music is for everyone: A handbook for providing music to people with special needs.* New Berlin, WI: Jenson Publications.

Goodman, K. D. (2007). *Music therapy groupwork with special needs children. The evolving process.* Springfield, IL: Charles C Thomas, Publishers, Ltd.

Hadsell, N. A. (1993). Levels of external structure in music therapy. *Music Therapy Perspectives, 11*(2), 61–65.

Hanser, S. B. (1987). *Music therapist's handbook.* St. Louis: Warren H. Green.

Lathom, W. (1981). How a music therapist determines goals and objectives. In W. Lathom, *The role of the music therapist in the education of severely and profoundly handicapped children and youth* (7–10). Lawrence, KS: National Association for Music Therapy.

Lathom-Radocy, W. (2014). *Pediatric music therapy* (2nd. ed.), Chapters one and two, 1–38. Springfield, IL: Charles C Thomas, Publishers, Ltd.

Sandness, M. I. (1991). Developmental sequence in music therapy groups: A review of theoretical models. *Music Therapy Perspectives, 9,* 66–72.

Schulberg, C. H. (1981). *The music therapy sourcebook: A collection of activities categorized and analyzed.* New York: Human Sciences Press.

Standley, J. (1991). *Music techniques in therapy, counseling, and special education.* St. Louis: MMB Music.

Zinar, R. (1987). *Music activities for special children.* West Nyack, NY: Parker Publishing.

Chapter Seven

MUSIC THERAPY FOR INDIVIDUALS WHO HAVE INTELLECTUAL DISABILITIES

Definition

The history of terminology used to define and describe persons with intellectual disabilities is quite complex. Over many years, various definitions and descriptions arose and receded (Davis, Gfeller, and Thaut 2008, 80–82). Farnan (2007) provides a history of terms used for this population. The term "mental retardation," found in much legislation, was used by the American Association on Mental Retardation, now called The American Association on Intellectual and Developmental Disorders (AAIDD), since 1959. The second edition of this book used the label *mental retardation*; the term was not revised at that time. The *Diagnostic and Statistical Manual of Mental Disorders (DSM-V)* (2013, 33) states that "*intellectual disability* is the term in common use by medical, educational, and other professions and by the lay public and advocacy groups." The levels are specified as "Mild, Moderate, Severe, and Profound," as determined by the child's adaptive functioning ability.

There are three essential features:

1. Deficits in general mental abilities – usually measured with tests of intelligence.
2. Impairment in adaptive functioning – considerations of personal independence and social responsibility. This is assessed by clinical evaluation and psychometric tests.
3. Onset in the developmental period. "Deficits are present during childhood or adolescence." (DSM-V, 38)

Intellectual disabilities are listed within a larger category – *neurodevelopmental disorders* – which includes communication disorders, autism spectrum disorders, attention deficit/hyperactivity disorders (ADHD), neurodevelopmental motor disorders, and specific learning disorders. These areas are discussed in later chapters.

Intellectual disability is not defined solely by deficits in intellectual functioning but also includes concurrent limitations or deficits in more than one adaptive skill area. Thus, subaverage intellectual functioning is a necessary but not a sufficient condition for a diagnosis of intellectual disability. In addition, although intellectual disability may be a lifelong condition, its symptoms must first be manifested during the *developmental period*, that time during which individuals mature and grow to adulthood, usually considered as any time from birth to eighteen years of age. With appropriate programs, improvement in functioning often occurs, and many who receive appropriate education and training may later blend into society.

Intellectual functioning usually is measured by one or more standardized tests and reported as an intelligence quotient (IQ) score. Individuals are considered to have significantly subaverage intellectual functioning when their IQ scores are 70–75 or below (AAMR 1992; APA 1994). This represents a score of approximately two standard deviations below the mean, allowing for a measurement error of five points. Both clinical assessment and standardized tests are used to determine intellectual and adaptive functioning:

> IQ test scores are approximations of conceptual functioning but may be insufficient to assess reasoning in real-life situations and mastery of practical tasks. . . . Thus, clinical judgement is needed in interpreting the results of IQ tests. (DSM-V 2013, 37)

Intellectually disabled persons manifest limits or impairments in adaptive functioning concurrently with intellectual limitations.

In persons with intellectual disability, adaptive skill limits occur in two or more areas and relate primarily to their limited intellectual functioning, not to other circumstances (e.g., sensory limits, cultural or language diversity). Often, adaptive functioning limits, rather than low IQ, are the presenting symptoms in individuals with intellectual disability (APA 1994).

Related Terminology

Since intellectual disability manifests itself during the developmental period, individuals with this condition are included in the larger category of *neurodevelopmental disorders*. The older term was *developmental disability* and that is the terminology in some legislation. According to Public Law 95-682, the Developmental Disabilities Bill of Rights Act (1978): "A *developmental disability* is attributable to a mental or physical impairment that begins before age 22 and is likely to continue indefinitely and that results in substantial functional limitation in *three* or more areas of major life activity" (AAMR 1992, 13). Because funding and services may be tied to this legislation, it is important to retain it.

Individuals with some genetic disorders also may have intellectual or cognitive deficits. Some genetic disorders, such as Rett syndrome or San Phillippo syndrome, are progressive, but intellectual disability is generally nonprogressive (DSM-V 2013, 38). One may label a relationship of intellectual disability to other conditions as *comorbidity*: "Co-occuring neurodevelopmental, medical, and physical conditions are frequent in intellectual disability, with rates of some conditions (e.g., mental disorders, cerebral palsy, and epilepsy) three to four times higher than in the general population" (DSM-V 2013, 40).

Snell (2006) discussed the terminology used in The Individuals with Disabilities Education Act (IDEA, Public Law 101-476, 1990, 2004). She stresses the need to define the individual's educational needs. Various states have slightly different definitions, so it is important for music therapists to know their state's definitions and use the correct terminology in writing the Individualized Education Plan (IEP). Schwartz (2006) explained that regulations in those revisions include music therapy (which had been in a footnote in Public Law 94-142, The Education for All Handicapped Children Act, 1975):

> As under prior law, the list of related services is not exhaustive and may include other developmental, corrective, or supportive services (such as artistic and cultural programs, art, music, and dance therapy) if they are required to assist a child with a disability to benefit from special education in order for the child to receive FAPE [Free Appropriate Public Education]. Therefore it is determined through the Act's evaluation and IEP requirements that a child with a disability requires a particular supportive service in order to receive FAPE; regardless of whether that service is included in these regulations, that service can be considered a related service under these regulations, and must be provided at no cost to the parents. (64 Federal Register 48, 12548, 1999, as stated by Schwartz 2006, 29)

Typically, particularly in educational settings, the broader label of developmental delay is used during preschool years. A diagnosis of intellectual disability, if appropriate, is made after age five (AAMR 1992). A child with a developmental delay shows a significant variation from normal development in cognitive, physical, communication, or socioemotional development or in adaptive or self-help skills, as determined by appropriate diagnostic instruments or procedures administered by an interdisciplinary team (ECIC 1992). Not every developmentally delayed child is or ever will be classified as intellectually disabled; deficits occurring in other areas do not necessarily impact cognitive or intellectual functioning. In a sense, *intellectual disability* is a much more specific term than *developmental disability* because, in intellectually disabled individuals, limits in adaptive functioning necessarily relate primarily to intellectual limitations rather than to organic or environmental factors (AAMR 1992).

Down syndrome is a congenital condition that is characterized by some degree of intellectual disability. Individuals with Down syndrome also have characteristic physical features, including small, flattened skulls, short flat-bridged noses, wide-set eyes, and short, broad hands and feet (Miller and Keane 1978).

Causes

Causes of intellectual disability include organic (biological) factors, environmental factors, or a combination of the two. Only about 25 percent of the cases can be traced to specific biological causes (Furman and Furman 1996). Sometimes, intellectual disability occurs because of prenatal factors, such as chromosomal disorders, various syndrome disorders, inborn metabolic errors, developmental defects in brain formation, or influences of malnutrition, drugs or toxins, maternal diseases, or irradiation during pregnancy. Other cases are caused by perinatal factors, such as placental insufficiency, abnormal labor or delivery, neonatal hemorrhages, seizures, respiratory disorders, infections, head trauma, or metabolic or nutritional disorders. Still other cases are due to postnatal causes, such as head injuries, various infections, demyelinating disorders, degenerative syndromes or disorders, seizure disorders, toxic or metabolic disorders, malnutrition, or environmental deprivation due to psychosocial disadvantage, child abuse or neglect, or chronic social/sensory deprivation (AAMR 1992). In about 30–40 percent of the cases, no clear etiology or cause for the intellectual disability can be determined, even with extensive evaluation and testing (APA 1994; DSM-V 2013, 39). Since intellectual disabilities have so many different causes, some view the category as "a final common pathway of various pathological processes that affect the functioning of the central nervous system" (APA 1994, 39).

Classification Systems

Throughout the years, various classification systems have been developed in an attempt to help clarify degrees of intellectual disability. Many systems have relied primarily on IQ measurements to assign a level or degree of severity to the disability. However, the current classification developed by AAIDD and used in DSM-V (2013) specifically avoids reliance on IQ scores to assign levels of disability. Instead, it emphasizes the person's functioning level and the intensity and type of support systems needed to help that person function as independently and productively as possible within his or her community. Since both types of classification systems are encountered in various settings, each is briefly described in the following paragraphs.

Physicians and psychiatrists frequently classify individuals who have an intellectual disability according to DSM-V (2013) guidelines. The current severity of the client's intellectual disability is now defined on the basis of adaptive functioning, including conceptual, social, and practical domains (DSM-V 2013, 34–36). Early intervention and appropriate programs and treatment throughout childhood may considerably improve functioning. Both necessary supports and programming must be considered. For some clients, there is enough improvement that the diagnosis of intellectual impairment is no longer appropriate. For more severely intellectually disabled clients, support may be needed throughout life. The goal remains to provide the support necessary for full participation in all activities of daily living.

Historically, many educators have used a different classification system, which groups individuals with intellectual disability by educational potential into the following four groups (Hewett and Forness 1974):

1. Slow learners or borderline retarded children
2. Educable mentally retarded (EMR)
3. Trainable mentally retarded (TMR)
4. Profoundly retarded children.

These terms have been replaced in most educational settings, but still may be found in literature from the 1960s and 1970s. Of course, the term *mentally retarded* is now replaced by *intellectually disabled.* In addition, children have individual assessments that lead to the Individualized Educational Plan (IEP), and that determines placement rather than the previously used grouping based mostly on IQ scores.

In recent years, many professionals have come to view intellectual disability not as a *trait* to be measured but as a *state* in which functioning is impaired in certain specific ways. This system departs significantly from previous classification systems. The result is a classification system for intellectual disability in which the person's *level of functioning* is the critical measure; thus, the classification is focused on an individual's adaptive behavior and level of support systems needed, not on severity of intellectual impairment (IQ scores):

> Rather than requiring subclassification into four levels of a person's intellectual disability (mild, moderate, severe, and profound), the system subclassifies the intensities and pattern of supports systems into four levels (intermittent, limited, extensive, and pervasive). (AAMR 1992, x)

For purposes of classifying severity of impairment, the person's strengths and weaknesses are described in reference to psychological, physical, and environmental dimensions, and a profile is developed of needed support levels (intermittent, limited, extensive, or pervasive).

> Thus, a diagnosis might well be "a person with intellectual disability who needs limited supports in communication and social skills." Another sample diagnosis

might be "a person with intellectual disability with extensive supports needed in the areas of social skills and self-direction." Such descriptions are more functional, relevant, and oriented to service delivery and outcomes. (AAMR 1992, 34)

The foundation for the current DSM-V (2013) definition of intellectual disability was in the 1992 AAMR classification system, which provided a more functional description of an individual's capabilities and adaptive behavior and his or her needs for specific levels of support within the various adaptive skill areas, as well as the three other dimensions: psychological/emotional considerations, physical/health/etiology considerations, and environmental considerations. This system recognized that intellectually disabled individuals have strengths in some adaptive or personal capabilities (e.g., good health and strong social skills but difficulty in communication, or good at functional math but not functional reading) despite limitations in two or more adaptive skill areas. It also underscored the importance of appropriate supports over sustained periods to help improve general life functioning. The classification process acknowledged that "numerous variations in adaptive skill functioning are possible across individuals diagnosed as having intellectual disability and even within a single individual over time" (AAMR 1992, 113).

The focus on individual needs in the 1992 AAMR classification system moves away from the historical conception of intellectual disability as representing global deficits and directs service delivery toward individual planning and functional supports. The recognition that limitations in some adaptive skill areas may be juxtaposed with strengths in other areas highlights intellectually disabled individuals' *capabilities* and facilitates planning targets and functional intervention strategies that will help individuals be integrated into the community as fully as possible in spite of the significant limitations resulting from intellectual disability. This shift of focus and emphasis from previous classification systems is resulting in many changes in service delivery, particularly in the area of adult services (Wager 2002). Wager (2000) provided a four-year case study of an adult 36-year-old male with autism and mental retardation (the term that was in use in 2000). Over the four years, he resided in a community group home with two other residents and 24-hour staff. During the four years, he increased the time he could attend to music activities (described in detail in Wager's article) and improved gross and fine motor skills. Although he could sing with the therapist, communication was very limited: "Playing and singing music provided a symbolic, non-verbal, non-threatening way to appropriately interact" (137). Changes in medication influenced his behavior. This study exemplifies co-occuring conditions (intellectual disability and autism), called comorbidity in DSM-V (2013), which often is seen in music therapy referrals.

Another case description of music therapy with adults with co-occurring conditions was provided by Ingbar (2003, 46), who describes her clinical experience of using MIDI activities with "adults with moderate or severe mental retardation [intellectual disability]." All could make music. In addition to the excitement of music making, these activities allowed the clients to work on motor, cognitive, and social skills.

The paradigm shift engendered by the 1992 AAMR classification system represents the third phase in the evolution of services for intellectually disabled individuals from the former phases of institutionalization and segregation. Braddock (2011) stated that the number of institutional residents with I/DD in the U. S. declined from 195,000 in 1966 to 34,000 in 2009. Phase 1, prevalent well into the twentieth century, included deinstitutionalization and community development. Phase 2, beginning in the 1970s, used a functional support model. In the adoption of this new definition and classification system for individuals with intellectual disability, "delivery systems must reorient their roles from being providers of program services to being providers and facilitators of individual supports." (AAMR 1992, 146). DSM-V (2013, 38) states that "Intellectual disability has an overall general population prevalence of approximately 1% and prevalence rates vary by age. Prevalence for severe intellectual disability is approximately 6 per 1,000." Kern, Rivera, Chandler, and Humpal (2012, 275) report a "ten-fold increase in prevalence over four decades." The emphasis is on individual need: "AAMR suggests that the trend is to provide individualized support and services rather than relying on the preexisting diagnostic categories to place people who may benefit from such services" (Farnan 2007, 82). In a school setting, the IEP reflects individualization. If the individual is in a treatment setting, that placement is short-term, requiring an IPP (Individual Program Plan). Braddock, Hemp, and Rizzolo (2004) reported that almost 300,000 persons received short-term residential care from 1977–2002, although only 20,000 were previously in this level of care. Thus, the shift from long-term care to integration in public schools or short-term care facilities is apparent. For music therapy services to be included, they must be stated in the IEP or IPP.

COMMON CHARACTERISTICS, PROBLEMS, AND NEEDS OF CLIENTS

As with any population, intellectually disabled individuals are a very heterogeneous group. Any individual client has a unique combination of abilities, needs, personality traits, strengths, and weaknesses that will impact his or her treatment program and functioning level; therefore, it is unwise to attempt to predict a particular person's skill levels or ceiling of abilities based on broad generalizations about a certain population. However, an awareness of some of the characteristics and problems commonly occurring in many intellectually disabled clients will be beneficial both to the therapist who desires to work with this population and to the reader who is trying to understand how music therapy intervention strategies may benefit this population.

Individuals with intellectual disability generally have fundamental difficulties in learning and performing various skills of daily living. Because of their intellectual disability, they have substantial limits in three specific areas, now called domains: conceptual intelligence, social intelligence, and practical intelligence (AAMR 1992):

> The *conceptual (academic) domain* involves competence in memory, language, reading, writing, math reasoning, acquisition of practical knowledge, problem solving, and judgment in novel situations, among others. The *social domain* involves awareness of others' thoughts, feelings, and experiences; empathy; interpersonal communication skills; friendship abilities; and social judgment, among others. The *practical domain* involves learning and self-management across life settings, including personal care job responsibilities, money management, recreation, self-management of behavior, and school and work task organization, among others. Intellectual capacity, education, motivation, socialization, personality features, vocational opportunity, cultural experience, and coexisting general medical conditions or mental disorders influence adaptive functioning. (DSM-V 2013, 37)

Obviously, many of the adaptive skill limitations found in individuals with intellectual disability may relate very closely to their substantial limitations in conceptual, practical, and social intelligence (AAMR 1992).

No particular personality patterns, behaviors, or physical features are uniquely associated with the general condition of intellectual disability (APA 1994). Layman, Hussey, and Reed (2013, 155) conducted a pilot study of an assessment tool to use in groups of children (mean age 9.5, SD=1.85) with severe emotional disturbances in a residential setting. Nine items were measured: "attention to task (physical and verbal), eye contact, pro-social skills (physical and verbal), empathy (physical and verbal), and managing negative affect (physical and verbal)." These skills also are needed by intellectually disabled children. However, since the pilot study was conducted with emotionally disturbed children, it should be studied with intellectually disabled children before generalizing results. Although they reported good inter-rater reliability and content and construct validity, the sample size of this pilot study was small (N=6). The assessment tool shows great promise and it should be replicated with emotionally disturbed children and tested with other populations, such as children with intellectual disabilities.

Many individuals have delayed development of motor skills (resulting in poor motor control and coordination, poor balance, poor spatial perception, and/or a poor body image). Many also have delays or deficits in language skills and need assistance developing functional communication. Often, intellectually disabled individuals also need intensive training to develop self-help skills (e.g., feeding, dressing, personal hygiene). Other common problems include low self-esteem, poor frustration tolerance, poor impulse control, short attention span, poor social skills, difficulty making independent choices, and an inability to structure leisure time.

Studying peer awareness of preschool children with developmental disabilities, Sussman (2009, 55) examined "the effects of musical and nonmusical elements on the sustained and alternating attention . . . towards their peers." Her results suggest that musical objects and musical context are effective in sustaining attention toward peers. This, too, was a pilot study with a small group (N=9) and needs replication. Increasing attention span is a very important goal for children with intellectual disabilities, so the study should be repeated with preschool children with that diagnosis, as well as other disabilities.

Of course, when intellectual disability is part of a specific syndrome, that syndrome's particular physical features (e.g., in Down syndrome) or behavioral symptoms (e.g., the intractable self-injurious behavior of Lesch-Nyhan syndrome) will be present. Also, generally speaking, the more severe the intellectual disability, the greater the likelihood that other conditions, such as seizures or other neurological impairments, neuromuscular difficulties, visual or auditory impairments, or cardiovascular conditions, will be associated with it (APA 1994). Individuals who have severe or profound intellectual disability often have multiple handicaps or disabilities which cause them to need extensive or pervasive support services.

Because of impairments in general intellectual functioning, individuals with intellectual disability have certain special learning needs. These include "(1) a slower rate of presentation, (2) more repetition, (3) smaller amounts of new material, and (4) concrete experiences" (Atterbury 1986, 35).

Chase (2004, 30) surveyed music therapists working with developmentally disabled children. DD was defined, as it had been by Boxhill (1995, 29), as "persons age 0–17 who have failed to progress at a normal rate in at least one of the following areas: (a) motor skills, (b) adaptive skills, (c) communication skills, (d) cognitive skills, and (e) social skills." This definition included children with intellectual disabilities as well as other impairments. Chase's purpose was to study assessment practices of music therapists working with children with DD. Ninety-five useable surveys were analyzed. The most frequently assessed areas included (28): "Motor (95%), Communication (83%), Social (79%), Cognitive (64%), and Music (35%)." The author stated the need for a standardized assessment instrument, which many others have noted.

As developmentally disabled individuals age, most will need special training in functional living skills, basic work skills, and responsible social behaviors. They also may need assistance in identifying and accessing support services that will enable them to continue to improve their functioning level and help them become more independent, productive, and integrated into their community. Most will live at home or in small group homes if they are unable to function independently. Their degree of satisfaction with life depends very much on having the best available support and continuing programs if they remain intellectually disabled. Their quality of life often depends upon their feeling that they can contribute to society (e.g., in work and social relationships) and can find respect and inclusion in community life.

Research suggests that intellectually disabled individuals demonstrate better skill generalization and retention when skills are taught as integrated parts of functional routines rather than in isolation (AAMR 1992). As people with intellectual disability move from more restrictive institutional placements to less restrictive living options, they often make significant improvements in their adaptive skills and their behavioral characteristics. Inclusion in integrated educational and community settings with peers without intellectual disability can be beneficial to many ID individuals. Peers can provide powerful models for language, behavior, dress, and social skills. Integrated and inclusive settings provide opportunities for both planned and spontaneous peer-to-peer instruction that usually is not possible in separate schools and community groups where all the individuals have disabilities.

SETTINGS FOR SERVICE DELIVERY

Until recently, intellectually disabled persons were institutionalized and segregated from the mainstream of society and considered unable to learn to care for themselves or become independent in any areas (AAMR 1992; Furman and Furman 1988). The second half of the twentieth century saw increasing recognition "that with special education programs these people can improve their daily living skills as well as their abilities to plan and make good judgments" (Furman and Furman 1988, 285). With this change in attitude came an increased advocacy for the rights of individuals with intellectual disability. Changes in legislation and educational practices and a movement toward deinstitutionalization in the 1970s and 1980s greatly expanded educational, vocational, and community living options for both children and adults. Many children who used to be institutionalized now receive support services in their homes and schools. Many adults now live in semi-independent living situations in group homes or apartments within the community at large and work in sheltered workshops or are employed in various community jobs that fit their skill capabilities. With the paradigm shift engendered by the 1992 AAMR classification, most service delivery systems are moving to a functional supports model that maximizes habilitation goals related to health (physical, psychological, and/or functional wellness) and fosters "characteristics of a satisfying life (choice, competence, respect, community presence, and participation in the environment)" (AAMR 1992, 115). The movement is toward deinstitutionalization:

> The expectation today is that supportive services are provided to promote the acquisition of adaptive skills which will prepare individuals to live in the community within the limits of their handicapping conditions. . . . Most retarded citizens live in homes, group homes or apartments with a prescribed level of assistance. (Furman & Furman, 1996, p. 129)

The institutionalized population now consists mainly of adults who are severely or profoundly impaired and who have major treatment and support needs, usually including multiple handicaps or disabilities (Furman and Furman 1996). Farnan (2007) notes that

> music therapists need to be aware of the sources of funding for services. The delivery of services is shifting from residential facilities to day programs and smaller homes. Funding is following the person wherever they go to live and prosper. Service and support providers work with brokers to select, arrange, and purchase desired and needed services. (82)

Before the age of 21 years, most intellectually disabled individuals receive educational, training, and support services through their local school districts' special education program. The Individuals with Disabilities Act (IDEA) (Public Law 101-476), the 1990 revision of the 1975 Education for All Handicapped Children Act (Public Law 94-142), assures a free, appropriate public education to all children, aged 3–21 years, who have disabilities, including those with intellectual disability. As Adamek and Darrow (2010, 175) explain,

> Music therapists usually work with small groups of students who have similar goals. Students with mild to moderate cognitive disabilities will most likely be educated in inclusive settings [with children without disabilities] while students with severe cognitive disabilities may be educated in self-contained classrooms for all or a portion of the day.

Furthermore, the Technology-Related Assistance for Individuals with Disabilities Act (Public Law 100-407) provides for assistive technology devices and services that an individual may need (Adamek 1996; Johnson 1996).

Public Law 99-457 of 1986 provides incentives to address the needs of handicapped or disabled children from birth through age 2 years (Adamek 1996; Humpal 1990). Therefore, early intervention services usually begin at birth or during the first two years of life. Children may come to an early intervention center for treatment, or professionals from early intervention programs may provide treatment in the child's home or day care setting. During these years, Individualized Family Service Plans (IFSPs) are written to address the needs of the child and family. When they are 3 years old, individuals usually are referred to special education programs in their local school district. After initial assessment and identification of the individual's unique areas of ability and disability, Individualized Educational Programs (IEPs) are written to guide instruction and programming. IEPs set educational/habilitative goals matched to the individual's specific functioning profile. They also provide for appropriate support services, placement in the least restrictive environment, and an annual evaluation of student progress.

Recent trends in special education have placed great emphasis on "inclusion" practices, providing for individuals receiving special education services to be educated with their "normal" peers to the greatest extent possible. For example, a student may be sent to a resource room for help or training in specific areas with a special education teacher or specific therapist for short segments of the day, while being mainstreamed (included in a regular classroom) for as much of the day as possible, perhaps with the assistance of an aide when necessary. For middle school and high school students with intellectual disabilities, Individualized Transitional Programs (ITPs) often complement IEPs and guide the transition from schools and education to community services and work.

Music therapists may work as employees of or consultants to school districts or early intervention programs (Humpal 1990; Wilson 1996). Their assistance is now even more important: "Due to the overwhelming evidence in favor of early intervention for intellectual disabilities, federal legislation requires educational services for children with disabilities between the ages of 3 and 5" (Davis, Gfeller, and Thaut 2008, 90). When IEP assessments find that music therapy can provide a unique means of helping students achieve their educational objectives, music therapists may provide traditional direct services, work with students in self-contained classes; work with students in inclusive classes, provide direct in-home services to students who are confined to their homes for medical reasons (Wolfe and Waldon 2009); provide consultation services to facilitate classroom instruction, inclusion, or music education; and/or provide staff development workshops (Wilson 1996). The decision of individual or group music therapy must consider the child's ability. From her experience in music therapy in a school setting, Goodman (2007, 78) notes that "the child must be ready to musically contribute, developmentally engage with others and tolerate the sensory impact of the group session." Music therapy is usually classified as a related service in special education settings.

Some music therapists also work with children and adolescents who have intellectual disability in other settings, such as private studios or clinics, the client's home, community programs, day care programs, private programs for developmentally disabled individuals, or special schools and institutions. Goodman (2007, 110) provides case examples of children in a school setting who need individual therapy in order to make progress and return to the group.

After age 21 years, individuals may receive support services through agencies in diverse settings, such as group homes, sheltered or specially structured work environments, day treatment programs for developmentally disabled individuals, community facilities, state schools, or special training centers. Some individuals also receive services in their own homes. Music therapists may work in any of these programs or settings as full-time or part-time employees, or they may provide services on a contractual or consultive basis.

After working with four developmentally disabled adults who shared an apartment, Hooper (2001, 126) concluded that "using non-threatening, non-verbal music activities to structure interaction increases the frequency of successful interaction." Furman and Furman (1996) predict that, as medical and technological advances increase life expectancy for intellectually disabled individuals, programs focusing on elderly clients will become more numerous. In addition, programs focusing on developing music skills may become an important means of providing individuals with "appropriate and dignified leisuretime activities which are immediately usable in the community" (291). Farnan (2007, 82) indicates that "the monies are not funneled solely to a facility for services. The monies now follow the person wherever that person goes to live."

In a recent survey of populations served by music therapists in which respondents were permitted to list as many categories as appropriate (AMTA 2013), 14 percent of 1,544 professional MT-BCs responding said they worked with individuals who were developmentally disabled. (The survey did not list a separate category for intellectual disability.)

HOW MUSIC IS USED IN THERAPY

In her review of music therapy literature related to intellectual disability, Reynolds (1982, 43) showed that "the use of music as a treatment mode for mentally retarded [intellectually disabled] individuals has changed in focus and scope as the field of music therapy has grown to meet the needs of this population." In the 1950s, typical goals in music therapy programs for mentally retarded clients included social adjustment, increased concentration, improved muscular coordination, self-control, emotional stability, and motivation and satisfaction of achievement (Brewer 1955; Gilliland 1959). In the 1960s, music therapy goals tended to focus on socialization, strengthening defenses, impulse control, intrusion on fantasy, sensory stimulation, and gratification (Lathom 1968). In the late 1960s and the 1970s, when behavior modification techniques began to receive a prominent place in education and training programs for the mentally retarded, music therapy goals "began to emphasize overt behavior rather than the former emphasis on psychoanalytical goals" (Reynolds 1982, 45). Several studies conducted during this period demonstrated that music could be an effective reinforcer of desired behaviors (Bellamy and Sontag 1973; Dileo 1975; Dorow 1976; Johnson and Phillips 1971; Jorgenson 1974; Metzler 1974; Remington, Foxen, and Hogg 1977; Saperston et al. 1980; Steele 1968; Underhill and Harris 1974; Walker 1972). Johnson and Zinner (1974) demonstrated that behaviors and concepts learned in music therapy sessions could be maintained and generalized to other aspects of the environment. In their surveys of music therapy research regarding intellectual disability, Furman and Furman (1988, 1996) found that contingent music was still the most frequently used music therapy procedure documented in music therapy studies involving intellectually disabled clients.

In the late 1970s and early 1980s, more educational and training programs were initiated for severely and profoundly disabled individuals, and music therapists began to develop intervention strategies geared specifically to the needs of this population (Carter 1982; Gonzales 1981; Lathom 1981b; Miorin and Covault 1979; Nordoff and Robbins 1977; Saperston et al. 1980). These music therapy techniques helped elicit and develop responses that enabled these individuals to become more aware of and responsive to people and objects in their environment, thus contributing to the growth and development of individuals who otherwise might show little progress in a clinical or educational setting (Furman and Furman 1988; Lathom 1981b; Madsen 1981; Nordoff and Robbins 1977).

As more and more clients have been mainstreamed or included in music groups with their "normal" peers, music therapists have also investigated and developed various techniques to facilitate the inclusion or normalization process (Atterbury 1990; Birkenshaw-Fleming 1993; Boxill 1989; Furman and Furman 1988; Gunsberg 1988, 1991; Hughes et al. 1990; Humpal 1991; Humpal and Dimmick 1995; Jellison and Duke 1994; Jellison and Flowers 1991; Krout 1986a; Lathom-Radocy 2014; Zinar 1987). Similarly, with the move toward deinstitutionalization and the introduction of a new classification system for intellectual disability that emphasizes adaptive functioning (AAMR 1992; DSM-V 2013), music therapy programs, too, have increasingly emphasized developing functional skills that can be useful in community settings (Coates 1987; Deats and Farnan 2008; DiGiammarino 1990, 1994; Furman and Furman 1988, 1996). Programs and services focusing on early intervention and the elderly client with intellectual disability also are increasing as medical and technological advances continue and as legislation mandates and funds services (Furman and Furman 1988, 1996; Humpal 1990). In addition, music therapy has been found to be a very effective intervention for increasing and maintaining communication responses, motor functioning, cognitive skills, and social and affective responses in individuals with Rett Syndrome (Hadsell and Coleman 1988; International Rett Syndrome Association 1987; Wesecky 1986; Wylie 1996). Furman and Furman (1996) provide an excellent survey and summary of the literature on music therapy and mental retardation (intellectual disability) published from 1970–1995. Lathom-Radocy (2014) extended the literature.

Many different types of music experiences (e.g., singing, listening, moving to music, playing musical instruments, creating music, discussing music, and reading music notation) can be structured to help intellectually disabled individuals reach nonmusical therapeutic goals. Music experiences and activities can be used (a) to *reinforce*, increase, or maintain desired behaviors; (b) to *structure* or serve as a vehicle for presenting the material or skill to be learned; and (c) to *stimulate* the production and development of desired social, perceptual motor, or academic skills and behaviors (Madsen 1981). Various music therapy techniques and experiences can help individuals with intellectual disability or other developmental disabilities improve their skills in many areas, including (1) communication skills; (2) academic, cognitive, or vocational skills; (3) motor skills; (4) social and emotional skills; (5) self-help or independent living skills; and (6) leisure skills (Boxill 1985; Carter 1982; Coates 1987; Davis 1992b; DiGiammarino 1990, 1994; Furman and Furman 1988, 1996; Grant 1989). While the next sections examine each of these areas individually to discuss commonly used music therapy strategies, one should remember that, in practice, all of these areas overlap and influence one another. In fact, one of the strengths and unique aspects of music therapy is that it can address skills in many areas and on many levels of development simultaneously (Grant 1989; Lathom 1981b; Lathom-Radocy 2014), thus facilitating the growth of the whole person in an integrated fashion.

Music Therapy Strategies to Improve Communication Skills

Intellectually disabled individuals have varying degrees of impairment in communication abilities. Some may have no functional speech and may need to develop ways of communicating nonverbally with basic sign language or simple communication boards. DSM-V (2013, 37) considers "co-occurring disorders that affect communication, language, and/or motor or sensory function" because they may affect IQ scores. Some children with intellectual impairments may have difficulty with awareness of or attention to auditory stimuli (auditory perception) or in interpreting and responding to communications from others (receptive language). Still others may need alternative ways to learn to develop and expand their functional verbal communication skills (expressive language). Various music therapy strategies can help in many of these areas.

For individuals needing help in developing the auditory perception skills necessary to attend to and understand spoken language, music therapists might use music experiences that require the client to locate, track, identify, and discriminate among sound sources (Grant 1989; Thaut 2005). Simple sound exploration activities using musical instruments, vocal sounds, and body sounds (e.g., clapping, tapping, tongue clicking) can stimulate the initial auditory awareness and attention necessary to language development (Boxill 1985; Monti 1985; Nordoff and Robbins 1971a, 1977). Thaut (2005, 2) notes that "speech and music both take on meaning within the cultural background, the social context, and the intents and expectations of the situation in which the communication takes place." Later, simple music activities employing matching, sequencing, and echo techniques can be used to develop auditory memory and sequencing skills (Grant 1989; Lathom-Radocy 2014).

Songs, movement-to-music activities, dances, and instrumental activities that require clients to follow directions or point to certain things named in the song can help clients develop *receptive language skills* (Grant 1989; Lathom-Radocy 2014). Spencer (1988) found that movement activities were generally more effective than instrumental activities in developing the ability to follow directions in adolescents and young adults with intellectual disability; however, significant change required at least sixteen to twenty treatment sessions. Of course, a particular client's individual preferences and skills require consideration when planning what approaches to use with that client.

In the area of *expressive language*, various musical experiences and techniques can elicit, stimulate, and increase an individual's vocalizations. These include vibroacoustic therapy (Skille 1989), soft instrumental background music (Cunningham 1986), and various vocal exploration and imitation exercises (Boxill 1985; Grant 1989; Nordoff and Robbins 1977). Research suggests that singing activities involving singing alone or in conjunction with actions, picture cards, or concept learning can be useful in encouraging spontaneous speech and increasing expressive language skills in preschool children with intellectual disability or developmental disabilities (Hoskins 1988). In addition, music therapy experiences can be structured so as to gradually increase an individual's expressive communication, first requiring him or her to supply one, then two, three, or more words within the context of a musical activity. Reading recognition and comprehension skills may also be increased via words that are presented in songs or with other musical activities. For example, pairing the words "walk," "run," and "hop" with descriptive music may help clients learn to associate printed words with their corresponding actions.

Music Therapy Strategies to Improve Academic, Cognitive, and Vocational Skills

Prior to learning any academic or vocational skills, individuals must have both the motivation to participate in the experience and certain behaviors, such as eye contact, the ability to discriminate and focus on specific auditory, visual, or tactile cues and stimuli, sufficient attention span, and the ability to follow directions. Music therapy experiences can help clients develop skills in all of these areas (Davis 1992b; Lathom 1981a, 1981b; Lathom-Radocy 2014; Nocera 1979). For example, unique musical sounds and rhythms can attract attention and elicit eye contact. Attention span can lengthen gradually as the duration of songs or musical experiences increases and as individuals are asked to wait longer and longer to have their turn to play an instrument or give a specific response within the context of the music activity. Various songs and musical games requiring clients to point to, match, or identify certain sounds, pictures, or objects can also help individuals learn to attend to and discriminate among different auditory, visual, or tactile stimuli. In addition, songs or musical games that incorporate specific commands or directions in the lyrics are effective in helping individuals learn to attend to and follow directions. The interest in musical sounds and rhythms, the pleasure of making music, and the gratification gained by participating in musical experiences often motivate even the most unresponsive clients to attend, respond, and participate.

Once individuals have learned to attend to the learning situation, many academic skills and concepts, such as identification of colors, shapes, numbers, body parts, clothing, as well as directionality, time and space concepts, etc., can be presented and practiced through various song lyrics, action songs, musical games, dances, or musical instrument activities (Boxill 1985; Lathom 1981a, 1981b; Lathom-Radocy 2014; Nocera 1979; Thaut 2005). For example, song lyrics can be written to describe or express certain concepts; or action songs, musical games, or dances can require individuals to point to or match or identify colors or numbers or shapes or body parts. Radocy and Boyle (2012, 164) note that "behavior and cognition are integrally related and mutually interdependent." Using colors, shapes, or numbers to correspond to various musical sounds or pitches on charts for song or ensemble playing can also give clients practice in identifying and recognizing colors, shapes, and numbers. When material is presented in a musical context, the melody and rhythm of the music help provide the structure necessary to help intellectually disabled individuals learn, process, and retain certain concepts. In addition, the natural repetition inherent in musical structure gives clients needed multiple presentations of information without the boredom of tedious drill. Davis, Gfeller, and Thaut (2008, 59) note that "the motivational quality of preferred music can help to grab a client's attention."

Research indicates that musical perception tasks can be used to assess that level of cognitive development in individuals with intellectual disability as well as in nonhandicapped children (Jones 1986; Rider 1978, 1981). Music intervention strategies employing a controlled increase in musical complexity then can be used to enhance cognitive development in individuals with intellectual disability by helping them move through the tasks associated with different stages of cognitive development. Goodman (2007, 140–141) provides case examples and goals and objectives for small groups; they include cognitive goals/objectives and procedure. Some research also indicates that exposure to certain types of stimulating music and rhythmic drum beats for a period of 15–20 minutes prior to academic instruction can increase muscle tone in hypotonic children with Down syndrome, leading to greater physical alertness and enhancing intellectual responsiveness to the learning tasks (Sekeles 1989).

Music therapists frequently use contingent music experiences, involving both active (e.g., instrument playing, dancing) and passive (e.g., listening) responses, to facilitate skill learning among intellectually disabled individuals (Furman and Furman 1988, 1996). Standley, Johnson, Robb, Brownell, and Kim (2008, 105–127) explain the behavioral approach to music therapy. These strategies are often very effective in increasing many different preacademic and academic skills (Dorow 1976; Holloway 1980; Saperston et al. 1980; Underhill and Harris 1974). However, it is important to note that music's reinforcing properties vary not only with individual reinforcement history but also with the degree of intellectual disability. A pilot study with profoundly disabled children (Ghetti 2002, 28) observed that "since individuals with multiple disabilities need longer periods of time for cognitive processing and take longer to learn, music therapy intervention may be more effective if it is presented more frequently during the school week." Although some individuals who have more severe levels of involvement do respond positively to contingent music programs (Walker 1972), those with greater degrees of impairment usually have the least consistent responses to contingent music (Furman and Furman 1988).

In addition to facilitating the development of attending behaviors and the learning of certain procedures and tasks, music may help to structure the general work or learning environment. For example, one study finds evidence that certain types of background music have significant positive effects on the work behavior of intellectually disabled adults participating in sorting tasks in a vocational training environment (Groeneweg et al. 1988). However, other studies suggest that easy listening music and distracting noises have no effect on the productivity of intellectually disabled workers (Wentworth 1991). Not all types of background music will have equally beneficial effects for all clients or for all tasks; clients' responses must be carefully observed and monitored for each situation. What is beneficial or reinforcing in one situation may not be so in another.

Music Therapy Strategies to Improve Motor Skills

The development of functional motor skills can be very important in helping individuals learn to interact with and learn from their environment (Boxill 1985). Intellectually disabled individuals may have delays in motor development or have various concurrent motor or nervous system difficulties that make voluntary control and coordination of movement difficult or impossible (Davis 1992b). These difficulties are described as comorbidity in DSM-V (2013), which also notes that medical and physical conditions are frequent in intellectual disabilities. Motor skills allow individuals to explore the environment and provide the foundation for much other learning. They are also an integral part of the performance of many daily living activities (e.g., feeding, bathing, dressing, etc.) that are a part of adaptive functioning. Therefore, the process of developing and refining motor skills for learning and functional activities is often an important part of therapeutic programs for intellectually disabled individuals. Because of its direct physical effects and its time-ordered structure (see Chapter Five), music can help stimulate motor responses and facilitate the development of motor control and coordination.

Many types of music experiences, including action songs, dances and movement-to-music activities, and the exploration and use of musical instruments, can be used to stimulate and develop motor responses (Boxill 1985; Grant 1989; Lathom 1981a, 1981b; Lathom-Radocy 2014; Nocera 1979). Movement-to-music experiences may be active or passive. Individuals may be required to perform activities independently or be guided through normal movement patterns by the therapist, who gradually diminishes the assistance as the individual's skills emerge and develop. Passive range of motion or movement-to-music activities can play vital roles in the maintenance of joint mobility and range of motion in individuals who have limited independent mobility. O'Konski et al. (2010, 121) note that "among older adults, diminished mobility is most prevalent among long-term care facility residents." Careful attention to the structure, mood, and physical and psychoemotional effects of the music that accompanies the exercises can enhance individuals' receptiveness and responsiveness to passive and active range of motion exercises. Dr. Oliver Sacks (2008, 257), a well-known author and a professor of neurology and psychiatry at Columbia University, wrote that "it is clear that music, above all else, can kick-start a damaged or inhibited motor system into action again."

Certain types of music also stimulate active movement and help individuals coordinate and control their actions. For example, Sekeles (1989) found that stimulating drum beats, stimulating music improvised by the music therapist,

and recordings of music from ecstatic healing rituals could help elicit spontaneous motor responses and increase muscle tone in hypotonic children with
Down syndrome, which lead to greater physical alertness and enhancing
responses to posture and motor control exercises. Various motor activities,
such as ball tossing, block stacking, engaging in exercise patterns, etc., can
also be structured by or choreographed to rhythmic music or song lyrics, and
may increase fluidity and coordination of movement. Dances, musical games,
or action songs can incorporate both gross and fine motor movements in
accordance with an individual client's needs. In addition, music activities can
be structured to include various motor skills that individuals need to practice,
thus reinforcing skill development (Holloway 1980).

Musical instruments can provide clients with many enjoyable opportunities
for developing and refining motor skills. According to Grant (1989), music's
rhythmic structure provides a unique means of programming the input,
cognitive processing, and output process of perceptual motor function, while
active participation in playing various instruments gives many possibilities for
the development and practice of specific movement patterns. The motions
required to play various instruments can help clients develop and refine
skills in reaching, grasping, releasing, arm extension, eye-hand coordination,
finger movements, and coordination of bilateral or unilateral movements
(Boxill 1985; Grant 1989; Lathom 1981a, 1981b; Lathom-Radocy 2014;
Nocera 1979). Experiences in playing musical instruments also can promote
appropriate hand usage in individuals with Rett Syndrome (Hadsell and
Coleman 1988; Wylie 1996). Instrumental activities may be structured to
require gross or fine motor movements, depending on individual needs.
For example, a hand drum may be sounded by a slap or tap (Hadsell and
Coleman 1988) by individuals with limited motor skills or may be played
with intricate finger patterns by those who are developing fine motor skills
(Sekeles 1989). As an individual's skills increase, the music therapist gradually
increases the difficulty of the movement required to play the instrument. For
example, an autoharp may be positioned farther away from an individual so
that individual will have to extend his or her arms more to strum the instrument. Or an individual may be challenged to play a rhythmic pattern faster
or be given a part that has faster notes or more chord changes. With various
adaptations, even those individuals with limited motor skills can play musical
instruments (Clark and Chadwick 1979; Rudenberg 1982).

Music Therapy Strategies to Improve Social
and Emotional Skills

In working with intellectually disabled clients, music therapists frequently
target improvement in social skills and the elimination of inappropriate or

self-stimulatory behaviors (Furman and Furman 1988, 1996; Lathom-Radocy 2014). The adaptive limitations associated with intellectual disability often include significant limits in social intelligence (DSM-V 2013); therefore, individuals who have intellectual disability often need help in acquiring and practicing appropriate social behaviors (Davis 1992b; Davis, Gfeller, and Thaut 2008). Group music experiences using songs, movement-to-music, and instrumental activities all can be structured to incorporate social skills such as parallel or cooperative play, appropriate greetings, sharing, taking turns, listening to others, and group awareness and cooperation (Boxill 1985; Grant 1989; Krout 1986a; Lathom 1981a, 1981b; Lathom-Radocy 2014; Nocera 1979). By playing instruments or dancing or singing together, individuals learn to work together, listen to each other, follow a group leader, and wait for their turn to sing, move, or play. The repetition and order of music help the clients predict what is coming, thus increasing their comfort level and helping them become more confident of their ability to participate with the group (Eyre 2011). Clients who participate in performing groups, such as bell choirs, bands, drum corps, and singing groups, also learn to improve self-discipline, impulse control, and social skills. In addition, these activities provide the group members with experiences that bring gratification and increase self-esteem. Since music activities are adaptable to different ability levels within a group (e.g., less coordination is needed to strike a bass drum than to strike the correct bar of a xylophone), group music activities can provide opportunities for clients of many different ability levels to work together and achieve success.

Music groups and improvised musical play experiences can also provide fun and nonthreatening opportunities for intellectually disabled individuals to associate and interact with their nondisabled peers (Boxill 1989; Gunsberg 1988, 1991; Hughes et al. 1990; Humpal 1990, 1991; Monti 1985). By using specific strategies, music therapists can facilitate the development of interaction between disabled and nondisabled individuals. For example, Humpal (1991) found that, for early childhood groups, parachute games and hoop or elastic rope dances to music were most effective in fostering interaction, while creative movement to music and line dancing were least effective. Music experiences using rhythm instruments, bean bags, circle activities, or partner dances were all moderately effective in promoting interaction. The following procedure summarizes a typical music therapy session:

1. Provide a clear structure for the session while allowing the children to choose options.
2. Model each musical task as necessary.
3. Task-analyze the musical task in order to present one step at a time to the children.
4. Model – practice-praise or correct.

5. Repeat musical materials as requested by the children but add variety in order to provide more developmental challenge.
6. Infuse language in a naturalistic manner as the session proceeds.
7. Evaluate responses on a regular basis. (Goodman 2007, 188)

Some intellectually disabled individuals may be very impulsive, lack emotional stability, or exhibit inappropriate behaviors, such as showing aggressiveness, talking out of turn, leaving their seats without permission, or participating in verbal or physical abuse. In many cases, contingent music activities can effectively increase appropriate social behaviors and eliminate inappropriate behaviors (Furman and Furman 1988, 1996; Krout 1986a; Madsen 1981). Inappropriate behaviors are called "off-task behaviors." Standley et al (2008) discussed the effect of reinforcement on on-task behavior. They reported that music is a very effective reinforce. They explain that "the Premack Principle is the use of high-occurrence stimuli to reinforce low-occurrence behaviors . . . music participation is a highly desirable and effective Premack activity." (113)

Songs and improvisational activities dealing with various emotions and feelings also may be useful in helping clients learn how to express emotions in appropriate and socially acceptable ways. In addition, song lyrics can be written to help clients learn and remember appropriate ways to express various emotions, such as anger.

Saperston (1989) developed a special, individualized, music-based relaxation training technique to help intellectually disabled individuals control or eliminate inappropriate behaviors. In this program, various music experiences, including songs, chanting, and recorded or improvised music that elicits physiological responses associated with relaxation, or combinations of different musical elements are used as reinforcements, structural prompts, or eliciting stimuli of desired behaviors to help clients circumvent behavioral problems. Pujol (1994) also found that pentatonic music was useful in increasing deep inhalations and relaxation responses in severely or profoundly impaired individuals.

Music therapists have also successfully used music in conjunction with intensive play techniques to decrease inappropriate or self-abusive behaviors, establish social rapport, and increase adaptive responses in clients who had severe or profound impairments (Carter 1982; Gonzales 1981; Miorin and Covault 1979). In this process, music, close body contact, and physical stimulation are used to establish rapport between the therapist and the client. Once rapport is established, the therapist continues to use these elements to evoke and develop positive responses, such as eye contact, appropriate affect, cooperative interaction, initiation of sounds, facial expressions, and purposeful motor actions, in the client. Relating this process to literature on sensory integration, Farnan (2002, 83) notes that "the pairing of rhythmic stimuli with specific movements is utilized to provide multisensorial stimulation and to develop improved sensory processing and integration." Other music therapists use improvisational music, based on the client's movements and vocalizations, to elicit and develop adaptive responses and appropriate interactions with severely or profoundly impaired clients (Boxill 1985; Nordoff and Robbins 1977; Pfeifer 1982).

Music Therapy Strategies to Improve Self-Help and Independent Living Skills

Because of limitations in practical intelligence accompanying intellectual disability, individuals often need support or specially structured programs to help them achieve the greatest degree of independence possible in self-help and self-care skills (DSM-V 2013). Music can assist in many of these areas, providing the structure, motivation, or reinforcement for appropriate skill development (Boxill 1985, 1989; Furman and Furman 1988, 1996; Lathom 1981a, 1981b; Lathom-Radocy 2014). For example, pleasurable music activities can provide effective positive reinforcement for self-care skills (Garwood 1988). In other cases, song lyrics may provide the necessary cues and structure to help clients learn and remember the sequence of steps needed for various dressing or personal hygiene routines (Kramer 1978). Other clients may be motivated to adhere to acceptable standards of personal hygiene and learn to take pride in their appearance to maintain their membership in a musical performance group. Increased motor skill coordination and independence developed in music experiences may also be transferred to functional areas like personal mobility, holding eating or grooming utensils, etc.

Music Therapy Strategies to Improve Leisure Skills

A final area where music therapy can be highly beneficial for intellectually disabled individuals is the development of meaningful and satisfying leisure-time activities. As these people are integrated more and more into the community, they must find ways of occupying their hours of free time when they are not involved in specific work or training programs. Music therapists can help them gain functional leisure and music performance skills that will help them enjoy and participate in many different types of music activities in their free time, either alone or with others, at their residence or in community settings (Coates 1987; Davis 1992b; DiGiammarino 1990, 1994; Furman and Furman 1996). The ability to find appropriate social contacts and leisure-time activities may make the difference between successful adjustment to community living and failure to adapt to their new independence from more structured and sheltered environments (Hooper 2001).

Intellectually disabled persons can learn to access and enjoy many music activities independently if they are given appropriately structured training which leads to generalization of skills to other settings and in the presence of people other than the trainer (Coates 1987; DiGiammarino 1990, 1994). Functional music leisure skills may include activities such as learning to operate audiovisual equipment, learning appropriate concert etiquette, learning to select and borrow or purchase recordings and tapes, learning to purchase concert tickets, becoming a member of a community chorus or band, attending and participating in community dances, and learning to play musical instruments. Most individuals without intellectual disability develop several of these skills incidentally through everyday experiences at home or in the community; however, "individuals with mental retardation [intellectual disability] . . . may need direct instruction in skills which will help them access music independently during leisure time" (DiGiammarino 1994, 19; Hooper 2001). According to Lathom-Radocy (2014, 67), appropriate social skills are necessary for interaction in community social groups. It is here the music therapist's skills become important, for the music therapist knows not only how to use, access, and teach various types of music skills but also how to structure and sequence training in a way that intellectually disabled persons can assimilate and understand. For example, the music therapist might employ certain types of special notation, symbolic representations, or cueing techniques to teach music performance skills, such as piano performance (Velasquez 1991).

Other music therapists are beginning to use personal computers and special applications of music education software to help intellectually disabled clients uncover and develop musical talent. For example, Spitzer (1989) used computers to help an individual with Down syndrome improve his singing range and accuracy so he was better able to join in singing groups. Individuals with mild retardation who had difficulty with traditional notation were also able to play and create melodies and spend many enjoyable hours in this way because of computer programs. Success with music and the computer also enhanced their motivation and level of concentration, "thereby allowing them to feel better about themselves in general" (Spitzer 1989). In short, technology helps clients achieve their goals in music therapy treatments:

> Through the combination of computer software and electronic musical instruments, music therapists utilize current technology to enable participants to work on goal areas of communication; expression of preferences; visual, auditory, and tactile stimulation; functional hand use; peer interaction; sensory development; and enjoyment. (Farnan 2007, 83)

As the clients gain functional music listening and performance skills, they are equipped with more tools that will help facilitate successful integration into the community. Although initial treatment may require many prompts and much interaction between the music therapist and the client, independent functioning by the client within the community setting is always the ultimate goal (Coates 1987; DiGiammarino 1990, 1994).

SPECIAL CONSIDERATIONS AND TIPS FOR SUCCESS

Music activities used with intellectually disabled individuals should be clear, direct, concrete, and incorporate multisensory experiences as much as possible (Atterbury 1990; Birkenshaw-Fleming 1993; Boxill 1985; Lathom-Radocy 2014; Nocera 1979; Zinar 1987). Material often must be presented at a slower rate and in smaller steps, and language and demonstrations used must be simple and concrete enough for the individual to understand. Gestures and verbal or physical prompts may be used initially to help clients achieve the desired responses, and then faded as the clients' skills emerge and develop. Group leaders may need to direct the client's attention specifically to important features of the lesson or experience and to review and summarize these clearly before going on to the next point. Color-coding or adaptive notation may help clients to perform skills independently. Electronic instruments or computer programs also may help unlock an individual's musical talent and independent performance abilities (Birkenshaw-Fleming 1993; Farnan 1993, 2007; Spitzer 1989).

When planning and selecting materials, the therapist must consider the clients' chronological ages as well as their level of intellectual and adaptive development. Songs and instruments should be age-appropriate and have wide appeal (Atterbury 1990; Birkenshaw-Fleming 1993; Boxill 1985; Nocera 1979; Zinar 1987). If clients are to be integrated in school or community settings, it is important that they experience the same types of vocal, instrumental, and listening activities as their nondisabled peers (Jellison and Flowers 1991).

Songs that have simple text and lots of repetition are generally most successful with intellectually disabled clients. Concrete representation of song content and use of familiar vocabulary will also facilitate participation (Atterbury, 1986). It is important that melodic range correspond to the client's singing range, which generally is lower and narrower than that of his or her non-disabled peers (Furman and Furman 1988, 1996; Larson 1977; Zinar 1987). It is also important to make sure that the accompaniment is not distracting and serves to enhance the meaning of any song lyrics (Birkenshaw-Fleming 1993; Boxill 1985; Nordoff and Robbins 1971a; Zinar 1987). Different types of accompaniment may positively or negatively influence vocal responses, especially among clients who are severely or profoundly impaired (Wylie 1983).

When structuring music experiences, the music therapist should find ways to actively involve the clients in making, responding to, and creating music (Birkenshaw-Fleming 1993; Boxill 1985; Nordoff and Robbins 1971a, 1971b). The therapist may need to make adaptations to instruments or to find ways to build the musical experience around the clients' movements or simple vocal responses, but with sensitivity and creativity on the part of the music therapist, most clients can become actively engaged in the music experience.

Of course, the therapist should structure activities to provide clients with successful experiences, but it is also important to provide the client with some degree of challenge. Although praise should be given for even the smallest accomplishments, praise never should be given falsely or indiscriminately. It is also very important to be specific when praising clients so that they will know what they are doing right and where they still need to improve.

As intellectually disabled individuals are integrated more and more into the community, functional skills that can be generalized to community use require an increasing emphasis (Coates 1987; DiGiammarino 1990, 1994; Furman and Furman 1988, 1996). The music therapist must remember that, although initial treatment may require many prompts and much interaction between the music therapist and the client, independent functioning by the client within the community setting is always the ultimate goal. Teaching methods and therapeutic strategies should promote generalized skills used by the individual in normalized environments: home, school, leisure, community, and work (AAMR 1992). As Standley et al. (2008, 115) maintain, "Since the world often lacks consistent and contingent reinforcement schedules, it becomes important to systematically teach clients to respond to reinforcers that occur naturally as consequences of their behavior."

Research also indicates that intellectually disabled individuals demonstrate better skill generalization and retention when skills are taught as integrated parts of functional routines rather than in isolation: "Rather than simply scheduled for instruction in discrete blocks of time, basic motor, language, and social skills are taught as they occur or are needed, naturally *embedded* within routine activities" (AAMR 1992, 131). Music therapy can be especially effective as a means of integrated instruction because music experiences naturally include all these areas.

In preparing individuals with intellectual disability to participate with their nondisabled peers in mainstreamed, inclusive, or community settings, the music therapist must pay special attention to the specific social behaviors required by that situation (Jellison and Duke 1994; Krout 1986a). Jellison and Duke (1994) found that teachers considering integrating intellectually disabled individuals into inclusive music settings rated social behaviors more important than musical skills. When conducting music therapy activities in an integrated or mainstreamed setting, planners must train other staff in the use of appropriate teaching techniques that will facilitate learning and integration within a music setting (Hughes et al. 1990; Madsen and Alley 1979).

Music therapists who work with individuals in programs for the intellectually disabled or developmentally disabled occasionally may encounter individuals who have a unique condition known as Williams syndrome. Although most individuals who have this chromosomal disorder have mild-to-moderate intellectual disability, they also have some mental strength, including strong verbal abilities and a great appreciation of and talent for music, with a good memory for songs, melodies, and lyrics (Lenhoff 1998; Stambaugh 1996). Generally, individuals with Williams syndrome learn better in one-to-one learning situations than in group classes, learn better through hearing and imitating than through written music notation, and, because of motor limitations, have the most success with voice, keyboard, and drums (Lenhoff 1998). In working with these individuals, it is important to (a) match instruments to the students' physical characteristics, (b) use short sentences and frequently address students by name to help maintain attention, and (c) anticipate escalating frustration and help students remove themselves from the situation or find alternate activities (Stambaugh 1996).

QUESTIONS FOR THOUGHT AND DISCUSSION

1. Discuss the major differences between the DSM-V (2013) classification system and the other systems of classification for intellectual disability described in this chapter. What impact do these have for the provision of music therapy services?
2. Describe several characteristics, problems, and needs which may be common to many intellectually disabled individuals. How do these special characteristics, problems, and needs impact the structure or methodology of music therapy treatment approaches?
3. Describe various ways that music therapy techniques and experiences can help individuals with an intellectual disability improve their skills in the general areas of (1) communication skills; (2) academic, cognitive, or vocational skills; (3) motor skills; (4) social and emotional skills; (5) self-help or independent living skills; and (6) leisure skills.

    Do techniques and approaches vary according to the individual's level of impairment? If so, how?
4. List several special considerations that may be important to remember when developing therapeutic intervention strategies for persons with intellectual disability. Why are these important? What are their implications for the structure of music therapy intervention strategies?
5. For the situations described below, (a) define the problem or areas of need for the client or group of clients, (b) describe one or more of the goals you

might pursue in music therapy sessions with the client(s), (c) describe music activities you might use to help the client(s) meet those goals, (d) tell how the music activities you described relate to the goals and needs of the client(s), and (e) mention any special considerations you might want to take into account when working with the client(s).

Situation 1:

Mark is a three-year-old boy with intellectual disability due to Down syndrome. Mark has been referred to you for music therapy. He can use a spoon to feed himself soft foods (although he still spills a lot) and can drink from a plastic cup without assistance. He can pull off his shirt, shoes, and socks, but he needs help putting them on. Mark can stand alone, but he walks with an unsteady gait. His mother says that he sometimes flaps his arms and bounces up and down to music from a radio or record as if he were dancing. Mark can imitate sounds, and he is just beginning to say "Ma" consistently. He recognizes familiar people and shows preferences for some people over others.

Situation 2:

You have been contracted to provide weekly music therapy sessions for a group of 10–12 older teenagers and young adults who have intellectual disabilities. Most have limited perceptual motor skills, short attention spans, limited communication skills, and limited means of personal expression. Some need work on impulse control. Many have needs in the areas of increasing their awareness and attention to people, objects, and events in their environment and/or of improving functional skills that will enable them to initiate responses and interact cooperatively and positively with others in group situations. Other programming for these individuals emphasizes functional living skills, attention span, and appropriate social behaviors.

SUGGESTIONS FOR FURTHER READING

Boxill, E. H. (1985). *Music therapy for the developmentally disabled.* Rockville, MD: Aspen Systems.

Boxill, E. H. (1989). *Music therapy for living: The principle of normalization embodied in music therapy.* St. Louis: MMB Music.

Carter, S. A. (1982). *Music therapy for handicapped children: Mentally retarded.* Washington, D.C.: National Association for Music Therapy.

Davis, W. B. & Farnan, L. A. (2008). Music therapy with children and adults with intellectual disabling conditions. In W. B. Davis, K. E. Gfeller, & M. H. Thaut, *An introduction to music therapy: Theory and practice.* (79–115). Silver Spring, MD: American Music Therapy Association.

DiGiammarino, M. (1994). Functional music leisure skills for individuals with mental retardation. *Music Therapy Perspectives, 12(1)*, 15–19.

Farnan, L. A. (2007). Music therapy and developmental disabilities: A glace back and a look forward. *Music Therapy Perspectives, 25(2)*, 80–85.

Farnan, L., & Johnson, F. (1988). *Everyone can move: Music and activities that promote movement and motor development.* New Berlin, WI: Jenson Publications.

Farnan, L., & Johnson, F. (1988). *Music is for everyone: A handbook for providing music to people with special needs.* New Berlin, WI: Jenson Publications.

Furman, C. E., & Furman, A. G. (1988). Music therapy research with mental retardation: Analysis and clinical implications. In C. E. Furman (Ed.), *Effectiveness of music therapy procedures: Documentation or research and clinical practice* (285–299). Washington, D. C.: National Association for Music Therapy.

Furman, C. E., & Furman, A. G. (1996). Uses of music therapy with people having mental retardation: An update of a previous analysis. In C. E. Furman (Ed.), *Effectiveness of music therapy procedures: Documentation of research and clinical practice* (2nd ed.) (279–296). Silver Spring, MD: National Association for Music Therapy.

Grant, R. E. (1989). Music therapy guidelines for developmentally disabled children. *Music Therapy Perspectives, 6*, 18–22.

Hadsell, N. A., & Coleman, K. A. (1988). Rett syndrome: A challenge for music therapists. *Music Therapy Perspectives, 5*, 52–56.

Humpal, M. E. (1990). Early intervention: The implications for music therapy. *Music Therapy Perspectives, 8*, 30–35.

Krout, R. (1986). *Music therapy in special education: Developing and maintaining social skills necessary for mainstreaming.* St. Louis: MMB Music.

Lathom-Radocy, (2014). *Pediatric Music Therapy.* Developmental disabilities. (Chapter three, 39–74). Springfield, IL: Charles C Thomas.

Lenhoff, H. M. (1998). Insights into the musical potential of cognitively impaired people diagnosed with Williams syndrome. *Music Therapy Perspectives, 16(1)*, 33–36.

Standley, J. (1991). *Music techniques in therapy, counseling, and special education.* St. Louis: MMB Music.

Standley, J., Johnson, C. M., Robb, S. L., Brownell, M. D. & Kim, S-H. (2008). Behavioral approach to music therapy. In A.-A. Darrow, *Introduction to approaches in music therapy* (2nd ed.), pp. 105–127. Silver Spring, MD: American Music Therapy Association.

Chapter Eight

MUSIC THERAPY FOR INDIVIDUALS WHO HAVE SPECIFIC LEARNING DISABILITIES

Definition

Some people display an educationally significant discrepancy between their estimated intellectual potential and their actual academic performance that cannot be explained in terms of physical, sensory, intellectual, or experiential problems. These individuals usually are classified as having some sort of learning disability. DSM-V (2013) states that Specific Learning Disability (SLD) is

> a neurodevelopmental disorder with a biological origin that is the basis for abnormalities at a cognitive level that are associated with the behavioral signs of the disorder . . . which affect the brain's ability to perceive or process verbal or non-verbal information efficiently and accurately. (68)

The Learning Disability Association of America (LDA 2015) states that 2.4 million students are diagnosed with SLD. IDEA legislation provides services to the SLD group, who comprise 41–47 percent (depending on the source) of all students receiving funding through this legislation. Learning disabilities are sometimes called invisible or hidden handicaps (NIMH 1993); there are no physical signs, and the people who have them usually have average or above average general intelligence.

Learning-disabled individuals have some brain processing malfunction that negatively affects "a student's ability to access information (input), make sense of information (integration), store and retrieve information (memory), and communicate information back to others (output)" (Adamek and Darrow 2010, 179). For example, individuals with learning disabilities may have impaired abilities to interpret what they see or hear, or they may have difficulties linking information from different parts of the brain.

Learning disabilities are manifested in many different ways as specific difficulties in written or spoken language, attention, coordination, or self-control. They often impede the individual's ability to do schoolwork or to read, write, or do math (NIMH 1993). The Learning Disabilities Association of America (2015) provides this list of specific disabilities:

1. Auditory processing disorder
2. Dysgraphia
3. Dyscalculia
4. Dyslexia
5. Language processing disorder
6. Visual perceptual/visual motor deficit
7. Nonverbal learning disability

While attention deficit disorder (ADD) or attention-deficit-hyperactivity disorder (ADHD) often may accompany learning disorders, these disorders are not in and of themselves considered learning disorders (APA 1994; NIMH 1993). Other disabilities that may commonly occur with SLD include speech and language disorders, autism spectrum disorder, disruptive and emotional behavior problems, and disabilities that involve motor function. However, ADHD is the most common comorbid condition, with about 50 percent having SLD (DSM-V 2013, 77; Hardman et al. 2008).

The term *learning disability* or *learning disorder* is not used to describe a single condition; rather, it is a broad umbrella term used for classification purposes to cover a wide variety of specific learning problems that have in common processing or learning difficulties in some specific area while development in other areas is average or above average (Adamek and Darrow 2010; APA 1994; Atterbury 1990; Birkenshaw-Fleming 1993; Gfeller 1992b; Gladfelter 1996; Hamill et al. 1981; Mercer 1987; NIMH 1993; Welsbacher 1975; Zinar 1987). Any two individuals classified as learning disabled likely will have many differences both in the type of deficits in perceptive, integrative, or expressive processes which impair learning and in the academic areas affected. Because of the great diversity of problems that may be associated with this condition, professionals have found it difficult to develop a single, succinct definition of learning disabilities.

School settings often use the definition of learning disabilities developed by the United States Office of Education for IDEA legislation. According to Adamek and Darrow (2010, 168–169), "students who qualify for special education services due to a learning disability must demonstrate a severe discrepancy between their potential and their achievement, as measured by intelligence tests and achievement tests."

However, many professionals prefer the definition that was prepared by the National Joint Committee for Learning Disabilities in 1981, which stresses a physiological, central nervous system basis for the disability, notes the uniqueness of the manifestation in each individual, and recognizes that learning disabilities exist in individuals of all ages (Gfeller 1992b; Mercer 1987):

> "Specific Learning Disabilities" (SLD) is a generic term that refers to a heterogeneous group of disorders manifested by significant difficulties in acquisition

and use of listening, speaking, reading, writing, reasoning, or mathematical abilities. The disorders are intrinsic to the individual and presumed to be due to central nervous system dysfunction. Even though a learning disability may occur concomitantly with other handicapping conditions (e.g., sensory impairments, mental retardation, social and emotional disturbance) or environmental influences (e.g., cultural differences, insufficient/inappropriate instruction, psychogenic factors), it is not the direct result of those conditions or influences. (Hamill et al. 1981, 336)

An individual may have more than one learning disorder. Learning disorders are differentiated from normal variations in academic achievement and from academic difficulties due to lack of opportunity, poor teaching, or cultural factors. The primary diagnostic criteria for learning disorders demonstrated that (1) reading, mathematical, and/or written expression abilities are *substantially* below those expected for the individual's chronological age, measured intelligence, and age-appropriate education; (2) these difficulties in reading, mathematical, and/or written expression abilities interfere *significantly* with areas of academic achievement or daily living requiring these abilities; and (3) if sensory deficits are present, the difficulties in reading, mathematical, and/or written expression abilities *exceed* those difficulties usually associated with the sensory deficit (DSM-V 2013).

One must remember that learning disabilities are disorders in psychological processing, not in general intellectual functioning, and they usually affect only specific, limited areas of learning or development (APA 1994; Atterbury 1990; NIMH 1993). Learning-disabled individuals have some dysfunction in the *way* they learn, but their basic capacity *to* learn remains intact.

Medical, psychological, and educational professionals use various terms to identify specific types of learning disabilities (Clayton and Morrison 1992). For example, *developmental reading disorder* is the term used to describe a condition in which all learning skills except reading (silent and oral) develop at normal rate. *Dyslexia* describes impairments in reading ability: Dyslexic individuals have difficulties with spelling, reading, and writing, and they may have trouble with reversals or left to right orientation. Dehaene (2009, 237) describes dyslexia as "a disproportionate difficulty in learning to read that cannot be attributed to mental retardation, sensory deficit, or an underprivileged family background. This definition makes it clear that not all poor readers are dyslexics." In *developmental arithmetic disorder* (*dyscalculia*), all learning skills except math develop at normal rate, while in *developmental expressive writing disorder*, all learning skills except expressive writing develop at a normal rate. Other terms employed in the broad classification of learning disabilities include *sequencing disorder* (reversing the order of numbers and words; mix-ups happen in speech and writing), *tracking disorder* (difficulty following objects; also causes difficulty staying on same line when reading), *fine motor skills disorder* or *dysgraphia* (difficulty with writing and small muscle tasks), *auditory figure-ground* or *discrimination disorder* (difficulty separating out competing sounds), *visual figure-ground disorder* (difficulty separating relevant visual stimuli), *visual closure disorder* (difficulty completing incomplete visual image), *auditory closure disorder* (listener unable to hear every spoken word said; unable to fill in gaps), *alexia* or *visual aphasia* or *word-blindness disorder* (confusion in letter recognition or symbol decoding, especially d, b and p, q, beyond normal developmental stages; involves reading of letters), *agraphia* or *dysgraphia* (confusion in letter recognition or symbol decoding, especially d, b and p, beyond normal developmental stages; involves writing letters), *perseveration disorder* (difficulty stopping a task when it is completed; trouble switching from one concept or task to next), or *left to right orientation disorder* (tendency to confuse right and left).

Developmental speech and language disorders, such as *developmental articulation disorder* (difficulty in articulation skills; may substitute or omit certain speech sounds), *developmental expressive language disorder* (difficulty in oral communication; may be mute, have difficulty learning new words, have a small vocabulary, or omit, substitute, or over-generalize words), *developmental receptive disorder* (difficulty in ability to understand others' speech), or *cluttering disorder* (speech is hurried, drops letters or syllables), sometimes are included in the classification or discussion of learning disorders (Clayton and Morrison 1992; NIMH 1993), as various receptive and expressive language difficulties may relate to specific neural processing problems and the resultant difficulties understanding certain aspects of speech may lead to academic difficulties. Communication disorders, including developmental speech and language disorders, are a separate category.

Causes

The exact causes of learning disabilities are not firmly established. Since learning disabilities manifest in so many different ways, they may have a variety of causes (APA 1994; DSM-V 2013; Gfeller 1992b; Mercer 1987; NIMH 1993). Current theories suggest that learning disabilities result from neurological processing dysfunctions caused by subtle disturbances in brain structures and functions. Recent research also suggests that "most learning disabilities do not stem from a single area of the brain, but from difficulties in bringing together information from various brain regions" (NIMH 1993, 10). Contributing causes to subtle disturbances in brain dysfunction may include (1) disruptions in fetal brain development occurring after the brain cells are becoming specialized and moving into place, resulting in errors in cell makeup, location, or connections; (2) genetic factors or heredity influences; (3) effects of maternal tobacco, alcohol, or other drug use during pregnancy on fetal brain development; (4) complications, trauma, or infections during pregnancy or delivery that may disrupt or alter fetal brain development; (5) environmental influences, such as toxins (e.g., cadmium and lead), allergic reactions to foods or additives, or radiation or chemotherapy treatment at an early age; and (6) acquired trauma after birth (DSM-V 2013; Mercer 1987; NIMH 1993). Although the impact of some of these factors can be diminished through medical intervention or nutritional and environmental changes, most conditions classified as learning disabilities cannot be cured, but rather must be managed (Gfeller 1992b; NIMH 1993). Learning disabilities usually are not outgrown, but most people are able to develop their personal strengths, adapt to them, and live fulfilling lives.

COMMON CHARACTERISTICS, PROBLEMS, AND NEEDS OF CLIENTS

As any population, learning-disabled individuals are a very heterogeneous group. Any individual client will have a unique combination of abilities, needs, personality traits, strengths, and weaknesses that will impact his or her treatment program and functioning level; therefore, it is unwise to attempt to predict a particular person's skill levels or maximal abilities based on broad generalizations about a certain population. Since learning-disabled clients' developmental patterns and subsequent behaviors are unique to each individual, it is especially difficult to make any generalizations about this condition. However, the neurological problems tend to lie in certain categories:

> Learning disabilities are neurologically based processing problems that affect a student's ability to access information (input), make sense of information (integration), store and retrieve information (memory), and communicate information back to others (output). (Adamek and Darrow 2010, 179)

In addition, the term "learning disabilities" is an umbrella classification for including a wide variety of specific learning problems. Each particular type of learning problem included under this general term has its own peculiar manifestations, which may or may not impact other areas. However, an awareness of some general characteristics, problems, and needs that may be found in many learning-disabled individuals may be beneficial both to the therapist who desires to work with this population and the reader who is learning how music therapy intervention strategies may benefit these individuals.

Most learning-disabled individuals have normal, near normal, or above average intelligence; however, they frequently have difficulty with intellectual achievement in school due to perceptual problems that make it difficult for them to select, retain, or process certain types of incoming sensory data (Atterbury 1990; Berry and Kirk 1980; Birkenshaw-Fleming 1993; Clayton and Morrison 1992; Gladfelter 1996; Hibben 1991; Mercer 1987; NIMH 1993; Zinar 1987).

These individuals often have jagged learning profiles, excelling in some areas but lagging far behind in others. Because developmental skills in reading, writing, speaking, listening, and math often overlap, individuals also may experience difficulties in more than one area (NIMH 1993). McCord and Fitzgerald (2006, 46) noted that "students with a learning disability that affects math learning are likely to struggle with reading music."

DSM-V (2013) lists these coding categories for Specific Learning Disability:

315.00 (F81.0) With impairment in reading
 Word reading accuracy
 Reading rate or fluency
 Reading comprehension
Note: *Dyslexia* is an alternative term referring to a pattern of learning difficulties characterized by problems with accurate or fluent word recognition, poor decoding, and poor spelling abilities. If dyslexia is used to specify this particular pattern of difficulties, it is important also to specify any additional difficulties that are present, such as difficulties with reading comprehension or math reasoning.

Colwell and Murlless (2002) examined the reading accuracy of learning-disabled children. Chanting and singing conditions were compared with regular reading conditions, which included sign language as a visual prompt. Accuracy while reading improved in all three conditions. According to Dehaene (2009, 2), "Surveys indicate that about one adult in ten fails to master even the rudiments of text comprehension." Shaywitz et al. (2002) reported that 5 to 17 percent of children in the United States suffer from dyslexia. It seems to have a genetic component, since it runs in families (Dehaene 2009). McCord and Fitzgerald (2006) reported a relationship between math and music reading:

315.1 (F81.2) With impairment in mathematics:
 Number sense
 Memorization of arithmetic facts
 Accurate or fluent calculation
 Accurate math reasoning
Note: Dyscalculia is an alternative term used to refer to a pattern of difficulties characterized by problems processing numerical information, learning arithmetic facts, and performing accurate or fluent calculations. If dyscalculia is used to specify this particular pattern of mathematic difficulties, it is important also to specify any additional difficulties that are present, such as difficulties with math reasoning or word reasoning accuracy. (67) (DSM-V 2013, 67)

An initial diagnosis of learning disabilities is not the music therapist's job. However, the therapist should be aware of this information before planning or executing music therapy sessions for this population. It should be in the child's IEP, and the special educator can further clarify the problem(s).

Learning-disabled individuals may feel bombarded by sights and sounds and be unable to focus their attention. They may try to read or add, but be unable to make sense of the letters or numbers. They may have important ideas or needs to express, but be unable to communicate them. These experiences can lead to a cycle of failure, frustration, and lowered self-esteem (NIMH 1993), which may lead to additional social and emotional problems or maladaptive behaviors (Berry and Kirk 1980; Mercer 1987; Pavlicek 2014; Smith and Neisworth 1975). Determination of the area or areas in which a particular individual's problems lie will help provide a framework for understanding that individual's particular strengths and weaknesses and suggest strategies for maximizing strengths and working around weaknesses.

The difficulties with information processing common to learning-disabled individuals may manifest in several ways (APA 1994; Atterbury 1990; Berry and Kirk 1980; Birkenshaw-Fleming 1993; Clayton and Morrison 1992; Hibben 1991; Mercer 1987; NIMH 1993; Nocera 1979; Smith and Neisworth 1975; Zinar 1987). Some of the more common manifestations include difficulties in selective attention (attending to or isolating visual and auditory information), sequencing, or symbol recognition; difficulties with spatial relationships, quantity perception, or time perception; difficulties in performing perceptual motor skills; difficulties in integrating visual and auditory input or output; difficulties in verbal expression or in understanding others; difficulties in mental organization, strategies, and pattern recognition; problems with memory or conceptual thinking; and general orientation and laterality problems. Other associated features may include hyperactivity, emotional lability, impulsivity, poor social skills, and difficulty listening to others or accepting authority; difficulty helping others or cooperating with others, difficulty expressing feelings or ideas; negative self-attitude or low self-esteem, demoralization; and feelings of failure, stress, and frustration. Although not all or even most of these behaviors and characteristics are found in every learning-disabled individual, one must recognize that any of these factors may be present and may contribute in some way to the individual's various academic or learning difficulties. Careful observation and testing are vital for determination of the areas in which a particular client's deficits lie, so programs of training and intervention can be matched to his or her particular needs. Music therapy can address many of these problems. With carefully planned musical tasks, it is possible for the learning-disabled student to be included in music groups in inclusive classes, as well as in small groups designed to address specific problems.

Learning disabilities usually are first diagnosed during the school years when teachers notice a child's persistent difficulties in reading, writing, or arithmetic that seem out of character for his or her level of ability and intelligence. Hock et al. (2009) reported that more than eight million adolescents have not mastered the reading skills required to successfully meet the requirements of secondary school or the workplace. After visual or hearing problems and inadequate instruction or opportunity are eliminated as causes for the child's difficulties, specific tests are used to pinpoint the exact nature of the individual's skill gaps. Appropriate educational plans and medical and psychosocial support systems can greatly reduce the impact of learning disabilities (Gfeller 1992b; NIMH 1993). Since learning disabilities can affect the individual and his or her family in many ways, support and specific plans for controlling or working around the learning disability may be needed in educational, medical, social, emotional, and practical areas. Adamek and Darrow (2008, 416) provide a useful list of Adaptive Strategies for use with disabled students. Many would be of value to music therapists working with learning-disabled persons.

Although learning disabilities usually are thought of in association with children, they may occur in adults, too (APA 1994; Berman 1982; Gfeller 1992b; Mercer 1987; NIMH 1993; Schulman 1986). Many adults who have mild forms of learning disabilities, such as mild dyslexia, have grown up without needed help. Consequently, they now may take twice as long as an average person to master certain tasks. Problems associated with learning disabilities may cause adults to have difficulties in the areas of employment, higher education, leisure activities, and social relationships (APA 1994; Dworkis 1994; Mercer 1987; NIMH 1993; Schulman 1986). Fortunately, recognition of learning disabilities in adults is increasing; and, once diagnosed, many special aids can be used to help remediate or bypass the problem. In addition to self-help sessions, specialized college programs are now available for learning-disabled adults (Berman 1982; NIMH 1993; Schulman 1986). Equal employment opportunities for learning-disabled individuals are mandated by the Americans with Disabilities Act of 1990, and state departments of vocational rehabilitation have many programs available to assist them in receiving training and counseling, and special equipment to help them sidestep their disability (NIMH 1993).

Learning disabilities are not a disease; they result from deficits in some aspect of information processing. They may be single or overlapping; they may affect only part of a person's routine or impact several aspects of school or work, family life, or social and leisure activities. Although learning disabilities usually cannot be cured, with proper identification of problem areas, appropriately structured programs of training and education, and adequate social, emotional, medical, and practical support, their negative effects on a person's life can be greatly diminished. Adults as well as children can benefit from appropriate programs specially designed to help them maximize their strengths and work around their areas of weakness. Most people, given appropriate supports and opportunities, can learn to adapt and lead fulfilling and productive lives.

SETTINGS FOR SERVICE DELIVERY

Learning-disabled individuals may receive special programs to help meet their specific needs in varied settings (NIMH 1993). The Individuals with Disabilities Act (IDEA) (Public Law 101-476), which is the 1990 revision of the 1975 Education for All Handicapped Children Act (Public Law 94-142), assures a free, appropriate public education to all disabled children, aged 3–21 years, including those who are diagnosed with learning disabilities. This law, as well as the Technology-Related Assistance for Individuals with Disabilities Act (Public Law 100-407), also provides for necessary assistive technology devices and services (Adamek 1996; Johnson, 1996). Millard (2007, 63) found that portable music players, like the video iPod, MP3 players, and hand-held computers, like the Palm Tungsten, are useful tools with children: "For the majority of these students, behavioral challenges and learning disabilities have often led to absenteeism and low grades, but using the iPods has instilled in them a fresh sense of enthusiasm." This technology could be highly useful in music therapy.

When IEP assessments find that music therapy can provide a unique means of helping students achieve their educational objectives, music therapists may be called upon to work with students in self-contained classes or in inclusive classes. In addition, they may provide direct in-home services to students confined to their homes for medical reasons, and/or provide consultation services or conduct staff development workshops to facilitate classroom instruction, inclusion, or music education (Wilson 1996; Montgomery and Martinson 2006). Music therapy usually is classified as a related service in special education settings.

Learning-disabled students usually spend as much of the school day as possible with normal peers in a regular classroom and attend special education classes or therapy sessions for several hours a week as needed. Severely disabled students may need instruction in separate all-day classrooms or in special schools for the learning disabled. Some parents choose to go outside the public school system, arranging for their child to work with trained tutors or therapists after school. Fitzgerald (2006, 40) noted that "parental involvement, particularly in a music program, is the key to success for many students."

Programs to assist learning-disabled adults continue to increase as the lifelong nature of most learning disabilities becomes more evident. Colleges and universities often have special programs that may include specific testing to determine areas of need and the development of strategies to help students maximize strengths while working around their areas of deficits. Special programs and help are available in many forms, and may include alternate provisions such as recorded books and lectures, allowing the student to record rather than write reports, or allowing the student to take tests orally or in rooms free from distraction. The American Council on Education provides a national clearing house on post secondary resources for people with learning disabilities (NIMH 1993).

Individuals with learning disabilities are also served by state departments of vocational rehabilitation (NIMH 1993) that can refer adults to counseling, health care, and high school equivalence programs. They also can help learning-disabled individuals identify areas of aptitude and assist in arranging for job training that sidesteps the individual's disabilities. In addition, these agencies can help individuals find special equipment (e.g., a special computer that reads books aloud) that enables them to receive training, retain jobs, or live independently.

Music therapists may work with both children and adults who have learning disabilities. They deliver services to these clients in many different settings, including public schools, private schools or clinics, music studios, or community programs. Music therapists may provide direct or consultant services and work with clients as individuals or in groups.

HOW MUSIC IS USED IN THERAPY

Since learning disabilities have many different manifestations, music therapy intervention strategies must be structured to recognize each client's unique strengths, weaknesses, and needs. Some approaches and techniques that are very effective with certain learning-disabled clients will be totally ineffective with others: "There is no standard method or approach deemed effective for all students with learning disabilities" (Gfeller 1992b, 201). Nevertheless, "many students . . . excel in music, since the information typically is presented through auditory, visual, and kinesthetic means."

Music therapy intervention strategies for learning-disabled clients may incorporate strict behavioral approaches or more client-centered or developmental approaches. Experiences may include various modes of music involvement, such as singing, listening, playing instruments, moving to music, notating music, reading music, and creating music, used alone or in combination. Specific music education approaches, such as Orff-Schulwerk and Dalcroze eurhythmics, have also been adapted for use in therapy with learning-disabled individuals (Hibben 1991). Madsen (2004) found that illustrations representing the lyrics offered valuable clues that allowed children to transition from the picture that illustrated the lyrics to the written words.

Various music therapy experiences may help learning-disabled individuals develop strengths, work around specific disabilities, and address associated problems such as low self-esteem, poor behavior control, poor social skills, attention deficits, poor listening skills, and low frustration tolerance. Denton and Vaughn (2008) reported that failure to learn to read and write leads to lack of motivation for older students. This finding was also noted by the National Joint Committee on Learning Disabilities (2008). Using song lyrics to improve decoding skills of SLD adolescents, Hines (2010, 21) found that "this is a promising technique of adolescents with disabilities who need remedial decoding instruction but who may have lost the motivation to engage in more traditional instructional practices due to repeated failures." Successful experiences with music can motivate and increase participation in the group activity.

Some music experiences can provide an alternate means of receiving, processing, or rehearsing information as well as affording alternate modes of expression. Jensen (2005) indicated that presentation through music, with its rhythms, contrasts, and patterns of information, may assist the brain in encoding new information. Music also may help an individual focus attention and motivate him or her to concentrate on or practice difficult movements, exercises, or concepts. For some individuals, music may be used as part of a behavioral program employing operant conditioning to provide unique rewards or reinforcements for academic learning or behavior control. In addition, the very structure of music experiences can facilitate behavior control and promote group cooperation, while success in music activities can lead to increased feelings of self-worth and self-esteem.

In general, music therapy programs and intervention strategies for learning-disabled individuals focus on one or more of the following areas (Atterbury 1990; Birkenshaw-Fleming 1993; Gfeller 1984, 1992b; Gladfelter 1996; Hanser 1987; Hibben 1991; Nocera 1979; Phipps 1975; Rink 1989; Sandbank 1989a; Steele 1984; Welsbacher 1975; Zinar 1987): (1) developing behavior control and increasing attention span; (2) improving visual and auditory skills, including perception, discrimination, memory, sequencing, and integration; (3) improving motor control and coordination; (4) supporting academic learning; (5) improving communication skills; (6) promoting social and emotional growth and development; and (7) supporting music education and assisting in leisure skill development.

Music Therapy Experiences Help Develop Behavior Control and Increase Attention Span

Behavior management often becomes a primary focus in early music therapy sessions with learning-disabled individuals because behavior control is necessary for learning and skill development to occur. The strong attention-attracting qualities of music, combined with its order and structure and its ability to function as a powerful reinforcer (Lathom 1981b; Lathom-Radocy 2014), can make music therapy sessions an ideal setting for developing impulse control and increasing on-task behavior in learning-disabled clients. For example, since music is often an enjoyable activity, various individual or group music experiences (e.g., listening to preferred music, taking music lessons, being able to participate in a music group) can be used within behavioral programs employing operant conditioning procedures to provide unique rewards or reinforcements for be-havior control (Gfeller 1992b). Through careful assessment, the music therapist can determine just what type of music activities or experiences are motivating or reinforcing to a particular individual, and then use these in devising a con-tingent music program to reinforce the desired response. The therapist must specify exactly what behaviors or responses will be reinforced. It is essential that the student clearly understand what specific behavior (e.g., remaining quiet until called upon, in-seat behavior, or both) is required to earn the music reward. Colwell and Murlless (2002) found increased on-task behavior during the music conditions compared with the reading instruction classes. However, "there seemed to be an inconsistent relationship between reading accuracy and on-task behavior" (17).

Music therapists frequently structure their treatment programs so that the music task's difficulty level and amount of structure complements the level of attention and behavioral control expected at each stage of the music therapy process (Hibben 1991; Steele 1984). For example, in early stages of the program, experiences are highly structured and geared for instant success, with all deci-sions being made by the therapist. As clients develop skills in attending and impulse control, they are given more opportunities to work independently or with partners and make some decisions about activities. They also may have to practice or rehearse music tasks before achieving success. In later stages, individuals are given more creative freedom in developing musical perfor-mances and may work in teams and make group decisions, with the therapist providing only indirect supervision. Thus, music experiences that are carefully structured to demand increased levels of attention and independence can help individuals learn to control and manage their own behavior by providing (1) a novel stimulus to attract attention, (2) structure and boundaries for activity, (3) reinforcement for cooperative, attentive behaviors, and (4) a pleasurable, successful experience.

As individuals gain more control over impulsive behaviors, they can more readily focus on selected tasks and activities that will help them gain skills in many areas. Initially, techniques like singing instead of speaking commands, using props (puppets, pictures, hoops, scarves) to complement songs or move-ments, and using instruments like drums and metallophones may help attract the attention of individuals with learning disabilities and help them enter into the song or activity (Birkenshaw-Fleming 1993). The music therapist starts with short experiences and gradually increases the length of the experience as the individual's ability to attend increases. By presenting materials in a highly structured manner, with clear objectives and careful step-by-step directions, and by having different modes of sensory input and response readily available, the therapist can increase the successful participation of learning-disabled indi-viduals (Atterbury 1990; Birkenshaw-Fleming 1993; Nocera 1979; Zinar 1987).

Many different types of music experiences help learning-disabled individuals increase their attention spans. For example, music listening activities that require clients to attend to, order, and remember auditory stimuli can help develop listening skills and concentration abilities. Music therapists can help clients focus their attention by asking them to listen for specific things in songs or recordings. Initial experiences are kept very short so that they stay within the clients' limited attention spans. Later, activities are gradually lengthened as the clients' listening and attending skills increase.

Instrumental activities requiring clients to wait for their turn to play or to play only at a certain point in the song also help develop attention span. Again, individuals will be asked to wait only a short time at first, with the waiting time gradually being increased as self-control and attention span develop. For example, a client might first be asked to wait until one other person has played the drum with a song before he takes a turn. Later, that client might be asked to wait for three or four others to play before getting a turn. Or the individual might be given the cymbal part to play in an ensemble, but have to follow a chart or conductor to play only at specified times.

Performing actions to songs can also help clients to focus on activities and increase attention to a specified task. If a song has a spot for a particular loud clap or certain rhythmic pattern (e.g., hands clapping together like the snap of an alligator's jaws or the rhythmic clapping pattern of the children's song "B-I-N-G-O"), the client must also listen to others so he or she will perform the action with the rest of the group at the appropriate time. This takes self-control and attention to task, but most will recognize how much better the song sounds when everyone performs the action together. Recording performances may assist individuals in monitoring their performance and finding ways to improve.

Music Therapy Experiences Improve
Auditory and Visual Skills

Since music is an auditory phenomenon, it seems natural to use music to help individuals improve their auditory perception and discrimination skills. Individuals with learning disabilities involving deficits in auditory perception or processing need to learn what to listen for, how to listen for it, and how to attach meaning to what they hear (Phipps 1975). Those who have difficulties with auditory memory and sequencing skills also may have problems remembering the series of tones in a melody or the sequences of words in song lyrics. The many simultaneous sounds in music may be confusing (Welsbacher 1975; Zinar 1987).

The music therapist can help individuals with deficits in auditory perception improve their skills by using experiences that direct their attention to specific sounds or sound characteristics. Visual aids and motor activities may facilitate learning. For example, individuals might be asked to bend low when they hear low pitches and stretch high when they hear high pitches. They also might move their hands or bodies up and down to indicate the rise and fall of pitches in a familiar melody or trace the contour of a notated melody with their finger or pencil. Music therapists also use activities employing contrasts in volume, tempo, timbre, and pitch level to help clients develop auditory awareness and auditory discrimination skills. This method is used in Auditory Perception Training (APT), which integrates different sensory modalities (visual, tactile, and kinesthetic) with sound discrimination (Thaut 2008, 196). In addition, songs and musical games that associate sounds with actions, commands, or objects may help clients learn to perceive and respond to auditory cues. For example, the music therapist might have clients play a game where they are asked to turn around when they hear a bell, walk when they hear a drumbeat, tiptoe when they hear a maraca, etc.

Rhythm pattern echo activities are also useful in developing auditory discrimination and auditory memory, but motor coordination problems may limit the ability of some learning-disabled individuals to perform rhythmic patterns (Gilbert 1983). Adding spoken rhythmic syllables or words to the rhythmic patterns may help some individuals reproduce the rhythmic patterns more easily (Atterbury 1983a; Zinar 1987). In addition, singing can improve auditory awareness and enhance memory training (Gladfelter 1996).

Regarding visual perception, it is important to remember that learning-disabled individuals with specific problems in distinguishing letters and numbers also may have difficulty distinguishing musical symbols. These individuals need special instructional methods that include multisensory activities and mnemonic devices to assist them in making sense of the visual symbols (Zinar 1987). Since learning symbols in music means not only learning a written sign but also learning to clap, sing, play, hear, and move in response to the symbol, music experiences may be particularly well suited to the type of multisensory instruction that will assist these individuals in refining their visual perception abilities by learning through complementary aural and motor activities that increase attention and aid learning by taking advantage of abilities they do have (Zinar 1987). Specific techniques may include special instruction in distinguishing notes and rests using mnemonic devices or aural and movement aids, using chants when practicing writing symbols, giving aural as well as visual instructions or examples, and showing symbols in different ways (e.g., felt or plastic models that can be manipulated). As individuals learn to correctly distinguish and identify letters, numbers, notations, and other symbols within the context of music experience, they simultaneously improve their visual perception, discrimination, and memory skills (Gladfelter 1996). Learning behaviors in music experiences that parallel skills needed in other areas also may help individuals master skills and then transfer them to other areas. For example, visual tracking skills required to read written music and then play it on a keyboard are similar to the left-to-right eye movement used in reading words. The motivation to produce music may help the individual succeed in learning this skill in a musical context and then transfer it to the correlated reading skill (Hanser 1987).

Music Therapy Experiences Support Academic Learning

Music therapy activities and experiences support academic learning in many ways. Various musical activities may be structured to allow learning-disabled individuals another means and modality in which to practice and demonstrate skills and basic cognitive concepts such as object classification, seriation, and spatial and temporal relationships (Gfeller 1984, 1992b). For example, Roskam (1979) found that music therapy activities requiring clients to match, sort, group, reproduce, and associate pitches, loudness levels, rhythm patterns, and tone qualities, used alone and in combination with language development activities, could help learning-disabled children improve their verbal skills and nonverbal auditory awareness, reading word recognition, and spelling. Musical instruments of varied shapes and sizes demonstrate different representations of the concepts of large/small and square/rectangle/circle/triangle, while music of different tempos can help illustrate concepts of fast and slow (Gfeller 1992b). In addition, songs requiring clients to hold up, point to, match, or identify various shapes, colors, numbers, etc., can help clients practice these skills. Instruments or pitches on a xylophone or piano can also be given color, letter, number, or shape codes which the clients must match to a chart to play a certain tune (Lathom-Radocy 2014).

Music, especially in the form of songs or rhythmic chants, can be used as a carrier of information to help learning-disabled individuals learn and retain certain academic information like grammar rules and multiplication tables (Gfeller 1983, 1992b; Gladfelter 1996; Zinar 1987). Shehan (1981) found that combining auditory and visual modes enhanced short-term memory of word pairs for learning-disabled children. These results may indicate that music activities employing visual aids could help some learning-disabled individuals learn to synthesize and integrate stimuli from two sensory modalities. Adamek and Darrow (2010) discuss sensory integration, especially for children with dyspraxia. Activities that require clients to connect visual symbols with the auditory stimulus of music have the additional benefit of giving clients opportunities to gain facility in decoding symbols and using symbols to process information. To maximize the benefits of music as a carrier of academic information, the music therapist will (1) structure the information to be learned into well-organized units to facilitate recall through "chunking," (2) pair the information with a familiar melody to assist memory processes and facilitate recall, and (3) use the novel presentation of information in musical jingles or rhythmic chants to increase motivation and attending (Gfeller 1983, 1992b). Adamek and Darrow (2010), and Adamek and Darrow (2008), also note the importance of working with the rest of the special education team to write appropriate IEP goals and determine the best procedures.

Music experiences can reinforce academic learning and reward the completion of academic tasks. Students who have short attention spans and poor ability to concentrate and focus on tasks (Gfeller 1992b) may be motivated to complete academic tasks accurately if this behavior is rewarded by a preferred music activity (e.g., listening to preferred music, taking music lessons, being able to participate in a music group). Through careful assessment, the music therapist can determine just what music activities or experiences motivate a particular individual and reinforce learning. When using music in this way, therapists must specify exactly what responses are to be reinforced. For example, reinforcing in-seat behavior will not necessarily increase the quality of academic work. Therefore, if using music is to improve academic outcomes, the therapist must link the music reward clearly to these outcomes, not just to good behavior (Gfeller 1992b).

Music Therapy Experiences Improve Communication Skills

Some learning-disabled individuals have communication difficulties due to difficulties in understanding or processing auditory or visual information or in oral and/or written expression. For many of these individuals, music can provide a nonthreatening or less threatening means of communication and speech and language development (Birkenshaw-Fleming 1993; Gladfelter 1996; Phipps 1975; Zinar 1987). Choruses and glee clubs can be a very valuable part of programs for learning-disabled individuals, for singing "assists in the sequencing of verbal ideas, reinforces sight vocabulary, enhances pronunciation, modifies speech behaviors, improves auditory awareness, and involves memory training" (Gladfelter 1996, 187). Songs, rhythmic chants, and musical games can help develop vocal fluidity, increase vocabulary, and improve enunciation. Learning to play simple wind instruments like recorders or harmonicas may also help individuals develop increased oral muscular coordination necessary for clear speech, while composition and improvisation experiences may help individuals gain confidence in their expressive skills. In addition, successful participation in verbal (e.g., singing, chanting, lyric writing) and nonverbal (e.g., instrumental performance or improvisation, creative movement to music) expressive experiences of music can do much to bolster self-confidence and enhance self-esteem. Furman and Humpal (2006, 90–93) provide examples of communication goals and objectives.

Music Therapy Experiences Promote Social and Emotional Growth and Development

Research suggests that learning-disabled individuals often have poorer social skills than do their nondisabled peers (Gresham and Reschly 1986). Jellison and Draper (2015) indicate that learning disabilities are underrepresented in music research. Since music therapy can address development of improved social skills, there is a need for more research with this population. Behaviors such as not listening to others, not accepting authority, not helping or cooperating with others, not expressing feelings, or using an inappropriate tone of voice often lead to poor teacher and peer acceptance (Atterbury 1990). Constant failure and frustration in academic work also can diminish learning-disabled individuals' feelings of self-worth and self-esteem.

Well-structured music groups can give all individuals, learning disabled and nondisabled alike, a chance to participate successfully in positive musical experiences. As a class becomes involved in producing and processing musical events, direct experiences with affective material may replace a focus on cognitive demands (Atterbury 1990). Structured music groups also create motivating environments in which individuals see appropriate behavior modeled by the therapist and learn to integrate these behaviors into interpersonal interactions (Gfeller 1992b; Gladfelter 1996; Hibben 1991; Lathom-Radocy 2014; Steele 1984). In addition, music therapy groups can enable individuals to integrate abilities and skills they work on separately in other classes or therapies and provide an opportunity to practice and use these skills in a normal social setting (Sandbank 1989a).

Various music therapy experiences incorporating listening, movement, improvisation, lyric analysis, composition, and song writing activities can help individuals who have difficulty with emotional expression learn to experience and express emotions appropriately. These experiences also can be structured to afford them opportunities to practice group cooperation and problem-solving skills (Gfeller 1984, 1992b; Hibben 1991). For example, Gladfelter (1996) used chorus and instrumental ensemble experiences to help learning-disabled students develop social skills, learn to function successfully as part of a large group, develop poise and self-confidence, develop the skills needed to cooperate with others in producing a pleasing musical product, and increase self-esteem through successful experiences. As Nocera (1979) observed, social and emotional benefits of music experiences can be of utmost value to learning-disabled individuals who have learning disabilities and even serve to enhance their success in other areas.

Music Therapy Can Support Music Education and Help Develop Leisure Skills

In public school settings, learning-disabled students are often mainstreamed or included with their same-aged peers in regular music classes (Atterbury 1990; Gfeller 1992b). However, because of the processing and perceptual difficulties associated with their particular learning disability, these students may need special adaptations or compensatory teaching strategies so they can benefit from and participate successfully in music instruction or classroom music activities. Music therapists, who are trained in working with the special needs of students with specific learning disabilities as well as in music techniques, may work with music educators to help them adapt activities or instructional methods to the student's unique learning (Atterbury 1990; Birkenshaw-Fleming 1993; Gfeller 1992b; Gladfelter 1996; Nocera 1979; Phipps 1975; Welsbacher 1975; Zinar 1987). For example, some students will need special aids to help them focus on the appropriate material, while others may need extra time or practice to be able to perform rhythm patterns. Those who have reading or language problems may need special adaptations when reading from songbooks or workbooks or when receiving instructions from the teacher:

> Adaptations are any adjustment in the environment, instruction, or materials for learning that enhances the student's performance and allows for at least partial participation. Adaptations should be made for individual students based on their specific learning needs and should be based on their abilities as well as their limiltations. (Adamek and Darrow 2010, 65)

In some situations, learning-disabled students may receive special instruction from music therapists to help them develop skills necessary to succeed in mainstreamed or inclusive settings (Gfeller 1992b; Krout 1986a).

As more and more adults are learning to play musical instruments, music therapists can provide valuable assistance to studio teachers or music store instructors who may find themselves working with learning-disabled adults. Music therapists might conceivably work with college or vocational programs that serve learning-disabled adults and develop a private practice to provide adaptive music instruction. Learning to play a musical instrument can enhance a person's self-esteem and self-confidence and also provide an enjoyable leisure activity which can be useful for stress reduction and as a means of personal expression. In addition, developing an interest or skill in music can lead to new opportunities for that person to interact with others through concerts, music appreciation or adult enrichment classes, community performance groups, and the like.

SPECIAL CONSIDERATIONS AND TIPS FOR SUCCESS

Learning-disabled individuals usually function best within an organized, structured environment. The music therapist should always remember to plan activities in a way that minimizes distractions. Moreover, "consistency, firmness, warmth, and acceptance on the part of the teacher [or therapist] play a major role in directing successful learning experiences" (Phipps 1975, 130).

Learning-disabled individuals will benefit most from an active music program that utilizes a multisensory approach to learning and engages several skills and senses in presenting or rehearsing any one concept (Atterbury 1990; Birkenshaw-Fleming 1993; Gladfelter 1996; NIMH 1993; Zinar 1987). By incorporating many modes of presentation and providing for many modes of responses, the music therapist most likely will find ways that teach to the individual's strengths and work around his or her areas of weakness. For example, individuals with difficulties in visual perception may be encouraged to use their auditory, oral, kinesthetic or tactile abilities or modes of expression, while individuals who have poor auditory memory skills might benefit from visual aids or movement cues.

When giving directions, the therapist should use a few carefully chosen words and speak in short sentences. Directions should be concrete and specific, and repeated exactly the same way each time they are given. Simple tactile or visual aids may help reinforce concepts. One must be extremely careful when using commercially available visual aids because some music books and seemingly attractive posters or charts may contain so much information that they cause visual overload for learning-disabled individuals. Adaptive devices, like frames, color cues, and arrows, can be used to help clients screen out extraneous information and focus on the information they need (Atterbury 1983b, 1990; Birkenshaw-Fleming 1993; Gladfelter 1996; Nocera 1979; Zinar 1987). In addition, specially adapted instructions may help individuals with specific learning disabilities learn music skills more easily. For example, Denckla (1990) found that a dyslexic individual learned piano more easily if the correspondence of the "music map" to the instrument was constantly emphasized and if he proceeded directly to the auditory and kinesthetic experience without worrying about naming the notes.

Because of their perceptual difficulties, learning-disabled individuals often need extra time to process and respond to information. Therefore, it may be necessary to adapt imitation, echo, and call-and-response activities by adding extra beats of rest or measures of instrumental accompaniment so the clients have adequate time to process the auditory information given before they are expected to respond (Atterbury 1986). At times, it also may be necessary to be ready to provide clients with alternative response modes (e.g., "show me" instead of "tell me"). Furthermore, some common music activities may be too "busy" for perceptually handicapped clients who have difficulty processing auditory stimuli and attending to more than one thing at a time. In order to provide successful experiences for learning-disabled clients, the music therapist may have to simplify these activities by limiting the number of accompanying rhythm patterns or limiting the number of actions requested to be performed (Atterbury 1990; Birkenshaw-Fleming 1993; Nocera 1979; Zinar 1987). It may be beneficial to have individuals practice movement patterns separately before applying them to instruments and to practice the sub-skills associated with a complex skill or movement (Gilbert 1983; Rink 1989). In addition, adding spoken rhythmic syllables or words to rhythmic patterns may help some learning-disabled individuals be able to reproduce rhythmic patterns more easily (Atterbury 1983a; Zinar 1987). Gladfelter (1996, 197–199) provides many additional practical suggestions for working in a music environment with learning-disabled students.

In the instruction of learning-disabled individuals, "manner of presentation is as important as content" (Gfeller 1992b, 202). Therefore, music therapists must be familiar with special teaching methods designed for the learning disabled and create approaches and intervention strategies in close consultation with the special education team, while considering the unique manifestations of a specific learning disability in the particular individual (Gfeller 1992b; Gladfelter 1996). It is also important for the therapist to practice good social skills and desired behaviors, such as taking care of equipment, using appropriate language, treating others with respect, obeying rules, etc., so that individuals in the group will see appropriate behavior and have a good model to imitate.

QUESTIONS FOR THOUGHT AND DISCUSSION

1. Discuss some of the special characteristics and needs of learning-disabled individuals. What implications do these have for music therapy programming?
2. Why and how are music experiences useful for helping learning-disabled individuals reach therapeutic goals? Are some types of experiences and activities more useful than others? Which ones? Why?
3. Describe some specific music therapy experiences that might be used to help learning-disabled individuals (a) develop behavior control and increase attention span, (b) improve auditory and visual skills, (c) improve motor control and coordination, (d) increase and practice academic skills, (e) improve communication skills, (f) increase social skills and enhance emotional growth and development, and (g) develop music and leisure skills. What special adaptations might you have to make in choice of music, instruments, mode of expression, etc., to fit these to the unique needs and preferences

of specific clients?

4. List several special considerations that are important to remember when developing therapeutic intervention strategies for learning-disabled persons. Why are these important? What are their implications for the structure of music therapy intervention strategies?

5. For each of the situations listed below, (a) define the problem or areas of need for the client or group of clients, (b) describe one or more of the goals you might pursue in music therapy sessions with the client(s), (c) describe music activities you might use to help the client(s) meet those goals, (d) tell how the music activities you described relate to the goals and needs of the client(s), and mention any special considerations you might want to take into account when working with the client(s).

Situation 1:

You have been asked to begin music therapy sessions for a group of eight learning-disabled children, aged 9–11 years. These children are easily distracted and have short attention spans. They have trouble organizing auditory perceptions due to poor auditory discrimination, memory, and sequencing skills. They also have a poor sense of spatial orientation and find it difficult to use symbols to process information.

Situation 2:

A 32-year-old man with dyslexia, poor concentration, poor spatial awareness, and poor motor coordination has come to you inquiring about piano lessons. He says he has always wanted to learn to play the piano, but never thought he could because of his learning problems. He recently heard that music therapists know how to teach music to people with special needs, and he wants to know if you could help him, too.

SUGGESTIONS FOR FURTHER READING

Adamek, M. S. & Darrow, A-A. (2010). *Music in special education.* Silver Spring, MD: The American Music Therapy Association.

Adamek, M. & Darrow, A-A. (2008). Music therapy in special education. In W. B. Davis, K. E. Gfeller, & M. H. Thaut (Eds.), *An introduction to music therapy theory and practice* (3rd ed.) (405–426). Silver Spring, MD: The American Music Therapy Association, Inc.

Bernstorf, E. D. & Welsbacher, B. T. (1996). Helping students in the inclusive classroom. *Music Educators Journal, 82*(5), 21–29.

Gladfelter, N. D. (1996). Music therapy for learners with learning disabilities in a private day school. In B. L. Wilson (Ed.), *Models of music therapy interventions in school settings: From institution to inclusion* (184–199). Silver Spring, MD: National

Association for Music Therapy.

Goodman, K. D. (2007). *Music therapy groupwork with special needs children.* Springfield, IL: Charles C Thomas.

National Institute of Mental Health (NIMH) (1993). *Learning disabilities.* Washington, DC: US Government Printing Office.

Chapter Nine

MUSIC THERAPY FOR HEARING IMPAIRED INDIVIDUALS

Definitions

Hearing impairment is a general term that includes all the different types and severities of hearing losses. This population includes individuals of any age who are *deaf*, deafened, hard-of-hearing, or partially hearing. People who are deaf have hearing impairments so severe that they cannot understand or process speech through their auditory sense, even with the assistance of hearing aids or fine amplification systems. For deaf individuals, the sense of hearing is nonfunctional for the ordinary purposes and activities of daily life; sounds, including speech, have no meaning or function for their daily activities. For these individuals, sounds are not processed auditorily but experienced as vibrations perceived tactilely by the skin and felt in the bones and body cavities (Zinar 1987). Individuals acquiring this degree of severe hearing impairment after they have acquired speech, may be classified as *deafened* rather than deaf.

Hard-of-hearing or *partially hearing* people have some degree of hearing loss but still have enough functional hearing to understand speech and process language through their auditory sense, with or without the aid of amplification systems. Although these individuals have some defect in their sense of hearing, they can obtain enough functional meaning from sounds that they can use their auditory sense for ordinary life purposes and activities. Usually, these individuals use some type of hearing aid.

Classification of Hearing Loss

Hearing losses may range in degree and severity from very slight to very extreme. Generally, the more severe the hearing impairment, the greater impact it has on the development of language and other communication skills (Bauch 2014; Gfeller 1992d). However, total deafness is very rare. By most estimates, at least 90 percent of individuals who have hearing impairments have some sensitivity to sound and some degree of usable or residual hearing (Boothroyd 1980; Gfeller 1992d; Matthias 1989; Zinar 1987).

Hearing impairments generally are classified by degree of decibel (dB) loss as *slight* (27–40 dB loss), *mild* (41–55 dB loss), *moderate* (56–70 dB loss), *severe* (71–90 dB loss), or *profound* (greater than 90 dB loss) (Darrow and Gfeller 1988, 1996; Darrow and Schunk 1996; Gfeller 1992d; Smith and Neisworth 1975). The amount of hearing loss greatly influences the individual's ability to participate in conversation and develop or maintain language and communication skills (Darrow and Gfeller 1988, 1996; Darrow and Schunk 1996; Gfeller 1992d; Gfeller and Darrow 2008). For example, individuals with *mild* hearing losses can usually understand normal conversational speech at a distance of three to five feet; however, they may miss as much as half of the conversation if they are unable to see the speaker or if the speaker's voice is soft. Individuals with mild hearing losses also may have some speech abnormalities or a limited vocabulary. While individuals who have mild losses usually only have problems hearing faint or distant speech, those who have *moderate* losses often have difficulty understanding even loud speech. Individuals with moderate hearing losses also frequently wear hearing aids and are likely to have some difficulties in speaking and participating in group discussions. Individuals who have *severe* hearing losses can only hear loud speech that is within one foot of their ears and usually have marked deficits in speech and language abilities. However, these individuals can still distinguish pitch, intensity, and tone color in music if the sounds are louder than 70 to 85 dB. In contrast, those persons who have *profound* hearing losses tend to be aware of vibrations more than tonal patterns and rely on vision rather than hearing as their primary means of communication.

Hearing losses also may be classified by time of onset. If an individual's hearing loss is present at birth, he or she has a *congenital* hearing loss. If the child is born in a hospital, hearing is tested by two types of screening before the infant leaves the hospital: The Auditory Brain Stem Response (ABR) tests for neural hearing ability, and the Transient Evoked Otoacoustic Emissions Test (TEOAE) tests for otoacoustic emission (OAE) in the cochlea. Cassidy and Ditty (2001) noted a gender difference, with female infants showing an advantage. This is important if music therapy is used in hospitals with newborns. The Mayo Clinic (Bauch 2014, 32) reported that hearing loss is found in 12,000 children each year, which makes it the most common birth defect. Hearing loss occurring after birth is called an *adventitious* or *acquired* hearing loss. In addition, the relationship of the onset of hearing loss to the individual's stage of language development may be considered. A hearing loss occurring before the individual acquires or develops speech and language skills is called a *prelingual* hearing loss. Hearing losses that occur after the individual acquires language are termed *postlingual* hearing losses. Generally, an individual will have greater speech and language deficits with a prelingual hearing loss than with a postlingual loss (Bauch 2014; Gfeller 1992d; Gfeller and Darrow 2008).

Types of Hearing Loss

There are two main dimensions to the sense of hearing: (1) the intensity with which the sound is received, measured in dB; and (2) the clarity with which the sound is received, which is related to frequency perception and is measured in cycles per second or Hertz (Hz). Hearing ability may be impaired along either or both of these dimensions. In the process of hearing, sound waves travel from a sound source to the listener, where they are collected by the outer ear and travel through the ear canal to the ear drum or *tympanic membrane*. The sound waves cause the tympanic membrane to vibrate and transmit the sound energy to the three small bones (*ossicles*) of the middle ear. These bones (hammer or *malleus*, anvil or *incus*, and stirrup or *stapes*) carry the sound waves to the inner ear (*cochlea*), where delicate hair cells receive sensory information on the pitch or frequency and intensity or magnitude of the sound signal. The auditory nerve then carries this information to the brain, where the signals are processed and interpreted. When any part of this process is disrupted or malfunctions, some degree of hearing loss or impairment results. The term *hearing impairment* usually implies that the hearing problem is permanent, while the term *hearing loss* is a general term that may describe either a temporary or permanent condition. Depending upon which part or parts of the auditory system are affected, hearing losses may fall into one of four categories: conductive, sensorineural, mixed, or central (Atterbury 1990; Bauch 2014; Darrow and Gfeller 1988, 1996; Gfeller 1992d). Hearing losses in any of these categories may be partial or total. Severity of impairment and possibilities for remediation vary with the type and extent of the loss.

A *conductive hearing loss* occurs when some disease, malformation, or obstruction in the outer or middle ear interferes with the travel of sound waves. The function of the cochlea may be normal (Bauch 2014). This type of loss affects the strength of the sound signal reaching the inner ear and usually results in a mild to moderately severe hearing loss across all frequencies. Sometimes these losses respond to medical treatment to remove the obstruction, clear the infection, or correct the malformation. If medical treatment is not an option, conductive hearing losses usually can be at least partially corrected by hearing aids or other amplification systems.

A *sensorineural hearing loss* is caused by damage to the nerve fibers in the inner ear or by damage to the auditory nerve. Because of this damage, hearing may be faulty or nonexistent at certain frequencies. Missing frequencies cause certain words that have consonant or vowel sounds at those frequencies or other environmental sounds that contain those frequencies to be unclear or distorted. Sensorineural losses may be slight or extreme. Persons with these losses may have difficulties with high frequencies, low frequencies, or various frequencies throughout the spectrum. These types of losses are generally more severe and difficult to treat because the inner ear and auditory nerve are less accessible and more delicate than the outer and middle ear structures. Ordinary hearing aids may be of little help in sensorineural losses, for ordinary hearing aids amplify all frequencies, not just the problem frequencies. *Presbycusis*, a decline in higher frequencies, occurs in older people. That and exposure to loud noise may cause sensorineural hearing loss (Bauch 2014).

A *mixed hearing loss* occurs when there is some degree of defect or damage both to the outer or middle ear structures *and* to the inner ear or auditory nerve. The extent to which hearing aids or medical procedures will improve hearing in mixed losses varies, depending on the type and extent of the losses.

A *central hearing loss* occurs when there is damage to the brain or central nervous system. In these losses, sound waves are transmitted clearly and at adequate intensity through all the ear structures; however, the individual has difficulty interpreting, understanding, or recognizing the sound because of damage or defects in some portion of his or her auditory processing centers.

Causes

Hearing losses occur due to various biological or environmental factors. Hearing losses that are present at birth can be caused by genetic abnormalities, viral disease or infection in the mother during pregnancy, drug or alcohol abuse by the mother during pregnancy, congenital malformations, lack of oxygen during birth, exposure to radiation or certain medications during pregnancy, severe injury or trauma during pregnancy or birth, or severe newborn jaundice due to problems like Rh incompatibility (Bauch 2014). After birth, things like serious viral infections, middle ear inflammations (*Otitis media*), accumulation of wax or fluid in the ear, foreign objects in the ear, injury or trauma, or prolonged exposure to loud noises can precipitate hearing impairments. In about half the cases of hearing loss, the exact cause is unknown.

Conductive hearing losses are frequently caused by infections or diseases that produce middle ear inflammation (otitis media), by injury or trauma from accidents, or from foreign objects being inserted into the ear. Certain birth defects, such as the malformations associated with cleft lip and cleft palate that hinder the eustachian tube's ability to equalize middle and outer ear pressure, can also cause conductive losses (Atterbury 1990). As many as half of all congenital sensorineural hearing losses are caused by inherited structural defects in the auditory mechanism. Other congenital causes of sensorineural losses include trauma or lack of oxygen during birth, infection in the mother during pregnancy, or drug or alcohol abuse by the mother during pregnancy.

After birth, sensorineural hearing losses may be caused by severe viral infections and injury or trauma. In addition, prolonged exposure to loud sounds, either in the environment or through headphones, is an increasingly common cause of temporary and permanent sensorineural hearing deficits (Bauch 2014; Jaret 1991). Presbycusis, the gradual loss of hearing associated with the aging process, also may result in sensorineural impairments caused by deterioration of hair cells at the base of the cochlea (high frequency receptors) and degeneration of neural pathways leading from the cochlea to the cortex (Bauch 2014). About a third of Americans who are over 64 years old have hearing loss, and half of those over 75 years old also show a loss, especially in upper frequency perception (Bauch 2014). Mixed hearing losses often result from genetic factors; they also may result from trauma, injury, or infection. Central hearing losses most often are caused by traumatic brain injuries, strokes, or brain tumors. All in all, "about 17 percent of Americans – 36 million – have some degree of hearing loss, ranging from mild to profound" (Bauch 2014, 11). Conductive hearing losses are more common than sensorineural hearing losses.

COMMON CHARACTERISTICS, PROBLEMS, AND NEEDS OF CLIENTS

As with any population, the hearing impaired are a very heterogeneous group. Any individual client will have a unique combination of abilities, needs, personality traits, strengths, and weaknesses that will impact his or her treatment program and functioning level; therefore, it is unwise to attempt to predict a particular person's skill levels or ceiling of abilities based on broad generalizations about a certain population. However, an awareness of some of those characteristics, problems, and needs common to many hearing-impaired clients will be beneficial both to the therapist who desires to work with this population and to the reader wishing to understand how music therapy intervention strategies may benefit these individuals.

Depending on the type, severity, and onset of their loss, hearing impaired individuals have various degrees of difficulty in (a) perceiving, understanding, and interpreting speech or environmental sounds; (b) producing intelligible speech; (c) developing language skills; and (d) interacting with others in social situations. If they had good language models at home, their degree of language difficulty is reduced. However, if their parents are also hearing impaired, the language model may be deficient. In the general population with normal hearing, "most children by ages 3 or 4 will have acquired most of the basic rules of grammar for their native culture simply by listening to language around them" (Gfeller and Darrow 2008, 379). Since most hearing impaired individuals must live and function within a hearing society, two of their biggest needs are: (1) learning to use whatever residual hearing they have to perceive, discriminate, and interpret sounds; and (2) finding ways to communicate with hearing individuals. Consequently, rehabilitative and educational programs for hearing impaired individuals often stress auditory training, speech and language development, and development of skills and strategies for communication and socialization with others (Darrow 1985; Darrow and Gfeller 1988, 1996; Darrow and Schunk 1996; Gfeller 1992d; Gfeller and Bauman 1988; Gfeller and Darrow 2008).

Those individuals who have early-onset severe hearing problems usually need intensive training to develop speech and language skills since they do not hear well enough to benefit from everyday language models and develop speech and language skills on their own. Generally, the greater the hearing loss, the more difficulty an individual has with speech and language (Gfeller and Bauman 1988). If the child learns manual communication, there may not be a deficit in language skills in the hearing-impaired child compared with hearing children. Transfering this knowledge to speaking or understanding speech requires special training. However, even individuals who have severe hearing losses can develop some speech skills, but they need intensive therapeutic training to develop proper speech rhythms, inflections, and enunciations.

Because hearing-impaired individuals acquire language skills more slowly than the average person and because poor language skills also affect performance on reading and in written tasks, they often lag behind their hearing peers in academic achievement. In addition, individuals who are deaf or hard-of-hearing may experience much frustration because they lack verbal skills to express their thoughts, wants, and needs. They often have a very literal interpretation of vocabulary and poor skills in grammar and syntax. Because of the great effort necessary to discriminate and interpret auditory stimuli, hearing impaired individuals often have short attention spans and experience difficulty especially in concentrating on auditory activities. Because of their difficulties in communicating with others, individuals who are deaf or hard-of-hearing also may have poor social skills.

When individuals acquire hearing losses as adults, they often retain enough speech and language skills to be understood by others and can develop some ability to compensate by using hearing aids and other assistive devices. For these individuals, the main problems associated with their acquired hearing losses involve (1) increasing social isolation because of difficulty hearing conversations or hearing television and radio and (2) vocational disabilities when job skills, such as the ability to use a telephone, hear instructions, or hear sounds important to work performance, are affected by the hearing loss (Bauch 2014; Gfeller 1992d; Gfeller and Darrow 2008). Persons who acquire hearing losses as adults, especially in their elderly years, may need the support of family and friends to help them admit their loss and motivate or encourage them to seek out and utilize assistive devices and strategies to help them maintain their abilities to communicate and socialize (Miller 1983).

Hearing Aids and Assistive Devices

Individuals who have hearing losses may use hearing aids or other assistive devices to enhance their residual hearing capacities (Atterbury 1990; Boothroyd 1980; Matthias 1989). These devices also help hearing impaired individuals become more aware of sounds and more perceptive of auditory cues. In addition, amplification of auditory stimuli can help individuals with moderate and severe hearing losses become more aware of their own voice. If a person can barely understand a conversation at 40 dB HL, he or she is considered to have a moderate hearing loss. (dB are measures of power ratios or sound pressure ratios [Radocy and Boyle 2012, 138–139]. HL is hearing loss.) If 70 dB HL is the threshold for hearing, the person has a severe loss (Bauch 2014). About 60 dB HL is required for participation in normal conversation. Thus, hearing aids can be important for sound and speech production as well as for speech and sound comprehension.

Hearing aids vary for different types and severities of hearing losses. Many hearing impaired individuals wear personal ear-level aids, which may be fitted behind or in the ear. Others use portable FM systems that include two units: The person speaking to the individual wears a unit containing a microphone and transmitter, while the individual wears a unit containing a receiver and hearing aid. Advances in technology are also giving rise to innovations such as "smart" hearing aids that help filter out background noise and cochlear implants, devices that act like an electronic inner ear to receive sound waves and then stimulate the auditory nerve (Atterbury 1990; Bauch 2014). In addition, hearing impaired individuals may use special devices that replace the usual auditory medium with visual communication, such as Teletype telephones (Telecommunications Device for the Deaf or TDD), decoders for close-captioned television programming, or flashing lights for telephone or doorbell rings (Bauch 2014; Matthias 1989).

Cochlear Implants (CI)

This assistive hearing device is sometimes available for people who have profound sensorineural hearing loss that affects both ears. Gfeller (2000, 123) explains how this device works: "Rather than amplifying the sound . . . a cochlear implant provides direct electrical stimulation to the surviving cochlear neurons, and the nerve impulses travel along the auditory pathways to the cortex where they are interpreted." Sometimes the CI is used together with a hearing aid on the other side of the head: "The concept of electrical and acoustic stimulation involves electrically stimulating the nonfunctional, high-frequency region of the cochlea with a cochlear implant and applying a hearing aid in the low-frequency range" (Miranda et al. 2014).

In one study, Innes-Brown, Marozeau, Storey, and Blarney (2013) used an integrated approach, including aural, visual, and kinesthetic modes of learning for students aged 9–13 years. Twenty children participated. Eleven had impaired hearing (six with a unilateral CI or CI and HA together and five with bilateral HI). Nine were normally hearing. They found that temporal cues were important in the perception of timbre as well as rhythm.

If the person had hearing before deafness occurred (postlingually deafened), he or she quite likely will have some memory of musical sounds. The sound from the CI is quite distorted when compared with the sound during the usual experience of listening to music. However, the hearing impaired listener may recognize some music from the rhythm, which is usually available in their perception. Perception of rhythm is the primary way many deaf students can respond to music and have pleasure from participation (Trehub, Mitani, Kanda, and Nakata 2006). Those who have never heard (prelingual deafness) may be able to use the device for improved hearing of speech, which has a more restricted frequency range. However, their experience with music may be unpleasant, because only some frequencies are represented and the cortex does not have musical sounds in storage for comparison.

Gfeller, Driscoll, Kenworthy, and van Voorst (2011) studied music therapy for preschool children who had cochlear implants. They found that most CI users could participate in music therapy if proper adaptations were made in the environment and music selection, as well as in the activities. The "practical tips" provided in the appendix to the article would be most helpful to clinicians (Gfeller et al. 2011, 49).

Gfeller et al. (2012) studied the components of both linguistic and musical excerpts in real-world experience of both CI users and normal-hearing adults. Background music was not recommended since it reduces speech recognition of both hearing and CI recipients. Age was a factor, with older listeners having more difficulty than younger listeners. The degree of residual hearing was another factor. The researchers recommended music with clearly structured lyrics presented in a quiet environment and combined with contextual cues. Even then, some CI recipients may not enjoy music. If so, music therapy may be inappropriate.

Bartov and Most (2014) studied identification of musical nursery rhymes by young children in several groups: Unilateral CI, bilateral CI, and bimodal CI-HA (CI with contralateral hearing aid). All three groups were better able to identify songs with words than presentations without the lyrics. This finding is consistent with other research (Hsiao 2008; Mitani et al. 2007; Vongpaisal et al. 2004, 2006, 2009). Rhythm can be an important cue (Gfeller 1998, 2000). When the child receives the implant at a younger age, success rates increase. When the child is asked to identify melodies when given only pitch cues, he or she has more difficulty (Stordahl 2002; Vongpaisal, Trehub, and

Schellenberg 2006). Stordahl (2002, 5) noted that "inplant recipients perform similarly to normally hearing adults in rhythmic perception, but less accurately on tasks that require perception of pitch, timbre recognition, or appraisal (that is liking of sound quality)." However, Gfeller (2001) designed a training program for adults with CIs and found that, with training, it is possible to improve timbre recognition, timbre appraisal, song recognition, and appraisal ratings of complex songs. She indicated that the learning style, previous experience, and ability to process information should be considered in a music training program for CI adults.

Nakata, Trehub, Mitani, and Kanda (2006, 148) found that "unlike their adult counterparts with cochlear implants, congenitally deaf children with implants seem to derive considerable pleasure from music." They can participate in music by singing (although pitch may be poor), dancing, and instrumental lessons (Gfeller, Witt, Spencer, Stordahl, and Tomblin 1998; Nakata et al. 2005; Vongpaisal et al. 2006). Van Besouw et al. (2014) conducted workshops for adult CI users in England to improve music listening strategies so music could be used in rehabilitation. The clients made positive changes in attitude and behavior toward music.

Gfeller (2007) summarized how music therapy was used with clients with hearing loss over the previous 30 years. During this time, the CI was introduced and changed the way music could be used with many clients. The Deaf President Now movement at Gallaudet University also occurred during this time period, which led to the controversy of "music for all" attitude that had preceded this movement.

Alternative Communication Methods

Some communication aid or alternative method of communication is essential for most individuals who have permanent hearing losses. They may use one or more of various methods to communicate among themselves and with the hearing world (Atterbury 1990; Darrow and Gfeller 1988, 1996; Darrow and Schunk 1996; Gfeller 1992d; Matthias 1989). The method used may vary with the degree of hearing impairment and the social or educational situation.

Individuals with less severe hearing losses often can speak and usually can understand the speech of others by using a combination of assistance from a hearing aid, speech reading (looking carefully at the speaker's lips, body, and facial expression as well as environmental cues to discern the basic thought of the speaker's message), and careful listening. People who emphasize using speech and speech reading together with amplification of residual hearing as the exclusive means of communication for hearing impaired individuals believe in an *oral communication* philosophy.

Many individuals with more severe hearing losses, especially those whose hearing impairment had an early onset, need alternative methods to enable them to communicate to the fullest extent possible (Darrow and Gfeller 1988, 1996; Darrow and Schunk 1996; Gfeller 1992d; Matthias 1989). *Cued speech* is a method used to supplement speech reading that uses different hand shapes or movements shown at a specific place on the face to visually represent the sounds or pronunciations of spoken syllables. This is of special use when the person is lip-reading, but some letters look the same. There are eight hand shapes for the consonant sounds, and the hand placement represents the vowels (Bauch 2014). *Fingerspelling* uses a system of hand shapes and positions to represent the letters of the written alphabet. People who use fingerspelling to communicate spell out their messages letter by letter. The Rochester Method of communication uses fingerspelling in combination with spoken English as the primary communication mode (Darrow and Gfeller 1988).

Systems of *sign-supported speech* or *manual communication* use various combinations of hand positions and gestures, along with fingerspelling, both to send and receive messages (expressive and receptive communication). Some of these systems, such as Signed English, Signing Exact English, Seeing Essential English, and Linguistics of Visual English, follow the grammar and syntax of spoken English. American Sign Language (ASL), however, is a manually produced language that has its own syntax and grammar, which is very different from spoken English (Bauch 2014; Darrow and Gfeller 1988, 1996; Darrow and Schunk 1996; Gfeller 1992d; Matthias 1989). Many members of the deaf community in the United States and Canada use ASL. When children with profound hearing impairments establish ASL as their first language, English is learned as a second language (Matthias 1989).

Total communication incorporates speech, speech reading, residual hearing, one or more forms of manual communication, and written language. These various modes of communication may be used simultaneously or chosen selectively depending on the specific situation. In the *total communication* philosophy, all methods that help the hearing impaired individual acquire or understand language are used and accepted (Darrow and Gfeller 1988, 1996; Darrow and Schunk 1996; Gfeller 1992d; Matthias 1989).

Some hearing impaired individuals may use other alternative communication devices, including pointing to pictures, letters, numbers, or words on specially constructed *communication boards* or using *electronic speech devices* that mechanically "speak" the words typed in by the user (Bauch 2014). Hearing dogs also may be used with HI persons, just as "seeing eye" dogs are used with visually impaired people. However, these dogs serve by using their paws or nose to nudge the person and lead them to the source of the sound. This can be very important in public places or in traffic when the person may not hear or see a car or pedestrian approaching from behind.

Historically, there has been much disagreement, both among educators of hearing impaired individuals and among members of the deaf community, about which of the various systems of communication mentioned above is most beneficial. Currently, however, many experts believe that most individuals benefit from a combination of approaches: "There is increasing consensus that whatever system or method works most successfully for the individual should be used to allow the hearing-impaired person access to clear and understand-able communication" (Darrow and Gfeller 1988, 140).

Deaf Culture

Gfeller (1992d) noted that those who work with persons who have significant hearing losses must also be aware of Deaf culture. When capitalized, the term *Deaf* refers primarily to an individual's affiliation with the Deaf community, a cultural alignment based not only on severity of hearing loss but also on social attitude. Individuals who are Deaf in their cultural orientation usually use American Sign Language as their primary system of communication and may seek out activities and organizations where they can socialize with other deaf people (Gfeller 1992d). Music does have a limited role in Deaf culture, although some members of the Deaf community consider music to be of little or no importance (Darrow 1993). The music therapist should be sensitive to Deaf culture: "Before initiating any significant rehabilitative program with deaf children, it would be advisable to learn more about Deaf culture in order to interact appropriately and sensitively" (Gfeller 1992d, 223).

People who align themselves with the Deaf community may include those who have congenital hearing losses, those who have one or more parents and/or grandparents who are deaf, and those who acquired hearing losses early in childhood and attended residential schools for the deaf (Gfeller 1992d). On the other hand, some severely hearing impaired individuals, especially those who acquired their losses well into adulthood or those who were raised by hearing parents and exposed primarily to an oral approach to communication, may not consider themselves to be part of the Deaf community (Gfeller 1992d; Matthias 1989). The degree to which an individual identifies with Deaf or hearing culture also influences that individual's perception of music's role and importance. Darrow (1993) found that the majority of subjects who primarily identified with Deaf culture ranked music as of little or no importance, while the majority of those who identified with hearing culture considered music to be very important.

SETTINGS FOR SERVICE DELIVERY

Hearing impaired individuals may receive special programs to help meet their specific learning needs in various settings, depending on the type, severity, and onset of their loss. Audiologists can help determine the degree and extent of the hearing loss and suggest appropriate amplification devices or acoustical measures that will make best use of residual hearing. Speech and language pathologists and teachers specially trained to work with hearing impaired individuals often assist these individuals in developing communication skills, either in private clinics, public schools, or special schools and residential programs.

The Individuals with Disabilities Act (IDEA) (Public Law 101-476), the 1990 revision of the 1975 Education for All Handicapped Children Act (Public Law 94-142), assures a free, appropriate public education to all disabled children, aged 3–21 years, including those with hearing impairments. This law and the Technology-Related Assistance for Individuals with Disabilities Act (Public Law 100-407) also provide for assistive technology devices and services that an individual may need (Adamek 1996; Johnson 1996). The Americans With Disabilities Act (ADA) prevents discrimination against those with physical and mental disabilities in the workplace. The regulations are available at www.ada.gov (Bauch 2014). Incentives for early intervention programs to address the needs of children from birth through age 2 years who have handicaps or disabilities are provided by Public Law 99-457 of 1986 (Adamek 1996; Humpal 1990). Special education services for deaf students or hard-of-hearing students are delivered according to the same general procedure outlined in Chapter Seven.

Individuals who acquire hearing losses later in life also may benefit from the services of audiologists and speech and language pathologists to help them learn to adjust to their hearing aids and/or develop effective compensatory strategies to help maintain their abilities to communicate and socialize with their peers and families. Associations for the deaf or hearing impaired also may provide valuable information on assistive communication devices or sources for assistive devices to aid individuals in performing vocational tasks or in perceiving environmental sound cues associated with activities of daily living (e.g., flashing light instead of ring for telephone).

Music therapists may work with both children and adults who have varying degrees and types of hearing impairments. They deliver services to these clients in many different settings, including public schools, private schools or clinics, music studios, nursing homes, rehabilitation centers, or community programs. Music therapists may provide direct or consultant services and work with clients as individuals or in groups. Kaiser and Johnson (2000, 227) looked at the effect of interactive experiences on music majors' perception of music for deaf students: "Following the interactive experience, all 23 subjects indicated they would consider music experiences for deaf students." This finding has implications for preparation of music educators as well as music therapists.

HOW MUSIC IS USED IN THERAPY

Many researchers, therapists, and educators have found that hearing-impaired people can perceive and enjoy music experiences, especially when accommodations are made for their auditory limitations and auditory input is supplemented by vibrotactile and/or visual input (Bang 1980; Buechler 1982; Darrow 1985, 1989, 1992; Darrow and Gfeller 1988, 1991, 1996; Darrow and Goll 1989; Darrow and Heller 1985; Darrow and Schunk 1996; Ford 1988; Gfeller 1992d; Humpal and Dimmick 1995; Solomon 1980). Like individuals who have normal hearing, hearing impaired individuals vary in their inborn musicality or musical aptitude. However, although hearing impairment may delay the development of musical skills and abilities, it does not necessarily preclude or impair their development (Darrow 1987a).

After investigating the perception of emotion in music, Darrow (2006) reported that students with sensorineural hearing loss may have difficulty assigning emotional meaning to music. Darrow and Novak (2007, 69), studying referential meaning in music (where the music sounded like an animal or bird to most listeners), found that "hearing loss is a greater deterrent to perceiving imagery in music than is vision loss. . . . [e]ven with considerable amplification, they may not have heard, or more likely, listened to the excerpts as well as hearing participants." The researchers recommended transposing music to allow children to listen to pitches that are present within their residual hearing range.

Because music has a much wider range and variety of frequencies and a greater intensity, music is generally more accessible to hearing impaired individuals than are speech sounds (Darrow 1989, 1991). Although hearing-impaired individuals may be more attuned and sensitive to music's rhythmic and vibrational aspects and be inclined to process auditory stimuli through their tactile sense (Darrow 1987a; Darrow and Goll 1989), it is important not to limit their musical experience to feeling vibrations (Ford 1988). Tonal aspects of music, as well as experiences in singing, moving, listening, and playing instruments, also can be used successfully with and have potential benefits for individuals with hearing impairments (Buechler 1982; Darrow 1985, 1991; Darrow and Gfeller 1991, 1996; Ford 1988; Sheldon 1997). Gfeller and Darrow (2008, 389) add songwriting and pairing music with textual information as a means to increase correct language usage and expand vocabulary.

Since the nineteenth century, music has been used in various ways as part of special education, training programs, or therapy for the hearing impaired. individuals (Darrow and Heller 1985; Solomon 1980). Today, music therapy strategies continue to benefit hearing impaired people, through (1) assessment of auditory functioning, (2) auditory training, (3) speech production, (4) language development, and (5) social skill development (Buechler 1982; Darrow 1989; Darrow and Gfeller 1988, 1996; Darrow and Schunk 1996; Gfeller 1992d; Gfeller and Darrow 2008; Lathom-Radocy 2014; Michel 1985). Working with speech pathologists, audiologists, and language specialists, music therapists bring an additional avenue for motivation and reinforcement of shared goal areas for hearing impaired clients as they strive "to find unique and exciting ways to use music as a tool to teach speech, language, and listening skills" (Darrow 1989, 65).

Music to Help Assess Auditory Functioning

As was mentioned earlier, total hearing loss is rare. Most hearing impaired individuals possess some degree of residual hearing. Since music has a much wider range of frequencies than speech, musical auditory stimulation often may be more accessible than speech sounds for individuals who have residual hearing (Darrow 1989, 1991; Gfeller and Darrow 2008; Michel 1985). Therefore, music experiences may help diagnose which frequency ranges are most impaired in a particular individual's hearing loss and what areas or ranges of functional hearing the individual might still possess (Michel 1985). As they carefully note clients' responses to various ranges and timbres of musical sounds, music therapists can provide audiologists, speech-language pathologists, and other professionals with much useful information for determining what residual hearing individuals possess and what types of sounds might be used to stimulate and develop their residual hearing potential.

Specially structured music activities also may be used to help individuals who are difficult to test prepare for audiological screenings. For example, Heyer, Downs, Kalloy, and Magdinec (1986) found that music therapists can use group sessions with a piano to condition many previously untestable subjects to respond successfully to an audiologist's pure-tone hearing screenings. By working in conjunction with audiologists, music therapists can develop protocols for those hard-to-test individuals who need prior conditioning to the tones and tasks in order to be measured by audiological screenings. Music therapists then can implement the protocols in groups, thereby freeing audiologists to devote more of their time to the actual screenings (Heyer et al. 1986).

Music Therapy Strategies to Assist in Auditory Training

Auditory training programs help hearing impaired individuals learn to make maximal use of any residual hearing, thus increasing their ability to become aware of, attend to, understand, and interpret speech and environmental sounds (Darrow 1989; Darrow and Gfeller 1988, 1996, 2008; Darrow and Schunk 1996; Gfeller 1992d). Since both speech and music require perception, interpretation, and performance of sound, and since the perception of music and speech requires discrimination along similar dimensions (e.g., sound/silence, pitch, duration, rhythm, loudness or intensity, sound quality or timbre), music activities and experiences can be a valuable supplement to auditory training programs by helping to motivate partipants' use of residual hearing and offering another way for them to practice listening skills (Bang 1980; Buechler 1982; Darrow 1989, 1991; Darrow and Gfeller 1988, 1996; Darrow and Schunk 1996; Gfeller 1992d; Michel 1985). In addition, music activities frequently increase attention to the task while decreasing some of the tedium and boredom often associated with repeated drill and practice (Darrow 1991).

Auditory training programs give hearing impaired individuals specific training and practice in developing listening skills, beginning with simple reflexive and alerting responses to sound and moving from gross discriminations to increasingly more subtle tasks. The ultimate goal is comprehension of speech to the maximum extent possible. Objectives in auditory training programs include increasing (1) attention to sound and the ability to detect the presence or absence of sound, (2) ability to discriminate sounds as same or different, (3) ability to recognize and identify sounds, and (4) ability to understand or comprehend sounds (Darrow 1989; Darrow and Gfeller 1988, 1996; Darrow and Schunk 1996). By working with audiologists and speech-language pathologists, music therapists can determine which objectives are most appropriate for individual clients. Using their knowledge of the frequency ranges, timbre characteristics, and vibrotactile qualities of various instruments and musical sound sources, music therapists then can devise specific interventions that will complement auditory training programs and motivate clients to use and develop their residual hearing abilities.

Music experiences are often very useful in the early stages of auditory training exercises because musical sounds have a wider range of frequencies (pitches) and intensities (loudness) than do speech sounds (Darrow 1989; Gfeller 1992d). In addition, the vibrations of music have a tactile as well as an auditory component. Even severely or profoundly impaired clients still may be able to perceive music's vibrational patterns through their tactile sense. Some have recommended that auditory training programs for the hearing impaired should use musical instruments to help the clients learn to distinguish vibrations and sensations in their environment. In this type of program, clients first are asked to sit near a piano or bass xylophone and to touch the instrument directly to feel its vibrations. When the vibrations stop, clients are to indicate this by word or gesture. Gradually, clients are asked to tell when vibrations stop and start with fewer and fewer direct visual and tactile cues.

Bang (1980) and Gfeller (1992d) describe similar structured experiences in sound awareness and detection using drums, bass tone bars, pianos, xylophones, and other musical instruments with vibrating surfaces that are easily felt. String instruments, such as the violin, that provide vibratory as well as auditory feedback, also may be useful for auditory training (Darrow 1991). In addition, enhancing the vibrotactile stimulation of sound sources by placing sound speakers near the individual (Buechler 1982) or by using specially manufactured platform mattresses (Darrow 1992; Darrow and Goll 1989) may help hearing impaired individuals learn to perceive sound and distinguish various sound characteristics. Brass instruments that produce a sustained sound may be more useful than sounds that decay after initial production (e.g., piano). Wind instruments vibrate very minimally; their main vibrations produce columns of vibrating air. Putting the bell near a drum head can set it in motion.

Tactile stimulation from the patterned vibrations of music also can provide cues that increase clients' abilities to discriminate and reproduce rhythm patterns and perceive pitch changes (Darrow 1992; Darrow and Goll 1989; Korduba 1975). The vibrotactile stimuli readily available from many musical sound sources can enhance auditory training experiences greatly by providing hearing impaired individuals with additional sensory input that is complementary or redundant to the information they can receive auditorily: "This additional support increases the amount of available information and solidifies existing concepts" (Darrow and Goll 1989, 123). Korduba (1975) found that deaf third-grade students could listen to rhythms presented on a bass drum and then reproduce them on a snare drum significantly better than third-grade students with normal hearing. Buechler (1982, 13) hypothesized that "it is very possible that the vibrations coming from the drum provided additional tactile cues to those students who, because of their deafness, had become more receptive to tactile stimuli."

In summary, music activities used in auditory training programs usually require individuals to (a) move or signify by gestures when sounds start or stop; (b) show differentiated responses to auditory stimuli with different levels of loudness, tempi, pitch, durations, timbres, or rhythms; (c) show recognition or identification of specified sounds, instrument timbres, words, or phrases; or (d) locate sound sources or follow moving sound sources (Bang 1980; Buechler 1982; Darrow 1989; Darrow and Gfeller 1988, 1996; Darrow and Schunk 1996; Gfeller 1992d). Generally, initial activities require clients to respond to very gross distinctions, with finer and finer discriminations being required as the clients develop their abilities to use their residual hearing. Buechler (1982), Darrow (1989), and Darrow and Gfeller (1988, 1996) give several examples of specific music therapy objectives and activities that may be used to complement auditory training programs for hearing impaired individuals. Darrow (1989) and Darrow and Gfeller (1988, 1996) also provide information on assessments and hierarchies for auditory processing that will assist the music therapist in planning appropriate interventions for hearing impaired clients.

Music Therapy Strategies to Improve and Reinforce Speech Production

Individuals who have normal hearing learn to speak by hearing others speak and trying to imitate those sounds. They then receive feedback from hearing their own voices, which enables them to adjust their pronunciation, inflection, or speech rhythm as necessary to better match the model. Hearing impaired individuals hear only distorted or partial speech models and receive distorted auditory feedback from their own speech production. Therefore, they often have some degree of speech impairment and need special intensive speech training to help them learn to use their voices to speak clearly, at a proper pitch level, and with appropriate rhythm and inflection (Darrow 1989; Darrow and Gfeller 1988, 1996; Darrow and Schunk 1996; Gfeller 1992d). Since music and speech have many common elements, such as intonation and inflection, tempo and rate, accent and stress, and rhythm, music activities often may encourage vocalization and improve and reinforce various aspects of speech production in hearing impaired individuals (Bang 1980; Buechler 1982; Darrow 1989, 1990; Darrow and Cohen 1991; Darrow and Gfeller 1988, 1996; Darrow and Schunk 1996; Darrow and Starmer 1986; Gfeller 1992d; Staum 1987; Zinar 1987). Although they usually are not trained as speech therapists, music therapists can work with speech therapists to identity a client's particular areas of need for speech production and develop specially structured music activities and experiences that will promote development in those areas and complement and reinforce the speech therapists' work. Common treatment objectives for enhancing speech production in hearing impaired individuals include: (1) increasing free vocalization and improving vocal imitation skills, (2) increasing awareness of rhythmic patterns and improving ability to speak with natural speech rate and rhythms, (3) increasing awareness of pitch movement and improving vocal intonation and inflection, (4) increasing awareness of vocal dynamics and phrasing, (5) increasing speech fluency, (6) improving vocal quality, and (7) improving articulation skills and speech intelligibility (Bang 1980; Buechler 1982; Darrow 1989; Darrow and Gfeller 1988, 1996; Darrow and Schunk 1996; Gfeller 1992d; Staum 1987). Gfeller and Darrow (2008) add that music can provide motivation to learn vocabulary words.

Many types of music experiences can be used to stimulate vocalization, encourage vocal play, and increase vocal awareness. Bang (1980) found that specially constructed, large wooden and metal tone resonator bars (frequency range of 64–380 Hz) are very useful in increasing sound and pitch perception and in eliciting vocal production in hearing impaired individuals. Others have used vocal play exercises, including the tactile perception of laryngeal vibrations, to stimulate initial vocalizations in deaf or hard-of-hearing individuals (Buechler 1982; Darrow and Gfeller 1988, 1996). In this technique, the client touches the therapist's throat and feels the laryngeal vibrations as the therapist vocalizes by singing tones or short phrases or playfully laughing. Then, the client's hand is placed his or her own throat, and the client is encouraged to vocalize in imitation of the therapist. Feeling his or her own laryngeal vibrations reinforces awareness of his or her own vocalization efforts.

Clients who do not vocalize in imitation of the therapist may begin to vocalize when they try to produce a sound on a reed horn. Amplification or electronic devices that provide both tactile and visual stimulation also can encourage and cue vocal production, provide feedback to help increase awareness of vocalizations, and facilitate improvement of vocal accuracy (Buechler 1982; Darrow and Cohen 1991). In addition, some hearing impaired clients may find auditory stimuli more accessible and perform better on vocal reproduction tasks when a 10-band graphic equalizer is used to adjust the stimuli to accommodate the individual subject's audiogram (Darrow 1990). Once clients have learned to vocalize freely and spontaneously, music therapists can refine skills by gradually adding more structure to vocal play exercises, using longer vocal phrases and encouraging more exact imitation.

Rhythmic programs have been an important part of speech development programs for deaf or hearing impaired individuals throughout the history of deaf education in this country (Darrow and Heller 1985; Solomon 1980). Music experiences that include rhythmic movement, rhythmic use of musical instruments, or rhythmic speech and chanting all can help increase clients' abilities to perceive rhythm patterns aurally and then reproduce them. The visual and tactile cues received from the vibrations of instruments, movements used, or rhythmic notation may provide additional sensory input that helps hearing impaired individuals increase their awareness of sensitivity to speech's rhythmic components. For example, when hearing impaired clients use their entire body for rhythmic expression in movement-to-music activities, they often achieve a better understanding of and a refined ability to reproduce speech rhythms (Darrow 1985). Some therapists and educators have found that experiences incorporating Dalcroze eurhythmics and Orff-Schulwerk techniques, with their inherent visual, imitative, and rhythmic aspects, can be used very successfully with hearing impaired clients (Darrow 1985; Darrow and Gfeller 1991). Speech rhythms, inflections, and patterns also can be played and experienced on percussion instruments, thereby helping clients become more aware of and better able to produce those patterns (Bang 1980; Buechler 1982; Darrow and Gfeller 2008; Gfeller 1992d). In addition, music notation can cue to the duration and rhythm of words and syllables, thereby helping clients improve their awareness of speech rhythms and increase their ability to speak with natural rhythms and inflections (Staum 1987).

Since speech's prosodic features include many melodic elements (rhythm, intonation, rate, and stress), group and individual singing experiences, vocal exercises, and private vocal instruction all can be structured to help hearing impaired individuals improve their vocal intonation, inflection, pitch, volume, and quality (Darrow 1989; Darrow and Cohen 1991; Darrow and Starmer 1986; Gfeller 1992d; Staum 1987). Instrumental, movement, or vocal exercises that help clients develop proper breath support and breathing techniques may also have positive effects on vocal quality and speech volume. In addition, various music activities, such as song practice using targeted words or sounds, can help clients improve or practice articulation skills (Darrow 1989).

Many more examples of specific music therapy objectives and interventions that may help hearing impaired individuals develop and improve various aspects of their speech production are given by Buechler (1982), Darrow (1989), and Darrow and Gfeller (1988, 1996, 2008). Darrow (1989) and Darrow and Gfeller (1988, 1996) also describe specific assessment procedures that will assist the music therapist in determining clients' particular abilities and needs in areas of speech production.

Music Therapy Strategies to Improve and Reinforce Language Development

Individuals who have serious hearing losses often lag behind their peers in language development since they lack regular exposure to everyday conversational models of language, syntax, and vocabulary from which hearing impaired individuals learn many words and rules of language (Darrow 1989; Darrow and Gfeller 1988, 1996; Darrow and Schunk 1996; Gfeller 1992d; Gfeller and Bauman 1988). Therefore, hearing impaired individuals usually need special training and intervention to help them develop and practice language skills, in whatever methods of oral and/or manual communication they choose to use. Signage has long been a means of communication: "Long before their vocal mechanisms are mature enough to verbalize, babies can learn to communicate their wants and needs using gestures or signs" (Miller 2005, 1). Usually, individuals with more severe hearing losses have greater difficulty in developing language skills (Gfeller and Bauman

1988). Poor language skills manifest themselves in problems with vocabulary, complex sentence structure, and multiple meanings of words. Delayed development of language skills also affects performance adversely in both reading and writing, which can seriously hamper academic development. In addition, poor ability to use language to communicate with others or to receive information from others diminishes opportunities for spontaneous interactions with others, thus hampering social and emotional development (Darrow and Gfeller 1988, 1996, 2008; Darrow and Schunk 1996).

Structured music experiences, which promote small group socialization, communication, and interaction and provide opportunities for using written, spoken, and/or signed language in singing, song signing, and song writing activities, can also foster many motivating and enjoyable opportunities for the development and practice of receptive and expressive language skills in safe, structured, socially appropriate environments (Darrow 1987a, 1989; Darrow and Gfeller 1988, 1996; Darrow and Schunk 1996; Galloway and Bean 1974; Gfeller 1987b, 1990; Gfeller and Bauman 1988; Knapp 1980; Prueter and Giles 1981; Warner 1981). According to Darrow (1989), music therapists most often work with the language components of syntax and semantics, while focusing on development of both receptive and expressive language skills. In addition, some music therapy experiences may ask clients to use various reading and writing skills.

After consulting with the speech/language pathologist to help determine the individual's specific needs, current level of functioning, and best methods for language remediation, the music therapist also assesses the individual's interests and level of functioning in areas specific to the music therapy context to help determine what types of music therapy experiences might best complement the individual's language development program (Darrow and Gfeller 1988, 1996; Lathom-Radocy 2014). More specific information on assessment procedures for various components of language development is given by Darrow (1989), Darrow and Gfeller (1988, 1996), and Gfeller and Bauman (1988). For maximum facilitation of language development, music therapists should also be familiar with and at least somewhat conversant in the client's primary method of communication (speech, signing system, etc.).

Typically, language development goals in music therapy for individuals with hearing impairments focus on one or more of the following areas: (1) increasing vocabulary (including both knowledge of word meaning and appropriate use of words); (2) increasing spontaneous, topic-related interaction within a group by increasing ability to understand and functionally use rules and behaviors that affect group communication; and (3) increasing complexity and completeness of sentences (Darrow 1989; Darrow and Gfeller 1988, 1996; Darrow and Schunk 1996; Gfeller 1992d; Gfeller and Bauman 1988). Music therapists structure music therapy interventions and sessions to encourage and reinforce interaction and communication continually by modeling appropriate uses of language and providing opportunities for clients to (a) participate in spontaneous and solicited dialogue, (b) practice using selected vocabulary words, (c) construct and interpret sentences, and (d) practice using appropriate grammar and syntax (Darrow 1989; Darrow and Gfeller 1988, 1996; Darrow and Schunk 1996). As these skills are practiced within the context of carefully structured music experiences, they are reinforced and refined to enable transfer to other settings.

Many different types of music experiences can be structured to help encourage and reinforce various aspects of language development for hearing impaired individuals. For example, action songs and movement-to-music experiences can introduce words and encourage clients to experience and demonstrate word meanings (Galloway and Bean, 1974; Gfeller 1990), while eurhythmics programs can facilitate development of total communication skills and enhanced emotional expression. Targeted vocabulary words also can be included in specially designed song lyrics. Individuals can practice the words and become more proficient in their chosen mode of communication (spoken language or sign language) as they sing or sign the lyrics. In addition, they can demonstrate word comprehension by holding up or pointing to appropriate pictures, graphics, or word cards at appropriate places in the song or by following directions contained in the song lyrics (Darrow 1989; Darrow and Gfeller 1988, 1996; Darrow and Schunk 1996; Gfeller 1990, 1992d; Gfeller and Bauman 1988; Prueter and Giles 1981; Warner 1981). Additional opportunities to learn and practice oral and/or manual language skills occur within the context of music therapy sessions as clients request preferred activities, respond to questions, discuss song lyrics, participate in performance groups (e.g., choirs that combine sign and song), or communicate with others in group movement or instrumental activities (Darrow 1987a, 1989; Darrow and Gfeller 1988, 1996; Darrow and Schunk 1996; Gfeller 1990, 1992d; Gfeller and Bauman 1988; Knapp 1980; Prueter and Giles 1981; Warner 1981).

Song-writing activities also can provide many unique and motivating opportunities for hearing impaired clients to develop vocabulary, practice sentence construction, use correct grammar and syntax, practice reading and writing skills, and use expressive language skills (Darrow 1989; Darrow and Gfeller 1988, 1996; Darrow and Schunk 1996; Gfeller 1987b, 1992d; Gfeller and Bauman 1988). Song writing can increase motivation and attention by providing a novel teaching method, while the lyrics and music provide a focus for thematic discussion and a structure for teaching listening, speaking, reading, and writing skills (Gfeller 1987b). Song-writing experiences may be as simple as having the client provide one word to complete a lyric phrase or as involved as writing original lyrics for an entire song. Discussion of lyrics, composition techniques, or group processes provide additional opportunities for increasing spontaneous, topic-related interactions.

Additional examples of specific music therapy objectives and interventions for language development with hearing impaired individuals appear in Darrow (1989), Darrow and Gfeller (1988, 1996, 2008), Gfeller (1990), and Gfeller and Bauman (1988).

Music Therapy Strategies to Improve and Reinforce Social Skills

Since many routine human interactions involve communication through the exchange of auditory information, "hearing impairment acts as a barrier to social contact" (Zinar 1987, 123). Because of distorted or missing perceptions of certain speech or environmental sounds, hearing impaired individuals find it difficult, if not impossible, to participate in incidental conversations or everyday social exchanges. Poor hearing and limited speech and language skills may also hamper their ability to understand instructions, ask questions, or express ideas and concerns. Moreover, they may have difficulty joining in many recreational, social, and leisure-time activities, unless special efforts are made to include them and find ways for them to communicate and participate with others. Thus, hearing impairments can impede the development of many basic social skills, including the ability to attend to others, share, take turns, follow directions, work cooperatively, and express feelings in socially acceptable ways (Lathom-Radocy 2014). Hearing impaired individuals who do not learn constructive and appropriate ways of interacting with others may experience social isolation and exhibit various social adjustment problems, such as immature behavior, poor emotional control, tantrums, withdrawal, inflexibility, egocentricity, or depression (Bauch 2014; Gfeller 1992d; Zinar 1987). Since many music experiences involve cooperative group activity and since music often can be perceived tactilely and visually as well as auditorily, music can be a useful tool for helping hearing impaired clients learn and practice many different levels and types of social skills, thereby improving their ability to interact both with other hearing impaired individuals and with persons who have normal hearing (Bang 1980; Buechler 1982; Darrow 1985, 1987a; Darrow and Gfeller 1991; "Deaf People" 1980; Donnelly 1991; Gfeller 1987b, 1992d; Michel 1985; Standley 1991a; Zinar 1987).

At a most basic level, an awareness of music's vibrations or the gratification experienced from playing musical instruments can lead an individual to increase attention to and interaction with others. For example, once an individual becomes aware of and intrigued with the sounds or vibrations made by rhythm instruments, rhythm instruments may be used as part of a contingency system to reward and increase attention to a designated task or person (Michel 1985) or as a means of interacting with others in a structured or improvisatory duet or small ensemble experiences (Bang 1980; Buechler 1982; Donnelly 1991; Standley 1991a). In addition, dance and rhythmic movement activities can help hearing impaired individuals improve their rhythmic perception and grace and gain confidence in movement while giving them opportunities to interact with others and develop social skills (Birkenshaw-Fleming 1993; Michel 1985). Structuring activities and choosing materials so that tactile or visual cues and stimulation supplement auditory input will facilitate the involvement and participation of hearing impaired clients. Group song writing or lyric discussion experiences, using topics such as friendship or cooperation, also can be used to explore and develop social skills (Gfeller 1987b).

With special methods of instruction, even individuals who have severe hearing losses can learn to play band and orchestral instruments and participate successfully in instrumental ensembles, bands, and orchestras ("Deaf People" 1980; Sheldon 1997; Zinar 1987). These ensemble performance experiences, as well as those involving percussion ensembles (Donnelly 1991), musical plays, or song-signing and total communication choirs (Darrow 1987a; Darrow and Gfeller 1988, 1996; Knapp 1980; Standley 1991a), can do much to increase clients' skills in working cooperatively with others. In addition, clients' self-esteem increases as they work hard to learn their parts, perform successfully, and have their accomplishments acknowledged and appreciated by others.

Since group music experiences are a normal part of human behavior and are commonly used by people in all parts of society in both formal and informal interactions, group music experiences can be very effective as part of mainstreaming or inclusion approaches to facilitate interaction between hearing impaired individuals and those with normal hearing. For example, traditional music play activities can provide a unique environment in which to motivate positive interactions between preschoolers with and without handicaps or disabilities (Hughes et al. 1990).

Since over half of all hearing impaired children who attend public schools attend regular music classes (Darrow and Gfeller 1991), music education settings frequently provide opportunities for integrating hearing impaired children with their normal hearing peers (Atterbury 1990; Birkenshaw-Fleming 1993; Darrow 1985; Darrow and Gfeller 1991; Humpal and Dimmick 1995; Knapp 1980). By using their residual hearing, most hearing impaired individuals can participate with peers in the traditional music education experiences of singing, playing, listening, moving, and creating, especially when appropriate instructional techniques and beneficial adaptations are used (Darrow 1985; see also "Special Considerations" section below). Generally, hearing impaired children succeed better in movement-to-music and instrumental activities than in listening or composition activities (Darrow and Gfeller 1991). Orff, Kodály, and Dalcroze techniques, with their strong visual, imitative, and rhythmic components, also facilitate successful participation by and inclusion of deaf or hard-of-hearing students (Darrow 1985; Darrow and Gfeller 1991). In addition, song-signing experiences, either within the music classroom or as part of a formal performing organization, can provide many unique and valuable opportunities for "cross-cultural exchange" between hearing impaired and normal hearing students (Darrow 1987a; Knapp 1980; Standley 1991a). Moreover, for some hearing impaired individuals, music experiences can provide important and unique avenues for personal achievement and increased self-esteem as well as many opportunities for enjoyable leisure-time activities (Darrow and Heller 1985; Donnelly 1991; Gfeller 1992d).

SPECIAL CONSIDERATIONS AND TIPS FOR SUCCESS

It is imperative that music therapists who work with hearing impaired clients consult and cooperate with the clients' speech/language pathologists and audiologists and learn to communicate in the clients' preferred mode of communication or use a qualified interpreter (Darrow 1989; Darrow and Gfeller 1988, 1996; Darrow and Schunk 1996; Gfeller 1990, 1992d; Gfeller and Bauman 1988). Music therapists who want to initiate rehabilitative programs with persons who align themselves with the Deaf community are also advised "to learn more about Deaf culture in order to interact appropriately and sensitively" (Gfeller 1992d, 223). Those who work with groups in which individuals use both speech or speech reading and sign language must remember to talk and sign at the same time (Knapp 1980). When planning intervention strategies and selecting music materials, music therapists also must consider the clients' language and communication abilities and/or deficits as well as their limited hearing abilities, and modify the language level of activities as needed (Darrow 1989; Gfeller 1992d). By making judicious use of visual aids, tactile or visual cues, vibrotactile stimulation, movement activities, and multisensory or multimodal presentation techniques to support and emphasize auditory information, music therapists can both facilitate the clients' participation and help them better understand the concepts or skills that are being presented (Atterbury 1990; Birkenshaw-Fleming 1993; Darrow and Gfeller 1988, 1991; Ford 1988; Gfeller 1992d). Research suggests that approaches and techniques such as Orff, Kodály, and Dalcroze that utilize strong visual, imitative, and rhythmic components, may be extremely useful and effective with hearing impaired individuals (Darrow 1985; Darrow and Gfeller 1991).

When using musical instruments with hearing impaired individuals, one must consider how the instrument's acoustical properties (frequency range, loudness, resonance) correspond to the hearing abilities of the client who will play it. For example, a client with no hearing in the upper frequencies would probably have a much more enjoyable musical experience playing a bass metallophone than playing a triangle. Since hearing impaired individuals already have limited sound perception abilities, it is especially important to use musical instruments with the best sound quality possible. Instruments that have a low frequency range or large vibrotactile surfaces, as well as those that have physical appeal or those that provide greater degrees of supplementary vibratory feedback, usually are most successful (Bang 1980; Buechler 1982; Darrow 1991; Darrow and Gfeller 1991). Several electronic, special amplification, and computerized devices, such as electronic instruments with built-in speakers or headphones, video learning screens or computer programs that visually represent sounds, or electronic pick-ups and amplifiers that can enhance the sound of acoustic instruments, also may be useful in working with hearing-impaired clients (Birkenshaw Fleming 1993; Buechler 1982).

Vocal work with hearing impaired individuals sometimes can be facilitated by special amplification devices, microphone headsets, computer programs, or electronic devices that give visual or tactile feedback about an individual's vocalization (Buechler 1982; Darrow and Cohen 1991). Kodály hand signals can also help provide supplementary visual and kinesthetic feedback (Darrow and Cohen 1991; Darrow and Gfeller 1991). In addition, songs may be more accessible to hearing impaired individuals if slightly lower keys or a range of the B below middle C to a twelfth above is used (Birkenshaw-Fleming 1993; Ford 1988).

Music experiences will be more accessible to hearing impaired individuals when the room is arranged so that they can sit very close to the sound sources. A very high-quality sound system is also desirable. Some clients will also benefit when auditory signals are adjusted with graphic equalizers (Darrow 1990) or when recordings that are specially arranged and acoustically mixed for easier perception by the hearing impaired are used (Market Space 1987). In addition, music therapists should eliminate or minimize extraneous environmental sounds (e.g., buzzing lights, noise of heater or fan or air conditioner, outdoor traffic) as much as possible, using room fixtures such as draperies, carpeting, and upholstery to absorb unnecessary noise (Darrow and Schunk 1996).

When working with clients who wear hearing aids, music therapists should understand how the hearing aids work and how they may be used most effectively in the music setting (Atterbury 1990; Bauch 2014). For example, in group activities, clients wearing hearing aids "should be positioned with their hearing aids toward the group" (Darrow and Schunk 1996, 209). Most hearing aids also have an automatic gain cutoff at the pain threshold. This may cause problems if the clients are asked to play or are seated near very loud instruments such as drums or cymbals. Every time the drum or cymbal is struck loudly, the sound intensity will trigger the hearing aid's automatic cutoff mechanism and cause the aid to shut off momentarily. Because of this, the clients will perceive a series of clicks or gaps in the music. Modern hearing aids can be programmed in many ways to meet the individual's auditory needs (Bauch 2014).

Finally, as more and more people fall victim to noise-induced hearing damage, music therapists may consider being advocates for hearing health and the prevention of hearing impairments. Exposure to loud noises in the workplace long has been recognized as a contributing factor to hearing loss; however, permanent hearing damage also can come from prolonged exposure to loud music or noise from many other common sound sources, including powerful speakers at concerts, personal stereo headphones, customized car stereos, personal listening devices, and television sets (Brody 1982; Jaret 1991; Levey, Levey, and Fligor 2011; Lovejoy and Estridge 1987; Tung and Chao 2013). Shargorodsky, Curhan, Curhan, and Eavey (2010) reported that 16 percent to 20 percent of children aged 10–12 years may have some kind of hearing loss which may be related to increased use of personal listening devices. People who live or work along busy flight paths or next to busy train tracks also may suffer noise-related damage. In addition to damaging hearing acuity, noisy environments may increase stress levels, irritability, and fatigue, and possibly contribute to increased blood pressure, cardiovascular injury, ulcers, accidents, and reduced work efficiency (Jaret 1991). Hearing loss from exposure to sound is fairly common: "Approximately 15 percent of Americans between ages 20 and 69 have some degree of high-frequency hearing loss due to exposure to loud sounds or noise at work or in leisure activities" (Bauch 2014, 82–83). High environmental noise levels also may disrupt sensory and motor skill development in infants and toddlers (Jaret 1991).

Some studies have addressed students in music environments. For example Jin, Nelson, Schllauch, and Carney examined the risk for noise-induced hearing loss (NIHL) in college students who were in a marching band compared with other college students. They did not find significant differences. This finding may be because they are working not with a steady level of intensity, but rather with one that fluctuates widely over time. Chesky (2008) and Chesky and Amlani (2014, 2015) studied sound levels in wind ensembles. They indicate that this is an environment with a dynamic noise level, in contrast to the steady noise level in a factory or other work environment, which has been the interest of authorities setting noise standards. They note that "music as a source is highly variable over time, includes an expanded frequency profile and is directly influenced by humans behaving musically" (17). This variation reduces the risk of hearing loss. They also studied flat attenuation hearing protection (musician earplugs). These have been designed from research with workplace noise monitoring and may have little reduction of sound from the low frequencies found in most music. Radocy and Boyle (2012, 147–149) also wrote about the potential for loss of hearing from loud sounds, including musical sounds.

Recent years have seen additional research on hearing loss related to use of personal listening devices (iPods, personal CD players, etc.). This is an outgrowth of concern for persons employed in very loud work situations. In both the United States and United Kingdom, guidelines have been provided to define the loudness levels that are acceptable without causing hearing loss. The Occupational Safety and Health Administration (OSHA 1998) and the National Institute for Occupational Safety and Health (NIOSH 1998) have established standards, which include use of MP3 players, CDs, and tapes. Epstern, Marozeau, and Cleveland (2010) studied listening habits of 64 listeners to determine if their listening levels exceeded the established noise guidelines. They found that their subjects listened at levels well below the regulations and were not at risk for hearing loss. However, they also reported that iPod output can exceed the level considered safe. They recommended that loudness and listening time be carefully monitored. Silcox (2010) recommends a hearing health surveillance program conducted by a professional with appropriate training.

More testing in musical settings is needed. Auchter and Le Prell (2014) conducted training in earplug use and the importance of ear protection. After training, 62 percent of the high school marching bands reported that they had used earplugs on some occasions. Rawool and Colligon-Wayne (2008, 1) studied the attitude of young people toward wearing hearing protection devices. They reported that "although 75% of the students were aware that exposure to loud sounds could cause hearing loss, 50% of the students appeared to be exposing themselves to potentially harmful loud music." Federman and Picou (2009) reported that when musicians perform in ensembles, the sound pressure level may be as high as 109 dB, and recreational listening devices can be used at 130 dB. The duration of time in which students are listening and the choice of lower levels for listening devices are factors. Loud concerts or nightclubs may add to the hearing loss related to loud sounds. The students surveyed by Rawool and Colligon-Wayne (2008) were unconcerned about hearing loss, although 66 percent reported tinnitus. The National Association for Schools of Music (2013–2014) as well as the National Association for Music Education (2014) now have safety accreditation standards.

Professional musicians are also at risk for developing hearing problems related to sound level exposure. O'Brien, Driscoll, and Ackerma (2012) studied eight Australian orchestras. Musicians indicated awareness of the problem, but solutions were complicated by legal, practical, and artistic concerns. These authors then conducted further research of 35 professional orchestral musicians during their personal practice (2.1 hours per day, five days a week). They found that "53% would exceed accepted permissible daily noise exposure in solitary practice, in addition to sound exposure during orchestral rehearsals and performances" (2748).

Thus, by alerting people to the dangers associated with prolonged exposure to loud sounds or noisy environments, music therapists might do much to improve the general health and well-being of the population at large as well as helping to prevent noise-induced hearing losses.

QUESTIONS FOR THOUGHT AND DISCUSSION

1. Briefly describe the different classifications and types of hearing loss. Discuss some impacts each might have on an individual's speech, language, and social skills. Also speculate on different adjustments or accommodations that might have to be made for different severities and types of hearing losses in the music setting; e.g., how might they impact choice of materials and experiences, instructional approaches, etc.?

2. Discuss some of the special characteristics and needs of hearing impaired individuals. What are their implications for music therapy programming?

3. Why and how are music experiences useful in making contact with hearing impaired individuals? Are some types of experiences and activities more useful than other? Which ones? Why?

4. Describe some specific music therapy experiences that might be useful in (1) assessing auditory functioning, (2) assisting with auditory training, (3) improving speech production, (4) promoting language development, and (5) improving social skills. What unique benefits does music provide in each of these areas?

5. List several special considerations that may be important to remember when developing therapeutic intervention strategies for hearing impaired persons. Why are these important? What are their implications for the structure of music therapy intervention strategies?

6. For each of the situations listed below, (a) define the problem or areas of need for the client or group of clients, (b) describe one or more of the goals you might pursue in music therapy sessions with the client(s), (c) describe music activities you might use to help the client(s) meet those goals, (d) tell how the music activities you described relate to the goals and needs of the client(s), and (e) mention any special considerations you might want to take into account when working with the client(s).

Situation 1:
   A group of six children, aged 7–8 years, has been referred to you for music therapy services. All of the children have moderate to severe hearing loss and wear hearing aids. Most can understand speech that is clear, loud, and distinct. These children make some speech sounds, but they have problems enunciating words clearly and have poor speech rhythm and

inflection. Other problems include a limited ability to localize sounds and extreme frustration because of their lack of verbal skills with which to express their thoughts, wants, and feelings to the hearing people around them.

Situation 2:

You are working at a community center that offers special programs for individuals who are deaf or hard-of-hearing as well as programs for the general public. The manager of the center is looking for some experiences that will integrate these two groups and is asking you for ideas.

SUGGESTIONS FOR FURTHER READING

Atterbury, B. W. (1990). *Mainstreaming exceptional learners in music.* Englewood Cliffs, NJ: Prentice-Hall.

Bauch, C. D. (Ed.) (2014). *Mayo clinic on better hearing and balance.* Rochester, MN: Mayo Clinic.

Birkenshaw-Fleming, L. (1993). *Music for all: Teaching music to people with special needs.* Toronto: Gordon V. Thompson.

Bruscia, K. E. (Ed.) (1991). *Case studies in music therapy.* Phoenixville, PA: Barcelona.

Buechler, J. (1982). Music therapy for handicapped children: Hearing impaired. W. Lathom & C. Eagle Jr., (Eds.). Washington, DC: National Association for Music Therapy.

Darrow, A-A. (1989). Music therapy in the treatment of the hearing impaired. *Music Therapy Perspectives, 6,* 61–70.

Darrow, A-A. (1993). The role of music in deaf culture: Implications for music educators. *Journal of Research in Music Education, 41(2),* 93–110.

Darrow, A-A. & Gfeller, K. E. (1996). Music therapy with children who are deaf and hard-of-hearing. In C. E. Furman (Ed.), *Effectiveness of music therapy procedures: Documentation of research and clinical practice* (2nd ed.) (230–266). Silver Spring, MD: National Association for Music Therapy. [Note: Pages 248–264 contain an annotated bibliography of research on music with individuals who are deaf or hard-of-hearing.]

Darrow, A-A. & Schunk, H. A. (1996). Music therapy for learners who are deaf/hard-of-hearing. In B. L. Wilson (Ed.), *Models of music therapy interventions in school settings: From institution to inclusion* (200–223). Silver Spring, MD: National Association for Music Therapy.

Gfeller, K. (1990). A cognitive-linguistic approach to language development for the preschool child with hearing impairment: Implications for music therapy practice. *Music Therapy Perspectives, 8,* 47–51.

Gfeller, K. & Bauman, A. A. (1988). Assessment procedures for music therapy with hearing impaired children: Language development. *Journal of Music Therapy, 25(4),* 192–205.

Gfeller, K. E. & Darrow, A-A. (2008). Music therapy in the treatment of sensory disorders. Part I: Hearing. In W. B. Davis, K. E. Gfeller, & M. H. Thaut (Eds.), *An introduction to music therapy, theory and practice* (3rd ed.) (365–390). Silver Spring, MD: American Music Therapy Association.

Lathom-Radocy, W. (2014). Music therapy for children who are deaf or hard-of-hearing. In W. Lathom-Radocy (Ed.), *Pediatric music therapy* (2nd ed.) (189–237). Springfield, IL: Charles C Thomas.

Miller, A. M. (2005). *Baby sing and sign* (2nd ed.). Olathe, KS: Love Language Publishers.

Standley, J. (1991). *Music techniques in therapy, counseling, and special education.* St. Louis: MMB Music.

Zinar, R. (1987). *Music activities for special children.* West Nyack, NY: Parker.

Chapter Ten

MUSIC THERAPY FOR INDIVIDUALS WHO HAVE VISUAL IMPAIRMENTS

Definition

Pfeiffer and Pinquart (2013) reported that there are about 150 million people with visual impairments in the world. Individuals who have severe visual impairments are generally classified as blind or as partially sighted. *Vision impairment* (VI) is the term used for persons who have 20/40 or worse vision in the better eye, even with glasses (CDC 2015). Usually, the term *blind* refers not only to individuals with no visual capability but also to legally blind persons (Codding 1982; Gfeller and Darrow 2008). Individuals are considered *legally blind* when the visual acuity of their better eye is 20/200 or less after correction or when their peripheral vision is so restricted that its widest diameter subtends an angle of no greater than 20 degrees (CDC 2015).

For educational purposes, children are sometimes classified as blind when they cannot read print but can learn to read braille, while they are classified as low sighted or low vision if they can learn to read print under special conditions, as with special optic devices or with specially enlarged print (Adamek and Darrow 2010; Smith and Neisworth 1975). Individuals who are classified as blind because they do not have enough vision to read print may still have some *residual sight*; that is, they may be able to perceive forms, motion, and light to some degree (Atterbury 1990; Lathom-Radocy 2014). There are varying degrees of blindness, depending on how much residual sight a person possesses (Birkenshaw-Fleming 1993; Gfeller and Darrow 2008). Individuals who perceive forms well enough to move around are said to have *guiding vision*, while those who can see only within a range of two to four feet have *perception of form and motion*. Those who cannot distinguish forms or motion but can distinguish day and night have residual *light perception*, while those who have no light perception whatsoever are classified as *totally blind*.

One may encounter several other terms describing various vision problems and conditions when working with visually impaired individuals (Adamek and Darrow 2010; Atterbury 1990; Birkenshaw-Fleming 1993; Codding 1982;

Lathom-Radocy 2014). The medical terms describe the cause of the disability. Persons with *myopia*, or severe near sightedness, are unable to see objects clearly at a distance; those with *hyperopia*, or farsightedness, can see distant objects clearly but have difficulty seeing close objects clearly (Lathom-Radocy 2014). Individuals who have *peripheral vision* only can see only out of the sides of their eyes; they have little or no straight-ahead vision. On the other hand, those with *tunnel vision* have only a narrow field of vision (20 degrees or less) straight ahead. Severe *astigmatism* causes a distorted image due to light rays in the eye not converging on a focal point because of irregularities in the curvature of the cornea. In *amblyopia*, a person's eyes do not track together. A person who has *strabismus*, or crossed eyes, is unable to focus both eyes simultaneously on the same point. *Nystagmus* is a muscle disorder that causes rapid, involuntary, rhythmic oscillation of the eyeball. Individuals who have *albinism* have a lack of pigment that filters out light rays and literally can be "blinded" by the sun. With *cataracts*, the lens of the eye loses its transparency, and vision becomes blurred and clouded. *Glaucoma* is an eye disease characterized by increased intraocular pressure that distorts the eye's ability to focus and may lead to blindness if untreated. *Retinitis pigmentosa* is a hereditary condition in which the retina (that part of the eye that contains that photoreceptive cells that receive the light images and send them to the brain via the optic nerve) gradually atrophies and degenerates. *Cortical blindness* is loss of sight due to an injury to the visual cortex; although the eye itself may be intact, the brain is unable to process or interpret visual stimuli.

Causes

Visual impairments may result when there are abnormalities or dysfunctions in any of the visual system's protective, refractive, directive, or receptive components (Codding 1982). *Protective structures* guard and defend the eye from injury and include the orbit, orbital fat, eyelashes, eyelids and their lining, and tears. The *TO-active components* focus the light and visual stimuli; they include the cornea, lens, vitreous body (jelly-like material that fills the eyeball), and retina. *Directive structures* are muscles that move the eyes up, down, or to the sides. *Receptive components* receive, transport, and interpret visual stimuli; they include the retina, optic nerve, and visual cortex (area of the brain where visual perception occurs).

Loss or impairment of vision may be caused by congenital defects, acquired eye disease, accidents and injuries, brain disorders, diseases affecting the whole body, or by unknown heredity factors (Birkenshaw-Fleming 1993; Codding 1982; Gfeller 1992d; Lovejoy and Estridge 1987; Miller and Keane 1978). Common causes of blindness in newborns include congenital cataracts, congenital glaucoma, and disorders of the retina or optic nerve. Some former major causes of blindness during childhood, including damage to the eyes due to high concentrations of oxygen given to premature newborn (*retrolental fibroplasia* or RLT) (Standley and Walworth, 2010) and blindness from maternal rubella or gonorrhea during pregnancy, have become much less common. Later in life, accidents, cataracts, glaucoma, inflammation of the cornea, cancer of the retina (*retinoblastoma*), or diabetes may cause loss of sight. Problems or conditions leading to visual impairments may be stable or progressive in nature; some are treatable by medication or surgery.

Compared to other types of disability classifications or handicapping conditions, the incidence of legal blindness (especially by itself, with no other handicaps or disabilities) is relatively rare in children and young adults (Codding 1988; Gfeller 1992d): "Total blindness, of congenital origin, seems to be the exception rather than the rule" (Codding 1988, 107). Among older adults, however, progressive decline in visual acuity is more common. In the United States, over half of those persons who are classified as legally blind are aged 65 years or older (Miller and Keane 1978).

When severe visual impairments are accompanied by other disabilities or handicapping conditions, individuals are said to have multiple disabilities (Codding 1988).

COMMON CHARACTERISTICS, PROBLEMS, AND NEEDS OF CLIENTS

As with any population, visually impaired individuals are a very heterogeneous group. The degree of impairment, its cause and time of onset, the expected course of the condition (whether it is stable or progressive), and the degree and type of support services available all have varying effects on the individual's level of functioning, needs, and treatment program. In addition, each client has a unique combination of abilities, needs, personality traits, strengths, and weaknesses that will impact his or her own particular responses and functional abilities; therefore, it is unwise to attempt to predict a particular person's skill levels or ceiling of abilities based on broad generalizations about a certain population. However, an awareness of some characteristics, problems, and needs which may be common to many blind or partially sighted clients will be beneficial both to the therapist who desires to work with this population and to the reader who wishes to understand how music therapy intervention strategies may benefit this population.

Since they have difficulty seeing where they are going, blind or partially sighted individuals often lack freedom and confidence in independent movement. Many consider this restriction in mobility to be the most debilitating factor of severe visual impairment (Atterbury 1990). Lack of mobility can also have detrimental effects on an individual's sense of independence and self-confidence. Individuals who have severe visual impairments need help in developing body awareness, spatial awareness, and locomotor skills; independent interaction with the environment continually must be encouraged.

Because so much knowledge and information is acquired visually during normal development, children who are blind or severely visually impaired from birth or early childhood may progress more slowly than their sighted peers in many areas, regardless of their overall level of intelligence (Codding 1982; Gfeller and Darrow 2008; Lovejoy and Estridge 1987). Early development of motor skills and language both rely on visual models of gross and fine muscle movements and lip and mouth positions. Later in life, much academic and practical skill information is acquired visually through pictures, demonstrations, and models. Individuals who have severe visual impairments have to acquire information and form concepts tactilely or auditorily rather than visually. They often must use their other senses to compensate for their impaired sight. Therefore, programs for these clients usually encourage high development of auditory skills. It is important to realize that other sense areas are not strengthened automatically when vision is impaired; developing skills in auditory and tactile perception requires training and practice (Gfeller 1992d). As Adamek and Darrow (2010, 215) explain, "Sounds, smells, and touch are probably not fully appreciated by individuals who rely on their sight."

As a consequence of the lack of visual stimulation or perhaps because of overprotection by well-meaning relatives, individuals who have severe visual impairments sometimes become quite egocentric and have difficulty participating cooperatively in group activities (Adamek and Darrow 2010; Codding 1982; Gfeller 1992d; Lovejoy and Estridge 1987). They may have difficulty relating to peers because of a lack of social opportunity. They must learn to interpret social cues that they cannot see, cues normally provided by "eye contact, facial expression, and gestures" (Gfeller and Darrow 2008, 394). Social cues must be taught through other senses. Pfeiffer and Pinquart (2013, 104) confirmed that visually impaired adolescents can use a computer to communicate with peers. They found that "a romantic relationship was a significant correlate of computer use in adolescents with visual impairment . . . the association between computer use and social relations was stronger in adolescents with visual impairment than in sighted peers."

Visual impairment may also be accompanied by emotional trauma and feelings of anxiety and insecurity, especially in clients who have deteriorating vision or became blind after birth. Therefore, blind or severely visually impaired individuals may also need emotional support and benefit from experiences that promote psychological security and increase self-esteem (Codding

1982; Gfeller 1992d; Josepha 1968; Lovejoy and Estridge 1987). In addition, since society is, for the most part, geared for sighted people, persons with severe visual impairments may experience extreme frustration as they try to fit in with society, be accepted and understood by others, and seek meaningful relationships outside the protected environments of home and school (Adamek and Darrow 2010; Codding 1982). Consequently, they may need to find outlets for emotional expression and release of frustration and develop ways of interacting successfully and appropriately with sighted individuals.

SETTINGS FOR SERVICE DELIVERY

The Individuals with Disabilities Act (IDEA) (Public Law 101-476), the 1990 revision of the 1975 Education for All Handicapped Children Act (Public Law 94-142), assures a free, appropriate public education to all disabled children, aged 3–21 years, including those with visual impairments. Public Law 99-457 of 1986 provides incentives for early intervention programs to address the needs of children, from birth through the age of 2 years, who have visual handicaps or disabilities (Adamek 1996; Humpal 1990). Since the passage of these laws, most visually impaired children attend public schools, with assistance from a certified teacher of the visually impaired (Lathom-Radocy 2014). Most attend regular classes. Some are seen in a resource room, separate class, separate school, residential facility, home or hospital (Dote-Kwan and Chen 1995).

Kern and Wolery (2001) set up musical stations and a path between them to assist a 3-year-old visually impaired boy during playground activities. However, they found that staff training was necessary to increase his socialization, interaction with musical materials, and mobility, as well as to reduce his stereotypic behavior. They observed that "reductions occurred when he became more involved in meaningful activities." This may have occurred because "he had sensory input from the outside world; thus, he did not need to supply self-stimulation by rocking or shaking his head" (162). Beginning music therapy with preschool children can provide the necessary sensory stimulation to initiate interaction with others. Many blind children who have been overprotected and have limited mobility expect all of their needs to be met by others. This is detrimental to later school adjustment in a classroom. Special education services for visually impaired children are delivered according to the same general procedure outlined in Chapter Seven.

Music programs have been an important part of education and training programs at special schools for the blind since Lowell Mason initiated a music curriculum at Perkins School for the Blind in 1832 (Codding 1988; Heller 1987). Today, school-aged children who are classified as blind or severely visually impaired are much more likely to be served in public schools than in special schools for the blind (Dote-Kwan and Chen 1995; Lathom-Radocy 2014; Zinar 1987). Especially when visual impairment is their only disability, these students frequently are mainstreamed or included in regular classes in public school settings and receive music instruction from music educators (Atterbury 1990; Codding 1988; Lathom-Radocy 2014; McReynolds 1988; Siligo 2005; Zinar 1987). Attentive behavior and the ability to select important stimuli amid competing background noise is essential for a visually impaired child to learn in a mainstreamed class. Robb (2003) demonstrated how music could function to increase attentive behavior in a group setting.

When music therapists work with individuals who have severe visual impairments in public school settings, they focus on using music to promote desirable physical, academic, and social changes, not on music instruction per se (Codding 1988). At times, music therapists may consult with music educators to help them adapt instructional materials and procedures for visually impaired students. Siligo (2005) recommended reading notation for students who have some sight. For those who are blind, braille music is one possibility, but many memorize the music from repeated listening to tapes or CDs. It is important that they listen to the entire piece, as well as their part, so they understand how the ensemble sounds (Siligo 2005, 32). Some music therapists also contract their services to various agencies or see clients privately for individual therapy or specially adapted music instruction (Moog 1987; Shoemark 1991).

As Gfeller and Darrow (2008, 398) pointed out, "Persons with visual impairment make up a small segment of children and young adults with disabilities." Since visual impairments affect adults more than children (Codding 1988), music therapists also may work with individuals who have visual impairments in geriatric centers and adult rehabilitation facilities. Although blindness or visual impairment may not be the primary reason individuals are in these settings, lack of sight certainly impacts their ability to function and interact with others and must be considered in planning and implementing rehabilitation programs.

Visually impaired individuals, then, may receive services in diverse settings, depending on factors such as age, degree of visual impairment, and existence of other impairments or disabilities. Music therapists, too, may work with both children and adults who have visual impairments in many different settings, including public schools, state schools or hospitals, special schools for the blind, private schools or clinics, adult rehabilitation facilities, geriatric centers or nursing homes, music studios, private practice settings, or community programs. Music therapists may provide direct or consultant services and work with clients as individuals or in groups.

HOW MUSIC IS USED IN THERAPY

When people think of blindness and music, images of talented musicians like Ray Charles and Stevie Wonder often come to mind. However, for persons with visual impairments, as for the population in general, extraordinary musical talent is the exception rather than the rule (Codding 1988; Gfeller 1992d; Gfeller and Darrow 2008). Nevertheless, the field of music, either in performance or in related activities like piano tuning, long has been considered by many to be a "natural" vocational choice for blind individuals (Fleming and Moore 2010; Zinar 1987). In the United States, many schools for the blind, beginning with Perkins School for the Blind in 1832 and the New York School for the Blind in the mid-1800s, developed and maintained outstanding music programs that rivaled those of public schools, continuing to train excellent musicians well into the 1970s (Codding 1988; Heller 1987; Zinar 1987). Music's therapeutic benefits for persons with severe visual impairments received some mention in these programs; however, most literature on these programs focused on music education rather than music therapy (Codding 1988; Josepha 1968). Music therapy, as a specific discipline, is a relatively recent addition to schools and training centers for individuals who are blind or severely visually impaired, first being introduced to any wide extent in schools for the blind in the mid-1970s (Codding 1988). As the implementation of Public Law 94-142 in the mid-1970s led to including more students with visual impairments in the public schools and to the provision of educational services for more severely disabled persons (Codding 1988; Zinar 1987), music therapy, with its emphasis not on music learning and musical excellence for their own sake, but on using music to enhance learning and skill development in nonmusic areas and to promote desirable changes in intellectual, social, motor, and emotional functioning, began to play a more prominent role in the education and training of individuals with severe visual impairments.

Goodman (2007, 198) stated that "the focus of therapy with visually impaired involves music as an auditory cue for special awareness and travel, provision of directional cues, as a contingency to establish, maintain or eliminate inappropriate nonmusic behavior (i.e., motoric stereotypic movement)." Often, however, given the long history of music education for blind or severely visually impaired individuals and the prominence of some blind professional musicians, "music therapy, as a profession, is misunderstood by others who provide services to the visually disabled client" (Codding 1988, 124).

Certainly, the development of musical skills may be beneficial and rewarding to individuals who are blind or severely visually impaired, and music skills may be developed during music therapy sessions, thereby making the distinction between music therapy and music education vague or obscure at times (Josepha 1968). However, music therapists always focus primarily on using music and its related learning and expressive experiences to help individuals gain skills or improve their functioning in nonmusical areas, such as sensory, motor, cognitive, language, self-help, social, and emotional development (Adamek and Darrow 2010; Codding 1982, 1988; Gfeller 1992d; Josepha 1968; Kersten 1981; Lathom-Radocy 2014; Michel 1976, 1985). Therapeutically directed music experiences can help (1) provide accessible, enjoyable sensory stimulation for individuals who have impaired vision, thus reducing self-stimulation; (2) develop motor skills and increase independent mobility; (3) develop auditory memory and discrimination; (4) develop and reinforce academic concepts; (5) enhance self-concept and assist in emotional development; (6) promote social interaction and increase communication with others; and (7) provide opportunities for relaxation, development of leisure skills, and aesthetic enrichment.

Music Therapy Experiences Provide Accessible, Enjoyable Sensory Stimulation and Help Reduce Self-Stimulation

Blind or severely visually impaired individuals, especially those who are very young, congenitally blind, or have additional disabilities, often engage in various types of self-stimulatory behavior, such as rocking, poking or rubbing the eyes, shaking the fingers in front of the face, moving the head side to side, head-rolling, head-bobbing, or head-banging (Codding 1982, 1988; Gfeller 1992d; Kersten 1981; Lovejoy and Estridge 1987). Some theorize that individuals with severe visual impairments who lack visual input and stimulation continue to engage in these mannerisms or ritualistic behaviors (sometimes termed *blindisms*) long beyond the normal period in infant development because these movements help relieve tension and frustration and/or provide satisfying sensations (Codding 1982; Kern and Wolery 2001; Kersten 1981). When individuals withdraw into self-stimulatory behaviors, however, it is difficult for them to attend to external cues and learn to interact successfully and appropriately with people and objects in their environment. Therefore, therapeutic and educational programs often try to reduce self-stimulatory mannerisms.

Although music experiences may have visual components, music is primarily an auditory phenomenon that is not dependent upon vision for its perception or performance. Therefore, music provides a source of sensory stimulation that is very accessible to blind or visually impaired individuals, as well as being something that is enjoyable to many and viewed by society as a very appropriate and even desirable means of sensory stimulation and enrichment. Music activities, such as listening or playing instruments, may be used as rewards for individuals who are working on reducing or extinguishing ritualistic behaviors (Codding 1982). Attractive music stimuli also may divert an individual's attention from self-stimulatory behavior and help focus attention on positive activities, such as grasping and playing instruments (Codding 1982, 1988; Gfeller 1992d; Kersten 1981). In addition, the motor activity involved in playing instruments or moving to music also may help individuals discharge tension and frustration in a socially acceptable manner, reducing the need to relieve tension by stereotypic mannerisms (Kersten 1981). Older persons with severe visual impairments also may learn to decrease tension and frustration and improve their control over stereotypic mannerisms by music-mediated relaxation exercises (Kersten 1981) or other music experiences (e.g., instrumental improvisation, song writing) that focus on emotional expression, anxiety control, or the development of alternative behaviors or coping mechanisms.

Music Therapy Experiences Develop Motor Skills and Increase Independent Mobility and Interaction with the Environment

One of the greatest needs of persons with severe visual impairments is that of developing skills to move about their environment as independently as possible. This process involves developing (a) an *awareness of one's body parts* and their position in space, (b) *orientation* skills that allow one to use various sensory processes to develop spatial awareness and establish one's position in relation to other objects in the environment, and (c) *mobility* skills to move fluidly and confidently from one place to another (Codding 1982; Gfeller 1992d; Goodman 2007). These areas also greatly impact an individual's ability to explore and learn from the environment (Adamek and Darrow 2010; Codding 1982).

Many different types of therapeutically directed music experiences can help blind or severely visually impaired clients develop body image, spatial awareness, orientation, mobility, and environmental exploration skills (Adamek and Darrow 2010; Atterbury 1990; Bachman 1991; Birkenshaw-Fleming 1993; Codding 1982, 1988; Gfeller 1992d; Jospeha 1968; Kersten 1981; Lathom-Radocy 2014; Michel 1976, 1985; Nocera 1979; Salas and Gonzalez 1991; Zinar 1987). Songs that require clients to move or touch body parts can be used to help them develop an accurate body image, which is one of the prerequisites to moving about in space successfully. As the clients gain skills and confidence, spatial concepts and simple locomotor and nonlocomotor movement patterns can be taught and practiced with action songs, musical games, and simple dances. Movement-to-music exercises and techniques from the Dalcroze eurhythmics approach, with their emphasis on large muscle movement, exploration of space, time, and energy, object awareness, tactile sensitivity, and consciousness of muscle movement, also may be very useful in developing confident and fluid movement in visually impaired persons (Atterbury 1990; Bachman 1991; Kersten

1981; Frego, Liston, Hama, and Gillmeister 2008). In fact, Dalcroze himself applied his approach to blind individuals and provided specific exercises directed toward them (Bachman 1991; Kersten 1981).

Initially, music therapists might have clients do movement activities on mats to provide a defined, safe place in which to move. Later, the therapist can encourage environmental exploration by having clients reach out to find and play instruments and by having them walk across the room to find an instrument that is being played. Clients who are reluctant to move independently may be encouraged to explore the space around them if a guide rope is strung across the room at waist height or if they are paired with sighted partners. Kern and Wolery (2001) described a playground modified with a ridged pipe connecting musical play stations so that a visually impaired child could move from one station to the next.

Scarves and streamers also may be used as aids to investigate the space around a client's body. Research demonstrates that rhythmic music facilitates travel training and promotes a smooth walking gait, even in congenitally blind individuals (Unkefer 1958, cited in Jospeha 1968). Auditory cues and techniques, such as pairing specific songs with specific rooms, also may be used to facilitate mobility training and teach travel routes (Codding 1988). Thaut (2008, 196) explains *Auditory Perception Training (APT)*, which includes "auditory perception and sensory integration." This method uses all the components of musical sound, integrated with other sensory modalities, with movement to music. Walking is a rhythmic activity for which rhythmic music can facilitate neurological organization.

Successfully exploring and playing instruments in music therapy sessions may give clients the incentive and confidence to explore other aspects of their environment. For example, engaging in creative clinical musical improvisation with a music therapist using drum, cymbal, tambourine, piano, guitar, and voice helped a blind four-year-old child develop the skills and confidence to reach out to and explore other aspects of the world (Salas and Gonzales 1991). The ability, motivation, and confidence to explore and interact with one's environment is very important to an individual's overall development, for it is by exploring, manipulating, and interacting with objects and people in one's environment that one develops and refines many basic physical, cognitive, social, and emotional skills. Pavlicevic (2000, 272) distinguished between music improvisation, as seen in jazz, and MT improvisation, during which the client and therapist both contribute; the finished product is not as important as the process, for the goal is "to create an intimate interpersonal relationship between therapist and client through the musical event."

Music Therapy Experiences Help Develop Auditory Memory and Discrimination

When individuals are blind or severely visually impaired, their ability to receive information through the visual sense is absent, reduced, or distorted. Thus, other sensory modalities, especially the auditory sense, become vitally important for environmental awareness, learning, mobility, and interaction with others. Since music is largely an auditory phenomenon, it can play an important role in developing, training, and refining auditory skills. In addition, because many types of music experiences also often involve tactile and kinesthetic components, music may help individuals integrate their aural, kinesthetic, and tactile senses (Herlein 1975; Thaut 2008).

Sapp (2011) used the program "Somebody's Jumping on the Floor," which uses rhythms and music to teach orientation and mobility (O & M) skills to young children (developmental level of 2–7 years). They must learn conceptual information, such as body parts and position words, as well as movement skills and orientation to auditory cues that help them move safely in their environment. Through the rhythm and word patterns of songs, children can repeat the activity many times and acquire improved movement skills.

Songs, chants, directed listening activities, movement-to-music games or exercises, and musical instruments all can be used as part of therapeutically directed music experiences designed to help individuals learn to become aware of and respond to sounds, localize and track sounds, discriminate among sounds or sound patterns, and recall and imitate sequences of sounds or words (Codding 1982, 1988; Moog 1987; Nocera 1979). Memory skills developed as part of music auditory training programs also may help visually impaired persons learn to recall longer and longer selections of vocal or instrumental music, thus enabling them to memorize parts needed to participate in instrumental or vocal performance ensembles.

Music Therapy Experiences Help Develop and Reinforce Academic Concepts

Most people acquire much of their general information and knowledge through their eyes. Although blind or partially sighted persons have the same range of intellectual capabilities as their sighted peers, they must rely on senses and experiences other than visual ones for most of their learning. Songs and musical games dealing with various academic concepts, such as colors, numbers, days of the week, months of the year, shapes, and simple relationships, can help individuals who have severe visual impairments acquire much basic academic information and vocabulary in nonvisual ways (Codding 1982, 1988; Lathom-Radocy 2014; Nocera 1979; Sapp 2011). Music also can be used as a structure to help individuals recognize and discriminate among common environmental sounds (Codding 1988; Michel 1985) or to teach the sequence of steps needed to perform basic self-help, dressing, and grooming skills (Adamek and Darrow 2008; Gfeller 1992d; Gfeller and Darrow 2008; Michel 1985). In addition, music activities can be formulated and structured to correspond to Piaget's stages of cognitive development (Codding 1982; Radocy and Boyle 2012; Rider 1978, 1981), affording children who are blind or partially sighted with auditory and tactile experiences that will provide stimulation and learning experiences vital to successful academic development. Thus, auditory and tactile experiences can be used in place of visual experiences to help children with severe visual impairments master basic skills, facilitating their movement through the sensorimotor, pre-operational, concrete operations, and formal operations stages of cognitive development.

Music Therapy Experiences Enhance Self-Concept and Assist in Emotional Development

Although visual impairments do not in and of themselves adversely affect emotional adjustment and self-concept, negative or overprotective reactions and attitudes of significant others to the disability and the visually impaired person can lead to feelings of helplessness, dependence, lack of acceptance, and low self-esteem (Codding 1982; Gfeller 1992d; Lathom-Radocy 2014; Pfeiffer and Pinquart 2013). Visually impaired people also may experience many frustrations as they try to get along in a world geared for sighted people, and these frustrations may lead to feelings of anger or anxiety (Birkenshaw-Fleming 1993; Kersten 1981). Through involvement in various types of music therapy experiences, blind or visually impaired individuals can learn to express feelings and emotions appropriately, find constructive ways of coping with frustrations, and achieve successes and personal accomplishments that will help foster a healthy self-concept (Birkenshaw-Fleming 1993; Codding 1982, 1988; Gfeller 1992d; Josepha 1968; Kersten 1981; Lathom-Radocy 2014; Nocera 1979; Salas and Gonzalez 1991; Shoemark 1991).

Many music activities, such as singing, writing songs, or playing musical instruments, can give blind or partially sighted individuals accessible, socially acceptable outlets for emotional expression. In addition, music, with its many timbres and wide range of dynamics, can provide a depth of expression that might otherwise be lacking for individuals who are unable to perceive the nuances associated with gestures and facial expressions. Music therapists have also used musical exploration experiences incorporating improvisational music therapy techniques to help blind clients develop increased self-confidence and more positive affect (Salas and Gonzalez 1991; Shoemark 1991). Moreover, as the visually impaired gain skills in singing or in playing a musical instrument, as they perform successfully with ensembles, or as they learn to move about freely and independently in dances, they can gain a sense of belongingness and feelings of mastery and accomplishment that will help increase their self-confidence and build their self-esteem: "Music allows for a degree of physiological and psychological equivalency with the sighted, a vital aspect of the self-image and esteem needs of nonsighted individuals" (Kersten 1987, 132).

Adults who have declining vision or individuals who experience visual impairments later in life also may need assistance both in learning to accept the changes imposed by their visual disability and in developing skills to minimize the impairment's impact on their daily life. Music therapy experiences that are structured to provide immediate success, personal gratification, and concrete evidence of personal accomplishment can help boost clients' confidence and self-concept and be important parts of their rehabilitation programs (Codding 1988; Gardstrom and Hiller 2010; Gfeller 1992d; Gfeller and Darrow 2008; Josepha 1968; Lathom-Radocy 2014). In addition, music experiences involving song writing, lyric discussion, or instrumental improvisation techniques can be used to help individuals express and work through some of the emotions and psychological issues associated with their visual impairment and its effect on various aspects of their lives. Music discussion need not be limited to lyrics. It can include other musical aspects, such as "listening and discussing any type of music; this process could conceivably revolve around purely instrumental (not-lyrical) works rather than song material" (Gardstrom and Hiller 2010, 47).

Music Therapy Experiences Promote Social Interaction and Increase Communication with Others

Music activities are often inherently social experiences. Whether they be one-to-one experiences involving interaction only between client and therapist or group activities involving interaction with visually impaired or sighted others, the music therapist can structure music experiences to foster social interaction and interpersonal communication (Birkenshaw-Fleming 1993; Codding 1982, 1988; Gfeller 1992d; Kersten 1981, 1987; Moog 1987; Nocera 1979; Nordoff and Robbins 1977; Salas and Gonzalez 1991; Shoemark 1991). For example, clinical improvisational techniques can be used in individual music therapy sessions to help clients learn to interact and participate with the therapist in music making. Shoemark (1991) found that interactional skills developed in individual music therapy sessions using piano improvisation also helped increase participation and cooperation in classroom activities.

Group music activities, such as dances, singing groups, or instrumental ensembles, can provide opportunities for visually impaired clients to interact and socialize with each other and/or with their sighted peers. As they participate in music groups, clients develop and practice social skills such as taking turns, listening to others, following directions, and cooperating with others. Group song-writing or composition projects, lyric discussion activities, or group improvisation exercises also may be structured to provide them with opportunities to learn group problem-solving skills. In addition, many music activities provide situations in which visually impaired individuals can communicate and interact as full participants, making physical contributions equal to those of their sighted peers. Kersten (1987, 64) observed that "this feeling of belonging and equality is extremely important because their other opportunities for social and physical interaction are often limited."

Music Therapy Experiences Provide Opportunities for Relaxation, Development of Leisure Skills, and Aesthetic Enrichment

Like all people, individuals who are blind or severely visually impaired need activities that are relaxing, that provide for constructive use of leisure time, and that enable aesthetic enrichment and fulfillment. Music activities provide experiences that are easily accessible through senses other than vision and that are not subject to visual values (Moog 1987; Zinar 1987). Music therapists, with their specialized knowledge of the needs and learning styles of visually impaired individuals and their knowledge of music activities and materials and ways these may be adapted, are well equipped to structure music experiences in ways that will promote full, successful involvement and participation by blind or partially sighted individuals.

Persons who have limited vision must concentrate intently and attend vigilantly to auditory and tactile cues in their environment. Robb (2003, 267) noted that "sighted children use their vision to maintain focused and sustained attention. Children with visual impairments must concentrate on an activity primarily through listening." This state of constant attention and alertness can lead to physical and mental tension and fatigue (Kersten 1981, 1987). Relaxation or movement exercises done to music can help relieve muscle tension, physical strain, and psychological tension, while also serving to reduce fatigue and revitalize mental processes (Birkenshaw-Fleming 1993; Kersten 1981, 1987; Zinar 1987). In addition, listening to music (live or recorded), moving or dancing to music, or actively participating in music making, either by singing or playing instruments, all can provide both enjoyable leisure-time activities and aesthetically rewarding experiences for visually impaired individuals. Although some adaptations of instructional methods may be necessary, blind or partially sighted individuals have few limitations to participation in most music activities (Atterbury 1990; Birkenshaw-Fleming 1993; Gfeller and Darrow 2008; Kersten 1981, 1987; Levinson and Bruscia 1985; McReynolds 1988; Moog 1987; Zinar 1987). As Coates (2012, 66) stated, "Musical tasks that sighted band students perform can be performed equally well by visually impaired band students with the assistance of accommodations and modifications." This is an example of inclusion, which is occurring in public schools. It takes special effort, but music teachers and therapists can make participation available to visually impaired students.

Moreover, since persons with limited vision cannot relate to or contribute equally with sighted individuals in many other types of leisure pursuits (e.g., watching or participating in athletic contests, attending art exhibits, plays, or movies), music activities can provide welcome opportunities for them to actively participate in leisure or recreational activities right alongside individuals who are not visually impaired (Birkenshaw-Fleming 1993; Codding 1982, 1988; Gfeller 1992d; Gfeller and Darrow 2008; Kersten 1981, 1987; Zinar 1987).

While job training is not usually the focus of music therapy, some visually impaired persons do develop musical interests and skills that eventually may enable them to support themselves economically (e.g., by performing or tuning pianos). Jacko, Cobo, Cobo, Fleming, and Moore (2010) described a music production training program called "Better Chance." This program, developed at the Miami Lighthouse for the Blind and Visually Impaired, allows visually impaired individuals to learn to use Musical Instrument Digital Interface (MIDI) technology. This training can be applied in music production and sound engineering, incorporating marketable skills that can lead to independence. This same facility provides a braille music distance learning curriculum accessible to any musician worldwide (Website 2015).

Some blind or partially sighted individuals have even become music therapists (Michel 1985), using their music skills to help children and adults with many different kinds of disabilities improve their physical, psychological, social, or emotional functioning. While music therapists certainly will encourage interested and talented clients in these pursuits, they also will recognize that music or music-related vocations are not right for every visually impaired client, even one who has musical talent. Certainly music can be a compensatory medium or device for visually impaired persons, but that is not music's only benefit: "Therapists must always take care not to overemphasize the compensatory benefits of music for the visually handicapped, but to focus attention on the individual behind the music-making" (Michel 1976, 34).

Finally, in a world that is devoid of visual stimulation and visual perceptions of beauty, music's many timbres, dynamics, and styles can bring a richness of aesthetic experiences that otherwise might be lacking. Music is one aesthetic area that is completely accessible without sight (Moog 1987).

SPECIAL CONSIDERATIONS AND TIPS FOR SUCCESS

Because visually impaired individuals have limited abilities to explore instruments visually or to observe others playing them, they must be given plenty of time to touch and hold instruments and experiment with ways of playing and moving them. Since individuals who have severe visual impairments learn more successfully from multisensory experiences (Codding 1982), tactile or movement experiences should reinforce verbal instruction whenever possible. When giving directions or instructions to groups that include blind or partially sighted persons, one must remember to verbally describe all visual demonstrations and verbally repeat any visually displayed information. In addition, one must learn to describe things in tactile as well as visual terms. Atterbury (1990), Birkenshaw-Fleming (1993), Codding (1982), and Zinar (1987) provide many other practical suggestions for making different types of music experiences more accessible to persons with limited vision.

Different types of adaptations for printed material, including magnification, special lighting, enlarged print, or braille, may be useful with different individuals, depending on their degree of visual impairment (Atterbury 1990; Birkenshaw-Fleming 1993; Codding 1982; Herlein 1975; McReynolds 1988; Smaligo 1998; Zinar 1987). A braille system of music notation exists; however, the sighted person must recognize that the braille system differs in concept from the print system of music notation and also involves a memory dimension (Herlein 1975; Siligo 2005). Special electronic devices, such as the Varispeech machine, the Optacon, or the Kurzweil reader, also may be useful in making materials accessible to blind or visually impaired individuals (Levinson and Bruscia 1985; Zinar 1987). Coates (2012, 64) recommends the music transcription software "Goodfeel" and "Toccato" to create braille documents: "Both programs come with an OCR scanning program called Shap-Eye, which scans, edits, and converts the music document into a notation interchange file format (NIFF) file or extensible markup language (XML) format." Printed materials should have large, black letters that contrast sharply with the background. Some students prefer a white symbol on a black background. Visual aids should also be large, simple, and uncluttered. In work with clients who read braille, it may be beneficial to label autoharp chord bars, resonator bells, and piano keys with braille letters. These clients also may be able to learn to read braille music notation.

Braille, large-print, and recorded music materials are available from the Music Division of the Library of Congress, Division for the Blind and Physically Handicapped, in Washington, D.C., as well as from other sources. For more extensive lists of resources and of organizations providing services and music materials to individuals who are blind or who have severe visual impairments, see Atterbury (1990), Coates (2012), Codding (1982), Kersten (1981, 1987), Siligo (2005), Smaligo (1998), and Zinar (1987).

QUESTIONS FOR THOUGHT AND DISCUSSION

1. How do varying degrees of visual impairment affect people's ability to interact with others and move about in their environment? What implications might this have for the structure and implementation of music experiences with this population?
2. Discuss some of the special characteristics and needs of visually impaired individuals. What implications do these have for music therapy programming?
3. Why are music experiences useful for therapeutic interventions with visually impaired individuals? Are some types of experiences and activities more useful or beneficial than others? Which ones? Why?
4. Describe some specific music therapy experiences that might be used with visually impaired individuals to (1) provide accessible, enjoyable sensory stimulation and reduce self-stimulation; (2) develop motor skills and increase independent mobility; (3) develop auditory memory and discrimination; (4) develop and reinforce academic concepts; (5) enhance self-concept and assist in emotional development; (6) promote social interaction and increase communication with others; and (7) provide opportunities for relaxation, development of leisure skills, and aesthetic enrichment. What unique benefits does music provide in each of these areas?
5. List several special considerations that may be important to remember when developing therapeutic intervention strategies for visually impaired persons. Why are these important? What are their implications for the structure of music therapy intervention strategies?
6. For each of the situations listed below, (a) define the problem or areas of need for the client or group of clients, (b) describe one or more of the goals you might pursue in music therapy sessions with the client(s), (c) describe music activities you might use to help the client(s) meet those goals, (d) tell how the music activities you described relate to the goals and needs of the client(s), and (e) mention any special considerations you might want to take into account when working with the client(s).

Situation 1:
　　Sean is a five-year-old blind child who has been referred to you for music therapy. This is his first year in a school setting. Up to this point in his life, Sean's mother has done almost everything for him. She rarely lets him move around without holding her hand, except when he is in the safe confines of a large playpen. Sean is a very demanding and egocentric child who is used to having his every wish immediately fulfilled. He is an only child, and he has had almost no contact with other children his own age. His expressive and receptive language skills approximate those of a

normal five-year-old child. Sean likes to manipulate objects and enjoys producing sounds on a piano or toy xylophone. He can walk, but he is reluctant to move around without holding someone's hand. Sean does not interact with his classmates; he either ignores them or pushes them away.

Situation 2:

Three young adult males who have become blind after injuries received in car and motorcycle accidents have been added to your music therapy group of developmentally disabled adults. Their short-term memory skills have also been impaired. These men need to learn to adjust to their lack of vision and find ways to interact successfully, appropriately, and cooperatively with others in spite of their visual impairments. They also need to find constructive outlets to discharge anger and frustration and learn appropriate ways to express their feelings. These individuals are still working on mobility skills; at the present time, they are a bit wary of moving about independently and lack confidence and freedom in independent movement. All three say they like music, especially rock music. They enjoy singing, and one used to play guitar before his accident.

SUGGESTIONS FOR FURTHER READING

Adamek, M. & Darrow, A-A. (Eds.) (2008). Students with vision loss. In *Music in special education* (2nd ed.) (215–237). Silver Spring, MD: The American Music Therapy Association.

Atterbury, B. W. (1990). *Mainstreaming exceptional learners in music.* Englewood Cliffs, NJ: Prentice-Hall.

Baker, F. & Wigram, T. (2005). *Songwriting: Methods, techniques and clinical applications for music therapy clinicians, educators, and students.* London: Jessica Kingsley.

Birkenshaw-Fleming, L. (1993). *Music for all: Teaching music to people with special needs.* Toronto: Gordon V. Thompson.

Brescia, K. E. (Ed.) (1991). *Case studies in music therapy.* Phoenixville, PA: Barcelona.

Codding, P. (1982). Monograph 2: Music therapy for visually impaired children. In W. B. Lathom & C. T. Eagle, Jr. (Eds.), *Music therapy for handicapped children* (43–95). Washington, D.C.: National Association for Music Therapy.

Codding, P. A. (1988). Music in the education/rehabilitation of visually disabled and multiply handicapped persons: A review of literature from 1946–1987. In C. E. Furman (Ed.), *Effectiveness of music therapy procedures: Documentation of research and clinical practice* (107–136). Washington, D.C.: National Association for Music Therapy.

Gfeller, K. & Darrow, A-A. (2008). Music therapy in the treatment of sensory disorders: Vision In W. B. Davis, K. E. Gfeller, & M. H. Thaut (Eds.), *An introduction to music therapy: Theory and practice* (3rd ed.) (390–404). Silver Spring, MD: The American Music Therapy Association, Inc.

Grocke, D. & Wigram, T. (2007). *Receptive methods in music therapy: Techniques and clinical applications for music therapy clinicians, educators, and students.* London: Jessica Kingsley.

Lathom-Radocy, W. (Ed.) (2014). Children with visual impairments or blindness. In W. Lathom-Radocy (Ed.), *Pediatric music therapy* (2nd ed.) (238–277). Springfield, IL: Charles C Thomas.

McReynolds, J. C. (1988). Helping visually impaired students succeed in band. *Music Educators Journal, 75(1),* 36–38.

Smaligo, M. A. (1998). Resources for helping blind music students. *Music Educators Journal, 85(2),* 23–26, 45.

Standley, J. (1991). *Music techniques in therapy, counseling, and special education.* St. Louis: MMB Music.

Taessch, R., (2002). *An introduction to music for the blind student: A course in Braille music reading.* Valley Forge, PA: Dancing Dots.

Zinar, R. (1987). *Music activities for special children.* West Nyack, NY: Parker.

Chapter Eleven

MUSIC THERAPY FOR INDIVIDUALS WHO HAVE ORTHOPEDIC IMPAIRMENTS

Definition

Orthopedics is the branch of medical science that deals with disorders involving the skeleton, joints, muscles, and fascia (i.e., the membranes that cover and separate the muscles). Orthopedically impaired individuals have some neuromuscular or skeletal disorder or condition that temporarily or permanently interferes with the normal functioning of their bones, muscles, and/or joints. All orthopedic impairments interfere in some way with a person's physical abilities, by adversely affecting mobility, muscular or joint strength, motor control and coordination, range of motion, muscle tone, muscle endurance, balance, posture, or locomotor patterns. Orthopedic impairments are often exclusively medical problems; they do not necessarily interfere with intellectual functioning. Other terms used to describe this general category of disability or impairment include *physically disabled, physically handicapped, physically impaired,* or *crippled* (Rudenberg 1982; Staum 1988; Thaut 1992a). Disabled person is the "correct" term in 2015. Many consider "crippled" and "handicapped" (although it is in some legislation) offensive.

Individuals who have orthopedic impairments may be described as *ambulatory, semiambulatory,* or *nonambulatory,* depending upon their ability to walk or move about independently or with varying types of assistance. Orthopedic impairments or handicaps also may be classified by degree, as *mild, moderate,* or *severe* (Atterbury 1990; Rudenberg 1982). Mildly impaired individuals may require little special physical therapy or medical treatment, while those with more severe impairments may require extensive therapy and special educational or medical services. However, many classification systems exist for orthopedic problems. DiPaola and Franko (2012) even describe apps that can be used to find the appropriate classification.

Causes and Associated Conditions

Orthopedic disabilities may result from either *congenital* (present at birth) or *adventitious* (acquired) neuromuscular or skeletal conditions or disorders, and may occur at any age. Any individual prognosis depends upon many factors, including the exact type of condition, disorder, or injury that caused the orthopedic impairment, the severity of the condition, and any associated disabilities, and the availability of necessary medical, rehabilitative, and other support services. Some orthopedic impairments may be relatively uncomplicated and easily treatable (e.g., simple fracture), while others may be more complex and permanent (e.g., cerebral palsy) or even degenerative or terminal (e.g., Duchenne muscular dystrophy). Conditions frequently associated with physical disabilities or orthopedic impairments include cerebral palsy, spina bifida, muscular dystrophy, multiple sclerosis, poliomyelitis, arthrogryposis, malformations and joint dislocations, arthritis, spinal cord damage, severe head injury, stroke, severe burns, fractures, amputations, and brittle bone disorders (osteogenesis imperfecta and osteoporosis) (Atterbury 1990; Rudenberg 1982; Staum 1988, 1996; Thaut 1992a).

Cerebral Palsy

Cerebral palsy (CP) results from damage to the brain's motor control centers. It is the most common motor disability in childhood (Accardo 2008, 17). As many as 10,000 babies born in the United States each year will develop cerebral palsy (Centers for Disease Control 2010); about 764,000 children and adults in the United States have cerebral palsy (United Cerebral Palsy [UCP] 2013). It is a nonprogressive disorder of the coordination of muscle action that results in disorders of movement and posture.

Eighty-five to ninety percent of all cases of cerebral palsy are congenital (CDC 2015; Lovejoy and Estridge 1987; Thaut 1992a). Congenital causes include complications connected with prematurity, lack of oxygen to the fetal brain, maternal infections or heavy smoking or heavy alcohol or drug use, exposure to toxic substances, cerebral hemorrhage, severe newborn jaundice, or severe birth trauma. The 10 to 15 percent of cases of cerebral palsy that may be acquired in childhood, adolescence, or adulthood most often are caused by head injuries (e.g., skull fractures and brain lacerations), brain infections (e.g., meningitis and encephalitis), or problems relating to blood flow to the brain (e.g., cerebral vascular accidents, clotting problems, heart defects, or sickle cell anemia) (CDC 2015). Most children who have cerebral palsy live to be adults; life expectancy depends in part upon the severity of the condition and any associated disabilities (Lovejoy and Estridge 1987; UCP 2013).

Cerebral palsy may be classified according to four main types of movement disorder (*spastic, dyskinetic* [includes athetoid, choreoathetoid and dystonic], *ataxic,* mixed, *atonic*). This may be further defined by body parts involved (*monoplegia* – one arm or leg affected; *hemiplegia* – one side of the body (both arm and leg) affected; *paraplegia* – only the legs affected; *diplegia* – major involvement in the legs, minor involvement in the arms; *triplegia* – three limbs affected, usually one arm and both legs; *quadriplegia* – both arms and both legs affected). Special consideration is given to "stiff muscles (spasticity), uncontrolled movement (dyskinesia) and poor balance and coordination (ataxia)" (CDC 2015). Most (77.4%) of individuals diagnosed with CP have *spastic cerebral palsy,* which is characterized by tight muscles (high muscle tone or *hypertonicity*), tense, stiff movements, and abnormal movement patterns and postures resulting from the inability of the muscles to relax and the disturbance of normal muscle reflexes. Others have *dyskinetic cerebral palsy,* characterized by involuntary, purposeless movements and abnormal, irregular movement patterns, as well as varying muscle tone. In *ataxic cerebral palsy,* damage to the cerebellum results in a poor sense of equilibrium and poor balance control, unsteady and uncoordinated movements, an unsteady gait, and lack of muscle tone and power. In mixed types, more than one type of cerebral palsy is present. Frequently, the mix includes both dyskinesia and spasticity, although ataxia or tremor also may be part of mixed conditions. *Atonic cerebral palsy* is found primarily in infants and is characterized by very low muscle tone (*hypotonia*).

Within each type of cerebral palsy, wide ranges of involvement and disability may occur. Those with mild involvement may have some awkward movements but usually can walk and talk, and often have normal intelligence. Those with moderate impairment may walk unsteadily, have difficulty controlling and coordinating hand movements, and have some speech difficulties. Those who have severe involvement frequently are nonambulatory, have many speech and communication problems, and often have other associated disabilities.

Cerebral palsy does not necessarily result in deficits in intelligence; in fact, about one-third of all the individuals diagnosed with cerebral palsy have average or above average intelligence. However, 30–50 percent of children with cerebral palsy will be intellectually disabled. This is most common in those diagnosed with spastic quadriplegia (National Institute of Neurological Disorders and Stroke [NINDS] 2015). Still, many individuals who have cerebral palsy have other impairments or disabilities (e.g., visual impairments, hearing impairments, perceptual problems, speech disorders, seizures, and learning disabilities), and over half have some degree of mental retardation (Atterbury 1990; Lovejoy and Estridge 1987; Rudenberg 1982; Thaut 1992a). There is no cure for cerebral palsy; however, interdisciplinary treatment, which may include things like medical services, physical therapy, speech therapy, special education, neurological services, orthopedic surgery, psychological services, social services, or vocational training, may help individuals develop skills to function as independently as possible.

Spina Bifida

Spina bifida (literally, "cleft spine"), the most common permanently disabling congenital birth defect in the United States (SBA National Resource Center 2015), results when one or more of the spinal rings in the vertebrae do not fuse properly during fetal development, thereby leaving an opening in the spine through which some or all of the spinal canal's contents may protrude (Atterbury 1990; Lathom-Radocy 2014; Lovejoy and Estridge 1987; Rudenberg 1982; SBA 2015; Thaut 1992a). In the mildest form, *spina bifida occulta*, skin covers the portion of the spine that had not fused properly; usually there is no protrusion of the spinal cord, and the nerve tissues remain intact. In the more severe forms, saclike protrusions expose either the *meninges* (coverings of the spinal cord) or the spinal cord and its nerves. This is called *myelomeningocele* or *spina bifida cystica* (SBA 2015). Spinal nerves do not develop past the opening in the spine. Therefore, depending on where the opening occurs, various nerve circuits, such as those needed for walking or for bowel and bladder control, may remain incomplete. Usually, the higher along the spinal column the location of the lesion or defect occurs, the greater the functional impairment. Many with spina bifida have some degree of *hydrocephalus*, in which the head is enlarged because the normal circulation of cerebrospinal fluid is blocked, and the fluid accumulates in the brain. Hydrocephalus is now commonly treated with a shunt operation where a tube is inserted to drain the excess fluid from the brain to some other part of the body.

Although early surgery may be performed to close the spinal opening or to reinsert or protect the meninges and spinal cord, later treatment usually is required to correct or compensate for the accompanying neurological deficits. While the disorders or impairments associated with spina bifida usually cannot be eliminated, various types of surgery, therapy, and medical treatment may help control them. Unless there are serious complications from hydrocephalus or severe infections, spina bifida usually does not affect an individual's intelligence, although learning disabilities are common in individuals with spina bifida (NINDS 2015). Also, while lower body paralysis may severely impact mobility, the lesions associated with spina bifida rarely impact the motor functioning of the arms or upper trunk.

Muscular Dystrophy

Muscular dystrophy (MD) is a degenerative genetic muscle disorder that is characterized by progressive muscle weakness. *Duchenne muscular dystrophy*, the most common and devastating type, primarily affects young males but in rare cases can affect girls (MDA 2015). MD occurs in about one of every 3,500 live male births. The estimated prevalence is 1.3 to 1.8 per 10,000 males, 5 through 24 years of age (CDC 2007). The genetic defect causing this condition, an absence of dystrophin, usually results in an onset of symptoms between ages two and five years, although symptoms may first occur as late as ages ten or eleven years. Muscles in the lower body and spine are affected first, with a gradual progression to other muscles. Initially, motor problems are minimal, with individuals having an abnormal swaying or waddling gait, difficulty climbing stairs, frequent falls, and a general lack of stamina. Children usually lose their ability to walk and become wheelchair-bound between the ages of ten and thirteen years. As the disease progresses, muscles become thin, reflexes disappear, bone deformities and muscle contractures become more prevalent, and respiratory and heart muscles also may begin to deteriorate. Death usually occurs before age twenty years, when muscle weakness becomes so severe that the individual succumbs to secondary complications such as heart failure or severe respiratory infections (Lovejoy and Estridge 1987; Thaut 1992a).

Other types of muscular dystrophy may also occur because of genetic defects (Lovejoy and Estridge 1987). *Limb-girdle muscular dystrophy* mainly affects the pelvic muscles. It can occur in both boys and girls, and ranges in severity from mild to extremely debilitating. Although death can result because of complications, death occurs less frequently than with Duchenne muscular dystrophy. Prognosis depends on the extent of muscle weakness and speed of muscle deterioration. *Facioscapulohumeral (FSH) muscular dystrophy*, a far more mild form of MD, primarily involves the face, arms, legs, shoulders, and chest or upper back, and can affect both males and females. Usually, symptoms do not appear until adolescence or adulthood, and progression is very slow. Another less common and less severe form of MD is *Becker muscular dystrophy*. Although its symptoms may resemble those of mild forms of Duchenne muscular dystrophy, initial symptoms usually appear at a later age, and individuals may maintain the ability to walk well into adulthood. Heart involvement is less common than in Duchenne muscular dystrophy. *Myotonic muscular dystrophy* is the adult form of the disease. Some with MD die in infancy; others live into adulthood with only moderate disability. Survival is related to type of MD and progression of the disorder (CDC 2015).

Multiple Sclerosis

Multiple sclerosis (MS) is a chronic, progressive disease resulting from damage to the myelin (covering of nerve fibers) and nerve fibers in the central nervous system that may involve the nerves affecting motor coordination and balance. MS most often strikes adults between the ages of 20 and 40 years;

periods of improvement usually alternate with periods of worsening symptoms. Symptoms and effects vary with the portion of the nervous system affected. Weakness, tremor of the limbs, impaired balance, and unsteady or stiff gaits are common motor problems associated with MS. In later stages, paralyses of various parts of the body may occur (Miller and Keane 1978). According to the National MS Society (2015), "Effective symptom management by an interdisciplinary team of healthcare professionals is one of the key components of comprehensive MS care."

Poliomyelitis

Poliomyelitis is a highly infectious viral disease that attacks the central nervous system and injures or destroys nerve cells that control the muscles, thereby causing temporary or permanent paralysis (Lovejoy and Estridge 1987; Miller and Keane 1978; Rudenberg 1982; Thaut 1992a; World Health Organization [WHO] 2015). Also known as *polio*, this disease most often affects the leg muscles, although it may affect any muscles, including those involved in breathing and swallowing. Five to ten percent die from paralysis of breathing muscles. Vaccination programs have now made the disease quite rare in this country. Due to a global effort, polio cases have decreased by over 99 percent since 1988 (WHO 2015). However, vaccination is still essential.

Arthrogryposis

Arthrogryposis multiplex congenita (AMC) is a congenital genetic condition characterized by stiff joints and weak muscles. The joint contractures are apparent at birth (Lathom-Radocy 2014). Depending on the extent and sites of involvement, these abnormalities in muscle and joint development result in various deformities such as turned-in shoulders, limited elbow flexion, pronated forearms, flexed wrists or fingers, dislocated hips, flexed or extended knees, curved spine (*scoliosis*), or turned-in feet (American Association of Neuromuscular and Electrodiagnostic Medicine (AANEM) 2015; Rudenberg 1982; Thaut 1992a). These deformities limit mobility and coordination to various extents. Various types of orthopedic surgeries may help correct some deformities. Although deformities and conditions associated with arthrogryposis may severely impact coordination and mobility, speech and intelligence usually are unaffected.

Malformations and Dislocations

Malformations and dislocations may occur in different bone structures and joints for various reasons throughout a person's life (Lovejoy and Estridge

1987; Miller and Keane 1978; Rudenberg 1982; Thaut 1992a). A dislocation occurs when two bones are out of place in the joint that connects them. *Congenital malformations* exist when infants are born with some bone structure that deviates from the normal in any way. Examples include *clubfoot* (a common hereditary foot malformation characterized by the heel being turned in under the ankle, the inner edge of the foot turned upward, and the sole and toes flexed downward), *clubhand* (hand and wrist deviated to one side as the result of a missing or shortened forearm bone), *webbed fingers, extra fingers, congenital flexed thumb* (thickened flexor tendon at the base of the thumb prohibits full extension), and some forms of *scoliosis* (abnormal spine curvatures to the left or right). *Congenital dislocations* usually occur when infants are born with bones displaced from joints because of some abnormality in bone development or joint construction that occurred during fetal development. One of the most common examples is *congenital dislocation of the hip.* Congenital malformations or dislocations may occur alone or in association with other conditions, syndromes, and deformities. Problems associated with congenital malformations and dislocations vary greatly according to the severity of the defect or to the severity of related conditions. Corrective treatment is available for most conditions, and may include various combinations of surgery, casting, bracing, splinting, and physical therapy.

Adventitious malformations or *deformities* of various bone structures and dislocations of various joints also have many causes. Deformities such as *scoliosis* (abnormal spinal curvature), *lordosis* (swayback), or *kyphosis* (humpback) may occur in connection with diseases (e.g., osteoporosis, rickets, muscular dystrophy, spina bifida, Marfan syndrome) that affect an individual's bones, muscles, or connective tissue. Contorted positions assumed in attempts to alleviate pain from tumors, injuries, spinal disk problems, or bone infections may also result in skeletal deformities. Pain is defined as "a multifaceted process made up of physiologic, psychosocial, and cultural parts" (Lukas 2004, 7). In addition, deformities may occur when bone fractures are not set properly or do not heal properly. *Adventitious dislocations* usually result from a blow or a fall, although some may occur in connection with extreme physical exertion. The most common sites for dislocation are *finger, thumb, shoulder, elbow, knee,* and *hip* joints. Problems associated with malformations and dislocations that occur later in life vary greatly and are often related to the severity of the defect or any associated diseases or conditions. Corrective treatment, which may include various combinations of surgery, casting, bracing, splinting, and physical therapy, is available for most orthopedic problems resulting from deformities or dislocations. In older persons with severe or chronic problems, the replacement of affected joints by artificial joints may be considered.

Arthritis

Among many bone disorders, "Arthritis is one of the most common diseases in the United States and is the leading cause of disability" (Hunder, 2006). It is characterized by inflammation or pain and stiffness in the joints. It is estimated that one in every five adults and 300,000 children in the U.S. have some type of arthritic disease (Arthritis Foundation 2015). Arthritis can occur in people of many different ages, from infants to elderly people. It can affect both the joints and the connective tissues throughout the body and causes pain, swelling, and stiffness. The damage to joints may be from many causes including the wearing away of (osteoarthritis), inflammation of the lining of joints (rheumatoid arthritis) and even genetic predisposition in some cases (Chang-Miller, 2013). Symptoms may come and go without warning; however, arthritis is a chronic condition that is always there even when symptoms are not present. Thus, arthritis usually requires long-term treatment and adjustments (Arthritis Foundation 1987; Chang-Miller 2013; Department of Health and Human Services 1986; Lovejoy and Estridge 1987; Miller and Keane 1978; Rudenberg 1982; Thaut 1992a).

One of the most common forms of chronic arthritis in children is *ideopathic arthritis* (JIA) (formerly called *juvenile rheumatoid arthritis* (JRA) (Chang-Miller, 2013). In the United States, about 300,000 children under the age of 16 years suffer from one of the three main forms of this disease: *systemic*, which involves the entire system, with symptoms like fever, rash, enlarged liver, spleen, and lymph nodes, muscle and skeletal aches and pains, and eventual inflammation of joints; *polyarticular*, which affects five or more joints, often affecting the small joints in the hands and feet along with ankles, knees, and hips; or *oligoarthritis* (formerly called *pauciarthritis*), which involves four or fewer joints. JRI affects girls more than boys; peak incidence occurs between two and five years of age. Older children may have an extended form of the disease involving multiple joints (Chang-Miller, 2013). Acute episodes of joint inflammation called flares are very painful and may vary in length from a few days to several weeks. There is no cure for JRI; treatment focuses on easing pain and preserving or, if possible, improving joint function. Many individuals who suffer from JRI, however, do experience remission.

In adults, the two main types of arthritis are

1. *rheumatoid arthritis*, which affects 1.2 million Americans, and is three times more common in women (Chang-Miller, 2013).
2. *osteoarthritis*, which is the most common form, especially among older adults (Arthritis Foundation 1987; Chang-Miller, 2013; Department of Health and Human Services 1986; Miller and Keane 1978).

Osteoarthritis, a degenerative joint disease caused by the disintegration or wearing away of the cartilage that covers the ends of the bone, occurs in about 27 million pople in the U. S. (Arthritis Foundation 2015). Women are affected more often than men. Joints that receive the most stress from weight-bearing over the years, such as fingers, knees, big toes, hips, and lower spine, are most likely to be involved. Symptoms vary from mild to severe, depending on the amount of degeneration. Pain and stiffness are felt when affected joints are used, and in more severe cases, movement at the joint may be restricted.

Rheumatoid arthritis, the more serious, virulent, and disabling disease, relates to inflammation and an abnormal response of the immune system. Both men and women are affected, but women over age 40 are at higher risk than men. This chronic systemic disease causes inflammatory changes throughout the body's connective tissues, affecting many joints, especially the small joints in the hands. Eventually, especially in more severe cases, the inflammation and thickening of tissue around various joints may lead to deformities or destruction of bones.

Treatment for individuals suffering from arthritic diseases is concerned with relieving pain, reducing inflammation, maintaining or restoring motion of the joint, preventing crippling deformities, helping maximize independent functioning, and reducing emotional stress. Various combinations of medication, balanced regimens of rest and exercise, applications of heat and cold, prescribed physical or occupational therapy, and adaptive or assistive devices may help treat or manage arthritis. For some individuals, surgical intervention involving joint repair or replacement may be recommended. Braces, casts, or splints may immobilize affected joints or help prevent deformities by maintaining good joint position.

Spinal Cord Damage

As reported by the Christopher and Dana Reeve Foundation (2015), 1,275,000 people (0.4% of the U. S. population) reported paralysis due to a spinal cord injury (SCI) .When the spinal cord is damaged in neck or back fractures, the flow of electrical impulses from the brain is interrupted, and various degrees of paralysis and loss of function result. SCI is diagnosed with consideration of the level, type, and severity of the injury to the vertebrae (NIH 2013). The site of the injury determines the extent of the damage; the farther up on the spinal cord the injury occurs, the more extensive the loss of function. When the spinal cord is damaged in the thoracic area or below, *paraplegia*, loss of use of the lower body movement and sensation occurs. Damage to the cervical area or below (to the thoracic area) of the spinal cord results in *tetraplegia* (formerly called *quadriplegia*), the loss of body movement and sensation below the neck. When spinal cord nerve pathways are completely destroyed, they do not regenerate and cannot be repaired by current medical techniques; thus, paralysis from spinal cord injuries is usually permanent. However, recent research offers new hope to persons who have been paralyzed by spinal cord injuries, challenging the belief that paralysis resulting from central nervous system damage is irreversible (National Paralysis Foundation, n.d.).

Paralysis often imposes many severe emotional, social, and occupational changes in a person's life. Therefore, treatment and rehabilitation of persons who have spinal cord injuries focuses on helping them adjust psychologically as well as helping them learn adaptive techniques to improve their daily functioning.

Severe Head Injury

Severe head injuries (closed head injuries, head trauma, traumatic brain injury) result from sudden mechanical force or blows to the head, such as may occur in accidents or falls, birth injuries, child abuse, contact sports, or motor vehicle accidents (Rudenberg 1982; Brain Injury.com). Brain injuries can be life threatening or result in residual dysfunctions in one or more sensory, motor, language, behavioral, or psychological areas, depending upon the extent and location of the brain injury. An injury within the skull is called closed head injury. If the skull is broken or penetrated, it is called open skull injury (Medline Plus 2015). Motor problems that can occur as the result of severe head injuries include *hemiplegia* (loss of movement and/or sensation on one side of the body), difficulties with motor control, motor planning, balance, or coordination, restricted range of motion, and limited muscle strength, loss of coordination, and endurance (Lucia 1987; Medline Plus 2015; Rudenberg 1982).

Severe Burns

Deep second-degree burns, presenting with blisters and some thickening of the skin, and third-degree burns, showing a widespread thickness with a white, leathery appearance (Healthline 2015), can cause temporary or permanent orthopedic handicaps because of contractures (i.e., permanent shortening and tightening of muscles), loss of body parts, or limitation of movement due to treatment procedures (Healthline 2015; Rudenberg 1982; Thaut 1992a). Thermal, chemical, or electrical agents, or radiation may cause burns. Third-degree burns, the most severe category, involve all skin layers and may involve tendons, muscles, and even bones. Nerves also are damaged. These burns do not heal spontaneously; they require skin grafting and often leave severe scars. Individuals who have third-degree burns often require prolonged periods of hospitalization and rehabilitation. Treatment may include bathing in special solutions, debridement (removal) of dead skin tissue, dressing changes, blood tests, physical or occupational therapy, and surgical procedures, such as skin grafts. These procedures may cause considerable pain. Lukas (2004, 7) noted that "if healthcare workers used music therapy consistently as an adjunct to decrease postoperative pain and anxiety levels in surgical patients, a positive physiological and psychological effect might be achieved." This holistic approach is noninvasive and cost effective.

Stroke

In a stroke, or *cerebrovascular accident* (CVA), the blood supply to the brain is temporarily blocked, thereby cutting off the brain's source of oxygen and damaging the brain cells (Davis, Gfeller, Thaut 2008; Prazich 1985). As the brain cells are damaged or die, the functions they control (e.g., speech, muscle movement, emotions, understanding) are lost or impaired (Miller and Keane 1978; National Stroke Association 2015; Prazich 1985; Zamula 1986). Motor problems that occur include paralysis (*hemiplegia*), muscle weakness (*hemiparesis*), difficulties in balance, or difficulties in coordination and motor planning and language.

Although there are about 7 million stroke survivors in the U. S., it is still the fifth leading cause of death. Nearly 800,000 new strokes occur each year. Someone dies from stroke every 4 minutes (National Stroke Association 2015). Among survivors, about 10 percent return to work without significant impairment, about 25 percent will be slightly disabled, about another 40 percent will be moderately disabled and require some special services, and about 10 percent will require institutional care (National Institute of Neurological Disorders and Stroke [NINDS] 2015; Zamula 1986).

Fractures

Fractures (broken bones) can impair movement either temporarily or permanently. Fractures most often are caused by trauma (e.g., in accidents, falls, severe blows to the affected part); they may also result from twisting caused by muscle spasms, indirect loss of leverage, or disease (osteoporosis) that causes decalcification of the bone (Medline Plus 2015; Miller and Keane 1978). As many as half of older women and a quarter of men over 50 years of age will break a bone due to osteoporosis (Medline Plus 2015). In simple or closed fractures, there are no open wounds. In compound or open fractures, the broken bone breaks through the soft tissues and skin, causing an open wound. Fractures are treated by aligning the broken ends of the bone and establishing bone continuity so healing can occur. Once the broken bone is set (and, in more severe breaks, internally stabilized by pins, nails, screws, or plates as necessary), the bone is immobilized by a cast or traction apparatus. Once the cast is removed, the patient will need to rebuild strength in the muscles that were not used while the bone was immobilized. After severe fractures or in cases where bones have not healed in proper alignment, range of motion or mobility may be permanently affected. Any muscle or nerve damage occurring along with a fracture also may impede a person's recovery of full function.

Amputations

Persons who have amputations lose all or part of a limb or limbs (Lovejoy and Estridge 1987; Medline Plus 2015; Miller and Keane 1978; Rudenberg 1982; Thaut 1992a). *Congenital amputations* occur when fetal limb buds fail to develop, resulting in the baby being born without limbs or parts of limbs. *Elective* or *acquired amputations* occur when a limb is removed due to an accident or surgery to treat or arrest certain medical conditions, such as blood vessel disorders, infections, bone tumors, gangrene, and malignancies. Most acquired upper limb amputations are the result of severe trauma, while most leg amputations are due to some type of blood vessel disorder. *Traumatic amputations* are often caused by accidents involving motor vehicles, farm machinery, or power tools, or by gunshot injuries.

Treatment and rehabilitation for individuals who have amputations includes exercises to strengthen surrounding muscles and prevent contractures and training in use of prosthetic devices (e.g., artificial limbs) for both functional and recreational activities. Since acquired amputations are usually very traumatic for a person, strong psychological support is necessary.

Brittle Bones (Osteogenesis Imperfecta)

For both children and adults, abnormally brittle bones resulting in frequent fractures and possible deformities and restrictions in mobility can be a problem. *Osteogenesis imperfecta* (OI), is a hereditary condition that affects both males and females and is marked by abnormally brittle bones that fracture easily (Miller and Keane 1978; Thaut 1992a). It is caused by defects in the four genes that produce collagen, the protein that creates bone (Healthline 2015). Limbs may become shortened or deformed by repetitive fractures and broken bones that heal in deformed positions. When the condition develops during intrauterine life (*osteogenesis imperfecta congenita*), the child is born with deformities. The condition also may develop after birth (*osteogenesis imperfecta tarda*), with fractures usually beginning when the child begins walking. While physical activities for children with this condition may be severely restricted, and repeated fractures and resultant deformities may limit mobility, they usually have normal intelligence and do well academically.

Osteoporosis, a disease in which bones become fragile and porous, makes them more likely to break. It usually affects people over 50 years old. More than 10 million Americans are at high risk for developing osteoporosis (NIH 2015). Peak bone mass usually is achieved by the age of 30 years. Although women are five times more likely to suffer from osteoporosis, men also can develop the disease (National Osteoporosis Foundation 1995). Principal causes include lack of physical activity, lack of estrogens or androgens, and a chronic low intake of calcium. Osteoporosis also may occur in connection with endocrine disorders, bone marrow disorders, and nutritional disturbances (Miller and Keane 1978). Complications of osteoporosis include increased risk of fracture (especially for spine, wrist, and hip bones), postural deformities, pain, and loss of mobility. Appropriate exercise (including stretching, strengthening, balance, and walking), proper posture, and proper diet can help build and maintain strong bones and help avoid osteoporosis and its devastating effects. Special weight-bearing or resistive exercises to help pre-serve bone, strengthen back and hip muscles, and maintain flexibility usually are part of prevention and treatment programs for osteoporosis. Treatment also may include adjusting diet to insure adequate calcium and vitamin D intake and prescribing medications that slow bone loss for men and women.

COMMON CHARACTERISTICS, PROBLEMS, AND NEEDS OF CLIENTS

As evident from the preceding paragraphs, the population of orthopedically impaired individuals is quite heterogeneous, including persons with widely varying temporary or permanent conditions and ranging in age from infants to the elderly. Different types of conditions or diseases that cause orthopedic impairments also have wide ranges of impact, from very mild to very severe.

In addition, individuals who have orthopedic or physical disabilities often suffer from multiple handicaps (Thaut 1992a). If an individual's orthopedic impairment is caused by some trauma or condition (congenital or acquired) that damaged a portion of the brain or nervous system, the damage rarely is confined to one isolated area and often impairs more than one area. Thus, although diseases and conditions that result in orthopedic impairments do not necessarily affect other areas of functioning, some physically impaired individuals also may have intellectual, sensory, or speech deficits. Generally speaking, the more severe or extensive the individual's impairments or dis-abling conditions, the more adaptations or assistance the individual will need to carry out tasks of daily living.

Of course, any individual client will have a unique combination of abilities, needs, personality traits, strengths, and weaknesses that will impact his or her treatment program and functioning level; therefore, it is unwise to attempt to predict a particular person's skill levels or ceiling of abilities based on broad generalizations. One must always remember that "each person is unique, and different adaptations must be made for each" (Birkenshaw-Fleming 1993, 47). However, an awareness of some of those characteristics, problems, and needs which may be common to many clients who have some kind of condition that causes an orthopedic impairment will benefit both the therapist who desires to work with this population and the reader who wishes to understand how music therapy intervention strategies may benefit this population.

Whether the impairment is congenital or adventitious, permanent or temporary, orthopedically impaired clients need to make some personal and social adjustments. Some of their most immediate or obvious needs involve finding ways to carry out their normal activities of daily living despite limitations in mobility, range of motion, coordination, or muscular strength and endurance. Those with certain conditions (e.g., cerebral palsy) may need special positioning or handling techniques to help them make maximal use of their motor abilities (Goodman 2007; Lathom-Radocy 2014; Rudenberg 1982), while those with other conditions may need to learn to use prosthetic devices, wheelchairs, or other adaptive devices. Clients who are in constant pain from their orthopedic impairments also need something to relieve their pain and enable concentration elsewhere. Most orthopedically impaired individuals must be encouraged continually to function as independently as possible. Many will need motivation to exercise regularly to improve or maintain muscle tone and joint function. Since immobility and muscle weakness increase susceptibility to respiratory infection, lung and breathing exercises may also be important.

Because many social activities, especially for children, often require physical mobility, those who have orthopedic impairments may lack opportunities to socialize with their peers (Lathom-Radocy 2014; Thaut 1992a). Therefore, they may need to seek out activities that can provide meaningful and enjoyable social experiences. Obvious physical deformities or lack of physical coordination also may lead to lack of social acceptance by peers, and individuals who have such problems may need help in finding ways to cope with the reactions of others and to be accepted despite their impairments. Individuals who have been overprotected because of their physical frailties also will need help in increasing their confidence in doing things independently to the extent of their abilities. Those who have a lower sense of self-worth because of their physical impairments will also need help increasing their self-confidence and self-esteem. Settings and activities that seek out and strengthen their talents and abilities while minimizing or compensating for their weaknesses will be most beneficial (Atterbury 1990; Rudenberg 1982; Thaut 1992a). The rhythm of music can provide temporal organization and appropriate arousal (Thaut 2008).

Lack of mobility or decreased ability to move independently can also adversely impact the social life of adults who have chronic conditions that cause orthopedic impairments. As moving about becomes more difficult, these persons may gradually stop participating in activities they formerly enjoyed, have fewer opportunities to interact with others, and gradually lose their social skills. This isolation can also decrease self-esteem.

Orthopedically disabled persons have the same needs for emotional development and emotional expression that all people do (Atterbury 1990; Birkenshaw-Fleming 1993; Lathom-Radocy 2014; Rudenberg 1982; Thaut 1992a; Zinar 1987); however, their physical disabilities may limit options for expressing emotions or releasing tension. For example, since clients who have a limited capacity for physical activity cannot use strenuous physical activity as an outlet for venting frustration, they must find other ways to express their frustration and release tension. Some may become verbally abusive and blame others for their condition. Others may withdraw into fantasy or regress into less mature behavior patterns. Still others may overcompensate by trying to excel in some other area. All these individuals need experiences that will restore their self-esteem, improve their self-image, and provide them with more appropriate ways to express their emotions and relieve tension and anxiety. Depending on the nature of their disability or condition, individuals may also need to find ways of coping with loss, grief, depression, or loneliness. In particular, those who have lost motor functions in traumatic accidents or those who suffer from degenerative, terminal conditions may have special needs for constant encouragement and emotional support from significant others as they find ways of coping with the realities of their condition. (For more information on the needs of those who are in rehabilitation settings or who are terminally ill, see Chapters Eighteen and Twenty.)

Along with the unique needs imposed by the particular condition or disability, orthopedically impaired individuals continue to have needs common to all people, including needs for independence, a feeling of accomplishment, opportunities to participate with others, opportunities to be involved in meaningful activities, enjoyable leisure and recreational experiences, outlets for emotional expression, sources of security and support, sources of comfort and love, intellectual stimulation, respect, and opportunities for aesthetic experience and fulfillment. Because of the limitations imposed by their conditions, they may need to find unique ways to meet these needs or have special adaptations made to enable them to participate with others or join in experiences as equal participants. Even those who suffer from degenerative, terminal conditions need "opportunities to participate equally in expressive musical experiences and occasions to experience musical perception and experience" (Atterbury 1990, 146). Physical impairments or deteriorations do not diminish a person's need for aesthetic experience. In fact, some of these individuals may have increased needs for aesthetic experience and expression as they seek ways to add meaning, fulfillment, and quality experiences to their lives.

SETTINGS FOR SERVICE DELIVERY

Orthopedically impaired individuals may receive special programs to help meet their specific needs in varied settings. Programs depend somewhat on age, the nature and extent of their disability, and any accompanying impairments. Young children may receive services at home or be seen in special early intervention programs, pediatric hospital units, burn centers, preschool programs, centers for the developmentally delayed, or clinics sponsored by agencies such as Easter Seals or United Cerebral Palsy (Humpal 1990; Jacobowitz 1992; Michel 1985; Rudenberg 1982; Rudenberg and Royka 1989; Staum 1988, 1996; Thaut 1992a). Public Law 99-457 of 1986 provides incentives for early intervention programs to address the needs of disabled children (Adamek 1996; Humpal 1990; Schwartz 2006h).

Since the Individuals with Disabilities Act (IDEA) (Public Law 101-476), the 1990 revision of the 1975 Education for All Handicapped Children Act (Public Law 94-142) assures a free, appropriate public education to all disabled children, aged 3–21 years, including those with orthopedic impairments, school-aged children most likely will receive services through their local school district. They also may receive assistive technology devices and services through the provisions of IDEA or the Technology-Related Assistance for Individuals with Disabilities Act (Public Law 100-407) (Adamek 1996; Johnson 1996). Special education services for orthopedically impaired children are delivered according to the same general procedure outlined in Chapter Seven.

Orthopedically impaired adults also receive services in widely varied settings, including general hospitals, state hospitals, state schools, rehabilitation centers, extended care facilities, nursing homes, physical therapy clinics, neurological institutes, VA hospitals, burn centers, biofeedback clinics, pain clinics, or private homes (Michel 1985; Staum 1988, 1996). In addition, agencies like United Cerebral Palsy provide day treatment programs and services for adult clients in some communities (Michel 1985).

Music therapists work with both children and adults who have various types of orthopedic impairments or physical disabilities. They may treat clients in any of the settings mentioned above as well as in music therapy clinics, music studios, community programs, or private practice. Music therapists may provide direct or consultant services and work with clients individually or in groups. Music therapists may also use their skills and training to help musicians overcome physical discomforts and problems related to music performance (Rider 1987; Taylor 1997).

HOW MUSIC IS USED IN THERAPY

Several different types of musical experiences, such as singing, listening, playing instruments, moving to music, and creating music, can all be structured in specific ways to have therapeutic benefits for individuals who have various orthopedic impairments or disabilities (Birkenshaw-Fleming 1993; Lathom-Radocy 2014; Michel 1985; Rudenberg 1982; Staum 1988, 1996; Thaut 1992a, 2008; Zinar 1987). The selected experience will depend on the client's needs, capabilities, and interests. While music therapy intervention strategies used with this population often primarily focus on increasing "efficient synergistically appropriate uses of muscles as they relate to movement" (Staum 1988, 79), music therapy experiences also may have important social, emotional, and personal benefits. From early intervention (Humpal 1990) to geriatric settings (Belgrave, Darrow, Walworth, and Wlodarczyk 2011; Bright 1972, 1981; Palmer 1977), therapeutically directed music experiences can be a valuable asset to educational, developmental, and rehabilitative programs for individuals who have various types of orthopedic impairments.

Music Therapy Interventions Help Elicit Movement and Decrease Pain Perception

As anyone who has ever found themselves unconsciously tapping their foot or drumming their fingers or rhythmically nodding their head to a march or a dance tune with a strong, lively beat will attest, music can stimulate movement. Musical instruments also arouse curiosity and interest, typically inviting and encouraging a person to make a sound. Music therapists working with orthopedically impaired persons can structure these inherent motivating aspects of music for a variety of purposes, "from stimulating exercise of large muscle groups to almost imperceptible movements in nonresponsive patients" (Staum 1988, 75). Thaut (2008, 85) explains that rhythm provides a temporal structure that can cue the control of movement.

Individuals who have orthopedic impairments or disabilities may be reluctant to move for various reasons, including the pain associated with their condition (e.g., arthritis, severe burns), the degree of neuromuscular involvement that renders movement extremely difficult (e.g., severe cerebral palsy, head injury, strokes), anxiety associated with fear of further injury or pain (e.g., brittle bone disorders), or, especially for those who have been overprotected, a lack of confidence in their abilities. Exercise and movement, however, are often vital aspects of the rehabilitation programs that are necessary to improve their level of functioning and help them reach their maximum level of independence. Therefore, music therapy interventions that help elicit and encourage movement and help decrease pain perception associated with movement can be most important in motivating individuals to participate actively in therapeutic movement programs and increase their functional independence (Bright 1972, 1981; Jacobowitz 1992; Michel 1985; Palmer 1977; Staum 1988, 1996).

Rhythmic, stimulating music frequently motivates even the most reluctant individuals to participate in simple movement or exercise activities (Bright 1972, 1981; Michel 1985; Palmer 1977; Staum 1988, 1996; Thaut 1992a). The auditory signal of music brings focus to the activity: "One of the most vital elements of attention is the ability to sustain focus in order to complete a task" (Thaut 2008, 201). Since music often is associated with fun and pleasure, movement performed or requested in the context of music experiences "may not be thought of as exercises, and therefore may be attempted more readily, without the expectation of failure" (Ford 1984, 11). Props like hoops or scarves used in conjunction with the movement-to-music experiences may further encourage movement. In addition, lyrics that request movements or action songs and music games may motivate some clients to participate. Because music can be adapted for diverse populations, it can meet the needs of many physically disabled individuals (Adamek and Darrow 2010). The musical lyrics can cue movement from individuals who are reluctant to move (Christenbury 1979; Lathom-Radocy 2014). The social aspects of dance or movement-to-music games and activities, along with the stimulating and motivating qualities of the music itself, also may encourage those who need help to allow themselves to be assisted to move, even if the movement is painful.

Individuals are usually more likely to want to move or exercise if the music is meaningful or enjoyable to them. Thus, it is important to consider an individual's preferences and cultural background when choosing music to accompany movement activities. Hearing preferred music may elicit movement even in seemingly nonresponsive clients. For example, contingent application of 15 seconds of preferred music (patient's preference determined from conversations with the patient's family) increased overt systematic responses in targeted behaviors (e.g., lateral head movement, mouth movement, eye focus, eye blinks, finger movement) for some comatose patients who were in a vegetative state (Boyle 1987, 1989). Wolfe (1980) also found that contingent music, controlled by special head devices with mercury switches that played the music only when the subject's head was erect, effectively improved head control in some subjects who had spastic cerebral palsy.

For some individuals, the pleasure obtained from making a sound on a musical instrument may provide the necessary motivation for movement. As they focus on the instrument and the sound being produced, clients may become less aware of pain associated with movement. For example, as Rudenberg and Royka (1989, 41) found, the pleasure and comfort associated with the experience of playing adapted instruments helped pediatric burn patients achieve "increased movement with lessened or decreased awareness of pain." If musical instruments are selected and adapted appropriately, they can be highly motivational tools for encouraging the development or rehabilitation of physical skills (Clark and Chadwick 1979; Elliott 1982; Ford 1984; Humpal 1990; Lathom-Radocy 2014; Rudenberg 1982; Staum 1988, 1996; Thaut 1992a). Once the client becomes motivated by an instrument and reaches out to play it, the therapist can shape and guide experiences to complement movements and exercises employed in physical and occupational therapy programs. Instruments can also be set up in particular ways to encourage proper body positioning or increased range of motion. In addition, music provides a cueing function to invite participation (Davis, Gfeller, and Thaut 2008).

Electronic instruments and computer music technology continue to advance. As new devices for inputting and controlling electronic and computer music appear, more musical possibilities are available for the music therapist who is striving to encourage and motivate movement in orthopedically impaired individuals with limited movement capabilities (Fegers et al. 1989; Howell, Flowers, and Wheaton 1995; Krout 1992a, 1995; Nagler and Lee 1989; Swingler 1994). Adamek and Darrow (2010, 283) indicate that "The Individuals with Disabilities Education Act (IDEA) considers assistive technology to be any piece of equipment or product that increases, maintains or improves the functional capabilities of individuals with disabilities." The use of web sites to obtain information may be facilitated by design of sites that consider accessibility, as well as their use and convenience (Loiacono, Djamasbi, and Kiryazov 2013).

A real-time interactive image and music composition interface, designed for a child with cerebral palsy, simultaneously presented audio and visual feedback stimuli (Azeredo 2007). The child had a short attention span, poor mobility in upper limbs, and was in a wheelchair. Over thirteen sessions, he exhibited improved quality of movement control as well as improved sound production.

Electronic technology, such as Soundbeam (www.midicreator.co.uk) and Midicreator (www.midicreator.co.uk), as well as specialized software and amplification and recording equipment can be used by people with disorders and impairments that make the usual way of playing instruments impossible (Magee 2006). Both the American Music Therapy Association (Professional Competencies 2003) and the National Association for Schools of Music (Handbook 2003–2004) require that music therapy students be familiar with the use of appropriate technology when working with clients (Crowe and Rio 2004).

Certain types of music therapy interventions also can be beneficial for individuals who have much pain because of their orthopedic condition or the treatment procedures associated with it. For example, music therapy interventions such as music listening combined with deep breathing, progressive muscle relaxation, and age-appropriate imagery can help severely burned patients decrease anxiety and tension prior to and during surgery or painful procedures (e.g., daily debridement) or exercises (Barker 1991; Christenberry 1979; Robb et al. 1995; Rudenberg and Royka 1989). Moreover, by providing a more relaxed, comforting, and soothing atmosphere, music can help divert the patient's attention, at least to some extent, from the pain. The use of music, relaxation, and imagery also may assist in the management of postsurgical pain for various orthopedic surgeries, such as corrective surgery for scoliosis (Good, Stanton-Hicks, Grass, et al. 2001; Lukas 2004; Steinke 1991). In addition, techniques like biofeedback and music (Godley 1987; Rider 1987) or vibroacoustic therapy, which combines music, vibration, and low frequency sound (Chesky and Michel 1991; Skille 1989), help manage or alleviate pain associated with arthritis or chronic muscle pain or fatigue. Other clients with chronic pain may benefit from techniques combining music and sound with meditation or imagery (Rider 1987; Weissman 1983). The music therapist should choose the music carefully, always keeping the goal in mind:

> Music that is familiar, active, and somewhat complex may be more effective in alleviating procedural pain. Music that is less active, less apparently structured, and more relaxing, however, may be useful in muscle relaxation and distraction from chronic pain. (Lathom-Radocy 2014, 344)

Music Therapy Interventions Have Positive Influences on Muscle Tone

As noted in Chapter Five, research shows that music with different amounts of rhythmic activity and different degrees of percussive or sustained sounds (stimulative vs. sedative music) has different effects on several physiological responses, including muscle tension, motor activity, and relaxation responses (Edwards et al. 1991; Gfeller 1992a; Hodges 1980; Radocy and Boyle 2012). Although individual preferences and experiences certainly affect the responses of a particular listener to a particular musical selection or style at any given time (Hanser 1985), stimulating music (music that is fast or lively, with strongly enunciated rhythms and detached percussive sounds; e.g., marches, fast dances) usually tends to stimulate muscular action and physical activity, while sedative music (music that is slower, with more sustained sounds, flowing melodies, as well as smoother, more quiet or monotonous rhythms; e.g., lullabies) tends to reduce physical activity, decrease tension, and promote relaxation (Gaston 1968a). More recent research by Thaut and his associates (2008) indicates that rhythmic music can be effective in gait training and upper extremity rehabilitation. Music therapists may make use of these general principles, along with the information on music style preferences gained from their assessments of particular clients, to suggest musical stimuli that will positively influence a client's muscle tone and help that client engage in motor tasks more efficiently or effectively.

Individuals who have low muscle tone (hypotonia) need to increase their muscle tone to maintain proper posture and effectively perform motor tasks. Music therapists have found that using various types of stimulating music (e.g., drum beats, recorded music, stimulating music improvised by the therapist) with these individuals often facilitates increased muscle tone and stimulates active movement, leading to greater physical alertness and enhancing responses to posture and motor control exercises (Sekeles 1989). When movement is synchronized with musical and rhythmic stimuli, muscles usually become more active and work more efficiently (Thaut 1992a; 2008). Therefore, techniques using rhythmic and musical stimuli to pace or time movements may be very useful in facilitating neuromuscular re-education for victims of strokes or traumatic brain injuries (Scholtz et al. 2015; Thaut, Schleiffers, and Davis 1991; Thaut et al. 1997). Exercising certain body parts by playing instruments or repeating dance movements also can help improve muscle tone in the body parts exercised (Rudenberg 1982; Staum 1988, 1996; Thaut 1992a).

Individuals who have high muscle tone (hypertonia), muscle stiffness, or spasticity need to find ways of relaxing their muscles. Relaxation exercises to soothing, sedative music prior to other activities may help some individuals calm and relax their muscles and then participate more effectively in activities requiring motor control (Rudenberg 1982; Thaut 1992a). Techniques combining sedative music with biofeedback-assisted relaxation training (Scartelli 1982) or combining low-frequency sound with music (Wigram 1995) also helped decrease muscle tone and promote relaxation in some spastic individuals. Continual advances in computer and electronic technology now provide the clinician with ways to control musical sound information (e.g., pitch, dynamics, timbre) by biological signals, offering new possibilities for music-facilitated relaxation (Krout 1995). In addition, techniques combining music and meditation or music and imagery have effectively reduced muscle tension in some clients (Rider 1987; Weissman 1983).

When working with individuals who have cerebral palsy, one must consider the type of cerebral palsy when selecting music. For example, some research has shown that sedative and stimulative music may have quite the opposite effects on individuals who have spastic cerebral palsy in comparison with those who have athetoid cerebral palsy: Generally, stimulative music seems more effective in promoting relaxation and controlled movement in clients with spastic cerebral palsy, while sedative music seems more effective for clients with athetoid cerebral palsy (Lathom 1961; Schneider 1954, 1957). Of course, individual responses will vary, and these guidelines will not apply to every individual who has a given type of cerebral palsy. (For example, see Scartelli [1982] above.) Although general guidelines may provide useful starting points, the music therapist must always carefully observe, assess, and evaluate individual preferences for and responses to particular techniques, experiences, and selections of music and plan or revise music-based interventions accordingly.

When working with clients who have severe physical handicaps, such as those with severe cerebral palsy, music therapists must work closely with trained physical therapists and occupational therapists to learn specific positioning and handling techniques that will help normalize muscle tone (e.g., neurodevelopmental treatment (NDT) techniques). Music therapists then can incorporate these techniques into their treatment programs (F. Johnson 1981; Rudenberg 1982), as they position clients or instruments in ways that will maximize normal muscle tone and facilitate normal movement patterns (Adamek and Darrow 2010; F. Johnson 1981; Rudenberg 1982). Using their knowledge of music's physiological and psychological effects, music therapists may work with physical therapists and occupational therapists to develop background music to accompany NDT exercises and help facilitate and structure normal, rhythmic muscle movement. For clients who are very tactilely defensive or who have a high degree of spasticity or athetosis, listening to certain types of music prior to working with the physical therapist may help them become calmer and more relaxed, thereby facilitating an atmosphere and state of being more conducive to treatment.

Music Therapy Interventions Help Strengthen Muscles and Joints, Increase Endurance, and Promote Physical Fitness

Almost all orthopedically impaired individuals must engage in some sort of motor development or rehabilitation program to help improve joint or muscle strength or function. Many types of music experiences can facilitate clients' involvement in and response to these programs. However, since music therapists usually do not have extensive training in kinesiology and functional motor assessment, they must consult with occupational and physical therapists or other motor rehabilitation specialists to see what particular types of exercises, movements, positions, or handling techniques are indicated (or contraindicated) for any individual client. Music therapists then use their expertise in music to plan music-based interventions that complement these efforts.

Many music therapy interventions that are used to help clients increase muscle or joint strength, improve range of motion, increase endurance, or promote physical fitness fall under the general category of "movement to music" (Thaut 1992a, 174) and use specially selected music to accompany, guide, or structure movement activities:

> Musical exercises offer a wide range of structural options to integrate patients into a group therapy setting where music applications can be scaled to each patient's level of functioning and yet contribute to a meaningful, musical group experience. (Davis, Gfeller, Thaut 2008, 282)

Depending on the situation, the music may be supplied by recordings or performed live by the therapist. The music's tempo and length can be adjusted to correspond to the individual's capabilities and to the desired speed and duration of the exercise. Demands can be increased gradually by playing the music for longer intervals as the individual gains strength (Michel 1985).

Appropriate background music can facilitate participation in and response to range-of-motion and muscle-strengthening exercises by (a) stimulating muscular activity, (b) facilitating desired changes in muscle tone, (c) motivating participation, (d) serving as a distraction from pain that may be associated with the movement, (e) setting a mood that matches and encourages the desired motor response, and (f) helping to rhythmically structure and synchronize movements (Gfeller 1988; Lathom-Radocy 2014; Lucia 1987; Michel 1985; Rudenberg 1982; Staum 1988, 1996; Thaut 1992a; Thaut et al. 1991; Zinar 1987). For example, range-of-motion and muscle-strengthening exercises can be a very necessary but very painful part of treatment and therapy for many individuals who have arthritis, cerebral palsy, spasticity, or contractures, as well as for those recovering from burns, fractures, strokes, or traumatic brain injuries. Carefully selected music can facilitate clients' responses to these exercises by helping relax muscles prior to exercise and by providing a more pleasant atmosphere and/or a diversion from the pain that is often associated with the movement (Christenberry 1979; Lathom-Radocy 2014; Rudenberg and Royka 1989). Vibroacoustic therapy techniques, which use music in combination with low-frequency sound vibrations, also have been useful in increasing range of motion and decreasing high muscle tone in some clients (Wigram 1995). Researchers have found that receiving vibroacoustic therapy treatment prior to range-of-motion exercises can significantly increase range of motion for some individuals with spastic cerebral palsy (Wigram 1995).

Research indicates that carefully chosen music also may enhance general fitness programs by increasing motivation and by helping structure temporal and quantitative factors related to the required exercise movements (Gfeller 1988; Thaut et al. 1991; Thaut 2008). Choosing music that incorporates client preferences as well as appropriate rhythmic and phrase structures further enhances participation by facilitating "active focus on an external event rather than on the discomforts that accompany strenuous exercise" (Gfeller 1988, 40). Thus, adding music to exercise routines may help increase endurance and frequency of activity, as well as alleviate the boredom and tedium generally associated with repetition (Denenholz 1959; Gfeller 1988; Palmer 1977; Staum 1988, 1996; Wolfe 1978). Individuals can also practice muscle or joint strengthening exercises in fun ways when specific, prescribed exercise movements are incorporated into dance routines or action songs. Some people who are reluctant to participate in structured exercise programs might be very willing or motivated to dance. Judicious planning and coordination of efforts by music therapists and physical therapists can make enjoyable dance experiences double as goal-directed exercise programs.

Exercise-to-music programs and movement-to-music experiences, then, can be an important part of general physical fitness programs for many different types of clients, including frail older adults (Bright 1972, 1981; Clair and Memmott 2008; Weissman 1983) by helping to improve breathing and circulation as well as assisting in maintaining muscle and joint function. Some clients may process and respond to exercise routines better when music is added. For example, music can provide persons recovering from strokes or traumatic brain injuries with important cues that help increase their attention and focus on the task (especially important for language-affected persons with right hemiplegia) and provide a rhythmic structure for organizing and maintaining muscular effort and increasing endurance (Adamek and Darrow 2010; Clair and Memmott 2008; Lucia 1987; Thaut et al. 1991). For some clients, performing exercises to a rhythmic accompaniment may improve stability of joints by facilitating an earlier onset and prolongation of muscle activation or by increasing co-contraction of antagonist muscle groups (Thaut et al. 1991).

Examples of specific movement-to-music and exercise-to-music programs for specific goals, types of movements, or body parts appear in Bright (1981), Lathom-Radocy (2014), Lucia (1987), Miller (1979), and Zinar (1987). Individuals who need to develop, strengthen, or reactivate large arm and shoulder muscles also can benefit from the arm movements associated with musical conducting (Tanner and O'Briant 1980; Staum 1988, 1996), while using hand signals associated with the Kodály approach to music education can promote wrist rotation and finger flexion and extension (Brownell, Frego, Kwak, and Rayburn 2008; Zinar 1987).

Other music therapy interventions make use of musical instruments to help clients increase muscle or joint strength, improve range of motion, increase endurance, or promote physical fitness. By carefully selecting instruments and matching them to the individual's needs and interests, music therapists can help the client develop increased range of motion in certain joints or strengthen specific muscle groups (Confrancesco 1985; Denenholz 1959; Farnan and Johnson 1988b; Ford 1984; Josepha 1964, 1968; Miller 1979; Rogers 1968; Rudenberg 1982; Rudenberg and Royka 1989; Staum 1988, 1996; Thaut 1992a, 2008; Zinar 1987). A careful analysis of basic physical abilities (e.g., muscle groups involved, range-of-motion and positioning requirements) needed to play many string, brass, woodwind, percussion, and keyboard instruments, such as that provided by Elliott (1982) or Adamek and Darrow (2010), will help therapists select the most appropriate and beneficial instruments for individuals with particular physical abilities and disabilities. Of course, an individual's preferences will also require consideration; individuals will be more motivated to play and practice instruments they like. Many traditional instruments can be adapted for successful use by orthopedically impaired clients (Adamek and Darrow 2010; Clark and Chadwick 1979; Josepha 1964; Rudenberg 1982; Zinar 1987). Others may learn to make music with computers, developing skills which also increase their muscle and finger strength (Spitzer 1989).

Musical instruments can be great motivational devices for encouraging movement and promoting sustained practice of a certain movement or sustained exercise of a certain muscle group. The pleasure and sense of accomplishment associated with making instrumental music often distracts an individual from the pain that may be associated with the movement and encourages the individual to keep on moving to make the sound. For example, Rudenberg and Royka (1989) noted that pediatric burn patients had increased movement with less pain when they were playing adapted instruments. In addition to providing pleasant stimulation, the aural feedback provided by the instrument may help an individual gauge improvement and progress. Instrumental instruction naturally links to a series of gradual goals (Elliott 1982), which easily can match physical therapy goals for increased range of motion, strength, and endurance. Individuals also gain added strength and endurance as they practice their instruments outside the therapy session and maintain the program at home (Elliott 1982).

By positioning instruments in certain ways, music therapists can encourage individuals to maintain proper posture. By gradually moving instruments farther away from individuals or by having individuals reach to xylophone bars or piano keys farther and farther from midline, music therapists can encourage increased arm extension and upper extremity range of motion. Music therapists also can add interest to passive motion exercises as they assist clients in moving their arms or fingers to produce instrumental sounds. For example, crashing a cymbal or tapping a tambourine as one is assisted to stretch and extend one's arm may help give purpose and meaning to the exercise while adding an element of fun. Rhythmic background music may facilitate rhythmic structure of the movement and activation of appropriate muscle tone, as the sound produced by the instrument played with the assistance of the therapist provides feedback on the movement and adds pleasure to the exercise. Some music therapists have also used musical instruments to increase hand-grasp strength in stroke victims (Confrancesco 1985; Thaut 2008). Others use specific instruments in hospital rehabilitation and therapy programs to strengthen particular joints or muscle groups and increase general physical endurance (Elliott 1982; Rogers 1968). Josepha (1964) found that, with special adaptations, piano and violin instruction could help amputees strengthen muscles and improve coordination in using a prosthesis. When music therapy is used, a group of clients with diverse abilities can make music together:

Group singing or instrumental ensembles can be arranged to bring together ambulatory and wheelchair-bound children, or children with skilled or impaired usage of hands and fingers, with or without sensory impairments, and engage them in social interaction through music. (Davis, Gfeller, and Thaut 2008, 173)

Thus, music therapy can be used to achieve both physical and social goals within the same group.

Music Therapy Interventions Help Regulate Physical Movement and Increase Motor Control and Coordination

Many orthopedically disabled individuals have difficulties timing and coordinating their movements. They need special programs to help them develop functional neuromuscular patterns, increase their control over their movements, and improve the coordination of their movements. Just like movement, music is a dynamic event, unfolding through time. By matching the qualities and rhythms of the music to the qualities and rhythm of the desired movement, music therapists can devise interventions that (a) help individuals perceive the rhythm and timing of normal movement patterns, (b) provide an enjoyable structure to facilitate the appropriate timing of movements, and (c) offer a rewarding and pleasurable means of practicing and working to improve movement control and coordination. Music therapists have used a variety of experiences involving movement to music, playing instruments, or contingent music listening to help develop functional motor behaviors, increase neuromuscular coordination and motor control, and improve mobility and locomotion in clients who have coordination or motor control problems resulting from cerebral palsy, traumatic brain injuries, stroke, arthritis, muscular dystrophy, severe burns, fractures, aging, or other conditions causing skeletal, joint, or muscular impairments (Bright 1972, 1981; Denenholz 1959; Farnan and Johnson 1988a, 1988b; Ford 1984; Josepha 1964, 1968; Kennedy and Kua-Walker 2006; Kwak 2007; Lathom-Radocy 2014; Lucia 1987; Michel 1985; Miller 1979; Palmer 1977; Rogers 1968; Rudenberg 1982; Staum 1988, 1996; Thaut 1992a; Thaut et al. 1991; Zinar 1987).

The rhythmic structure of music can be very beneficial in helping individuals time their movements or perceive the rhythmic flow and structure of desired movement patterns. As music is chosen to match the desired movement, the structure of music helps organize responses and make them purposeful:

As the body responds to rhythm, reflexes and random movements can be changed to functional or purposeful movement. The signal, music, stimulates the person's nervous system, and can draw a motor response. (Farnan and Johnson 1988a, 11)

When rhythmic techniques are used to teach and accompany movement skills in neuromuscular reeducation programs, some individuals may experience quicker recovery of motor skills because of improved anticipation and timing of muscular effort (Thaut et al. 1991). Movement-to-music experiences can help individuals perceive normal, symmetrical movement patterns and then practice and reinforce these patterns (Birkenshaw-Fleming 1993). By moving or being assisted to move to recorded music, by performing actions to songs, and by doing exercises or dancing that require movements in various directions, individuals can learn to become more aware of the position of their body in space and learn to control and coordinate their movements to perform specific actions. Coordination and control are approached gradually through successive steps of approximation, with difficulty, number, extent, and independence of movements gradually being increased as the individual's skills develop. Walking to music or a steady beat can also facilitate locomotion and gait training (de l'Etoile 2008; Staum 1988, 1996; Thaut 1992a; Thaut 2008). In addition, music's structure may help individuals who are recovering from strokes or traumatic brain injuries focus on tasks and sustain consistent muscular efforts by helping them organize their movements to a rhythmic beat (Bhogal et al. 2003; Davis, Gfeller, and Thaut 2008; Lucia 1987; Mauritz 2002; Teasell et al. 2003; Thaut et al. 1991, 2008). The cues provided by musical structure or song lyrics may also assist in motor planning, thus facilitating the development of functional motor patterns that an individual can use in daily routines (Lathom-Radocy 2014; Lucia 1987; Staum 1988, 1996). For example, Gervin (1991) used song lyrics to train a patient recovering from a brain injury to dress independently. The external cues and pacing provided by the lyrics and music helped structure the activity and overcome the patient's difficulties in initiation, sequencing, and motor planning (Lathom-Radocy 2014).

Many individuals who have severe neuromuscular impairments resulting from conditions like cerebral palsy, stroke, or traumatic brain injury need help developing or relearning functional movement patterns. For some, musical instruments may provide motivation for them to use their hands and arms and to develop functional hand skills (Adamek and Darrow 2010; Farnan and Johnson 1988b; Ford 1984; Michel 1985; Rogers 1968; Rudenberg 1982; Staum 1988, 1996; Thaut 1992a; Zinar 1987). As individuals reach out to touch, grasp, hold, manipulate, and release instruments, they develop important functional hand skills that they then can use to perform other activities of daily living (Confrancesco 1985; Farnan and Johnson 1988b). As skills develop, music therapists can help encourage increased control and coordination by gradually asking individuals to play faster beats, more complex patterns, or more intricate rhythms. More complex instruments like xylophones, keyboards, guitars, and other band or orchestral instruments also have been used to help develop motor skills and increase motor control and coordination in individuals who have physical handicaps (Adamek and Darrow 2010; Denenholz 1959; Elliott 1982; Howell et al. 1995; Rogers 1968; Staum 1988, 1996). When these instruments are specially adapted, they can also be used by individuals with upper limb amputations (Edelstein 1987, 1989; Josepha 1964) or others with unique physical limitations (Birkenshaw-Fleming 1993; Clark and Chadwick 1979; Rudenberg 1982). In addition, electronic instruments and computers help individuals with severe physical impairments use instrumental instruction as a means of improving motor control and coordination (Howell et al. 1995).

Severely orthopedically impaired clients may require special treatment techniques, such as neurodevelopmental treatment (NDT) or sensory integration, to help them develop functional, controlled movement patterns. Music therapists can work with physical and occupational therapists to learn these techniques and find ways to incorporate them into music therapy treatment programs (James 1986; F. Johnson 1981; Rudenberg 1982). Music therapists who work with severely impaired clients must also be aware that clients' positions can greatly affect their motor control (Adamek and Darrow 2010; Farnan and Johnson 1988b; Rudenberg 1982). Rudenberg (1982, 12–13) lists several guidelines for reducing the influence of abnormal reflexive activity and abnormal muscle tone in clients who have severe cerebral palsy.

Brown and Jellison (2012) identified and systematically reviewed music research with children and youth published in peer-reviewed journals between 1999 and 2009. Two reviewed studies categorized participants and CP: Perry (2003) and Kwak (2007).

Perry (2003) studied communication development in 10 school-aged children with severe and multiple disabilities, including cerebral palsy, epilepsy, microcephaly, visual problems, and Norrie's Disease. None had functional communication skills and none were autistic or hearing impaired. One of the goals was to use music to provide a reason to communicate. They also had social goals. The study "demonstrated a number of possible avenues for developing social closeness and shared experience despite difficulties with being able to communicate, being motivated to communicate, and limitations in avenues of mutual interest" (241–242).

Kwak (2007) studied the effect of Rhythmic Auditory Stimulation (RAS) on gait performance in children with spastic cerebral palsy. (RAS is defined as "a neurologic technique using the physiological effects of auditory rhythm on the motor system to improve the control of movement in rehabilitation and therapy" (Thaut 2008, 139).) A physical therapist worked with a control group and a self-guided training group. In addition, the self-guided group had RAS self-guided training. Kwak used RAS techniques in the therapist-guided group. She found that the therapist-guided group made significant gains in stride length, velocity, and symmetry. This led to three conclusions: (a) RAS does influence gait performance of people with CP; (b) individual character-istics, such as cognitive functioning, support of parents, and physical ability play an important role in designing a training application, the effectiveness of RAS, and expected benefits from the training; and (c) velocity and stride length can be improved by enhancing balance, trajectory, and kinematic sta-bility without increasing cadence.

By careful positioning of both client and equipment, music therapists can use many instrumental and movement-to-music experiences to facilitate motor control and coordination. Clients may also increase tolerance for positioning equipment as they use it in the music therapy situation, where the music activity distracts them from the pain or restrictions of the equipment. In addi-tion, operant conditioning procedures involving contingent music listening can help develop functional motor behaviors (Staum 1988, 1996) or increase maintenance of desired positions and postures in some clients (Wolfe 1980).

Mondanero (2008) studied psychosocial care of pediatric patients with epilepsy. He was particularly concerned with using music during the Video-Electroencephalogram (VEEG measures electrical activity in the brain) placement of electrodes on the patient's scalp: "The music therapist meets the patient on a nonverbal level by providing a repetitive and predictable pattern of musical phrases" (105). This nonverbal technique allows the technologist to work while the child is relaxed and calm. He also presented psychoeducational materials and medical play opportunities to allow the child to understand the process and epilepsy.

Silverman (2009) studied the effect of a single-session psychoeducational music therapy session on verbalizations and perceptions in psychiatric pa-tients. Psychoeducation is "a mutual process between a psychiatric consumer and some type of educator attempting to increase the knowledge and illness management skills of the consumer" (106). It is especially effective because the patient shares information and is involved in his/her own treatment. It is considered an evidence-based practice (EBP).

Music Therapy Experiences Facilitate Communication and Emotional Expression

Orthopedically disabled people have the same needs for communication and emotional expression as all people; however, their physical disabilities may limit their options for expressing ideas and emotions. Some conditions that result in orthopedic impairments also may have associated speech or language disorders (e.g., severe cases of cerebral palsy, other conditions that affect muscles associated with speech or respiration, some strokes or traumatic brain injuries). Since both verbal and nonverbal communication and emotional expression are a natural part of many music experiences, which usually are perceived as enjoyable and nonthreatening and can be readily adapted for participation by individuals of varying levels of abilities and disabilities, music therapy experiences can provide needed outlets for communication and emotional expression for many orthopedically impaired clients (Lathom-Radocy 2014).

A systematic qualitative analysis of responses from six participants, diagnosed with chronic, progressive Multiple Sclerosis (MS), was conducted by Magee and Davidson (2004). The participants' verbal responses were recorded during interviews conducted after 10 music therapy sessions. Responses were categorized, and three categories emerged as representative of the subject's experience in music therapy: "the experience of each music in the sessions, the experience of living with the chronic illness and methods for coping with the emotional consequences of illness" (43). These responses support the use of music as therapy. They corroborate studies that indicate that music therapy is effective in building positive self-concept and feelings of identity (Clarkson and Robey 2000).

Music therapy interventions can stimulate communication by providing enjoyable motivating activities that offer clients opportunities for self-expression and verbal or nonverbal communication, and favorite music activities can also effectively reward desired communication behavior (Thaut 1992a). For those clients who have speech and language difficulties associated with their orthopedic impairment, music experiences can provide a nonthreatening atmosphere in which to practice verbal communication skills as well as afford a potent avenue for nonverbal communication. For many of these individuals, music therapy interventions also can effectively complement many speech therapy goals.

Because physical impairments may limit options for releasing tension and frustration, many orthopedically impaired individuals must find alternative ways to express strong emotions. Depending on the nature of their disability or condition, some individuals also may need to cope with feelings of loss, grief, depression, or loneliness. Music, a language of the emotions (Whitwell 1993), offers a natural, socially acceptable way of meeting clients' needs for emotional development and emotional expression. As they participate in music experiences by singing, writing songs, or choosing songs to express the way they feel or by playing musical instruments, moving, or relaxing to music, individuals can express a wide range of emotions and find new ways to relax and relieve tensions. Specially structured music therapy experiences also can offer individuals assistance in coping with frustrations or emotional problems that may be associated with their disabilities. In addition, songs can offer comfort and emotional security to those individuals who have been scarred or disfigured by accidents or whose lifestyles have been drastically altered by the effects of strokes, spinal cord injuries, or traumatic brain injuries

(Moore and Bowen 2008; Rudenberg and Royka 1989). Song-writing experiences also can be effective for helping patients release and discuss feelings related to their injuries (Christenberry 1979; Krout 2005b). For those involved in rigorous physical rehabilitation programs, the opportunity to participate in fun and enjoyable creative music experiences can provide a much needed emotional outlet to help them release tension and cope with the strain and frustrations they are experiencing (Barker and Brunk 1991). As family members become involved in music therapy experiences, music can give patients and families new ways to communicate, provide ways to address emotionally charged topics, give them help and support in coping with multiple losses and adjusting to new life situations, and offer needed avenues of emotional release (Barker and Brunk 1991; Davis, Gfeller, and Thaut 2008; Magee and Bowen 2008; Rudenberg and Royka 1989).

Since "access to musical experiences can be provided on many different levels of sensory, physical, and intellectual ability" (Thaut 1992a, 177), music therapists can readily structure many different types of experiences in singing, song writing, music listening, playing musical instruments, improvising or composing music, or moving to music to fit an individual's unique abilities and need for expression (Edelstein 1987, 1989; Ford 1984; Rudenberg 1982; Thaut 1992a, 2008). Recent advances in technology now allow even individuals with severe physical limitations increased opportunities to create music independently by using computers and adaptive electronic equipment (Adamek and Darrow 2010; Fegers et al. 1989; Howell et al. 1995; Krout 1992a, 1995; Nagler and Lee 1989; Swingler 1994). One computer system that makes music possible for children with limited movement is the movement-to-music (MTM) system (Tom et al. 2007). As technology continues to advance, more and more individuals with physical limitations will have increased access to emotional expression through interaction with musical instruments and musical composition.

Music Therapy Experiences Increase Self-Esteem and Provide Opportunities for Personal Enrichment

Problems like lack of mobility, decreased independence, physical deformities, lack of motor coordination, or physical frailties all may adversely impact an individual's self-confidence and self-esteem. Along with the unique problems or needs imposed by their particular condition or disability, orthopedically impaired individuals continue to have needs common to all people, including needs for independence, success, a feeling of accomplishment, enjoyable leisure and recreational experiences, intellectual stimulation, and opportunities for aesthetic experience and fulfillment. Physical impairments or deteriorations do not diminish a person's need for aesthetic experience. In fact, some individuals with physical impairments may have increased needs for aesthetic experience and expression as they seek ways to add meaning, fulfillment, and quality to their lives. Through successful participation in music experiences, individuals can increase their feelings of confidence and self-esteem as well as develop viable avenues for personal expression and leisure-time enjoyment in which they can participate throughout their lives (Birkenshaw-Fleming 1993; Edelstein 1987, 1989; Ford 1984; Jacobowitz 1992; Josepha 1964, 1968; Michel 1985; Rider 1987; Rogers 1968; Rudenberg 1982).

Birkenshaw-Fleming (1993, 54) observed that "developing a good self-image is very important for students with physical problems, especially as they grow older and become more aware of their disabilities." As these individuals participate successfully in carefully structured music experiences, they can gain feelings of competence and increased confidence and self-esteem as they learn to independently control and interact with various aspects of music (Schmid and Aldridge 2004). Developing musical performance or compositional skills and talents also may boost self-esteem and self-confidence for many individuals. In addition, these skills can provide them with new avenues for personal enrichment, aesthetic expression, meaningful accomplishments, and participation in "normal" activities that are valued by society.

With the use of adaptive devices (Adamek and Darrow 2010; Birkenshaw-Fleming 1993; Clark and Chadwick 1979; Edelstein 1987, 1989; Elliott 1982; Josepha 1964; Rudenberg 1982; Zinar 1987) or computer technology, adaptive switches and input devices, and electronic instruments (Fegers et al. 1989; Howell et al. 1995; Krout 1992a, 1995; Nagler and Lee 1989; Swingler 1994), even individuals with severe physical limitations can participate independently and successfully in musical performance and composition experiences. Persons who have had upper limb amputations or who are paralyzed on one side also may learn to play instruments by making use of adaptive devices (Davis, Gfeller, and Thaut 2008; Edelstein 1987, 1989; Elliott 1982; Josepha 1964) or may find much enjoyment and enrichment from the extensive amount of piano literature written for one hand (Edel 1994).

Other individuals may find additional aesthetic and personally enriching leisure opportunities through developing an active interest in and appreciation for listening to music, either alone or at concerts and community events (Birkenshaw-Fleming 1993; Ford 1984; Lathom-Radocy 2014). Ford (1984, 13) noted that, by developing music listening skills and interests as well as singing or playing skills, orthopedically impaired individuals "will be able to enjoy music as an active force throughout life." Listening to music can be a source of comfort, enjoyment, learning, and personal enrichment no matter what the person's level of ability or disability (Birkenshaw-Fleming 1993). As music therapists structure experiences to facilitate the acquisition of academic information, enhance the experience of and memory for certain concepts, and set moods conducive to learning (e.g., promote attention and reduce anxiety), music can also serve to enhance cognitive learning processes and promote the development of academic and language skills in orthopedically impaired individuals (Ford 1984; Lathom-Radocy 2014; Thaut 1992a, 2008; Thaut, Peterson, Sena, and McIntosh 2008).

Music Therapy Experiences Provide Opportunities for Socialization and Increase Social Skills

Since many social activities, especially in childhood, are built around movement or require independent physical mobility (Thaut 1992a), orthopedically impaired persons may have limited opportunities to participate in social experiences with their peers. Lack of mobility or decreased ability to move independently also can adversely impact the social life of adults who have chronic conditions that cause orthopedic impairments. Specially structured music experiences can be very beneficial in developing, improving, or helping maintain socialization skills in clients of all ages, including preschoolers (Furman and Humpal 2006; Hughes et al. 1990) to school-aged children (Adler 2006; Atterbury 1990; Birkenshaw-Fleming 1993; Ford 1984; Humpal and Dimmick 1995; Jacobowitz 1992; Josepha 1964, 1968; Michel 1985; Nordoff and Robbins 1971a; Rogers 1968; Rudenberg 1982; Rudenberg and Royka 1989; Thaut 1992a; Zinar 1987) to adults (Barker and Brunk 1991) to geriatric clients (Bright 1972, 1981; Clair 2008; Glassman 1983; Palmer 1977; Weissman 1983). They give orthopedically impaired individuals opportunities to interact with their peers (both disabled and nondisabled) in meaningful and productive ways. Music experiences can also facilitate communication and healthy, enjoyable interaction between disabled individuals and family members (Barker and Brunk 1991; Rudenberg and Royka 1989). Wheeler and Stultz (2008, 590) note that "music aids and promotes two-way communication. It is a motivator and support in the development of this communication."

Because music is accessible on many different physical, intellectual, and emotional levels, music experiences can be structured to include individuals of widely diverse physical and intellectual abilities, giving them each a part in producing a meaningful product or achieving an enjoyable experience. For example, ambulatory and nonambulatory clients can participate together in group singing or instrumental experiences or even in dance and movement-to-music experiences (especially if these incorporate adapted movements or wheelchair dancing for nonambulatory clients). Music play experiences and traditional music learning activities can promote interaction and socialization among children with and without disabilities (Atterbury 1990; Birkenshaw-Fleming 1993; Hughes et al. 1990; Humpal and Dimmick 1995; Kennedy and Kua-Walker 2006; Zinar 1987). As physically disabled children interact with others in music settings, they receive important socialization experiences while they learn music skills. As individuals of all ages work with others to write group songs, produce instrumental improvisations, perform in instrumental or vocal ensembles, dance, or present musical plays, they develop skills in interacting and working cooperatively with others (Barker and Brunk 1991; Ford 1984; Glassman 1983; Jacobowitz 1992; Josepha 1964, 1968; Michel 1985; Nordoff and Robbins 1971a; Palmer 1977; Rogers 1968; Rudenberg 1982; Rudenberg and Royka 1989; Tanner and O'Briant 1980; Thaut 1992a; Weissman 1983).

New electronic and computer technologies enable clients with severe physical limitations to work together with others in music performance groups. For example, synthesizers with electronic control devices matched to an individual's physical abilities allow orthopedically disabled clients to participate in ensembles with nonhandicapped individuals (Fegers et al. 1989). Individuals using switches connected to specific electronic or computer-controlled drum sounds can learn to work together to produce the sound of a large drum set (Krout 1995). During activities such as these, clients learn to focus on and attend to each other, thereby improving their social awareness and sense of group as they concentrate on the sounds and work cooperatively to play the desired musical patterns.

Clients also may have the opportunity for leadership roles as they conduct musical ensembles (Ford 1984; Tanner and O'Briant 1980) or direct musical plays. In addition, by leading or performing in ensembles or by participating in musical plays or talent shows, individuals have increased opportunities for social recognition as well as for interaction with others. For older adults, the enjoyment and satisfaction gained from music experiences like performing in vocal or instrumental ensembles, attending concerts or music appreciation programs, participating in musical plays or talent shows, or writing group songs, may motivate them to participate coninually in group activities, helping them maintain their social skills and giving them ways to continue to interact with others in meaningful and satisfying ways (Bright 1972, 1981; Glassman 1983; Lathom-Radocy 2014; Palmer 1977; Tanner and O'Briant 1980; Weissman 1983).

SPECIAL CONSIDERATIONS AND TIPS FOR SUCCESS

When serving orthopedically impaired clients, music therapists must work closely with physical and occupational therapists to learn exactly what exercises or types of movements the clients should be encouraged to do or exactly how the clients should be moved and positioned (Farnan and Johnson 1988b; James 1986; F. Johnson 1981; Rudenberg 1982; Thaut 1992a; Zinar 1987).

The therapist will also need to consider the expected prognosis or developmental course of a client's condition to know what reasonably can be expected of the individual at various stages and in what particular ways the individuals and/or family members may need support as they deal with various stages of recovery or progressive deterioration (Atterbury 1990; Barker and Brunk 1991; Birkenshaw-Fleming 1993; Christenberry 1979; Rudenberg 1982; Rudenberg and Royka 1989). This evaluation may require a family assessment (Adamek and Darrow 2010).

Traditional musical instruments often require adaptation for successful use by orthopedically impaired clients. For example, handles or mallets may have to be adapted to fit the client's grasping ability, or special stands may be necessary for the individual to hold and position instruments. The music therapist also should be aware that, even with the use of simple rhythm instruments, certain instruments require more effort to produce sound than others. One may facilitate participation by first having an individual play instruments requiring less effort (e.g., wrist bells, hand drum), then gradually moving to instruments requiring more effort (e.g., rhythm sticks, drum with mallet) as the individual's skills develop. Farnan and Johnson (1988b, 45) provide a useful chart ranking the relative difficulty of common rhythm instruments.

When using musical instruments to mobilize, exercise, or strengthen certain muscles or limbs, the therapist should observe the individual carefully to make sure the complex act of playing the instrument is not creating undue tension or strain elsewhere (Staum 1988, 1996). While musical instruments can be very motivating and effective tools for developing increased muscle strength, range of motion, and motor control and coordination for many individuals, they may not offer the most direct means of rehabilitation for all individuals or all orthopedic disorders (Staum 1988, 1996). The music therapist who works with severely orthopedically handicapped individuals should also strive to remain aware of technological developments that offer increased access to music playing and composition through the use of computers, adaptive switches and control devices, and electronic instruments.

Many resources are available to help music therapists find materials that are useful for persons who have various orthopedic impairments. For example, Edel (1994) has compiled a resource list of over 1,000 piano pieces for one hand alone that range in difficulty from basic to virtuoso. Special tape players and music materials are also available from the Library of Congress Division for the Blind and Physically Handicapped in Washington, D.C. Several excellent, practical ideas for adapting activities, instruments, and equipment to maximize independent participation by individuals who have physical disabilities and various orthopedic impairments appear in Atterbury (1990), Birkenshaw-Fleming (1993), Clark and Chadwick (1979), Edelstein (1987, 1989), Elliott (1982), Farnan and Johnson (1988a, b), Humpal and Dimmick (1995), Rudenberg (1982), and Zinar (1987).

Neuromusculoskeletal Disorders Related to Playing Instruments

Music therapy interventions may also be useful in increasing self-esteem and positive attitudes in musicians who experience performance problems involving muscle pain and fatigue. For example, Rider (1987) found that music therapy interventions involving a combination of guided imagery and music, music improvisation, biofeedback, systematic desensitization, and cognitive restructuring effectively decreased a 34-year-old cellist's problems with shoulder pain and fatigue and with anxiety during solo performance, thereby increasing performance quality, self-esteem, and positive attitude toward performance.

Because music therapists are musicians and spend many hours per day playing their instrument or singing, it is important that they avoid playing related disorders for themselves and those they treat. Pianists and organists can get tendinitis, thoracic outlet syndrome, carpal and cubital tunnel syndrome, and focal dystonia. Lister-Sink (2015, 16) has worked with musicians with these disorders for over 25 years, and she reports that this can occur in as many as 93 percent of pianists:

> The Performing Arts Medicine Association (PAMA) and the National Conference on Keyboard Pedagogy (NCKP) are beginning to develop and share resources for students and teachers . . . in 2012, the National Association of Schools of Music (NASM) required all member institutions to be responsible for providing information on injury-prevention and on maintaining vocal, hearing and musculoskeletal health.

Much of the injury occurs from poor posture while playing as well as inefficient muscle use and strain from repetition which leads to overuse injury. Good biomechanical principles should be used to prevent injury.

Kok, Vlielend, Fiocco, and Nelissen (2013, 1471) compared musculoskeletal complaints among musicians and nonmusicians. They found that from a sample of eighty-three students from a music academy and 494 medical students that "non-musicians have on average less complaints than musicians (p=0.01)." The complaints they investigated included "the right hand, wrists, left elbow, shoulders, neck, jaw and mouth."

There is now a field called *performing arts medicine*. Wind players, as well as keyboard performers, often have playing-related disorders. Steinmetz et al. (2014, 783) conducted a study of embouchure problems of 585 professional brass players. They stated that "embouchure problems can potentially lead to focal dystonia." Embouchure fatigue and cramping (a symptom of dystonia) preceded more serious problems. Their study revealed "a high relative frequency of embouchure problems in professional brass players."

String players also have playing-related injuries, such as temporomandibular (joint of the lower jaw) dysfunction, which occurs from holding the violin against the lower jaw for extended periods of time. This can cause poor jaw alignment. Dawson (2006) suggests preventive measures.

Music therapists are responsible for carefully observing clients' posture and playing habits, as well as for monitoring their own performance practice. Many injuries can be avoided by attention to pain signals, which indicate fatigue and need for changes in neuromuscular function.

QUESTIONS FOR THOUGHT AND DISCUSSION

1. Discuss some of the special characteristics and needs of orthopedically disabled individuals. What implications do these have for music therapy programming?
2. Are some types of music experiences and activities more useful than others in therapeutic programs for orthopedically impaired individuals? If so, which ones? Why?
3. Describe some specific music therapy experiences that might be used with orthopedically impaired individuals to (1) help to elicit movement and decrease pain perception; (2) positively affect muscle tone to facilitate movement or relaxation; (3) help strengthen muscles and joints, increase endurance, and promote physical fitness; (4) help regulate physical movement and increase motor control and coordination; (5) facilitate communication and emotional expression; (6) increase self-esteem and provide opportunities for personal enrichment; and (7) provide opportunities for socialization and increase social skills. What unique benefits or qualities does music bring to each of these areas?
4. List several special considerations that may be important to remember when developing therapeutic intervention strategies for orthopedically impaired persons. Why are these important? What are their implications for the structure of music therapy intervention strategies?

For each of the situations listed below, (a) define the problem or areas of need for the client or group of clients, (b) describe one or more of the goals you might pursue in music therapy sessions with the client(s), (c) describe music activities you might use to help the client(s) meet those goals, (d) tell how the music activities you described relate to the goals and needs of the client(s), and (e) mention any special considerations you might want to take into account when working with the client(s).

Situation 1:
    Wayne, a six-year-old boy with a diagnosis of athetoid cerebral palsy,

has been referred to you for music therapy services. The physical therapist thinks that, given enough training, Wayne eventually will be able to use his upper extremities for functional movements. At this time, however, Wayne exhibits many jerks, writhing, and uncontrolled movements. He cannot grasp or hold objects for more than two or three seconds. Wayne also has poor eye-hand coordination: Whenever he tries to reach out to touch or grab something, he usually misses on the first and second attempts. Wayne has normal intelligence and often becomes frustrated by his inability to control his movements. The more frustrated he becomes, the more tense he gets, and the less he can control his movements. Consequently, Wayne needs to learn to relax so he can make the most efficient, controlled movements of which he is capable.

Situation 2:

You are working as a music therapist on a hospital unit for patients recovering from orthopedic injuries. The physical therapists have asked you to help them devise programs that will decrease the patients' pain during range of motion exercises. They have also asked you to help devise activities that will motivate reluctant patients to participate in exercises designed to increase joint and muscle strength or to improve muscular control and coordination.

SUGGESTIONS FOR FURTHER READING

Atterbury, B. W. (1990). *Mainstreaming exceptional learners in music.* Englewood Cliffs, NJ: Prentice-Hall.

Birkenshaw-Fleming, L. (1993). *Music for all: Teaching music to people with special needs.* Toronto: Gordon V. Thompson.

Bruscia, K. E. (Ed.) (1991). *Case studies in music therapy.* Phoenixville, PA: Barcelona.

Clark, C. & Chadwick, D. (1979). *Clinically adapted instruments for the multiply handicapped.* Westford, MA: Modulations.

Complete Guide to Repetitive Strain Injury: What You Need to Know About RSI and Carpal Tunnel syndrome (2004). Hoboken, NJ: John Wiley & Sons.

Edelstein, J. E. (1989). Musical options for upper limb amputees. In M. H. M. Lee (Ed.), *Rehabilitation, music and human well-being* (213–225). St. Louis: MMB Music.

Elliott, B. (1982). *Guide to the selection of musical instruments with respect to physical ability and disability.* St. Louis: Magnamusic-Baton.

Farnan, L. & Johnson, F. (1988). *Everyone can move: Music and activities that promote movement and motor development.* New Berlin, WI: Jenson.

Farnan, L. & Johnson, F. (1988). *Music is for everyone: A handbook for providing music to people with special needs.* New Berlin, WI: Jenson.

Godley, C. A. S. (1987). The use of music in pain clinics. *Music Therapy Perspectives, 4,* 24–28.

Howell, R. D., Flowers, P. J., & Wheaton, J. E. (1995). The effects of keyboard in experiences on rhythmic responses on elementary school children with physical disabilities. *Journal of Music Therapy, 32*(*2*), 91–112.

James, M. R. (1986). Neurophysiological treatment of cerebral palsy: A case study. *Music Therapy Perspectives, 3*, 5–8.

Lathom-Radocy, W. (Ed.) (2014). Children with orthopedic impairments. In W. Lathom-Radocy (Ed.), *Pediatric music therapy* (2nd ed.) (278–337). Springfield, IL: Charles C Thomas.

Nagler, J. C. & Lee, M. H. M. (1989). Music therapy using computer music technology. In M. H. M. Lee (Ed.), *Rehabilitation, music and human well-being* (226–241). St. Louis: MMB Music.

Rudenberg, M. T. (1985). Music therapy for orthopedically handicapped children. In W. B. Lathom & C. T. Eagle, Jr. (Eds.), *Music therapy for handicapped children* (36–116). Washington, DC: National Association for Music Therapy.

Rudenberg, M. T. & Royka, A. M. (1989). Promoting psychological adjustment in pediatric burn patients through music therapy and child life therapy. *Music Therapy Perspectives, 7*, 40–43.

Standley, J. (1991). *Music techniques in therapy, counseling, and special education.* St. Louis: MMB Music.

Staum, M. J. (1988). Music for physical rehabilitation: An analysis of literature from 1950–1986 and applications for rehabilitation settings. In C. E. Furman (Ed.), *Effectiveness of music therapy procedures: Documentation of research and clinical practice* (65–104). Washington, D.C.: National Association for Music Therapy.

Staum, M. J. (1996). Music for physical rehabilitation: An analysis of literature from 1950–1993 and applications for rehabilitation settings. In C. E. Furman (Ed.), *Effectiveness of music therapy procedures: Documentation of research and clinical practice* (2nd ed.) (61–105). Silver Spring, MD: National Association for Music Therapy.

Thaut, M. H., Mertel, K., & Leins, A. K. (2008). Music therapy for children and adults with physical disabilities. In W. B. Davis, K. E. Gfeller, & M. H. Thaut (Eds.), *An introduction to music therapy theory and practice* (3rd ed.) (143–180). Silver Spring, MD: American Music Therapy Association.

Zinar, R. (1987). *Music activities for special children.* West Nyack, NY: Parker.

Chapter Twelve

MUSIC THERAPY FOR INDIVIDUALS WHO HAVE COMMUNICATION DISORDERS OR IMPAIRMENTS

Definitions

The American Speech and Hearing Association [ASHA] (1993, 1) has defined communication disorders as "an impairment in the ability to receive, send, process, and comprehend concepts or verbal, nonverbal and graphic symbol systems." Communication disorders may range in severity from occasional misarticulations or sound repetitions to complete inability to use speech and language for communication. According to ASHA (1993), communication disorders occur in two broad categories. *Speech disorders* hamper the clear production of sounds. *Language disorders* include problems with both comprehension and use of symbol systems in interpersonal communication.

Speech and language pathologists, more commonly referred to as speech therapists, specialize in human communication, normal speech and language development, and communication disorders (ASHA 1980; Michel and Jones 1991). Their clinical services include assessing and treating speech and language disorders, helping individuals understand the types and severities of communication disorders, and assisting individuals who have communication disorders in finding ways to achieve more normal communication in social, school, and/ or work settings (ASHA 1980). Their methods vary with the nature and severity of the disorder, the individual's age, and the individual's awareness of the problem. Music therapy can be integrated with goals of speech-language therapy when the two professions work together (Geist, McCarthy, Rodgers-Smith, and Porter 2008). The authors found that "children who demonstrate a motivation to exhibit more communicative behaviors when music is present vs. when it is not will most likely benefit more from collaboration" (315).

Hobson (2006) described collaboration between music and speech therapists in the treatment of neurogenic communication disorders (NCD). She explained that these disorders are the result of nervous system pathology (58), and she recommended communication training for individuals with this diagnosis (61 and 64). If the left hemisphere, which is usually dominant for speech functions, is damaged, the goal is to work for right hemisphere redistribution, which is possible because of neuroplasticity (Brookshire 2003; Thaut 2008). This is a neurological principle used in neurologic music therapy (NMT) and cognitive rehabilitation. As noted by Thaut (2008, 191), "Sacks (1998) provides numerous examples of music's power to reorganize the brain."

Collaboration usually brings about more effective client care. However, it may pose a risk when professional identity is blurred. This can lead to territorialism, where each discipline feels a threat. Funding realities, which must focus on the most cost-efficient service delivery, may lead to defensive behavior with fear of letting others do things usually thought to be unique to music therapy. Hobson (2006, 69) describes professional documents that delineate professional roles and responsibilities of speech and language pathologists (SLPs) and music therapists (MTs). Collaboration requires frequent communication, mutual respect without excessive "territorialism," and a clear understanding of professional competency of both the MT and the SLP, as defined in the Scope of Practice of both AMTA and ASHA.

Types of Speech and Language Disorders

Speech and language disorders may be grouped into several broad categories. Individuals who have communication disorders or impairments may have difficulties in one or more of these areas in varying degrees of severity. Speech or language problems may exist by themselves or be associated with other conditions, such as hearing impairments or other sensory deficits, cerebral palsy, learning disabilities, traumatic brain injuries, mental retardation, autism, speech-motor deficits, severe environmental deprivation, or psychosocial problems (APA 1994; Lim 2009; Lovejoy and Estridge 1987; Whipple, Gfeller, Driscoll, Olesen, and McGregor 2015).

Articulation Disorders

Speech sound disorders have an estimated prevalence of 2 percent to 25 percent of children aged 5 to 7 years (Law, Boyle, Harris, Harkness, and Nye 2000). Since these disorders involve phonological production, they sometimes are called *phonological disorders*. Individuals who have articulation disorders fail to produce speech sounds that are expected and appropriate to their age and dialect, and these difficulties often interfere with social communication or with academic or occupational achievement (ASHA 1980; DSM-V 2013; Lovejoy and Estridge 1987; Miller 1982; Timler 2008).

Individuals who have articulation disorders have difficulty producing speech sounds clearly. They may substitute one sound for another (e.g., "wight" for "light" or "wabbit" for "rabbit"), omit sounds (e.g., "at" for "hat" or "han" for "hand"), and/or distort sounds (e.g., "shlip" for "sip" or /s/ in "say" pronounced like /z/). A lisp (/s/ pronounced as /th/; e.g., "yeth" for "yes") is a common example of a slight distortion. Depending on the severity, articulation disorders may affect speech intelligibility minimally or make speech completely unintelligible. Usually sound omissions are viewed as more severe than sound substitutions. Sound distortions typically are viewed as least severe. Phonological disorders also may involve errors in selecting or ordering sounds within words or syllables.

It is important to realize that some sound substitutions, omissions, or distortions are a normal part of language development or regional dialect. Thus, assessment of speech abilities must always take into account an individual's developmental age and cultural context (APA 1994; ASHA 1980; Lovejoy and Estridge 1987; Michel and Jones 1991; Timler 2008).

Fluency Disorders

Individuals with fluency disorders have disturbances or disruptions in the natural rhythm and time patterning of their speech that are inappropriate for their age or developmental level (ASHA 2015; Lovejoy and Estridge 1987; Mansson 2007; Miller 1982). Some dysfluencies that occur in young children in the normal course of language development are not considered to be disorders.

One of the most common and widely recognized fluency disorders is *stuttering*. Individuals who stutter frequently repeat or prolong sounds, syllables, words, or phrases when they speak (ASHA 2015; DSM-V 2013, Lovejoy and Estridge 1987; Mansson 2007; Yairi and Ambrose 2013). The diagnosis of stuttering may be made "by age 6 for 80%–90% of affected individuals, with age at onset ranging from 2 to 7 years" (DSM-V, 46). When onset is in adults, it is called adult-onset fluency disorder. The extent of the disturbance may vary from one situation to another, often becoming more severe when there is particular pressure to communicate. Other types of speech dysfluencies include *interjections* (word or phrase inserted into an utterance that has no grammatical connection to it; e.g., "uh," "oh"), *broken words* (pauses or breaks within a word), *audible or silent blocking* (pauses in speech that may filled with interjections or left silent), and *circumlocutions* (substituting words to avoid problem words).

Voice Disorders

Individuals who have voice disorders have problems with vocal quality, vocal pitch, or vocal loudness or intensity. Individuals with overly harsh, hoarse, breathy,or nasal speech have problems involving *vocal quality*. Those whose speech is higher (shriller) or lower than is standard for their age or sex and those who speak in a monotone or have breaks in their voice have problems with *vocal pitch.* Individuals who have problems with *vocal loudness* or *intensity* speak too loudly or softly or may lose their voice (e.g., as in *aphonia* associated with chronic laryngitis). Unlike many other speech problems, some voice disorders may be temporary (ASHA 1980; Lovejoy and Estridge 1987; Miller 1982).

Delayed Language

Children who exhibit a marked slowness in developing language skills necessary to express and understand thoughts and ideas are said to have delayed language (ASHA 1980; Miller 1982). Children who have delayed language may have receptive language disorders (impaired ability to understand language), expressive language disorders (problems using speech/language to communicate meaning or problems using age-appropriate language and speech patterns), and/or auditory processing difficulties (problems distinguishing, focusing on, or remembering certain sounds) (APA 1994; Lovejoy and Estridge 1987).

Children who have *receptive language disorders* have difficulties comprehending the meaning of words or sentences. In milder cases, children may have difficulty understanding the subtleties of language (e.g., that the remark "You forgot your book" contains an implied message to go back and get the book) or difficulties understanding only certain types of words (e.g., spatial terms) or certain types of statements (e.g., more complex structures, like "if-then" sentences). In more severe cases, children have difficulty understanding even basic vocabulary and simple sentences. Since a child's ability to develop expressive language depends on acquiring receptive language skills, most receptive language disorders in children also include some expressive language disorder component (APA 1994).

Children with *expressive developmental language delays* fail to develop speech skills expected for their age (ASHA 1980; DSM-V 2013; Lovejoy and Estridge 1987). They may have a limited amount of speech and a limited vocabulary, use simplified and limited varieties of grammatical structures, and use a limited variety of sentence types. They may have difficulty recalling words and difficulty learning new words. They may make frequent word-finding or vocabulary errors or may change the order of letters in words (e.g., "aminal" instead of "animal"). They also may use unusual word order in sentences or omit critical parts of sentences. Conti-Ramsden et al. (2012, 1716) investigated "the longitudinal trajectories of verbal and nonverbal skills in individuals with a history of specific language impairment (SLI) from childhood to adolescence." They found, as a whole, that there is stable skills growth throughout the 10-year time frame for expressive language, receptive language, and nonverbal skills. However, "different patterns of growth of nonverbal skills are observed from childhood to adolescence" (1717). Other studies (Botting 2005; Mawhood et al. 2000; Stothard et al. 1998) have found a decline in standard scores measuring nonverbal skills. Since music is a nonverbal skill, this finding is important for music therapists. It indicates that nonverbal skills may not be on a regular, stable projectory, but may develop unevenly. Thaut (2008, 71) notes that "musical activities are frequently mentioned in the clinical literature as very effective tools to enhance delayed speech and language development in children."

Children who have problems or deficits in some areas of auditory process-ing have difficulty discriminating sounds, associating sounds and symbols, processing sounds, or storing, recalling, or sequencing sounds and ideas. Some may be easily distracted by irrelevant background noises, while others may have difficulty shifting their attention from one sound to another. Some may be unable to remember sounds even for a short time, and others may respond to a certain sound differently each time it is heard. Because of these symptoms, children with auditory processing problems may often appear to have attention deficit hyperactivity disorders or learning disorders (DSM-V 2013; Lovejoy and Estridge 1987).

Aphasia

Aphasia is the loss or impairment of speech and language abilities because of damage or injury to certain cortical regions often as the result of a stroke or head injury (Adamek and Shiraishi 1996; Cohen 1995; Miller 1982; Taylor 1989). Traditionally, speech was considered to be a left hemisphere process. While Wernicke's and Broca's areas in the left hemisphere are of great impor-tance, producing and understanding speech is very complicated, involving both hemispheres. It is now known that "both language and music represent their sound categories bilaterally in auditory cortex" (Patel 2008, 73). Depend-ing on location and extent, the damage may affect expressive language skills, receptive language skills, or both expressive and receptive language skills. For example, a lesion in Wernicke's area of the brain (*Wernicke's* or *receptive aphasia*) causes deficits in a person's ability to *comprehend* spoken or written language. In addition, individuals who have Wernicke's aphasia often are unable to find the proper words to communicate their intended messages, so they may produce fluent but nonsensical speech. In contrast, a lesion in Broca's area (*Broca's* or *expressive aphasia*) causes deficits in a person's ability to articulate speech (Carter, Aldridge, Page, and Parker 2009). Although they are able to understand speech reasonably well, individuals who have Broca's aphasia have difficulty expressing themselves in meaningful words, phrases, or sentences. They may have problems retrieving words to name objects or express ideas, or they may have difficulties when they try to combine words into phrases or make sentences. Thaut (2008, 168–169) describes Musical Speech Stimulation (MUSTIM) as a technique to be used with clients with aphasia.

Two related communication disorders caused by brain damage or injury are apraxia and dysarthria (Adamek and Shiraishi 1996; Cohen 1992, 1995; King 2007; Miller 1982; Taylor 1989; Thaut 2008). These may be found in conjunction with aphasia in some patients. In *apraxia*, the brain centers that control motor programming are damaged, and the motor memory needed for speech articulation is impaired. Individuals who have *verbal apraxia* may know what they want to say, but they cannot remember how to make their oral muscles produce the correct sounds. Apraxia causes a disruption in motor planning (King 2007, 14). In *dysarthria*, the neuromotor mechanisms that regulate speech movements are damaged, resulting in incoordination of the muscles needed to produce speech and disturbances in respiration, vocal pitch, and phonation. "Dysarthric speech is characterized by limited verbal intelligibility, vocal intensity, and vocal range, as well as abnormal speech rates" (Cohen 1995, 70). It is "a neuromuscular impairment that causes weakness or rigidity of movement" (King 2007, 14).

Haneishi (2001) developed a music therapy protocol for use with Parkinson's patients who had hypokinetic dysarthria. She addressed the problems of phonation and respiration through singing. The Music Therapy Voice Protocol (MTVP) allowed examination of the effects of music therapy on "speech intelligibility, phonation, maximum vocal range, vocal fundamental frequency, vocal fundamental frequency variability, and mood of individuals with Parkinson's disease (PD)" (287). Her results were generally significant, and participation led to improved mood and reduced fatigue.

Communication Disorders Associated with Other Conditions

Some conditions may affect the mechanisms associated with the production or development of speech, thereby causing problems, impairments, or delays in speech and language. For example, malformations like *cleft palate* (a condition that occurs when the bones and tissues of the hard and soft palates fail to fuse) adversely impact vocal quality and phonation. The speech of individuals with cleft palates is characterized by hypernasality, nasal emissions (air escaping through the nasal passages during speech), and misarticulations (Lovejoy and Estridge 1987; Miller 1982). These speech problems should be differentiated from Speech Sound Disorders, as are speech difficulties related to "congenital or acquired conditions, such as cerebral palsy, deafness or hearing loss, traumatic brain injury, or some other medical or neurological conditions" (DSM-V 2013, 44).

Individuals who have *cerebral palsy* (see Chapter Eleven) may also experience speech and language difficulties. When cerebral palsy affects the motor control centers that govern the muscles for speech and/or breathing and breath control, individuals may have articulation, fluency, and/or voice disorders. If the impairments are extremely severe, the individual may be unable to develop oral speech.

Since hearing profoundly influences one's ability to develop or maintain speech and language skills, individuals who have *hearing impairments* may also have speech and language difficulties (Darrow and Gfeller 1988; Gfeller 1992d; Lovejoy and Estridge 1987; Zinar 1987). Problems may include delayed language development or various voice, fluency, and articulation disorders. Generally, the more severe the hearing impairment, the greater impact it will have on the development of language and other communication skills. (See Chapter Nine for more information.)

In addition, individuals who have conditions such as *mental retardation* (see Chapter Seven), *learning disabilities* (see Chapter Eight), *autism* (see Chapter Thirteen), *severe environmental deprivation,* or *psychosocial problems* (see Chapters Fourteen and Fifteen) may also have associated speech and language impairments. Rainey Perry (2003) noted the importance of singing for children who are at a preverbal communication level. It provides a reason for communication. For more information on developing or remediating communication skills in these individuals, the reader is encouraged to consult the chapters discussing those conditions.

Causes

Many different physical, emotional, and environmental factors may cause communication disorders (ASHA 1980; DSM-V 2013; Lovejoy and Estridge 1987). Some speech and language impairments are the result of congenital or developmental factors or conditions (e.g., faulty development of brain and central nervous system centers related to language processing and speech production, hearing impairments, cleft palate, cerebral palsy) or are acquired later in life through injury to the brain or to any of the mechanisms involved in speech and language. Problems with physical or mental development, psychological or emotional problems, and inadequate speech and language models in the home environment may also adversely impact speech and language development. In addition, voice disorders may be caused by excessive throat clearing, yelling, or screaming; and allergies or smoking can cause varying degrees of laryngitis.

Speech or language problems that have the same manifestation also may have entirely different causes in different individuals. For example, children may have an impairment or delay in expressive language that is not associated with any known injury to the brain (*developmental type*), or individuals may *acquire* an expressive language impairment after brain injury resulting from severe head trauma.

COMMON CHARACTERISTICS, PROBLEMS, AND NEEDS OF CLIENTS

As with any population, individuals who have communication disorders or impairments are a very heterogeneous group. Factors such as the type and severity of the speech or language impairment, its cause and time of onset, the existence of associated conditions or impairments, and the degree and type of support services available will have varying effects on the individual's level of functioning, needs, and treatment program. In addition, each individual who has a speech or language impairment will have a unique combination of abilities, needs, personality traits, strengths, and weaknesses that will impact that individual's particular responses and functional abilities. Therefore, it is unwise to predict a particular person's skill levels or ceiling of abilities based on broad generalizations about a certain population. However, an awareness of characteristics, problems, and needs common to individuals who have various types of communication disorders will benefit both the therapist who desires to work with this population and the reader who is trying to understand how music therapy intervention strategies may benefit this population.

When individuals have difficulty communicating with others, they often become isolated from friends, family, or society in vocational, educational, social, and emotional areas (ASHA 1980; DSM-V 2013). Individuals who have communication disorders also may have emotional or self-confidence problems that arise from and/or contribute to their speech and language difficulties (DSM-V 2013; Lathom-Radocy 2014; Wells and Helmus 1968). In addition, they may feel angry, frustrated, or alienated because of the negative reactions of others to their poor speech or because of their inability to easily express their thoughts and ideas to others (Cohen 1994). Consequently, clients often need experiences that will enhance their self-esteem and self-confidence, provide outlets for emotional expression and release of anger and frustration, and present opportunities for interacting and communicating successfully with others.

Individuals who have speech impairments may have varied problems, including poor coordination of breath and vocal mechanisms, poor articulation, lack of vocabulary, inability to remember speech sounds, inability to speak in complete sentences, poor grammar and syntax skills, inaccurate speech rhythms and inflections, and mixing up the order of words in a sentence or the order of syllables within a word (DSM-V 2013; Nocera 1979).

Clients with communication disorders seldom exhibit all of these problems, but they demonstrate a cluster of them consistently. Therapeutic goals may include increasing the ability to vocalize, improving breath and muscle control necessary for speech, increasing verbalization, developing accurate speech rhythms and inflections, and improving receptive and/or expressive language skills. La Gasse (2013) studied speech motor entrainment and the underlying mechanism as well as how an external stimulus, e.g., a metronome beat, may impact oral motor movements. She studied subjects in three age groups, but found that "children as young as seven have an oral motor synchronization response that is similar to adults" (20).

Individuals with communication disorders resulting from malfunction of or injury to the brain centers used in processing or producing speech and language (e.g., aphasia) may have difficulty with many different aspects of speech and language. For example, they may have a speaking voice that is pitched too high or too low, have a limited vocal range, or have difficulty controlling the intensity of their voice, have a speech rate that is uneven or abnormally fast or slow, or be difficult to understand (Cohen 1992). Other individuals may be able to understand speech but not be able to produce it (Cohen 1995; DSM-V 2013; Miller 1982; Taylor 1989). Rhythmic speech cuing (RSC) may be used to improve the production of intelligible speech: "RSC has been shown to be effective in fluency disorder rehabilitation for stuttering and cluttering, in rate control to enhance intelligibility in dysarthric patients, and in facilitating rhythmic sequencing in apraxia" (Thaut 2008, 170). Some individuals also may have problems with certain aspects of language, such as abstractions or spatial terms (APA 1994; Bernstorf and Welsbacher 1996), or they may have difficulty focusing on the main idea or take longer than normal to respond (Adamek and Darrow 2010; Bernstorf and Welsbacher 1996; Lathom-Radocy 2014; Lovejoy and Estridge 1987). Again, therapeutic interventions will be tailored to the individual's specific needs and problems, with the primary goal of giving the client some system of functional communication.

Augmentive Communication Systems

Some individuals have impairments or conditions, such as deformity of or damage to the vocal mechanism, certain types of brain damage, or profound hearing loss, that leave them unable to use oral speech for communication. These individuals need some alternative to oral speech, some augmentive means of communication (Gadberry 2012; Geist, McCarthy, Rodgers-Smith, and Porter 2008); Goodman 2007; Humpal and Dimmick 1995; Miller 1982; McCarthy et al. (2008, 407) explained that Augmentative and Alternative Communication Systems (AAC) include "gestures, eye gaze and signs, picture communication boards, and electronic systems with speech output." These systems allow persons who cannot speak to meet their communication needs:

Augmentative voice output communication can include things like using a voice output communication aid to talk to friends, pointing to pictures in a communication book to order at a restaurant, or using a computer to type and send e-mail. It is anything that can improve someone's ability to communicate. (Binger and Light 2006)

Gadberry (2012) investigated expressive communication and therapist prompts within music therapy sessions with nine clients, aged 4 to 9 years. Seven were diagnosed with autism spectrum disorder, one with Down syndrome, and one with Angelman syndrome. All used an AAC system. The study compared music therapy interventions with and without the system present. Generally, the AAC system is an aid to receptive communication and comprehension. Her study indicated that communication was better with the system present. It also reduced off-task behavior. Music therapists should learn to use the AAC system if it is recommended for the client.

Several different types of augmentive or alternative communication systems are currently available, including (1) signing or manual communication systems, such as American Sign Language (ASL) (see Chapter Nine for more information); (2) Blissymbolics, a system of symbols designed by Charles Bliss to represent words and concepts (Blissymbolics Communication Foundation 1978); and (3) electronic or manual communication boards, which use letters, words, or pictures to represent items and needs the clients encounter in their daily environment. Communication boards usually are designed by speech therapists, and are tailored to fit the individual's specific communication needs and physical and mental capabilities. The speech therapist helps the individual and those with whom the individual wishes to communicate learn how to use the system. Individual picture symbol cards (Coleman, McNairn, and Shioleno 1995; *Picture Communication Symbols Combination Book* 1994) and various electronic devices and speech synthesizers (Binger and Light 2006; Humpal and Dimmick 1995) also may be used to help nonverbal individuals communicate.

SETTINGS FOR SERVICE DELIVERY

Individuals having communication disorders or impairments may receive special programs and services to help meet their specific needs in various settings. Treatment settings may vary according to the type and severity of the impairment, the precipitating cause, and the time of onset (i.e., whether a congenital or developmental problem or one acquired later in life). Speech and language pathologists, usually the primary professionals who help these clients develop or improve their communication skills, provide services in many different types of facilities, including private clinics, public and private schools, colleges and universities, hospitals, rehabilitation centers, nursing homes, community clinics, state and local health departments, and state and federal government agencies (ASHA 1980).

Many children who have speech and language disorders receive services through their local school district. The Individuals with Disabilities Act (IDEA) (Public Law 101-476), the 1990 revision of the 1975 Education for All Handicapped Children Act (Public Law 94-142), assures a free, appropriate public education to all children, aged 3–21 years, including those who have speech or language impairments. Both this law and the Technology-Related Assistance for Individuals with Disabilities Act (Public Law 100-407) also provide for necessary assistive technology devices and services (Adamek 1996; Johnson 1996). Incentives for early intervention programs to address the needs of children, from birth through the age of 2 years, who have communication disorders are provided by Public Law 99-457 of 1986 (Adamek 1996; Adamek and Darrow 2010; Humpal 1990). Special education services for children who have speech or language impairments are delivered according to the same general procedure as that outlined in Chapter Seven.

When the IEP assessment suggests that music therapy may help students achieve their educational objectives, music therapists may provide traditional direct services; work with students in self-contained or inclusive classes; provide direct in-home services to students who are confined to their homes for medical reasons; provide consultation services to facilitate classroom instruction, inclusion, or music education; and/or provide staff development workshops (Wilson 1996). Music therapy usually is classified as a related service in special education settings.

Individuals who acquire speech or language impairments later in life also may benefit from the services of speech and language pathologists to help them learn to adjust to their losses and/or to develop compensatory strategies to help maintain their abilities to communicate and socialize with their peers and families. This may be especially important for individuals who have suffered brain damage due to head injury or stroke. Moore and Bowen (2008, 306) note that "in addition to being a channel for shared activity, music offers opportunities for emotional connection, increased intimacy and closeness between relatives."

HOW MUSIC IS USED IN THERAPY

Speech and song have many similarities, sharing common features of fundamental frequency, variation and range of frequency or pitch, rate or rhythm, vocal intensity, correct breathing patterns and breath support, coordinated phonation, and accurate diction (Cohen 1992, 1994; Coleman, McNairn, and Shioleno 1995; Michel and Jones 1991; Patel 2010; Staum 1989). Both speech and song are natural vehicles for human expression. In addition, involvement in music experiences increases many skills necessary for speech and language development, such as auditory attention and perception, auditory discrimination, auditory memory, a sense of body image and spatial relationships, motor planning and muscular coordination, vocabulary development, social interaction skills, and development of imagination and creativity (Adamek and Darrow 2010; Zoller 1991). Rhythm, an important part of music, organizes the sound: "Rhythm gives 'life' to music, and a 'feel' or 'sense' of rhythm as the dynamic force within music facilitates a person's interactions with music, both as a performer and a respondent." (Radocy and Boyle 2012, 166). Therefore, music experiences, especially those involving singing, may help individuals improve speech and language skills. In fact, researchers have long noted the close connection between speech pathology and music therapy and continue to explore relationships between the two fields (Adamek and Darrow 2010; Cohen 1994; Michel 1985).

Music therapists treating individuals who have speech and language disorders must work closely with speech and language pathologists to determine the specific needs of each client (Lathom-Radocy 2014; Michel 1976, 1985; Michel and Jones 1991). At times, music experiences may enhance traditional speech therapy approaches, as when songs are used to practice and drill specific words or sounds (Zoller 1991). However, since "music provides an alternative neurological pathway for learning" (Coleman, McNairn, and Shioleno 1995, 3), music therapy approaches can make many unique contributions to treating persons with communication disorders (Cohen 1994; Michel 1985; Miller 1982; Thaut 2008). For example, music experiences can present material in an enjoyable, nonthreatening way, provide structure for the learning task and for the occurrence of appropriate responses, help cue or facilitate speech and language responses, and provide immediate positive reinforcement (Coleman McNairn, and Shioleno 1995; Michel and Jones 1991; Standley and Hughes 1997; Staum 1989). By providing multisensory learning and expressive experiences that involve the whole person, music promotes emotional engagement, increases motivation to participate in the task or treatment, and helps alleviate some of the boredom usually associated with repetitive drill (Coleman, McNairn, and Shioleno 1995; Davis, Gfeller, and Thaut 2008; Miller 1982; Staum 1989; Zoller 1991). In addition, "almost all reports in the literature suggest that both children and adults enjoy musically adapted speech learning experiences" (Staum 1989, 64). Adamek and Darrow (2010, 342–343) discuss "Adaptations Specific to Students' Language and Communication Limitations." The strategies they explain would be especially valuable in a public school setting.

Music experiences may address several needs of clients who have various types of speech and/or language disorders. For example, therapeutic music experiences may focus on (1) increasing breath and muscle control, (2) stimulating vocalization, (3) developing receptive and/or expressive language skills, (4) improving articulation skills, (5) improving speech rate and fluency, and/or (6) correcting voice disorders. Music therapy approaches may also facilitate speech and language development or rehabilitation in individuals who (7) have cleft palates, (8) have aphasia, or (9) use augmentive communication systems. Finally, music therapy interventions can help individuals with communication disorders (10) increase self-confidence, emotional expression, and social interaction. The next sections of this chapter exemplify ways therapeutic music experiences can help clients gain skills in each of these areas.

Therapeutic Music Experiences to Increase Breath and Muscle Control

In order to produce speech sounds, an individual must have a certain amount of breath and muscle control. Music activities, such as playing simple wind instruments (e.g., kazoo, flutophone, Melodica) (Thaut 2008), practicing breathing or blowing exercises to music (e.g., blowing bubbles to a song about bubbles), doing breathing and vocal exercises associated with singing instruction, and participating in singing and chanting, can help individuals develop the breath and muscle control (Cohen 1994; Miller 1982; Nocera 1979; Wells and Helmus 1968; Zoller 1991). In discussing Speech Stimulation (STIM) Davis, Gfeller, and Thaut (2008, 166) recommend using familiar lyrics because "such songs have been repetitively heard and reproduced . . . the patient's mental representation of these songs is tied not only to their musical and lyrical content, but also to their specific motor program as related to the act of singing." Vocal warmups usually include breathing exercises. Playing simple instruments also can develop respiratory muscles and breath control (Cohen 1992, 1994). Some clients may learn to play more advanced wind instruments (Haas, Pineda, and Axen 1989). The aesthetic rewards inherent in making music can be important factors in motivating clients to develop and practice breath control and breath support skills. As they experience success in developing breath and muscle control in music contexts, clients may also develop the confidence they need to transfer and apply these skills to speech production.

Therapeutic Music Experiences to Stimulate Vocalization

Before individuals can speak in words, they must learn how to use their vocal mechanisms to produce sounds. Vocalizations are preverbal behaviors that are part of speech development. Once an individual produces vocal sounds, these may be shaped over time into words and communicative speech (Cunningham 1986; Lathom-Radocy 2014; Staum 1989).

Music often acts as "a nonverbal catalyst to evoke vocal participation" (Staum 1989, 64). For example, various types of specially selected background music can help elicit and increase vocalizations in children with cerebral palsy (Adamek and Darrow 2010; Ditson 1961), disadvantaged kindergarten children (Goolsby, Frary, and Rogers 1974), children and adults with intellectual disability (Cunningham 1986; Pujol 1994), and individuals who are speech delayed or mute (Staum 1989). Some research found that soft music and flute melodies in major keys were particularly useful in significantly increasing vocalizations (Cunningham 1986; Pujol 1994). However, since all clients have individual preferences and unique responses, music therapists always must carefully observe each client's responses to various types of music and musical instruments to determine what particular background music (style, form, tempo, volume, etc.) or instruments will promote vocalizations for a particular individual or group of clients most effectively.

Sometimes, vocalizations can be encouraged and shaped as the therapist imitates the client's spontaneous sounds and then shapes or extends or structures them through vocal or instrumental improvisations (Loewy 1995; Nordoff and Robbins 1977). In other instances, contingent music may be used as a reinforcer to increase free verbalization (Talkington and Hall 1970; Walker 1972). Other participatory music experiences, such as humming, singing with sustained vowel sounds, singing or echoing consonant sounds or syllables, or vocally imitating instrument, animal, or familiar environmental sounds (e.g., sirens, horns, jets, wind) within the context of songs, may also encourage individuals to vocalize and stimulate the use of expressive speech (Loewy 1995; Nocera 1979). Adamek and Darrow (2010, 189) note that "auditory awareness and auditory discrimination, skills needed for language development, can be addressed through music activities focusing on being aware of sounds, locating sounds, tracking sounds, and identifying sounds."

Many musical vocal stimulation experiences can be structured to follow the normal sequence of language development (Loewy 1995; Michel and Jones 1991). For example, Loewy (1995) suggested a series of music techniques to stimulate and activate vocalization at each stage of Van Riper's (1984) model of language acquisition. At the earliest stages, Loewy suggests tonal/vocal holding techniques to match and extend the child's cry and rhythmic drum beating to match and help organize the child's sounds. At the babbling/lalling stage, vocal mirroring techniques encourage vocal play and development. Later, vowels and phonemes are used in vocal improvisation and rhythmic consonant play, and specific action words are used and explored with instruments and in songs. Perhaps most importantly, while carefully sequenced music experiences help encourage vocalization within the context of an individual's particular stage or level of speech and language, they simultaneously help "integrate the cognitive, physical, and emotional aspects of growth" (Loewy 1995, 71).

Therapeutic Music Experiences to Develop Receptive and Expressive Language Skills

Specially structured music experiences may help clients develop, practice, and reinforce receptive and expressive language skills (Adamek and Darrow 2010; Coleman, McNairn, and Shioleno 1995; Humpal 1990; Lathom-Radocy 2014; Michel and Jones 1991; Miller 1982). Music may be especially useful in helping in the development of the listening, sound discrimination, and auditory sequencing and memory skills that are important in the development of *receptive language skills* (Michel and Jones 1991; Miller 1982; Zinar 1987; Zoller 1991). Sounds of musical instruments and singing voices readily attract the attention of most clients, thus providing a useful starting point for auditory awareness training. At first, music therapists may address basic auditory awareness and perception skills by asking clients to make gross discriminations (e.g., sound/no sound, fast/slow, loud/soft, high pitch/low pitch) in listening, movement, singing, and instrumental experiences. As the client's skills emerge and develop, these activities can be structured and adapted to lead the client to gradually make finer discriminations of sound qualities, pitches, dynamics, tempos, or rhythms. Music activities and experiences that gradually ask clients to remember more sounds, lyrics, and rhythms or more complex sequences of sounds, musical events, or directions can help develop auditory memory and sequencing skills.

When individuals have good receptive language skills, they understand what words mean and can follow directions. Music therapists can structure various activities readily to help individuals develop and practice these skills. For example, songs, dances, and musical games can require individuals to follow simple directions, identify or move specific body parts, or identify colors, pictures, objects, letters, numbers, etc. Clients also can demonstrate an understanding of language by pointing to pictures or word cards that go with song lyrics, performing actions or answering questions to demonstrate an understanding of song lyrics, or sequencing picture cards to tell the story of a song. Michel and Jones (1991, 16–18), Miller (1982, 43–45), and Nocera (1979, 24–54, 99–100), give several detailed suggestions of music activities that may be useful in developing auditory perception and receptive language skills. Davis, Gfeller, and Thaut (2008, 169) discuss Auditory Perception Training (APT) as a means for individuals to regain speech and language. This utilizes the components of music: "time, tempo, duration, pitch, timbre, rhythmic patterns, and speech sounds." Radocy and Boyle (2012, 25) discussed the components of music: "Whatever the culture, music involves an organization of sounds and silences, encompassing various pitches, loudness levels, and timbres, all of which occur within a rhythmic framework." Due to dysfunctional sensory systems, it is important to consider the organization of auditory stimuli in music, which can help the individual organize sensory input (Kalas 2012).

Different types of music experiences also may help motivate individuals to develop and practice various *expressive language skills.* For example, group singing effectively may reinforce communication, improve expressive language skills, and increase self-initiated speech (Cohen 1994). Individuals who have speech impairments or delayed language development may also become more confident in using expressive speech when asked to do this in the enjoyable, nonthreatening context of music experiences (Hoskins 1988; Lathom-Radocy 2014; Michel and Jones 1991; Miller 1982; Zinar 1987):

> Children will frequently sing something they rarely or never say, and can often do so without demonstrating the same difficulties they have when they are speaking the same words. This can lead to increased self-confidence, and can encourage the child to use the words in everyday speech. (Miller 1982, 31)

Sequentially structured songs and musical games can gradually encourage the development of expressive language skills, by first asking individuals to produce vowel or consonant sounds (e.g., sing with "ah" or "oo" or "buh"), then to sing one or two words or fill in the missing words to song lyrics, and then to sing phrases and whole songs (Michel and Jones 1991; Miller 1982). Hoskins (1988) also found that music activities like action songs; singing activities used to teach concepts like body parts, colors, and numbers; and antiphonal songs using picture word cards were particularly useful in encouraging spontaneous speech and improving expressive language skills in preschool children who had language delays. In addition, clients can also develop and practice expressive language skills as they participate in song-writing experiences, supplying single words, phrases, or complete lyrics for original songs or parodies. Adamek and Darrow (2010, 190), Davis, Gfeller, and Thaut (2008, 160–167), Goodman, (2007, 195–197), Lathom-Radocy (2014, 173–182), Michel and Jones (1991, 19–26), and Zinar (1987, 175–176) provide several excellent examples of specific music activities for developing expressive language skills.

Music experiences also may be used to increase vocabulary, teach rules of grammar and syntax, and develop, improve, or reinforce reading and writing skills. Musical experiences, such as songs, chants, musical games, song-writing activities, listening experiences, and movement or instrument-playing experiences that incorporate the use of written symbols or directions, all may be structured to present information on these subjects, practice these skills, provide a structure for learning and remembering the information, or reinforce the learning (Coleman, McNairn, and Shioleno 1995; Lathom-Radocy 2014; Michel and Jones 1991; Miller 1982; Standley and Hughes 1997; Staum 1989; Zoller 1991). Moreover, the multisensory aspect of music experiences can facilitate the learning and retention of material. For example, Madsen (1991) found that first graders learned more new vocabulary when the words were presented with music paired with gesture than when paired with gesture alone. In addition, music experiences can accommodate a wide variety of learning styles.

Some music therapists have structured therapeutic music interventions to complement various approaches to language development. Gfeller (1987b) used song writing in a language experience approach to increase reading and writing skills, and found that song writing increased motivation to participate and increased attention to the material by adding a novel teaching method. The lyrics and music also provided themes for discussion and a structure for teaching language skills. Many concepts that are necessary for success in reading can be taught through music (Lathom-Radocy 2014, 177–178). In another research project, music activities structured to complement a cognitive linguistic approach to language development (a) increased multisensory and motor involvement in learning (instrumental and music-movement experiences), (b) encouraged dialogue and group interaction (question-and-answer, call-and-response, echo, or fill-in songs), (c) motivated and engaged client participation, and (d) provided opportunities for clients to experience and practice language skills in a different context (Gfeller 1990). Another researcher found that, when books' texts were set to music in a music-enhanced whole language approach, music became a structural prompt to pair the sung word to the written word, thereby helping children "link oral to written language through rhyme, rhythm, and repetition of vocabulary and story structure" (Colwell 1994, 240).

In early intervention settings, specially designed music activities can provide effective avenues for practicing language patterns, learning how to use books and printed materials, increasing language comprehension, and beginning to decode written language (Standley and Hughes 1997). Research suggests that music activities that intentionally target and focus on specific skills are most effective in teaching prereading and writing concepts (Standley and Hughes 1997). Coleman, McNairn, and Shioleno (1995) provide several examples of songs and music activities that may be used to increase specific literacy skills. Register (2004, 2) measured effects of music on learning letter names, phonemic awareness, and concepts in a study of kindergarten children with normal development but low socioeconomic backgrounds, comparing results with those from a television program designed to teach early literacy behaviors: "The Music/Video and Music-Only group achieved the highest increases in mean scores from pre to posttest on 4 of the 7 subtests." This research led to a follow-up study of reading skills of second-grade students and students who were identified as having a specific learning disability:

Analysis of pre/posttest data revealed that students with a specific disability in reading improved significantly from pre to post on all three subtests: word decoding (p = .04), word knowledge (p = .01), reading comprehension (p = .01), and test total (p = .01). (Register, Darrow, Standley, and Swedberg 2007, 23)

Both the control group and test group made significant gains from pre to posttest.

Therapeutic Music Experiences to Improve Articulation Skills

Since individuals must be able to discriminate between correct and incorrect sounds to articulate words properly, musical experiences focusing on improving sound discrimination skills (e.g., same/different) may provide an important foundation for improving articulation skills (Michel and Jones 1991; Zinar 1987; Zoller 1991). Initial experiences may use instrumental sounds (e.g., identifying instruments by sound only, telling whether two sounds were played by the same or different instruments), with later experiences moving to finer distinctions of verbal sounds. For example, individuals may be asked to listen to two versions of a lyric to identify which uses the correct word sounds and which contains errors.

One of the most obvious beneficial musical experiences for individuals who have articulation disorders is the use of specially devised songs, chants, or musical games that help them practice certain speech sounds or words (Cohen 1994; Michel and Jones 1991; Miller 1982; Staum 1989; Zinar 1987; Zoller 1991). The process may begin by setting specially targeted sounds or syllables to melodies or chants for the individual to sing. Articulation requires motor control and muscular coordination (Davis, Gfeller, and Thaut 2008). After mastering specific sounds, the individual may then be asked to sing targeted words in songs that use these sounds. Michel and Jones (1991, 19–21), and Zinar (1987, 182–187) provide good examples. Singing and music can motivate individuals to practice their articulation exercises by providing a more pleasurable way of communicating and by relieving some of the boredom often associated with the repeated drill necessary to improve articulation skills.

Music's rhythmic structure may provide additional benefits to persons with articulation disorders. Zoller (1991, 275) suggested that individuals speak poems rhythmically while clapping, walking, or tapping the beat, for "rhythm often unconsciously helps correct misarticulations." The rhythmic and melodic cues provided by setting words to music may also help individuals remember sound sequences within words, another skill that is important to proper articulation (Staum 1989).

Therapeutic Music Experiences to Improve Speech Rate or Fluency

Music's rhythmic and melodic structure also may help individuals achieve a more normal *speech rate*. Individuals who speak too rapidly may learn to speak more slowly by singing question-and-answer songs that have slow or moderate tempi and one syllable per note. The structure involved when the therapist sings questions and the client sings responses may help individuals relax and slow their speech rate (Michel and Jones 1991). Rhythmic games and exercises that involve walking, tapping, or playing instruments to the basic beat or melodic rhythm of songs may help individuals become more aware of tempo and speech rate (Davis, Gfeller, and Thaut 2008; Miller 1982). Speaking or chanting words or phrases rhythmically, as well as saying and clapping the rhythm of familiar words, are other music- and rhythm-based techniques that may help individuals achieve a more appropriate speech rate (Davis, Gfeller, and Thaut 2008; Miller 1982). Cohen (1988) found that superimposing a rhythm on verbal structure by tapping the beat while singing or by tapping the beat while practicing a tape of functional sentences helped decrease excessively fast speech rates in brain-damaged individuals. Persons with neurological impairments who received singing instruction (including breathing and vocal exercises and group singing) also showed some improvement in speech rate (Cohen 1992; Cohen and Masse 1993). For persons with neurogenic communication disorders who had an abnormally slow speech rate, vocal instruction paired with Visi-Pitch™ feedback helped increase speech rate and vocal intensity (Cohen 1995).

Music's rhythmic and melodic structure also can help decrease *fluency disorders*. Although Galloway (1974) reported that, contrary to popular belief, singing cannot cure stuttering, various studies have shown that white noise and rhythmic stimulation can significantly reduce stuttering (Altrows and Bryden 1977; Brayton and Conture 1978; Silverman 1976; Yairi 1976). Michel and Jones (1991) noted that researchers have hypothesized that some stuttering problems may relate to difficulties with speaking rate, controlling the breath stream, and synchronizing the breath stream with sound production at the vocal cord level, and that many techniques in singing instruction may help alleviate these difficulties. Therefore, they recommend that music therapists "apply techniques of good singing instruction, vocalizing, breathing, etc., with stutterers" (Michel and Jones 1991, 23). Since stuttering problems often increase in stressful situations, stutterers may benefit from music relaxation techniques (Michel and Jones 1991). Conceivably, there may be instances in which rhythmic or melodic structure could cue both relaxation and fluency for some individuals. Clearly, many questions about stuttering and its causes and treatments remain to be answered (Davis, Gfeller, and Thaut 2008; Michel and Jones 1991; Miller 1982).

Therapeutic Music Experiences to Correct
Voice Disorders

Since singing and speaking both involve elements of vocal frequency (pitch), inflection (melodic contour and pitch change), sound quality, and intensity (loudness), singing can be a valuable therapeutic tool to help correct various voice disorders (Cohen 1992, 1994; Miller 1982; Nocera 1979; Staum 1989; Zinar 1987). Because breath control affects vocal resonance and voice timbre, individuals who have problems with *vocal quality* (overly harsh, hoarse, breathy, or nasal speech) may benefit from breath control exercises to music or from learning proper breath support and control as part of vocalization exercises and singing instruction (Cohen 1994; Miller 1982). Davis, Gfeller, and Thaut (2008, 163) describe vocal intonation therapy (VIT), which "addresses the rehabilitation of abnormal pitch, loudness, timbre, breathing, and prosody of speech."

Humming or playing simple wind instruments like the kazoo or flutophone also helps develop breath control and support and helps individuals learn to direct their air stream for more open, less nasal sounds (Miller 1982; Wells and Helmus 1968; Zinar 1987). Therapeutic Instrumental Music Playing (TIMP) is "the use of musical instrument playing to facilitate engagement in physical exercise and to stimulate functional movement patterns in motor therapy (Davis, Gfeller, and Thaut 2008, 294).

Various music experiences can also positively influence *vocal pitch* and *inflection.* For example, individuals whose speech is higher (shriller) or lower than is standard for their age or sex may benefit from music-movement and singing games that have them recognize and imitate high or low sounds and pitches. Using hand signals that correspond to high, medium, and low pitches may help emphasize proper intonation and pitch level placement. Singing instruction and training utilizing songs and vocal exercises have effectively improved the fundamental speaking frequency (vocal pitch) of hearing impaired children (Cohen 1994; Davis, Gfeller, and Thaut 2008, 386; Darrow and Starmer 1986) and persons with neurological impairments (Cohen 1992; Thaut 2008). Specially adapted music education software used with a personal computer that increased singing range and accuracy in an individual with Down syndrome also caused his speech to become clearer and pitched in a higher, more appropriate frequency range (Spitzer 1989).

Music can also be a valuable asset in teaching or practicing correct inflectional patterns for individuals who speak in a *monotone* or who have problems with proper *vocal inflection* (Lathom-Radocy 2014; Miller 1982; Staum 1989; Wells and Helmus 1968; Zinar 1987). When melodies and phrases of songs are carefully constructed so that the melodic and rhythmic treatment of the lyrics corresponds to the natural rhythms and inflections of speech, singing songs can help clients learn and practice correct rhythmic and inflectional patterns for words, phrases, and sentences (Nordoff and Robbins 1971a). As individual clients learn to use more inflection through singing or chanting, the music can be gradually faded (Staum 1989). Matching tones with a piano, moving or making diagrams to show the pitch contour of a phrase, and echo songs and chants are all experiences that can help increase awareness of vocal pitch and inflection. Miller (1982, 47–48), Nocera (1979, 102–103), and Zinar (1987, 181–183) provide several examples of music- and rhythm-based experiences designed to improve vocal inflection.

When individuals speak too loudly or softly (disorders of *volume* or *intensity*), experiences in singing or playing the same song at different intensity levels may help them become aware of differences in degrees of loudness and learn to control their own level of speaking, singing, or playing. Relating musical dynamic markings to speech situations, practicing getting gradually louder or softer (with voices or instruments), or using echo songs may also help individuals learn to use appropriate loudness in singing and speaking (Zinar 1987). Those who speak too softly may need to develop breath control and lung capacity. They may benefit from vocal and breathing exercises, singing sustained tones and gradually being encouraged to sing longer songs and phrases, vocally imitating the sounds of chimes or drums, playing the harmonica or kazoo, or learning to play a wind instrument (Wells and Helmus 1968; Zinar 1987). Cohen (1995) found that a treatment regimen including breathing exercises, speech tasks set to diatonic ascending and descending patterns that slightly exaggerated normal speech prosody, singing familiar songs, and Visi-Pitch™ feedback helped individuals with neurogenic communication disorders improve their vocal intensity. Subjects noted that combining singing and Visi-Pitch™ feedback enhanced their therapy and gave them an incentive to practice at home. Again, music has a great ability to motivate individuals to participate in treatment and to practice repetitious drills (Staum 1989; Thaut 2008). It provides a reinforcing stimulus for vocal production, which is used in Therapeutic Singing (TS) (Thaut 2008, 175–176).

Music Therapy for Individuals Who Have Cleft Palates

Cleft palates result from incomplete closure of facial parts during the embryonic period (Spraycar (Ed.), *Stedman's Medical Dictionary* 1995). Individuals with cleft palates often have problems with hypernasality and poor breath-stream control. Several music experiences involving singing and playing simple wind instruments can help alleviate these problems (Michel 1968; Michel and Jones 1991; Wells and Helmus 1968; Zinar 1987). As mentioned above, humming and kazoo playing may be effective in reducing nasal sounds (Michel 1968; Wells and Helmus 1968; Zinar 1987). Playing simple wind instruments like the harmonica, flutophone, melodica or pianica, whistle, or reed horn also may develop velopharangeal closure and help eliminate nasal emission of air (Michel 1968; Michel and Jones 1991; Wells and Helmus 1968), while trumpet instruction can help older clients learn to direct their airstream properly (Wells and Helmus 1968). In addition, group singing and vocalizing experiences can help develop proper control of breath stream and provide a pleasurable way to practice correct speech sounds and improve tone quality (Michel 1968; Michel and Jones 1991; Thaut 2008).

Music therapy interventions not only help individuals who have cleft palates increase ability to discriminate sound quality, improve breath stream control, and practice articulation exercises, but also provide outlets for expressing feelings of frustration and aggression and help individuals increase self-confidence as they make positive accomplishments in developing musical skills (Michel 1968).

Music Therapy for Speech and Language Rehabilitation in Individuals with Aphasia

The benefits of singing for stimulating speech in individuals who have neurological impairments have been noted for many years. Cohen (1994) summarizes early anecdotal records (dating back to 1745) and research, all of which note how individuals with expressive aphasia who have little or no speech often maintain singing ability. While the ability of music therapy interventions to help a particular individual may depend on many factors, including the individual's premorbid experience with music and the exact site and extent of brain damage (Cohen 1994; Taylor 1987b, 1989), music therapy techniques can be effective in treating speech dysfunctions for many individuals with traumatic brain injuries (Adamek and Shiraishi 1996).

Early reports in the music therapy literature observed that individuals who were unable to speak due to a brain injury often were still able to sing songs that were learned before the injury. For some clients, these songs could provide a springboard for redeveloping some language ability (Goodglass 1963; Palmer 1953; Thaut 2008). Since those early years, many different music- and rhythm-based interventions have been developed to help restore speech and communication abilities in persons with aphasia.

Melodic Intonation Therapy

In the early 1970s, Melodic Intonation Therapy (MIT) was developed as a strategy to recover some functional speech in adults with aphasia who were not responding to more traditional speech therapy techniques (Albert, Sparks, and Helm 1973; Baker 2000; Brookshire 2003; King 2007; LaGasse 2012; Sparks, Helms, and Albert 1974; Sparks and Holland 1976; Thaut 2008). In MIT, short phrases and sentences are intoned at a slow tempo to simple, unfamiliar melodic patterns that have a limited pitch range (designed to resemble the natural inflections of speech), with a precise rhythm that emphasizes the words' normal stress and inflection. Baker (2000, 110) indicates that "both verbal and music language contain similarities with respect to rhythm, timbre and pitch, and they both aim to convey some form of message." The client is led through a sequence of specific steps and levels that gradually increase the length of intoned phrases and sentences, decrease dependence on the therapist, and minimize the client's reliance on the intonation. Techniques used in the MIT process include verbal cuing, hand tapping, control by hand signals, unison repetition, and eventual fading of the melodic patterns. For a complete description of the method, see Sparks and Holland (1976).

MIT techniques assume that the brain's right hemisphere may have unimpaired language areas and that singing is distributed in many areas (Hobson 2006; Thaut 2008). The right hemisphere, then, also responds to the "musical" qualities of speech (rhythm, stress, inflection), especially when they are exaggerated. MIT presumably is effective because melodic intonation that exaggerates the rhythm, stress, and melodic contour of words and phrases employs speech functions contained in the undamaged right hemisphere, thereby stimulating and assisting the ususally dominant (for speech) left hemisphere (Kraus and Galloway 1982): "MIT utilizes a patient's unimpaired ability to sing to facilitate speech production" (Thaut 2008, 166). The best candidate for MIT is an adult with aphasia who has normal verbal comprehension but limited verbal output, who is emotionally stable, and who makes an active effort at self-correction.

Lucia (1987), a music therapist, has adapted MIT techniques for group use, focusing on word retrieval through songs and rhythmic chant. According to Lucia, this approach is most useful for patients who have damage to the left frontal lobe (Broca's aphasia) or bilateral damage in which the right temporal lobe is still relatively intact. Kraus and Galloway (1982) also have successfully used MIT techniques to help develop speech in children who have apraxia and language delays. LaGasse (2012) provides "Implications for Music Therapy Clinical Practice." Generally, when used in music therapy, the method has been modified. Music therapy presents many ways to provide a more motivating approach to using this method. She concluded that "music therapists should consider utilizing more appropriate treatment techniques for children with DAS [Developmental Apraxia of Speech], using the motivational and structural elements of music in order to promote engagement and speech communication" (55).

Rhythm and Melody in Speech Therapy

This technique, developed by a music therapist (Rogers and Fleming 1981), uses both musical and therapeutic principles, and it employs "carrier melodies" to stimulate speech in persons with left hemisphere brain damage. The technique "capitalizes on residually intact melody and rhythm at some neurophysiologic level wherein correlates of speech/language share neural pathways with those elements of music salient to verbal communication, i.e., rhythm and melody" (36). In contrast to MIT, this method uses familiar melodies "to take advantage of any 'automatic' ability present" (34). After selecting a familiar melody with intervals and rhythms approximating those of conversational speech for use as the carrier tune (e.g., "Yankee Doodle"), the therapist establishes the patient's ability to hum or sing the carrier melody. Next, phrases are added to the melodic pattern. Tongue exercises performed to the music help patients prepare to speak/sing the words. Later, a two-note pattern introduces new words to increase vocabulary. Finally, the carrier melody and two-note patterns are reduced and eliminated, and more complex phrases are substituted, using melodies involving three pitches (e.g., C, D, E). Rogers and Fleming used the method in both group and individual sessions, and noted that "the simplicity of the program lends itself to family participation and carry-over to practice in the home during weekend passes and after discharge" (35).

Other Techniques

Other music-based techniques also can enhance communication abilities in persons with aphasia and related disorders. Skille (1989) found that vibroacoustic therapy, a method in which musical sound waves are applied directly to the body, increased vocal sound production in persons with aphasia. Cohen (1992) by using singing instruction and weekly Visi-Pitch™ feedback on vocal intensity, fundamental frequency, and percentage of pause time to help clients with both expressive aphasia and dysarthria increase their speech rate and vocal intensity. Cohen and Masse (1993) found that singing and rhythmic instruction successfully increased verbal intelligibility in persons with neurogenic communication disorders. Cohen (1988) also worked with a patient who had right hemisphere brain damage and found that tapping the beat during singing or rhythmic speech helped decrease the patient's excessively fast speech rate.

Taylor (1987b; 1989) gives several recommendations for using music-based treatment interventions with aphasic clients, including the following:

1. Tailoring the music therapy intervention to the specific needs, strengths, abilities, and preferences of each client, to maximize music's ability to

effectively treat the specific speech and language disorders of that individual;

2. Using slower than normal tempos to increase the time available to perceive and form syllables and words; also using slowed conversational speech, emphasizing key words;

3. Using songs with few words, frequent repetitions, and fairly regular, repeated rhythm patterns for singing activities;

4. Singing songs more than once so clients have a chance to correct errors;

5. Pointing to the printed lyrics while singing, using large song cards or typed sheets with one song per page;

6. Using melodic settings of the words that enhance normal speech accents and inflections; and

7. Working separately on elements tempo, rhythm, pitch control, loudness, tone quality, articulation, breath control, so success in one area will generate motivation to work on other areas.

Taylor (1989, 177) also suggests using song writing to help improve expressive language and believes "treatment objectives should include social, emotional and nonlanguage motor skills in addition to specific communication behaviors."

Therapeutic Music Experiences Using Augmentive Communication Systems

Individuals who use augmentive communication methods may readily participate in music experiences if the therapist is willing to learn the individual's system of communication and utilize it in giving instructions and allowing the individual to respond. For example, individuals who use communication boards may respond to questions or contribute to song-writing exercises by using their boards. Herman (1985) worked with children who used Blissymbols and had them point to symbols to identify feelings represented by music, contribute to group "story songs," or tell what feelings they wanted to express. As mentioned in Chapter Nine, signing and manual communication systems can be used to express song lyrics, and signs and singing can be used together for total communication experiences (Darrow 1987a; Knapp 1980). Music can also have a positive effect on learning signs. Adamek and Darrow (2010) discuss picture exchange communication system (PECS). Conversation is initiated by use of pictures and symbols: "Using PECS, a student learns the meaning of a set of pictures or symbols by exchanging those symbols for something he or she wants or needs" (196). Use of AAC systems requires training and practice to adapt the system to music therapy.

Technology now enables nonverbal individuals to have an active "voice" in many music experiences (Humpal and Dimmick 1995). For example, switches may activate tape players containing loops of repeated words or phrases in a song. Individuals who have augmentive communication devices that produce synthesized speech sounds may use these to supply words or phrases to songs or contribute to discussions or group compositions. Symbolic communication training (SYCOM) can be used with ACC to "stimulate communication structures in social interaction patterns" (Thaut 2008, 176). This system is used to express emotional communication. Technology also allows individuals with severe physical limitations increased opportunities to create music independently via computers and adaptive electronic equipment (Adamek and Darrow 2008; Fegers et al. 1989; Howell et al. 1995; Krout 1992a, 1995; Nagler and Lee 1989; Swingler 1994). Goodman (2007, 162) discussed use of Boardmaker: "a touch activated communication system, [which] contains over 3,000 picture communication symbols which the music therapist can select in order to help the child communicate in music."

Therapeutic Music Experiences Increase Self-Confidence, Emotional Expression, and Social Interaction

The opportunities for nonverbal communication inherent in group music activities can be very important to individuals who cannot use speech for communication. By playing instruments or moving to music, individuals may express themselves and their feelings without the trauma, difficulty, or embarrassment of attempting to speak. Opportunity for self-expression through music, a socially acceptable, meaningful form of communication, "may serve to alleviate some of the frustration that often accompanies speech impairments and give the child [or adult] an opportunity for ventilation of feelings" (Miller 1982, 2). Individuals who have acquired communication impairments due to brain injuries also may benefit from music therapy interventions, such as song writing, instrumental improvisation, or discussion of song lyrics that help them process social and emotional issues related to their injury and losses (Adamek and Shiraishi 1996; Taylor 1989).

Speech problems may cause individuals to have a lack of self-confidence (Wells and Helmus 1968). As they participate in creative music experiences like song writing, instrumental improvisation, and creative movement to music that allow them to express their own feelings and personalities, individuals "visibly grow in power and self-possession" (Herman 1985, 35). Individuals also increase their self-confidence and self-esteem as they participate successfully in music experiences, see their speech skills improve from practice in music situations, or acquire skills in singing or playing musical instruments (Haas, Pineda, and Axen 1989; Michel 1968). Lathom-Radocy (2014, 179) explains that "positive reinforcement of correct responses is far more effective than constant attention to speech problems."

Music therapy experiences often occur in group settings and provide opportunities for social interaction in the context of enjoyable activities. Group instruction provides many additional social and emotional benefits not present in individual instruction (Cohen 1992; Rogers and Fleming 1981). Participating in group singing or instrumental experiences can help increase cooperation, decrease shyness, and increase interaction with others (Michel 1968). As Adamek and Darrow (2010, 190) confirm, "Through music making with others, students can work on taking turns, sharing, listening, self-expression, leadership, and other social skills needed for active involvement with others." Group music experiences for individuals with aphasia also help increase social awareness, encourage successful interactions within a peer group, provide emotional support systems, give opportunities to see fellow patients at varying stages of progress, provide a safe environment to test new skills, and offer a forum for sharing issues, frustrations, concerns, and complaints (Cohen and Masse 1993; Rogers and Fleming 1981). Following their work in music therapy with persons who had aphasia, Cohen and Ford (1995, 54) observed,

> The music therapy session provided them with a comfortable environment in which they were able to produce some words and apparently feel successful. Music therapy was valuable for them because it fostered participation and provided a means of expression, both verbal and nonverbal.

Research suggests that preschool children who have speech and language disorders can participate successfully in basic group music activities with their nondisabled peers (Cassidy 1992; Furman and Humpal 2006; Hoskins 1988). Language function is important to social interaction. Thus, the practice of "mainstreaming" or including children who have communication disorders in "regular" music classes gives them opportunities to interact successfully with their peers and helps them practice various communication skills.

SPECIAL CONSIDERATIONS AND TIPS FOR SUCCESS

When music therapists work with clients who have speech and language disorders, it is essential that they consult and cooperate with speech therapists. Such cooperative efforts can have important beneficial results for the clients (Gfeller and Bauman 1988; Lathom-Radocy 2014; Michel 1976, 1985; Michel and Jones 1991; Michel and May 1974).

The music therapist who uses music intervention to develop language skills should be familiar with the normal sequences of language development and with common language assessment tools (Michel and Jones 1991). This will help the therapist determine the client's current level of functioning and help provide a sequence for skill development. Pairing concrete stimuli (e.g., pictures or gestures) with the aural/verbal stimuli of spoken words may help individuals respond correctly (Adamek and Darrow 2010; Cassidy 1992). Instructions and activities should use language that matches the client's functional language abilities and should not attempt to teach too many items or give too many examples at one time (Michel and Jones 1991).

Since many individuals with communication disorders may have emotional problems that arise from or underlie their speech and language problems, it is important to consider their emotional needs in the total treatment plan (Adamek and Darrow 2010; Lathom-Radocy 2014; Michel 1968; Michel and Jones 1991; Miller 1982; Taylor 1989; Wells and Helmus 1968). Since poor communication skills also negatively affect socialization, it may be important to help individuals develop and have opportunities to practice appropriate social interaction skills.

QUESTIONS FOR THOUGHT AND DISCUSSION

1. Discuss some of the general characteristics and needs of individuals who have communication disorders. What implications do these have for music therapy programming?
2. Describe some general ways music experiences facilitate the acquisition of speech and language skills. Do some types of music experiences or modes of musical expression seem to facilitate the acquisition of speech and language skills more readily than others? If so, which ones? Why?
3. Describe at least three different types of augmentive communication systems. How might each of these be incorporated into music therapy experiences?
4. Describe some specific music therapy experiences that might be used to (1) increase breath and muscle control, (2) stimulate vocalization, (3) develop receptive and/or expressive language skills, (4) improve articulation skills, (5) improve speech rate and fluency, (6) correct voice disorders, (7) facilitate speech and language development in individuals who have cleft palates, (8) facilitate speech and language rehabilitation in individuals who have aphasia, (9) incorporate the use of augmentive communication systems, and (10) increase client's self-confidence, emotional expression, and social interaction. What unique benefits does music provide in each of these areas?
5. List several special considerations that may be important to remember when developing therapeutic intervention strategies for persons who have communication disorders. Why are these important? What are their implications for the structure or implementation of music therapy intervention strategies?

6. For each of the situations listed below, (a) define the problem or areas of need for the client or group of clients, (b) describe one or more of the goals you might pursue in music therapy sessions with the client(s), (c) describe music activities you might use to help the client(s) meet those goals, (d) tell how the music activities you described relate to the goals and needs of the client(s), and (e) mention any special considerations you might want to take into account when working with the client(s).

Situation 1:

Because Mary seems to enjoy listening to music and playing the piano, she has been referred to music therapy in the hope that she can gain some needed nonmusical skills through music activities. Mary is ten years old, and she does not articulate consonant sounds clearly. Although her neurological evaluation showed that she should be able to develop the coordination needed for clear speech, Mary seems to have great difficulty coordinating the movements of her lips, tongue, and teeth. Mary rarely practices the exercises that the speech therapist gave her; she says they are boring and don't do any good.

Situation 2:

You are working as a music therapist in a long-term care facility. Twelve of the residents have some degree of expressive aphasia. They are on the waiting list for speech therapy services. Many are depressed and frustrated by their lack of ability to communicate and socialize with others. Your administrator heard something about how music might help individuals with aphasia regain some speech, and she wants you to start a music group that might help these residents communicate and interact with others successfully.

SUGGESTIONS FOR FURTHER READING

Adamek, M. S. & Shiraishi, I. M. (1996). Music therapy with traumatic brain injured patients: Speech rehabilitation, intervention models, and assessment procedures. In C. E. Furman (Ed.), *Effectiveness of music therapy procedures: Documentation of research and clinical practice* (2nd ed.) (267–278). Silver Spring, MD: National Association for Music Therapy.

Cohen, N. S. (1994). Speech and song: Implications for therapy. *Music Therapy Perspectives, 12(1)*, 8–14.

Coleman, K., McNairn, P., & Shioleno, C. (1995). *Quick tech magic: Music-based literacy activities.* Solana Beach, CA: Mayer-Johnson.

Hobson, M. R. (2006). The collaboration of music therapy and speech-language pathology in the treatment of neurogenic communication disorders. Part I and

Part II. *Music Therapy Perspectives, 24(2),* 58–65, 66–72.

Lathom-Radocy, W. (2014). Speech and language impaired children. In W. Lathom-Radocy (Ed.), *Pediatric music therapy,* (2nd ed.) (153–188). Springfield, IL: Charles C Thomas.

Loewy, J. (1995). The musical stages of speech: A developmental model of pre-verbal sound making. *Music Therapy, 13(1),* 47–73.

Michel, D. E. (1985). Speech and language disorders and disabilities. In D. E. Michel (Ed.), *Music therapy: An introduction, including music in special education* (2nd ed.) (43–47). Springfield, IL: Charles C Thomas.

Michel, D. E. & Jones, L. (1991). *Music for developing speech and language skills in children: A guide for parents and therapists.* St. Louis: MMB Music.

Miller, S. G. (1982). Music therapy for speech impaired children. In W. B. Lathom & C. T. Eagle, Jr. (Eds.), *Music therapy for handicapped children,* Vol. 2 (117–163). Washington, D.C.: National Association for Music Therapy.

Musselwhite, C. & Showalter, S. (1990). *Augmentive communication activity book.* Ashville, NC: The Irene Wortham Center.

Standley, J. (1991). *Music techniques in therapy, counseling, and special education.* St. Louis: MMB Music.

Standley, J. M. & Hughes, J. E. (1997). Evaluation of an early intervention music curriculum for enhancing prereading/writing skills. *Music Therapy Perspectives, 15(2),* 79–86.

Staum, M. J. (1989). Music as motivation for language learning. In R. R. Pratt & H. Moog (Eds.), *First research seminar of the ISME commission on music therapy and music in special education: Proceedings of 1986* (62–68). Bad Honnef, W. Germany: MMB Music.

Taylor, D. B. (1987). The theoretical basis for the use of music with aphasic patients. In R. R. Pratt (Ed.), *The fourth international symposium on music: Rehabilitation and human well-being* (165–169). New York: University Press of America.

Taylor, D. B. (1989). A neuroanatomical model for the use of music in the remediation of aphasic disorders. In M. H. M. Lee (Ed.), *Rehabilitation, music and human well-being* (168–178). St. Louis: MMB Music.

Zoller, M. (1991). Use of music activities in speech-language therapy. *Language, Speech, and Hearing Services in Schools, 22,* 272–276.

Chapter Thirteen

MUSIC THERAPY FOR INDIVIDUALS ON THE AUTISM SPECTRUM

Definition

Autism is a neurological disorder that affects brain function, causing a lifelong developmental disability. DSM-V (2013, 53) gives these essential features of autism spectrum disorders:

> Persistent impairment in reciprocal social communication and social interaction (Criterion A).

> Restricted, repetitive patterns of behavior, interests, or activities (Criterion B).

Parents of autistic children observe these difficulties and usually bring their child for diagnostic observation in early childhood. The problems tend to limit or impair everyday functioning (Criteria C and D) (53).

Autism is manifested by a variety of characteristic behaviors, including (1) disturbances and deficiencies in speech, language, and communication, especially nonverbal language (DSM-V 2013), (2) difficulties in relating to other people and failure to develop normal socialization, (3) abnormal responses to sensory stimuli, (4) resistance to any change in routines or in the environment, and (5) uneven rates of development (e.g., relatively normal motor skill development, delayed or uneven or out of sequence development of communication or cognitive skills). For a diagnosis of autism, these features must become evident in early childhood, but may not be noted until social demands require customary behavior (Autism Society of America 1995; DSM-V 2013; Lovejoy and Estridge 1987; Powers 1989; Snell 1996). Although some symptoms may become less severe over time, most continue to affect the individual, at least to some extent, throughout his or her life.

DSM-V (2013) classifies autism as one of the neurodevelopmental disorders. It may occur with intellectual or language impairments, but those should be stated in the diagnosis. Delayed or abnormal functioning in social interaction, language for social communication, or symbolic or imaginative play are usually evident before 3 years of age.

The syndrome of autism was first identified by Kanner (1943), who used the term *infantile autism* to describe the condition, since the symptoms become evident in infancy. Other terms or labels have been used to describe the syndrome, but current terminology recognizes that autism is on a spectrum of disorders. The term *autism spectrum disorder* (ASD) is used in the current literature. It is differentiated from Rett syndrome, selective mutism, language disorders and social (pragmatic) communication disorder, intellectual disability (intellectual developmental disorder) without autism spectrum disorder, stereotypic movement disorder, attention-deficit/hyperactivity disorder, and schizophrenia (DSM-V 2013, 57–58).

Causes

When the syndrome was first identified, autism was thought to be caused by improper parenting, early emotional trauma, lack of parental affection, or faulty mother-child relations in early infancy. However, accumulated research since the 1960s has largely discounted these theories (Atterbury 1990; Birkenshaw-Fleming 1993; Del Olmo 1998; Lovejoy and Estridge 1987; Siegfried 1997; Thaut 1992d; Toigo 1992).

Although the exact cause of autism remains unknown, there is now considerable evidence that autism is a neurodevelopmental disorder (Atterbury 1990; Del Olmo 1998; Kern 2013; Lovejoy and Estridge 1987; Thaut 1992d; Toigo 1992). Diverse kinds of damage or abnormal development in brain centers handling sensory input may cause autistic individuals to react differently to sensory stimuli (light, sound, touch) and to have difficulty handling sensory input (Berger 2002). These reactions interfere with learning and the ability to function normally in society. Furthermore, as individuals withdraw, "brain damage could be compounded as the brain is denied the stimulation necessary for normal development" (Toigo 1992, 15).

Current evidence shows no single brain structure or system that is defective in autistic individuals, but suggests that "molecular defects are spread throughout various parts of the brain in such a way that the ability to process complex information is diminished" (Siegfried 1997, 7D). Kern (2013, 29) explores various theories of causation of ASD: (1) the role of hormones (particularly androgens/testosterone) in ASD; (2) the mechanisms that may underlie differences in neural connectivity in various areas and pathways in the brain; (3) multiple genetic markers; (4) autoimmunity; and (5) environmental factors that may be interacting with biological or genetic mechanisms to cause autism, and he supports each of these theories with the current (2005–2011) research.

Researchers continue to explore genetic, chemical, and biological causes of autism (Lovejoy and Estridge 1987; Siegfried 1997). Factors currently under investigation include (a) a combination of at least three genes that together generate the range of autistic symptoms, (b) defects in the nerve endings that receive chemical signals in the brain, (c) problems with the chemical messenger molecule, serotonin, or (d) problems in the brain's fetal development (Siegfried 1997). Although clues are increasing, researchers are still a long way from understanding exactly what causes autism. Ockelford (2013, 26) noted that "it may be that autism, as the term is commonly used, is indeed not 'one thing,' but an umbrella term for many different types of cognitive impairment (with potential areas of overlap) . . . the search for a single neurological cause is in any case likely to be frustrating."

Course of Disorder

By definition, autism has its onset in early childhood. It affects one percent of the population and is four times more common in boys than in girls (DSM-V 2013). Reschke-Hernandez (2011, 169) stated that this "is one of the most prevalent exceptionalities of childhood in the United States." The last decade has seen a dramatic increase in the number of reported cases, which may reflect change in definition of ASD, better screening, or increased efforts to report. Of course, there may be an actual increase in the number of individuals with ASD. This has led to the need for more music therapists to serve this population (Groene 2003).

Often, autistic children show lack of interest in social interaction at or shortly after birth. Symptoms become more apparent after the age of 2 years, when deficits in communication and social skills and developmental delays and differences become easier to define. Thompson (2012) notes that children with ASD may not follow a predictable sequence of attainment of social skills, as seen in typically developing children. With properly structured individualized treatment programs, many autistic individuals can gain some communication, cognitive, and social skills and decrease some of their stereotypical behaviors. Generally, those individuals who are able to develop communicative speech and have higher overall intelligence have the best prognosis (DSM-V 2013; Lovejoy and Estridge 1987; Powers 1989).

There is little information about ASD in old age (DSM-V 2013). Autism is a lifelong disorder, so symptoms continue to be present into and through adulthood. Only a small number of individuals with autism are able to live independently as adults; about one-third can achieve some degree of partial independence given appropriate environmental supports (APA 1994; Powers 1989).

COMMON CHARACTERISTICS, PROBLEMS, AND NEEDS OF CLIENTS

Like any group of individuals, people who have autism vary widely in their abilities and behavior, so symptoms and behavioral manifestations of the syndrome will differ somewhat among individuals (DSM-V 2013; Lovejoy and Estridge 1987; Powers 1989; Snell 1996). This is especially true since the spectrum was adopted. Factors such as the severity of the impairment, the existence of other disabilities, the client's age, and the degree and type of support services available also affect an individual's level of functioning and prognosis. In addition, each individual's unique combination of abilities, personality traits, strengths, and weaknesses will impact his or her particular responses and functional abilities. Therefore, it is unwise to attempt to predict a particular person's skill levels or ceiling of abilities based on broad generalizations about a certain population. However, an awareness of some characteristics, problems, and needs common to many individuals on the autism spectrum will be beneficial both to the therapist who desires to work with this population and to the reader who is trying to understand how music therapy intervention strategies may benefit this population.

Autistic children often look physically normal and healthy; however, their abilities to communicate and interact with others are severely impaired. Manifestations of autistic behaviors vary widely, but all individuals on the autism spectrum display, to some degree: (1) difficulties in social interaction and relating to other people; (2) severe language dysfunctions; (3) unusual, abnormal, and erratic reactions to routine sensory stimuli; (4) repetitive and restricted behaviors, activities, and interests and obsessive needs for sameness, order, and routine; and (5) disturbances in developmental rates or sequences (Atterbury 1990; Autism Society of America 1995; Birkenshaw-Fleming 1993; DSM-V 2013; Lim 2009; Lovejoy and Estridge 1987; Nelson, Anderson, and Gonzales 1984; Paul 1982; Powers 1989; Snell 1996; Thaut 1992d). Kalas (2012, 431) stated that joint attention deficit is one of the most common manifestations of the social behavior of persons with ASD: "Joint attention is the process of engaging another person's attention to share in the experience of observing an object or event." This is important because a child is expected to direct attention to someone else, imitate, and be aware of how his or her own behavior interacts with that of others.

Difficulties in Social Interaction and Relating to Others

The word *autism* is derived from the Greek word meaning "self." Individuals on the autism spectrum appear to be detached, aloof, and isolated from their surroundings. They seem to live in a world of their own, unaware of people in their environment. They have difficulty understanding or expressing emotion (Whipple, Gfeller, Driscoll, Oleson, and McGregor 2015) and rarely form emotional attachments; they usually avoid eye contact and physical contact. They may appear to be apathetic and unresponsive and have few, if any, social affective gestures (e.g., smile, frown, wave). Instead of seeking to share enjoyments, interests, and achievements with others or enjoying simple social play or games, they tend to treat people like objects and involve them in activities only as tools or mechanical aids

Difficulty in relating to others frequently is one of the first signs of autism, already becoming noticeable in early infancy. As babies, autistic individuals often are indifferent or averse to being held (e.g., stiffen when picked up) and may not act cuddly or want to be cuddled. As toddlers, they rarely make meaningful eye contact or respond with social smiles and do not enjoy adult interaction games like "peek-a-boo." As they grow, autistic children may become more aware of parents and other familiar adults, but have little or no interest in establishing peer friendships, have difficulty mixing with other children, and lack the ability to play cooperatively with others. They may be oblivious to other children. They usually have no concept of the needs of others and may not notice another's distress. As they grow older, individuals with autism may have some interest in friendship but have difficulty establishing friendships because they do not understand the conventions of social interaction.

Severe Language Dysfunctions

Inability to use language for functional communication is a primary feature of autism (Lim 2009). All autistic children have severe difficulties understanding and communicating with language: "Extreme deficit in the ability to communicate in the broadest sense, specifically, the ability to use speech for purposive communication (even when the child has speech), is the common denominator of early childhood autism" (Boxill 1985, 161). Both verbal and nonverbal communication skills and receptive language skills show marked and sustained impairments. As Lim (2009, 104) explains, "Children with ASD frequently have various kinds of language deficits; however, semantic, pragmatic, and prosody deficits are the most pervasive." (See previous chapter for definitions of these aspects of speech.) The prognosis for autistic individuals closely correlates with their ability to develop speech or a functional system of communication. If individuals can communicate with those around them, they have a better chance of being able to live and function successfully in the world.

Although autistic individuals hear speech clearly, they seem to have difficulty processing and understanding the meaning of speech sounds:

> Speech sounds (i.e., phonology), linguistic form (i.e., syntax), questions for requests, turn-taking abilities, and communication gestures are usually spared in children with ASD. However, intonation/vocal quality (i.e., prosody), linguistic function (i.e., pragmatics), semantics, questions seeking information, adding to conversational topic, and expressive gestures are usually impaired. (Lim 2009, 104)

To the individual with autism, human speech may just sound like senseless noise. Perhaps because of these processing difficulties, the development of spoken language is often delayed or absent. Approximately 40 percent to 50 percent of autistic individuals never speak. Others often develop their own special language or repeat the words and sounds of others (*echolalia*). Echoing may occur immediately after a person speaks or be repeated at another time. For example, some individuals on the autism spectrum may remember whole passages from conversations or television programs and repeat them at various intervals over a long period of time. This has had redefinition as a speech function in ASD children. It is now thought to be a developmental behavior with communication purposes (Lim 2009, 105).

Autistic individuals who do develop some functional speech often are unable to initiate or sustain conversations. Their speech is often characterized by abnormal pitch, volume, intonation, rate, rhythm, or stress. In addition, it may be flat (lacking intonation or emotion) or have inappropriate changes in tone. They seldom use appropriate nonverbal communication features, such as gestures and facial expressions (Brownell 2002). Their speech also frequently contains grammatical errors, stereotyped or repetitive use of language, or jargon that is meaningful only to the individual or those who are familiar with the individual's communication style. Because of disturbances in language comprehension, autistic individuals may be unable to understand simple questions, directions, or jokes. Frequently, they have little or no ability to engage in imaginative play or simple imitation games.

Music activities may be used as a part of behavioral strategies to encourage, reinforce, and structure verbal interactions. Songs and chanting techniques can also help students acquire and practice signed and spoken vocabulary and language patterns. Buday (1995) found that autistic children learn signs more effectively when they were taught with music and speech than when they were taught with only rhythm and speech. In addition to the positive effect on speech and sign imitation, participation in the music condition influences the children to show less hand flaying, fewer head movements, and less incoherent babbling. This suggests that music activities designed to improve expressive language skills in individuals with autism will be most successful when they employ a melodic component in addition to a rhythmic component.

Abnormal, Erratic Reactions to Routine
Sensory Stimuli

Autistic individuals tend to have unusual reactions and responses to things they can see, hear, touch, smell, or taste. They are frequently over-responsive (*hypersensitive*) or under-responsive (*hyposensitive*) to various types of sensory input (e.g., light, sounds, touch, pain). In addition, these reactions may be very inconsistent, varying from day to day and within sensory categories (e.g., not hypersensitive to *all* lights, *all* loud sounds, etc.). Autistic individuals sometimes are placed on a "sensory processing continuum" (Grandin 1995, 52), with those at the high-functioning end having mild sensory over-sensitivity problems and those at the lower-functioning end continually receiving severely distorted visual and auditory information. Fortunately, music is usually not distorted, so children can interpret the signal correctly (Lim 2009).

Many autistic individuals are hypersensitive to certain or all sounds. However, responses are often erratic. For example, an individual "may overreact with startle reflex or tantrum to the sound of a dropped pencil but be oblivious to a loud siren" (Thaut 1992d, 182). Or an individual may be distressed by the sound of a distant lawn mower but not seem to notice a human voice in the same room. Autistic individuals also may have difficulty screening out sounds and may be enthralled by background noises (e.g., sound of heater; buzz of lights), becoming frenetically active or immobile and passive for long periods of time as they attend to these background sounds.

Autistic individuals also have erratic and unusual responses to other types of sensory stimuli. Some may not show pain when injured or may show no fear of dangerous situations. Some may be fascinated with lights and color patterns or be preoccupied with certain surfaces or avoid certain textures. They may respond to motion in abnormal ways: some spin excessively with no dizziness; others fear certain movements, like the movement of elevators. It is common for these individuals to perseverate on anything with a repetitive motion.

Autistic children also tend to use different senses than their peers to explore the world (including people and objects) around them. Sometimes, children with autism use taste, smell, and touch more than vision and hearing to learn and explore (Lovejoy and Estridge 1987; Powers 1989). Thus, they tend to lick, mouth, and touch things (and people) in learning situations. Some children show a need for increased sensory input, perhaps as a way of making sense of a world that seems to lack order: "To a child with sensory processing problems, the environment may be confusing, painful, or even frightening" (Davis, Gfeller, and Thaut 2008, 124).

Repetitive and Restricted Behaviors, Activities, and Interests; Obsessive Need for Sameness, Order, and Routine

Autistic individuals frequently engage in bizarre, repetitive motor manner-isms, or *stereotypical behaviors*, involving the hands (e.g., hand or finger flapping, finger flicking, twisting or staring at their fingers or hands, hair pulling, bang-ing their head or ears) or the whole body (e.g., rocking, twisting, whirling, darting and lunging, or statue-like posturing) (Adamek and Darrow 2010). Stereotypical and perseverative behaviors are a barrier to social interaction for many individuals with autism. Some music therapists have reported that stereotypical behaviors may be decreased by their joining in the musical behavior (e.g., reflecting it with improvisation) and then using musical structure to broaden the behavior into purposeful activity or active responses to the changes in the music (Nordoff and Robbins 1977; Toigo 1992). Some feel these are *self-stimulatory* behaviors that autistic individuals use to create their own sensory input (Paul 1982; Thaut 1992d), while others suggest these repetitive motor mannerisms may relate to the individual's desire for sameness or their love of repetitive movement (Lovejoy and Estridge 1987). Autistic individuals also may develop habitual abnormal movement patterns, like walking or run-ning only on their tiptoes or holding their hands or bodies in odd postures. Kern (2013, 26) notes that these repetitive behaviors "may serve a variety of functions, such as self-regulation, communication or diversion."

Autistic individuals frequently develop fascinations, preoccupations, or fixations with certain objects (e.g., light switches, record players, vacuum cleaners, washing machines) or parts of objects (e.g., buttons, parts of the body) (DSM-V 2013). They may develop strong attachments to meaningless, inanimate objects, like a rubber band or a piece of string, and become very upset if that object is removed. Repetitive movement also frequently fascinates these individuals, and they may become utterly absorbed in watching electric fans or toy tops, repeatedly opening and closing doors, or repeatedly spinning wheels or other objects. While both fixations and stereotypical behaviors can interfere with learning, communication, and socialization, fixations differ from stereotypical behaviors like hand flapping and twirling in that they are directed toward something *external*. If channeled correctly, fixations can motivate learning (Toigo 1992). For example, if an individual is fixated on vacuum cleaners, one might use vacuum cleaners to teach counting concepts. Berger (2002, 33) reminds us that "if we accept the hypothesis that what the brain does, it does for a reason, then we must also assume that every behavior results from some form of physiologic prerequisite." The atypical behavior of one with ASD may be a functional response for that individual, even though it is hard to understand.

Autistic individuals, who usually have a very restricted range of interests, frequently become preoccupied with one narrow interest, like amassing facts about dinosaurs or airplanes or statistics for a certain sport or team (Lathom-Radocy 2013). Most autistic individuals also have an obsessive desire for order; everything must be in exactly the same place every time. They may arrange toys, blocks, eating utensils, or other objects the same way over and over again. Often, the system used to arrange or sort the objects is known only to the individual. These individuals have a strong need and desire to maintain sameness in their lives and are very resistant to changes in their environment or routines. They may become extremely distressed over seemingly small changes, like a piece of furniture being moved or slight change in the route taken to school. Autistic individuals frequently develop many nonfunctional rituals and routines (e.g., continually touching certain objects in the same order) that they adhere to inflexibly.

Disturbances in Developmental Rates or Sequences

Autistic individuals characteristically have very uneven patterns of development, with disturbances or low abilities in some areas and normal or high abilities in others. Development in one area often lags far behind that in another. For example, a 7-year-old child may be able to dress and undress appropriately but may be unable to use a toilet. Even in the same general skill area, the rate of development may be uneven. For example, a child may sit up at an early age but not learn to walk for years (Lovejoy and Estridge 1987). DSM-V (2013, 56) noted, "Autism spectrum disorder is not a degenerative disorder, and it is typical for learning and compensation to continue throughout life."

There is a gap between adaptive functioning and intellectual ability (DSM-V 2013). Most investigators agree that distribution of IQ levels for autistic individuals is similar to that of the general population (Thaut 1992d): Some are highly intelligent, others have average intelligence, and still others are mildly or seriously intellectually disabled. Whatever their intelligence level, autistic individuals usually have uneven cognitive abilities (DSM-V 2013). For example, an individual may have advanced math or reading skills but be unable to carry on a normal conversation. Many autistic individuals have certain isolated areas of ability, such as rote memory or special abilities in math, art, or music (subjects that do not depend on the use of language). Some have cognitive deficits, like difficulties with abstract thinking, difficulties making sense of auditory and visual information, and problems organizing and sequencing information. Many higher-functioning autistic individuals have a vocabulary that is higher than their level of language comprehension.

Characteristics of Autistic Adults

With appropriate treatment and therapy, many autistic individuals are able to gain some communication skills, develop basic functional skills, and decrease their stereotypical behaviors. Autistic adults usually do not acquire new behavior problems, nor do they lose the progress they have made in controlling their behavior and meeting their own needs. Usually, they do not develop new medical problems (e.g., seizures) that they did not have as children or adolescents. However, although some symptoms may become less severe, autistic adults continue to have some degree of difficulty in all of the previously described areas (DSM-V 2013; Lovejoy and Estridge 1987; Powers 1989). Those with higher intelligence and better language skill development may still have difficulty in social situations and show behavior that lacks the usual reciprocity of social interaction (e.g., responding to cues of when and how to enter a conversation and what is appropriate to say) (DSM-V 2013). Several studies have shown that music therapy interventions can help autistic individuals increase eye contact, attention span, appropriate social behaviors, and awareness of people and objects in their environment, while decreasing instances of bizarre and self-abusive behaviors (Mahlberg 1973; Saperston 1973, 1982; Stevens and Clark 1969).

In addition to difficulties in social functioning and communication, autistic individuals may also maintain a very limited range of interests and activities, including some fixations. If properly directed, however, these interests and fixations might be developed into a career. For example, a person with autism who was fascinated with cattle chutes ended up with a career in animal science (Grandin 1988; cited in Toigo 1992). Artistically talented individuals might be able to work as graphic artists (Toigo 1992), and musically talented individuals have become successful composers and pianists (Euper 1968). Since autistic adults still have problems understanding how others think and feel, however, even those who function well enough to have careers may still need persons who serve as "career mentors" and help them "deal with job-related social complexities" (Toigo 1992, 17).

Whatever the level of functioning, autistic adults still require considerable structure and routine. They frequently show an interest in rote activities, like memorizing sports statistics, bus schedules, or historic dates. They function best in a predictive, supportive environment that provides a balance between encouraging productivity and providing enough care and structure to help the individual feel secure and less anxious (Thompson 2012). Most retain a need for environmental sameness and consistency, and some may continue to become upset or throw temper tantrums when changes occur.

As autistic individuals reach adulthood, treatment and therapy programs often begin to phase out academic training and place more emphasis on functional life skills and increasing independence. In addition, the focus shifts from *changing* behaviors to *channeling and redirecting* behaviors (e.g., flip through a magazine instead of flapping hands). Autistic adults continue to need structured training programs to help them improve and maintain communication skills, self-care skills, social skills, impulse control, ability to follow directions, and appropriate behaviors. Berger (2002, 153) notes that "the autistic spectrum system may require and will certainly benefit from life-long, ongoing music therapy treatment." DSM-V (2013, 53) states that "adults who have developed compensation strategies for some social challenges still struggle in novel or unsupported situations and suffer from the effort and anxiety of consciously calculating what is socially intuitive for most individuals."

RECOMMENDED TREATMENTS

Although there currently is no cure for autism (Berger 2002; Kern, Rivera, Chandler, and Humpal 2012), various treatment techniques can benefit many individuals on the autism spectrum. Programs that include a combination of approaches in a structured, individualized treatment plan are usually most successful (Grandin and Scarino 1986; Lovejoy and Estridge 1987; Snell 1996; Thaut 1992d). Good treatment programs promote the development of functional language and communication skills, social and interpersonal skills, independent living and self-help skills, cognitive skills, sensorimotor skills, and generalization of learned behaviors, as well as help individuals learn to control and diminish nonfunctional stereotypical and ritualistic behaviors (Lovejoy and Estridge 1987; Snell 1996; Thaut 1992d). These behaviors are nonfunctional and can greatly impede the productive motor functioning of autistic individuals. However, some music therapists have found that rhythmic activities that first match the tempo and rhythm of these movements, and then change tempo or rhythm, can be useful in interrupting stereotypical or perseverative movement patterns. Once these patterns are interrupted and broken, rhythmic music activities then can broaden the client's rhythmic movement responses into purposeful activity, as the client responds flexibly to or interactively with the music of the therapist (Nordoff and Robbins 1977; Thaut 1992d; Toigo 1992).

Music can facilitate the development of cognitive skills in autistic individuals by (1) conveying nonmusical information, (2) being part of the structure or background of the learning environment, or (3) serving as reinforcement for learning (Thaut 1992d). Structuring the learning environment by alternating periods of instruction with periods of music listening can have many beneficial effects for some autistic individuals.

Currently, there is emphasis on evidence-based practice (EBP) (Humpal and Kern 2013). This requires the therapist to be familiar with current research and to choose the techniques that evidence supports. The therapist's clinical judgment and expertise must always be used, with consideration of the client, his/her family, and the surrounding culture. This is not something new in the profession. Even in the first issue of the *Bulletin of the National Association for Music Therapy* (1952, 1:1:10), there was a report of the Music Research Association, "which was organized in July 1948 for the purpose of promoting research in the field of music therapy, training workers, and bringing music to local hospitals." Research abstracts also were reported from the Music Therapy Research Committee at the first music therapy conference in Chicago in 1951. Therefore, the music therapy profession always has promoted and encouraged research and tried to build a basis for treatment. This emphasis is important to continue. The book *Music in Therapy* (1968) was organized around "three essential considerations for any discipline – theory, practice, and research" (Schneider, Unkefer, and Gaston 1968, 4). These remain essential considerations.

Since functional language and communication skills are crucial to inter-actions with others and are prime indicators of success in later life for autistic individuals, language development is often the main focus of early interven-tion and educational programs (Snell 1996; Thaut 1992d). With increasing frequency, parents of autistic children are considered partners in treatment. They receive training in educational and behavior management techniques so they can help reinforce their child's program at home (Kern et al. 2012; Lovejoy and Estridge 1987; Thaut 1992d). Autistic individuals generally make the most progress when behavior expectations, as well as management and interaction techniques, rewards, and consequences are consistent across all settings they encounter.

SETTINGS FOR SERVICE DELIVERY

Individuals on the autism spectrum receive special programs and services in varied settings, depending on their age, specific needs, level of functioning, and the types of services available in their community. Both children and adults with ASD receive music therapy. Kern et al. (2012, 282) reported that "most respondents saw their clients with ASD in public schools (K–12) (36.9%) followed by the family's home (34.9%), and in private practice (29.2%)." Other settings may include early intervention centers, public or private centers for persons who have various developmental disabilities, special clinic or treatment centers for individuals on the autism spectrum, special vocational training programs or sheltered workshops, and group homes. Walworth (2013) discussed family-centered practice, which allows the therapist to work with the child and parents in a natural environment. This setting allows parent involvement, which is likely to be continued after the therapy sessions. As both parent and child learn to communicate and interact through improvisational music sessions guided by the therapist, the child's tolerance for physical contact, social responsiveness, and emotional closeness gradually increases (Alvin and Warwick 1991).

Many autistic children are served by special education programs from their local public school system. Kern et al. (2012, 288) reported that "the top three goal areas selected when serving individuals with ASD were communication (97.9%), social (90.6%), and emotional (43.1%) skills." IEPs also provide for appropriate support services in areas of need, placement in the least restrictive environment, and an annual evaluation of student progress in the program. The student usually is included with peers in a regular classroom for as much of the day as possible.

When the IEP assessment finds that music therapy may provide a unique means of helping students achieve their educational objectives, music therapists may be asked to provide traditional direct services, work with students in self-contained classes, work with students in inclusive classes, provide direct in-home services to students who are confined to their homes for medical reasons, provide consultation services to facilitate classroom instruction, inclusion, or music education, and/or provide staff development workshops (Wilson 1996). Music therapy is usually classified as a related service in special education settings.

Lazar (2007) presented a nonstandardized four-step assessment model at a music therapy conference:

Step 1: Can IEP goals be supported by using music?
Step 2: Is additional support required?
Step 3: Is music a documented learning strength?
Step 4: Are music resources already available?

When these four steps are documented, music therapy is added to the child's IEP: "Music based strategies developed by the music therapist can be implemented throughout the child's educational programming as well as across settings and disciplines to maximize the child's learning through music and to provide multiple opportunities for generalization of skills" (Martin, Snell, Walworth, and Humpal 2013, 87). Kern et al. (2012) indicate that the complexity of ASD diagnosis requires collaboration of a variety of professionals to meet the child's needs.

HOW MUSIC IS USED IN THERAPY

The literature is filled with reports showing that almost all individuals on the autism spectrum respond positively to music, often showing unusual musical interests and abilities (DeMyer 1974; Edgerton 1994; Euper 1968; Ockelford 2013; Snell 1996; Thaut 1992d). After reviewing the literature on the musical behaviors of autistic children, Thaut (1992d) concluded that the evidence indicated that individuals with ASD (a) often perform much better in musical areas than they do in other areas, (b) often perform better in musical areas than many normal children do, and (c) usually respond to music more frequently and more appropriately than they respond to other auditory stimuli. As Lim (2009, 112–113) pointed out, "The perception of musical elements appears to be intact in children with ASD." Although little is known about the exact reasons for this responsiveness, people have speculated that music is attractive and pleasurable to autistic individuals because it bypasses language and is less specific than speech (Alvin and Warwick 1991; Euper 1968) or "perhaps because it is an absolutely predictable phenomenon in an unpredictable world" (Toigo 1992, 17). Katagiri (2009) explains that predictable procedures reduce the confusion of a child with ASD. This occurs within the stimulus as well as the sequence of events in the session: "Musical cues that facilitate emotional responses are embedded in music's tempo, sound level, timing, intonation, articulation, timbre, vibrato, tone attacks, tone decays, and pauses" (Katagiri 2009, 17). This was also recognized by Pasiali (2004, 13) in discussion of directions embedded in song lyrics to promote social skills in which she gave three case studies and a useful song protocol. Music can help individuals with autism channel or control abnormal or excessive emotional responses (Snell 1996; Toigo 1992).

Kern and Aldridge (2006) used embedded music therapy interventions during outdoor play of children with ASD. They set up a musical play station on the playground. The children with ASD were attracted to the instruments, which brought them into the vicinity of typically developing peers. This gave them motivation to interact with their peers.

Kern, Wakeford, and Aldridge (2007) used songs embedded in ongoing classroom routines. The music provided prompts for hand-washing, toileting, and cleaning up routines being taught to a 3-year-old child with ASD. The procedure was a collaboration among the occupational therapist, music therapist, and teacher. "Both the song and lyrical interventions [verbal directions] were beneficial for all selected multiple-step tasks" (48). The child was most resistant to changes in toilet training, but that may have been a reflection of developmental stage.

Left to their own devices, however, autistic individuals may use music as a device or stimulus to isolate themselves and further remove themselves from the real world (Benenzon 1981; Hoffman 1974). For example, some individuals will sit quietly for hours, repeatedly listening to favorite pieces of music, while totally unaware of their surroundings. If the therapist is using music to make contact with autistic individuals and help them gain skills in various areas, it is essential that the therapist be present to structure and guide the music experiences, leading the persons into constructive, reality-oriented activities that promote increased attention to and contact with the people and objects around them (Benenzon 1981). Kalas (2012) found that it was important to consider the complexity of the music:

> For children in the severe range of functioning, music that is simple, with clear and predictable patterns, may be most effective in eliciting responses to bids for joint attention. On the contrary, for children in the mild/moderate range of functioning, music that is more complex and variable may be most effective in eliciting responses to bids for joint attention. (430)

Not all autistic children respond to music. Some find it provides more stimulation than they can process (Lathom-Radocy 2014). Therefore, it is important to consider responses of each child to determine if music produces a positive response. Since many autistic individuals are attracted to music, placing the nonmusical information in a musical setting or context "may motivate, facilitate attention and perception, and enhance memorization of the information" (Thaut 1992d, 191).

Lim (2010b) used applied behavior analysis (ABA) verbal behavior (VB) with children with ASD to enhance verbal and nonverbal communication behavior: "Collectively, social communication and functional language abilities are regarded as the most critical areas to address in supporting the development of individuals with ASD" (95). ABA is an abbreviation of a sequence that was identified in language research in the 1960s. An outgrowth of B. F. Skinner's operant conditioning, it includes the antecedent that precedes the behavior, the actual behavior, and the consequence that follows the behavior. Through behavior modification, it is possible to shape the desired response. Music is a powerful reinforcer to use as a consequence for desired language behavior. Lim and Draper (2011, 535) reported that "pairing target verbal behavior with musical experiences establishes effective automatic reinforcement, and it can increase the frequency of the communicative behaviors and social interaction in children with ASD." Both music listening and active music making function as efficient reinforcers for many autistic individuals (Thaut 1992d).

As music therapists keep in mind the client's long-term goals, they structure increasingly more challenging musical activities and experiences to encourage the client to move forward to new levels of growth and development. In this way, progress continues and music therapy does not "degenerate into a form of musical coddling" (Nordoff and Robbins 1971b, 108). Kaplan and Steele (2005, 7) investigated the primary goal areas for children with ASD: "(a) behavioral/psychosocial skills, (b) language/communication skills, (c) perceptual/motor skills, (d) cognitive skills, [and] (e) musical skills, as well as (f) modifying physiological responses." (They recommend working on the first two goal areas before moving on to the other areas.)

Music Therapy Assessment

The unusual behaviors and many severe deficits in communication, social interaction, and sensory processing skills associated with autism often make it difficult for evaluations relying on visual and verbal means of communication to assess the individual's potential. It has been suggested that "uneven and inconsistent skills in communication, social interaction, and sensory processing in children with ASD may mask abilities as well as deficits" (Martin, Snell, Walworth, and Humpal 2013, 80). Many music therapists have developed their own assessments, formed over many years of clinical experience. However, it may be useful to use a preexisting assessment tool. This is of importance in establishing goals and reporting baseline behavior of an ASD child. One tool is the SCERTS model, which can be used by multidisciplinary team members. The acronym stands for *social, communication, emotional regulation,* and *transactional support* (Wetherby, Rubin, and Laurent 2003). This model was investigated by Walworth, Register, and Engel (2009, 210) to determine which areas of this tool are used in music therapy sessions and the frequency of domains within sessions: "Results of the descriptive analysis revealed that all three domains of social communication, emotional regulation, and transactional support were addressed within music therapy sessions." Walworth (2007, 14–15) exemplified goals that related to the SCERTS model. Because this is a multidisciplinary model, it is gaining national acceptance. Walworth (2007, 20) states that "music therapists need to be aware of this major shift in treatment of children with ASD and train themselves to participate effectively as a SCERTS interdisciplinary team member." Awareness and participation in the SCERTS model can help music therapists establish goals: "A validated systematic assessment also may offer specific information that can lead to the development of appropriate goals that may be musically tailored to the precise needs of each individual" (Martin, Snell, Walworth, and Humpal 2013, 91).

Since music therapy assessments do not depend on verbal and visual communication but rely on reactions to and interactions within music experiences, "a music therapy assessment may provide a glimpse of hidden potentials" (Snell 1996, 170). In music therapy assessment sessions, the music therapist can adapt the music to support and encourage the individual, ensuring a positive experience that will keep the individual engaged in music making. As the music therapist observes the client's responses to different musical experiences and interprets their relationships to nonmusical skill areas (e.g., communication, social, or cognitive abilities), important assessment information that complements the findings of other professionals is often gained (Snell 1996).

Individual assessment may also increase the speed of clinical effectiveness. Careful assessment of a client's musical preferences enables the music therapist to use preferred musical activities and experiences in initial interventions so that the client responds favorably to the music environment more quickly, heightening the therapist's ability to begin using music experiences to develop skills in other areas (Adreon 1994; Griggs-Drane and Wheeler 1997). Since autistic individuals often have unusual responses to sensory stimuli (perhaps because of sensory processing abnormalities), music therapists must carefully observe and analyze each client's responses to different types of music stimuli, noting whether the stimuli elicit normal responses, little or no arousal, hyperreactive responses, or paradoxical reactions (e.g., client defensively withdraws and shows no response to excessive stimuli, or client over-responds because she or he is not receiving enough sensory input) (Nelson, Anderson, and Gonzales 1984; Toigo 1992). A client's behavior may differ not only between musical and nonmusical environments, but also *within* the musical environment itself, depending on what particular musical styles, instruments, frequencies, modes of activity, etc., are being used and how these are perceived and processed by the client.

Griggs-Drane and Wheeler (1997) recommend the use of *functional assessment procedures* to help the music therapist define musical, environmental, and transitional variables that influence the client's behavior so that the therapist can use the information to develop more effective music therapy intervention strategies and behavioral support plans. During the assessment session, a wide variety of musical styles, instruments, and experiences are used. In addition to observing the client's behavior before, during, and after the session, the therapist notes and analyzes musical variables (such as song name and style, instruments or voices used), key, live or recorded presentation, and selection duration in relation to the client's responses. From this functional assessment, music therapists are able to determine which musical styles, keys, instruments, and modes of experiences are likely to be most reinforcing for that particular client and which are aversive or not tolerated. How the client responds will have definite implications for the type of stimuli that may be most effective in working with that particular client. Assessment information also may help the therapist plan sessions alternating preferred and less-preferred activities, a structural technique that can be very effective in helping autistic individuals gain new skills (Adreon 1994; Griggs-Drane and Wheeler 1997). Pairing a nonpreferred activity with a preferred stimulus also can reinforce and facilitate performance of the nonpreferred task (Griggs-Drane and Wheeler 1997; Snell 1996).

Music therapists who use clinical improvisation techniques as their primary mode of intervention also rely on careful observation, analysis, and assessment of the client's responses within the session to determine what music interventions will be most helpful in facilitating the client's positive growth and development (Alvin 1978; Alvin and Warwick 1991; Boxill 1985; Nordoff and Robbins 1968, 1971b, 1977; Walworth, Register, and Engel 2009).

Nordoff and Robbins (1977) developed two rating scales for evaluating autistic individuals and measuring changes in their behavior. One scale describes levels of participation and qualities of resistiveness in the client's relationship to the therapist in musical activity, beginning with the nonrelating attitudes of the profoundly autistic state and progressing to awareness, acceptance, coactivity, and constructive participation in group work. The second scale rates the client's level of musical communicativeness as demonstrated by his/her instrumental, vocal, or body movement responses, again moving from noncommunicativeness to fragmentary responses to more sustained responses and free, confident participation and communication in musical experiences. In addition to their function as rating instruments, these scales "have proved to be important guides to therapists in imparting a sense of orientation and perspective in therapy, and in suggesting clinical approaches at various stages and in different situations" (Nordoff and Robbins 1977, 179). As therapy progresses, the Nordoff-Robbins music therapy sessions are videotaped and analyzed to determine the progress and need for new strategies (Guerrero and Turry 2013). Boxill (1985, 50–63) has also developed a music therapy assessment for use with individuals on the autism spectrum, as well as for those who have other developmental disabilities.

General Approaches and Techniques

Most of the literature and research recommends using highly structured approaches in the education and therapy of autistic individuals (Edgerton 1994). However, both music therapy interventions employing highly structured, behavioral techniques (Adreon 1994; Burleson, Center, and Reeves 1989; Castellano and Wilson 1970; Lim 2010; Mahlberg 1973; Staum and Flowers 1984; Watson 1979) and those employing freer, improvisational techniques (Alvin 1978; Alvin and Warwick 1991; Boxill 1985; Edgerton 1994; Guerrero and Turry 2013; Nordoff and Robbins 1968, 1971b, 1977; Saperston 1973) have been used effectively with autistic clients. Highly structured, *behaviorally oriented* music therapy approaches use behavior analysis and systematic instruction coupled with reinforcement, which often employs preferred music activities (Adreon 1994). In this type of approach, "a firm directive strategy involves specific, frequent, clearly defined expectations of the child while being very careful not to let the child escape planned activities" (Nelson, Anderson, and Gonzales 1984, 103). In *clinical improvisation*, however, the music therapist strives to meet the client at his or her level through music and places few demands on the client, at least in the initial stages of therapy. Perhaps this seemingly less-structured approach also works effectively with autistic individuals because the improvised music itself structures the experience.

Several types of techniques, including vocalization/singing/chanting, dances/action songs, music-movement experiences, playing musical instruments (improvisation, structured performance, imitative games), musical games, Orff-Schulwerk activities (Colwell, Pehotsky, Gillmeister, and Woolrich 2008), music-listening experiences, and background music, have been used successfully in treating autistic individuals. The music therapist, through the music, "helps the child move from a fragmented world into an integrated one, from unaware experiencing to *aware* experiencing" (Boxill 1985, 161). The client's responses are reflected and translated into musical structures.

Brownell (2002) studied musically adapted social stories presented in four case studies. He concluded that "a musically adapted version of social stories is an effective and viable treatment option for modifying behaviors with this population" (117). He explains "social story" according to the definition initiated by Gray and Garrand:

> A social story is a short story that adheres to a specific format and guidelines to objectively describe a person, skill, event, concept, or social situation. The goal of a social story is to share relevant information. This information often includes (but is not limited to) *where* and *when* a situation takes place, *who* is involved, *what* is occurring, and *why*. (Gray and Garrand 1995, 171; as stated in Brownell 2002, 120)

Thus, social stories convey information, rather than give instructions. Brownell (2002, 122) provides the steps necessary to produce a social story. As the child's social skills develop, some higher-functioning school-aged individuals with autism may eventually be able to be included in some regular class settings (Atterbury 1990; Snell 1996).

Whipple et al. (2015, 85) discuss the many ways in which music is a powerful tool for therapy:

> Prior research indicates that music can be effective in conveying basic emotions to persons with ASD. . . . Music may be both motivating and effective as a therapeutic tool for improving recognition or expression of emotions, communications, and social skill acquisition.

For the child to understand emotions and respond correctly, there must be emotional understanding, which Katagiri (2009, 16) explained "involves the ability to recognize others' emotions and express one's emotions, using situational and expressive cues." While developing children typically learn these skills through imitation, children with ASD need specific training, probably because of their neurological deficits. Other studies reporting a relationship between emotional understanding and music (both as a background and in song texts) include Brownell (2002), Heaton et al. (1999), and Pasiali (2004).

Many music therapists combine improvisational and more highly structured, behaviorally oriented music intervention strategies in working with individuals with ASD (Nelson, Anderson, and Gonzales 1984; Saperston 1982; Snell 1996; Thaut 1984; Toigo 1992). The early stages of music therapy, which aim to establish contact with the client, promoting feelings of safety and security, often employ less-directive interventions (e.g., clinical improvisation techniques) that allow for more open-ended responses on the part of the client. In later stages, music therapists frequently use more directive interventions that place more demands on the client's attention, interaction, and responses and seek to develop specific, targeted perceptual, language, cognitive, social, or motor skills.

The American Music Therapy Association (2007, 5) established the Music Therapy and Autism Task Force/Think Tank to "explore and offer recommendations for future directions for music therapy and autism." There is a clear need for more evidence-based practice, but until additional research can be done, music therapists must rely on "clinical wisdom" and experience, as well as the available research. It is desirable for practice to be based on research evidence (Kern et al. 2012). However, an accumulation of "clinical wisdom" without the rigor of data collection and interpretation should not be ignored, because it provides the base for future research and practice.

From survey data, Kern et al. (2012, 289) reported that "music therapy techniques most frequently used with this population included singing and vocalization (98.6%), instrument play (98.6%), movement and dance (84%), free and thematic music improvisation (73.3%), and songwriting and composition (55.7%)." Therapeutically directed music experiences have been used to stimulate responses, reinforce responses, provide cues and structure for responses to occur, develop communication and interaction, focus attention, and mask distractions. In recent years, the use of computer-based techniques has become more frequent. This includes making music videos and use of various apps (Kern et al. 2012).

Stages of Development in Music Therapy Treatment

Music therapy with individuals on the autism spectrum is often a very slow process; one must frequently work months or even years before seeing much progress (Alvin 1978; Alvin and Warwick 1991; Nordoff and Robbins 1971b, 1977; Saperston 1982; Thaut 1984). The response time to musical cues may be much longer than anticipated (Humpal and Kern 2013; Lathom-Radocy 2014). In one case reported by Thaut (1984), it took two years of music therapy sessions for a ten-year-old boy to begin to respond to piano mood improvisations contrasting happy and sad by imitating the patterns on the piano and adding appropriate facial expressions and body postures. When possible, music therapists usually initially work with an autistic client in order to help develop and increase basic social responses. As the individual's skills develop, the music therapist can then gradually introduce the client to a group setting where these skills can be used and practiced. As Snell (1996, 176) observed, "Acceptance of and participation in a group setting might be a significant accomplishment for the student who has a severe inability to accept change and a low tolerance for sensory input."

Many authors speak of three general stages of development in music therapy treatment process with individuals on the autism spectrum (Alvin 1978; Alvin and Warwick 1991; Benenzon 1982; Nordoff and Robbins 1971b; Saperston 1982; Snell 1996; Thaut 1984). Although state names differ, most authors agree on the general developmental progression and focus of therapy in each stage.

In the *first stage* of treatment, the music therapist tries to establish contact with the client, using music experiences to elicit and support the client's limited responses, which are usually nonverbal. Through this process, the client begins to feel safe and secure in the music environment, and the beginnings of musical communication are established. Music can be a unique, nonthreatening way "of gently entering the client's world before demanding that he enter ours" (Toigo 1992, 19). The therapist's presence may be introduced gradually within the context of the music experience. Since individuals with ASD usually relate better to objects than to people, musical instruments may be particularly useful in initiating contact with these clients. The instruments may be structured to insure success, for example, bars may be removed from Orff instruments so all sounds are pleasant.

In the *second* or *intermediate stage*, specific forms of musical activity and responses are developed, and more demands are made on the client. The music therapist now becomes more involved in directing and shaping responses as musical processes are used to develop and reinforce basic perceptual, language, social, cognitive, and motor skills. Although some autistic individuals have relatively strong gross and fine motor skills, others have little functional hand use, delays in motor development, poor body awareness, poor laterality, and/or many nonfunctional stereotypical movements (Thaut 1984). Clients commonly exhibit problems with motor coordination and motor planning (Nelson, Anderson, and Gonzales 1984), as well as difficulty with sensorimotor integrations (e.g., coordinating movements with auditory cues) (Thaut 1992d; Toigo 1992). As individuals develop skills in playing musical instruments, motor control and coordination increases, along with skills in laterality patterns and right/left awareness (Thaut 1984d, 1992d; Toigo 1992).

As the client develops skills and gains more awareness and confidence, there is more reciprocal communication and cooperation between client and therapist in the context of musical experiences. Activities at this stage also help prepare the client for group work as a "my turn-your turn" concept and imitation skills are developed. For example, once a client begins to respond musically with an instrument, the therapist can gradually introduce techniques requiring more interaction (e.g., question-and-answer musical structure) or song lyrics that give directions or ask for specific responses from the client (Thaut 1992). After the client has experienced musical give-and-take in instrumental activity, he or she may be stimulated to join the therapist in singing at least portions of the song that structures the improvisation (Guerrero and Turry 2013; Nordoff and Robbins 1971b, 1977).

In the *third* or *complex stage*, the client is able to respond confidently and expressively in the music situation. The therapist aims to help the client integrate skills and use them to communicate with and relate constructively to the people and the world around him or her. Playing instruments combines the sensory input from the moving muscles and the feel of the instrument or mallet with auditory stimulation of the sound the movements produce. As the individual sings while moving or playing instruments, he or she also integrates auditory and movement-related stimuli. The client may be introduced gradually to group music therapy settings to help increase his or her abilities to relate and respond appropriately to and to communicate and work cooperatively with other people. It is interesting to note how closely these general stages of music therapy treatment with individuals with ASD correspond to Sears's (1968) classifications of processes in music therapy: (1) experience within structure, (2) experience in self-organization, and (3) experience in relating to others.

McCarthy, Geist, Zojwala, and Schock (2008) surveyed music therapists to determine how many worked with speech-language pathologists, and the nature of their collaboration. They found that "responses (N = 847) indicated the majority of participants reported they had worked with SLPs at some point in various roles and in various settings" (405). They also found that 67.5% of their caseload of individuals with ASD or a pervasive developmental disorder (now included in the autism spectrum disorders) used augmentative and alternative communication (AAC), which may require close collaboration with a speech-language therapist.

Gadberry (2011) surveyed the use of AAC during music therapy sessions. She found that only 14.6% of respondents use AAC with all clients who use this form of communication elsewhere; 33.8% of music therapists used AAC for most of the identified clients. The number using AAC related to the number of music therapists trained to use the system. AAC was used to promote literacy as well as for expressive communication.

A technique used with speech goals, including improvised or composed songs designed to stimulate the client to sing answers to questions instead of echoing words, can help decrease echolalia (Boxill 1985; Nordoff and Robbins 1971b, 1977). However, echolalia may be a stage of speech acquisition. Children who produce echolalia may achieve a higher level of speech production after treatment (Lim 2010a; Prizant and Weatherby 2005).

SPECIAL CONSIDERATIONS AND TIPS FOR SUCCESS

Since autistic individuals have a need for order and clear routines, expectations, and standards, it is important to provide structure, consistency, and predictability in music therapy treatment approaches. Structure can be provided by the music itself as well as by the session. Music therapy sessions with individuals with ASD are usually most successful when they use consistent opening and closing songs or rituals and follow a familiar, consistent pattern of songs and experiences within the body of the session. The technique of beginning and ending with preferred activities and then alternating more difficult tasks with easier, well-liked tasks during the session is often successful. The easiest, most favorite activities are often placed at the end of the session to help end the session with positive experiences.

Since autistic individuals have difficulty adapting to change, it is important to prepare them for changes in activity. Musical phrases that signal the end of activities or specially devised "transition songs" may be useful in this regard (Boxill 1985; Snell 1996). Many individuals with autism also respond well to activity schedules – a sequence of pictures, words, and/or symbols that maps out the sequence of tasks or schedules for the individual. These activity schedules provide stable consistent visual cues that "engage learners with autism, enhance learning, and reduce challenging behavior" (Griggs-Drane and Wheeler 1997, 90).

It is important to remember that many autistic individuals are hypersensitive to some sounds. The therapist may need to adjust choices of music, instruments, and loudness for comfort level. When using a device for individual listening, showing how to adjust the loudness and tone controls for comfort may help prevent behavior outbursts caused by overstimulation. Kalas (2012) explains that some children may experience sensory overload as a response to environmental events (sound of florescent lights, traffic noise, other children who move around, etc.), and complex music may add to the sensory overload leading to sensory disorganization. Music therapists also need to be aware that some autistic individuals may not process auditory input normally, which may lead them to respond abnormally to sound. Some clients may experience echoes of auditory stimuli, and others may be unable to tolerate multiple sounds and complex harmonies (Toigo 1992). Careful observation and assessment are crucial to the therapist's determinations of which sounds, instruments, keys, tempos, rhythms, musical styles, etc., are pleasant and reinforcing to the client and which are aversive. During the course of therapy, musical stimuli and experiences should be expanded gradually at a level the client will tolerate.

Gentle physical support or prompts (e.g., touch or support at shoulder, elbow, wrist) may be needed to encourage autistic individuals to initiate appropriate responses. These prompts should be faded as the client's skills emerge and develop. Adaptations of facilitated communication procedures also may have important implications for using musical instruments with individuals with ASD. As Birkenshaw-Fleming (1993, 94) observed, "supporting/holding the hand or arm might be just the impetus necessary for some people to focus their minds on learning to play an instrument."

QUESTIONS FOR THOUGHT AND DISCUSSION

1. Discuss some of the special characteristics and needs of autistic individuals. What implications do these have for music therapy programming?
2. Why and how are music experiences useful in making contact with autistic individuals? Are some types of experiences, activities, or instruments more useful than others? Which ones? Why?
3. Describe the three general stages of music therapy treatment used with individuals with ASD and compare them to Sears's (1968) classifications of processes in music therapy (experience within structure, experience in self-organization, and experience in relating to others). What types of music experiences are most useful at each stage of treatment? Why?
4. Describe some specific music therapy experiences that might help autistic individuals (a) develop speech and language, (b) improve social interaction, (c) develop identification and appropriate expression of emotions, (d) increase cognitive skills, or (e) improve sensorimotor skills. What unique benefits does music provide in each of these areas?
5. List several special considerations that may be important to remember when developing therapeutic intervention strategies for persons with ASD. Why are these important? What are their implications for the structure of music therapy intervention strategies?
6. For each of the situations described below, (a) define the problem or areas of need for the client or group of clients, (b) describe one or more of the goals you might pursue in music therapy sessions with the client(s), (c) describe music activities you might use to help the client(s) meet those goals, (d) tell how the music activities you described relate to the goals and needs of the client(s), and (e) mention any special considerations you might want

to take into account when working with the client(s).

Situation 1:

A five-year-old autistic boy has been referred to you for music therapy. He rarely gives eye contact or shows any social responsiveness to the people around him. He frequently rocks or flaps his hands. His parents report that he likes to listen to the classical music station on the radio. He has shown occasional interest in the tambourine and drum that are in his classroom. His teacher reports that he likes to spin the jingles on the tambourine.

Situation 2:

You have been asked to provide music therapy sessions for a group of four boys, aged 7–9 years, all of whom have been diagnosed as autistic. One knows a few basic signs; another is verbal but echolalic; the other two are nonverbal. The students rarely interact socially with one another. They are all used to using individualized activity schedules as a structural aid in their classroom. Their teacher reports that they show an interest in tapes of children's activity songs, but rarely follow the directions. When she tries to use rhythm instruments, they bang on them indiscriminately or use them for self-stimulation. She has noticed that they occasionally stop and listen when she plays a few beats on the triangle or resonator bells. The teacher would like to see her students increase their awareness of each other while they continue to work on basic color, number, clothing identification, and body part concepts.

SUGGESTIONS FOR FURTHER READING

Adamek, M. S. & Darrow, A-A. (Eds.) (2008), Students with autism spectrum disorders. In *Music in special education* (2nd ed.) (193–214). Silver Spring, MD: American Music Therapy Association.

Adamek, M. S., Thaut, M. H., & Furman, A. G. (2008). Individuals with autism and autism spectrum disorders (ASD). In W. B. Davis, K. E. Gfeller, & M. H. Thaut (Eds.), *An introduction to music therapy theory and practice* (3rd ed.) (117–142). Silver Spring, MD: American Music Therapy Association.

Alvin, J. & Warwick, A. (1991). *Music therapy for the autistic child* (2nd ed.). New York: Oxford University Press.

Berger, D. S. (2002). *Music therapy, sensory integration and the autistic child.* London: Jessica Kingsley.

Birkenshaw-Fleming, L. (1993). *Music for all: Teaching music to people with special needs.* Toronto: Gordon V. Thompson.

Boxill, E. H. (1985). *Music therapy for the developmentally disabled.* Rockville, MD:

Aspen Systems.

Bruscia, K. E. (Ed.) (1991). *Case studies in music therapy.* Phoenixville, PA: Barcelona.

Griggs-Drane, E. R. & Wheeler, J. J. (1997). The use of functional assessment procedures and individualized schedules in the treatment of autism: Recommendations for music therapists. *Music Therapy Perspectives, 15*(2), 87–93.

Kern, P. & Humpal, M. (Eds.) (2013). *Early childhood music therapy and autism spectrum disorders.* London: Jessica Kingsley.

Lathom-Radocy, W. (2014). Pervasive developmental disorders. In W. Lathom-Radocy (Ed.), *Pediatric music therapy* (75–98). Springfield, IL: Charles C Thomas.

Nelson, D. L., Anderson, V. G., & Gonzales, A. D. (1984). Music activities as therapy for children with autism and other pervasive developmental disorders. *Journal of Music Therapy, 21*(3), 100–116.

Ockelford, A. (2013). *Music, language, and autism.* London: Jessica Kingsley.

Paul, D. W. (1984). Music therapy for emotionally disturbed children. In W. B. Lathom & C. T. Eagle, Jr. (Eds.), *Music therapy for handicapped children*, Vol. 2 (3–59). Washington, D.C.: National Association for Music Therapy.

Snell, A. M. (1996). Music therapy for learners with autism in a public school setting. In B. L. Wilson (Ed.), *Models of music therapy interventions in school settings: From institution to inclusion* (156–183). Silver Spring, MD: National Association for Music Therapy.

Thaut, M. H. (1984). A music therapy model for autistic children. *Music Therapy Perspectives, 1*(4), 7–13.

Toigo, D. A. (1992). Autism: Integrating a personal perspective with music therapy practice. *Music Therapy Perspectives, 70*(1), 13–20.

Whipple, C. H., Gfeller, K., Driscoll, V., Oleson, J., & Mcgregor, K. (2015). Do communication disorders extend to musical messages? An answer from children with hearing loss or autism spectrum disorders. *Journal of Music Therapy, 52*, 78–116.

Chapter Fourteen

MUSIC THERAPY FOR CHILDREN AND ADOLESCENTS WHO HAVE MENTAL OR BEHAVIORAL DISORDERS OR SEVERE EMOTIONAL DISTURBANCES

Definitions

Children and adolescents who have mental disorders, behavioral disorders, or severe emotional disturbances *consistently* and *chronically* exhibit behaviors that are personally or socially deviant, maladaptive, or inappropriate. DSM-V (2013, 20) states that

> A mental disorder is a syndrome characterized by clinically significant disturbance in an individual's cognition, emotion regulation, or behavior that reflects a dysfunction in the psychological, biological, or developmental processes underlying mental functioning. Mental disorders are usually associated with significant distress or disability in social, occupational, or other important activities.

Since this definition includes behavior and emotion regulation, the older categories for behavioral disorders or severe emotional disturbances are included and not listed as separate categories in DSM-V.

Abnormal behavior is defined in terms of cultural norms, and it is, therefore, often difficult to determine precisely at what point behaviors are inappropriate or abnormal enough to be classified as disorders. One must consider many factors, including the behavior's frequency, persistence, duration, and intensity and the circumstances in which it occurs (DSM-V 2013; Thaut and Gfeller 1992). Many children or adolescents may exhibit some abnormal or inappropriate behaviors in isolated circumstances; however, those with diagnoses of mental disorders exhibit "higher frequencies of inappropriate behaviors and less than average amounts of appropriate behaviors" (Paul 1982, 2). DSM-V (2013) notes that the behavior occurs in many situations. Many different terms describe mentally disordered children and adolescents: "mentally ill, emotionally disturbed, behaviorally disordered, and having a psychiatric disorder" (Crowe 2007, 3). Various degrees and types of persistent, repeated problem behaviors that significantly impair social or academic functioning are the common factor in all the conditions or disorders described by these labels (APA 1994; Michel 1985; Paul 1982). These problem behaviors can be addressed in music therapy (Crowe 2007; Walworth 2007).

Mental Disorders

Examples of common psychiatric or mental disorders of childhood and adolescence include *schizophrenia spectrum and other psychotic disorders* (psychotic state with delusions or hallucinations with onset after years of normal development), *bipolar and related disorders* (previously called manic-depressive), *depressive disorder*, or *anxiety disorder* (e.g., phobias, panic disorders). These are disorders that are defined in DSM-V (2013), as compared with terms used in educational legislation and practice. *Disruptive* and *impulse-control* are terms used in education; *conduct disorders* (repeated and persistent behavior patterns that violate basic rights of others or age-appropriate rules and norms of society and that may include aggression to people or animals, deliberate destruction of other's property, persistent deceitfulness or theft, or repeated serious violations of rules) is a DSM-V classification as well as education term. Others that overlap include *oppositionally defiant, anxiety disorder, attention deficit/hyperactivity, psychotic behavior*, and *motor disorders* (Adamek and Darrow 2008, 139; DSM-V 2013). Substance-related and addictive disorders are among the DSM-V classifications. In addition, some may receive clinical attention because of relational problems (significantly impaired functioning in parent-child or sibling relationships) or problems related to abuse or neglect.

Emotional/Behavioral Disorders

Many definitions of emotional and behavioral disorders apply in considerations of remediation and therapy for children with these problems. Newcomer (1980, 6) argues, "Generally, if a person acts in a manner that is detrimental to him-or herself and/or others, he or she may be considered in a state of emotional disturbance." According to Federal legislation related to educating disabled individuals, children and adolescents are seriously emotionally disturbed when they demonstrate one or more of the following characteristics to a marked degree over a long period of time:

(A) An inability to learn which cannot be explained by intellectual, sensory, or health factors;

(B) An inability to build or maintain satisfactory interpersonal relationships with peers and teachers;

(C) Inappropriate behaviors or feelings under normal circumstances;

(D) A general pervasive mood of unhappiness or depression;

(E) A tendency to develop physical symptoms or fears associated with personal or school problems.

    (*Federal Register*, 1977, 42478, since issued as Individuals with Disabilities Education Improvement Act [IDEA]. 20 USC 1400 et seq., 2004)

This special education designation includes those who have diagnoses of childhood schizophrenia or autism. It does *not* include those who are socially maladjusted, unless they are also seriously emotionally disturbed.

Emotional and Behavioral Disorders (E/BD)

Children or adolescents who are capable of learning more socially acceptable and personally gratifying behaviors but who repeatedly respond to their environment in marked socially unacceptable and/or personally unacceptable ways are classified as having *emotional and behavioral disorders* (Kauffman 1977; Smith, Katsiyannis, and Ryan 2011).

In the past few decades, increased attention has also been focused on "at-risk" children and adolescents, those who, because of various circumstances (e.g., drug or alcohol abuse, poverty, unstable home structure, homelessness, AIDS infection, affected prenatally by crack or fetal alcohol syndrome, lead poisoning, repeated failure experiences in school), are at risk of not completing their education, of drug or alcohol addiction, of becoming teenaged parents, of becoming involved in gangs and criminal activities, or of suicide (Taylor, Barry, and Walls 1997).

These students may not be identified, but are simply looked upon as acting out or misbehaving individuals. Smith, Katsiyannis, and Ryan (2011, 185) indicate that

> they are less likely to be educated in less restrictive environments. Currently, only slightly over a third (37.3%) of students with E/BD spend more than 80% of their time inside the regular education classroom, as compared with over half (56.85%) of students with other disabilities.

Many of these students are in residential settings (Data Accountability Center 2010). Again, because of the uniqueness of each situation, an exact definition of this category is difficult. At-risk tendencies are reflected in attitudes, choices, and acting-out behaviors, such as delinquency, problems with authority figures, suspension or expulsion from school, lack of involvement in school activities, high absentee or tardiness or truancy rates, history of failure in school, dropping out of school, unprotected sexual intercourse at an early age, pregnancy, and/or substance abuse (Taylor et al. 1997). The 2004 IDEA amendments called for "Response to Intervention" (RTI) to "integrate assessment and intervention within a multilevel prevention system to maximize student achievement and to reduce behavior problems" (National Center on Response to Intervention 2010, 2). There now is a focus on behavior as well as academics (Smith, Katsiyannis, and Ryan 2011). This procedure does not replace comprehensive evaluation of at-risk students.

COMMON CHARACTERISTICS, PROBLEMS, AND NEEDS OF CLIENTS

As with any population, children and adolescents who have mental or behavioral disorders or severe emotional disturbances are a very heterogeneous group. Factors such as the type and severity of the impairment, the cause and time of onset, the existence of associated conditions or impairments, and the degree and type of available support services all have varying effects on the individual's level of functioning, needs, and treatment program. In addition, each individual will have unique combinations of abilities, needs, personality traits, strengths, and weaknesses that will impact his or her particular responses and functional abilities. Therefore, it is unwise to attempt to predict a particular person's skill levels or ceiling of abilities based on broad generalizations about a certain population. However, an awareness of some of those characteristics, problems, and needs which may be common to children and adolescents who have mental or behavioral disorders or severe emotional disturbances will benefit both the therapist who desires to work with this population and the reader who is trying to understand how music therapy intervention strategies may benefit this population.

Children and adolescents who have mental or behavioral disorders or severe emotional disturbances frequently are troubled by a high degree of tension and anxiety. They may exhibit disruptive, withdrawn, or bizarre behaviors, causing trouble for themselves and people around them. Those with more mild disturbances require constant structuring to keep them on task, while those with very severe disturbances may be unable to function within the boundaries of reality. Depending upon their level of learning skill and adaptive development, these clients often may need help developing basic academic, motor, communication, or social skills.

Since most children and adolescents with mental or behavioral disorders or severe emotional disturbances have problems developing and maintaining satisfactory interpersonal relationships, social skill development is usually a primary area of need. Many of these clients also need help in improving their self-concept, learning positive coping strategies, developing self-control in dealing with fear and frustration, and learning to predict consequences of behavior and to interact cooperatively and appropriately with others. While most adolescents experience stress in learning to cope with these areas, diagnoses of an emotional or behavioral disorder, or mental illness, are "related to the (1) frequency, (2) duration, and (3) intensity with which a behavior occurs or the emotion is experienced, as well as the circumstances surrounding the behavior or emotion" (Davis, Gfeller, and Thaut 2008, 210–211).

Several major categories or groupings may be delineated within the general population of children and adolescents who have mental or behavioral disorders or severe emotional disturbances. These may include schizophrenia or other psychotic disorders; anxiety disorders; mood disorders; eating disorders (anorexia, bulimia); disruptive, impulse-control, and conduct disorders; attention/deficit/hyperactivity disorders (included with neurodevelopmental disorders in DSM-V); disruptive mood dysregulation disorders; substance abuse or dependence; abuse and neglect. Juvenile offenders are not a separate DSM-V category, but will be discussed separately because of the severity of their behavior disorders. Those who are at risk will also be discussed. (DSM-V 2013; Paul 1982; Taylor et al. 1997). This text discusses autism in Chapter Thirteen, and schizophrenia and other psychotic disorders, anxiety disorders, mood disorders, and eating disorders (anorexia, bulimia) in Chapter Fifteen. Common characteristics and needs of youths in the remaining categories are described below.

Children and Adolescents Who Have Severe Emotional Disturbances

Children and adolescents who have severe emotional disturbances almost constantly have difficulty functioning in the family, at school, or in the community because of behavior that interferes with others. Soshensky (2007, 206) notes various examples:

> Rage and aggression, injurious behavior (toward self and others), isolation and withdrawal, inability to sustain attention or respond to limits, chronic dishonesty, criminal activity (such as shoplifting), acute anxiety, aural or visual hallucinations in the case of underlying psychosis, among others.

These clients have severe impairments that may include problems of identity, poor body image, perceptual problems, emotional lability, phobias, extreme anxiety, severe language disorders, bizarre or ritualistic behaviors, hallucinations, and severely delayed developmental stages. Relationships with other people and social interaction abilities usually are grossly impaired. Some clients may seem oblivious to other people, not play with peers, or withdraw and refuse to make eye contact. Some may engage in behaviors that are injurious to themselves or others (e.g., biting themselves, head banging, or engaging in prolonged temper tantrums or violent outbursts). Lower-functioning clients often lack basic self-help and personal hygiene skills (APA 1994; Newcomer 1980; Nowicki and Trevisan 1978; Paul 1982).

Adamek and Darrow (2010) note that the terms emotional disturbance and behavior disorder are sometimes used interchangeably. In special education, the term behavioral disorders is preferred (Turnbull, Turnbull, and Wehmeyer 2010).

Abused Children and Adolescents

Children and adolescents who have been abused through physical violence, neglect, continual terrorism, continual rejection, and/or sexual exploitation may also display certain behaviors that cause them to be classified as behavior-disordered or emotionally disturbed (Paul 1982). Some may be withdrawn and quiet, while others may be aggressive and destructive. Problems with asser-tiveness or anger management are common (Slotoroff 1994). Many also have difficulty expressing feelings, low self-esteem, a poorly developed sense of self, poor internal controls, inadequate coping and defense mechanisms, much fear and anxiety, an extreme sensitivity to criticism, and an inability to trust people and establish effective relationships. Other characteristics that abused children or adolescents may exhibit include short attention span, low frustra-tion tolerance, fear of failure, emotional outbursts, poor impulse control, and delayed physical, academic, and/or social development (Clendenon-Wallen 1991; Friedlander 1994; Isenberg-Grzeda 1995; Paul 1982; Slotoroff 1994). DSM-V (2013, 715) states that "affective problems may include feelings of sadness, apathy, or anger about the other individual in the relationship."

Children and Adolescents Who Have Attention-Deficit/ Hyperactivity Disorders

Children and adolescents who have attention deficit disorders (ADD) or attention-deficit/hyperactivity disorders (ADHD) have persistent difficulties with paying attention and focusing on important tasks and/or difficulties delay-ing and controlling impulsive behaviors (Children and Adults with Attention Deficit Disorders [C.H.A.D.D.] 1995; DSM-V 2013). Individuals may have both attention deficit and hyperactivity problems, or they may have prob-lems predominantly with inattention or with hyperactivity and impulsivity (DSM-V 2013). Children and adolescents with ADD or ADHD do not neces-sarily have emotional disturbances; however, without proper diagnosis and treatment, they may develop behavioral disorders, depression, or even sub-stance abuse (C.H.A.D.D. 1995). These are considered comorbid diagnoses (DSM-V 2013).

ADHD involves a set of behavioral characteristics that impair a child's ability to function in his or her environment. Though biologically based, these characteristics are influenced by psychological and social factors. None of these behavioral characteristics taken alone would necessarily be considered abnormal. But taken in combination, or because of their intensity or pervasiveness, or because of the nature of the child's environment, they can create problems in the classroom, home, and other places. Moreover, they can initiate a spiral of problems (Bain 1991, 20).

Children with ADHD may seem to be constantly in motion, fidgeting, continuously changing activities, or talking incessantly. They frequently exhibit many of the following symptoms of inattention and/or of hyperactivity-impulsivity: short attention span; difficulty sustaining attention; easy distraction; failure to give close attention to details; inattention to verbal directions; difficulty following through on instructions (failure to finish tasks, chores, etc.); constantly shifting from one uncompleted task to another; difficulty organizing tasks and activities; frequent loss of materials necessary for tasks; fidgeting with hands or feet or squirming in seat; difficulty remaining seated as requested; difficulty waiting turns; blurting out answers before questions are completed; interrupting or intruding on others' activities or conversations; difficulty playing quietly; engaging in physically dangerous activities without considering the consequences. These characteristic behaviors of ADHD are *chronic* and *persistent*, showing repeated occurrences. Symptoms may be evident in early childhood, and some have symptoms even as adults (Bain 1991; C.H.A.D.D. 1995; DSM-V 2013; Paul 1982).

Treatment of ADHD children and adolescents usually focuses on controlling or eliminating their problem behaviors at home, at school, and in the community. However, since their behaviors often cause these individuals to experience criticism, rejection, and failure, "possibly the greatest problems that ADHD children face are in the areas of their own self-esteem and their peer relationships" (Bain 1991, 173). Many have low self-confidence, feel low appreciation for and acceptance of themselves, and do not feel loved and accepted by others. Therefore, they need experiences to help them develop an internal sense of mastery, areas of competence, and ways of interacting appropriately and successfully with their peers (Lathom-Radocy 2014).

Children and Adolescents Who Have Disruptive Behavior Disorders

Individuals who exhibit disruptive behavior disorders have problems in regulating their emotions, which stimulate aggression, destruction of property, and abuse of others' rights. This diagnosis includes oppositional defiant disorder, intermittent explosive disorder, as well as conduct disorder, and antisocial personality disorder (DSM-V 2013). At one time, these individuals were categorized as socially maladjusted, but that term is no longer used.

Children and adolescents who have a *conduct disorder* exhibit behavior that is aggressive to people and animals, destructive of property, and deceitful; it may include theft or serious violation of rules (DSM-V 2013, 469–470). This behavior occurs in many settings and persists for at least 12 months. They show a pattern of interpersonal relationships characterized by lack of remorse or guilt, callous affect and lack of empathy, lack of concern about performance, and shallow or deficient affect (DSM-V 2013, 470). They *chronically and persistently* engage in behaviors that violate the basic rights of others or major age-appropriate rules and societal norms. They may repeatedly bully, threaten, or intimidate others; initiate physical fights; use weapons (e.g., brick, bat, knife, gun) that can seriously harm others; be physically cruel to animals or people; engage in crimes of theft like mugging, purse snatching, extortion, or armed robbery; or commit crimes of physical violence like rape, assault, or homicide. Individuals who have conduct disorders also may deliberately destroy the property of others through arson, breaking or smashing, or other acts of vandalism. They may engage in theft or deceitful behaviors, such as breaking into others' houses or cars, conning others, shoplifting, or forgery. In addition, these clients often have a pattern, beginning before the age of 13 years, of staying out late at night without parental permission, running away from home and staying away overnight or for a more lengthy period, or being truant from school. They also are likely to have disturbed peer relationships. When onset is in childhood, the condition is more likely to persist into adulthood than with adolescent onset; in addition, males are more likely to have conduct disorder if onset is in childhood, but the ratio is more balanced with adolescent onset (DSM-V 2013, 471). Individuals who have conduct disorders usually have little concern for the feelings, well-being, or wishes of others. While they project a tough image, they may have low self-esteem. They frequently are easily irritated, have poor frustration tolerance, tend to blame others for their own mistakes, have outbursts of temper, and engage in reckless or high-risk acts. Conduct disorder is often associated with illegal substances, smoking, drinking, and an early onset of sexual activity. Individuals also may have ADHD, learning disabilities, anxiety or mood disorders, or substance-related disorders.

Children and adolescents who have an *oppositional defiant disorder* show "a pattern of angry/irritable mood, argumentative/defiant behavior, or vindictiveness lasting at least 6 months" (DSM-V 2013, 462). These individuals frequently lose their temper, argue with adults, defy or fail to comply with requests of adult authorities, deliberately and persistently test limits, deliberately do things that annoy others, are verbally aggressive, or blame their mistakes or misbehaviors on others. They may be touchy and easily annoyed or spiteful and vindictive. They are often stubborn, resist taking directions, and refuse to compromise or negotiate with adults. Oppositional symptoms usually become evident during the preschool years and not later than early adolescence. Symptoms frequently occur first in the home setting; over time, they may spread to school and community settings. While individuals who have oppositional defiant disorder exhibit the disobedience and opposition to authority that also are observed in conduct disorder, they do not engage in serious aggression toward animals or people, deliberate destruction of property, or patterns of theft and deceit. However, oppositional defiant disorder may be comorbid with ADHD or conduct disorder. Problems may persist into adulthood in the form of "antisocial behavior, impulse-control problems, substance abuse, anxiety, and depression" (DSM-V 2013, 464). Their behavior leads to conflict in their home, school, and after-school activities. This conflict can then lead to further emotional problems.

A related diagnosis is *intermittent explosive disorder*. This occurs in children of age six years or older. The behavior is impulsive, with a rapid onset, and aggressive; the individual appears to have little control. These individuals display behavior that is not consistent with environmental cues and seems greatly exaggerated. The aggressive outburst usually lasts less than 30 minutes and is characterized by "temper tantrums, tirades, verbal arguments or fights, or assault without damage to objects or without injury to animals or other individuals" (DSM-V 2013, 467). Although their outward behavior may show impulsivity and aggression, many of these individuals are actually insecure, fear failure, and have a poor self-concept. They frequently are not able to foresee consequences of behaviors and often have unstable and ineffective interpersonal relationships. Many also have depressive disorders or emotional impairments that interfere with learning (ADHD, conduct disorder, or oppositional defiant disorder). Most have needs in the areas of exploring and expressing feelings appropriately; increasing their self-esteem; learning to interact positively and successfully with others; acquiring skills for constructive use of leisure time; developing problem-solving, anger management, and coping skills; and improving functional academic and job-related skills. Individuals under the age of 18 years who have been in trouble with the law may be described by various terms, including *juvenile offenders, youthful offenders,* or *juvenile delinquents*. Those who repeatedly violate rules and laws exhibit *delinquent behavior* (e.g., repeated cheating in school, extreme hostility or disrespect to authority figures, frequent fighting or stealing, carrying weapons, substance use or abuse); when they violate governmental laws they are classified as *juvenile offenders* (Gardstrom 1996; Michel 1985; Paul 1982; Zhang, Barrett, Katsiyannis, and Yoon 2011). They may have committed *status offenses* (e.g., truancy, curfew violations), acts that are illegal only when committed by juveniles, *misdemeanors* (e.g., trespassing, simple traffic violations), or more serious *felonies* (e.g., nonviolent crimes like car theft or violent crimes like armed robbery, rape, or murder).

Children and Adolescents Who Are Juvenile Offenders

The definition and age limit of "juveniles" differs. Age ranges from 14–21 years. Before 1999, juvenile crimes were not separated from those of adults. Before coming into contact with the juvenile justice system, these young people typically have displayed chronic patterns of antisocial behavior, such as cheating or missing assignments in school, being hostile and aggressive or aloof and withdrawn, being disrespectful to or defying authority, destroying property, fighting, stealing, carrying weapons, or using illegal substances (Gardstrom 1996; Michel 1985).

Aggression is often the most problematic antisocial behavior manifested by juvenile offenders. Many live in poverty areas and are influenced by gangs. The family situation often is disorganized. There is a high frequency of learning disabilities in this population. Based on data from 1,337 youths with a mean age of 14.81 years who were in a Connecticut detention center, Grigorenko et al. (2015) concluded that 24.9 percent of these youths tested as learning disabled. This led to poor scores in reading and mathematics. Zhang et al. (2011, 12) found "that offenders with disabilities had much higher risks for second and third referrals than those without disabilities and had their first contact with the juvenile justice system at an earlier age."

Children and Adolescents Who Have
Substance-induced Disorders

This category includes intoxication, withdrawal, and other substance/medication-induced mental disorders. DSM-V (2013, 481–482) includes ten classes of drugs, and each is described and coded: "All drugs that are taken in excess have in common direct activation of the brain reward system, which is involved in the reinforcement of behaviors and the production of memories." Adolescents or older youth who have substance use disorders show a "cluster of cognitive, behavioral, and physiological symptoms" (DSM-V 2013, 487) to such an extent that their health, safety, social or interpersonal relations, or performance at work, school, or home are impaired (DSM-V 2013; Paul 1992). Individuals who develop patterns of substance abuse and dependence often use chemical substances or alcohol to help them escape or try to cope with their problems. They may withdraw from family or friends or give up favorite recreational activities because of substance use. Some may enjoy the "high" or feelings of euphoria they get when they are under the influence of their drug of choice. Others may begin substance use because of peer pressure, a desire to rebel, or a quest for adventure (Paul 1982). Occasional or experimental use frequently develops into habitual substance abuse and substance dependence. The substance may be used even when it leads to recurrent physical, psychological, or social problems.

The problem of substance abuse becomes evident when individuals repeatedly (a) demonstrate intoxication or other substance-related symptoms that leave them unable to fulfill their obligations at school, work, or home (e.g., repeated absences due to substance use; substance-related expulsions or suspensions from school; neglect of family or household); (b) use substances in physically hazardous situations (e.g., driving a car, operating machinery, swimming, rock climbing); (c) are arrested for substance-related problems (e.g., disorderly conduct, driving under the influence, assault and battery); or (d) have persistent interpersonal problems (e.g., arguments, physical fights) caused or exacerbated by the use or effects of the substance (APA 1994). Many adolescents who have problems with substance abuse or dependence are depressed or insecure. They have a poor self-concept, low self-esteem, and ineffective or unstable relationships with others. Many also dread the future, have a fear or history of failure, have difficulty developing or conceiving long-range goals, and/or show an inability to perceive the consequences of behavior (Paul 1982). Lathom-Radocy (2014, 126) reminds therapists of the importance of their therapeutic approach: "In treatment, the client should always be viewed as capable of change and competent to assume responsibility for choices that he or she makes."

At-Risk Children and Adolescents

Since children and adolescents are at risk for many different reasons and each situation is unique, it is difficult, if not impossible, to describe the "typical" at-risk student. However, the literature does delineate several descriptive characteristics and high-risk behaviors that may indicate certain young people are likely to be at risk (Taylor et al. 1997).

As adolescents test new roles and greater independence from authority figures, they are more likely to engage in risk-taking behaviors. These include substance abuse, sexual behavior without effective contraception, and risk taking in vehicle use (Lathom-Radocy 2014, 120). At-risk children and adolescents often are poverty-stricken, have a history of low grades and failure in school that contributes to decreased motivation and lack of self-esteem, have low-level reading and academic skills, prefer gainful employment to school, have friends or relatives who have dropped out of school, have problems and stresses at home (e.g., dysfunctional family situation, emotional and/or physical abuse), feel alienated from the school environment, feel like outsiders because of numerous school transfers and family moves, or engage in self-destructive behaviors like substance abuse or early sexual intercourse. More obvious high-risk behaviors usually become evident during adolescence, when students may engage in delinquent or acting-out behavior, defy or rebel against adult authority figures, be repeatedly truant or tardy, have frequent suspensions or expulsions from school, develop a pattern of substance abuse, engage in unprotected sexual intercourse (that may result in teen pregnancies), or drop out of school. Usually, males are more likely to drop out of school and/or commit violent, aggressive acts, while females are at risk of becoming pregnant and have a greater tendency to attempt suicide.

Some children are at risk because they are homeless (Staum and Brotons 1995; Turnbull, Muckle, and Masters 2007). They are deprived of emotional and social stability and frequently display delays in developing academic and behavioral skills. They may need enrichment programs to help them develop interaction and group participation skills. Many also need experiences that will provide success, motivation, and security, and improve their self-concept and feeling of self-worth.

TREATMENT APPROACHES

Several different treatment approaches, such as those based on *biomedical models, cognitive-behavioral models, psychotherapeutic models, behavioral models,* and *multimodal models,* have been developed to treat children and adolescents who have mental or behavioral disorders or severe emotional disturbances (Atterbury 1990; Brooks 1989; Cassity and Cassity 1994a, 2007; Davis, Gfeller, and Thaut 2008; Silverman 2007). The approach used depends somewhat on the setting. For example, behavior modification techniques based on behaviorist principles are most likely to be used in school settings (Atterbury 1990). Outside the school setting, acute care facilities for adolescents often use psychotherapy as the primary treatment method, while chronic care facilities rely more on behavior modification (Brooks 1989).

Biomedical Model

Those approaching treatment from a biomedical model maintain that biological factors (e.g., biochemical imbalances, genetic problems, physical abnormalities or illnesses) underlie emotional and behavioral disorders. They emphasize the impact of biological processes on human behavior. A specific diagnosis (e.g., schizophrenia, autism, psychosis, neurosis, conduct disorder) is given by a medical doctor (psychiatrist), who prescribes the course of treatment. Treatment often includes some type of medication or drug therapy (Reed 2002). In cases in which environmental stresses are believed to contribute to the individual's problems, a biomedical approach also may employ environmental changes or treatment interventions that alter a person's responses to stresses (e.g., relaxation training, biofeedback) in conjunction with or in lieu of drug therapy.

Psychotherapeutic Models

In psychotherapeutic approaches, the psychiatrist, psychologist, or social worker looks beyond overt behaviors to try to determine underlying causes: Presenting behaviors are viewed merely as symptoms of more severe disabilities or underlying conflicts. Psychotherapists help individuals find and examine the causes of their maladaptive behaviors and learn better coping methods.

Those who work from a *psychoanalytic* or *psychodynamic* orientation (based on the theories of Freud and others) use various techniques to gain insight into an individual's unconscious conflicts, motivations, and symbols. Maladaptive behaviors are not dealt with directly, but decrease as individuals gain insight, work out underlying conflicts and anxieties, and build ego strength. Psychotherapists who work with young children may also use *play therapy* techniques, in which children reveal problems and anxieties on a fantasy level while playing with dolls, clay, or other toys, to help gain insight into their clients' behaviors and responses (Kaplan and Sadock 1991).

Some psychotherapists work from *humanistic* therapy models, such as Rollo May's existential therapy, Carl Rogers's person-centered therapy, or Perls's Gestalt therapy (Thaut and Gfeller 1992). According to this model, emotional or behavioral disorders result when individuals fail to find meaning in their lives. These therapists try to develop a supportive relationship that enables clients to feel secure enough to confront basic questions about the meaning of life and attain insights about their own life. Humanistic approaches emphasize each individual's uniqueness, value, and worth, and maintain the belief that all individuals have the capacity to control their own lives and make good decisions. Therapists often aim to help clients move to a state of "self-actualization" (Maslow 1968), moving beyond the basics of existence to a life filled with meaning and a sense of well-being.

Those who follow *cognitive* treatment models maintain that disordered thinking about oneself and the world leads to emotional and behavioral disorders. Treatment focuses on (a) helping clients become aware of negative or irrational thought patterns or beliefs that create stress or cause feelings of inadequacy, (b) confronting these and identifying life experiences in which they operate, and (c) finding ways to reverse the negative or irrational thinking and thus alter behavior. Some therapists combine a cognitive model with a behavioral model; this is referred to as a cognitive-behavioral therapy (Davis, Gfeller, and Thaut 2008). The cognitive-behavioral model is gaining more acceptance and will likely be used for some time.

Behavioral Models

Behavioral models focus on the maladaptive or disruptive behaviors that affect the individual's ability to learn or to interact successfully and appropriately with others. These approaches are based on the work of Pavlov, Watson, Thorndike, and B. F. Skinner (Atterbury 1990; Davis, Gfeller, and Thaut 2008; Kaplan and Sadock 1991). Therapists who work from a behavioral orientation believe that all behaviors are learned and therefore can be unlearned. Focus is on observable behavior, not underlying processes. Overt behaviors are observed, measured, and quantified to determine what behaviors need to be changed. Treatment plans use behavior modification techniques and principles of reinforcement and stimulus-response learning to decrease and extinguish inappropriate behaviors and responses and increase more adaptive, appropriate behaviors and responses. Brooks (1989, 37) noted that, even when treatment facilities use psychotherapy as the primary treatment approach, "some form of behavior therapy is used for daily maintenance of the adolescent. Behavior therapy in such settings enhances the psychotherapeutic process because it provides a safe, concrete structure the adolescent needs." This is the model often used in school settings.

Eclectic or Multimodal Models

While particular therapists or clinics may favor a certain treatment model or approach, most therapists realize that no existing treatment model is effective for every client in every situation. Therapy teams often find that an eclectic approach, drawing from many models and combining the best features of several approaches, is most helpful in meeting a particular client's unique needs (Davis, Gfeller, and Thaut 2008; Thaut and Gfeller 1992). For example, experts have found that many ADHD clients benefit most from a multimodal approach (e.g., parent training in behavior management, appropriate educational program, individual and family counseling when needed, medication if required) that uses multiple types of interventions (medication, behavior therapy, family therapy, psychological and educational intervention) to help the client achieve therapeutic goals (Bain 1991; Children and Adolescents with Deficit Disorders [C.H.A.D.D.] 1995). Adamek and Darrow (2010) indicate that the two favored approaches are applied behavioral analysis (ABA) and positive behavioral support (PBS).

Some therapists who work in psychiatric settings use Lazarus' (1976, 1989) multimodal therapy model (MMT) to help classify a patient's problems and types of therapeutic interventions. This very eclectic model employs varied therapeutic approaches to address the problems it identifies. "The Multimodal model involves comprehensive assessment and intervention across a person's

BASIC-ID (or basic identity)" (Cassity and Cassity 1994a, 134). Therapists using this model carefully assess and describe clients' *behavior* (habits, actions, gestures, reactions); *affect* (emotions, moods, feelings); *sensation* (how clients perceive what they see, hear, touch, taste, smell; including negative sensations such as tension, pain, dizziness, and client preferences or fixation); *imagery* (recurring dreams, vivid memories, clients' self-image or body-image); *cognitive* problems (ideas, values, beliefs, opinions, or attitudes that interfere with happiness or functioning); *interpersonal* relations (ways clients socialize or interact with others and any problems with the way clients treat or are treated by others); and *drug* use or health concerns (medication or drug use or abuse, any concerns about state of health or physical well-being). While multimodal assessment attends to specific problems within each modality, it also focuses on the interaction among modalities, thereby recognizing that a problem in one area or modality influences functioning in other areas. Noting in what order clients exhibit BASIC-ID responses ("modality firing order") during a given response pattern can help a therapist determine what events trigger affective responses or emotional disturbances (Cassity and Cassity 1994a, 138–139).

SETTINGS FOR SERVICE DELIVERY

Children and adolescents who have mental or behavioral disorders or emotional disturbances may receive special programs and services to help meet their specific needs in a variety of settings, depending on the type and severity of their impairments. These may include outpatient and inpatient mental health facilities for children and adolescents, youth homes, private or public rehabilitation/educational facilities or clinics, private therapy, programs related to the juvenile justice system, or public schools. Public Law 99-457 of 1986 provides incentives for early intervention programs to address the needs of handicapped or disabled children from birth through the age of 2 years (Adamek 1996; Adamek and Darrow 2010; Humpal 1990). Adamek and Darrow (2010, 6) reported that "during the fall of 2007, over 300,000 children of this age group and their families received services."

Music therapists work with both children and adolescents who have mental or behavioral disorders or emotional disturbances. They deliver services in many different settings, including outpatient and inpatient mental health facilities for children or adolescents, special education programs in public or private schools, public or private clinics, substance abuse treatment programs, youth homes, juvenile corrections programs in long-term public or private rehabilitation/education settings, music studios, community programs, and private therapy settings.

HOW MUSIC IS USED IN THERAPY

Many aspects of music make it a useful therapeutic tool for children and adolescents who have various mental or behavioral disorders or severe emotional disturbances. Layman, Hussey, and Laing (2002, 164), who conducted a pilot study on a music therapy assessment for severely emotionally disturbed children, stated that "'severely emotionally disturbed' (SED) refers to a rather diverse group of diagnoses including behavior disorders, schizophrenia, affective disorders (including mania and depression), autism, anxiety disorders, and attachment disorders." Some of these are medical diagnostic descriptions, as noted in DSM-V; some are educational descriptions.

The common factor is that these are emotionally damaged children who may be seen in residential settings as well as in public schools. All need assessment for the therapist to arrive at a working IEP. The assessment is used to identify strengths and weaknesses and is essential for accountability, since it is used as a baseline from which to note improvement or need for program. According to Layman, Hussey, and Laing (2002, 173), "The Beech Brook Music Therapy Assessment measures children on the basis of their behavioral and social functioning, emotional responsiveness, language and communication abilities, and musical skills."

As music therapists structure activities to focus on nonmusical behaviors and skills that can be learned and practiced through music experiences, music becomes something that children and adolescents with emotional or behavioral disorders can "identify with, relate to, and become an integral part of" (Levis and Lininger 1994). For those having severe emotional disturbances or psychoses, music's rhythm, order, and structure can provide a link to reality (Sears 1968/2007) and provide stability that may be a significant factor in bringing meaning and order to other aspects of their lives (Salas 1990). Since music is a potent means of nonverbal communication (Gaston 1968a), it can be an effective tool for establishing contact with those who have difficulty expressing feelings and ideas verbally. Whipple et al. (2015, 84) noted that there may be deficits in both expressive and receptive communication skills, as well as poor nonverbal skills, e.g., not responding to gestures or facial cues, and there may be "pragmatic deficits that manifest as sharing too much, not enough, or irrelevant information." As clients learn to express themselves and their feelings through music activities, such as playing musical instruments, singing, moving to music, or creating improvisations and songs, they also learn to relate more appropriately to others and begin to channel impulses into socially acceptable behaviors. Since music is a powerful affective medium that is integrally connected to emotions (see Chapter Five), it can be an effective medium for promoting desirable changes in moods and feelings (e.g., decrease depression, anxiety, anger; increase motivation, relaxation), thereby developing more desirable affective behaviors that support therapeutic change and growth (Thaut 1989a). In addition, music experiences can be structured to help clients learn to identify and appropriately express emotions, which can positively influence their ability to interact appropriately with others. Whipple et al. (2015, 86) studied "symbolic representation of emotions or movements within musical excerpts." They found that most children recognize concepts of happiness and sadness, while anger, fear, and disgust are less well identified. This finding is confirmed by other studies with different populations of children.

The gentle persuasion to group activity inherent in music (Gaston 1968a) may motivate shy or withdrawn clients to begin to interact with others in the music setting. Instrumental ensembles and dances may improve nonverbal communication and cooperation, while group singing, music discussion groups, and song writing activities can facilitate verbal expression and inter-action. As clients participate in rhythmic activities, instrumental ensembles, singing, and movement-to-music experiences, their imitation skills and amount of on-task behaviors also frequently improve. In addition, the experi-ences of successfully participating in music groups and learning musical skills also increase clients' self-esteem and contribute to improved self-image.

Since music is usually an important part of adolescent culture, music therapy may be a particularly useful modality for enhancing treatment with adolescents (Brooks 1989; Crowe 2007; Frisch 1990). When music therapists approach adolescent clients through the clients' preferred music, they are seen as "safe" adults with whom the adolescents may communicate through the common basis of music (Brooks 1989; Wooten 1992). Therapeutically structured music experiences provide positive, nonthreatening activities that offer a predictable, familiar context in which clients are able to relax and have a safe framework for taking risks and exploring difficult issues. These music experiences also offer nondirective and nonconfrontational control as the clients respond to the music's structure and the music experience, not the adult authority. Especially in the initial stages of therapy, "the adolescent psychiatric inpatient may trust and relate to the music more quickly and more deeply than to another person" (Frisch 1990). As well as being a way of establishing communication with adolescents, the adolescent's preferred music can give the therapist in-sight into the patient's emotional issues (Wooten 1992). For example, Metzger (1986) found that adolescent psychiatric patients who had a history of violence, sexual abuse, or drug abuse often chose to listen to songs with themes related to their diagnosis and showed excitement over or fascination with songs about sex, violence, drugs, and Satanism.

Doak (2003) studied the relationship among adolescent psychiatric diagnoses, music preference, and drug preferences. A large percentage of adolescents who abuse drugs also have comorbid psychiatric issues. Frequently, their psychological problems relate directly to drug use, as they try to self-medicate their depression, loneliness or isolation, and feelings of low self-esteem. Doak (2003, 72), who provides a list of preferred drugs, as well as preferred music in the article's Appendix, found "significant correlations between diagnosis and drug preference and diagnosis and music preference." Her finding supports the idea that adolescents may use drugs and music to alleviate psychological pain. [It should be noted that this article was published in 2003, so drug choices and music choice have likely changed. If you are using this information with clients, please obtain more currect information.]

General Music Therapy Intervention Strategies and Goals

When working with children and adolescents who have mental or behavioral disorders or severe emotional disturbances, music therapists structure different types of music experiences in many ways to help clients learn nonmusical behaviors that will help them relate more effectively and appropriately to the surrounding world. Whether the treatment model is primarily behavioral, psychodynamic, cognitive, humanistic, or eclectic, the music experience is an essential ingredient in the music therapy session. Whatever the treatment philosophy, music is both the primary tool used to establish contact with clients and the primary means through which clients learn and develop desired nonmusical skills and behaviors.

Often, music therapy approaches with children and adolescents who have mental or behavioral disorders or severe emotional disturbances incorporate *active physical involvement* because they make or respond to music through playing or improvising on musical instruments, dancing or moving to music, singing or vocalizing, or composing songs or lyrics. Other more *passive approaches* center on music listening, using contingent music listening to modify behavior, teaching music-mediated relaxation and stress reduction techniques, using song lyrics as a basis for discussion, or employing guided imagery and music. Some research suggests that music therapy experiences based on passive listening may be a better first approach for clients who are more fragile and have strong needs for structure and security, while more active experiences (e.g., improvisation or rhythmic training on drums and other percussion instruments) may be better first experiences for clients who have aggressive, acting-out behaviors and/or severe attention deficit problems (Montello and Coons 1998).

According to Friedlander (1994), music therapy approaches in psychiatric settings for children may be grouped into two broad categories: music activity therapy and music psychotherapy. In *music activity therapy*, the emphasis is on structuring music activities to provide individuals with successful experiences within the music group while also increasing social, motor, and expressive skills or improving the client's internal organization. Therapeutic music experiences may include Orff-Schulwerk activities, instrumental ensembles, group singing, exercises to music, music as a reward for desired behaviors, song writing, lyric discussion, or music for stress reduction.

In *music psychotherapy*, the emphasis is on using the client's personal experience with music to explore personal issues, with the goal of acquiring and consolidating a sense of confidence and self-worth. In *child music psychotherapy*, music therapists who have additional training in psychotherapy use music experiences such as improvisation, music listening, and creating new music to evoke or express imagery and emotion. However, unlike in adult music psychotherapy, the therapist does not interpret the musical metaphors and images the children generate. Instead, change and learning come from the meaningful interpersonal interchanges experienced in the music activities that result in corrective emotional experiences (Friedlander 1994). At first, the music therapist strives to "establish a safe musical container within which to accept the unique musical contributions of individual members" (Friedlander 1994, 95–96). Soshensky (2007, 206) discussed a "psychotherapeutic, re-constructive approach for analytical and cathartic-oriented music therapy practice for children with emotional disturbance." He notes,

> In music therapy, dynamical systems include the music itself with its movement, energy and patterns of relationships, all aspects of human functioning (physical, cognitive, behavioral), and the process of therapy itself, including the thoughts and intentions of the therapist. (217)

In later stages of child music psychotherapy, clients explore their differences and learn to interact cooperatively and constructively with others in musical experiences and to use music to express feelings, share with each other, and support one another.

Music therapists who serve adolescent patients in psychiatric settings treat adolescents with diagnoses of conduct disorders most frequently, followed by those with diagnoses of affective disorders, adjustment disorders, substance abuse, anxiety disorders, and psychotic disorders (Cassity and Cassity 1994b). The majority of music therapy interventions with adolescents address interpersonal, affective, or cognitive problems; with children, the majority address interpersonal, behavioral, cognitive, or physical problems (including problems with motor skills or receptive/expressive language) (Adamek and Darrow 2010; Cassity and Cassity 1994a, 1994b).

A careful assessment of clients' nonmusical and musical behaviors and preferences are a key part of developing effective music therapy treatment strategies. Important assessment areas include music attitudes and preferences; how the client uses music, music skills and rhythmic abilities; interpersonal relationships; eye contact; attention span; posture, grooming; expressive abilities (verbal and nonverbal); concentration, retention, and problem-solving abilities (Cassity and Cassity 1994b). Current literature indicates that applied behavior analysis (ABA), positive behavioral support (PBS), and cognitive behavior modification are effective with problem behaviors (Adamek and Darrow 2010).

Cassity and Cassity (1994a, 47–80) and Zinar (1987, 15–30) provide several examples of general types of music interventions that may be used to help children and adolescents who have mental or behavioral disorders or severe emotional disturbances reach various goals. Davis, Gfeller, and Thaut (2008, 234–236) list categories of music activities used with children and adolescents with behavior disorders:

> Listening and responding to music
> Playing and composing music
> Moving to music
> Music combined with other expressive arts
> Music for recreation and enjoyment
> Music for relaxation.

Music Therapy Interventions for Children and Adolescents Who Have Severe Emotional Disturbances

Children and adolescents who have such severe disorders that they have lost contact with reality and have grossly impaired relationships and abilities to interact with other people still may be attracted to and reached through music. Creative or improvisational music therapy techniques, in which the therapist improvises music based on the child's movements, vocalizations, behaviors, or instrument playing to reach out to the child and establish contact through musical sounds, are frequently successful in establishing communication with severely impaired children (Nordoff and Robbins 1971b, 1977). Once contact and communication are established, the improvised music can help structure interactions, facilitate personality development, and lead to a working relationship between child and therapist and between child and peers: "The patient's musical personality, once affirmed and withstood, can change and grow within the musical relationship(s)" (Steele 1987, 33).

By listening to the child's musical responses, reflecting these, setting them in a musical context (e.g., adding harmonies, form), and introducing variety, the music therapist structures the environment to let the music and the musical relationship move the child toward growth and positive change. For example, Steele (1987) described how a group of 6- to 9-year-old emotionally disturbed children learned to share a basic beat in drum improvisations, which paved the way for them to accompany, imitate, and vary a melodic theme played

by the therapist. As they became involved in more complex musical interactions, these children also learned to organize and control their responses
and cooperate with and relate more constructively and appropriately to the
other individuals in the music group. In another instance, as a 6-year-old girl
who had a profound fear of novel experiences and unfamiliar objects learned
to tolerate new musical instruments in passive listening experiences and in
active music activities involving playing and improvising on instruments, she
began to have a fear-free acceptance of other new objects, persons, and experiences (Hoelzley 1991). In this case, the music therapist used improvisational
music activities in combination with the behavioral techniques of reciprocal
inhibition and counterconditioning as the client was gradually exposed to
new instruments.

Music therapy techniques also have been incorporated successfully into
various therapeutic educational approaches used to treat children with severe
emotional disturbances. For example, specific music experiences have been
matched to the various levels of the Developmental Therapy curriculum,
resulting in an approach known as Developmental Music Therapy (DMT)
(Graham 1975; Wood et al. 1974). In DMT, music therapists structure the
musical environment and plan therapeutic music intervention strategies to help
the children sequentially develop needed behaviors, communication skills,
and socialization skills. As clients progress, the focus moves from eliciting
simple pleasure responses to music (Stage I), to developing individual skills for
musical success (Stage II), to learning skills for increasingly more demanding
types of group participation and involvement (Stages III–V).

Since music is a positive, reinforcing stimulus for many children, music
therapy also may be an integral part of a behaviorally oriented, levels system
approach (Cleveland Music School Settlement Music Therapy Department
1985; Presti 1984). Music therapists who use this approach carefully plan,
structure, and sequence experiences to help clients learn more appropriate
behaviors. Targeted behaviors are shaped successively through the use of
various types of specifically designed music activities to secure attention and
cooperation, elicit desired behaviors, and/or reinforce the intervention process.
Behavioral expectations, reinforcement, and consequences are specified for
each level, so clients are reponsible for their own behavior choices. By progressing through the levels as they learn to acquire, become proficient in,
maintain, and generalize desired behaviors, clients are encouraged to "invest
in the process, to learn the value of effort exerted and results achieved, and
to strive toward goals that will improve social conduct and interaction"
(Cleveland Music School Settlement Music Therapy Department 1985, iii).

Other music therapists and researchers have found that selected background
music, used alone (Mitchell 1966) or in conjunction with play therapy (Cooke
1969), can decrease anxiety levels of children who have psychoses or severe

emotional disturbances. Soothing instrumental background music can also increase these clients' accuracy in performing sorting tasks (Burleson et al. 1989). In addition, music therapists have used singing, vocal dynamics groups, various instrumental activities, movement-to-music, music listening, music improvisation, music composition, and music with computers to help children who have severe emotional disturbances (1) achieve greater self- and group-awareness, (2) increase concentration and on-task behavior, (3) improve communication and self-expression, (4) identify and express emotions and feelings accurately and appropriately, and (5) increase cooperation with others (Cassity and Cassity 1994a; Crowe 2007; Davis, Gfeller, and Thaut 2008; Salas 1990; Spitzer 1989; Wasserman 1972; Werbner 1966).

Music therapists who work in *adolescent psychiatric settings* most often use structured music experiences to help their clients develop better interpersonal skills (e.g., increased self- and group-awareness, appropriate interactions with peers and adults, more cooperative behaviors, improved communication with adults), better affective processes (e.g., appropriate identification and expression of feelings, decreasing anxiety or stress reactions, increasing impulse control, decreasing depression or suicidal feelings), and better cognitive processes (e.g., positive self-statements and increased self-esteem, sense of identity, organizational skills, decision-making and problem-solving skills, coping skills, insight into peer and family interactions) (Brooks 1989; Cassity and Cassity 1994a). Adolescents often do not communicate with adults; however, as they relate to the music used in therapy, they may also begin to see the music therapist as a "safe" adult, one with whom they can establish trust and communicate, in and through the musical experience. Goldbeck (2012, 397) evaluated the use of music therapy to provide a nonverbal approach for implementing "evidence-based principles of CBT (cognitive behavioral therapy), referred to as Multimodal Music Therapy (MMT)." She utilized both free and structured improvisation and communicative/dialogue music playing. She combined this approach with other cognitive-behavioral interventions, "such as psycho-education, social skills training, exposure to anxiety-evoking stimuli, and homework assignments" as well as expression through art and parent training. Her results indicated that MMT was more effective than TAU (treatment as usual) when remission of anxiety was measured. It is important to note that the post-treatment assessment conducted four months after treatment indicated that the remission of anxiety persisted. Since music activities can be structured to be nonthreatening, offering nondirective and nonconfrontational control, adolescents often engage in music-mediated therapeutic processes with little resistance. Brooks (1989) called music therapy an excellent "sneak" therapy for adolescents, one in which they readily engage and through which they can work on any treatment goals. Haines (1989) noted that adolescents often respond more quickly in music, usually working together already in the first session.

Frisch (1990, 20) observed that adolescents who have severe emotional disturbances frequently have difficulty using words to relate to other people; therefore, especially at the beginning of therapy, "the adolescent psychiatric inpatient may trust and relate to the music more quickly and more deeply than to another person." In addition, Frisch proposed that the musical symbols and structures adolescents choose to use can give the therapist an indication of where the client is in terms of identity formation, self-development, related-ness, and ego strength. She further suggested that the symbols and structural elements of the music used in music therapy provide adolescent patients with a safe medium for introspection that helps in developing ego strength and resolving identity crises.

Music experiences and techniques that can be useful in treating adolescents who have severe emotional or psychiatric disturbances include learning to play musical instruments, participating in music ensembles, rhythm training, improvisation, music listening and discussion, music-assisted relaxation, song lyrics substitution, song writing, guided imagery and music (GIM), group singing, musical storytelling, and making music videos (Brooks 1989; Edgerton 1990; Edison 1989; Ficken 1976; Frisch 1990; Haines 1989; Henderson 1983; Montello and Coons 1998). As adolescents take turns playing instruments and participate in structured instrumental ensembles, they develop impulse control and learn to take turns and cooperate with others (Frisch 1990). Rhythmic training can help adolescents who have difficulty controlling behaviors and impulses channel and contain their "out of control" energy into a structured drumming format (Montello and Coons 1998). As they learn to expand their expressive range and style, adolescents can experiment with and learn to control changes and transitions. Eventually, the ego strength and impulse control gained through success in music will carry over into other areas of life (Frisch 1990).

Instrumental activities can be a part of a behavioral approach with older children and adolescents. In a study by Edison (1989), middle school students earned tokens for learning to perform rock or rap songs on keyboard, guitar, or percussion instruments. These tokens, as well as those earned for good behavior in the classroom, could be used to purchase preferred roles in a music video. Students gained improved interpersonal skills through these experiences, achieving more stable results when they received specific in-struction in generalizing those skills to the classroom.

Song writing is frequently a useful music therapy tool in both individual and group work with adolescents. For individuals, song writing can be a vehicle for self-expression and a means of developing self-esteem; for groups, it can be a tool for developing group cooperation and cohesion, increasing self-esteem, and providing an outlet for self-expression (Edgerton 1990; Ficken 1976; Haines 1989). Song writing experiences usually begin with a very structured approach (e.g., filling in the blanks to complete a statement) so that the client may succeed easily and not be overwhelmed or threatened by the experience. Sometimes, the music therapist suggests a musical structure for the client's lyrics or uses precomposed tunes. At other times, the client improvises to determine the melody. Edgerton (1990) suggested that it is valuable to have the clients determine the musical setting because the clients are unable to "front" when they must work to make all the parts (rhythm, harmony, melody, etc.) fit together so the song will "sound good."

Music therapy techniques also can help adolescent clients learn to express and work through feelings. In working with a 17-year-old girl with a diagnosis of adjustment reaction and borderline personality disorder who had been admitted to an inpatient psychiatric unit after a suicide attempt, Dvorkin (1991), working from a psychodynamic framework, mirrored the client's actions in music and then used improvised musical dialogues to help the client explore the meaning behind her actions. Other techniques included using composed songs as transitional objects to help bring primary issues, such as abandonment, to consciousness. Composed songs also helped the client comfort herself and contain and control her rage. As the client selected songs to respond to her own emotional needs, she used the musical structure as a tool to experience and work through feelings and find ways to cope. Henderson (1983) also found that group music therapy sessions using activities involving group discussion of moods and emotions expressed in songs, composing stories to recorded music, and drawing to music helped adolescent psychiatric patients increase their ability to correctly identify moods and emotions. In addition, after participating in these experiences, the group members showed an increased feeling of group cohesion and used more group pronouns (e.g., "our" instead of "my") to express feelings.

Music Therapy Interventions for Abused Children and Adolescents

Abused children and adolescents frequently have a poor self-concept and low self-esteem, high degrees of fear and anxiety, and problems with assertiveness or anger management. They are among those with greatest risk for psychopathology (Soshensky 2007). Often, music therapists initially will use structured, nonthreatening music performance experiences with "guaranteed success" (e.g., individual lessons on an instrument, improvisational musical dialogues between music therapist and client, group instrumental ensembles) to help encourage these clients to interact with others and develop social skills (Paul 1982). Clients may be more comfortable with music experiences that allow nonverbal interaction and expression than they are with therapeutic experiences requiring verbal responses (Lathom-Radocy 2014). Thus, instrumental music experiences can be important in establishing initial contact and communication with these clients. Many find experiences using musical instruments to be less threatening than vocal experiences because musical instruments allow for some distancing of affect (Isenberg-Grzeda 1995).

As music therapists use musical instruments in exploratory improvisational sessions and in structured dyadic or ensemble experiences, they begin to engage clients in therapeutic group experiences that emphasize cohesiveness, identification, and universality. These experiences are also helpful in increasing positive relations with others, social coping skills, and problem-solving abilities (Friedlander 1994). As clients succeed in playing musical instruments or participate successfully in music ensembles, their self-esteem also improves. In addition, they gain skills that can be used in many school settings or for enjoyable leisure time activities (Paul 1982).

If clients are comfortable verbalizing in the music therapy setting, initial music therapy approaches may include small group sessions that use music listening and discussion to encourage social interaction and promote verbal expression (Paul 1982). Some music therapists find that experiences based on passive listening are a better first approach for clients who are more fragile and who have strong needs for structure and security (Montello and Coons 1998). Music therapists have also used song-writing activities, improvisational musical dialogues, musical stories or fantasies, music dramas, painting or drawing to music, and guided imagery and music experiences to help abused children and adolescents achieve therapeutic goals (Boyd 1989; Dvorkin 1991; Isenberg-Grzeda 1995; Lindberg 1995; Paul 1982; Ritholz and Turry 1994). Goodman (2007, 167) gives a case example of the use of musical drama.

Both individual and group music therapy sessions can be effective treatment settings for abused children and adolescents. Goodman (2007, 77, 86) discusses considerations in deciding if group or individual music therapy is most desirable. In *individual sessions*, music experiences are used to help increase self-esteem, facilitate expression of feelings or emotions, facilitate communication and creative expression, assist in relaxation, and develop leisure skills (Boyd 1989). Treatment frequently begins in a less directive fashion, letting the client explore musical experiences using music as an expressive tool. As therapy progresses, the therapist may employ more directive techniques in order to offer the client a series of challenges that will facilitate and encourage growth (Ritholz and Turry 1994). Sometimes, musical fantasy and improvisational creative music therapy techniques can decrease a client's isolation and increase a client's ability to participate in a shared relationship with the therapist (Goodman 2007; Ritholz and Turry 1994). In other instances, song writing experiences or improvised musical dialogues may be structured to help clients express and address their feelings (Dvorkin 1991; Isenberg-Grzeda 1995; Lindberg 1995). According to Lindberg (1995), the act of creating songs gives abused adolescents a means of expressing painful and hidden emotions, which then leads them to discover strengths and increase their assertiveness in expressing ideas and their confidence in decision making. Precomposed songs (e.g., those written by popular recording artists) also may help bring issues to a client's conscious awareness or be used as a structure to help clients express feelings or comfort themselves (Dvorkin 1991). In addition, Slotoroff (1994) found that structured and improvisational drumming techniques, used in a cognitive behavioral therapy framework to help clients increase awareness of their thoughts and feelings and practice ways of changing their behavior, were very effective in helping abused female adolescents feel more empowered and become more assertive, exhibiting positive responses after being seen in only one or two sessions.

Group music therapy sessions with abused children or adolescents frequently focus on facilitating social interaction and increasing social skills, the development of trust between group members, and opportunities for positive esteem and recognition by others (Boyd 1989). Music techniques used in group sessions include instrumental improvisation, instrumental ensembles, Orff-Schulwerk experiences, music listening and lyric discussion/analysis, song writing, rap writing, playing rhythm instruments, creative movement to music, relaxation to music, guided imagery and music, and choosing songs to portray personality, feelings, or emotions (Boyd 1989; Clendenon-Wallen 1991; Paul 1982). Initially, simple, safe, "instant success" activities, such as simple rhythm instruments, listening, or exercise/movement-to-music experiences, are used to help the clients feel safe in the music environment and develop trust in the therapist and each other (Friedlander 1994; Paul 1982). As the clients develop a feeling of trust and cohesion, the music therapist introduces more challenges by structuring activities to explore and address issues that help the clients move toward positive growth and change. Often, music therapists will develop activities or sessions around a single issue, problem, or need that is common to most group members.

Music Therapy Interventions for Children and Adolescents Who Have Attention Deficit/Hyperactivity Disorders

Music therapists seldom see ADHD clients who are not on medication. This fact affects clinical observation of music's effect as well as the research on music therapy with this population. Jackson (2003, 316) noted that "the existing literature clearly identifies medication as the most widely used form of treatment for ADHD despite some controversy over whether it is the best or most appropriate treatment in all cases."

Music can be used in many different ways to improve the behavior and concentration of children and adolescents who have attention-deficit/hyper-activity disorders. For example, contingent music used within a behaviorally oriented approach may help eliminate disruptive behaviors and/or increase acceptable social behaviors. Wilson (1976) demonstrated that interrupting rock music selections played as background music during art class when specified disruptive behaviors occurred quickly eliminated those undesirable behaviors. In another study, recorded music used to reinforced appropriate social behaviors improved the walking habits and car-riding behaviors of a hyperactive boy (Reid et al. 1975). Jackson (2003, 308) surveyed board-certified music therapists to determine music therapy methods and their perceived effectiveness with this population: "In general, respondents indicated that music therapy treatment is effective according to their treatment outcomes, and they perceived that others also feel music therapy is an effective treatment." The most frequent method used was music and movement, "followed by instrumental improvisation, musical play, and group singing" (306). The three most frequent goals indicated by respondents were behavioral, psychosocial, and cognitive goals. When a multidisciplinary approach is used, there is more likelihood of continuity of care and generalization of positive results.

Background music played before or during tasks also may decrease the activity level and increase the attentiveness of ADHD children. The *iso principle*, which states that the therapist should start at the client's current activity level, and then modify the music in the direction of the desired activity level, seems appropriate with ADHD children. Scott (1970) found that hyperactive boys' arithmetic scores improved significantly when they worked on their math problems while rock music was playing in the background. Cripe (1986) also found that when ADD children listened to rock music with a repetitive rhythm through headphones at a maximum level of 58 dB, their activity level decreased. In these studies, rock music was a preferred stimulus, although it likely would increase activity for many other children. However, just any background music will not necessarily decrease the activity level and increase the attentiveness of ADHD children. Windwer (1981) found that when a tape of instrumental background music with a progressive increase in tone frequency, tempo, and percussive elements was played during art class, the activity level of hyperactive children increased rather than decreased. Windwer suggested that, in this instance, a tape of music that progressively decreased in tempo, pitch, and intensity may have been more effective in decreasing activity and increasing attentiveness. Thus, optimal amounts of stimulation need to be determined through careful observation of behavioral responses if background music is to be an effective aid to decrease activity and increase attentiveness in hyperactive children. Other researchers have suggested that it may be more beneficial to expose children with attention and memory difficulties to music *prior* to cognitive processing tasks rather than using background music during the tasks.

Other music therapy approaches work through direct involvement of

ADHD children and adolescents in experiential music activities. Children are frequently attracted to musical sounds and musical instruments. The pleasure they derive from making music and from being involved in music experiences can encourage children with ADHD to stay focused on tasks and modulate their behavior to produce desirable or pleasant musical products. For example, when using gong improvisation with a group of hyperactive children, Fles (1995) found that after a brief period of experimentation in playing as loudly as they wanted, the children, on their own, decreased the loudness level of their playing to a tolerable level of sound. After several sessions, they even began to produce very subtle effects. Caught up in the musical experience of playing the gong, "these usually restless children modulated their behavior because the softer sounds gave them personal satisfaction and aesthetic pleasure" (Fles 1995, 89).

When ADHD children participate in experiential music activities like singing, playing instruments, and movement to music, the music helps increase their tolerance for group activity by holding them together in sound (Hibben 1991b). Music can provide structure (e.g., stop when the music stops; play instrument for one verse and then pass it to the next person), boundaries in time (e.g., length of turns or task), repetition to reinforce learning of social routines or academic concepts, internal cues (e.g., song lyrics reminding child how to behave), rhythmic structure or pacing for movement or activity, and closure (Hibben 1991b; Jones 1996). Montello and Coons (1998) and Rickson and Watkins (2003) recommend a highly structured group for ADHD boys. Based on data from their pilot study, groups that encourage creativity and spontaneity were found to be less effective and led to increased acting-out behavior. Rickson and Watkins (2003, 295) stated that "boys with ADHD might become overstimulated in a less structured situation." Lathom-Radocy (2014, 117–118) noted that ADHD children functioned better in a structured situation "as if they seek boundaries. Too many stimuli or uncertain expectations are likely to lead to loss of control." A list of areas requiring consistent attention is provided.

Music therapists also can use rhythm and musical structure (e.g., repeated chorus that can be anticipated or focused on) to help clients increase and maintain their attention to task. Increased on-task behavior usually is achieved gradually, by having the child participate in the musical task for increasingly longer periods of time (e.g., 1 minute, then 2 minutes, etc.) (Cassity and Cassity 1994a; Lathom-Radocy 2014). This gradual increase in length can occur subtly and unobtrusively, as verses or repetitions are added to a song, as the length of music accompanying movement activities gradually increases, or as the client gradually is given longer compositions to play.

Many ADHD children and adolescents also have a low frustration tolerance that causes them to quit, make excuses, yell, or become aggressive toward the objects or people involved as soon as tasks become difficult. When these clients are interested in learning to play musical instruments, music therapists design instructional approaches that assure the clients as much success as possible while simultaneously helping them increase their frustration tolerance and their ability to attend to and complete increasingly more difficult tasks (Jones 1996; Paul 1982). Often, the reward of making music will help keep the client working on the desired task, especially when successful completion of less preferred, more difficult tasks (e.g., note drills, repeating musical exercises until they are played correctly) is rewarded with preferred activities (e.g., composing own songs).

Adamek and Darrow (2010, 149) suggest that "reinforcing students who *are* doing what you want them to do creates a more positive learning environment than admonishing students who *aren't* doing what you want them to do." For example, in individual music therapy sessions with a 9-year-old boy who was hyperactive, impulsive, depressed, and had aggressive acting-out behaviors, Herman (1991) used the autoharp to attract attention and initiate interaction. A key to increasing this client's frustration tolerance and willingness to experiment with music was the realization that musical mistakes just "floated away." Succeeding music therapy sessions then helped the boy (1) gain expressive freedom (techniques included mirror, echo, and start-stop musical games and sand or water play to background music), (2) enjoy creative expression (painting and molding clay to music), and (3) learn structure (using a color-coded note system to play keyboard melodies and chords). Later, small group sessions (first with only one peer, then with two more), using musical games (e.g., conducting, reflection drumming, rhythm work, dancing) to increase frustration tolerance and develop appropriate interactions with peers were used to help the boy work cooperatively with others. Herman reported that, following this course of music therapy (120 sessions), the boy could stay on task for 15 minutes, follow most directions, stay in a group and behave appropriately, and had an increased frustration tolerance, an increased ability to wait his turn without frustration, improved social skills, clearer verbal communication, and decreased aggressive behaviors and temper tantrums.

Music Therapy Interventions for Children and Adolescents Who Have Disruptive Behavior Disorders

Interpersonal problems, such as uncooperative, disruptive, or socially inappropriate behaviors, are the most frequent types of problems treated by music therapists in psychiatric settings for both children and adolescents (Cassity and Cassity 1994a). Since music experiences are rewarding to and viewed positively by most children and adolescents, including those who have behavioral disturbances or disorders, the desire to learn musical skills or participate in preferred musical experiences or listen to preferred music can be a powerful motivator to control behavior. In addition, music experiences that are structured to promote positive interactions and cooperative participation with others can help children and adolescents learn and practice more appropriate social behaviors in the context of enjoyable music activities (e.g., working cooperatively with others in an ensemble to produce a satisfying musical product; working cooperatively with others to plan and record a music video). As individuals learn more appropriate ways of interacting with others in music groups and develop increased self-confidence and self-esteem through successful participation in music experiences, they can transfer these more desirable behaviors to other areas of their lives.

Various music therapy interventions may help clients with behavioral or conduct disorders develop more cooperative behaviors. Often, the therapist seeks to involve the client in an *instrumental group* by assigning responsibilities or musical roles so that group success depends on each client's cooperation (Cassity and Cassity 1994a; Cleveland Music School Settlement Music Therapy Department 1985; Crowe 2007d; Presti 1984). This approach may be structured to include behavior management techniques, where points are received for appropriate behavior in music, or be structured as a levels system (see description in "emotional disturbances" section above). Other music therapists use a variety of *music experiences* (e.g., listening, singing, music games, music ensembles, music improvisation or composition) *centered on themes* related to developing cooperative behaviors, combined with a systematic program of behavioral expectations, positive reinforcements, and consequences to help clients understand and experience cooperation (Levis and Lininger 1994).

Goodman (2007, 77) discussed the question of individual or group placement. She notes that "a specific and carefully considered rationale for initial individual vs. group music therapy placement for the child is nonexistent." This judgment is made by the therapist and the IEP team, with many factors to be considered. In individual music therapy sessions, a music therapist might use *improvisational music techniques* to help children or adolescents develop more appropriate and cooperative behaviors (Nordoff and Robbins 1977; Shoemark 1991). For example, Shoemark (1991) used piano improvisation with a boy who was blind and had behavioral disturbances to help develop a relationship that encouraged positive interactions and cooperative participation. As the boy learned to interact spontaneously and cooperatively with the therapist in music making, his participation and cooperation in other areas of life also increased. In other instances, musical interaction and skill development in individual sessions may be structured from a more *behaviorist* point of view, using a system of rewards for appropriate behaviors and completion of tasks or structuring instruction on a levels system (Cleveland Music School Settlement Music Therapy Department 1985; Kivland 1986; Paul 1982). When the therapist has a good relationship with the client, the therapist's attention as well as the music may be powerful reinforcers (Gfeller and Thaut 2008, 226).

Computer and *electronic music resources* also may be used in individual or group sessions to help adolescents who have behavioral disorders increase on-task behavior, self-expression, problem-solving and decision-making skills, and improve relations with peers (Krout 1992b; Krout and Mason 1988). Since these instruments are versatile and attractive to most adolescents, they may help motivate clients to learn age-appropriate music skills that they can use to participate successfully in school or community music programs and use throughout their lives for leisure time enjoyment. Music therapy sessions stress "music learning within socially acceptable boundaries" (Krout and Mason 1998), so clients gain usable skills that will help them express feelings appropriately and cooperatively with others.

Despite their tough image, many children and adolescents who have disruptive behavior disorders actually have low self-esteem. Increasing self-esteem can be targeted as a specific music therapy goal. As these clients experience success in music activities and learn new musical skills, their self-confidence and feelings of self-worth also may increase. Activities might be structured so that clients have opportunities to make positive statements about themselves or name specific things they did well in a music session. For example, Kivland (1986) used the format of individual piano lessons to help a 12-year-old girl with a conduct disorder learn to decrease negative self-statements and increase her ability to accept praise from others. Clear goals were presented for each lesson, so the girl knew what was expected for success. After 12 weeks of lessons, her negative statements about herself decreased, she consistently was able to list three things she did well in each lesson, and she could accept praise from others. While her self-esteem and musical skills increased, her relations with her peers also improved as they saw her accomplishments in music.

Music therapy interventions can also help children and adolescents who have disruptive behavior disorders learn to channel aggressive impulses and express anger in more appropriate ways. Clients may select songs that express the anger they feel and then be asked to identify appropriate ways to ventilate the anger (Cassity and Cassity 1994a). Some clients may feel more comfortable expressing their angry feelings through musical instruments. As they learn to control their playing (e.g., vary dynamics and rhythms) and express their feelings in a musical framework, they may find ways of controlling their behavior. For example, structured and improvisational drumming techniques can help adolescents with conduct disorders increase awareness of their thoughts and feelings and practice ways of controlling their anger and impulsive behavior (Crowe 2007b; Slotoroff 1994). The discipline of learning to play a musical instrument through individual or group music lessons can also help clients learn self-control (Cassity and Cassity 1994a; Nemeth 2006) while simultaneously providing them with a socially appropriate outlet for emotional expression.

Some clients with behavioral disorders learn to control their anger and behavioral outbursts through *music-based relaxation training*. Saperston (1989) used music in the form of concept songs and chants as structural prompts to help an intellectually disabled client who had behavioral disturbances learn to perform relaxation skills. Singing activities helped focus the client's attention on the relaxation task. The music therapist then directed the relaxation response, having the client lie still and perform breathing and muscle relaxation exercises with songs, chants, and rhythmic accompaniment to increase the client's awareness of relaxed feelings. Next, the songs and chants were faded and replaced with background music and verbal cues. Finally, music therapy sessions focused on developing transfer and generalization skills, helping the client recognize situations in which the procedure should be implemented, and helping him practice and perform the relaxation procedure in different settings. Other music-mediated relaxation techniques, such as progressive muscle relaxation to music, guided imagery and music, and music and bio-feedback, also may help children and adolescents with behavioral disorders learn to relax and help control their anger and disruptive, impulsive behaviors (Cassity and Cassity 1994a; Crowe 2007d).

Music Therapy Interventions for Juvenile Offenders

Skilled manipulation (Fulford 2002), low self-esteem, and a lack of confidence which may be masked by the appearance of a dominating personality or aggressive behavior characterize juvenile offenders (Rio and Tenney 2002). Many have a dual diagnosis with mood disorders, substance abuse, conduct disorder, or attention deficit and hyperactive disorder (ADHD).

Music therapy treatment goals for juvenile offenders generally fall under one of four behavioral domains: emotional, social, physical, or cognitive/academic (Gardstrom 1996). Wyatt (2002, 81) explained that "group music therapy experiences present rich opportunities for juvenile offenders to learn interpersonal problem-solving and conflict resolution skills that broaden their inventory of nonaggressive solutions to difficult situations." Since music addresses needs at a deeper, more expansive level, "the use of music and other creative arts therapies can affect aspects of treatment that are untouched by approaches relying on verbal communication alone" (Skaggs 1997b, 74). Nonverbal responses can lead to verbal communication as skills are generalized through music (Fulford 2002). Kaser and Bullard (2007, 188–190) found improvisation to be useful with juvenile offenders; they offer specific suggestions for music therapy procedures with this type of group. Justice (2007, 140) provides further information on conducting a music improvisation group.

Music therapy interventions in the *emotional domain* help clients (a) identify, explore, and express feelings, values, opinions, and ideas, and (b) build self-esteem. Since music experiences are multimodal and multidimensional, "they allow increasing access to inner feelings and provide diverse modes for expressing them" (Skaggs 1997b, 74). For example, music activities such as group singing of popular songs, dedicating songs to people, selecting songs to describe people, and choosing songs to express feelings have been shown to enhance the self-concept of clients who are juvenile delinquents while decreasing their feelings of rebellion and distrust (E. Johnson 1981; Rio and Tenney 2002). Improvisational activities are also useful vehicles for helping youths in juvenile corrections programs share feelings and express both self-worth and self-doubt (Edelman 1978; Fulford 2002; Rio and Tenney 2002). These nonverbal activities, which do not allow clients to hide behind words or tough talk, tend to promote honest and constructive responses.

In her work with male juveniles who were convicted sex offenders, Skaggs (1997b) found that techniques using guided imagery and music (Kaser and Bullard 2007, 191), improvising feelings and stories on Orff instruments, and of holding favorite music days (clients bring in CDs; discuss, analyze how music affects or can be used to manage behavior) were useful in helping clients identify feelings, develop empathy with their victims, and learn ways of managing volatile feelings and of controlling behaviors. Other music therapists have used song lyrics to stimulate discussion about themes relevant to the client's current situation or rehabilitation process, or developed songwriting experiences with varying degrees of structure to help the client express feelings or increase their self-awareness (Fulford 2002; Gardstrom 1996).

Gaining skills in music performance or in successfully using technical musical production materials can also help incarcerated youths gain self-esteem while they develop technical and possible vocational skills. Technical advances, electronic instruments, and computer music have made music performance and production available to an increasing number of individuals. For example, Sheedy (1995) used the WaveRider, a system of hardware and software that takes readings from the body (e.g., muscle groups, heart rate, brain waves) and converts them to musical sound, with boys in a Wisconsin juvenile prison. The boys were eager to participate in the program and intrigued and motivated by the equipment. In addition to being useful in encouraging relaxation, initiating self-awareness, and encouraging experimentation, the process of using the WaveRider was very effective in facilitating introspective dialogue among the group members.

In the *social domain*, music therapy interventions help meet clients' needs for "peer interaction, appropriate competition, relaxation, and leisure" (Gardstrom 1996). Various music experiences can be structured to decrease isolation, foster positive relationships and interactions, increase verbal interaction and self-disclosure, develop leadership skills, and give opportunities for healthy competition. Music experiences may provide the motivation for appropriate behaviors (e.g., facilitate appropriate group participation through group listening, singing, rhythm instrument, or movement-to-music experiences) or be used as a contingency for appropriate behavior (e.g., background music during free time stopped when any person fails to observe one of the established group behavior/interaction rules) (Michel 1985).

Performance groups or improvisational experiences on musical instruments frequently are used to help juvenile offenders develop social skills such as following directions, listening to others, making positive contributions to a group, cooperating with others, and giving and receiving constructive feedback (Edelman 1978; Fulford 2002; Gardstrom 1996; Gooding 2011; Kaser and Bullard 2007; Michel 1985; Sheedy 1995; Skaggs 1997b). These techniques can be combined easily with group-oriented treatment models for the rehabilitation of youths who have delinquent behaviors, such as Positive Peer Culture (Gardstrom 1987). When this structure is applied to music therapy treatment, peers meet in groups and assume responsibility for their own behavior and that of other group members. The music therapist serves as a facilitator, suggesting music experiences that are appropriately challenging and using questioning techniques to help maintain group focus and increase insight. Challenging opportunities for growth and the chance to develop social and leisure skills may be provided through experiences like learning to play musical instruments (e.g., electric guitar, keyboard, percussion), learning to create music spontaneously (e.g., vocal or instrumental improvisation), or cooperating with group members to produce a musical product (e.g., group song writing). At first, group music experiences are relatively low-risk, involving whole group responses, minimal personal sharing, and minimal music skill requirements (e.g., learning a group rap chant). Later, group music experiences include higher-risk, more challenging activities, such as forming a band, where individuals learn responsibility to the group, learn to accept responsibility for helping each other, and are rewarded for working cooperatively with others by a more pleasing musical product.

Based on a review of the literature, ten guidelines for music therapy with this population are listed below:

1. Keep the attention and motivation of juvenile offenders by using a variety of interventions.
2. Incorporate music listening into the sessions.
3. Use caution when selecting recorded music for the session.
4. Set consistent limits on behavior for the protection of the group members.
5. Utilize proportional interventions to redirect behavior.
6. Adolescents generally enjoy percussive instruments, such as the djembe,

conga, and metallophone.

7. Reframe negative exchanges to engage the adolescents in the therapeutic process.
8. Avoid power struggles.
9. Provide structure as needed.
10. Be honest. (Wyatt 2002, 81–82)

Wyatt discusses these guidelines in greater detail.

In the *physical domain*, music therapy interventions that involve motor activity (e.g., dance, creative movement, or exercise to music; playing instruments; singing with sign language) can help provide clients with regular exercise and constructive physical activity that is vital to rehabilitation: "Movement can be a powerful tool for personal expression or to enhance self-awareness" (Gfeller and Thaut 2008, 235). In addition, these music therapy interventions involving motor activity can help clients improve general fitness and body image, develop or improve their gross and fine motor skills, and reduce physical stress (Gardstrom 1996). Movement-to-music experiences, in particular, can be valuable tools for helping clients gain confidence in using their bodies to interact with others in socially acceptable ways and in helping them learn to appreciate personal boundaries and personal space (Reed 2002). Song writing or music listening/discussion activities also can be used to help generate open discussion about physical topics important to teens (e.g., sexuality, pregnancy, anatomy, feelings of anxiety over rapidly changing bodies) (Brooks 1989; Gardstrom 1996). In music listening, it is important to consider the musical style and familiarity to the client, as well as whether the lyrics are appropriate to the desired therapeutic goals (Thaut 2008).

Music therapy interventions that focus on the *cognitive domain* may be structured to help clients increase their attending skills and their ability to follow directions, improve short- and long-term memory skills, and reinforce or teach specific academic concepts (Gardstrom 1996; Lathom-Radocy 2014). Other cognitive-behavioral techniques used by music therapists include "modeling, feedback, transfer training and problem solving" (Gooding 2011, 440). Music experiences may be used as a reinforcer for desired academic skills (e.g., being allowed to listen to favorite music or participate in music group only after successful completion of assignments) or as a vehicle for teaching specific academic concepts (e.g., practicing reading and writing skills through lyric analysis or song-writing activities, song lyrics or rap chants that help clients learn and practice information like math facts or state capitals).

The motivational elements and multisensory nature of music experience may have important benefits for youths who are used to experiencing failure in academic subjects or have difficulty learning through more traditional means. For example, successfully expressing themselves nonverbally through instrumental or movement-to-music experiences may give some clients the confidence they need to try expressing themselves in written form. As they grow comfortable using words to express themselves in the context of music experiences (e.g., song writing), they may be more likely to try verbally expressing themselves in other contexts. In working with juvenile sex offenders, Skaggs (1997b, 78) observed that "story-telling on musical instruments flowed into story-telling through writing and art." In addition, creative music experiences (e.g., composition, song writing, group ensembles, producing music videos) help clients develop organizational, problem-solving, and decision-making skills that they can use in many areas of life.

Music Therapy Interventions for Children and Adolescents Who Have Problems with Substance Abuse

DSM-V (2013, 481) states, "All drugs that are taken in excess have in common direct activation of the brain reward system, which is involved in the reinforcement of behaviors and the production of memories." Clients who music therapists see in treatment programs for substance abuse are usually of adolescent age or older (Cassity and Cassity 1994a). The adolescents' preferred music, which is usually currently popular music, often is used as a common ground to establish contact and communication with the patient, and adolescents usually perceive music therapists who use this music as "safe" adults with whom to relate (Brooks 1989; Lathom-Radocy 2014; Michel 1985; Wooten 1992). The adolescents' musical choices may also give the therapist insight into the patients' emotional and behavioral issues (Metzger 1986; Wooten 1992): "Through musical expression and interaction, the client's strengths and resistances are revealed in dynamic, tangible form" (Soshensky 2007b, 153).

Once the music therapist has established communication with the patients, music can also be used as a "means for introducing and discussing alternative coping skills" (Wooten 1992, 97). For example, patients may be asked to listen to selected songs, discuss and analyze their lyrics, and process the themes and values suggested by the lyrics as a means of helping them become aware of the effects of chemical dependency and the consequences of various lifestyle choices or as a means of generating discussion about feelings of helplessness, powerlessness, loss of relationships, and alternative responses to situations (Cassity and Cassity 1994a; Gardstrom 1987; James 1988b; Silverman 2003a). Discussion of song lyrics used in the framework of a values clarification approach has been shown to positively influence participants' self-concept and sense of control over the environment, thereby increasing confidence in themselves and their ability to recover from chemical dependency (James 1988b). Music therapists also can help patients see how certain music may be linked with their substance abuse behaviors and help them learn to break these links by avoiding music with negative influences (Metzger 1986; Michel

1985). In addition, music therapists can help clients learn to use music to in-fluence their moods positively (an alternative "high") or to use music-based relaxation techniques as a chemical-free way to manage stress (Cassity and Cassity 1994a; Michel 1985):

> Feeling safe and taking part with others in music without the use of drugs can be a powerful experience for many clients in addiction treatment, since their primary associations with music and socialization may have been drug-related (going to clubs "high," drinking while "hanging-out and listening to music with friends," etc.). (Soshensky 2007b, 152)

Some music therapists have found that performance-oriented groups are more beneficial with adolescents than verbal/insight-oriented groups (Cassity and Cassity 1994a). Group instrumental ensemble experiences or cooperative group projects like producing an accompaniment to poetry or making a music video can help clients learn to (a) work cooperatively with others, (b) explore different aspects of interpersonal communication, and (c) develop or improve decision-making and problem-solving skills (James and Freed 1989). Other music therapists have used instrumental improvisation to role play dif-ferent situations and increase clients' awareness of different options for solving problems (Gardstrom 1987). Music performance always involves some risk, and therapists must be certain the goal is centered on the client's needs and not their own need for recognition. Soshensky (2007b, 160) indicated,

> Inherent components of performance – preparation, risk-taking, the need to "show-up," and the potential for acknowledgment/recognition – can also provide an opportunity to address some of the core character pathologies of addiction such as narcissism, grandiosity, and unreliability.

James and Freed (1989) have developed a sequential model for developing group cohesion and applied it to music therapy interventions in a residential treatment program for adolescents with chemical dependency. In the first stage, *Goal-Setting Activities*, assessments are conducted and clients are given an orientation to the format and rationale of the music therapy group, including a discussion of how progress in music therapy impacts the clients' treatment goals. In the next stage, *Individual/Parallel Play Activities*, music is used as a stimulus to encourage identifying with and relating to others in the group. Activities focus on what the group members have in common and may include experiences in music-assisted relaxation, identifying moods and feelings expressed by music, and song lyric analysis. By moving slowly in the beginning stages of therapy, music therapists establish a healthy therapeutic atmosphere that will facilitate the group's ability to accomplish tasks at the next levels. Stage three, *Cooperative Group Activities*, uses creative music performance experiences that require clients to interact more and work toward a group goal. Music activities at this stage include group compositions made up of individual contributions, improvisations led by the music therapist, performance groups with clients taking turns being conductors, music videos or musical puppet shows created by the clients, or group poetry writing accompanied by instruments. Goodman (2007, 131–132) also listed group goals that would be useful at this stage. In stage four, *Self-Disclosure Activities*, music is used as a nonverbal language to support individual group members' expressions of feelings and emotions as they communicate personal issues and receive insight and feedback from their peers in an accepting, nonjudgmental atmosphere. Musical experiences may including choosing songs to express feelings, moving to music that mirrors their feelings, peers choosing songs or improvising on instruments or moving to music to show the moods they perceive other group members to have, or individuals improvising or creating tone poems to express their feelings. In the final stage, *Group Problem-Solving Activities*, music therapy experiences are used to support and stimulate verbal therapy. Activities from all of the preceding stages may be used, with their content focused more specifically on individual issues and skill-building to transfer new behaviors to real life situations.

Gallagher and Steele (2002, 118) listed five stages of treatment: "engagement, crisis intervention, stabilization, active treatment, and recovery." They worked with dually diagnosed substance abuse/mentally ill clients. A list of the goals and interventions used is provided (120), as well as discussion of documentation and evaluation. They note that "music therapy . . . can reach those who are resistant to other therapies, and it can assist clients in learning new skills to maintain sobriety and improve mental health" (121).

Individual music therapy sessions may also be useful for adolescents who have substance abuse problems. For example, individual sessions using experiences in piano performance and relaxation and imagery to music helped a 16-year-old girl increase self-esteem, improve her relations with peers, decrease drug abuse, and learn to better organize and control her life (Lefebvre 1991). As she learned she could control her life and positively influence her moods during music therapy sessions, the girl eventually came to this realization: "It's up to me now as to how things are going to be from now on" (Lefebvre 1991, 229).

Music Therapy Interventions for At-Risk Children and Adolescents

In recent years, both music therapists and music educators have begun to pay more attention to the role music can play in meeting the special learning needs of children and adolescents considered to be "at-risk." In music education as well as in music therapy programs, music helps these individuals gain skills in nonmusical areas. For example, participating in music ensembles or school music classes can help increase self-esteem, provide a sense of belonging, allow for expression of emotions in safe and positive ways, and develop many basic skills necessary for successful employment (e.g., creative thinking, decision making, problem solving, the ability to see things in the mind's eye, self-management, teamwork, the ability to monitor and correct performance, the ability to work with diversity) (Taylor et al. 1997). As "at-risk" children and adolescents experience positive change, pleasure, creations of beauty, and aesthetic enrichment in music, they discover that there are positive things in the world and that artists can transform their world into a more beautiful, interesting, and provocative place. Success in music or other arts experiences may help provide a sense of hope to those children and adolescents whose world seems full of hopelessness. Participating in creative music experiences also gives them opportunities to have an active part in creating beauty and demonstrating positive accomplishments. As they learn music skills, they discover that work and self-discipline (practice) *do* yield positive results (increase in skills, improvement in performance). For many, successful experiences in music may be a key factor in encouraging them to stay in school and succeed in other academic areas (Taylor et al. 1997).

Frequently, at-risk children and adolescents need help learning basic attending and social skills (e.g., staying with group, listening, following directions, taking turns, keeping hands to self, not talking out of turn, working cooperatively) for classroom success. Smith (2012) described a therapeutic music video group of adolescent girls who chose to call themselves the "Sparkling Divas." Music therapy sessions included songwriting, use of pop music, video production, and lyric discussion to create a "safe space," a place "where they could be playful . . . for an hour a week, leaving their responsibilities at the door" (20). The music therapist used both Apple's iMovie and GarageBand to assist these young ladies in a music video experience. Smith concluded,

> Although only a moment in time for these girls, the relationships that they were able to build with each other, and the creativity they experienced together, gave them a sense of their worth and potential – something that can inspire them as they tackle the challenges that will undoubtedly arise in their lives. (24)

Kolb and Hanley-Maxwell (2003) define social skills as "a complex set of skills that include communication, problem-solving and decision making, assertion, peer and group interaction, and self-management" (163). Music therapists often help clients develop these skills by combining a systematic program of behavioral expectations, positive reinforcements, and consequences with music experiences that teach and give the students a chance to experience and practice the desired behaviors (Cleveland Music School Settlement Music Therapy Department 1985; Gooding 2011; Krout 1986a,

1986b; Levis and Lininger 1994; Staum and Brotons 1995). For example, by using a simple token contingency in a "Good Listening Game," Krout (1986b) helped increase listening skills, on-task behavior, and correct responses to questions in 10- to 12-year-old students who were classified as under-achievers and exhibited many disruptive behaviors. Students earned tokens, redeemable for group music listening time, when they correctly answered written questions about prerecorded musical compositions.

Music therapists sometimes work outside the school setting (e.g., in homeless shelters), using music activities as an enrichment/treatment program to help at-risk children develop interaction skills needed to function successfully in group learning situations (Staum and Brotons 1995). Children and adolescents often have experienced frequent failures with traditional learning methods in school. Music-based learning activities may give these students experiences that are more compatible with their learning styles and emotional needs, thus providing an effective, alternative method of learning to students who have academic delays and difficulty learning through more traditional means (Taylor et al. 1997). For example, music experiences can be structured to teach basic concepts (e.g., colors, numbers, multiplication facts) through song or rap lyrics or through music games (Lathom-Radocy 2014). Music activities also can reinforce learning from other subjects and make the information more relevant to students' lives and interests (e.g., learning fractions by calculating subdivisions in rhythms and meters, exploring history through music of a particular period) (Taylor et al. 1997). In addition, music lessons can serve as effective reinforcers to increase academic achievement and appropriate social behaviors in disadvantaged or at-risk students (Michel 1971; Michel 1985; Michel and Farrell 1973).

Active participation in music activities also can help build self-esteem in those whose learning styles favor "hands-on" experiences. For example, self-esteem can be developed and enhanced as students learn simple skills (e.g., playing basic chords on guitar or ukulele to accompany simple songs) in music lessons (Michel 1971; Michel and Farrell 1973). Ensembles, such as school or community choirs or bands, can also be structured therapeutically to help participants develop self-confidence and leadership abilities. In addition, these ensembles provide opportunities for self-expression and group decision making and facilitate clients' adjustment to the school or community (Ragland and Apprey 1974; Taylor et al. 1997). The WaveRider program described earlier in this chapter (see section on juvenile offenders) has also been used in public schools with at-risk students to help them develop self-esteem, self-direction, and group cooperation skills while they receive technical and vocational training in the media arts (Sheedy 1995).

Music Therapy Interventions in Family Therapy

Family relationships and interactions can greatly impact the behavior and well-being of any individual within the family group. With this in mind, some families have been given an Individualized Family Service Plan (IFSP) to document and guide the intervention process (Furman and Humpal 2006, 83). This can include children from birth through age 2 years, under Part C of IDEA. In family therapy, family members are treated together, and "family relations and processes are explored as potential causes of mental disorder in one or more of the family members" (Kaplan and Sadock 1991, 72). Miller (1994, 45) found that involving the family together in a meaningful music experience may enhance the effects of events occurring in the session.

Music and musical instruments are things that usually interest and are valued by both children and adults (Hibben 1992). Since music offers a means of nonverbal communication, and since musical instruments usually evoke interest and curiosity, family members may participate more readily in music experiences than they do in verbal therapy (Miller 1994). In addition, music experiences can readily include even young children in family work (Hibben 1992). Experiences using musical instruments can facilitate nonverbal expression of emotions by creating involvement while allowing safe distancing. Songs and song writing may help families express feelings that are difficult to verbalize, bring families together, build bridges between generations, and facilitate sharing experiences and family stories (Bailey 1984; Hibben 1992).

Music also offers a neutral context for assessment of family relationships and may provide a metaphor for family functioning (Hibben 1992; Miller 1994). For example, observing family members as they improvise on melodic or rhythmic percussion instruments can give the therapist much information on family roles, communication patterns, balance of power, and symptoms of dysfunction. By addressing adverse patterns of interaction and communication, music interventions may allow family members to recognize the dysfunctional patterns and practice more functional ways of interacting and communicating. Interventions such as improvisation and musical role playing, echoing, soloing, playing duets, playing mood themes, conducting, and having adults guide children, can facilitate self-expression of individual family members, enhance family communication skills, and address issues of structural power imbalances within the family. Miller (1994) also found that, because of the extra visual, auditory, and kinesthetic cues and associations inherent in music experiences, the learning that takes place in music therapy sessions may be more readily accessible to and more likely to be retained by all family members. Therefore, multisensory music therapy interventions, combined with or in addition to standard "talking" therapy, can help the treatment process move faster. Adamek and Darrow (2010, 355) discuss a family systems approach, which is "a way of working with families that emphasizes the interdependency of family members rather than focusing on individuals in isolation from the family." If one part of the family is affected, the whole is affected because they function as an interrelated system, rather than as a group of individuals. What happens to one member has bearing of the function of all others in the family. The United States Census Bureau (2013) considers a family to be a group of two people or more (one of whom is the house holder) related by marriage, birth, or adoption and residing together.

Other family music therapy sessions may be designed less to examine family interactions as the source of pathology than to help other family members learn how to relate most appropriately and constructively to a child or adolescent who has an emotional disturbance or behavior disorder. Music can help establish positive contacts among family members. Family members can also learn how to use music experiences at home to help structure the environment or help the child or adolescent control his or her behavior (e.g., contingent music, music-mediated relaxation, songs to cue appropriate behaviors, removing detrimental music).

Finally, if individuals are to maintain the new skills and behaviors they have learned in the clinical setting and generalize them to the home and community, the family must learn how to support these new behaviors. Therefore, sessions with family members may also be helpful toward the end of the treatment process to help clients learn to generalize their new skills and behaviors and apply them outside the therapy setting (James and Freed 1989).

SPECIAL CONSIDERATIONS AND TIPS FOR SUCCESS

For children and adolescents who have mental or behavioral disorders or severe emotional disturbances, "music represents a neutral, nonauthoritative force that allows them to relax and participate without fear" (Birkenshaw-Fleming 1993, 101). Therefore, music therapy sessions with these clients are often most successful when directions and structure are provided through music or as part of a musical experience rather than verbally whenever possible. For example, instructions such as "sit down" or "now stop" might be sung to a simple melodic phrase (e.g., sol-do) or chord sequence (e.g., V_7-I). In addition, songs and musical games can be used to structure length of turns (e.g., play/move/sing for certain number of beats/measures; use "now pass the _____ to" as part of lyrics), control movement from place to place, or focus attention on action while distributing or collecting instruments (Atterbury 1990; Birkenshaw-Fleming 1993; Zinar 1987). Therapists should strive to keep any verbal instructions short, simple, and concrete and to reinforce these instructions with visual aids or demonstrations whenever possible.

Children and adolescents who have mental or behavioral disorders or severe emotional disturbances usually function best in a secure, warm, structured, stimulating, success-oriented environment. Music therapists can help promote such an environment by (a) starting with highly structured activities and gradually reducing structure as clients gain skills and confidence, (b) breaking large tasks down into smaller, more manageable steps, and (c) leading clients through activities with examples and clear instructions before asking them to improvise or make original contributions. Structuring sessions so that groups begin and end with routine, "ritual" activities also promotes security and predictability. In addition, alternating fun, easy, familiar activities with more difficult ones helps keep clients involved and interested in the process.

When working with these clients, the therapist should emphasize the positive and build on the clients' strengths. Praise is important, but it must be genuine and given very specifically, by telling the individual exactly what was good and how it can be made better. It is also important for teachers and therapists to provide good role models of desired social and interpersonal behaviors: "Besides teaching academic skills, motor skills, social skills, etc., it is important that the children learn and see models of love, joy, peace, patience, kindness, goodness, faithfulness, gentleness, and self-control" (Paul 1982, 71).

Many children and adolescents who have mental or behavioral disorders or severe emotional disturbances need firm, consistent discipline and behavior management approaches. Usually, especially in group situations, these clients function best when there are clear, consistent expectations for behaviors. A few simple group rules for expected behaviors, along with consequences for infractions, should be clearly stated (Atterbury 1990; Cleveland Music School Settlement Music Therapy Department 1985; Presti 1984; Zinar 1987). These rules may be devised with the help of the group if the clients are functioning at a high enough level. It also may be helpful to post these rules so they are readily available for reference.

In any work with children and adolescents who have mental or behavioral disorders or severe emotional disturbances, it is very important to set up or adapt the environment so as to minimize distractions. Therapists and teachers should consider the social and psychological implications of various group formations (Nocera 1979, 262–263) and use formations that maximize feelings of inclusion and cooperation and help focus attention on activity. Activities should also be structured carefully to minimize distractions and maximize on-task behavior. In planning, it is also important to pay special attention to transitions between activities, for these are times when problem behaviors occur. In addition, if therapists and teachers know the warning signs of imminent behavior outbursts, they often can do something to diffuse the situation before an outburst occurs (e.g., change activity, tempo, response mode, or dynamic level; position self closer to individual; point to chart of expected behaviors as reminder). Teachers and therapists also must carefully monitor their own reactions and take time to stop and think before they react or respond to inappropriate behaviors (Atterbury 1990).

Music that clients listen to in their leisure time can also positively or negatively influence their behavior and levels of tension and anxiety. Music therapists should make clients and staff aware of how music affects and influences behavior, so they realize that a simple action like turning off or changing the music could help diffuse a potential crisis situation. After observing that incidents of sexual acting out and physical aggression on a psychiatric unit increased when adolescent patients listened to certain types of popular music, Metzger (1986) suggested that facilities establish an objective policy (by committee) on what types of music were suitable for leisure time use, which were suitable only if used under supervision in a therapy session, and which did not serve any clinically beneficial purpose. The latter category included "music that tends to intensify or perpetuate the problems of patients, and is too shallow for use in discussions" (22). Bushong (2002) examined the related literature on the relationship between popular music and antisocial behavior. The subject has been discussed from many theoretical and philosophical positions. Some of these include the drive reduction theory, modeling, and social learning theory. He concluded that "there appears to be enough evidence to support a position that, most likely, popular music is both a reflection of, and an exacerbating influence on, attitudes, values, and behaviors, when the idiosyncrasies of the indivudal and the stimulus are considered" (77). Perhaps the greatest concern should be for viewing violent or sexually explicit videos with a music background that heightens the effect.

Lefebvre (1991) lists several additional important considerations for music therapy with adolescents who have mental or behavioral disorders, including (1) taking time to *listen* to the adolescent; (2) thoroughly assessing clients, through both active and receptive techniques, to gain as complete an understanding as possible of the client's musical past (perhaps having the client do a "family music tree"), current music preferences and skills, and any musical goals; (3) letting the clients take an active part in setting treatment goals and evaluating progress; (4) using activities that are relevant to teenage needs and interests to motivate clients; (5) being flexible enough to change plans in response to the unpredictability of teenagers; (6) knowing when to empathize with clients and when to challenge them, being aware of how adept adolescents are at manipulation; and (7) giving the teenage client responsibility for his and her own life.

QUESTIONS FOR THOUGHT AND DISCUSSION

1. Discuss some of the special characteristics and needs of children and adolescents with (a) severe emotional disturbances, (b) a history of abuse, (c) attention-deficit/hyperactivity disorders, (d) disruptive behavior disorders, (e) a history of juvenile offence, (f) substance abuse problems, or (g) "at-risk" problems. What implications do these have for music therapy programming? Describe music therapy experiences that might be useful for each of these groups.

2. Do some types of music experiences and activities seem more useful than others in working with children and adolescents who have mental or behavioral disorders or severe emotional disturbances? If so, which ones? Why?

3. Which music therapy approaches described in this chapter reflect a psychodynamic orientation? humanistic orientation? cognitive orientation? behavioral orientation? eclectic or multimodal orientation? Do any reflect a biomedical orientation? How does the orientation affect the structure or implementation of music therapy strategies? How does it affect the interpretation of client responses?

4. What unique benefits can music provide in family therapy situations?

5. List several special considerations that may be important to remember when developing therapeutic intervention strategies for children and adolescents who have mental or behavioral disorders or severe emotional disturbances. Why are these important? What are some implications for the structure of music therapy intervention strategies?

6. For each of the situations described below, (a) define the problem or areas of need for the client or group of clients, (b) describe one or more of the goals you might pursue in music therapy sessions with the client(s), (c) describe music activities you might use to help the client(s) meet those goals, (d) tell how the music activities you described relate to the goals and needs of the client(s), and (e) mention any special considerations you might want to take into account when working with the client(s).

Situation 1:

You have been asked to conduct music therapy sessions with Carla, a 15-year-old girl who has been admitted to the adolescent unit of a county psychiatric hospital after an unsuccessful suicide attempt. Carla has a history of alcohol and drug abuse. She exhibits extreme fear and anxiety, is shy and withdrawn, and has low self-esteem and a poor self-image. She rarely interacts with others and often retreats into a world of fantasy. Carla sometimes laughs or cries for no apparent reason; she has difficulty expressing feelings accurately and appropriately.

Situation 2:

You have been asked to conduct music therapy sessions for a group of four boys, aged 7–9 years, who have been diagnosed with attention-deficit/ hyperactivity disorder. All have a short attention span, difficulty completing tasks and following directions, and are easily distracted. They are fascinated by musical instruments, but they have difficulty using them appropriately for longer than 30–60 seconds at a time. Their teacher wonders if you can do anything to increase their attention span and help them learn more appropriate behaviors so they can be more successful in group learning situations.

SUGGESTIONS FOR FURTHER READING

Adamek, M. S. & Darrow, A-A. (Eds.) (2010). Students with behavioral disorders. In *Music in special education* (137–158). Silver Spring, MD: American Music Therapy Association.

Atterbury, B. W. (1990). *Mainstreaming exceptional learners in music.* Englewood Cliffs, NJ: Prentice-Hall.

Brooks, D. M. (1989). Music therapy enhances treatment with adolescents. *Music Therapy Perspectives, 6,* 37–39.

Bruscia, K. E. (Ed.) (1991). *Case studies in music therapy.* Phoenixville, PA: Barcelona.

Cassity, M. D. & Cassity, J. E. (1994). *Multimodal psychiatric music therapy for adults, adolescents, and children.* St. Louis: MMB Music.

Cassity, M. D. & Cassity, J. E. (1994). Psychiatric music therapy assessment and treatment in clinical training facilities with adults, adolescents and children. *Journal of Music Therapy, 31,* 2–30.

Clendenon-Wallen, J. (1991). The use of music therapy to influence the self-confidence and self-esteem of adolescents who are sexually abused. *Music therapy Perspectives, 9,* 73–81.

Crowe, B. J. (Ed.) (2007). Music therapy practice for specific disabilities; Music therapy for children and adolescents with emotional/behavioral disturbances. *Music therapy for children, adolescents, and adults with mental disorders* (149–230). Silver Spring, MD: American Music Therapy Association.

Davis, W. B., Gfeller, K. E. & Thaut, M. H. (Eds.) (2008). Music therapy in the treatment of behavioral-emotional disorders. In *An introduction to music therapy theory and practice* (3rd ed.) (209–246). Silver Spring, MD: American Music Therapy Association.

Friedlander, L. H. (1994). Group music psychotherapy in an inpatient psychiatric setting for children: A developmental approach. *Music Therapy Perspectives, 12(2),* 92–97.

Frisch, A. (1990). Symbol and structure: Music therapy for the adolescent psychiatric inpatient. *Music Therapy, 9(1),* 16–34.

Gardstrom, S. C. (1987). Positive peer culture: A working definition for the music therapist. *Music Therapy Perspectives, 4,* 19–23.

Gardstrom, S. C. (1996). Music therapy for juvenile offenders in a residential setting. In B. L. Wilson (Ed.), *Models of music therapy interventions in school settings: From institution to inclusion* (127–141). Silver Spring, MD: National Association for Music Therapy.

Goodman, K. D. (2007). *Music therapy groupwork with special needs children*. Springfield, IL: Charles C Thomas.

Humpal, M. E. & Colwell, C. (Eds.) (2006). Typical goals and treatment objectives, settings, and service delivery models. In *Early childhood and school age educational settings* (68–119). Silver Spring, MD: American Music Therapy Association.

Isenberg-Grzeda, C. (1995). The sound image: Music therapy in the treatment of the abused child. In C. B. Kenny (Ed.), *Listening, playing, creating: Essays on the power of sound*. Albany, NY: State University of New York Press.

James, M. R. & Freed, B. S. (1989). A sequential model for developing group cohesion in music therapy. *Music Therapy Perspectives, 7,* 28–34.

Lathom-Radocy, W. (2014). Other behavior disorders. In W. Lathom-Radocy, *Pediatric music therapy* (114–152). Springfield IL: Charles C Thomas.

Metzger, L. K. (1986). The selection of music for therapeutic use with adolescents and young adults in a psychiatric facility. *Music Therapy Perspectives, 3,* 20–24.

Paul, D. W. (1982). Emotionally disturbed. In W. B. Lathom and C. T. Eagle, Jr. (Eds.) *Music therapy for handicapped children*, Vol. 2 (3–59). Washington, DC: National Association for Music Therapy.

Presti, G. M. (1984). A levels system approach to music therapy with severely behaviorally handicapped children in the public school system. *Journal of Music Therapy, 21(3),* 117–125.

Skaggs, R. (1997). Music-centered creative arts in a sex offender treatment program for male juveniles. *Music Therapy Perspectives, 15(2),* 73–78.

Slotoroff, C. (1994). Drumming technique for assertiveness and anger management in the short-term psychiatric setting for adult and adolescent survivors of trauma. *Music Therapy Perspectives, 12(2),* 111–116.

Standley, J. (1991). *Music techniques in therapy, counseling, and special education*. St. Louis: MMB Music.

Taylor, J. A., Barry, N. H., & Walls, K. C. (1997). *Music and students at risk: Creative solutions for a national dilemma*. Reston, VA: Music Educators.

Zinar, R. (1987). *Music activities for special children*. West Nyack, NY: Parker.

Chapter Fifteen

MUSIC THERAPY FOR ADULTS WHO HAVE MENTAL OR BEHAVIORAL DISORDERS

Definitions

Adult psychiatry deals with the prevention and treatment of mental, emotional, and behavioral disorders in adults. Although psychiatric illnesses and disorders may vary greatly in severity and observable symptoms, all are "primarily characterized by behavioral or psychological impairment of function, measured in terms of deviation from some normative concept" (Kaplan and Sadock 1991, 117). Just as children and adolescents, adults who have mental or behavioral disorders consistently and chronically exhibit behaviors that are personally or socially deviant.

The American Psychiatric Association (APA) *Diagnostic and Statistical Manual of Mental Disorders, 5th Ed.* (DSM-V) (2013, 20) defines a *mental disorder* as a

> syndrome characterized by clinically significant disturbance in an individual's cognition, emotion regulation, or behavior that reflects a dysfunction in the psychological, biological, or developmental processes underlying mental functioning. Mental disorders are usually associated with significant distress or disability in social, occupational, or other important activities.

Although mental disorders may vary in manifestations and degrees of severity, they all are characterized by persistent, abnormal patterns of problem behaviors (Michel 1976, 1985). Therefore, these clients sometimes are described as having *behavior disorders* or *behavioral disorders* (Gaston 1968b; Michel 1976, 1985). These terms are not DSM-V classifications and are more likely to be used in school settings (Adamek and Darrow 2010; Turnbull, Turnbull, and Wehmeyer 2010).

DSM-V (2013) changed the classification and terminology used in mental health facilities. The most common classifications will be briefly described, but a full list of all mental illnesses is beyond the scope of this book. Ten categories that are supported by music therapy literature will be listed. These classifications, and others, are more fully explained in DSM-V.

Schizophrenia Spectrum and Other Psychotic Disorders

Schizophrenia spectrum and other psychotic disorders are primarily characterized by loss of contact with reality. Individuals who have disorders on the schizophrenia spectrum have delusions, hallucinations, disorganized thinking, and/or disorganized or abnormal motor behavior (DSM-V 2013, 87). They commonly exhibit a flat or inappropriate affective response and avolition (lack of motivation for self-initiated activity). Because of their severely impaired abilities to think, respond emotionally, communicate, interpret reality, and behave appropriately, these individuals usually have severe difficulties relating appropriately to others and are often unable to function independently in society. The APA's listing of schizophrenia spectrum disorders includes schizophrenia, schizotypal (personality) disorder, schizophreniform disorder, schizoaffective disorder (bipolar type, depressive type), delusional disorder, catatonia, and brief psychotic disorder (DSM-V 2013, xv).

The schizophrenia spectrum is sometimes referred to as *psychotic disorders*: "Psychotic disorders are recognized to have an organic biochemical or structural cause or predisposition. The organic cause predisposes the client to a disorder, while environmental factors may worsen or trigger the manifestation of that disorder" (Crowe 2007c, 4). *Neurosis* is no longer used and has been relaced by *anxiety disorders* (DSM-V 2013).

Bipolar and Related Disorders

Bipolar and related disorders were formerly called *manic-depressive disorder.* Bipolar I includes a manic episode (increased energy leading to elevated and expansive activity and irritable mood). It may be followed by a depressive episode. Bipolar II requires at least one episode of major depression and at least one hypomanic episode. Other disorders in this category include cyclothymic, substance/medication-induced bipolar and related disorder, and bipolar and related disorder due to another medical condition.

Depressive Disorders

Depressive disorders are characterized by depressed mood, little interest in activities, decreased appetite, sleep disturbance, fatigue, or suicidal thoughts that adversely influence the way an individual thinks, feels, and interacts with the environment. These include major depressive disorder, persistent depressive disorder (dysthymia), premenstrual dysphoric disorder, substance/medication-induced depressive disorder, and depressive disorder due to another medical condition.

Anxiety Disorders

"Anxiety" is defined as "anticipation of future threat" (DSM-V 2013, 189). It is similar to fear, but when a person experiences fear the threat is real or perceived as such, whereas anxiety leads to vigilant, preparedness for anticipated events. Most anxiety disorders relate to objects or situations that are cognitively perceived as threatening. They include specific phobias (animal, natural environment, blood-injection-injury, or specific situations), as well as social anxiety disorder, panic disorder, agoraphobia (fear of situations where escape might be difficult or where help may not be available, such as being outside the home alone or in a crowd or enclosed space), generalized anxiety disorder, and substance/medication-induced disorder.

Personality Disorders

Personality disorders are enduring patterns of inner experience with onset in adolescence or early adulthood. Behavior deviates from cultural expectations, is pervasive and inflexible, and after a period of stability, may significantly disrupt social, emotional, or occupational functioning. It includes Cluster A: paranoid, schizoid, schizotypal; Cluster B: antisocial, borderline, histrionic, narcissistic; and Cluster C: avoidant, dependent, obsessive-compulsive, and generalized personality disorder.

Obsessive Compulsive Disorder

Obsessive compulsive disorder (OCD) is characterized by obsessions and/or compulsions. The person is driven to think or act in response to the preoccupation. OCD relates to anxiety disorders, since the person experiences anxious feelings in trying to control the behavior. Another related disorder includes body dysmorphic disorder (preoccupation with some perceived flaw or defect that may not be apparent to others), hoarding disorder, trichotillomania (hair-pulling disorder), excoriation (skin-picking) disorder, substance/medication-induced OCD, and other unspecified obsessive compulsive and related disorders.

Trauma- and Stressor-related Disorders

Trauma- and stressor-related disorders are characterized by psychological distress that follows trauma or a stressful event. There many be anxiety or fear related to the event. This category includes reactive attachment disorder, and disinhibited social engagement, both due to social neglect (absence of adequate caregiving during childhood). It also includes posttraumatic stress disorder (PTSD), acute stress disorder, and adjustment disorders.

Feeding and Eating Disorders

Feeding and eating disorders occur when persistent disturbances in eating cause inadequate consumption or absorption of nutrition. This condition leads to health problems as well as psychosocial dysfunction. It includes pica (eating of nonnutritive or nonfood substances, such as dirt or objects in the environment); rumination disorder (regurgitation of food over a period of at least a month); avoidant-restrictive food intake (lack of interest in eating, which leads to nutritional deficiency); anorexia nervosa (fear of gaining weight that leads to significantly low weight, which has health consequences); bulimia nervosa (binge eating followed by attempts to control weight gain, such as purging or misuse of laxatives or diuretics, or excessive exercise); binge eating (intake of excessive amounts of food, not followed by attempts to control weight).

Disruptive, Impulse-Control, and Conduct Disorders

Disruptive, impulse-control, and conduct disorders involve difficulty controlling behavior or emotions to avoid violating the rights of others. This brings the individual into conflict with others or society. It often involves relationships with authority figures. Included are oppositional defiant disorder, intermittent explosive disorder, conduct disorder, antisocial personality disorder, pyromania (deliberate fire setting), kleptomania (failure to resist temptation to steal objects), and other specified disruptive, impulse-control, and conduct disorders.

Substance-related Disorders

In *substance-related disorders*, the substance is used continuously, despite related problems. This abuse eventually leads to changes in brain circuits, which may persist. The pathological use of substances leads to impaired control in substance use, craving, unsuccessful attempts to stop or decrease use, and intense desire for the substance. These disorders lead to social impairment, represented by difficulties in social, occupational, and recreational aspects of life. This area includes alcohol-related disorders; cannabis-related disorders; hallucinogen-related disorders; inhalant-related disorders; opioid-related disorders; sedative-, hypnotic-, or anxiolytic-related disorders; stimulant-related disorders, and tobacco-related disorders. Gambling disorder is in this category, although it is not substance related.

As noted previously, this is not a comprehensive list because that would be beyond to scope of this book. It is assumed that music therapy majors will take course work in abnormal psychology, which will include additional and more comprehensive information about these disorders.

Causes

No exact causes are known for most disorders; however, both biological (e.g., brain abnormalities, deficiencies in various neurotransmitters, genetics) and environmental factors (e.g., traumatic experiences, family relationships) may contribute to many adult psychiatric problems (DSM-V 2013; Goetinck 1996b; Thaut and Gfeller 1992). There is growing evidence that most mental disorders have some biological component (Siegfried and Goetinck 1996; Taylor 1997): "At root, 'mental' illnesses are all disorders of thought or emotion, stemming from physical problems – the biological equivalent of faulty wiring – in the brain" (Siegfried and Goetinck 1996, 1F).

Moore (2013) systematically reviewed the neural effects of music on emotion. The term "emotion regulation" is used in the DSM-V definition of mental disorder. Moore (2013, 198) explains,

> Emotion regulation (ER) is an internal process through which a person maintains a comfortable state of arousal by modulating one or more aspects of emotion. The neural correlates underlying ER suggest an interplay between cognitive control areas and areas involved in emotional reactivity.

She found a relationship and suggested guidelines for some of the musical characteristics and certain strategies that might lead to ER in music therapy sessions. The preliminary guidelines include "using music considered happy and pleasant, with predictable, consonant harmonies. . . . Music listening, singing, and improvisation may assist in facilitating emotion regulation" (236–237).

COMMON CHARACTERISTICS, PROBLEMS, AND NEEDS OF CLIENTS

As with any population, mentally ill adults differ greatly in observable behavior. Factors such as the type and severity of the behavioral disorders, the cause and time of onset, the existence of associated conditions or impairments, and the degree and type of support services available will all have varying effects on the individual's level of functioning, needs, and treatment program. In addition, each individual will have a unique combination of abilities, needs, personality traits, strengths, and weaknesses that will impact his or her particular responses and functional abilities. Therefore, it is unwise to attempt to predict a particular person's skill levels or ceiling of abilities based on broad generalizations about a certain population. However, an awareness of some characteristics, problems, and needs which may be common to adults who have various types of mental or behavioral disorders will be beneficial both to the therapist who desires to work with this population and to the reader who is trying to understand how music therapy intervention strategies may benefit this population.

In the acute phases of the illness, adults who have mental or behavioral disorders often display behaviors of "intense confusion, agitation, excitability, fearfulness, or withdrawal" (Nowicki and Trevisan 1978, 153). They need to learn and develop positive coping mechanisms to deal with the stresses and responsibilities of daily life. They also may need to find ways to control and channel aggressive or destructive impulses. In addition, many need help in developing or improving decision-making or problem-solving skills.

Adults who have mental or behavioral disorders frequently lack the skills necessary to recognize and express feelings and emotions in an accurate and appropriate manner. Disturbances of affect, such as emotional lability, inappropriate outbursts of laughing or crying, or no affect, also may be present. Socialization is another common problem area for these clients. Usually, they have been unable to establish or maintain effective interpersonal relationships. Many clients also have a limited sense of trust in their own abilities and have low self-esteem. Of course, those clients who have severe psychotic disorders will need assistance in reestablishing contact with reality before they can begin to develop skills in communication, socialization, and expression of feelings. Some also may need to learn or relearn basic daily living skills (taking care of themselves and their house or apartment, budgeting, etc.).

Obviously, each particular mental disorder will have its own unique manifestations. For example, adults who have *schizophrenia* have symptoms such as delusions, hallucinations, impaired thinking, disorganized speech and behavior, emotional dysfunctions (e.g., affect that is blunted or reduced in intensity, flat affect, or inappropriate and unusual emotional reactions), social withdrawal, decreased ability to experience pleasure, and lack of motivation or perseverance (Davis, Gfeller, and Thaut 2008; DSM-V 2013; Siegfried and Goetinck 1996; Taylor 1997). Individuals who have schizophrenia also show markedly lower functioning in work, interpersonal relations, and/or self-care during the active phase of the disturbance (DSM-V 2013).

Adults who have *major depressive disorders* feel sad or empty most of the time and show a markedly diminished interest in, or ability to derive pleasure from, activities. They may have insomnia or hypersomnia, a significant increase or decrease in appetite, and a significant weight loss or gain. Most usually feel tired or fatigued, seem unable to make decisions or complete tasks, have trouble concentrating, feel worthless, and have recurrent thoughts of death or suicide (DSM-V 2013; Siegfried and Goetinck 1996; Taylor 1997). These symptoms cause significant clinical distress or impairment in social or occupational functioning (DSM-V 2013).

Bipolar and related disorders is another frequently encountered category in facilities for treatment of mental illness. Those who have *manic episodes* have a persistent abnormally elevated or irritable mood, inflated self-confidence and feelings of grandiosity, and decreased need for sleep; are extremely talkative and have racing thoughts; are easily distracted; have increased activity; and may be involved excessively in pleasurable activities that have a high potential for painful consequences (e.g., buying sprees, foolish investments, sexual indiscretions) (DSM-V 2013; Siegfried and Goetinck 1996). Again, the severity of the mood disturbance causes marked impairment in occupational functioning and in usual social relationships or activities (APA 1994).

De l'Etoile (2002) noted that the effect of emotional states on cognitive processes has been studied since the 1970s. Negative states, such as depression, have been found to effect memory and the time needed to process information and retrieve memories. Learning may be more difficult. Expanding on research by Thaut and de l'Etoile (1993), she studied the effect of background music on encoding and recall by subjects. The mood induction process revealed experience with positive mood music moved subjects toward expressing a more positive mood, as indicated by responses on bipolar scales.

Adults who have *personality disorders* perceive or relate to their environment in unusual, inflexible, maladaptive ways that lead to disruptions in their social, occupational, or emotional life (APA 1994; Thaut and Gfeller 1992). This diagnosis includes twelve disorders that cluster under this one main heading. Clients with these diagnoses usually have difficulty forming or sustaining interpersonal relationships. They may perceive themselves and/or others in unusual ways and rarely recognize how their behaviors may contribute to their problems. Some may have problems with impulse control.

Posttraumatic stress disorder is listed under the category of *trauma- and stressor-related disorders* (DSM-V 2013, 265–290). Symptoms may include nightmares; efforts to avoid thought, conversations, activities, people, or places that arouse recollections or are associated with the trauma; guilt feelings or depression; restricted affect; difficulty falling or staying asleep; irritability; difficulty concentrating; hypervigilance; and exaggerated startle responses. There are other common symptoms. Bloch et al. (2010, 27–28) studied the effects of music relaxation on sleep quality in people with schizophrenia: "Results showed an improvement in sleep latency and sleep efficiency after music relaxation played." Participants were 32 outpatient adults (aged 18–70 years), recruited from an Israeli clinic, who had been diagnosed with schizophrenia. The music composed for the study was recorded on a CD. This study should be replicated with subjects who have PTSD.

Individuals who have *feeding and eating disorders* often feel out of control in many or all areas of their lives (physical, emotional, mental, and behavioral). They try to substitute constant control over their eating behavior for the perceived lack of control over other aspects of their lives (Parente 1989; Taylor

1997). These individuals also have a disturbed perception of body shape and weight (DSM-V 2013).

Adults who have *substance-induced disorders* such as *alcohol use disorder* or misuse of other substances, engage in continued use of the substance, even when harmful consequences are apparent. Regular use affects the central nervous system, causes harmful changes in behavior, such as impaired control with increasingly larger doses, and results in health, social, and occupational impairments (DSM-V 2013; Thaut and Gfeller 1992). When individuals are addicted to or dependent on a substance, they feel their psychological and spiritual well-being depends upon the experience gained from the particular substance (Skaggs 1997a). Substance-dependent people have an increased tolerance for the substance, need continually greater amounts to achieve intoxication or the desired effect, have withdrawal symptoms when they abstain from the substance, and need the substance for daily functioning (DSM-V 2013; Thaut and Gfeller 1992). They are unable to reduce or control substance use; spend much of their time trying to obtain and use the substance or recover from its effects; reduce or give up important social, occupational, or recreational activities; and continue substance use despite having persistent problems that they know likely are caused or exacerbated by the substance.

These are only a few of the diagnoses frequently seen in psychiatric music therapy. Please refer to DSM-V (2013) for more complete descriptions of each diagnosis.

TREATMENT APPROACHES

Treatment for psychiatric disorders often involves a combination of approaches and interventions, including "a structured environment, a regime of medication, a variety of psychotherapeutic interventions, and a program of activity therapies" (Smeltekop and Houghton 1990). For more acute phases of more severe disorders (e.g., schizophrenia, major depression), patients may require hospitalization, especially if they pose a danger to themselves or others. While medication may be very helpful in stabilizing individuals with severe psychosis, they are more likely to avoid relapses if they also receive training in basic life skills (Goetinck 1996a). Treatment has moved from large psychiatric institutions to short-term inpatient and increased community-based treatments. Public Law 88-164 led to funding for community-based mental health facilities (Braswell 1968; Crowe 2007c).

Individuals with mental disorders are unique, and no one treatment or combination of treatments will be right for every person who has a particular disorder. The length of time available for treatment also will impact the choice of treatments. In short-term settings, treatment is intensive, very time-limited, and focuses on stabilizing patients, decreasing anxiety, helping them learn coping and problem-solving skills, and helping them recognize and change maladaptive behaviors (Murphy 1992; Wolfe 1996). More in-depth or insight-oriented interventions usually take longer periods of time.

Walworth (2003) studied the effects of music on induced anxiety levels. After testing initial anxiety levels, Walworth induced anxiety via the Stroop color-word test, in which subjects must say words that are the names of colors although the actual words are printed in different colors, e.g., "red" might be presented in blue. There were three conditions: No music, experimenter-chosen songs, and subject-selected songs. There was less anxiety during both song conditions, compared with that experienced during the no-music control condition. This study needs replication with clients who are experiencing anxiety as part of their mental illness. Generally, music therapists make the following assumptions: "When selecting music for patients or clients, the preference of the patient/client needs to be considered. Many times music used to reduce anxiety and increase relaxation is slow in tempo and instrumental (no lyrics)" (Walworth 2003, 4). These assumptions need further research to study effects of preference and tempo and differences between vocal and instrumental music.

Some therapists who work in adult psychiatric settings use Lazarus's (1976, 1989) *multimodal therapy model* to help classify a patient's problems and types of therapeutic interventions (Adelman 1985; Cassity and Cassity 1994a; Cassity and Theobold 1990; Wilson 1990a). Therapists who use this model carefully assess and describe clients' BASIC-ID: *Behavior* (habits, actions, gestures, reactions), *Affect* (emotions, moods, feelings), *Sensation* (clients' perceptions of what they see, hear, touch, taste, or smell; includes negative sensations, such as tension, pain, dizziness, and client preferences or fixation), *Imagery* (recurring dreams, vivid memories, clients' self-image or body-image), *Cognitive* problems (ideas, values, beliefs, opinions, or attitudes that interfere with the client's happiness or functioning), *Interpersonal* relations (ways clients socialize or interact with others; any problems with the way clients treat or are treated by others), and *Drug* use or health concerns (medication or drug use or abuse, any concerns about state of health or physical well-being). While multimodal assessment attends to specific problems within each modality, it also focuses on interaction among modalities, thereby recognizing that a problem in one area or modality influences functioning in all other areas. The multimodal therapy model is very eclectic; a variety of therapeutic approaches may be used to address the problems it identifies.

As in child psychiatry, many different models exist for guiding the treatment of adults who have mental or behavioral disorders. Scovel (1990) identified six general psychotherapeutic treatment models currently in use in adult psychiatry: (1) the biomedical model, (2) the behavioral model, (3) the psychodynamic model, (4) the cognitive model, (5) the humanistic model, and (6) the holistic-wellness model. Crowe (2007, 8–9) does not include biomedical or holistic-wellness models, but adds organic model, systematic-cybernetic model, developmental model, and transpersonal model. The choice of model reflects the therapist's training, the facility's philosophy and treatment approach, and the model that the team thinks will be most effective for each client. Most facilities employ more than one model.

In the *biomedical model*, mental disorders and the abnormal behavior that accompanies them are believed to be rooted in errant organic, physiological, or biochemical processes. Those who use this model search for germs or diseases, genetic history or abnormalities, or brain biochemistry to see what might cause or influence the syndrome. After diagnosis, treatments addressing the biological abnormalities (e.g., drugs or chemical therapies, relaxation training to decrease muscle tension and stress responses) are prescribed.

The *behavioral model* holds that individuals learn abnormal or maladaptive behaviors through conditioning; therefore, behaviors can be unlearned with appropriate therapy and training. The focus is not on underlying causes, but on the exhibited behaviors. Behaviors are carefully observed, and specific undesirable behaviors are targeted for change. Classical or operant conditioning (pairing learning with positive or negative reinforcers) techniques are used to help the client develop desired behaviors and diminish maladaptive responses. Often, contingencies are set up to help increase desired behaviors. A token economy system (clients receive tokens for desired behaviors, which may then be exchanged for privileges, rewards, desired music, etc.) or biofeedback techniques may be used. Other techniques include modeling, systematic desensitization, self-management programs, and assertiveness training. The therapist assumes an active and directive role by structuring the environment and providing rewards and consequences to help the client achieve the desired changes. Change and progress are measured by a decrease in abnormal, maladaptive behaviors and an increase in new, more adaptive behaviors.

Persons who subscribe to a *psychodynamic model* believe that abnormalities and mental disorders result from hidden personality conflicts. Treatment helps patients uncover, identify, and work through these unconscious conflicts. As patients gain insight into the causes of their distress and work through conflicts, they make positive personality changes. Approaches in this model are based on the theories of Sigmund Freud, Alfred Adler, Carl Jung, Harry S. Sullivan, Erick Fromm, or Erik Erickson, and include techniques like free association, dream and imagery interpretation, and fostering transference. guided imagery and music (GIM) relates to this model.

Cognitive models assert that the emotional and behavioral problems of psychiatric disorders result from disordered thinking about self, others, and the world. Cognitive therapies include Ellis' rational emotive therapy (RET), Maultsby's rational behavior therapy, Beck's cognitive therapy, Meichenbaum's cognitive behavior modification, Glasser's reality therapy, and Berne's transactional analysis (TA). In cognitive approaches, therapy focuses on guiding the patient to discover unrealistic, irrational, or self-defeating thoughts; challenging these ideas; and assisting the client in developing healthier responses and thought patterns. Emotional and behavioral problems are eliminated as the thoughts that promote them are changed. As client's ways of thinking and behaving become more logical, realistic, and mature, he or she develops the ability "to react more appropriately to life situations that demand a feeling response" (Scovel 1990, 103). Techniques include examining thinking for "musts" and "shoulds," modifying "shoulds," changing language, completing homework that tests new assumptions through open-ended questions, imagery, and role playing.

Cassity (2007) conducted a Delphi poll to ask psychiatric music therapists to forecast music therapy in 2016. Cognitive behavioral therapy, an approach focusing on altering thoughts, behaviors, and emotions, was predicted to become the choice theoretical orientation. The National Institutes of Mental Health (NIMH) has stated that cognitive behavioral therapy (CBT) is the treatment of choice for evidence-based psychotherapy. Silverman (2008, 462–467) analyzed CBT research and the existing music therapy research and created a useful table of music therapy research. Other requirements that Cassity predicted were Board Certification, evidence-based treatment (EBT), advanced credentials (beyond the initial degree), and more emphasis on informing the client and his/her family about music therapy and benefits of this type of treatment.

According to *humanistic models*, emotional and behavioral disorders occur when individuals fail to find or establish meaning in their lives. A key concept is humanistic theorist Abraham Maslow's (1968) idea of "self-actualization," which is a level of life rich in meaning and filled with a sense of well-being and completeness, the highest level of his hierarchy of human needs. Therapists who follow a humanistic approach give unconditional acceptance to the client and focus on the here-and-now of the therapeutic relationship. By relating to the client with genuine caring, acceptance, understanding, and respect, the therapist helps the client move beyond defenses and mental or emotional blocks to confront the basic questions of life, find meaning, and move to a higher level of functioning. Therapeutic techniques are experiential, oriented to building a trusting relationship and designed to help the client make choices, build an internal frame of reference, and take personal responsibility to find purpose and meaning in life. Humanistic models of therapy include Fritz Perls's Gestalt therapy, Rollo May's existential therapy, and Carl Rogers's client-centered therapy.

Recently, the holistic movement, with its emphasis on considering all aspects of the person (physical/ biological, mental/psychological, social, and spiritual) and treating the individual rather than the disease, has exerted an increasing influence on health care. The *holistic-wellness model* maintains that "the individual is an integrated whole with resources to promote personal health" (Scovel 1990, 104), and that abnormalities occur when body, mind, and spirit are not in harmony or are not functioning in unity. The therapist's role is to educate, become involved with the clients, and share experiences with them, thus helping the clients gain information and promoting techniques that will help clients develop self-responsibility, better stress management, better health and fitness, and effective ways of counteracting environmental stressors. In a holistic approach, clients are encouraged to look within themselves to find healing. Techniques include imagery and visualization, meditation, acupuncture, bodywork, psychic healing, awareness training, applied kinesiology, and chiropractic therapy. Focus is on self-responsibility, self-care, self-examination, and self-healing to achieve a balanced state of wellness. The newer emphasis on recovery would fit in this model. Psychiatric illness is not considered a life-long illness; with proper treatment the client can "recover" and learn to live a satisfactory life (Anthony 1993; Solli, Rolvsjord, and Borg 2013). Clients may not be symptom free, but rather may learn how to manage the illness in a manner that allows them to live in society.

Although the treatment models described above differ in their emphases and ways of understanding mental disorders, they all try to alleviate distress and affect growth and change. Whatever model is used, treatment follows the basic steps of (1) identifying the syndrome or disorder, (2) searching for a cause, (3) sorting out various possibilities and trying specific treatments, and (4) communicating the results in the language of the particular model (Scovel 1990). Since no one approach will work for every client with a particular disorder, an eclectic approach that draws from more than one theory or treatment model (e.g., a combination of medication and behavioral or cognitive approaches) often is recommended (Goetinck 1996a; Scovel 1990; Smeltekop and Houghton 1990; Wilson 1990a). Silverman (2007) surveyed music therapists working in the mental health field and reported that, while behavioral or psychodynamic approaches are used, an eclectic psychological philosophy is most used. Music therapists can work within the framework of any of these treatment models to devise goal-directed music interventions that help clients achieve positive growth and change. However, it is important to use the appropriate terminology related to the theoretical framework to communicate with other professionals on the team.

SETTINGS FOR SERVICE DELIVERY

Adults who have mental or behavioral disorders may receive special programs and services to help meet their specific needs in various settings. Years ago, many were confined to large mental hospitals. Although the census of these hospitals dropped dramatically in the last half of the twentieth century, long-term hospitalization remains a viable option in the continuum of mental health services (Wilson 1990b). However, since the introduction of psychotropic medications in the mid-1950s and the passage of the Community Mental Health Center Act (Public Law 88-164) by the U.S. Congress in 1963, there has been an increasing move toward deinstitutionalization and community-based treatment for adults who have mental disorders. Short-term hospitalizations are becoming increasingly common (Murphy 1992; Silverman 2009b; Wolfe 1996). Now patients have a decentralized network of services to respond to their needs at various levels of illness and disability. The components of this network include (1) community-based services designed for individuals able to live in the community while receiving treatment (e.g., outpatient clinics, community residences, after-care programs, half-way houses), (2) community hospital programs for those who are temporarily unable to function in the community or who may pose a danger to themselves or others (e.g., psychiatric units in general hospitals, community mental health center inpatient units), and (3) other sheltered settings for those who refuse traditional services but cannot function independently.

As society recognizes that a growing number of prisoners have severe mental problems, psychiatric services also are available in correctional and forensic settings (Thaut 1992b). One reason for the increase in mental illness among prisoners "may be that the deinstitutionalization of many psychiatric patients over the last 20 years and the lack of community-based outpatient psychiatric programs have victimized many patients by driving them into criminal activity, due to lack of adequate health and welfare services" (Thaut 2009, 247). Differentiating between correctional and forensic settings, Codding (2002, 59) defined *corrections* as a period of incarceration imposed by court action, whereas a *forensic* setting is confinement against one's will due to the likelihood of dangerous behavior, as suggested by a criminal history and/or probable psychiatric illness. Surveying music therapists practicing in correctional psychiatry, Codding found that very dedicated therapists served a large and diverse population. She described the demographics of this group of therapists and their goals and objectives. The therapists listed 36 objectives, with the following four listed by the highest percentage (over 90%) of surveyed music therapists:

1. To provide a non-threatening, motivating reality focus for use of leisure time and release of energy
2. To promote personal self-esteem
3. To promote acts of self control within a structured arts environment
4. To provide for appropriate release of tension, stress or anxiety; to promote the knowledge and use of coping skills and stress reduction techniques (64).

In work with adult male sexual offenders, Watson (2002, 109) used drumming and improvisation to achieve goals chosen by the residents and adopted by the therapist: "self-expression and awareness of emotions, appropriate social interaction, cooperation, and coping skills." This population showed anxiety, anger, and depression, as well as poor ability to identify, express, and regulate emotions. The group made considerable gains from the drumming intervention – results that were also reported by Hoskins (1988) from similar work.

In addition, there is a growing emphasis on finding ways to link patients with community support services after discharge from the hospital, treatment program, or prison. Many newly discharged clients need programs that will provide financial support, appropriate living arrangements, medical care, vocational rehabilitation, counseling, and leisure time activities to help them achieve a successful transition to community living (Wilson 1990b).

Music therapy has a long history of use in psychiatric hospitals (Michel 1985; Tyson 1981), and the field of mental health is still one of the largest employers of music therapists. Today, music therapists are established members of the interdisciplinary treatment team in many psychiatric hospitals (Choi 1997). In one survey, most staff members at psychiatric hospitals that had music therapy departments and music therapy clinical training programs viewed the functional role of music therapists highly favorably, but saw music therapy more as a supportive treatment than as a primary intervention (Choi 1997). Music therapists who work with adult males in psychiatric hospitals most often treat those who have psychotic disorders, followed by those who have affective or mood disorders, substance abuse problems, personality disorders, anxiety disorders, and adjustment disorders. Music therapists who work with adult female patients again most frequently treat those who have psychotic disorders, followed by those who have personality disorders, affective or mood disorders, substance abuse problems, adjustment disorders, and anxiety disorders (Cassity and Cassity 1994b).

Music therapists also work with adults who have mental or behavioral disorders in many other settings, including community mental health centers, Veterans Administration hospitals, drug/alcohol treatment programs, prisons or correctional programs, psychiatric units of general hospitals, public or private clinics, acute care inpatient or outpatient programs, music studios, community music schools, or in private practice (AMTA 1998; Eyre 2011; Goldberg 1989; Michel 1985; Wilson 1990b). Music therapists may provide direct or consultant services and work with clients as individuals or in groups. Music therapy can be part of both acute and chronic care programs and can be adapted to many different treatment models (Cassity and Cassity 1994a; Scovel 1990; Wilson 1990a). Some music therapists who also have training in psychotherapy use music therapy as a primary intervention to facilitate exploration of personal issues (Goldberg 1989): "Music is seen as a multidimensional activity that triggers unconscious dynamics and leads the person to integrate unconscious affect and thought with conscious thinking and behaving in the context of any musical activity" (Leite 2007, 63).

HOW MUSIC IS USED IN THERAPY

The beneficial effects of music on the mind, spirit, and emotions have been noted since primitive and ancient times. The field of mental and behavioral disorders has continued to be a prime venue for the therapeutic use of music in modern times. Tyson (1981, 7) observed that "music therapy is a hospital-developed practice; it evolved particularly in psychiatric hospitals, which have borne the major responsibility for the care of the mentally ill in the United States for more than two hundred years."

In state mental hospitals during the 1920s–1940s, group music activities provided some of the safest early group experiences for patients with serious mental illnesses, and music programs were conducted on the wards and in large groups to reach as many patients as possible (Tyson 1981). One of the music therapy's goals was to use music to stimulate and reinforce any positive responses, thus awakening or restoring the patient's interest in music, which could then be used "as motivation for new learning and relationships, and reintegrating the patient into the social community" (Tyson 1981, 11).

As concepts in mental health care changed from custodial approaches to an emphasis on rehabilitation, musical activities in psychiatric hospitals moved from being regarded as mainly recreational or entertainment to being a part of therapeutic or educational methods that counteracted destructive processes and helped patients use some of their own physical and mental powers to improve their conditions (Tyson 1981). The advent of tranquilizing drugs in the mid-1950s modified much of the acute, disturbed, psychotic behavior of individuals in mental institutions and made it possible to address their deeper psychological needs. Activity came to be seen as an important component of rehabilitation and recovery, and "hospitals began to mobilize all possible activities, music included, into full schedules designed to encourage growth processes and resocialization" (Tyson 1981, 12). In the 1960s, music therapists most commonly used music activities (a) to assist patients in establishing or reestablishing interpersonal relationships and (b) to increase or establish patients' self-esteem through self-actualization (Gaston 1968b; Tyson 1981).

In the 1970s–1980s, music therapy practice continued to reflect changes in the field of mental health, as music therapists began to work in community mental health programs, private hospitals, and private practice, as well as in state and federal hospitals. During this time, music therapy program offerings also became more diverse, with less emphasis on performance-based activities (chorus, band) and more emphasis on activities with multidimensional approaches (creative movement and music, music listening and discussion, song writing, improvisation, guided imagery and music, etc.) that were based on assessments of the psychological, behavioral, and social needs of individual clients and had specific therapeutic goals and objectives (Braswell, Maranto, and Decuir 1979a; Cassity and Cassity 1994a; Lathom 1982; McGinty 1980; Tyson 1981; Wilson 1990b).

With shorter hospital stays now becoming the norm, music therapists are working to develop treatment models that can achieve beneficial results in only a few sessions (Murphy 1992; Silverman 2009; Wolfe 1996). Acute care groups often focus on needs common to clients of varying diagnoses: (1) relaxation/anxiety management skills, (2) verbal interaction skills, and (3) leisure community skills (Wolfe 1996). In the 1960s and 1970s, the concept of expert-led and deficit-oriented treatment was predominant in very large psychiatric institutions, where many persons spent the rest of their life after admission. In the light of the civil rights movement, patient rights became more predominant, and deinstitutionalization moved most patients to community-based mental health facilities. The concept of "recovery" is described as

> a deeply personal, unique process of changing one's attitudes, values, feelings, goals, skills and/or roles. It is a way of living a satisfying, hopeful, and contributing life, even with limitations caused by the illness, recovery involves the development of new meaning and purpose in life as one grows beyond the catastrophic effects of mental illness (Anthony 1993, 7).

With this concept, patients are not "cured" in the sense of free of all symptoms, but rather learn a means of living satisfactory lives and keeping the symptoms under control. They can determine where and how they want to live, and make their own choices. This has led to a new way to understand mental illness, with the emphasis placed on the client's strengths and the expectation that the client will live in the "least restrictive environment" and be self-determined and in control of his/her life (Solli, Rolvsjord, and Borg 2013).

Why Music Is Useful in the Treating of Mental Disorders

Some of music's strengths in treating adults who have mental or behavioral disorders are its flexibility, its almost universal appeal to people of all ages and levels of functioning, its ability to organize behavior and bring people together, and its usefulness as a vehicle for emotional expression (Gaston 1968a; Goldberg 1989; Sears 1968/2007; Thaut and Gfeller 1992). As Goldberg (1989, 42) observed:

> A uniqueness of music in the psychiatric setting is its flexibility. Music brings people together in a cohesive, supportive way; it provides external organization,

narrows and focuses attention, and calms. Music reflects, evokes, and contains affect, stimulates imagery, and facilitates insight, support, and psychological safety. But most of all, its special quality lies in its unique ability to mirror the paradoxical, ambiguous, fleeting, dynamic nature of human emotions.

Since music is flexible and allows for participation at a wide variety of ability levels, music experiences used for therapeutic interventions can be readily adapted to the client's functioning level. For example, simple experiential music activities, such as singing, playing musical instruments, selecting recorded music for listening activities, or moving to music, can help establish contact with clients who have severe psychotic disorders by providing safe, nonverbal relating experiences and a nonthreatening structure for reality orientation. Because of its inherent order and structure and its power to serve as a means of nonverbal communication and as a gentle persuasion to join in activity (Gaston 1968a; Sears 1968/2007), music provides a "here-and-now" orientation that demands clients' attention and moment-by-moment commitment to the music experience. Music experiences also provide an important and unique way for clients to identify, experience, and express feelings in more appropriate ways. In addition, music may serve as a structure or reinforcer to control impulsive behaviors and practice more controlled cooperative behaviors.

For higher functioning clients, experiences such as relaxation to music, guided imagery and music, instrumental improvisation, lyric discussion, and song writing can reduce stress and anxiety, facilitate relaxation, increase self-esteem and feelings of well-being, improve verbal communication and social interaction skills, increase appropriate expression of feelings, and improve decision-making and problem-solving skills. In addition to helping clients improve their mental, social, and behavioral functioning, music therapy sessions also can provide clients with skills and abilities (e.g., singing with a group, playing instruments, exhibiting appropriate behavior while listening to music, following a conductor) that can be used in normal environments (Hadsell 1974). Moreover, as goal-directed music experiences are used to foster the development of group cohesion, provide a unique mode for expression of feelings, and offer experiences in support, leadership, creativity, and play, music therapy services can play an important role in assisting adult psychiatric patients in their transition from the institution to the community (Langdon et al. 1989).

Since most people perceive music as a nonthreatening, enjoyable stimulus, participation in music therapy experiences may produce less fear and anxiety than other types of treatment. Heaney (1992, 79) found that most adult psychiatric patients viewed music therapy very favorably and suggested that this may relate to the way music therapy interventions emphasize "increased socialization and group cohesion, provision of safe, expressive outlets for emotions, and the learning of new skills or the rekindling of previous interests which foster positive self-esteem." Eyre (2011, 166) studied patient experiences from participation in a therapeutic chorale; she concluded that, in addition to increasing self-esteem, participation in this type of group leads to increased confidence and improved social skills, emotional coping and expression, and cognitive skills. Music experiences also frequently stimulate the interest of apathetic clients and help motivate them to participate in goal-directed activities. As clients participate and cooperate in music therapy treatment, "the music therapist also actively promotes an attitude of cooperation with other aspects of treatment" (Smeltekop and Houghton 1990, 122). In addition, music therapy interventions can complement treatment with psychotropic medications by addressing aspects or manifestations of the disease or syndrome (e.g., lack of insight, lack of judgment, impaired memory, poor affective expression, poor communication or socialization skills) that chemical interventions do not reach (Smeltekop and Houghton 1990).

Recent advances in biomedical research techniques have also shown that music therapy interventions can directly influence neurological, biochemical, and physiological functions that relate to emotional regulation and amelioration of psychiatric disorders (Moore 2013; Taylor 1997). However, it is important to realize that simple exposure to music alone does not necessarily promote positive changes. For the therapeutic use of music to be most successful, the therapist must carefully plan and direct the music interventions so that they promote positive growth and change. Used without planning and direction, music can at times intensify pathology, as when individuals with antisocial personality disorders use certain songs to validate their pathological thoughts and values. As Taylor (1997, 83) explained:

> While the music alone does not rehabilitate the patient, it can affect reality contact through sensory stimulation and kinesthetic feedback. It is also used to structure interpersonal interaction and serve as a basis for participation in social groups or society at large.

General Music Therapy Intervention Strategies and Techniques

As with other client populations, music therapy interventions with adults who have mental or behavioral disorders can take a variety of forms, depending on the client's interests, preferences, abilities, and needs. Specific experiences used with particular clients are based on information gained in the music therapy and general assessments and are appropriate to the client's chronological and developmental age (Bruscia 1988; Cassity and Cassity 1994a, 1994b; Crowe 2007e; Thaut and Gfeller 1992; Wilson 1990a, 2002; Wolfe 1996). Music therapy interventions may employ *active* music-making techniques (e.g., singing, playing instruments, improvising or composing music, moving to music) or more *passive* techniques that are based on music listening (e.g., directed listening, listening and discussion, music for relaxation, guided imagery and music). While many interventions use familiar music that clients prefer to help establish rapport or use the lyrics of popular songs to help clients focus on a particular topic or treatment issue for discussion, others effectively use less familiar, classical music to stimulate clients' imagery or their expression of unique inner feelings (Summer 1994).

Music therapists may work with clients in individual or group sessions. Group music therapy is most often used in acute care settings. In addition to being more economical, group music therapy is more efficient at strengthening and building clients' interpersonal skills and is very effective in helping clients develop relevant, functional skills that can help them cope and function more effectively in their communal life (Murphy 1992; Wolfe 1996). Music also may be used as general environmental stimulus to help control behavior. For example, when music from two local radio stations was played during patient free time in the courtyard of a state mental hospital for patients who were hospitalized with behavioral problems, almost twice as many inappropriate behaviors (e.g., disruptive, exploitative, sexually assaultive, and self-abusive behaviors; property destruction; selling contraband) occurred when the rock/rap station was playing than when the easy listening/country western station was used (Harris, Bradley, and Titus 1992). The researchers noted that while the easy listening music possibly drove away persons more likely to act inappropriately and attracted those more prone to not act inappropriately, the change in music effectively controlled patients' behavior in a cost-free, instantaneous way where "frequent widespread attempts to control behavior in the mall area had been fruitless" (15).

Levels of Intervention

According to Wheeler (1983, 1987), music therapy clinical practice with adult psychiatric clients falls into three general categories, (1) supportive music therapy as activity therapy, (2) insight music therapy with reeducative goals, and (3) insight music therapy with reconstructive goals. These are further discussed in Gfeller and Thaut (2008, 238–241). Goldberg (1989) also distinguished two major types of music therapy practice used with adult psychiatric patients: music activity therapy (similar to Wheeler's level one) and music psychotherapy (similar to Wheeler's levels two and three). Music psychotherapy may use focused experiences, with themes determined by the therapist based on patient issues, or *open* experiences, where themes emerge from needs, images, feelings that arise from musical experience. Music therapists who use reconstructive insight music therapy or music psychotherapy techniques *must* have advanced clinical training in both psychotherapy and music psycho-therapy procedures (Goldberg 1989; Unkefer 1990; Wheeler 1983, 1987).

Music activity therapy emphasizes changing behavior, not understanding it, as music therapists actively involve clients in structured, success-oriented, goal-directed music experiences to help them experience and practice healthy behaviors. While participating in music activities, clients learn more adaptive and functional behaviors and develop behavioral and emotional control necessary to function in daily life. Goals include increasing internal/external organization, improving interpersonal interaction and relationships with peers, decreasing withdrawal and internal preoccupations, and increasing self-esteem. Techniques include Orff-Schulwerk activities, relaxation to music, exercises or movement-to-music, group singing, structured song writing, structured instrument playing, and other structured music experiences. Crowe (2007) explained that the interventions are product-oriented and are useful with severe mental disorders. Techniques she included were musical instruction, ensembles, movement, singing, composition, use of technology, and rhythmic activities (31–33). Peterson (2007) added drumming group experiences.

In *music psychotherapy* approaches, the focus is on exploring the client's personal issues. Techniques may include instrumental improvisation, music listening with discussion of lyrics or emotional reactions to music, or guided imagery and music. Music experiences are not limited merely to a short cata-lyst role at the beginning of the session; they are "used to expand, highlight, or contain emotional responses throughout the group session, depending on the needs of the group members" (Goldberg 1989, 40). Crowe (2007) explained that the verbal interaction between the client and therapist, or perhaps other group members, is included with active participation in the music therapy session. She included various uses of songs, movement, and listening.

Silverman (2009b, 55) surveyed music therapists to "identify songs psychiat-ric music therapists use during lyric analysis interventions and to identify the clinical objectives these clinicians address during lyric analysis interventions." In a previous survey (2007), he found that 61.8% of the responding music therapists used lyric analysis. In this study he asked the music therapists to list the ten most effective songs they used. There was much disagreement, but the most frequent favorite was "Lean on Me" by Bill Withers. The list of songs (n = 172), performing artists, and the theme or objective area are listed on pp. 56–58. Most therapists used the songs they listed because the songs reflected issues they believed would be helpful for discussion topics. One should note that the response rate was low, which requires caution in generalizing about the results.

In contrast to music psychotherapy with children, where the therapist does not interpret musical metaphors and images (Friedlander 1994), in music psychotherapy with adults, the metaphors and images generated with the client in music usually are processed verbally with the client (Goldberg 1989). Thus, music therapists who use these techniques must have advanced clinical training in psychotherapeutic techniques (Goldberg 1989; Unkefer 1990; Wheeler 1983, 1987).

Insight music therapy with reeducative goals uses music experiences to stimulate discussion of feelings, which leads to insights that help the clients reorganize their values or behavioral patterns, thereby resulting in less anxiety and improved functioning. Music therapy interventions emphasize identifying feelings and attitudes, exploring self-defeating attitudes and healthier ways of relating to others, creative problem solving, and using material presented in the musical experience or the feelings elicited by the musical experience to facilitate insight and behavioral change. In this level, music-based experiences and follow-up processing and discussion focus on relatively *conscious* material, such as the behavior patterns and feelings presented in the here-and-now interactions between the therapist and clients. As compared with music activity therapy, verbal processing plays a more prominent role in the therapeutic process.

In *insight music therapy with reconstructive goals*, the focus shifts to using therapeutic music experiences to help clients achieve insight into *unconscious conflicts* that negatively affect their behavioral patterns, thoughts, and feelings. The music therapist uses images and feelings elicited from music experiences that tap deeper levels of emotion and personality – e.g., Priestley's (1975) analytical improvisation techniques or Bonny's (1975) Guided Imagery and Music technique – to help the clients achieve insight into the causes of their current distresses or maladaptive behaviors and to help them work through these conflicts and fears, which leads to positive personality changes. It is important to note that many states require licenses for private psychotherapeutic practices; therefore, trained music therapists who wish to use music psychotherapy techniques in private practice may need to complete additional graduate coursework and have a certain number of hours of supervised clinical work so they can meet the requirements for a counseling license in their particular state (Goldberg 1989).

While each of these levels of music therapy may be useful in various situations, certain levels are generally more appropriate with specific types of clients (Goldberg 1989, 1994; Unkefer 1990; Wheeler 1987). General, activity-oriented music therapy (level 1) is used with clients who have severe mental disorders (e.g., chronic schizophrenia, organic mental disorders) and more extreme personality disorganization, while insight music therapy with reeducative (level 2) or reconstructive goals (level 3) is more useful with those who have mental disorders with less severe personality disorganization (e.g., substance abuse, depressive disorders, anxiety disorders, personality disorders). To benefit from insight music therapy with reconstructive goals, clients "have to be able and motivated to commit themselves to usually long-term therapy that challenges existent personality structures" (Unkefer 1990, 147). It is highly recommended that music therapists who use insight-oriented techniques with reconstructive goals or music psychotherapy obtain advanced clinical training in psychotherapeutic and music psychotherapy techniques (Goldberg 1989; Unkefer 1990; Wheeler 1983, 1987).

Categories of Musical Experience

Using Wheeler's (1983) levels of practice along with ideas from Yalom's (1983) level of inpatient group psychotherapy, Unkefer (1990) classified programs and techniques used in music therapy treatment of adults with mental disorders into six general categories: (1) music performing, (2) music psychotherapy, (3) music and movement, (4) music combined with other expressive arts, (5) recreational music, and (6) music and relaxation. Each category includes several techniques, any of which, depending on factors such as the exact nature of their presenting symptoms, their individual skills and preferences, the time and setting available for therapy, etc., may be beneficial to adults who have various mental or behavioral disorders. Music therapists who work in psychiatric settings frequently employ many of these techniques in assessing and treating clients (Cassity and Cassity 1994a). Silverman (2007, 388) listed the following techniques used by music therapists working in mental health, as indicated by a survey: "music assisted relaxation, improvisation, songwriting, lyric analysis, and music and movement." In 2011, he conducted a randomized clinical effectiveness study of the effect of songwriting on knowledge of coping skills and working alliance in psychiatric patients. He defined *working alliance* (also called *therapeutic alliance*) "as the relationship between the person receiving therapy and the person providing it" (Silverman 2011c, 107–108). He used group songwriting to present psychoeducational concepts of coping skills. Clients supplied lyrics about common problems with which acute psychiatric patients must cope. The control condition was a scripted psychoeducational session focusing on coping skills, but without music. Eighty participants were in two groups in 16 randomized sessions (with 48 attending the music sessions, and 41 in the control group). While there were no statistically significant differences between the two groups in knowledge of coping skills, working alliance, or enjoyment, the music therapy group tended to have slightly higher means in these measures, suggesting that music therapy can be as effective as psychoeducation." (112)

Justice (2007) discussed relaxation techniques used in music therapy. When using music relaxation it is important to remember that

> highly disorganized clients (those with psychotic disorders, high levels of agitation, etc.) have a greater need for external structure. Clients with symptoms of

depression or anxiety will have periods of disorganization and will need more structure, while clients with good self-organization skills will need less external structure during muscle relaxation techniques. (37)

She explains several relaxation techniques (36–39).

Music performing techniques include group instrumental improvisation, instrumental or vocal performance ensembles, group singing, individual instrumental or vocal music lessons, and individual music improvisation/interaction. In directing these techniques therapeutically, the therapist uses the context of music performance activities to increase skills such as appropriate socialization, cooperation, communication, expression of feelings, and frustration tolerance. In all of these performing activities, clients' self-esteem also increases as they master tasks and experience success in music performance.

Iliya (2011) used vocal techniques in her work with homeless/mentally ill clients. Common mental illnesses in this population include schizophrenia, bipolar disorder, and depression. Techniques included "vocal improvisation, group singing, individual singing, toning, and chanting" (14). Her goals were "socialization, self-expression, self-esteem, and mind/body connection" (14). In work of this type, group therapy is preferred over individual sessions. Singing is the preferred method for work on body/mind connection because deep breathing, diaphragmatic action, and vocal production help people feel a body connection. This also facilitates relaxation. Iliya (2011, 20–22) provided a case history of a homeless person's experience with vocal methods. She found that this experience allows her clients to do something creative and meaningful with others.

According to Unkefer (1990), *music psychotherapy techniques* use music and music-based activities (a) to provide affective experiences that evoke thoughts, feelings, or associations; or (b) to act as an objective focal point to elicit discussion or explore new behaviors or rediscover old skills. Techniques may include instrumental improvisation, GIM, lyric discussion, music listening with discussion of emotional reactions, song writing, and the like. Discussing music therapy improvisation for adult psychiatric settings, Nolan and Ierardi (2007, 49) note,

> It is the musical experience that reinforces awareness of the self, and others, as well as the cause-and-effect relationship of interaction with musical objects and reality-based auditory stimuli. This primary connection of the external world of reality with internal psychic states is fundamental to the acquisition of further treatment gains.

Gardstrom and Hiller (2010) define song discussion as an activity "in which the client and therapist listen to a song together and then discuss the meaning and relevance of the song to the client's life" (147; based on Bruscia 1998a). They deliberately used the term *song discussion*, rather than music discussion and/or lyric discussion, which have different connotations. The primary difference is that the discussion should include aspects of the music as well as the lyrics. This method is used in music psychotherapy to allow thoughts and emotions to surface and be available for discussion, which can lead to "improved self-awareness, release of emotions, development of healthy interpersonal relationships, healing of emotional trauma, and discovery of greater meaning and fulfillment in life" (148). Song selection, which is very important in this type of music therapy, requires consideration of the client's treatment stages and of the lyric content, as well as the client's cognitive ability to listen and process the content. The client's musical preference and familiarity with the music also require consideration.

Initially, group or individual approaches and activities may be *supportive*, as the music therapist structures music experiences to identify and clarify thoughts or feelings expressed by the client and to facilitate/support appropriate interpersonal behavior. Later, group or individual approaches and activities may become more *interactive*, as the music therapist structures music experiences to express and reflect themes/issues relevant to the client in a group process, or to clarify individual attitudes, feelings, motivations, or conflicts, thus facilitating the client's efforts to identify, express, and resolve conscious conflicts, to form new, healthier responses, and to practice the new behaviors. At the deepest level of music psychotherapy using *catalytic music group or individual therapy*, music experiences are used as a catalyst to tap unconscious levels of clients' emotional processes, which then can be processed and used to help the clients achieve insight and reorganize their existing personality structures to achieve healthier functioning. Obviously, use of these methods requires additional clinical training in psychotherapy and music psychotherapy techniques (Goldberg 1989; Unkefer 1990; Wheeler 1983, 1987).

Music and movement experiences used in treating adults with mental or behavioral disorders include (a) movement awareness, (b) movement exploration, (c) movement interaction, (d) expressive movement, (e) dance, and (f) music and exercise. As these techniques are therapeutically directed, movement-to-music activities provide a context and structure to help clients increase body awareness and comfort in movement, physical fitness, social interaction skills, nonverbal expression of feelings, and self-confidence, while decreasing tension and anxiety. Live or recorded music can support and facilitate these experiences in several ways: (1) a *background accompaniment* to facilitate participation by matching the mood and tempo of the activity and providing sensory and psychological stimulation for the clients; (2) a *timing cue* to structure movements; (3) a *catalytic stimulus* to provide a theme for expression or interaction through music; (4) a *representational accompaniment* to reflect or lead the character, tempo, flow, and mood of the movement; (5) a *content accompaniment* to help enhance the experience of internal aspects of the external movement characteristics; (6) a *designative accompaniment* to direct specific ways of moving (e.g., turn on trills, move up as music melody ascends); or (7) a *dance accompaniment* (Unkefer 1990). This encourages an interactive response, which obtains and holds the client's attention. The movement is in response to the music, the therapist, and others in the group. The effect of expressive movement has been studied by a number of researchers (Cevasco et al. 2005; Silverman 2003b, 2006, 2007, Unkefer and Thaut 2002).

Silverman and Marcionetti (2005) studied the effect of three conditions on auditory hallucinations: reading, interactive live music making, and recorded music. Results were not significant, but clients found that both music listening and active music making suppressed auditory hallucinations. The study needs replication with a larger group of subjects because it included only seven subjects. This type of research is very hard to conduct because results are confounded by medication, the client's inability to participate because of active symptoms, and irregular attendance. Although the researchers tried to find subjects each day for six months, only seven of them met the criteria. However, when these results are combined with other studies (Gallagher, Dinan, and Baker 1994; Margo, Hemsley, and Slade, 1981; Silverman 2003b), a pattern is apparent. Music does seem to interfere with auditory hallucinations. However, more research is needed.

Music therapists who work with adult psychiatric clients also may use *music combined with other expressive arts* in some of their treatment techniques. Gfeller and Thaut (2008, 235) state that "musical stimuli can act as a catalyst for expression of thoughts and feelings in an art or literary medium." For example, music might be used to set a mood or provide a theme for clients to express themselves through fine arts such as drawing, sculpting, or drama. Music also may be used with prose or poetry, as clients develop musical accompaniments for existing works or as music experiences stimulate expressive writing. These multisensory experiences often provide additional means of expression for nonverbal or withdrawn clients, helping them to express feelings without words or providing a structure to organize thinking and encourage expression through language (Cassity and Cassity 2006; Davis and Furman 2008; Siverman 2003; Unkefer 1990; Unkefer and Thaut 2002). When the music therapist works with other creative arts therapists (e.g., art therapists, dance therapists, psychodramatists, poetry therapists), they may use a team approach to provide these multisensory experiences for clients, with each therapist taking the lead in facilitating the experience in his/her area of expertise.

Frequently, music therapists use *recreational music activities* to help clients get comfortable with music making so music later can be used as a tool for more in-depth group participation and therapeutic goals. These activities also provide initial steps toward resocialization and help clients develop constructive leisure-time skills. Experiences may include (a) *musical games* (e.g., music bingo, name that tune, concentration games, instruments play games), (b) *music appreciation awareness* (listening to and discussing or creating/performing a variety of types of music to encourage attention and on-task behavior and provide opportunities for asserting individual preferences and opinions in a nonthreatening atmosphere), (c) *recreational music performance groups* (vocal and/or instrumental; emphasis on enjoyment and participation), and (d) *leisure-time skill development.* Leisure skills gained in music therapy can be an important part of a client's plan for post-discharge use of leisure time and can play a vital role in assisting the client in his/her transition from an institution to the community. The goal is often just to let the client relax and have fun with others (Cassity and Cassity 2006; Gfeller and Thaut 2008; Langdon et al. 1989; Silverman 2006, 2007; Unkefer 1990; Unkefer and Thaut 2002; Wolfe 1996).

Finally, since many adult psychiatric patients experience tension and anxiety, music and relaxation techniques can be an important part of music therapy programs (Cassity and Cassity 2006; Justice 2007; Unkefer 1990; Unkefer and Thaut 2002; Wolfe 1996). Music and relaxation training may occur in group or individual settings and utilize various techniques. These include (1) *music with progressive muscle relaxation training*, where appropriate music is paired with progressive muscle relaxation techniques and music becomes a conditioned stimulus for relaxation); (2) *music for surface relaxation*, in which clients learn to select music with characteristics that will help them relax and provide temporary relief from anxiety or stress); (3) *music imagery*, where clients listen to music in a relaxed state with therapist-suggested, open-ended scenarios to promote imagery or aid concentration or relaxation (*not* intended to reach deep intrapsychic material such as may occur in the specialized music psychotherapy technique Guided Imagery and Music (Bonny 1989); and (4) *music-centered relaxation*, where music is used as a stimulus or focus to divert clients' attention from unpleasant thoughts and suppress feelings of anxiety, fear, or tension (Unkefer 1990). Justice (2007) warns that patients who are highly disorganized or those with depression or anxiety who have times of disorganization need a more externally structured experience.

Music Therapy with the Multimodal Therapy Model

Some music therapists use Lazarus's (1976, 1989) multimodal therapy model to help assess clients and structure and integrate music therapy interventions in psychiatric settings. Thomas (2007, 127) states that in acute inpatient care, "multidisciplinary and multimodal interventions are provided in a 24-hour, secure, and protected treatment environment that is medically staffed and psychiatrically supervised." In this short-term intervention, stabilization and assessment to identify goals for follow-up treatment in a community setting are the primary goals. Justice (2007, 135) notes that community mental health services may be delivered in "group homes, community mental health centers, day treatment programs, clubhouses, or supported living programs." Music therapy activities can connect with one or several areas of a client's BASIC-ID (behavior, affect, sensation, imagery, cognition, interpersonal relations, drugs) and be useful both for assessing a client's current level of functioning and for helping a client gain skills in needed areas (Adelman 1985; Cassity and Cassity 1994a, 1994b; Wilson 1990a). Music therapy interventions may be structured to help clients increase concentration, attention span, and on-task behaviors; increase eye contact; increase ability to appropriately identify and express feelings and emotions; alter existing mood states (e.g., decrease depression or negative thought patterns); increase frustration tolerance, increase impulse control; decrease anxiety; facilitate muscle relaxation and release motor tension; increase self-esteem and improve self-concept (through success experiences, skill acquisition, positive sensory and social feedback); improve cognitive organization and memory skills; improve decision-making and problem-solving skills; increase ability to structure time and follow through on tasks; increase awareness of self and others; increase interaction and cooperation with others (through nonverbal as well as verbal means); increase group cohesion; and stimulate and/or structure perceptions and motor activity to increase alertness, increase coordination and confidence, and encourage social participation (Cassity and Cassity 1994a, 2006; Thaut and Smeltekop 1990).

Music Therapy Interventions for Schizophrenic Adults

A large percentage of music therapists work in psychiatric treatment facilities that include both inpatient and outpatient services. The duration of inpatient treatment has decreased significantly: "The current length of stay in most inpatient hospital settings for acute psychiatric care has been reduced to an average of 7–10 days or less" (Thomas 2007, 125). Many of these patients will require readmission some time after they return to the community, which is called *recidivism* or the "revolving door" policy (Silverman 2007). This pattern has changed the type of goals that music therapy can address, and treatment often continues in outpatient settings.

The most frequently treated adult client groups are those who have schizophrenia and other psychotic disorders (Cassity and Cassity 1994b). Since the 1950s, schizophrenia has been recognized as a neurological disorder or brain disease whose symptoms various psychotropic drugs may reduce (Goetinck 1996a; Siegfried and Goetinck 1996; Taylor 1997; Thomas 2007). Music therapy interventions can complement medication by treating and reducing symptoms (e.g., apathy, poor social skills, lack of involvement with others, blunted or inappropriate affect) that medications do not reach (Smeltekop and Houghton 1990).

Many clients with schizophrenia or other psychotic disorders have severely disorganized personalities and initially benefit most from experiential music activities (e.g., singing, playing musical instruments, moving to music, selecting music for listening activities, using music for relaxation) that provide a "here-and-now" orientation and demand moment-by-moment attention to the task (Nowicki and Trevisan 1978; Silverman 2003b; Unkefer 1990; Wheeler 1987; Wolfgram 1978). Since verbal methods often do not reach individuals who have severe psychoses, performance activities such as movement-to-music, instrumental improvisation, or those that provide opportunities for nonverbal relating experiences can be very important in establishing contact with these clients and helping them begin to become aware of and interact cooperatively with others. Oliver Sacks (2008, 331), a well known neurologist and psychiatrist, wrote:

> Psychiatrists speak of schizophrenic people as having "negative" symptoms (difficulties making contact with others, lack of motivation, and, above all, flat affect) as well as "positive" ones (hallucinations, delusions). While medication can damp down the positive symptoms, it rarely has any effect on the negative ones, which are often more disabling – and it is here . . . that music therapy can be particularly useful and may help open up isolated, asocial people in a humane and uncoercive way.

Regarding the auditory event of imaging music, Sacks (2008, 34) wrote that "imagining music can indeed activate the auditory cortex almost as strongly as listening to it." Perhaps this is one reason that familiar and preferred music is more effective in most music therapy sessions.

Recent research revealing that music reaches the brain's emotional centers without the need for higher cortical analysis also suggests a biomedical explanation for music's effectiveness as a vehicle for establishing contact with individuals who have schizophrenia or other psychoses. Taylor (1997, 113–114) suggests that frequent participation in producing music requires the brain to relate immediately to ongoing perceptions and thereby helps a psychotic person appropriately process and react to external stimuli.

Many music therapists have had success using improvisational music therapy techniques to establish contact with and elicit communication and cooperative interactions from adults who have schizophrenia or other psychotic disorders (Aigen 1990; Nolan 1994; Nowicki and Trevisan 1978; Pavlicevic et al. 1994). After conducting descriptive analysis of music therapists' roles, Silverman (2007, 408) reported,

> It would appear that the psychiatric music therapists who participated in this study did not favor one particular technique, although improvisation,

sing-alongs, lyric analysis, and music-assisted relaxation were cited more frequently than other interventions.

Silverman (2003b) conducted a meta-analysis "to determine the influence
of music on the positive and negative symptoms of schizophrenia and/or psychosis" (31). A meta-analysis compares a number of qualitative studies. From
this analysis, he reported that "the data revealing that music therapy techniques and passive listening were consistent indicate music powerful in com-
bating the symptoms of psychosis" (37).

Evidence is being required for third-party funding and to establish music
therapy positions in many psychiatric facilities. Silverman (2010, 4) called for
evidence-based treatment (EBT); i.e., "interventions that have been proven to
be effective via numerous rigorous well-controlled and randomized research
methodologies. This will allow music therapists to better articulate and support
the effectiveness of music therapy. He discussed four areas of EBT that music
therapy can best serve: (1) integrated dual-disorder treatment (for example,
drug abuse/mental illness), (2) illness management and recovery, (3) family
psychoeducation, and (4) medications (information and education for the
client).

Grocke, Bloch, and Castle (2009, 97) studied the effect of group music
therapy on quality of life (QoL) for clients with severe and enduring mental
illness (SEMI). The tests conducted after ten, one-hour weekly music therapy
sessions showed significant changes in five aspects of quality of life, which
indicated that the clients felt a better QoL, improved health and more support
from friends. Techniques used included singing, song writing, and instrumental
improvisation. Participants' diagnoses included "schizophrenia and bipolar
disorder, stabilized on medication" (94). Silverman (2009a) noted that many
studies focus on treatment with less concern about QoL, although life satisfaction is an important variable which affects the well-being of the individual.

Music Therapy Interventions for Adults Who Have
Mood Disorders

Mood or affective disorders are the second most frequent disorders seen
by music therapists who work in psychiatric hospitals. The National Alliance
on Mental Illness reports that

> an estimated 16 million American adults – almost 7% of the population – had at
> least 1 major depressive episode last year. . . . Women are 70% more likely than
> men to experience depression, and young adults aged 18–25 are 60% more
> likely to have depression than people aged 50 or older. (NAMI 2015a, 1)

Most of these people either get no help or are treated in outpatient facilities.
Few receive inpatient treatment.

Many music therapists have found that successful participation with others in music activities and gaining skills in playing musical instruments help increase self-esteem in clients who are depressed or have low self-esteem (Cassity 1976; Cassity and Cassity 1994a; Crowe 2007e; Morgan 1975; Unkefer 1990). Activities such as improvising on musical instruments, discussing music or song lyrics, and writing songs also can help clients learn to identify and express feelings accurately and appropriately (Behrens 1988; Cassity and Cassity 1994a; Cordobes 1997; Dickens and Sharpe 1970; Ficken 1976; Langdon et al. 1989; Nolan and Ieradi 2007; Unkefer 1990; Wolfgram 1978, 1980). In addition, music psychotherapy approaches utilizing metaphoric music improvisation and Guided Imagery and Music (GIM) can help severely depressed individuals gain access to feelings, images, and insights (Leite 2007; Warja 1994).

For many clients, music seems to be a "safer" vehicle than words for experiencing and expressing feelings and emotions. For example, Cordobes (1997) found that, while both game playing and song writing helped develop group cohesion in depressed adults, subjects used a greater number of emotional words and focused more on treatment issues during the song writing condition. Since it provides avenues for nonverbal as well as verbal expression, music allows comfortable modes of participation for clients who are reluctant to verbalize and provides authentic physical experiences of affect for those who hide behind verbal intellectualizations (Langdon et al. 1989).

Thompson (2007) discussed the use of metaphors in songwriting with psychiatric patients in a rehabilitation program. She defined metaphor as "another means of communication [which] may take the form of a word, turn of phrase, object, symbol, anecdote, or story that represents complex emotions or situations" (p 4). She explained four stages of the songwriting process: (1) brainstorming, (2) explicating meaning, (3) creating the music, and (4) adding the final touches. Two examples of client-written songs exemplify each stage (7–9). She was working in a setting where the group included both inpatient and outpatient clients, with turnover each session. Thus, each session had to stand on its own as a therapeutic experience for the persons who attended at that time.

Werner, Swope, and Heide (2009) studied relationships among ethnicity, music experience, and depression. They looked at depression among various ethnic groups and the place of music in their lives. They found correlations between music experience variables and depression, as well as differences in musical expression among ethnic groups. Some cultures teach a more restricted expression to music. This should be considered in planning music therapy sessions.

Taylor (1997) reported that the Expressive Emphasis Technique was very successful in treating adults with severe clinical depression and suicidal behavior: suicidal episodes decreased in frequency throughout treatment, reaching zero at or near the beginning of phase three, and positive personality traits of extraversion, self-confidence, and motivation became evident during the music therapy session and began to generalize as the treatment progressed.

Some research suggests that musical-rhythmic tasks may help distinguish mania from other mental disorders during a disorder's psychotic phase. Cohen (1986) found that subjects with mania were superior to subjects with other psychotic disorders on tests of rhythmicity and tempo reproduction; subjects with mania also scored significantly higher on rhythmicity than on tempo, and the speed of item presentation did not affect their performance.

Music therapy interventions may address various needs of manic patients (Cassity and Cassity 1994a; Unkefer 1990). For example, activities such as singing, structured dances or movement-to-music, and instrumental improvisation may help channel energy or provide structured, appropriate outlets for energy release. Music programs that move progressively from more stimulating to more relaxing music or music and relaxation training can help individuals decrease physical restlessness, while involvement in goal-oriented performance or movement-to-music experiences or guided music listening experiences may help focus attention and increase concentration (Johnson 2007). Task-oriented music activities may also provide reality orientation, structure, and practice in impulse control, while music psychotherapy techniques can help clients learn to appropriately identify and express emotions.

Music Therapy Interventions for Adults Who Have Anxiety or Stress Disorders

Because music has the ability to affect both physiological and mood/emotional responses (see Chapter Five), it can be a powerful tool for reducing stress, tension, and anxiety. Jellison (1975) showed that background music can reduce stress responses and help induce relaxation under stress. Music can also be combined with relaxation training (Alley 1977; Gfeller and Thaut 2008) and biofeedback techniques (Epstein, Hersen, and Hemphill 1974; Scartelli 1984; Wagner 1975) to reduce tension and stress responses and to facilitate relaxation responses (Silverman 2007). However, since individual preference for the type of music being played often affects the listener's response, one must consider individual preferences in order to achieve maximum benefits in using music to facilitate reduction of tension and stress (Hanser 1985; Logan and Roberts 1984; Prueter and Mezzano 1973; Stratton and Zalanowski 1984; Taylor 1973). Although precategorized selections of stimulative and sedative music may be useful in some cases, they may have subtle elements which will evoke unpredicted responses in some individuals:

> For instance, slow, arhythmic music which otherwise meets all criteria for
> sedative music may appear foreign or frightening to some listeners. Researchers

must use care in generalizing beyond a single musical selection until more exhaustive efforts to quantify the effects of different music have been undertaken. (Hanser 1985, 199)

Today, music-assisted relaxation training programs are an important part of many music therapy programs in acute care mental health settings (Cassity and Cassity 2006; Unkefer and Thaut 2002; Wolfe 1996). Techniques often involve pairing selected music with progressive muscle relaxation, self-suggestion, guided imagery, or biofeedback. Patients learn exercises through repetition with guidance from the therapist, and then they are encouraged to include them in their daily lives for self-maintenance. Treatment interventions combining selected music with vibroacoustic stimulation can also help clients decrease anxiety, increase feelings of calmness and relaxation, increase self-confidence in facing stressful situations, and decrease psychosomatic symptoms (Brodsky and Sloboda 1997; Wigram 1995). For some clients, using music plus vibrotactile stimulation within a cognitive-behavioral framework was just as effective as traditional psychotherapeutic counseling in reducing symptoms of anxiety (Brodsky and Sloboda 1997). This equal effectiveness is important, for some clients who shy away from more traditional treatments may perceive music-based treatments as less threatening and, therefore, be more willing to participate in music-based interventions.

Many music therapists use some form of Guided Imagery and Music (GIM) procedures to help clients decrease anxiety, facilitate relaxation, and increase feelings of well-being (Blake and Bishop 1994; Bonny 1978b, 1989; Gfeller and Davis 2008; Peach 1984). Hammer (1996) found that state anxiety, or perceived situational stress, decreased significantly in subjects in a GIM group and recommends this intervention for use with clients dealing with acute or chronic stress. In addition, Hammer's research indicated that GIM treatment programs "may have an overall effect on improving one's ability to react to stress, improving concentration and general contentment, and improving one's ability to relax in general" (67). In their work with musicians who had severe performance anxiety, Brodsky and Sloboda (1997) found that music-based relaxation and imagery training used within a cognitive behavioral framework were equally as effective as traditional counseling and psychotherapy in reducing stress and performance anxiety. A specific form of music and imagery treatment, the Bonny method of Guided Imagery and Music, has also been used very effectively to treat individuals who have been abused or have witnessed or been a victim of some horrible event that resulted in post-traumatic stress disorder (Blake and Bishop 1994; Ventre 1994b). Used with individuals or in groups, GIM techniques can help clients (a) decrease their hyperarousal and increase their concentration and physical/psychological relaxation, (b) gain access to memories, images, and the feelings associated with them, and (c) increase feelings of hope and empowerment by unlocking inner resources and directing energy to realistic solutions or resolutions, freeing the self from the effects of the past and healing/reconnecting with ordinary life and plans for a more fulfilling future (Burns and Woolrich 2004). GIM techniques can be a very powerful form of music psychotherapy, and music therapists who use GIM techniques require special, advanced clinical training.

Music therapists who work with clients who have anxiety or stress disorders may also use intervention techniques that involve clients more actively in making or responding to music. For example, instrumental improvisation or performance techniques or movement-to-music activities can help reduce tension and anxiety by providing constructive outlets for physical energy and relief of muscular tension (Morgan 1975; Unkefer 1990; Wolfgram 1978). Using music therapy as an adjunct to group therapy in a stress treatment program, Lienhard (1981) taught clients to listen to themselves by listening to music and their reactions to it. Instrumental improvisation activities were used to help make clients aware of the tone and loudness of their communication. In addition, playing instruments served as a vehicle for tension release in many clients. Lienhard also employed music listening/discussion activities, using song lyrics as a catalyst for discussion to help clients (1) identify areas of stress, (2) identify and express feelings associated with stressful areas, (3) ventilate emotions, (4) share with the group and receive feedback, and (5) determine alternative positive coping mechanisms to deal more successfully with stressful situations. Other music therapists have used drumming techniques (Peterson 2007) (e.g., improvisational drum groups, community drum circles, 1:1 sessions improvising and interacting with the therapist, storytelling with drum accompaniment) to help clients with posttraumatic stress disorder increase awareness of and express feelings; learn to modulate and control emotions; practice ways of changing or controlling behavior; increase feelings of control and empowerment; and, in group settings, help build feelings of group connectedness and group cohesion (Borczon 1995; Burt 1995; Slotoroff 1994; Watson 2002).

Music therapists may work within the framework of many different theoretical orientations as they structure music therapy interventions to help treat adults who have problems with stress or anxiety. For example, Tyson (1987) used an analytically oriented approach based on a psychoanalytic interpretation of the symbolic content of the client's singing and playing and interactions with the therapist to treat a client with generalized anxiety disorder. Working with the client using singing and instrumental lessons, Tyson noted a close relationship between the client's musical problems and his unconscious psychological conflicts. As the client analyzed the body movements he used in singing and playing, these became subjects for free association, searches for their psychodynamic meaning, and an experiential basis for creative problem solving and self-discovery.

Other music therapists work within cognitive or cognitive/behavioral orientations (Brodsky and Sloboda 1997; Bryant 1987; Cassity and Cassity 2006; Gfeller and Thaut 2008; Luce 2001; Maultsby 1977; Murphy 1992; Unkefer and Thaut 2002), using song lyrics, music listening/discussion, music performance or music improvisation, or music/movement techniques as vehicles to help clients change their disordered ways of thinking and build healthier, more adaptive ways of thinking and relating to the world and others around them. A typical music therapy session structure in this orientation may include (1) an introduction by the therapist, focusing the clients on the task; (2) a music warm-up, with the therapist modeling response; (3) a music experience (e.g., improvisation, creating a group song); (4) therapist-facilitated verbal processing and discussion of the musical experience and how clients' responses, experiences, and reactions relate to treatment issues; and (5) closure, led by the therapist (Murphy 1992). Therapists have found that music activities often reach clients on an immediate, emotional level that is able to bypass verbal rationalizations and defenses. As Murphy (1992, 105) observed, "While words can accomplish the same end results, for some patients it is the nonverbal experience that may best bring to conscious awareness recurrent, self-defeating patterns."

Still other music therapists take a biomedical approach, structuring music interventions to take advantage of the direct effect music has "on specific physiological processes whose functional variations are indicators of anxiety, tension or stress" (Taylor 1997, 103). Many of the music-facilitated relaxation techniques mentioned earlier fall in this category. Sometimes the cause and effect are difficult to distinguish. Biological changes occurring as a result of some mental illnesses are assessed and may be treated pharmacologically. When a neurobiological basis for the illness is identified, behavioral or emotional disorders must be treated along with the physiological dysfunction (Cassity and Cassity 2006; Silverman 2007; Unkefer and Thaut 2002). One example of a mental illness leading to physiological dysfunction is in the dual diagnosis of substance abuse and depression: "Abusing substances can also lead to mental health problems because of the effects drugs have on a person's moods, thoughts, brain chemistry and behavior" (NAMI 2015b).

Music Therapy Interventions for Adults Who Have Feeding and Eating Disorders

Various types of music therapy interventions from a variety of orientations have been used to treat clients who have anorexia (Justice 1994; Parente 1989; Siegel 2007; Taylor 1997) or bulimia (Justice 1994; Nolan 1989). Being "out of control" is a prominent theme for many clients with eating disorders (Parente 1989; Taylor 1997), and "music therapy can provide support experiences in which the patient has control, new ways of expressing herself and coping with emotions, and connections with other people" (Justice 1994, 105). Using a process musical theater structure where clients developed, practiced, and performed music reviews using songs based on clients' fears and major issues, Parente (1989) helped anorexic clients (a) identify, evaluate, and change faulty and self-destructive thought patterns; (b) discover new skills and behavior patterns; and (c) practice these new skills to transfer them to their daily lives. As part of the music therapy process, clients brought in "songs or musical selections expressing personal affirmations, current personal objectives, or troublesome thoughts and feelings" (47), some of which were then selected for inclusion in the musical review. As they participated in the musical theater ensemble and rehearsed and performed songs and scenes for the show, clients practiced control of fear or phobias; learned to substitute positive attitudes and behaviors for destructive thoughts, emotions, or activities; learned to exercise personal power to improve their situation; supported one another and developed or strengthened meaningful friendships; and improved their self-esteem/self-confidence as they accepted, learned, and performed their roles and began to see themselves as capable, worthwhile individuals.

Justice (1994) also used music therapy interventions within a cognitive/ behavioral framework to help clients with anorexia or bulimia increase self-awareness and self-esteem, increase awareness of irrational or destructive feelings and behaviors, decrease anxiety that may be experienced as they try to discontinue their eating disorder behaviors, and find new ways to control and cope with emotions. She presented three different levels of music therapy experiences that have been helpful in facilitating therapeutic processes with clients who have eating disorders: (1) music-reinforced relaxation, using music to complement, support, and ground muscle stretching, deep breathing, pro-gressive muscle relaxation, and directed imagery techniques; (2) structured music therapy groups, using music and movement, hand bells and choir chimes, group singing, or instrumental improvisation; and (3) insight-oriented music/creative arts and imagery techniques, using group adaptations of the Bonny method of Guided Imagery and Music (GIM) or drawing or writing in response to stories or poems read to music. In *music-reinforced relaxation*, the music helps direct the clients away from obsessive thoughts connected with their eating disorders or control issues and nonverbally paces the experience. Learning music-reinforced relaxation techniques gives clients a method of self-regulation that helps them cope with stress and anxiety, increases their awareness of their physical and emotional reactions, and provides new options for dealing with anxiety without giving in to their old urges (Taylor 1997). In *structured music therapy groups*, clients have opportunities to experience success and connect with others and share experiences on a nonverbal level, which may be less threatening than trying to connect and share in verbal therapy groups. As clients participate successfully in music experiences, they begin to view themselves as an integral part of the group and begin to see their value as a person is based on qualities other than weight. These nonthreatening, structured experiences also help prepare the clients for more *insight-oriented music therapy techniques*, which use music experiences to help clients move past the defenses of or inability to use words, connect with deeper issues through symbol and metaphor, and help clients begin to identify and resolve the issues and feelings underlying their eating disorders.

Working from a more psychodynamic perspective, Nolan (1989) showed how music, in the form of structured and unstructured group improvisational techniques, could serve as a transitional object designed to interrupt the binge/purge cycle in the treatment of bulimia. Nolan hypothesized that "musical expression, as a transitional object, may serve the purpose of redirecting unconscious feelings from the unsuccessful coping mechanism of bulimic behavior to conscious awareness and expression leading to mastery" (51). The experience of improvising and then discussing and processing roles and group process as members listened to a tape of the improvisation (a) helped reinforce reality contact for these clients, (b) assisted in identification of functional parts of their ego, (c) helped identify and intrude on distorted thoughts, and (d) provided a safe environment for testing new interpersonal behaviors. The act of playing musical instruments also provided clients with a wide range of expressive sounds over which they could have control, giving them a means of expression and a way to connect personally and subjectively with the music.

Focusing on the idea that being of out of control was one of the main issues for anorexic persons, Taylor (1997) developed Control Reversal Therapy (CRT), a music therapy procedure that reverses the usual locus of control in therapy sessions by giving control to the *client* and using experiential musical activities to generate feelings of internal control. Individual sessions are structured so that clients control the musical activity and participate on their own terms. Techniques include having the client (a) teach the therapist to sing/play specific songs or to play certain instruments, (b) use a rhythm instrument to signal or control the therapist's improvisations, (c) write song lyrics about a relevant topic and then choose the musical setting for these lyrics (therapist may offer suggestions, but clients must approve each note), (d) create music using interactive computer programs, or (e) use instruments to represent important people in the client's life. Hilliard (2001) also used song lyric analysis and song composition. This leads to "verbal dialogue and cognitive restructuring that help individuals reach their target goals" (Sieget 2007, 173). Reactions and feelings raised by these experiences are processed with the therapist's guidance. Taylor has had great clinical success with CRT since 1988, with patients needing 12 sessions or less to make dramatic positive changes.

Music Therapy Interventions for Adults Who Have Problems with Substance-Induced Disorders

Music touches all aspects of a person – physical, psychological, emotional, social, and spiritual. Since "many researchers emphasize the need to treat the 'whole person' as opposed to 'their addiction'" (James 1988a, 65), music therapy techniques can be valuable for treating adults who have problems with substance abuse or addiction. Music therapy interventions can be structured readily to complement many goals of addiction or alcoholism treatment programs, such as decreasing isolation, motivating clients to participate in treatment, increasing peer interaction and group involvement, facilitating group cohesion, increasing awareness of addictive behaviors and their consequences, clarifying values, accessing and expressing feelings and emotions, improving social skills, developing new coping skills, facilitating expression of issues and feelings related to recovery, decreasing tension and anxiety, facilitating relaxation and stress reduction, improving problem-solving skills, improving impulse control, developing a healthy self-image, finding constructive leisure-time activities, and providing assistance in relapse prevention (Bednarz and Nikkel 1992; Cassity and Cassity 1994a; Freed 1987; James 1988a; Skaggs 1997a; Soshensky 1997b; Treder-Wolff 1990; Wheeler 1985). In addition, music therapy interventions can enhance all treatment stages from engagement to recovery (Bednarz and Nikkel 1992; Skaggs 1997a; Treder-Wolff 1990). Initially, techniques like discussing music interests or lyrics, improvising with rhythm instruments, or participating in music ensembles may help encourage rapport and facilitate interaction with and comfort in the group. Experiences allowing for nonverbal interaction and nonverbal expression, such as activities using rhythm instruments or sessions involving music and art (e.g., drawing to music), may be particularly useful in increasing clients' involvement (Wheeler 1985). For many clients in this population, however, movement-to-music experiences may tend to decrease enjoyment and increase tension levels (Wheeler 1985). Therefore, movement-to-music experiences are usually not a good choice for initial music therapy interventions.

As treatment progresses to more active intervention, "music is a channel of communication that penetrates the rigidity of defenses brought into early recovery, and is an objective conveyor of social attitudes and beliefs that can be used as a tool for exploration" (Treder-Wolff 1990, 68). Techniques used to help clients recognize addictive and maladaptive behaviors and share feelings associated with them include (a) lyric analysis and discussion of songs related to addiction or treatment issues; (b) choosing songs from a list of titles to share something about one's feelings or life experiences; (c) group instrumental improvisations that can give insight into habits, feelings, or ways of interacting; (d) free or structured song writing procedures; and (e) guided imagery and music (GIM). These same techniques can be used later to help clients explore issues on a deeper level by facilitating insight, assisting in development and practice of new coping and problem-solving skills, and facilitating the recovery process. Siegel (2007, 173) explains that "it is through spontaneous verbalizations, movements, or art that unconscious awareness is accessed and healing occurs" in GIM sessions.

Music therapy interventions also may help clients become more aware of subtle social messages in advertising jingles for addictive products or of certain types of music/songs that are associated with or cue their substance abuse (Michel 1985; Treder-Wolff 1990). When clients become aware of these influences, music therapists can help them discover ways to counteract them. In addition, as clients recover and try to maintain an abstinent life style, they may continue to use music-based relaxation techniques or music/leisure activities (listening, playing instruments, playing or singing in community or church musical groups) to deal with stress, structure leisure time, and find new ways of socializing with others (Bednarz and Nikkel 1992; James 1988a; Treder-Winkelman 2003; Wolff 1990).

Many music therapists have found that structured songwriting experiences are particularly useful in helping clients express feelings related to their individual situations, addiction, and recovery process (Freed 1987; James 1988a; Treder-Wolff 1990). Soshensky (2007b, 158) noted that a sense of realization can be achieved in one session, even if refinement of the finished product may require additional sessions: "The therapist needs to be ready, remaining alert and prepared to support a client's process as it emerges."

Music therapists also use GIM techniques to help clients deal with the chronic stress and anxiety that may be associated with recovery (Hammer 1996; James 1988a) or to help clients view life from different perspectives, access and build trust in their inner resources, identify and express emotions and feelings, resolve internal conflicts and heal old hurts, modify moods, develop internal control and support systems, discover optional modes of behavior, and find models for healthy responses (Skaggs 1997a). In addition, techniques learned and insights gained during GIM sessions can assist clients in maintaining their recovery when treatment has ended. For example, "the music inside" can help clients get through the day by supplying all the things clients had formerly relied on their drugs to supply: support and strength during difficult times, the comfort of a familiar friend, a means of uplifting sagging spirits, and facilitation of their abilities to move through emotional pain. Thus, music becomes "a readily accessible, economical and healthy choice" that both helps clients recover from addictions and assists them "in maintaining sobriety and continuing the healing and growth process" (Skaggs 1997a, 46).

Music Therapy Interventions for Adults Who Have Antisocial Personality Disorders or Who Are in Correctional Facilities

Adults who have *antisocial personality disorders* may use certain songs to validate their pathological thoughts or values. Under the guidance of a music therapist, however, this same music can be used within the context of lyric analysis/discussion activities to help clients examine their role models, values, and goals (Taylor 1997). Instrument playing activities that require taking turns or waiting to play one's part can help clients learn to control impulsive behaviors. These activities also can have a positive effect on brain processes that control behaviors. In addition, playing instruments can serve as a means of personal expression, a valuable leisure-time skill, and a means of developing self-esteem. Group instrumental experiences also can be structured to provide opportunities for increasing problem-solving skills and practicing cooperative interactions with others.

Of special concern are the impulsivity, lack of regard for personal safety or that of others, deceitfulness (which may lead to conning others), and irritable or aggressive behavior (DSM-V 2013). These behaviors may lead to sudden outbursts of aggressive behavior, either aimed at someone or just the environment, or clients may decide to leave the facility suddenly (called "elopement"). Thus, the therapist must be very vigilant in watching for cues of increased tension or loss of control. These adults likely had conduct disorder before the age of 15 years, so many of the same behaviors persist into adulthood.

Some research suggests that music therapy interventions may be an initial nonthreatening treatment approach with men who have physically abused women or children (Cassity and Theobold 1990). Treatment approaches utilized music therapy experiences within the framework of cognitive/behavioral restructuring, anger management training, and relaxation training. Music therapy techniques included movement-to-music experiences to increase awareness of behavior, sing-alongs to elicit on-task behavior and cooperation as opposed to disruptive behavior, xylophone improvisation to facilitate appropriate nonverbal and verbal interaction, lyric writing to encourage expression of feelings, music listening/discussion and group music composition activities to promote cooperative interactions and facilitate discussion of treatment issues, and instrumental performance activities to improve impulse control and increase decision-making and organizational skills.

In a discussion of anger management and aggression, Hakvoort (2002) provided a case example of the use of music therapy intervention to help a client increase his self-regulation skills. Fulford (2002, 114), working in a maximum security unit of a state psychiatric facility, stated that "the energy used in drumming also releases stress and/or tension while providing a safe outlet to express anger or frustrations."

Correctional and Forensic Music Therapy

Music therapy techniques can assist in the rehabilitation of forensic mental health patients by helping them gain new skills and behaviors that will enable them to function more appropriately and adaptively upon return to society (Elliot and McGahan 1987; Hanser 1987; Michel 1985; Mitchell 1978). For example, music skills learned in music therapy sessions can provide activities for constructive use of leisure time (Michel 1985), either for personal enjoyment or for participating in community vocal or instrumental groups. In one instance, patients who played together in a music combo in prison continued to play together after their release, even supplementing their income through this activity (Michel 1976, 1985). After six years of research in providing music programs to prisoners, Elliot and McGahan (1987, 170) were "convinced that music is one of the potentially most effective instruments for rehabilitation available to present-day society."

Prisoners who choose to be involved in music programs (e.g., instruction in music theory, instrumental music, or vocal music) can begin to rebuild their lives as they make positive decisions and take concrete actions to participate in music tasks which demand group cooperation and consideration of others (Elliot and McGahan 1987). The mastery of even simple music tasks can help them build feelings of confidence and group cohesiveness. In addition, forensic mental health patients develop increased social and personal adjustment as they learn to conform to group expectations, experience group cohesiveness, and discover how each individual plays a unique role in cooperating with others to achieve a group goal. As their willingness to accept instruction and their skills increase, patients also learn to put forth more effort in the face of challenges, leading to increased self-confidence, self-esteem, self-satisfaction, and pride in their physical self-image.

Hanser (1987) found that loosely structured music groups, in which participants were able to choose the activities and goals they wished to work on in their music therapy hour, helped increase self-esteem in patients of a state correctional facility for women. In addition, these experiences provided the women with an opportunity to be themselves and to learn to trust others. Music and art therapy programs also can help prisoners express feelings and frustrations in socially acceptable ways, thereby relieving anxieties and tensions which can lead to prison unrest. Moreover, these programs reinforce individuality and self-expression amid boring prison routines, thus making the prison environment more humanized and civilized (Mitchell 1978).

Some music therapists work in the field of correctional psychiatry, treating patients who have various psychiatric disturbances (Kaser 1993; Kaser and Bullard 2007; Nolan 1983, 1994; Thaut 1987, 1989b, 1992b). Involvement in structured therapeutic music interventions can have several benefits for prisoners who have psychiatric problems. These include (a) increasing reality contact; (b) engaging mood and emotional responses that promote active thinking and motivation toward goal achievement; (c) increasing self-esteem and learning respect for others; (d) providing a means to express, reflect upon, and deal with thoughts, feelings, and memories; (e) reducing tension and anxiety; (f) decreasing hostile and aggressive behaviors; (g) increasing constructive social interaction and improving group awareness and cohesiveness; (h) facilitating positive mood states and increasing coping abilities; (i) increasing physical and mental alertness; and (j) promoting ability to experience, identify, express, and perceive emotions accurately and appropriately (Thaut 1987, 1992b). Music therapy techniques can be particularly effective in helping imprisoned patients feel more relaxed and in helping improve their mood and increasing positive thoughts about themselves and their lives (Kaser and Bullard 2007; Thaut 1989b).

Research and practice suggest that three types of music therapy techniques work very successfully with prisoners who have severe mental health problems (Thaut 1987, 1989b, 1992b). *Music group therapy techniques* use guided music listening and supportive verbal interaction to help patients learn to respect and cooperate with others. In this process, prisoner-patients also are guided to set achievable personal goals (e.g., soothe and relax mind, recall good memories, increase inspiration or motivation to make progress or complete tasks, release or express inner feelings and thoughts, get mind off problems, relieve tension, clear confusion, think about loved ones) and then learn to select music experiences that will help them accomplish these goals. In the second category of techniques, *instrumental group improvisation*, the music therapist structures and guides simple improvisation tasks that have patients play pitched and nonpitched percussion instruments, keyboards, or guitars. Through these experiences, prisoner-patients learn to express and communicate feelings, practice appropriate social interactions, experience success, release tension, and increase reality contact. Finally, music therapy programs in correctional psychiatry may use *music and relaxation techniques*, which teach patients progressive muscle relaxation to sedative music of their choice.

A few prisoner-patients also may benefit from insight-oriented guided imagery and music (GIM) techniques used in combination with supportive group music therapy experiences. Summer (1988) and Kaser and Bullard (2007, 191) caution that imagery "of any kind is contraindicated for individuals with active psychosis, such as the hallucinations that can be present in schizophrenia." This type of dual diagnosis is common in forensic hospitals (for example, schizophrenia and drug use). Nolan (1983) found that in some cases, GIM experiences can assist in temporarily lifting individuals' defenses so they can learn to recognize and deal with feelings that negatively impact their behavior and relations to others. As noted earlier, advanced training is essential for using GIM with any population.

Individual music therapy sessions may benefit some prisoner-patients. For example, Nolan (1994) used music improvisation techniques to work with a 32-year-old prisoner who was fearful, isolated, did not speak, and possibly had hallucinations. The therapist used a xylophone arranged in a pentatonic scale to engage the prisoner in an improvisatory duet with the therapist playing the guitar. After successfully playing the duet and then hearing the tape of it, the prisoner-patient began to speak. Nolan hypothesized that as the prisoner-patient entered into the musical exchange, the musical experience elicited mental processes not effected by the psychosis and increased his level of functioning. In another instance, Kaser (1993) worked in a correctional setting with a prisoner-patient in the mid-stages of Alzheimer's disease and found that, although the man was unable or unwilling to communicate his feelings verbally, he would communicate through songs he selected or sang. As he began to sing and express his feelings through songs he recalled, the prisoner-patient became more relaxed and less agitated. As his behavior improved in music therapy, he also behaved more appropriately on the cell block.

Kaser and Bullard (2007) used both free and structured group improvisation in their work in a maximum-security state hospital for adult male felons diagnosed with mental illness. They provide a case study (195) that exemplifies the use of a music therapy improvisation group for a 60-year-old pedophile in the sex offender commitment program. Within this facility, their therapy goals and treatment objectives are as follows:

To reduce resistance and help to develop a more positive attitude toward the therapeutic experience
To improve reality testing and integration
To reduce stress, frustration, and anger through positive physiological effects
To develop awareness of and the ability to express feelings
To develop interpersonal skills (180).

To work successfully in correctional settings, music therapists must understand rules, behavior codes, and social dynamics that are peculiar to the prison setting, always remembering that security takes priority over all other concerns and programs (Thaut 1987, 1992b). Music therapists need to work cooperatively with security staff and be competent in handling security issues. The music therapist also must know something of the patient's personality structure and criminal record to understand the behavior patterns and emotions that may be linked with his or her crime and expectations for the future. While therapy sessions in correctional settings must adapt to the limitations and restrictions of the prison system and usually do not have the degree of emotional sharing and openness that are present in other situations, therapeutic interventions that are brief, time-limited, focused on the here-and-now, and linked to clearly defined treatment goals (e.g., decreasing symptoms, increasing appropriate psychosocial functioning, adjusting to and coping with the reality of the present situation, preparing for reintegration with society for patients who are about to be released) can be very useful in facilitating the inmate's therapeutic progress. While this is a challenging and difficult form of music therapy, Kaser and Bullard (2007, 197) note that "when individuals are incarcerated for long periods of time in a very controlled, secure setting, the effect of producing and experiencing music is a powerful experience."

SPECIAL CONSIDERATIONS AND TIPS FOR SUCCESS

Music therapists who work with adults who have behavior disorders or mental illnesses have several responsibilities that include (1) creating a warm, nonthreatening environment that bolsters self-esteem and motivation by emphasizing successful experiences; (2) defining limits and expectations for appropriate group behavior; (3) directing and redirecting the client's attention to the task at hand; (4) being aware of individual responses and the significance of interaction; and (5) perceiving and addressing the clients as adults (Wolfgram, 1978). Whatever the therapist's philosophical orientation, it is important to establish clear and specific goals and objectives. When this is done, appropriate affective or social behaviors that may at first seem very nebulous can become directly observable and specific, thereby enabling both therapist and clients to determine whether progress is being made (Cooper 1985; Hanser 1984). For treatments to be most successful, music therapists also must structure their interventions to work within and support the particular orientation or treatment philosophy of the facility or program in which they are working (Gfeller and Thaut 2008; James 1988a; Wilson 1990a). A community-related approach to music therapy can facilitate the client's reintegration into society (Braswell 1968; Justice and Crowe 2007a; Rubin 1973, 1975; Wilson 1990b). For higher functioning clients, "it is essential that the therapist stress the importance of the program and even explain what is to be accomplished by it" (Nowicki and Trevisan 1978, 155). Having these clients write or choose their own goals is one way of encouraging them to take responsibility for their own actions (Cooper 1985; Nowicki and Trevisan 1978). It is also important to remember that a therapist's concern for the client, reflected in actions as well as words, can affect the client's progress: "If the therapist is frequently late or inconsistent with the group, the clients tend to interpret it to mean that therapy is not important, and, further, that their mental health is not important" (Nowicki and Trevisan 1978, 155).

QUESTIONS FOR THOUGHT AND DISCUSSION

1. Discuss some of the special characteristics and needs of adults who have mental or behavioral disorders. What implications do these have for music therapy programming?

2. Why are music experiences useful in making contact with adults who have mental or behavioral disorders? Are some types of experiences and activities more useful than others for certain types of clients? Which ones? Why?

3. Describe the six different models that may be used to guide the treatment of adults who have mental or behavioral disorders. Which music therapy approaches described in this chapter reflect a biomedical orientation? behavioral orientation? psychodynamic orientation? humanistic orientation? cognitive orientation? Do any reflect a holistic-wellness orientation?

4. Describe Wheeler's three levels of music therapy practice with adult psychiatric clients. What is the difference between music activity therapy and music psychotherapy? Why do music therapists need advanced training to use in-depth music psychotherapy or insight music therapy with reconstructive goals?

5. Describe some specific music therapy experiences that might be used in treating adults who have (a) schizophrenic disorders, (b) mood disorders, (c) anxiety or stress disorders, (d) eating disorders, (e) problems with substance abuse or addiction, or (f) who are in correctional facilities. What unique benefits does music add to treatment in each of these areas?

6. List several special considerations that may be important to remember when developing therapeutic intervention strategies for adults who have mental or behavioral disorders. Why are these important? What are the implications for the structure of music therapy intervention strategies?

7. For each of the situations listed below, (a) define the problem or areas of need for the client or group of clients, (b) describe one or more of the goals you might pursue in music therapy sessions with the client(s), (c) describe music activities you might use to help the client(s) meet those goals, (d) tell how the music activities you described relate to the goals and needs of the client(s), and (e) mention any special considerations you might want to take into account when working with the client(s).

Situation 1:
      You are working as a music therapist in a psychiatric hospital. One of the groups is comprised of five schizophrenic patients, aged 25–35 years. All have a history of previous hospitalizations, but none have been in the hospital for more than a week during their current admission. These patients are not yet stabilized on medication. They are confused and disoriented. Their problems include lack of reality orientation, inability to relate to others, disorganized and inappropriate verbalizations, and short attention spans.

Situation 2:

You are working at a university clinic. A 20-year-old female with anorexia has contacted you about starting private music therapy sessions. She has heard that music therapy techniques can sometimes be useful in helping people overcome anorexia. So far, no other treatment she has tried has had a lasting effect. She says her life seems out of control. She enjoys music, and wonders whether music therapy could help her.

SUGGESTIONS FOR FURTHER READING

Bednarz, L. F. & Nikkei, B. (1992). The role of music therapy in the treatment of young adults diagnosed with mental illness and substance abuse. *Music Therapy Perspectives, 10,* 21–26.

Blake, R. L. & Bishop, S. R. (1994). The Bonny method of Guided Imagery and Music (GIM) in the treatment of post-traumatic stress disorder (PTSD) with adults in the psychiatric setting. *Music Therapy Perspectives, 12(2),* 125–129.

Brescia, K. E. (Ed.) (1991). *Case studies in music therapy.* Phoenixville, PA: Barcelona.

Cassity, M. D. & Cassity, J. E. (2006). *Multimodal psychiatric music therapy for adults, adolescents, and children.* St. Louis: MMB Music.

Cassity, M. D. & Cassity, J. E. (1994). Psychiatric music therapy assessment and treatment in clinical training facilities with adults, adolescents and children. *Journal of Music Therapy, 31(1),* 2–30.

Crowe, B. J. & Colwell, C. (Eds.) (2007). *Music therapy for children, adolescents, and adults with mental disorders.* Silver Spring, MD: American Music Therapy Association.

Gfeller, K. E. & Thaut, M. H. (2008). Music therapy in the treatment of behavioral-emotional disorders. In W. B. Davis, K. E. Gfeller, & M. H. Thaut (Eds.), *An introduction to music therapy: Theory and practice* (3rd ed.) (209–246). Silver Spring, MD: American Music Therapy Association.

Goldberg, F. S. (1989). Music psychotherapy in acute psychiatric inpatient and private practice settings. *Music Therapy Perspectives, 6,* 40–43.

Justice, R. W. (1994). Music therapy interventions for people with eating disorders in an inpatient setting. *Music Therapy Perspectives, 12(2),* 104–110.

Langdon, G. S., Pearson, J., Stastny, P., & Thorning, H. (1989). The integration of music therapy into a treatment approach in the transition of adult psychiatric patients from institution to community. *Music Therapy, 8(1),* 92–107.

Nolan, P. (1983). Insight therapy: GIM in a forensic psychiatric setting. *Music Therapy, 3,* 43–51.

Nolan, P. (1989). Music as a transitional object in the treatment of bulimia. *Music Therapy Perspectives, 6,* 49–51.

Parente, A. B. (1989). Feeding the hungry soul: Music as therapeutic modality in the treatment of anorexia nervosa. *Music Therapy Perspectives, 6,* 44–48.

Silverman, M. J. (2003). The influence of music on the symptoms of psychosis: A meta-analysis. *Journal of Music Therapy, 40,* 27–40.

Silverman, M. J. (2007). Evaluating current trends in psychiatric music therapy: A descriptive analysis. *Journal of Music Therapy, 44*, 388–414.

Skaggs, R. (1997). *Finishing strong: Treating chemical addictions with music and imagery.* St. Louis: MMB Music.

Solli, H. P., Rolvsjord, R., & Borg, M. (2013). Toward understanding music therapy as a recovery-oriented practice within mental health care: A meta-synthesis of service users' experiences. *Journal of Music Therapy, 50*, 244–273.

Taylor, D. B. (1997). *Biomedical foundations of music as therapy.* St. Louis: MMB Music.

Thaut, M. H. (1987). A new challenge for music therapy: The correctional setting. *Music Therapy Perspectives, 4*, 44–50.

Thaut, M. H. (2008). Group music psychotherapy in correctional psychiatry. In W. B. Davis, K. E. Gfeller, & M. H. Thaut (Eds.), *An introduction to music therapy: Theory and practice* (3rd ed) (247–259). Silver Spring, MD: American Music Therapy Association.

Treder-Wolff, J. (1990). Affecting attitudes: Music therapy in addictions treatment. *Music Therapy Perspectives, 8*, 67–71.

Tyson, F. (1981). *Psychiatric music therapy: Origins and development.* New York: Fred Weidner & Sons.

Unkefer, R. F. & Thaut, M. (Eds.) (2002). *Music therapy in the treatment of adults with mental disorders.* St. Louis: MMB.

Wheeler, B. L. (1987). Levels of therapy: The classification of music therapy goals. *Music Therapy, 6*(2), 39–49.

Wolfe, D. E. (1996). Group music therapy in acute mental health care: Meeting the demands of effectiveness. In C. E. Furman (Ed.), *Effectiveness of music therapy procedures: Documentation of research and clinical practice* (2nd ed.) (106–143). Silver Spring, MD: National Association for Music Therapy.

Wyatt, J. G. (2002). From the field: Clinical resources for music therapy with juvenile offenders. *Music Therapy Perspecives, 20*(2), 80–88.

Chapter Sixteen

MUSIC THERAPY FOR INDIVIDUALS WHO HAVE SEVERE MULTIPLE DISABILITIES

Definition

DSM-V (2013) describes four severity levels of intellectual disabilities: mild, moderate, severe, and profound. This chapter basically concerns individuals at the severe level, although the term *severely/profoundly* sometimes is used to indicate that categories may overlap. DSM-V further categorizes each level into conceptual, social, and practical domains.

Severely disabled individuals have limited ability to form concepts and will need assistance with problem solving throughout their life. Although they may have ability to use single words or short phrases, speech is very limited, if present at all. They may understand some social speech and gestures and may form relationships with familiar people. These individuals need constant supervision and support because of their limited ability to participate in activities of daily living. Even as adults, they need support and supervision to participate in work or recreation, and they are unable to make decisions for their own welfare or others. With long-term training, some progress is possible, and all staff should continue to strive for the highest achieveable level for each individual even though progress will be slow. Some also have a tendency for self-injury, but they are in the minority (DSM-V 2013, 36). In addition, "individuals with intellectual disability, particularly those with more severe intellectual disability, may also exhibit aggression and disruptive behaviors, including harm of others or property destruction" (DSM-V 2013, 40).

Multiply disabled individuals have two or more conditions that seriously interfere with functioning and learning (Pfeifer 1982, 1989). This is common in intellectual disability "with rates of some conditions (e.g., mental disorders, cerebral palsy, and epilepsy) three to four times higher than in the general population" (DSM-V 2013, 40). This term does not specify any *type* of disability, but refers only to the *number* of disabilities that impact a person's functioning. For example, one individual with multiple disabilities may be blind and have intellectual disability, while another may have cerebral palsy, an intellectual disability, speech impairments, and visual impairments. Still another multiply disabled individual may have severe emotional disturbances, neuromuscular difficulties, and a seizure disorder, whereas a fourth may be nonambulatory, nonverbal, and have a chronic medical condition. Yet another individual may be hemiplegic and have expressive aphasia. These disabilties are severe and pervasive.

Cause

Many individuals who have severe and multiple disabilities are born with these problems. Disabilities may arise from various causes, such as genetic abnormalities, abnormal fetal development, prenatal trauma or injury, lack of oxygen at birth, or injuries during delivery. Other individuals acquire severe and multiple disabilities later in life as a result of diseases, accidents, brain or spinal cord injuries, or strokes. More information on the causes of a particular disability can be found in the chapter that discusses clients having that specific disability.

COMMON CHARACTERISTICS, PROBLEMS, AND NEEDS OF CLIENTS

As in any population, individuals who have severe multiple disabilities are a very heterogeneous group. Rarely do any two clients have the identical combination of disabilities with the identical degree of impairments. In addition, each client has a unique combination of abilities, needs, personality traits, strengths, and weaknesses that will impact his or her treatment program and functioning level. Music therapists assess the individual's strengths and use that information in program planning. Focusing on strengths is more valuable than concentrating on deficits. Therefore, individual assessment is essential in determining a particular client's unique learning needs and capabilities, and it is unwise to attempt to predict a particular person's skill levels or ceiling of abilities based on broad generalizations about a certain population. However, an awareness of some characteristics, problems, and needs common to many multiply disabled clients may be beneficial both to the therapist who desires to work with this population and the reader who is trying to understand how music therapy intervention strategies may benefit this population.

Individuals with multiple disabilities often have numerous severe physical, mental, and/or social/emotional problems and delays which cause them to need numerous support services (Atterbury 1990; Codding 1988; Coleman 1996; DSM-V 2013; Farnan 1996; Pfeifer 1982). Many have low levels of environmental awareness and limited abilities to respond to the people and objects around them. They may take a longer time to process and respond to information and directions, and their responses may be more subtle. Many have impaired motor control and coordination abilities; some have very limited mobility or are completely nonambulatory. Many of the most severely impaired individuals have few if any functional movements. Some cannot sit independently and need to be positioned in adaptive equipment.

Multiply disabled individuals may have visual or hearing impairments or be very tactilely defensive. Many have some degree of speech or language impairment, and the more severely impaired frequently are nonverbal. They may be able to make some sounds; however, in most cases, speech never develops. Some may be able to communicate with simple sign language, assistive technology, or communication boards, but others are totally unable to communicate and must rely on others to anticipate their needs. Some individuals have complex medical needs and chronic medical conditions. They may have tracheotomies that enable them to breathe, be tube-fed, and/or experience seizures (which may or may not be controllable by medication). Educational and therapeutic programs for these individuals often emphasize areas such as sensory stimulation; increasing functional motor, communication, and social skills; and learning basic self-help and survival skills.

It is important to remember that multiply disabled individuals do have *some* areas of strength and ability that can be nurtured and developed, even if these may seem to be hidden or masked by the severity of the individual's impairments. Whatever the degree or number of their impairments, all individuals have basic human needs and longings to respond to and communicate with others, to love and to be loved. Although responses may be small (e.g., a change in breathing pattern, eyes widening slightly, a slight turn of a head, a small movement of a finger), *they are responses* that can be developed and expanded with patient work and guidance. More than one disability does not make an individual incapable of developing *some* level of functional skills and responses in *some* area of life. Although a client with multiple disabilities might not make great gains in skill development, "the therapist is always about the business of helping the client to do his or her best, with hopes of always moving in the right direction" (Pfeifer 1989, 60).

SETTINGS FOR SERVICE DELIVERY

Depending on the nature and severity of impairments, age, and available community resources, individuals with severe multiple disabilities receive services in various settings. Many infants and school-aged children and adolescents receive services from special education programs administered by their local public school system. The Individuals with Disabilities Act (IDEA)

(Public Law 101-476), the 1990 revision of the 1975 Education for All Handicapped Children Act (Public Law 94-142), assures a free, appropriate public education to all children, aged 3–21 years, including those who have severe multiple disabilities.

From birth through 3 years of age, young children with multiple disabilities may receive services from early intervention programs in their homes, at day care centers, at special clinics, or at early intervention centers. From ages 3–21 years, individuals who have severe multiple disabilities often receive public school special education services "in segregated special schools, self-contained special education classrooms on age-appropriate campuses, or in fully inclusive placements in their home school" (Coleman 1996, 142).

Some individuals with multiple handicaps receive services in other settings, including residential treatment settings; day programs in public or private centers for individuals with developmental disabilities, cerebral palsy, or physical handicaps; group homes; rehabilitation centers; and nursing homes. With the deinstitutionalization that began in the late 1970s, residential centers have declined steadily as more community placement options have become available. Residential facilities now usually admit only persons with severe disabilities, such as profound intellectual disability and medically fragile conditions (Farnan 1996, 114–115).

As individuals age, placement options often grow more limited, and appropriate settings for service delivery may be harder to find. However, as public awareness of the need increases, more community placement options gradually may become available. Those who acquire severe multiple disabilities later in life as a result of diseases, accidents, brain or spinal cord injuries, or strokes often receive services in rehabilitation or nursing home settings.

Ockelford, Welch, and Zimmermann (2002) surveyed 393 schools in England that had educational/therapeutic responsibility for children with severe learning difficulties (SLD) or profound and multiple learning difficulties (PMLD). Ninety-four percent of the responding schools had a designated music coordinator, and over a third of the population was served by a music therapist. The surveyed music coordinators "stated that musical objectives appeared regularly on individual education plans for most pupils with SLD and PMLD" (181). Much of the music is presented by the child's teacher or by others who often have limited training in music.

Controversy regarding the provision of inclusive education for severely disabled students persists. Palmer, Fuller, Arora, and Nelson (2001) analyzed written comments from 140 parents of students with severe disabilities. In addition, 460 answered questions, using a Likert scale, that assessed their opinions regarding inclusive educational placements for their child. The children were described in this way:

22% were unable to walk and 22% had difficulty walking; 39.1% were not toilet trained at all and 28.1% had toileting accidents during the day. Further, 22.8% had seizures; 39.1% needed to be monitored due to behavioral or emotional problems; and 22.6% needed close supervision during the day due to poor health or a physical condition. (469)

They answered in regard to their own child and to students with severe disabilities in general. Some reasons for inclusion included better opportunity for academic or functional skill progress due to greater expectation for performance and more stimulation in an inclusive setting. Among the reasons many parents opposed inclusion was the belief that the child's disability would not allow participation in a general classroom. They thought the child would require more personal care than would be available from a general classroom teacher and feared that their child would distract other students. Most of the respondents "stated a desire to have their children in an environment that emphasized basic living or functional skills" (473). Some even feared that the child would be mistreated or ridiculed by other students.

Placement decisions are not easy; and, with the increased effort to include as many children as possible in the general classroom, the job of individual assessment becomes even more important. Placement should be in the "least restrictive environment" to serve the needs of the child, not the funding source. When assessment finds that music therapy can help students achieve their educational objectives, music therapists may be asked to provide traditional direct services; work with students in self-contained classes or with students in inclusive classes; provide direct in-home services to students who are confined to their homes for medical reasons; provide consultation services to facilitate classroom instruction, inclusion, or music education; and/or provide staff development workshops (Lathom-Radocy 2014; Wilson 1996, 2002).

Music therapy usually is classified as a related service in special education settings. Related services are defined in IDEA legislation (IDEA Regulations, 34 C.F.R. 300.13). In addition, the legislation specifies inclusion of other services "if they are needed to assist a student with a disability in benefiting from special education" (Downing 2004, 196). This statement includes music therapy; thus, is it imperative that the music therapist participate in designing the child's IEP and clearly state how this service will benefit the student's educational progress. This should be stated objectively and based on data recorded during the assessment period.

The list of related services is not exhaustive and may include

other developmental, corrective, or supportive services (such as artistic and cultural programs, art, music and dance therapy) if they are required to assist a child with a disability to benefit from special education in order for the child to receive FAPE [Free, appropriate public education]." (U.S. Department of Education 1999, 12548)

Furthermore, the National Information Center for Children and Youth with Disabilities (NICHCY, 2001, 5) states,

> The purpose of related service roles of art, dance, and music therapists is to
> - Assess the functioning of individual students;
> - Design programs appropriate to the needs and abilities of students;
> - Provide services in which music, movement, or art is used in a therapeutic process to further the child's emotional, physical, cognitive, and/or academic development or integration; and
> - Often act as resource persons for classroom teachers.

HOW MUSIC IS USED IN THERAPY

Almost all individuals, even those who have severe multiple disabilities, respond positively to some form of music. Nordoff and Robbins (1977, 1) describe "Music Child" – "that entity in every child which responds to musical experience, finds it meaningful and engaging, remembers music, and enjoys some form of musical expression." This entity often lies dormant in individuals who have severe multiple disabilities. As music therapists find that particular music, instrument, rhythm, or mode of response that attracts the individual's attention, the individual's inborn musicality begins to be awakened. Music therapists then structure music experiences to support, shape, and develop the individual's responses, thus facilitating increased awareness and perception and the development of appropriate interactions and skills.

The response may be subtle. Ghetti (2002, 22), reporting her work with profoundly handicapped individuals, indicated that "individuals with severe and profound disabilities exhibited pupil dilation when presented with pleasant visual, tactile and auditory stimuli, and demonstrated pupil constriction when presented with unpleasant stimuli." She studied the effect of rhythmic stimulation, song singing, and multisensory rhythm instrument playing on alert behavior states of profoundly disabled children in comparison with baseline behaviors. She found no difference among conditions, but the response of these children is so subtle that it would have been difficult to evaluate. She had a small sample size, which is common in research with this population because each individual is quite different from every other one. In addition, she noted that "individuals with multiple disabilities need longer periods of time for cognitive processing and take longer to learn" (28). For this reason, she suggested that music therapy intervention may be more successful if presented more than once per day for short periods of time (such as about 20 minutes). Operant conditioning has been demonstrated to be effective for this population, and has "demonstated that this population is indeed capable of learning" (23).

Music is a multisensory stimulus, something that is heard, felt (vibrations), and seen (watching performer or instrument). Multisensory approaches are critical to work with individuals whose sensory systems are often severely impaired (Davis and Farnan 2007; Farnan 1996). When music enters the environment, its pitch, rhythm, and/or the tactile sensation of its organized vibrations can attract the individual's attention and provide a new and direct way for that person to relate to the environment. Music can be both a stimulus for and a reinforcer of responses, thereby motivating clients to reach out to their environment, rewarding these attempts with pleasurable stimuli, and providing structures within which they can learn and practice new skills.

Music experiences can help prepare clients for learning experiences by decreasing levels of tension, distractibility, and hypersensitivity and by positively influencing muscle tone. Music also functions as a vehicle for emotional release and expression and as a means of verbal and nonverbal communication by providing opportunities for socialization and interaction with others. When music experiences are structured therapeutically, they can help individuals who have severe multiple disabilities increase environmental awareness, eye contact, attention span, awareness of self and others, functional social behaviors, functional motor skills, auditory and visual discrimination, receptive and expressive communication skills, cooperative and appropriate interactions with others, appropriate expression of emotions, basic self-help skills, and functional academic concepts (Boxill 1985; Coleman 1996; Cormier 1982; Farnan 1996; Farnan and Johnson 1988b; Kay 1981; Krout 1987; Lathom 1981a, 1981b; Lathom and Eagle 1982; Lathom-Radocy 2014; Nordoff and Robbins 1971a, 1971b, 1977; Rainey Perry 2003; Pfeifer 1982).

General Approaches and Techniques

If music therapists are to work effectively with clients who have severe multiple disabilities, they must learn to (1) carefully *observe* the client; (2) *change* or *adapt* the environment, techniques, or activities, as necessary, based on the client's responses; and (3) *set realistic goals*, based on the information gathered in observing and responding to the client, that will help the client improve basic functional and adaptive skills in his or her areas of need (Pfeifer 1982). Davis and Farnan (2008, 105–106) described preacademic skills necessary for learning: attention, following directions, and eye contact. These skills are generally not developed in severely multiply disabled individuals and, thus, give direction to goals needed in music therapy.

One must also adjust expectations and realize that individuals with severe multiple disabilities often take a very long time to develop responses or learn adaptive skills (Atterbury 1990; Coleman 1996). Responses may be more subtle, and response time within activities may be longer (Farnan 1996; Wheeler and Stultz 2008). As the individual works repetitively on the same learning tasks over many months and years, the therapist's ability to add slight variations to the music strategies and approaches can help maintain interest and attention, as well as promote generalization of that skill or concept. Repetition in various modes of expression also provides opportunities for different levels of participation and for introducing learning through various sensory pathways.

Music therapists who work with groups of individuals who have multiple disabilities face special challenges, for it is extremely unlikely that any two individuals will have identical conditions, impairments, and needs (Atterbury 1990; Farnan and Johnson 1988b; Krout 1987). However, with careful planning, music therapists can use the same activity to help different individuals work on different goals or objectives (Farnan and Johnson 1988b; Krout 1987). For example, the goal for one individual might be to hold his head up and look at the therapist during the "hello" song, while the goal for another individual during the same song might be to vocalize with the therapist, and the goal for a third individual might be to wave "hello" at the appropriate place in the song. The key is to structure activities so each individual can participate at his or her own level of ability, while spontaneously changing and adapting the activity, as necessary, based on the client's responses and/or immediate needs.

Another challenge in working with groups of individuals who have severe multiple disabilities is the "high degree of therapist involvement required to include the students in educational activities" (Krout 1987, 3). Often, unless each client has his or her own assistant, the therapist must move from individual to individual, giving them prompts or physical assistance to participate in activities. Frequently, a group session with severely multiply disabled individuals may seem more like a series of individual sessions. However, the music does provide a stimulus and focal point to which all clients can perceive and attend, even if the therapist is working directly with one client. Directing other group members to attend to the individual "performing" (or being assisted to perform) can help clients increase their awareness of others, sound localization, and attention span. Group members also can learn by watching others respond and be encouraged to participate themselves as they see their peers try to participate. For example, some individuals are more likely to vocalize if they are in a group and hear their peers vocalizing.

Several music therapists suggest that an effective way to plan group sessions for severely multiply disabled individuals is to proceed from a general session outline (Coleman 1996; Farnan and Johnson 1988b; Krout 1987). In this approach, the general progression of activities within each session remains the same (e.g., greeting song, warm-up movement-to-music or action song, instrument play, targeted preacademic or academic skill, singing, instrument play, movement-to-music, cool-down/session review, closing song), although the particular experience within each category may vary from session to session (e.g., use drum for instrument play one week, triangle the next). Of course, many different general session structures are possible, depending on the age of the clients, the needs and capabilities of the various individuals within the group, the time and space available, the equipment available, the particular music therapy objectives for the group members, etc. Coleman (1996), Davis and Farnan (2008, 109), Farnan and Johnson (1988b), and Krout (1987) provide several examples of music therapy session outlines for various age and ability groups of clients with multiple disabilities.

Therapeutic Music Experiences to Increase General Awareness and Responsiveness

Many individuals who have severe multiple disabilities seem to have very little, if any, awareness of the people, objects, and events around them. Before they can develop other adaptive skills, they must make some response to surrounding stimuli, no matter how subtle (e.g., change in facial expression, dilation or constriction of pupils, slight vocalization, increase or decrease in movement or respiration, slight movement or turning toward sound source). Music activities are often effective in eliciting awareness responses from these clients, even when other treatment intervention modalities have failed. Music provides a powerful sensory stimulus that is almost impossible to ignore (Lathom 1981b) and can be adapted to allow for many different response levels (Sears 1968/2007). As music is used creatively to reflect, mirror, and match the client's "here-and-now," and as it is used to identify and symbolize the relationship emerging between the client and therapist, an awakening of responsiveness often begins to occur. Boxill (1985, 71) terms this "*a continuum of awareness*, the creative process of using music functionally as a tool of consciousness to awaken, heighten, and expand awareness of self, others, and the environment."

Several different types of music experiences establish contact with and elicit initial responses from clients with severe multiple disabilties. These include (1) music in combination with intensive-play or play therapy techniques (Carter 1982; Gonzales 1981; Miorin and Covault 1979; Monti 1985); (2) music improvisations built around the client's vocal, movement, or instrumental responses (Boxill 1985; Nordoff and Robbins 1971b, 1977; Pfeifer 1982); and (3) sensory stimulation experiences using the auditory and tactile input from musical instruments to attract attention and elicit responses, with gradual exposure to "hands-on" experiences with instruments (Cormier 1982; Farnan 1996; Schmidt 1981). Positioning clients on a specially designed, wooden sound floor may help them feel the vibrations of live music and increase their responsiveness to the musical stimuli (Farnan 1996).

Some music therapists are now having great success using electronic and high technology music resources to establish initial responses in multiply disabled individuals. Campbell, Milbourne, Dugan, and Wilcox (2006) reviewed research on assistive technology (AT). Children between the ages of 2.5 to 60 months used switch activation (e.g., "head turn; head movement; leg movement; touch") to produce an outcome or consequence. They mention that one outcome was music, which was reinforcing for the child. The 12 studies that met criterion included infants and young children diagnosed with cerebral palsy, severe or multiple disabilities, severe motor delays, or Down syndrome. These studies provide relatively strong evidence that

> children younger than a year old and with a variety of types of disabilities including cognitive disabilities may be successfully taught to operate switches to activate toys or provide other outcomes when switch activation uses an existing movement and results in outcomes that are reinforcing to the child. (Campbell, Milbourne, Dugan, and Wilcox 2006, 6)

Six of the included articles discussed computer use with young disabled children. In using computer software programmed for learning experiences, the investigators found that the children "preferred software that included bright colors, sound, and animation" (7). This should be further explored in music therapy research.

Swingler (1994) described Soundbeams, a technology that uses ultrasonic beams controlled by body movements to play electronic musical instruments at a distance without physical contact. Since the system may be set up so that tiny finger or head movements control the beams, it may be particularly useful in reaching those who have limited motions and limited abilities to respond to the world around them. Computers, synthesizers, specially adapted switches and MIDI-input devices, and music composition software also can create new possibilities for participation and responses for individuals who have severely limited abilities by allowing them to independently control and initiate musical sounds (Krout, Burnham, and Moorman, 1993).

As they learn to interact with others through these technological resources, clients develop increased eye contact, attention to task, and communication with others.

Therapeutic Music Experiences to Decrease Self-Stimulatory or Self-Abusive Behaviors

Some individuals with severe multiple disabilities engage in various self-stimulatory or self-abusive behaviors, which often are a barrier to appropriate interactions with the people and objects around them. Some music therapists have reported stereotypical or self-stimulatory behaviors may be decreased by joining in the behavior musically (e.g., reflecting it with improvisation) and then using musical structure to broaden the behavior into purposeful activity as the client interrupts or modifies his or her behavior in response to the changes in the music (Nordoff and Robbins 1977).

Since music is an attractive stimulus that catches the attention of even many individuals who have severe multiple disabilities, it can also be used effectively with behavior modification techniques, serving as a reinforcer or contingent stimulus to help clients increase eye contact, attention span, appropriate social behaviors, and awareness of surrounding people and objects, while decreasing instances of bizarre and self-abusive behaviors (Mahlberg 1973; Saperston 1973, 1982; Stevens and Clark 1969). Farnan (2007) notes that reducing an undesirable behavior requires offering an appropriate replacement behavior.

Music therapists can use active music making as well as passive music listening techniques to help individuals learn to channel and control responses. For example, Cormier (1982) reported that playing an electric piano with headset helped a nine-year-old boy who had developmental delays, vision and hearing impairments, and many autistic-like behaviors decrease his hyperactive behaviors and increase his attention span. Cormier (1982, 12) observed: "The very act of playing at the piano provided spatial limitations so needed by J." In another example, Clarkson (1991), working with a nonverbal, self-abusive, violent adult autistic male found that, as music therapy sessions utilizing structured and improvised instrumental and vocal activities and dancing to recorded music provided appropriate outlets for self-expression, his tantrums, violent outbursts, and ritualistic behaviors markedly decreased, while his abilities to communicate and interact appropriately with others increased. Griggs-Drane and Wheeler (1997) also found that the aggressive, self-stimulatory behaviors of an adolescent female with multiple handicaps decreased during music therapy sessions. In addition, tapes with recorded music presented to the client after the session helped de-escalate the aggressive behaviors that frequently occurred when the music session ended.

Therapeutic Music Experiences to Increase Adaptive Social Responses and Promote Appropriate Social Interaction Skills

As multiply disabled individuals learn to respond to and interact with adults and peers through specially structured music experiences, they can develop many basic social skills, like looking at the speaker, responding to their name, smiling in response to pleasurable stimuli, looking at others, singing or playing instruments, and participating cooperatively in partner or group activities. In intensive play programs, a progression of prerecorded instrumental music (6–7 minutes of slow music, 7–9 minutes of fast music, 6–7 minutes of slow music) provides the environment and structure for movement activities involving close physical contact and stimulation that develop desired social skills like tolerating physical contact; indicating an awareness of others by smiling, vocalizing, or giving eye contact; moving cooperatively with another person; or engaging in simple imitation games. These techniques have been effective in building basic social behaviors in children with multiple disabilities and profound developmental delays who normally are unresponsive, unaware, and often fearful of physical contact and movement (Carter 1982; Gonzales 1981). Davis and Farnan (2007, 108–109) gave a case history and sample music therapy session plan for a 17-year-old with severe intellectual disability. Although he did not have multiple disabilities, the session example would still apply.

Music also may be used with traditional play therapy approaches, which employ musical sounds, body percussion sounds (e.g., clapping, stamping), and exploration of musical instruments to facilitate interaction with others and the environment (Monti 1985). The extensive range of sound possibilities available through music increases the likelihood that a sound can be found to attract the individual's attention and serve as a starting point to develop responsiveness and interaction with others.

Music experiences also can facilitate social interactions between multiply disabled infants or young children and their parents or siblings. Witt and Steele (1984) described a case where a multiply disabled 14-month-old girl learned to increase eye contact and positive interactions with her mother, to play appropriately with rhythm instruments and sound-producing toys, and to respond to her name through music therapy sessions involving both mother and child. Approaches included singing early childhood action songs while assisting the child to participate, providing rhythmic experiences using various instruments and sound-producing toys to attract attention and encourage interaction, and using listening experiences to promote attention and eye contact. The mother would rehearse activities under the therapist's guidance and then continue to implement activities at home during the week, also involving other family members. The music activities gave family members a structure for interacting positively with the child and helped the child develop basic social skills and responses: "The most important gain, however, was the improvement the family felt in their ability to relate to their handicapped member in a meaningful way" (Witt and Steele, 1984, 19).

After the individual develops basic social awareness responses in music activities, these responses gradually may be expanded through more complex and more demanding partner and group music experiences. In individual sessions, a music therapist might use improvisational music techniques to develop increased interactive responses between the client and the therapist (Boxill 1985; Nordoff and Robbins 1971b, 1977; Rainey Perry 2003; Wheeler and Stultz 2008). For example, Shoemark (1991) used piano improvisation with a blind boy who had behavioral disturbances to help develop a relationship that encouraged positive interactions and cooperative participation. As the boy learned to interact spontaneously with the therapist in music making, his participation and cooperation also increased. More behaviorally oriented techniques that use music or music activities to reinforce desired social behaviors like eye contact and attention to task also can increase these responses in individual sessions (Witt and Steele 1984).

Wheeler and Stultz (2008) compared musical relatedness and communication of typically developing infants with children with multiple severe disabilities. They used Greenspan's model of psychosocial development (Greenspan and Wieder 2000), which describes nine stages of child development. However, Wheeler and Stultz found that only the first three stages applied to their study population. In stage one, the child develops regulatory behavior to allow adjustment to changes in stimulation. Stage two, which centers on relationship formation, is usually seen in an infant of about 5 months of age. In the third stage, intentional two-way communication is fostered, and this stage usually is achieved by a 9-month old infant. The child learns that his or her behavior can have consequences. A music therapist working with an individual at this stage "can promote opportunities for the child to make the connection between wanting something, taking action, and achieving a goal" (587). This study addresses the ways in which a therapist may use a developmental framework to help children progress in their abilities to self-regulate and focus on the environment, enjoy closeness with attachment figures, and engage in two-way communication. The investigators' videotapes of sessions revealed that multiply disabled infants and children exhibit needs and themes during development similar to those of children who are developing more normally. This study also gives guidance to the formation of music therapy goals by therapists who are working with individuals who are still in one of these first stages of development.

Rainey Perry (2003) used improvisational music therapy with severely and multiply disabled children to study musical interaction. Ten school-aged children participated; cerebral palsy was the most common medical diagnosis. Video recordings were analyzed to identify the child's communication development level. Rainey Perry found that "both turn taking and playing and singing together were found to be important forms of communication during music therapy" (227). These children displayed the communication difficulties previously identified in descriptions of severely intellectually disabled children (lack of attention to objects, lack of interaction, lack of motivation, limited means of interaction, insufficient arousal, little interest in the outside environment). Rainey Perry also noted that "it was often important for the therapist to wait for the child to initiate and respond" (237). With consistency and adequate wait time, these children do present brief indications of awareness and pleasure in music therapy (Adamek and Darrow 2010).

In group sessions, structured music activities involving singing, moving to music, or playing instruments with others can help individuals with multiple disabilities learn to participate and cooperate with others as they play/sing/move all together or as they wait their turn to play and learn to share with others (Coleman 1996; Farnan 1996; Farnan and Johnson 1988a, 1988b; Kay 1981; Krout 1987; Lathom 1981b; Lathom and Eagle 1982; Lathom-Radocy 2014; Nordoff and Robbins 1971a; Wheeler and Stultz 2008).

Music activities can be structured so individuals with widely varying abilities can participate simultaneously. Some may sing all the words of a song; others may vocalize on a single syllable (Krout 1987). Some may play a complicated rhythmic or ostinato pattern; others may play one cymbal crash or a steady drum beat. With appropriate adaptations of traditional instruments (Clark and Chadwick 1979; Coleman 1996; Rudenberg 1982), or with electronic instruments and technological innovation, many multiply disabled individuals eventually can participate independently in instrumental ensembles. New electronic and computer technology and special switches and control devices make it possible for even those clients with severe physical limitations to work together with others in music performance groups (Farnan 2007; Fegers et al. 1989). Technology also enables clients who cannot play traditional instruments to make the sounds of these instruments. For example, by using switches connected to specific electronic or computer-controlled drum sounds, clients can work together to produce the sound of a large drum set (Krout 1995). Cooperative ensemble experiences like this help the clients focus on each other and improve their attention and sense of group as they concentrate on the sound being produced and work to play the desired sound patterns.

Music activities also can provide opportunities for multiply disabled individuals to interact with their nondisabled peers. In some cases, individuals with disabilities may participate in ensembles with nondisabled peers (Fegers et al. 1989). In other instances, nondisabled students may function as "peer-helpers" in music classes for students who have multiple disabilities (Atterbury 1990; Dykman 1979). A peer-helper can help move the individual's feet or arms rhythmically, move the individual's wheelchair for wheelchair dances, and help hold instruments. As the students interact, they learn to cooperate in positive ways and develop new ways to socialize with persons who differ from them.

Therapeutic Music Experiences to Improve Motor Functioning

Many individuals with severe multiple disabilities have limited functional motor skills. Those who are nonambulatory and immobile may need range-of-motion exercises to help them maintain or increase joint and muscle function. However, some individuals have such high muscle tone that these exercises become very difficult to perform. Music therapists can use their knowledge of the physiological effects of different types of music on muscle tone to provide background music that will help reduce a client's overly high muscle tone, provide sensory stimulation, and facilitate responses to range-of-motion exercises (Farnan 2007; Schmidt 1981). Action and body-part songs also can provide structure for movement exercises. Awareness of the body is part of self-identity, which is the beginning of understanding self as separate from others (Lathom-Radocy 2014). As individuals are given assistance to participate in these movement-to-music experiences, they can be guided through normal movement patterns and increase their awareness of body position and body parts.

In addition to facilitating appropriate muscle tone, musical stimuli may provide the incentive or motivation for clients to maintain proper posture or positioning. Wolfe (1980) used an operant conditioning procedure involving contingent music listening to help individuals with cerebral palsy increase their ability to maintain an upright head position. Kraut (1987) found that the desire to participate in music activities could also help an individual who had multiple handicaps and poor head control learn to keep his head upright for longer periods of time. In addition, individuals who need to adjust to new positioning equipment may learn to tolerate it more readily in the music therapy situation, where interest in the music activity may distract them from the pain or the restrictions of the equipment.

Musical stimuli, particularly the sounds of musical instruments, may also motivate clients to increase their purposeful active movements (Farnan 2007; Farnan and Johnson 1988b; Schmidt 1981; Witt and Steele 1984). As sound attracts the individual's attention, the individual will look toward the sound source and then gradually reach toward it. At first, individuals may need assistance to reach out to touch and feel instruments (Farnan 1996, 1997; Schmidt 1981), but as their tolerance for tactile stimulation and their abilities to direct their movements increase, this guidance gradually can be faded.

Playing basic rhythm instruments can help individuals develop many functional hand skills, such as reaching, touching, grasping, holding, manipulating, and releasing (Farnan and Johnson 1988b). However, some multiply disabled individuals, especially those who are very tactilely defensive and who startle or have a seizure in response to the slightest touch, may need very gradual exposure to "hands-on" experiences with instruments over the course of many months. Still, with patience and carefully structured experiences (first listening, then being close enough to feel the vibrations, then being assisted to touch and play the instrument, and, finally, perhaps reaching out to play it themselves), most individuals are eventually able to tolerate touching and playing instruments. For example, as Schmidt (1981, 24) reported, "A girl who used to seizure when the guitar was strummed within one foot of her body now, after 14 months, tolerates having her own hand used to strum the guitar for two to three minutes with no seizure activity."

Movement-to-music activities can also be very beneficial in helping individuals who have severe multiple disabilities increase their motor control and coordination and their sense of body image and awareness of self in space (Boswell and Vidret 1993; Farnan and Johnson 1988a, 1988b; Lathom 1981b; Lathom and Eagle 1982; Lathom-Radocy 2014). Programs may include passive movements to music, active rhythmic movements to music, action songs and movement imitation songs or dances, songs or movement-to-music experiences that direct clients to move particular body parts or move their whole bodies in certain ways, creative movement responses to music, and relaxation exercises to music.

> Adults and children with severe and profound needs . . . usually have difficulty coordinating even basic movements, due to physical and cognitive limitations. Nonetheless, music therapy experiences that promote movement enable these individuals to interact more fully within the environment. (Davis and Farnan, 101)

Therapeutic Music Experiences to Facilitate Personal Expression

The opportunities for self-expression through music can be very important for individuals whose severe multiple disabilities allow them very limited means of personal expression. As individuals learn to make choices (e.g., choose an instrument to play, choose a note or word to fit in a song) and express preferences (e.g., for instruments, particular songs, types of music), they develop functional skills needed for a more independent life (Farnan 1996). Even those who are nonverbal can find ways to express themselves in music (Davis and Farnan 2007). For example, individuals who use communication boards may respond to questions or contribute to song-writing exercises by using their boards (Adamek and Darrow 2007). Working with children who used Blissymbols, Herman (1985) had them point to symbols to identify feelings represented by music, contribute to group "story songs," or tell what feelings they wanted to express. Signing and manual communication systems can be used to express song lyrics, and signs and singing can be used together for total communication experiences (Darrow 1987a; Knapp 1980). Technology now even makes it possible for nonverbal individuals to have an active "voice" in many music experiences (Humpal and Dimmick 1995). For example, switches may activate tape players containing tape loops of repeated words or phrases in a song (Coleman 1996; Humpal and Dimmick 1995). Individuals who have augmentive communication devices that produce synthesized speech sounds may use these to supply words or phrases to songs or contribute to discussions or group compositions. Adamek and Darrow (2010) remind music therapists to be sure that their device includes appropriate music symbols.

Music experiences also help stimulate emotional responses and develop appropriate means of emotional expression. At a basic level, individuals develop emotional responses as they indicate excitement, pleasure, or other emotions aroused by musical stimuli (Pfeifer 1982). Emotional responsiveness is further demonstrated when individuals respond by synchronizing their instrument playing to match the tempo and dynamic changes of the therapist's improvisation (Nordoff and Robbins 1971a, 1977; Pfeifer 1982; Shoemark 1991). This ability to participate freely in expressive musical activities also can positively influence the individual's general emotional state. For example, Shoemark (1991) noted that as a boy with multiple disabilities developed communicative responsiveness and spontaneous creativity in his piano improvisations with the music therapist, his positive affect and mood also increased. In addition, expressive music experiences (e.g., singing, playing the drum) can be a means of venting and releasing one's innermost feelings (Pfeifer 1982), which can be very important to clients who have limited means of personal expression.

As they sing or vocalize, move creatively to music, play instruments, create songs or improvisations, or choose songs that tell something about themselves or their feelings, individuals who have severe multiple disabilities gain new and appropriate avenues for self-expression: "It is important to keep in mind that most behaviors that might be considered inappropriate are actually an attempt to communicate needs" (Davis and Farnan 2008, 99). Participation can be encouraged at each individual's level of ability (Krout 1987). For example, verbal individuals may be encouraged to sing song lyrics, those who use sign may be encouraged to sign lyrics, and nonverbal individuals may be prompted to vocalize on "ah." With appropriate adaptations, many individuals eventually can learn to play some instruments independently (Adamek and Darrow 2010; Birkenshaw-Fleming 1993; Clark and Chadwick 1979; Coleman 1996; Edelstein 1987, 1989; Elliott 1982; Lathom-Radocy 2014; Rudenberg 1982; Zinar 1987) and use them to express feelings and emotions. Adamek and Darrow (2010, 70–71) describe many ways simple instruments may be adapted to allow children with more severe disabilities to participate. Recent advances in technology now allow even individuals who have severe physical limitations increased opportunities to create music independently through the use of computers and adaptive electronic equipment (Fegers et al. 1989; Howell et al. 1995; Krout 1992, 1995; Krout, Burnham, and Moorman 1993; Nagler and Lee 1989; Swingler 1994). With these technological tools,

> a whole range of people, for whom the possibility of making any kind of musical performance would have been regarded as remote if not downright

inconceivable, have discovered that the development of creative musical expression and performance is now entirely possible for them. (Swingler 1994, 5)

Therapeutic Music Experiences to Develop Functional Academic and Life Skills

Once individuals with severe multiple disabilities develop basic awareness of and attention to music experiences, music therapy activities can be structured to help them progress gradually through higher levels of awareness and increase their basic academic and functional life skills (Coleman 1996; Farnan 1996; Kay 1981; Krout 1987; Pfeifer 1982). The content of the academic work remains basic: "Academic work usually is related to learning tasks of daily living and self-care (e.g., feeding, toilet training, basic hygiene, and dressing skills)" (Lathom-Radocy 2014, 46). Individuals may learn to follow directions and improve their imitation skills as they participate in action songs and musical games that require them to respond to verbal directions or imitate one-step and two-step sequences. Colors, numbers, shapes, and spatial concepts can be learned and practiced in structured music activities using songs, movement-to-music, or musical instruments. Music experiences can also be structured to improve skills in making choices, matching, and sorting. In addition, multiply disabled individuals often can learn and practice the sequence of steps for specific life skills (e.g., spreading peanut butter on a cracker or brushing teeth) more easily when these steps are set to song lyrics (Griggs-Drane and Wheeler 1997). Music also can establish an environment that makes it easier for multiply disabled individuals to acquire life skills. For example, when such individuals received feeding training in a music-controlled environment, they remained calmer and more attentive (Ayres 1987). In addition, the trainers said clients felt more patient and tolerant when the background music was used.

SPECIAL CONSIDERATIONS AND TIPS FOR SUCCESS

Even though the clients discussed in this chapter often have severe and numerous physical, mental, and/or social/emotional problems and delays, they still deserve treatment with dignity and respect. Therapists should talk to them as they would to any person of their age. Selections of music and music materials should be as age-appropriate as possible. Even if the therapist does not think the client can understand, the therapist still should explain what she or he is doing and wants the client to do. The therapist should use short, concrete statements, using gestures and vocal tone to help convey the message. Music therapists should describe what the clients are seeing, hearing, and feeling to help them label their experiences. It is also important to use many kinds of sensory experiences and multisensory stimulation: "The pairing of rhythmic stimuli with specific movements is utilized to provide multisensorial stimulation and to develop improved sensory processing and integration" (Farnan 2007, 83).

Because multiply disabled individuals often take longer to process the information and make a response, therapists must be sure they wait long enough for the individual to respond. Music therapists who work with clients who have severe multiple disabilities often need to "fine tune" their observation skills so that they become aware of very subtle responses, like a slight change in the client's breathing pattern or a widening of the eyes to a certain musical stimulus. Since these individuals often take many months or even years to learn and develop skills and responses, it is important to work on skills that will be functional for the individual in the long term. Therapists must be prepared to repeat the same information in many different ways to give clients opportunities to learn and practice skills: "Creative repetition is the key with this population" (Coleman 1996, 155).

Because multiply disabled individuals often have very limited motor skills, instruments or materials frequently require adaptation to allow clients to participate as independently as possible (Clark and Chadwick 1979; Coleman 1996; McCord and Fitzgerald 2006). When physically assisting instrument play or movement, the therapist should encourage as much independence as possible. For example, even though individuals may be unable to play tambourine independently, they may be able to move their hands or fingers to tap the tambourine when the therapist supports and guides their movement at the wrist or elbow and holds the tambourine in front of them. In some instances, computers, electronic instruments, and adaptive switches and control devices can enable even individuals with very severe multiple handicaps to control musical sounds and make music independently (Adamek and Darrow 2010; Fegers et al. 1989; Krout 1992, 1995; Krout, Burnham, and Moorman 1993; Swingler 1994).

Any of the special considerations mentioned for specific disabilities also apply when an individual has that condition in combination with some other impairment. In addition, many of the music therapy intervention strategies listed for individuals who have severe developmental disabilities, autism, or severe motor limitations are often useful and effective with multiply disabled individuals. Because many may have complex medical needs and conditions, "the music therapist practicing in this type of setting must have knowledge of infection control practices, emergency procedures, child development, education, and rehabilitation" (Farnan 1996, 114).

In order to coordinate their treatment approach with that of other treatment team members, music therapists working with multiply disabled individuals must become familiar with the various theories and practices associated with abnormal/normal development, alternative communication, sensory integration, and neurodevelopmental treatment and learn to incorporate those theories and techniques used by the other professionals in their facility into music therapy treatment programs (F. Johnson 1981; Kalas 2012). Music therapists must also become aware of the methods of observation and assessment that are useful and appropriate for work with multiply disabled clients (F. Johnson 1981). In addition, music therapists should learn which methods of observation, assessment, and data collection are most useful and appropriate and find ways to individualize treatment within group settings (Coleman 1996; Farnan 1996; Farnan and Johnson 1988b; F. Johnson 1981; Krout 1987; Pfeifer 1982, 1989).

QUESTIONS FOR THOUGHT AND DISCUSSION

1. Describe some of the general characteristics and needs of multiply disabled individuals. What implications do these have for music therapy programming?
2. Why and how are music experiences useful in making contact with multiply disabled individuals? Are some types of experiences and activities more useful than other? Which ones? Why?
3. Describe some specific music therapy experiences that might be used to help multiply disabled individuals (a) increase general awareness and responsiveness, (b) decrease self-stimulatory or self-abusive behaviors, (c) increase adaptive social responses and promote appropriate social interaction skills, (d) improve motor functioning, (e) facilitate personal expression, and (f) develop functional academic and life skills. What unique benefits does music provide in each of these areas?
4. List several special considerations that may be important to remember when developing therapeutic intervention strategies for multiply disabled persons. Why are these important? What are their implications for the structure of music therapy intervention strategies?
5. For each of the situations listed below, (a) define the problem or areas of need for the client or group of clients, (b) describe one or more of the goals you might pursue in music therapy sessions with the client(s), (c) describe music activities you might use to help the client(s) meet those goals, (d) tell how the music activities you described relate to the goals and needs of the client(s), and (e) mention any special considerations you might want to take into account when working with the client(s).

Situation 1:
    Sue is a 19-year-old female who is nonambulatory and has cerebral

palsy, spastic quadriplegia, and severe intellectual disability. She has flexion contractures at her elbows, hips, and knees, severe scoliosis, and very limited movement in her arms and legs. She sometimes can grasp and hold objects that are placed in her hands and occasionally uses her hands to slowly push objects placed on her wheelchair tray. However, these movements are too slow and limited to be of much functional use. Sue's most consistent and controlled movements are with her head, and the occupational therapist is teaching her to use a head stick and a switch controlled by head movements.

Sue is nonverbal, but she does answer yes-no questions with eye movements (eyes up and down = "yes"; eyes side to side = "no"). She has a receptive vocabulary approximating that of a 4-year-old child and can identify most letters of the alphabet, numbers 1–10, and basic colors. She eye-points to communicate with her language board, which contains about 20 pictures and symbols for familiar people, food, objects, places, and feelings. Sue is a very social person, but has difficulty interacting with others because of her physical and speech limitations.

Sue enjoys music. She often smiles and turns toward the music source when music is playing. When Sue sees staff or ambulatory peers moving and dancing to music, she tries to move her arms and legs, too. Sue also tries to use what limited movement she has in her arms and hands to play musical instruments. With much concentrated effort, Sue can slowly draw her fingers across the strings of a guitar or autoharp held in front of her or ring bells suspended from a line or bar.

Situation 2:

You have been asked to provide music therapy services for a group of six children and adolescents who have multiple disabilities and who range in age from 7–16 years old. All are nonverbal and nonambulatory and have severe-to-profound intellectual disabilities along with numerous medical and physical difficulties. Four have spastic quadriplegia and many muscle contractures; two have floppy muscle tone and some jerky athetoid movements. All have few if any functional movements; they are completely dependent on others to meet their needs. Three are tube-fed; two have tracheotomies. All have short attention spans, limited awareness of or interest in their environment, and limited abilities to respond to and interact with others. Staff members have noticed some slight changes in behavior, affect, and muscle tone when different types of music are played in the room, but these responses are currently inconsistent and unpredictable.

SUGGESTIONS FOR FURTHER READING

Adamek, M. S. & Darrow, A-A. (Eds.) (2010). Students with cognitive disorders: Mental retardation, learning disabilities, and traumatic brain injury In *Music in special education* (159–181). Silver Spring, MD: American Music Therapy Association

Atterbury, B. W. (1990). *Mainstreaming exceptional learners in music.* Englewood Cliffs, NJ: Prentice-Hall.

Birkenshaw-Fleming, L. (1993). *Music for all: Teaching music to people with special needs.* Toronto: Gordon V. Thompson.

Bruscia, K. E. (Ed.) (1991). *Case studies in music therapy.* Phoenixville, PA: Barcelona.

Clark, C. & Chadwick, D. (1979). *Clinically adapted instruments for the multiply handicapped.* Westford, MA: Modulations.

Coleman, K. A. (1996). Music therapy for learners with severe disabilities in a public school setting. In B. L. Wilson (Ed.), *Models of music therapy interventions in school settings: From institution to inclusion* (142–155). Silver Spring, MD: National Association for Music Therapy.

Cormier, L., Sr. (1982). Music therapy for deaf-blind children. In W. B. Lathom & C. T. Eagle (Eds.), *Music therapy for handicapped children.* Vol. 1 (97–120). Washington, DC: National Association for Music Therapy.

Farnan, L. (1996). Music therapy for learners with severe disabilities in a residential setting. In B. L. Wilson (Ed.), *Models of music therapy interventions in school settings: From institution to inclusion* (113–126). Silver Spring, MD: National Association for Music Therapy.

Farnan, L. & Johnson, F. (1988). *Everyone can move: Music and activities that promote movement and motor development.* New Berlin, WI: Jenson.

Farnan, L. & Johnson, F. (1988). *Music is for everyone: A handbook for providing music to people with special needs.* New Berlin, WI: Jensen.

Krout, R. (1987). Music therapy with multi-handicapped students: Individualizing treatment within a group setting. *Journal of Music Therapy, 24(1),* 2–13.

Monti, R. (1985). Music therapy in a therapeutic nursery. *Music Therapy, 5(1),* 22–27.

Nagler, J. C. & Lee, M. H. M. (1989). Music therapy using computer music technology. In M. H. M. Lee (Ed.), *Rehabilitation, music and human well-being* (226–241). St. Louis: MMB Music.

Pfeifer, M., Sr. (1982). Multihandicapped. In W. B. Lathom & C. T. Eagle, Jr. (Eds.), *Music Therapy for Handicapped Children,* Vol. 3. (2–34). Washington, DC: National Association for Music Therapy.

Pfeifer, M., Sr. (1989). A step in the right direction: Suggested strategies for implementing music therapy with the multihandicapped child. *Music Therapy Perspectives, 6,* 57–60.

Standley, J. (1991). *Music techniques in therapy, counseling, and special education.* St. Louis: MMB Music.

Zinar, R. (1987). *Music activities for special children.* West Nyack, NY: Parker.

Chapter Seventeen

MUSIC THERAPY IN MEDICAL TREATMENT SETTINGS

DEFINITION

Medical treatment involves diagnosing and prescribing measures to cure or alleviate illness, disease, injury, or pain; it also is the science and art of preventing diseases and improving and preserving health. Individuals may seek or require medical treatment for various acute or chronic conditions, injuries, diseases, or life events (e.g., labor and delivery) that impact their daily functioning. Medical treatment may be long- or short-term and occur in various settings, depending on the exact nature of the condition, injury, or disease and the patient's particular needs and life situation. Some treatments may involve hospitalization, surgery, or specific medical procedures (e.g., injections, lumbar punctures, bone marrow aspirations, debridement, cardiac catheterization, dialysis, chemotherapy). Treatment also may include various types of medication or lifestyle changes.

Conditions that cause acute or chronic health problems include heart disease, pulmonary (lung) disease, kidney disease, severe burns, broken bones, severe infections, cystic fibrosis, severe allergies, asthma, hemophilia, sickle cell anemia, leukemia, cancer, diabetes, or epilepsy. This chapter deals mainly with those conditions that are treated in general hospital, outpatient, office, or clinic settings.

COMMON CHARACTERISTICS, PROBLEMS, AND NEEDS OF CLIENTS

The population of individuals who are treated in medical settings is extremely diverse (Gfeller 1992c; Lathom-Radocy 2014; Maranto 1991, 1996; Standley, 1986, 1996b). Clients or patients vary in age (newborns to elderly); diagnosis or condition; type, intensity or urgency of treatment needed (emergency to planned surgery or procedure, acute vs. chronic conditions, wellness programs vs. disease treatment); state of general health; and types of support available. Individuals also have different prognoses, durations of treatment or hospitalization, and responses to their illness or treatment. In addition, each disease or condition presents its own unique set of problems and challenges. Despite this great diversity, some general physical and psychosocial needs common to many individuals undergoing medical treatment or experiencing acute or chronic illnesses are identifiable (Gfeller 1992c; Hurley 1987; Schwankovsky and Guthrie 1982; Wolfe and Waldon 2009). "Every patient paints a different picture due to his or her individual experiences and diagnosis." (Hanson-Abromeit 2008, 4)

Because many conditions or medical procedures are painful to some degree, one of the most common *physical needs* of many patients is finding a way to reduce, increase their tolerance for, or decrease their perception of pain (Gfeller 1992c; Spintge 1989; Wolfe and Waldon 2009). Patients who have conditions that are exacerbated by stress, or who are experiencing extreme stress because they must learn to deal with chronic illnesses or a change in life style, also may need to learn effective relaxation and stress reduction techniques. No matter what their particular medical condition, patients are often anxious about treatment procedures, anesthesia, impending hospitalizations (Hannan 2008; Spintge 1989), or changes that their illness or condition may bring to their lives. Therefore, a common *psychosocial need* is anxiety reduction.

Severe illnesses or accidents may also cause an individual to experience several losses: loss of former self-image, loss of independence (at least for a time), and loss of home and privacy if hospitalization is required. Consequently, many patients need emotional and psychological support to help rebuild self-esteem and facilitate their adaptation to treatment procedures or the revised life style that their condition may mandate (temporarily or permanently). Chronically ill persons, in addition to needing good medical care, also need comprehensive social and psychological services to help them deal with the daily complications and difficult circumstances that accompany many chronic conditions (Hurley 1987).

Other common psychosocial needs of individuals who need treatment for acute or chronic medical conditions include (1) learning to adapt to the illness and the limitations it imposes; (2) helping other family members adjust to the illness; (3) dealing with the stresses and confinements of hospitalization; (4) learning and using age-appropriate coping strategies and defense mechanisms; (5) decreasing fear and anxiety; (6) normalizing the environment as much as possible; (7) finding ways to continue school, work, and/or social contacts; (8) preventing or remediating developmental delays or regressive behavior patterns; (9) finding ways to return to normal physical activity and daily routines to the fullest possible extent; and (10) facing issues of one's own mortality (Schwankovsky and Guthrie 1982).

SETTINGS FOR SERVICE DELIVERY

Individuals who have acute or chronic medical conditions may receive treatments and services in various settings, depending on factors such as their age and the exact nature and severity of their condition. These include hospitals, outpatient facilities, clinics, doctors' offices, and home health care programs. School-aged children who have chronic health impairments may receive services from special education programs administered by their local school system. In these cases, health-related services necessary for the child to participate in his or her educational program are specified in the child's individualized educational plan (IEP).

Music therapists serve individuals of all ages with various acute or chronic medical conditions in diverse settings such as general hospitals, children's hospitals, clinics, outpatient facilities, hospice programs, wellness programs, home health agencies, childbirth education programs, performing arts medicine programs, and special education settings (Adamek and Darrow 2010; AMTA 1998; Gfeller 1992c; Maranto 1991, 1996; Schwankovsky and Guthrie 1982; Standley 1996b). Music therapy interventions can complement and facilitate medical treatment in areas such as labor and delivery, neonatal care, pediatrics, coronary intensive care, pulmonology, surgery, anesthesia, pain control, radiology, oncology, burn units; for specific medical procedures (e.g., laceration repair, lumbar punctures, kidney dialysis, bone marrow transplants, debridement, dressing changes, cardiac catheterization, bronchoscopy); or for specific chronic medical conditions (e.g., asthma, cystic fibrosis, diabetes, epilepsy, heart disease, hemophilia, lead poisoning, leukemia, nephritis, sickle cell anemia) (Froehlich 1996; Gfeller 1992c; Hanson-Abromeit and Colwell 2008; Maranto 1991, 1996; Schwankovsky and Guthrie 1982; Standley 1986, 1996b; Wolfe and Waldon 2009). Music therapists may work as full-time, part-time, or contract employees or as consultants. They may provide direct services (e.g., prescribed individual or group interventions with patients) and/or indirect services (e.g., designing general music listening programs; staff development training; establishing/maintaining a tape/music library to meet patient needs; organizing or supervising volunteers who provide diversional, recreational, or entertainment music experiences for patients).

HOW MUSIC IS USED IN THERAPY

As was noted earlier, music has been associated with healing and treating diseases since ancient times. Since the late 1970s and early 1980s, as more research tools and methods demonstrating the efficacy of music therapy as a viable tool for medical treatment have become available (Spintge 1991), "the fields of medicine and music have been experiencing a renaissance in the appreciation of music as an important component in the world of medicine" (Taylor 1988, 86). Today, applications of music in medical settings are based on scientific knowledge about the physical, psychological, and socioemotional effects of music that are substantiated by research (Gfeller 1992c; Hanson-Abromeit and Colwell 2008; Maranto 1991, 1996; Spintge 1989, 1991; Standley 1986, 1996b; Taylor 1988, 1997). Music therapists function as cooperative members of the medical team. Specific tasks include assessing the patient's needs and planning music therapy intervention strategies designed to meet these needs. Specifically structured music experiences within the context of a therapeutic relationship help the patient reach the prescribed medical/therapeutic goals. The overall goal is to enable him or her to regain as full a degree of health as possible (Gfeller 1992c; Hanson-Abromeit and Colwell 2008; Maranto 1991, 1996).

Music therapy interventions can meet both physical and psychosocial needs of children or adults who require treatment for acute or chronic medical conditions. Studies have found that music therapy procedures are particularly useful in helping patients respond more favorably to medical treatment procedures and in facilitating their ability to deal with hospitalization (Barrickman 1989; Chetta 1981; Christenberry 1979; Dunn 1995; Froehlich 1984, 1996; Gfeller 1992c; Jacobowitz 1992; Malone 1996; Marley 1984; McDonnell 1984; Perez 1989; Robb 1996; Robb et al. 1995; Rudenberg and Royka 1989; Schwankovsky and Guthrie 1982; Standley 1996b). Hannon (2008, 108) categorized the following clinical objectives for pediatric patients: pain reduction and management, anxiety reduction, infant pacification, decreased respiratory distress, and increased coping skills.

Standley's (1996b) meta-analysis of research literature related to the use of music in medical treatment yielded the following generalizations: (1) women usually have greater responses to music than do men; (2) music has a slightly greater effect on children and adolescents than on adults, with infants showing the least response to music; (3) music has greater effects when some pain is present, but becomes less effective as pain increases; (4) effects of music vary with patient diagnosis, prognosis, and related levels of pain and anxiety; (5) live music presented by a trained music therapist has greater effects than recorded music; (6) studies using patients' preferred music demonstrate the greatest effects; and (7) results vary according to the specific dependent measures.

Functions of Music Therapy in Medical Settings

Maranto (1991, 1) defines *medical music therapy* as "the use of music therapy strategies in the treatment of illness and the maintenance of health." In medical settings, music therapy interventions may be used (1) *as* medicine, when music or music-based experiences affect the patient's health *directly* on a biomedical and/or psychosocial level (e.g., listening to music or doing music-mediated relaxation exercises to decrease pain perception, using music based interventions to help the patient achieve lifestyle changes needed to promote health), or (2) *in* medicine, when music or music-based experiences support or facilitate medical procedures (e.g., music listening or music and imagery to positively affect mood or decrease tension during procedures; various active and passive music-based techniques to reduce distress and anxiety related to illness, condition, or treatment) (Maranto, 1991). Sometimes, music therapy interventions function as primary treatments (e.g., music instead of pain medication). At other times, they are equal partners with medical treatments (e.g., using music and visualization/imagery in conjunction with respiratory therapy exercises to improve breathing). Music therapy interventions also may be used to augment, enhance, or support medical treatments (e.g., music-based experiences to motivate patients to participate in the treatment program).

Crowe (1985) identified five uses of music in the general hospital setting: (1) to decrease patients' overall anxiety level through guided relaxation techniques, (2) to assist in pain management, (3) to help patients actively cope with anxiety and stress and stimulate verbalization of fears and concerns, (4) to humanize an otherwise sterile environment and emphasize wellness rather than illness, and (5) to support the patients' religious/spiritual needs.

At times, music therapy assessments also can provide information that may be helpful in giving a more complete picture of a patient's diagnosis, condition, problems, or needs. For example, patients may reveal fears, concerns, and anxieties in music and creative arts sessions that they do not mention in other settings (Froehlich 1996). Music therapists who are trained and accredited in Guided Imagery and Music (GIM) procedures have found that imagery associated with the pathway linking mind and body may be used as a projective diagnostic tool that complements standard medical and psychological procedures. For example, in situations where a patient is extremely ill or has had some trauma and is depressed or highly stressed, GIM techniques can elicit relevant physical imagery that elucidates psychological underlays, stress factors, or physical traumas or abuses that impact the patient's condition, or GIM imagery may indicate areas that are of critical concern to the patient (Short 1991). Of course, music therapists then share their findings with the other members of the medical team. When the treatment team is aware of the patient's fears or concerns, they are better able to prioritize treatment approaches to meet the needs of the patient and enhance treatment effectiveness.

Cost-Effectiveness of Music Therapy Interventions

Music therapy can be a very cost-effective addition to medical treatment settings. Research shows that patients who participate in prescribed music therapy programs often have "shorter hospital stays and fewer side effects or complications, with little or no additional costs to the facility" (Standley 1996b, 35). Many music therapy interventions are very effective in decreasing patient anxiety and increasing patient relaxation (Crowe 1985; Froehlich 1996; Hannon 2008; Maranto 1996; Schwankovsky and Guthrie 1982; Standley 1986, 1996b; Taylor 1997), and "physicians . . . have long recognized that a relaxed patient requires less medication, experiences less pain, and recovers more quickly than a patient whose level of anxiety creates a state of mental and physical turmoil" (Crowe 1985, 46). Research has also demonstrated that structured application of analgesic (pain relieving) and anxiolytic (tension and anxiety relieving) effects can reduce the use of or need for sedative or analgesic drugs, decrease amounts of anesthesia or postoperative medications needed, shorten recovery periods and hospitals stays, and decrease total medical costs (Halpern 1989; Hannon 2008; Lukas 2004; Maranto 1996; Spintge 1989; Standley 1986, 1996b; Taylor 1997).

Effective, appropriate music therapy programs can be started with relatively minimal expenditures for basic equipment (Crowe 1985). In contrast to disciplines that rely heavily on nonreusable supplies, music therapy programs use reusable and long-lasting materials (Clark and Ficken 1988; Crowe 1985). Music therapy programs are also highly cost-effective because of their flexibility (Crowe 1985). Music therapists can work effectively in many areas of medical treatment (e.g., surgery, orthopedics, general medical care, pediatrics, maternity, oncology/palliative care) and use their interventions to address and remediate many different patient problems. In addition, many music therapy services can be provided in groups, allowing for serving a greater number of patients. As Crowe (1985, 48) observed,

> Because of the flexibility of music therapy and the predominance of group participation, the hospital receives maximum financial benefit from the decision to hire professional music therapists who provide services to an optimum number of patients meeting a broad spectrum of their needs.

General Music Therapy Goals and Treatment Techniques

Since many patients who seek medical treatment are dealing with pain, *pain abatement* is one of the more common and important uses of music in medical settings. Music therapy interventions can decrease awareness of pain, increase pain threshold or pain tolerance, reduce the need for or provide an alternative to pain medication or sedatives, decrease stress and its physiological results, and alter or eliminate the psychological perception of pain (Bonny 1978b, 1983; Brown, Chen, and Dworkin 1989; Chesky and Michel 1991; Colwell 1997; Crowe 1985; Eagle and Harsh 1988; Gfeller 1992c; Gfeller,

Logan, and Walker 1990; Godley 1987; Locsin 1981; Maranto 1996; Mitchell and MacDonald 2006; Rider 1985; Schwankovsky and Guthrie 1982; Selm 1991; Spintge 1989; Standley 1986, 1996b; Steinke 1991; Taylor 1997; Wolfe 1978). Many music therapy interventions for pain management employ some type of structured music listening as a distraction from pain, a focus for attention, a stimulus for relaxation, or a masking agent (e.g., mask unpleasant sounds of dental drills, hospital equipment noises, or sounds of other patients). Often, treatment is more effective when the patient is involved in choosing the music from a selection of programs provided by the therapist (may include various musical styles, but all programs have certain structural elements known to facilitate relaxation or pain reduction) or chosen from his or her own preferred music (Maranto 1996; Mitchell and MacDonald 2006; Spintge 1989; Standley 1996b). A notable exception to this is the special classical music programs used with Guided Imagery and Music (GIM) techniques that also have proven effective in reducing pain (Bonny 1978b, 1983). In addition, some research has shown that "entrainment music" that contains a definite mood shift from unpleasant to pleasant or from tension to relaxation is significantly effective in reducing pain (Rider 1985). For some patients, more stimulating music, such as drumming tapes or live drum music (Scartelli 1991) or rock music (Gfeller, Logan, and Walker 1990) may be the most effective in reducing pain.

Many factors, including the patient's age, medical condition, general health, music preferences, familiarity of music, and specific therapeutic goals, impact the selection of music for listening-based interventions (Gfeller, Logan, and Walker 1990; Maranto 1996). Not all music will be equally effective for all patients. Music listening experiences may be presented together with the suggestion they will reduce pain (Lavine, Bucksbaum, and Poncy 1976; Melzack, Weisz, and Sprague 1963), with structured relaxation techniques (Clark et al. 1981; Godley 1987; Standley 1986, 1996b), in conjunction with biofeedback (Godley 1987; Rider 1985), or with imagery techniques (Bonny 1978b; Godley 1987; Rider 1985). For some individuals, pain reduction may be facilitated when vibroacoustic stimulation is paired with the listening experience via a vibroacoustic recliner (Colwell 1997) or table (Chesky and Michel 1991). Other more active music-making techniques, such as singing and playing instruments, also may be used as distractions to help manage pain (Colwell 1997).

In addition to its use as an audioanalgesic, music may be used as a cognitive/affective structure to help patients control or manage pain (Brown, Chen, and Dworkin 1989; Selm 1991). Examples include experiences that present positive or relaxing statements through song lyrics, use songs as a nonthreatening medium to explore and challenge distorted or irrational beliefs, and use music-mediated relaxation or GIM approaches to decrease tension and anxiety and increase feelings of overall well-being.

In addition to pain relief, music therapy interventions may (a) decrease fear and anxiety about a condition or treatment procedure, (b) help individuals cope with the trauma of hospitalization and/or illness, (c) facilitate relaxation, (d) promote stress reduction, (e) increase muscular function, (f) structure movements or exercises, (g) increase motivation to participate in treatment, (h) facilitate healing or recovery processes, (i) structure and/or reinforce healthy lifestyle changes, (j) increase expression of feelings, (k) serve as an outlet for expressing frustration, (l) provide emotional support, (m) decrease isolation, (n) facilitate communication between patients and families or patients and therapists, (o) reinforce or serve as a vehicle for learning health principles or self-care routines, (p) structure pleasurable interpersonal interactions, and (q) normalize the medical environment (Chetta 1981; Christenberry 1979; Froehlich 1996; Gfeller 1992c; Hannon 2008; Herman 1981; Maranto 1996; Perez 1989; Schwankovsky and Guthrie 1982; Standley 1986, 1996b; Taylor 1997; Tims 1981; Wolfe and Waldon 2009). Music therapists use a variety of techniques, both active and passive, directive and nondirective, within the context of the therapeutic relationship to help individuals meet these goals. Techniques include music listening, GIM, Orff-Schulwerk activities, group or individual music improvisation, musical/rhythmic games, movement to music, singing, playing musical instruments, music lessons, music ensembles, lyric discussion, song writing, music-mediated relaxation, exercise to music, vibroacoustic therapy, music and biofeedback, contingent music, participating in musical plays, and producing music videos (Bonny 1983; Froehlich 1996; Hannon 2008; Herman 1981; Levine-Gross and Swartz 1982; Maranto 1996; Perez 1989; Schuster 1985; Schwankovsky and Guthrie 1982; Skille 1989; Standley 1986, 1996b; Tims 1981). Some composers are also working to compose music that they believe will affect people directly on a cellular level to accelerate the healing process (Halpern 1989).

Whatever music therapy techniques are used in medical settings, they must be structured to fit the medical model, using specific objectives that are relevant to medical diagnosis, prognosis, and treatment time line (Standley 1986, 1996b). Like any drug or treatment, the music therapy interventions in medical settings should be prescribed specifically or ordered by the physician or treatment team for specific purposes (Spintge 1989). Music therapists must also be able to describe music therapy treatment benefits in medical, not musical terms (Standley 1986; Taylor 1997). In addition, music therapists must work cooperatively with other medical personnel, communicating professional observations and striving to find ways to schedule and incorporate music therapy interventions so they enhance treatment and do not jeopardize or interfere with crucial medical routines (Froehlich 1996; Standley 1986, 1996b). For music therapists to work successfully in a medical setting, "it is important that medical staff consider music therapy a priority due to its perception as a benefit rather that a disruption" (Standley 1986, 102).

Music Therapy Interventions in Labor/Delivery

Since the 1980s, music has been used in connection with prepared childbirth methods as (1) an attention-focusing stimulus, (2) a distraction stimulus to divert attention from pain, (3) a stimulus for pleasure response, (4) a conditioned stimulus for relaxation, and (5) a structural aid to breathing (Browning 2001; Clark 1986; Clark, McCorkle, and Williams 1981; Hanser, Larson, and O'Connell 1983). Clark, McCorkle, and Williams (1981, 98) reported that women who participated in a music therapy-assisted childbirth program "experienced significantly more positive perceptions of their childbirth experience than have their non-music therapy counterparts." With the music therapy-assisted approach, women perceived more support from significant others, spent more time practicing Lamaze techniques at home, and reported less anxiety and pain during childbirth. Hanser, Larson, and O'Connell (1983) also found that a specifically designed program of background music could make the labor experience more pleasant by decreasing the expectant mother's behavioral manifestations of tension and verbalizations associated with pain. Browning (2001, 79) reported that "the results of this study seem to indicate that women who receive music therapy during labor are more relaxed, perceive more personal control, and feel more positive about their birthing experience." However, it did not reduce requests for analgesia nor the amount used. In addition, Stein (1991) discovered that when patients who were undergoing Caesarean deliveries listened to structured tape programs of soft, melodious music in their preferred style of music (easy listening, classical, country/western, or jazz) via headphones, their anxiety decreased.

Music therapy interventions may play an important role in the treatment of patients who have high-risk pregnancies. Working with women hospitalized during pregnancy because of high-risk complications, Winslow (1986) used group and individual music therapy sessions to help the women express their anxieties and find effective ways of coping with their feelings. These sessions helped increase these patients' quality of life while decreasing their anxiety and increasing their compliance with and responsiveness to medical treatment. Techniques used in individual sessions included music with progressive muscle relaxation and talking to the baby in utero. Group music therapy sessions were conducted weekly and used sing-alongs of children's songs and lullabies to help increase socialization and group discussion of concerns. Most of the participants felt an increased degree of control over their lives, felt less anxious, had fewer somatic complaints, had a more positive attitude, and experienced increased physical relaxation.

In another study, progressive muscle relaxation training paired with music effectively decreased the state anxiety levels of adolescent girls in their third trimester of pregnancy (Liebman and MacLaren 1991). After reviewing the literature related to music therapy in obstetrics, McKinney (1990, 60) concluded that music therapy interventions using music listening, music-enhanced relaxation and/or imagery, GIM, and the singing of lullabies and children's songs "may have the potential to shorten labor and reduce obstetrical complications as well as to increase the patient's sense of well-being through the alleviation of anxiety and the reduction of conflicting feelings and issues."

In addition to facilitating the labor/delivery process and helping increase the mother's sense of well-being, music therapy interventions can play significant roles in integrating siblings into the birth process. For example, songs can act as a catalyst to help children express how they feel about becoming older siblings. Music activities can also be used to initiate positive interactions between older siblings and the new baby. In one hospital setting, siblings were allowed to go to the nursery to sing "Happy Birthday" to the new baby as part of a "Welcome to Life" program (Linderman and Fridley 1981).

Music Therapy Interventions in Neonatal Care

Although Standley's (1996b) meta-analysis indicated that, by age, infants showed the least response to music, perhaps because of their lower degree of neurological and musical development, research and clinical observation demonstrate that many infants do respond positively to music and that selected music therapy interventions can play an important role in neonatal care. Various studies have shown that the rhythmic stimulation of the mother's heartbeat can effectively calm and quiet newborns (Murooka 1975; Smith and Steinschneider 1975). Murooka (1975) found that recordings of the sound of blood pulsating through maternal veins and arteries and recordings of these sounds combined with classical music effectively stopped the crying of newborns and served as a natural sleep inducer. Sedative music also has a calming and stabilizing effect on premature infants (Lorch et al. 1994). According to Standley and Wolworth (2010, 6), "it is now known that the 30–35 gestation week fetus is hearing maternal and nearby environmental sounds and is beginning to respond." Thus, the baby is familiar with the sound of the mother's heartbeat and is able to respond to music in the environment.

Appropriate music stimulation is usually pleasing to and well-tolerated by infants. For example, Cassidy and Standley (1995) found that music stimulation was not contraindicated even in the first week of life for very low birth weight infants, for whom sensory stimulation was usually restricted. In fact, short periods of listening to lullabies reduced their distress and had positive effects on oxygen saturation levels, heart rate, and respiration rate, thereby helping premature infants thrive. Because music effectively reduces tension and stress-related responses in newborn and premature infants, "staff at a large hospital in central Wisconsin believe that the use of music may have lifesaving significance in their attempts to give premature babies a better chance to survive" (Taylor 1997, 108).

Chapman (1975) suggested that musical stimuli might help premature infants conserve energy, thereby enabling them to use more calories for weight gain. Standley and Walworth (2010, 21) provide a useful "Developmental Chart for Severely Premature Infants." Caine (1991) also found that presenting taped lullabies and children's songs in 30-minute increments to infants in the newborn intensive care unit (NBICU) significantly reduced initial weight loss, increased caloric intake and average daily weight, and decreased both time in the NBICU and total hospital stay.

Music also may be used to stimulate learning and development. For example, assisted participation in body part songs may stimulate tactile exploration (hand to mouth, face, head, nose, eyes) and movement that is necessary for development (Standley 1991). Standley and Wolworth (2010) provide a "multimodal stimulation protocol" that can increase the infant's tolerance for stimulation without excessively stimulating him or her. This can shorten the length of time the infant must remain in the hospital (Standley 1998).

In addition to having positive effects on newborns, music interventions can help promote bonding and positive interactions between newborns and their parents. For example, since music is not contraindicated even for premature infants, it may be a tool for nurturing bonds between parents and their critically ill infants, whom they may not be able to hold, feed, bathe, or touch (Cassidy and Standley 1995). Songs can also structure positive interactions between parents and newborns, act as a catalyst for play, decrease stress and tension, give parents tools for stimulating or calming their infants, and facilitate daily care (Standley 1991). To increase bonding and personalization, parents might add their own words to songs and lullabies. Owens (1979) speculated that music therapists could help produce happier babies and parents and possibly even prevent early child abuse by teaching parents how stimulation is important to infant development, showing them ways to use music to stimulate and soothe their infants, and teaching them basic behavioral principles to promote desired behaviors and guard against the formation of undesirable contingent behaviors.

Music Therapy Interventions for Children or Adolescents Who Have Acute or Chronic Medical Conditions

Music therapy interventions can help meet both the physical and psychosocial needs of children and adolescents who have acute or chronic medical conditions. For example, music therapy techniques may play a particularly significant role in helping children and adolescents (and their families) deal with the trauma of hospitalization and respond more favorably to treatment procedures (Barrickman 1989; Chetta 1981; Christenberry 1979; Dunn 1995; Froehlich 1984, 1996; Hanson-Abromeit and Colwell 2008; Jacobowitz 1992; Lathom-Radocy 2014; Malone 1996; Marley 1984; McDonnell 1984; Newton and Redmond 1995; Perez 1989; Robb 1996; Robb et al. 1995; Rudenberg and Royka 1989; Schwankovsky and Guthrie 1982; Standley 1996b; Wolfe and Waldon 2009). In addition to facilitating pain management and tension/anxiety reduction, music therapy interventions can provide (a) opportunities for expressing and dealing with feelings related to hospitalization, injury, or one's medical condition; (b) diversionary experiences and opportunities for socialization; (c) normalization experiences that provide opportunities to continue age-appropriate motor, language, and social development; and (d) integrative experiences that help children with chronic conditions or traumatic injuries fit changes resulting from the injury or medical condition into their lives so they can make adjustments and live life to the fullest.

Many techniques used with children and their families involve active music making procedures "because children are people of action" (Froehlich 1996, 17). Music therapists may use singing, rhythm bands, Orff-Schulwerk experiences, movement-to-music, relaxation to music, music games, improvisation, song writing, music video production, and many other techniques in their work with hospitalized children. Music therapy interventions frequently are integrated with child life practices (Froehlich 1996; Rudenberg and Royka 1989), and "puppets, instruments, objects for manipulation, and toys can assist the therapist in establishing a relationship of trust" (Barrickman 1989, 14), especially with young children who may be shy, confused, or fearful and reluctant or unable to communicate verbally. Chetta's (1981) study indicated that songs can be used to familiarize children with medical equipment and procedures and that songs and other music therapy activities can effectively reduce children's preoperative anxiety. Marley (1984) also found that music therapy activities, such as relaxation to music, musical/rhythmic exploration and imitation games, movement to music, and simple songs, combined with direct interaction with the music therapist, could significantly reduce stress-related behaviors in hospitalized infants and toddlers. In a more recent study, Malone (1996) found that live singing of age-appropriate children's songs with guitar accompaniment was an effective, noninvasive means of pain management and stress reduction for even very young pediatric patients. In addition, music therapy sessions can be very beneficial to pediatric trauma patients, who often must be deprived of the most basic comfort of being held. Music activities can help reduce anxiety and increase feelings of security and safety by creating "a compensatory holding environment through the use of sound, rhythm, and association to familiar songs" (McDonnell 1984).

Robb (2000) developed a contextual support model of music therapy to use with hospitalized children, based on a motivational theory by Skinner and Wellborn (1994). It is built around concepts of music therapy containing "elements of structure, autonomy support, and involvement that lead children to become more actively engaged with their environment" (Robb 2000, 118). This model allows more adaptive coping. When an environment is chaotic and disorganized, with inconsistent and unpredictable expectations, children have more difficulty in making good choices. Music therapy offers structure through the musical elements, therapist's consistency, and environmental organization. It supports autonomy by providing the opportunity for choice, and thus an increased sense of control, in an environment where others make most decisions and choices. The therapist's involvement is seen as conveying interest in the child and being "emotionally available" to meet the child's emotional and social needs. In a later article, Robb (2003, 30) explains how to design music therapy interventions for hospitalized children using the contextual support model that employs "three aspects of music interventions; session structure, the client-therapist relationship, and the music itself provide elements of structure, autonomy support, and involvement." She also provides a diagram of the model (30).

Many music therapy experiences, such as those using Orff-Schulwerk activities, instrumental improvisation, music-listening, matching music to the child's mood or emotions, musical stories and games, fill-in-the blank song and chants, song writing, and musical dramatizations, also can stimulate children to discuss their fears and feelings associated with their hospitalization or medical condition (Barrickman 1989; Dunn 1995; Froehlich 1984, 1996; Jacobowitz 1992; Perez 1989). Froehlich (1996) suggested that music therapists who work with hospitalized children follow a crisis intervention model to structure interventions that help children cope with the trauma of hospitalization and illness. In this model, therapists first use structured music experiences to help assess the individual patient and determine any particular needs or conflicts. Once these are determined, music therapists use music experiences to build a trusting relationship with the patient, facilitate the patient's expression of feelings, help the patient find alternative ways of coping and positive support systems, and offer the patient hope for the future. Froehlich (1996, 25–36) also gives several examples of ways Orff-Schulwerk activities may be used with hospitalized children within the framework of this model.

Pediatric patients who have traumatic injuries such as burns may receive many benefits from music therapy techniques. For example, when a combination of music listening, deep breathing, progressive muscle relaxation, and imagery were used prior to reconstructive surgery, the pediatric patients' anxiety significantly decreased as compared with standard preoperative preparation

(Robb et al. 1995). Music-assisted relaxation techniques also gave patients new coping strategies and provided ways for them to be involved actively in their own care. In addition, these music experiences used within a therapeutic relationship provided emotional support and comfort to both the patient and the family.

Music therapy experiences involving singing, movement-to-music (whole body or isolated body parts), and playing instruments can provide much needed and enjoyable "normal" sensory stimulation for pediatric burn patients. In addition, these experiences also may be structured to complement and facilitate physical therapy and respiratory therapy goals (Christenberry 1979; Rudenberg and Royka 1989). As the child feels secure and experiences pleasure and success in the music therapy setting, various music activities (e.g., singing, instrumental improvisation, fill-in or question-and-answer songs, lyric analysis and discussion, song writing) may be structured to help the child increase self-expression and build the psychological strength needed to cope with painful and sometimes frightening treatments, deal with various losses, and adapt successfully to different stages of recovery (Christenberry 1979; Froehlich 1996; Lathom-Radocy 2014; Rudenberg and Royka 1989). Song-writing experiences using fill-in-the-blank scripts, group song writing, instrumental and vocal improvisation, lyrical narration with instrumental accompaniments, and writing lyrics related to discharge may be particularly useful for helping adolescents increase self-expression, self-esteem, communication, psychological adjustment and coping skills, and socialization (Lathom-Radocy 2014; Robb 1996). Recent research shows that music therapy interventions that provide patients with active coping strategies and promote self-expression also have important physical benefits, such as increased immune function (Lane 1991, 1994; Robb 1996, 2000).

Usually, when a child is hospitalized or traumatically injured, the child's whole family needs help coping with feelings of anger, fear, and loneliness that may be associated with the health crisis. By including parents and other family members in music therapy sessions, the music therapist can reduce the stress and anxiety of both the child and the family, facilitate communication and expression of fears and feelings, and provide the child and the family members with meaningful ways of relating to each other in structures that safely contain emotions. In addition, by giving the child and family members active roles in facilitating the child's health and well-being and providing them with something positive and constructive to do, family music therapy sessions can help both the child and the family deal with the events of the medical crisis and its aftermath (Dunn 1995; Froehlich 1996; McDonnell 1984; Newton and Redmond 1995). For example, a musical story may provide a young child with an avenue to express feelings of fear and anxiety directly in a way that does not overburden anxious and worried parents (Jacobowitz

1992). In addition, active involvement in music experiences may provide important distraction from pain, worry, and waiting for the parents as well as the child (Barrickman 1989).

Children and adolescents who have chronic medical conditions also can benefit from music therapy interventions. Herman (1981) found that music activities, such as playing instruments, singing, writing songs, moving to music, and presenting musical plays, helped provide severely asthmatic children with outlets for venting frustration and expressing emotions. Moreover, singing and playing wind instruments had the added medical benefit of helping the children develop and maintain their optimum level of respiratory status (Haas et al. 1989; Herman 1981; Lathom-Radocy 2014; Michel 1985; Schwankovsky and Guthrie 1982). As the children experienced success in music activities and acquired musical skills, their self-esteem also increased. In addition, group music activities provided opportunities for socialization and positive interactions with others.

Music therapy experiences also can be structured to meet the physical and psychosocial needs of children who have other chronic health impairments, (Lathom-Radocy 2014), such as cystic fibrosis, diabetes, epilepsy, heart disease, hemophilia, leukemia, nephritis, and sickle cell anemia. Schwankovsky and Guthrie (1982, 121-122) provide several examples of how various music activities can provide these individuals with enjoyable ways to improve their physical status. The activities provide sensory stimulation and appropriate levels of physical activity; improve coordination and sensorimotor skills; decrease anxiety and tension; increase socialization, self-esteem, and self-expression; facilitate positive interactions with peers; increase coping skills and psychosocial adjustment; provide developmental learning experiences and peer interaction; and improve self-concept (Hanson-Abromeit and Colwell 2008; Lathom-Radocy 2014).

Colwell, Davis, and Schroeder (2005) studied the effect of artistic composition (art or music) on the self-concept of hospitalized children. Self-concept is the mental regard one has of oneself and the surrounding environment. Their data indicate that a participation in a composition process, either art or music, can improve a patient's self-concept. There were differences in subcategories, and these need further research. This study is an important pilot study, but there were some limitations in its scope: "patients participated in one 45 to 60 minute session targeting either an art composition or a music composition that reflects who they are or something about their hospital experience" (53). If patients had experienced both conditions and more than one session of each, different results might have occurred. Subjects were randomly assigned to a group, rather than having a choice in selecting art or music.

Music Therapy Interventions for Adults Who Have Acute or Chronic Medical Conditions

With adults, music therapy interventions have been used successfully in coronary intensive care units, prior to and/or during surgery, to facilitate postoperative recovery; in radiology; in oncology; for headache or chronic pain patients; with gynecological procedures; with burn patients; in podiatry; with dental patients; and with specific medical procedures, such as laceration repairs, lumbar punctures, or kidney dialysis (Maranto 1996; Standley 1986, 1996b).

As noted earlier, one of the most common uses of music therapy interventions in medical settings is the use of music listening, music-assisted relaxation, or music and imagery to reduce pain perception and to decrease tension or anxiety (Bonny 1978b, 1983; Brown, Chen, and Dworkin 1989; Chesky and Michel 1991; Colwell 1997; Crowe 1985; Eagle and Harsh 1988; Gardner, Licklider, and Weisz 1960; Gfeller 1992c; Gfeller, Logan, and Walker 1990; Godley 1987; Hanson-Abromeit and Colwell 2008; Lathom-Radocy 2014; Locsin 1981; Maranto 1996; Mitchell and MacDonald 2006; Rider 1985; Selm 1991; Spintge 1989; Standley 1986, 1996b; Steinke 1991; Taylor 1997; Wolfe 1978). Mitchell and MacDonald (2006) found that preferred music increased tolerance for pain and a perception of control better than nonchosen relaxing music. Subjects chose many types of music, which suggests that the action of making a choice is more important than the musical characteristics. Familiar music was more effective than the therapist's choices, which may have been unfamiliar to the client. The theoretical basis for this study was the gait theory (Melzack and Wall 1965), which proposes that "a distracting outside task will reduce mental resources able to be allocated to pain" (Mitchell and MacDonald 2006, 296).

In other music therapy interventions, adult patients take a more active role in music making through individual or group improvisations, instrumental or vocal solos, song requests, lyric discussion, or song writing. These activities also help reduce anxiety, serve as outlets for emotional expression, and may even provide some patients with the motivation they need to continue living and participate cooperatively in medical treatments (Levine-Gross and Swartz 1982; Tims 1981). Those individuals who have medical conditions that force them to pursue less strenuous leisure activities than those to which they were accustomed may develop music skills or music-related interests that can provide them with new leisure-time interests that they also can pursue outside the hospital setting.

Music Therapy in Specific Areas

Music Therapy in Surgery

Research suggests that music therapy interventions can have beneficial effects (1) as part of preoperative procedures (Lukas 2004), (2) in the operating room during surgical procedures, and (3) postoperatively, during recovery (Lukas 2004; Standley 1986, 1996b; Taylor 1997). In her review of over 30 studies that examined music's influence on physiological and psychological parameters associated with surgery, Maranto (1996, 46–52) found that most interventions involved music listening, often selected by the patient from programs offered by the therapist; and that music interventions usually influenced both physiological and psychological measures positively. Structured music interventions also helped decrease patients' fear, anxiety, and awareness of pain; reduced the amount of anesthesia or pain medication needed; and, in some cases, decreased recovery time (Maranto 1996; Taylor 1997).

Whipple (2003, 77) described a program called Surgery Buddies, which was designed to "provide anxiety reduction for pediatric surgical patients and their caregivers." In the facility where she was employed, a music therapist was assigned to each surgery patient. Preoperative sessions attempted to build a sense of control in each patient by utilizing observed coping skills and focusing attention on positive affect. Parents often participated and found that music therapy provided distraction and support when they were in an anxiety-producing situation.

Structured music listening experiences, used alone or combined with imagery or various relaxation techniques, can provide a very effective, noninvasive way of decreasing presurgical stress, fear, and anxiety. Patients who listened to classical music selected for its relaxing or calming qualities over loudspeakers in the preoperative area, experienced substantial decreases in anxiety (Bonny and McCarron 1984). Listening through headphones to individually selected music programs (from a choice of prerecorded music tapes of various styles constructed by the therapist for their anxiety-reducing qualities) also can decrease presurgical anxiety effectively (Milukkolasa et al. 1996). In addition, listening to preferred relaxing music (selected from taped music programs of various styles compiled by the music therapist) combined with vibrotactile stimulation from a Somatron™ mattress can effectively reduce presurgical anxiety (Walters 1996). This method also decreased time in surgery and the amount of postoperative medication needed in women awaiting scheduled gynecological surgery (Walters 1996).

Music used during surgery may have both physical and psychological benefits for patients. Hannon (2008, 121–124) provided a detailed case history of a severely depressed 16-year-old medical/surgical patient. This case history demonstrates the patience and consistency needed by the therapist to allow time for behavioral change to occur.

During surgery, the patient yields many controls. Music therapy can help return some control by providing the patient with individualized choices (e.g., music selection, setting or adjusting the loudness level, choosing the scene for imagery, determining self-suggestion statements and active techniques to be used for stress reduction or pain management) (Krout 2007; Robb 2003). As these choices increase the patient's sense of control, they also tend to decrease the need for medication and facilitate both the patient's response to surgery and his or her recovery (Cowan 1991; Mandel 1988; Whipple 2003). In addition, music techniques can have specific benefits during particular surgical procedures. For example, patients undergoing punch biopsy, in-office gynecological procedures showed significantly lower respiratory rates and overt pain scores when they used music listening combined with basic relaxation procedures, as compared with nonmusic controls (C. A. Davis 1992). In addition, those using the music had fewer procedural complications and required less time to complete the medical procedures.

While listening to preselected music through headphones can have some beneficial effects, such as decreased anxiety and a reduced need for anesthesia (Bonny and McCarron 1984), the presence of the music therapist also can be very important in helping the patients achieve optimum benefits from music interventions. The music therapist can facilitate patient responses by focusing the patient's attention on the music and/or the music-assisted relaxation or imagery procedures, by providing comfort and reassurance, observing patient responses, and by changing music programs or techniques as necessary to meet the patient's changing needs (Cowan 1991; Mandel 1991). For example, Cowan (1991) found that therapist-assisted techniques like imagery, breathing exercises, stroking or direct pressure, or autogenic suggestions used in combination with music listening were very helpful in calming, relaxing, and comforting patients during surgery, thus increasing the quality of patient care. The presence of both the music and the music therapist are vital in giving a patient the most effective, positive surgery experience (Cowan 1991; Mandel 1991).

Music therapy interventions also can assist in postoperative recovery by helping increase alertness, providing distraction from pain, facilitating relaxation, decreasing tension and anxiety, and reducing the need for postoperative medication (Bonny and McCarron 1984; Cowan 1991; Hannon 2008; Lukas 2004; Taylor 1997). Bonny and McCarron (1984) recommended that music listening programs used in recovery rooms have faster tempi and include more stimulative music to facilitate the patient's return to normal consciousness. However, since responses to music are very individualized, indiscriminate use of music in recovery rooms may hinder rather than help the patient's progress.

Mandel (1991), a music therapist herself, related a personal surgical experience in which the music tape played in the recovery room did not match her mood and actually increased her agitation rather than serving its intended purpose of decreasing tension and anxiety. She wished there had been an attending music therapist in the recovery room who could have observed her reaction and turned off the music or offered her another selection that would have been more relaxing for her individual needs and mood at that moment. Mandel observed that, despite previous knowledge and training, in the postsurgical state in the recovery room, "I was unable to monitor the music myself effectively. The music and my lack of control became factors detrimental to my initial recovery" (111). She suggested that, even in the recovery room, "it seems necessary to have a music therapist serve as coach, observe patient responses, and plan and implement changes as they are indicated" (112). Cowan (1991) also recommended that the music therapist be with the patient in the recovery room, offering music therapy interventions as a means of increasing alertness, providing distraction from pain, or facilitating relaxation.

Music Therapy with Organ Transplant Procedures

Since music is pervasive in society, it is generally well received by most patients. Music is also a very flexible therapeutic tool that can meet patients' needs at various physiological, psychological, and social response levels. For these reasons, music therapy interventions may be particularly useful in addressing the emotional and social factors associated with the anticipatory and recovery phases of organ transplantation processes.

Gibbons and McDougal (1987) and Ghette and Walker (2008) have suggested several ways that music therapy interventions might benefit kidney, liver, and bone marrow transplant recipients, donors, and their families. For example, in the *pretransplant phases*, music therapy procedures could be structured to present information and facilitate discussions to help patients and family members realize the risks associated with the transplant procedures and help them form realistic expectations about post-transplant quality of life. During the *waiting period*, active or passive music-mediated relaxation and stress reduction procedures could help reduce anxiety and tension. Music therapy interventions also may address agitation or depression that may be associated with fear of organ rejection, surgical risks, or prognosis. In addition, as in any surgical procedure, music therapy techniques can help patients manage physical pain and provide sensory stimulation and pleasurable experiences in a sterile hospital environment. Through music and imagery experiences, patients may even "travel" from the hospital environment for a time. In the *post-transplant phase*, structured experiences involving improvisation, playing musical instruments with others, group singing or listening, song writing, or lyric discussion could help recipients deal with feelings of indebtedness or guilt toward their donors, facilitate the establishment or reestablishment of social relationships, and support self-esteem and self-concept, which may be decreased when physical limitations force employment or lifestyle changes.

Ghetti and Walker (2008, 161–163) provide a useful form for "Pediatric Hematology/Oncology Music Therapy Assessment," as well as a "Sample Music Therapy Summary Assessment Note." They also provide "Pediatric Hematology/Oncology Music Therapy Goals" and objectives (166–167). These forms would be most helpful for a music therapist working in a unit that treats bone marrow transplant patients.

Music Therapy in Coronary Care

Listening to special programs of taped music can increase the pain tolerance of patients in coronary intensive care units while helping to decrease their heart rates and lessen anxiety and depression (Bonny 1983). Listening to self-selected tapes of anxiolytic music can also facilitate emotional relaxation and provide distraction from pain for cardiac patients in intensive care (Spintge 1989). In addition, some research has found that patients who listened to anxiolytic music consistently demonstrated "a statistically significant reduction ($p < .01$) of stress response in the cardiovascular and endocrinological systems" (Spintge and Droh 1987, 91).

In cardiac rehabilitation programs, music therapy interventions can be structured to address and reduce patient fears (e.g., of death or of job loss), decrease pain and stress, and motivate patients to cooperate with and participate in their treatment program (Taylor 1997). MacNay (1995) found that adding preferred music to a cardiac rehabilitation exercise program decreased the patients' perceived feelings of exertion and estimations of time spent exercising and increased positive moods. These results suggest that adding patients' preferred music to cardiac exercise programs may help motivate some patients to participate in vital rehabilitation exercises and also may increase endurance and performance levels. While assessing patients' use of music during cardiac rehabilitation, Metzger (2004) found that clients enjoyed listening to music and using it as a distraction during exercise but did not use music as a specific stimulus for exercise. Other ways that music can be used in cardiac rehabilitation include providing positive reinforcement, changing mood, and alleviating stress. Further research is needed in this area.

Mandel (1996) also found that several music therapy techniques can facilitate stress management for individuals referred to music therapy by their cardiologist: small group discussion of live and taped music or lyrics, music relaxation and imagery, song writing, identification of song lyrics or titles that describe stressful situations or coping techniques, using songs to express personal feelings, and nonverbal expression of feelings on musical instruments.

Music Therapy with Patients Who Have Severe Burns

Music therapy interventions may address both physiological and psychological needs of patients who have severe burns. *Physically*, music therapy interventions may provide sensory stimulation and reduce sensory deprivation that may be associated with the sterile hospital environment; help distract from or reduce the pain associated with the burns, dressing changes, debridement, or skin graft operations; motivate physical movement and exercise necessary for rehabilitation; facilitate relaxation and stress reduction; and encourage deep breathing to help restore respiratory function and prevent respiratory complications (Barker 1991; Christenberry 1979; Neugebauer 2008; Taylor 1997). Techniques used to achieve these goals include music and progressive muscle relaxation (PMR), singing, humming, hand-clapping, guitar strumming, exercise or movement-to-music, listening to sedative music, and music with imagery. Barker (1991, 137) noted that using music interventions during painful treatment procedures such as daily debridement also has beneficial effects for the staff: "During music/PMR conditions, the burn technicians were more relaxed and jovial with the patients."

Severely burned adult patients also undergo various stages of *psychological adjustment* as they recuperate. Music therapy interventions may benefit patients through all of these stages (Christenberry 1979). In the first stage, *physiological emergency*, patients experience many physiological stresses, and they may have recurrent nightmares related to their accident or periods of delirium or disorientation and confusion. Experiential music activities (e.g., singing or listening to familiar songs) may provide a foundation for reestablishing order and contact with reality. Other interventions, such as structured music listening, music and imagery, or music-mediated relaxation techniques, also may help reduce stress, tension, anxiety, and pain perception accompanying this early experience of burn injuries (Neugebauer 2008; Taylor 1997; Wolfe and Waldon 2009). During the second stage, *psychological emergency*, patients are physically stable but are becoming increasingly aware of the losses associated with their injuries and are "involved in a transition from denial to recognition" (Christenberry 1979, 144). Music therapy activities employ techniques like song writing, lyric discussion, improvisation, and guaranteed-success experiences in singing, playing instruments, moving-to-music, or composing music to help patients express feelings, fears, and frustrations and build or rebuild self-esteem. During the third stage, *social emergency*, patients may confront changes in their lifestyles and may have to deal with differences in interpersonal relationships as they prepare for discharge and return to society. In this period of great emotional adjustment, patients may become shy, suspicious, withdrawn, discouraged, or depressed. Prior to discharge, music therapy sessions can help patients discuss problems they may face outside the hospital, continue to work on increasing self-esteem, structure and enhance communication between the patient and family members, and possibly provide patients with music skills that they can use for their own enjoyment or to participate in community music groups (Lathom-Radocy 2014; Taylor 1997). Cristenberry (1979, 146) argues the need for continued therapy after discharge: "Ideally, music therapy should be continued on an out-patient basis to help in the readjustment to life outside the hospital."

Music Therapy with Hemodialysis

Many patients with kidney disease must repeatedly undergo an invasive blood-cleansing procedure known as *hemodialysis.* Music therapy interventions that reduce stress and anxiety may help keep a patient's emotions under control so that blood pressure will not be a problem during this procedure (Taylor 1997). There is some evidence that listening to specially selected, preferred music reduces the anxiety of adult hemodialysis patients (Schuster 1985). Biomedical data now explain how music is able to produce these effects (Taylor 1997). Normally, an aversive stimulus such as the invasive hemodialysis procedure would stimulate reactions from the amygdala and hypothalamus that would produce blood pressure changes and release of stress-related hormones. However, music therapy interventions involve the amygdala and hypothalamus with reactions to musical stimuli, making them less able to respond or react to the aversive stimulus. As Taylor (1997, 76) explains:

> With musically stimulated impulses occupying neural pathways throughout the brain, the orbitofrontal cortex is less able to focus on self-concerns in determining emotional responses. The positive responses are sustained and replicated as the individual's brain stores conditioned emotional responses resulting from the effects of music on the medial division of the medial geniculate nucleus in the thalamus.

Thus, the anxiety-reducing effects of music can have important benefits for adult patients undergoing hemodialysis.

Music Therapy in Pulmonology

Various types of music therapy interventions, including singing, breathing exercises to music, listening to tapes of sedative music, relaxing to music, and playing simple wind instruments to improve exhalation ability, are beneficial to individuals who have respiratory problems (Christenberry 1979; Mandel 1996; Maranto 1996; Rider et al. 1991; Wade 2002). For example, music may motivate some patients to perform necessary deep-breathing exercises.

Chlan and Heiderscheit (2009) developed a tool for assessing music preference in critically ill patients receiving mechanical ventilator support. An artificial airway allows these patients to breathe. Because of the endotracheal tube or tracheostomy, however, patients are unable to speak. Since music therapists have found that preferred music is most desirable in most situations, they must find a way to communicate so that patients can indicate preference. This may be through eye blinks, a squeeze of the hand, or change of eye focus. The authors devised a protocol for using a music preference assessment tool and provide a copy (44–45). It is important that they included a place for patients to indicate music they do *not* like. They also include a case scenario (46).

Michel (1985) found that singing and playing wind instruments helped individuals with asthma increase their ability to use abdominal breathing. Bouhuys (1964) also studied the use of wind instruments to encourage deep breathing.

Other research has found that singing improved the clinical status of patients with pulmonary edema and that singing in vocal ensembles increased the patients' relaxation responses (Rider et al. 1991). In addition to exercising the lungs and requiring individuals to use about 90 percent of their vital capacity, singing stimulates the cough reflex and helps patients with chronic respiratory conditions clear secretions from their airways (Bolger and Judson 1984). Staum (1996, 75) suggested that singing's success as a treatment modality for patients who have respiratory problems "is possibly due to its sustained nature and to its ability to stop, start, and successively time respiration." Wade (2002, 31) compared effects of vocal exercises/singing to music-assisted relaxation on peak expiratory flow rates of asthmatic children: "Results indicated that subjects showed an increase or maintenance of lung functioning after singing, while results for subjects were not consistent following the relaxation condition."

Toning (chanting-sustained vocal sounds on individual pitches) also effectively increases deep breathing and reduces heart rate in many pulmonary patients (Rider et al. 1991). Other music-based techniques that benefit pulmonary patients include using music to accompany breathing exercises, using music-assisted relaxation techniques, and being involved in small group music therapy sessions that use techniques such as lyric discussion, matching songs to personal feelings, song writing, and instrumental improvisation to encourage expression of feelings and frustrations and to decrease anxiety (Mandel 1996). Some respiratory patients have developed their lungs and intercostal and abdominal muscles and increased their endurance and breath control by learning to play wind instruments (Staum 1988, 1996). Engen (2005) used vocal exercises and group singing with patients with emphysema.

Music therapy techniques can also facilitate patients' responses to bronchoscopy procedures. For example, Metzler and Berman (1991) found that listening to tapes of classical and semiclassical sedative music decreased tension and anxiety in patients undergoing bronchoscopy procedures. During the music condition, bronchoscopy patients showed significantly less increase in heart rate, increased neck relaxation, and had warmer hands (a factor that is associated with increased relaxation).

Music Therapy to Affect Immune Response

Research demonstrates that stress decreases immune system activity, thus increasing a person's susceptibility to infection (Taylor 1997). Edwards (2005) notes that the person's appraisal of the threat or situation is the most important element in the stress response. Therapists should not impose their own estimation of a procedure's likely stress level without considering the patient's ability to cope. Immune system responses can be enhanced through many techniques, including imagery and music (Bartlett et al. 1993; Lane 1991, 1994; Rider 1985; Taylor 1997; Tsao et al. 1991). Some research has shown that secretory IgA levels can be increased by conscious thought and the use of music, suggesting that "sedative music can be an effective method for enhancing the immune system" (Tsao et al. 1991, 113). Other research has found that when subjects listened to relaxing selections of music from their preferred genre (e.g., contemporary jazz, new age, classical), their cortisol levels decreased significantly, thereby supporting the theory that music facilitates immune system recovery (Bartlett et al. 1993). Taylor (1997) suggested that a closer look at how music influences the biological structures that control the immune system shows how music may accomplish these effects. After a detailed explanation of the biomedical processes involved, he summarizes: "In short, music can calm neural activity in the brain, resulting in decreased glucocorticoid production and associated recovery of normal white blood cell activity" (108).

Music Therapy in Oncology

Children undergoing cancer treatment may experience suppression of the immune system. This condition is of importance to music therapists, as well as to all others who enter the person's room. It is essential that patients do not acquire further illness from germs they may receive from interaction with others: "These immunosuppressed children may be placed in isolation in their rooms or wear masks to cover their nose and mouth in order to prevent contracting an illness" (Ghetti and Walker 2008, 152). This danger must be of concern when introducing musical instruments or other equipment into the hospital room.

Research and clinical evidence show that music therapy interventions, such as music listening, music-mediated relaxation, music and imagery, song writing, and lyric discussion, can have many benefits for cancer patients. Daveson (2001, 114) listed factors to consider in creating goals for children with cancer: the child's personal coping style, stage of illness, diagnosis, present medical status in relation to referral time, levels of anxiety and pain, disease trajectory, developmental status, individual treatment protocol, and situational specific factors.

Burns (2012, 10) analyzed 22 research articles published in English that met her criteria of adult cancer patients receiving music as the primary intervention and a design that included a "Comparative, Clinical, or a Randomized Controlled Trial." Her references provide a good list of the current research on music therapy with cancer patients. Some of the benefits mentioned in the literature include (a) assisting in pain management, (b) increasing relaxation and decreasing tension and anxiety, (c) increasing positive mood, (d) decreasing feelings of fear and isolation, (e) enhancing ability to communicate and express feelings, and (f) decreasing chemotherapy's side effects (Burns 2001; Burns et al. 2005; Daveson 2001; Maranto 1996; Taylor 1997; Waldon 2001). Music therapy experiences such as song selection or instrumental improvisation also can be structured to enhance communication between patients and their families by helping them express and explore emotions and ideas that seem too threatening to verbalize or express in other ways (Bailey 1984; Bright 1986; Burns et al. 2005; Clair 1996b; Edwards 1976; Froelich 1996; Ghetti and Walker 2008; Gilbert 1977; Hamilton and Bailey 1981; Martin 1989, 1991; Munro 1984; Ridgway 1983; Whittall 1991). Burns, Sledge, Fuller, Daggy, and Monahan (2005) studied preference and interest in participation in music therapy by cancer patients. They found that adult cancer patients were interested in participation with a preference for listening.

Some research in music therapy and oncology has focused on music therapy for patients undergoing stem cell transplants (formerly called bone marrow transplants). Gibbons and McDougal (1987) concluded that interventions could be structured to impact socioemotional factors that affected the waiting and recovery processes of patients and their family members. Boldt (1996) developed a specific music therapy protocol for stem cell transplant patients to help increase their feelings of psychological well-being, physical comfort, and exercise endurance. Techniques included deep breathing exercises, progressive muscle relaxation to slow instrumental music, range-of-motion exercises to music, patient-selected songs sung with guitar accompaniment, and patient-selected music to accompany exercise routines. The use of music increased the patients' cooperation and participation in activities, self-reported relaxation and comfort, sense of well-being, and physical comfort. Boldt noted that patients who previously had used music as a coping device or intervention for pain relief or relaxation were more willing to participate in the music therapy exercise program. Kennelly (2001) also studied music therapy in the stem cell transplant unit for adolescent patients. He provides a case history of an adolescent boy with leukemia and addresses his emotional needs. Adolescents are going through a difficult stage of development, and cancer makes it even more difficult for them to cope with natural changes, e.g., "peer acceptance, body image, and emerging independence" (104). Cancer often leads to feelings of loss of control, social isolation, and anger or frustration. Kennelly concluded that "music therapy provided Jack with opportunities to acknowledge, support, and explore his feelings regarding his hospitalization during BMT with his own songs and improvisations; his own creative outputs were vitally important in assisting this process" (108).

Waldon (2001, 232) studied the effects of group music therapy on mood states and cohesiveness in adult oncology patients. Those attending group music therapy "significantly improved self-reported mood state (as measured by the POMS-SF [The Profile of Mood States-Short Form])." Group cohesiveness has to do with the perceived support the client receives from being in the group. Her data did not support a conclusion of increased group cohesiveness, but this may have been related to irregular attendance because of some subjects withdrawing from the study as their treatment progressed.

Music Therapy for Chronic Pain Management

Individuals who have chronic pain often seek medical treatment to find ways to alleviate or better manage their pain. Recently, treatment of chronic pain patients has begun to focus not only on the person's physical processes, but also on his/her affective and cognitive processes, in an attempt to change the person's subjective painful experience, thus improving the person's ability to cope with or manage pain more effectively (Selm 1991). In addition to having definite effects on biomedical processes that relate to pain and pain perception (Mitchell and MacDonald 2006; Taylor 1997), music therapy interventions also can positively impact cognitive and affective processes that affect pain perception. Techniques include using music as a cue for relaxation and tension/anxiety release through music-mediated relaxation, biofeedback and music, and guided imagery and music (GIM) (Colwell 1997; Godley 1987; Selm 1991); singing or playing musical instruments to distract attention from the pain (Colwell 1997); assisting learning by presenting verbal material related to pain management in song lyrics or by discussing relevant songs (Selm 1991); or using music experiences as a nonthreatening way to explore cognitive distortion and challenge irrational beliefs (Selm 1991).

Lesiuk (2010, 138) studied "the role of music-based intervention in the context of a high-cognitive demand occupation, namely computer information systems designing." This is a complex activity, for which the affect infusion model, stating that mood is an important variable when a task is complex, is appropriate. Music, therefore, can be used to prevent or reduce anxiety. Lesiuk's study links the concepts of mood and anxiety: "Both the quantitative results and narrative comments reflect the finding that music listening is an anxiolytic treatment in times of stress" (Lesiuk 2010, 149; Lesiuk 2000, 2005).

After learning music-based pain control procedures under the music therapist's guidance, many patients then can use these music-based techniques as self-regulation procedures to facilitate relaxation and pain relief (Colwell 1997; Godley 1987; Hannon 2008; Selm 1991). Godley (1987) found that approximately 70 percent of the chronic pain patients who received music therapy interventions decreased their use of medication, with many substituting listening to their music tape for medication. Using music also increased patients' positive attitudes, optimism about their health, and faithfulness in practice of relaxation and pain management techniques. Selm (1991, 94) concluded: "Research suggests that music enhanced self-regulation training methods may be more effective than those without music for persons with chronic pain."

In a meta-analysis of music research in medical/dental treatment, Standley (1996b) found that, by population groups, headache patients showed the second greatest response to music interventions. Music-based relaxation training has reduced pain effectively in both tension and migraine headaches. In one study, relaxation training with music and imagery was superior to biofeedback training in relieving migraine headaches (Chance 1987). One year after training, patients in the music group had only one-sixth as many headaches as before training, and the headaches were shorter and less severe. Using music-based relaxation techniques, some patients were even able to end a developing migraine headache before it became very painful.

Music-based interventions are also effective in relieving some of the chronic pain associated with arthritis. Vibroacoustic therapy combining music, vibration, and low frequency sound effectively decreases pain for some arthritic patients. Some research indicates that the combination of music and vibration is more effective in reducing pain than music alone or a placebo condition (Chesky and Michel 1991; Skille 1989). Other research has shown that listening to anxiolytic music reduces pain associated with movement or range of motion exercises for arthritic patients (Spintge 1989). Adding music to prescribed exercise routines or using musical instruments to motivate and structure movement can also distract individuals from the pain associated with movement. Edwards (2005, 40) notes that "it is becoming more widely understood and accepted that psychological and physiological components of health can not be separated."

Music Therapy and Performing Arts Medicine

In recent years, a new medical specialty, *performing arts medicine*, which is concerned with treating health-related problems of performing artists, has emerged (Brotons 1994a; Habboushe and Maranto 1991; Maranto 1991; Taylor 1988, 1997). A significant portion of this specialty is devoted to treating musicians' specific medical and psychological problems. Performing arts medicine for musicians focuses on treating (a) those medical problems resulting from playing/singing or practicing that directly affect musical performance and (b) those that are not directly caused by playing/singing but still directly affect musical performance. Musicians may seek treatment for problems such as nerve compression syndromes, tension and fatigue, muscle or tendon disorders, cardiac irregularities, problems with the respiratory apparatus or the vocal cords, overuse syndromes, vision problems, performance anxiety, the affects of aging, or brain damage that results in amusia (Habboushe and Maranto 1991; Taylor 1997). *Amusia* literally means "without music" but has diverse manifestations and causes. For a brief discussion, see Radocy and Boyle (2012, 462–463). Since music therapists have a thorough knowledge of music and music performance as well as a knowledge of therapeutic and rehabilitation processes, they may have valuable insights into the problems of performing musicians and be able to structure effective treatment interventions to help improve the musician's medical and psychological functioning. By bringing this unique perspective to the treatment team, music therapists can provide a bridge between physician and musician, as well as between music and medicine (Habboushe and Maranto 1991; Rider 1987).

Music therapy interventions may be very helpful in treating performing musicians' problems. For example, Rider (1987) used a combination of music psychotherapy involving GIM and music improvisation techniques, biofeedback, systematic desensitization, and cognitive restructuring to relieve a cellist's problems with shoulder pain and fatigue, breathing, and anxiety experienced when playing solos. Rider noted that, after music therapy treatment, the cellist's self-esteem, positive attitude toward performance, and performance quality also increased. Using music therapy techniques to treat performance anxiety, Brodsky and Sloboda (1997) found that counseling supplemented with music relaxation and imagery techniques or with music plus vibrotactile stimulation from a Somatron Acoustic Massage™ power recliner were just as effective as traditional cognitive-behavioral psychotherapeutic interventions in reducing performance anxiety. In addition, they found that musicians were more willing to participate in music therapy interventions than in traditional psychotherapy.

When working with musicians who have performance anxiety, the music therapist must remember that individual performers may need different strategies for relaxation since all performers do not experience anxiety in the same ways or for the same reasons. Performance anxiety may have various physiological (e.g., increased heart rate, shortness of breath, nausea, sweating, shaking), psychological/emotional (e.g., exaggerated apprehension, fear of failure, generalized panic), cognitive (e.g., loss of confidence, lack of concentration due to worrying, memory lapses), or behavioral (e.g., trembling knees or hands, stiff arms or neck, deadpan face) manifestations in different individuals. Alleviation often involves adequate preparation and learning to focus on the music rather than potential negative aspects. Radocy and Boyle (2012, 312–318) discuss this topic with emphasis on LaBlanc's (1994) "ll-level hierarchical model of sources of performance anxiety." These levels are explained, as well as some ways to alleviate performance anxiety, in the Radocy and Boyle section. Brotons (1994a, 78) explains, "By studying individual differences, performers with different anxiety modes can be matched to the most appropriate treatment interventions."

SPECIAL CONSIDERATIONS AND TIPS FOR SUCCESS

Since clients who have acute or chronic health impairments suffer from specific medical problems, it is imperative for music therapists to consult with medical personnel to learn exactly what medical precautions or restrictions apply to individual clients. It is also beneficial for to be aware of the client's prognosis and the expected effects the condition will have on the client. This type of knowledge will help music therapists anticipate the client's needs. It is also extremely important for music therapists to be aware of any special procedures necessary in the event of crisis or emergency situations, such as acute asthma attacks, diabetic insulin reactions, or epileptic seizures.

Like any drug or intervention, the use of music in medicine should be prescribed individually (Spintge 1989). As in any setting, music therapy interventions in medical settings should be used for specific purposes, taking into account each patient's individual preferences, needs, and responses and matching the music and the type of intervention (e.g., active or passive) to these (Maranto 1996; Standley 1996b). When music is used properly, "the data suggest that there may be no medical procedure where music cannot be used for the benefit of the patient" (Spintge and Droh 1987, 100).

Music therapists who work in medical settings must learn to structure their treatments and reporting procedures to comply with the medical model's requirements and expectations. According to Standley (1996b, 36), "Music therapy patient objectives should be specific, and should be relevant to medical diagnosis, course of treatment, and discharge timeline; benefits should be described in medical, not musical terms." Music therapists working in medical settings also should pay particular attention to biomedical research that relates to music therapy. As music therapists learn to apply biomedical findings to their clinical practice and learn to describe the effects of music therapy interventions in terms and parameters familiar to other health professionals, they will elevate their professional status as they are "able to be understood on the same medically sound basis as other disciplines" (Taylor 1997, 122).

Music therapists who work in hospital settings need to develop methods for quick, precise assessment charting and documentation methods (Douglass 2006; Jacobowitz 1992; Standley 1996b). Because of factors such as uncertain scheduling due to other treatments, medical crises, and patients being transferred or discharged without notice, music therapists who work in hospital settings must also learn to maintain a balance between structure and flexibility (Jacobowitz 1992). At times, the music therapist must work around tubes and medical equipment or adapt to different treatment settings. Strict infection control procedures must be observed in many medical settings. The music therapist should always remember that "in a hospital, the medical condition of the patient has priority" (Perez 1989, 248) and adapt music therapy interventions and approaches to the patient's current condition, needs, and location.

QUESTIONS FOR THOUGHT AND DISCUSSION

1. Discuss some of the special characteristics and needs of individuals with various acute or chronic medical conditions. What implications do these have for music therapy programming?
2. Why and how are music experiences useful in making contact with individuals who have various types of acute or chronic medical conditions? Are some types of experiences and activities more useful than others for certain conditions or needs? Which ones? Why?
3. Describe some specific music therapy experiences that might be used when working in (a) labor/delivery, (b) neonatal care, (c) the care of hospitalized or health impaired children, (d) surgery areas (prior to, during, or following surgery), (e) areas serving organ transplant patients and their families, (f) coronary care, (g) severe burn care, (h) hemodialysis, (i) pulmonology, (j) areas concerned with immune response, (k) oncology, (l) chronic pain management, and (m) performing arts medicine. How do music therapy interventions help facilitate medical treatment or provide unique ways to meet the medical and/or psychosocial needs of patients in each of these situations?
4. Discuss some special considerations that may be important to remember when developing therapeutic intervention strategies for persons who have acute or chronic medical conditions or when working as in a medical setting. Why are these important? What are their implications for the structure of music therapy intervention strategies and the reporting/documentation of treatment outcomes?
5. For each of the situations described below, (a) define the problem or areas of need for the client or group of clients, (b) describe one or more of the goals you might pursue in music therapy sessions with the client(s), (c) describe music activities you might use to help the client(s) meet those goals, (d) tell how the music activities you described relate to the goals and needs of the client(s), and (e) mention any special considerations you might want

to take into account when working with the client(s).

Situation 1:

A 4-year-old child entering the hospital for surgery is very anxious and frightened about the procedure. Parental concern about the child's fears and his condition are making his parents very anxious, too, but they are trying to hide this from the child because they don't want him to get more upset. The doctor has asked you to help in finding ways to calm and relax the child and parents and help them express and deal with their fears and concerns. She also would like you to help explain the procedure to the child in a way he can understand.

Situation 2:

A young mother-to-be in the sixth month of her pregnancy wants to have a medication-free childbirth experience and has heard that music might be helpful in relieving or distracting her from the pain. She is in good health, and her doctor supports her plan. She and her husband have contracted with you to develop a music therapy-assisted childbirth program for them.

SUGGESTIONS FOR FURTHER READING

Barrickman, J. (1989). A developmental music therapy approach for preschool hospitalized children. *Music Therapy Perspectives, 7,* 10–16.

Boldt, S. (1996). The effects of music therapy on motivation, psychological well-being, physical comfort, and exercise endurance of bone marrow transplant patients. *Journal of Music Therapy, 33(3),* 164–188.

Brown, C. J., Chen, A. C. N., & Dworkin, S. F. (1989). Music in the control of human pain. *Music Therapy, 8(1),* 47–60.

Bruscia, K. E. (Ed.) (1991). *Case studies in music therapy.* Phoenixville, PA: Barcelona.

Clark, M. E. (1986). Music therapy-assisted childbirth: A practical guide. *Music Therapy Perspectives, 5,* 23–27.

Cowan, D. S. (1991). Music therapy in the surgical arena. *Music Therapy Perspectives, 9,* 42–45.

Crowe, B. (1985). Music therapy and physical medicine – expanding opportunities for employment. *Music Therapy Perspectives, 5(1),* 44–51.

Froehlich, M. A. R. (Ed.) (1996). *Music therapy with hospitalized children: A creative arts child life approach.* Cherry Hill, NJ: Jeffrey Books.

Gibbons, A. A. & McDougal, D. L. (1987). Music therapy in medical technology: Organ transplants. In R. R. Pratt (Ed.), *The fourth international symposium on music: Rehabilitation and human well-being* (61–72). Nyack, NY: University Press of America.

Hanson-Abromeit, D. & Colwell, C. (Eds.) (2008). *Medical music therapy for pediatrics in hospital settings.* Silver Spring, MD: American Music Therapy Association.

Harvey, A. W. (Compiler) (1988). *Music and health: Sourcebook of readings.* Richmond, KY: Music for Health Services Foundation.

Jacobowitz, R. M. (1992). Music therapy in the short-term pediatric setting: Practical guideline for a limited time frame. *Music Therapy, 11(1),* 45–64.

Lathom-Radocy, W. (2014). Health-impaired children. Part 1 (338–351); Other health-impaired children. Part 2 (352–418). In W. Lathom-Radocy, *Pediatric music therapy* (2nd ed.). Springfield, IL: Charles C Thomas.

Maranto, C. D. (Ed.) (1991). *Applications of music in medicine.* Washington, DC: National Association for Music Therapy.

Maranto, C. D. (1996). Research in music and medicine: The state of the art. In M. A. R. Froehlich (Ed.), *Music therapy with hospitalized children: A creative arts child life approach* (39–66). Cherry Hill, NJ: Jeffrey Books.

McKinney, C. H. (1990). Music therapy in obstetrics: A review. *Music Therapy Perspectives, 8,* 57–60.

Robb, S. L. (2003). Designing music therapy interventions for hospitalized children and adolescents using a contextual support model of music therapy. *Music Therapy Perspectives, 21(1),* 27–40.

Rudenberg, M. T. & Royka, A. M. (1989). Promoting psychological adjustment in pediatric burn patients through music therapy and child life therapy. *Music Therapy Perspectives, 7,* 40–43.

Schwankovsky, L. M. & Guthrie, P. T. (1982). Other health impaired. In W. B. Lathom & C. T. Eagle, Jr. (Eds.), *Music therapy for handicapped children,* Vol. 3 (117–173). Washington, DC: National Association for Music Therapy.

Selm, M. E. (1991). Chronic pain: Three issues in treatment and implications for music therapy. *Music Therapy Perspectives, 9,* 91–97.

Spintge, R. (1989). The anxiolytic effects of music. In M. H. M. Lee (Ed.), *Rehabilitation, music and human well-being* (82–100). St. Louis: MMB Music.

Standley, J. M. (1986). Music research in medical/dental treatment: Meta-analysis and clinical applications. *Journal of Music Therapy, 23(2),* 56–122.

Standley, J. M. (1996). Music in medical/dental treatment: An update of a prior meta-analysis. In C. E. Furman (Ed.), *Effectiveness of music therapy procedures: Documentation of research and clinical practice* (2nd ed.) (1–60). Silver Spring, MD: National Association for Music Therapy,

Standley, J .M. & Walworth, D. (2010). *Music therapy with premature infants* (2nd ed.). Silver Spring, MD: American Music Therapy Association.

Chapter Eighteen

MUSIC THERAPY IN PHYSICAL REHABILITATION PROGRAMS

DEFINITIONS

According to *Stedman's Medical Dictionary, 26th ed.* (Spraycar, 1995), *reha-bilitation* is the process of restoring an individual's ability to function as normally as possible in his or her daily life and to work following a disabling injury, disease, or illness, or to help the person learn to function in a new normal manner. *Physical rehabilitation programs* work to restore functional abilities in cognition, communication, physical skills (e.g., motor learning and motor skills), activities of daily living, and psychosocial skills to individuals who have injuries or illnesses that have caused physical, cognitive, sensory, and/or perceptual deficits (Sandness 1995). Interventions are directed toward helping patients achieve the maximum degree of independence possible in physical, psychological, and social/emotional functioning so that they can return to the community to enjoy the best quality of life possible (Brunk 1992). The three most common groups of individuals who physical rehabilitation programs serve are survivors of traumatic brain injuries, strokes, and spinal cord injuries.

A *traumatic brain injury* (TBI) is a severe injury to the brain that causes widespread, diffuse damage. Each year, more than two million Americans suffer brain damage from a blow to the head (Beil 2015). "Temporal organization and appropriate arousal–universally important functions in perception, attention, memory, and executive function–can be modulated by music in patients with, for example, demented or traumatic brain injury" (Thaut 2008, 78). Other terms used to describe this condition include *closed head injury* (used when the brain is injured without skull penetration) or *head trauma*. Thaut, Thaut, and LaGasse (2008, 277) explain that closed head injuries result from "(1) compression of brain tissue, (2) tearing of brain tissue, and (3) shearing, as areas of the brain slide over other areas." Traumatic brain injuries usually are caused by sudden mechanical force or blows to the head such as may occur in accidents or falls, assault, gunshot wounds, or motor vehicle accidents (Brunk 1992; Lucia 1987; Rudenberg 1982; Thaut 1992c). Lack of oxygen (e.g., in near-drowning) or lack of blood supply to the brain (e.g., following cardiac arrest) also may cause TBIs. TBIs can be life threatening or result in residual dysfunctions in one or more sensory, motor, language, behavioral, or psychological area, depending upon the extent and location of the injury.

Most individuals who experience brain injuries are unconscious or in a comatose state for some period of time. A *coma* is "a state of unconsciousness from which the patient cannot be aroused, even by powerful stimuli" (Miller and Keane 1978, 235). A person in a coma lacks consciousness and environmental awareness (Beil 2015). The longer patients are in a coma, the more likely they are to have widespread, severe brain damage (Thaut 1992c). Conciousness usually is defined by wakefulness and awareness; coma is a state of profound unconsciousness from which one cannot be roused. In between there are several levels, including sleep and vegetative state, in which a person can be awake (as indicated by an EEG) but not aware. In a vegetative state, they are "able to open their eyes and make sounds but uncoupled from true consciousness. Or so it seems" (Beil 2015, 18). New research indicates that people in a vegetative state may respond to some commands, which can be seen on functional magnetic resonance imaging (fMRI) scans. Laureys and Schiff (2012, 478) note that "some patients, with severely injured brains and very longstanding conditions of limited behavioral responsiveness, may nonetheless harbor latent capacities for significant recovery." These findings should indicate that clinicians must carefully treat the patient who seems vegetative as if he or she can hear and respond.

Daveson (2010) developed the *Music Therapy Assessment Tool for Low Awareness States* (MATLAS). The test assesses five behavioral reponse categories: "(a) visual, (b) auditory, (c) awareness of musical stimuli, (d) verbal commands, and (e) arousal" (413). She reported findings from 33 music therapy assessments of patients in low-awareness states, which include vegetative state (VS) and minimally conscious state (MCS). Many of the VS patients were referred for sensory regulation group therapy, and many of the MCS patients were referred for individual music therapy. Further work is needed to establish the test's reliability and validity, but it is an important contribution to establishing assessment standards for this group of patients. Giacino, Fins, Laureys, and Schiff (2014) discuss clinical management of patients with prolonged disorders of consciousness.

In a *stroke*, or *cerebrovascular accident* (CVA), the blood supply to the brain is temporarily blocked, closing the brain's source of oxygen and causing damage to brain cells (Davis, Gfeller, and Thaut 2008; Prazich 1985). About two-thirds of all strokes are *ischemic strokes* or *infarctions*, resulting from blockages or clots that gradually form in arteries leading to the brain. When the obstruction is only temporary, a *transient ischemic attack* (TIA) occurs, sometimes known as an incomplete, "mini," or "little" stroke. TIAs are brief, lasting only a few seconds to no more than 30 minutes, followed by a complete return to normal functioning. However, they usually are a warning sign that a complete stroke may occur in the future. *Hemorrhagic strokes* occur when blood vessels in or around the brain leak or burst, as the result of artery walls being weakened by disease and breaking, a sudden increase in blood pressure that ruptures arteries, or a cerebral aneurysm (thin tissue in a section of an artery wall that bulges and eventually breaks).

As brain cells are damaged or die during a stroke, the functions they control (e.g., speech, muscle movement, emotions, understanding) are lost or impaired (Miller and Keane 1978; Prazich 1985; Zamula 1986). Brain damage caused by strokes usually is more localized and specific than the diffuse brain damage that occurs in TBIs (Brunk 1992; Thaut 1992c). A million Americans suffer strokes or cardiac arrest each year. This can cause lack of oxygen to the brain and serious brain damage (Hall, Levant, and Defrances 2012).

Spinal cord injuries are usually result from accidents or traumatic injuries (NINDS 2011; Rudenberg 1982; Thaut 1992a). The National Institute of Neurological Disorders and Stroke (NINDS) provides information regarding the incidence and costs of spinal cord injuries:

> Accidents and violence cause an estimated 10,000 spinal cord injuries each year, and more than 200,000 Americans live day-to-day with the disabling effects of such trauma. The incidence of spinal cord injuries peaks among people in their early 20s, with a small increase in the elderly population due to falls and degenerative diseases of the spine. Because spinal cord injuries usually occur in early adulthood, those affected often require costly supportive care for many decades. . . . For the nation, these costs add up to an estimated $10 billion per year for medical and supportive care alone. (NINDS, 2011, 5)

Spinal cord damage from neck or back fractures interrupts the flow of electrical impulses from the brain. This interruption causes various degrees of loss of function and paralysis, including *paraplegia* and *quadriplegia*: "Paraplegia refers to paralysis of the lower part of the body, including motion and sensation. Quadriplegia refers to paralysis of all four limbs" (Thaut, Mertel, and Leins 2008, 150). The farther up on the spinal cord the injury occurs, the more extensive the loss of function. When spinal cord nerve pathways are completely destroyed, they do not regenerate and cannot be repaired by current medical techniques; thus, paralysis from spinal cord injuries is usually permanent. However, recent research offers new hope to persons paralyzed by spinal cord injuries and challenges the belief that paralysis resulting from central nervous system damage is irreversible (NINDS 2011). For example, scientists have found that nerve tissue can be transplanted into the brain and grow and survive there and that embryonic nerve cells can survive and function in the central nervous system of an adult host. In addition, new drugs are being discovered that minimize the process of paralysis and improve recovery following injury, and techniques like computer stimulation and biofeedback are in use to help restore functional control to previously useless muscles (National Paralysis Foundation, n.d.). Research continues on ways to apply these findings to the rehabilitation of individuals who have spinal cord injuries.

After injuries to the brain or nervous system, some patients may experience a gradual, spontaneous return of some cognitive, physical, or sensory functions that were lost immediately following the incident. Known as *spontaneous recovery*, this usually occurs within three to six months of the injury; therefore, a prognosis usually is not given until after this period. Spontaneous recovery of some functions may continue for another 12–18 months; however, patients usually should start rehabilitation as soon as possible after their injury (Lucia 1987).

COMMON CHARACTERISTICS, PROBLEMS, AND NEEDS OF CLIENTS

As with any population, individuals served by rehabilitation programs are a very heterogeneous group. Factors such as the type and severity of the impairment, the cause and time of onset, the existence of associated conditions or impairments, and the degree and type of support services available all have varying effects on the individual's level of functioning, needs, and treatment program. In addition, each individual will have a unique combination of abilities, needs, personality traits, strengths, and weaknesses that impact his or her particular responses and functional abilities.

Government agencies, such as the Joint Commission on Accreditation of Healthcare Organizations (JCAHO) and the Commission on Accreditation of Rehabilitation Facilities (CARF) that set standards for physical rehabilitation programs emphasize providing therapeutic, educational, and training services that are consistent with the individual patient's needs and help the patient develop and maintain the highest possible level of independent functioning and community reintegration (Sandness 1995). Thus, a measure of how well patients can function independently in various aspects of life activities is an important indicator of their treatment needs. Many physical rehabilitation programs use the *Functional Independence Measure* (FIM) from the Uniform Data System for Medical Rehabilitation to indicate the severity of a patient's disability (Sandness 1995, 77). A patient's FIM score can change during the rehabilitation process as the patient makes progress in increasing independent functioning in some area of life activities.

The FIM contains 18 items in six categories of life activities: self-care, sphincter control, mobility, locomotion, communication (receptive and expressive), and social cognition (includes social interaction, problem solving, and memory). These items are rated on a seven-level scale that represents gradations of independent or dependent behavior and reflects the amount of help needed by the patient in each area. In levels 1 and 2, "complete dependence," the patient contributes less than 50 percent to less than 25 percent of the effort required for an activity. In levels 3–5, the patient is able to expend 50 percent to 75 percent or more of the effort, but requires physical assistance or supervision from another person to complete the activity. Patients functioning at levels 6 or 7 do not require assistance or supervision to perform the activity and are rated as "independent" in those areas.

The FIM is a useful tool for providing a general idea of the patient's overall level of functional independence and his or her progress toward independence during treatment. Douglass (2006) notes the importance of identifying positive coping and the social and developmental characteristics of hospitalized children. She developed an assessment form (76–78), which was field tested and found reliable and easy to use.

Other assessment tools specific to various population groups (e.g., coma patients) also are used to determine physical rehabilitation clients' needs. Some of these assessments are described briefly in the following sections, which are concerned more specifically with the characteristics and needs of individuals who have traumatic brain injuries, are comatose, have had strokes, or have spinal cord injuries.

Individuals with Traumatic Brain Injuries

Survivors of traumatic brain injuries (TBIs) may have functional deficits in several areas, including speech and language, vision and/or hearing, motor function (e.g., paralysis, limited range of motion, limited muscle strength or endurance, difficulties with balance or motor planning), cognition (e.g., difficulties with concentration, memory, recalling sequences, reasoning, problem solving), and socioemotional areas (e.g., labile affect, depression, poor motivation, poor self-image, difficulty initiating activities or carrying them through to completion, impulsivity or over activity, rigidity, poor self-awareness, inappropriate social behaviors, lack of social judgment) (Brunk 1992; Chance 1986; Lucia 1987; Thaut 1992c). Magee et al. (2011, 5) note that in some TBI patients, the frontal lobe's control of emotional impulses results in many inappropriate behaviors. Persons who have had TBIs "are often irritable, quarrelsome, anxious, easily depressed, and excitable" (Chance 1986, 64); these qualities may affect their ability to interact effectively with others. TBI patients also may become confused and agitated by even slight variations in routine, may laugh uncontrollably, or may become verbally abusive when they are under stress.

At some point in their recovery, individuals facing chronic disability will experience feelings of grief over the losses they have sustained (Bright 1986). Anger at their helplessness, with the doctors, with society, etc., is often a part of the grief over disability (Bright 1986). It is important that professionals offer TBI patients considerable emotional support, along with assistance in gaining physical, cognitive, and social skills, to help them adapt successfully to the changes that have occurred in their lives. Because self-esteem is critical to the way individuals adapt to loss and change (Bright 1986), it also is important to provide experiences that bolster or increase the patient's self-esteem.

Rehabilitation from traumatic brain injury is a long process, and individuals usually pass through several stages or phases of recovery (Brunk 1992; Claeys et al. 1989; Jeong and Lesiuk 2011; Thaut 1992c). In the *early* or *acute phases* of TBI, there is global suppression of cognitive functions and little or no response to stimuli. The patient may be in a coma. As patients emerge from this phase, they often experience severe agitation and confusion and are disoriented in time and place. In the *middle* or *intermediate phases*, patients generally are oriented to time and place but still experience moderate confusion and may have disoriented, disorganized, or agitated responses to stimuli. With appropriate environmental structure, their performance and responses generally improve. At this stage, most TBI patients have marked to severe attention deficits, severe memory deficits, difficulties with problem solving and judgment, and social difficulties. During the *later phase*, patients may continue to have some cognitive impairments (e.g., mild-to-moderate memory, problem-solving, or organizational difficulties); however, their performance usually improves with direction, repetition, and learning compensatory strategies for persistent deficits. With practice, social relationships and behaviors usually improve, and many patients regain a generally positive self-image. However, as they work on accepting their residual deficits and try to find ways to return to as many of their preinjury responsibilities as possible during this stage, patients also may experience depression, anger, or anxiety. Behaviors and cognitive functioning levels of TBI patients often are described by levels of the Rancho Los Amigos Scale (Brunk 1992; Claeys et al. 1989), which is discussed in the next section of this chapter.

Individuals who have traumatic brain injuries frequently respond best to multimodal, transdisciplinary treatment processes that begin with the development of rapport between client and therapist (Claeys et al. 1989, 71):

> TBI clients appear to respond to relationships far more than to techniques or processes. Thus, the more transdisciplinary training and clinical practice that occurs, the greater likelihood of the most therapeutic combination of relationship and technique occurring.

In working with individuals who have TBIs, it is important to incorporate positive expectations into all aspects of rehabilitation. Therapists should try to focus on abilities rather than disabilities and structure interventions to work with the patient's strengths. Rehabilitation programs often offer many services, including physical therapy, occupational therapy, speech therapy, psychotherapy, nutrition or dietary planning, creative arts therapies, therapeutic recreation, and group and family counseling (Brunk 1992; Chance 1986). Programs frequently focus on cognitive training or retraining, functional skills training (e.g., learning skills and routines for self-care, housekeeping, leisure, work or school, business and finance, consumer events, and personal/social activities), and environmental management (modifying the environment to minimize the effects of the individual's limitations) (Chance 1986).

Individuals Who Are Comatose or Emerging from Comas

Individuals suffering brain injuries from head trauma or a stroke often are comatose for at least a short time after their injury. The amount of time spent in coma impacts the patient's chances of recovery. Generally, "the longer a person is comatose the more likely the existence of severe and widespread brain damage" (Thaut 1992c, 259).

Patients in deep coma states do not respond to their environment (Boyle 1989; Brunk 1992). They often appear to be in a sleep-like or vegetative state. Although they may seem to be awake at times, there is no external evidence of communication or complex behavior. Most movements are random and reflexive. Therapists who work with coma patients try to find some type of stimulation that will produce consistent alerting and orienting responses to help them gradually move out of the coma and begin to purposefully respond to and interact with their environment (Beil 2015; Boyle 1987, 1989; Claeys et al. 1989).

Several assessment scales have been developed to assess the severity of comatose states by rating various responses and behaviors of coma patients. Two of the most common are the Glasgow Coma Scale (Boyle 1989; Sandness 1995; Thaut 1992c) and the Rancho Los Amigos Scale (Brunk 1992; Claeys et al. 1989; Sandness 1995; Thaut 1992c). The *Glasgow Coma Scale* uses numerical scales to rate three areas of response: (a) *eye opening* (1 = none; 2 = to pain; 3 = to speech; 4 = spontaneous), (b) *motor response* to pain stimulus or command (1 = no response; 2 = extension; 3 = abnormal flexion; 4 = withdrawal; 5 = localizes pain; shows purposeful movement; 6 = obeys command), and (c) *verbal response* (1 = none; 2 = incomprehensible; 3 = inappropriate; 4 = confused; 5 = fully oriented). Adding the three ratings gives an assessment of coma severity: A total of 13 or more is a mild coma, 9–12 is moderate, and 8 or below is severe (Thaut 1992c).

The *Rancho Los Amigos Scale* uses eight levels to describe the cognitive functioning and behaviors that patients emerging from a coma typically demonstrate (Claeys et al. 1989; Thaut 1992c). In *Level I, no response,* the deepest comatose state, the patient seems to be in a deep sleep and is completely unresponsive to stimuli. In *Level II, generalized responsiveness,* the patient still appears to be asleep most of the time, but has limited, inconsistent, nonpurposeful, nonspecific responses (e.g., physiological changes, body movements, vocalizations) to pain or sensory stimulation. Responses are often the same, regardless of the type of stimulation. At *Level III, localized responses,* patients react specifically, although still inconsistently, with responses being differentiated according to the type of stimulus. Patients are beginning to be more aware of and responsive to some people. They may be alert for three or more minutes at a time, and may begin to follow simple commands, such as closing eyes or squeezing hand. At *Level IV, confused-behavioral,* patients become more active, exhibiting confused, bizarre, agitated, nonpurposeful, and sometimes aggressive behaviors, apparently related to internal confusion. Patients do not seem to discriminate between people and objects and attend only very briefly to environmental events. If patients are able to talk, their speech is frequently incoherent or inappropriate to the environment. However, Level IV patients are beginning to take some independent actions and show some signs of processing information, even though they usually lack short- and long-term recall skills. As patients progress to *Level V, confused,* they are becoming more alert and are able to follow simple commands fairly consistently. However, responses to more complex tasks and new learning often are fragmented and confused. Patients are unable to sustain attention for any length of time and have difficulty focusing on one task. With structure patients can perform some previously learned tasks, but are usually unable to learn new information. Patients may be able to converse on a superficial social level for short periods, but verbalizations often are inappropriate or confabulatory. Memory functions remain severely impaired. In *Level VI, confused-appropriate,* patients can follow simple commands consistently and show goal-directed behaviors, but depend on cues and external structure for direction. They are usually able to perform previously known self-care activities with minimal assistance. Although many memory and processing deficits remain, memory and attention span are increasing, as are awareness of self and others. Responses may be confused but are usually appropriate to the situation. Patients at this stage generally have more depth and detail for past memories than for recent memories. Patients who progress to *Level VII, automatic-appropriate,* behave appropriately and are oriented within hospital and home settings. They can perform daily routines automatically and are able to learn some new information, although usually at a decreased rate. With structure they can initiate some social or recreational activities, but they still have impaired judgment, planning, and problem-solving skills. At *Level VIII, purposeful and appropriate,* patients are alert, oriented, responsive to the environment, and able to recall and integrate past and recent events. They can learn new activities and perform activities without supervision once they have been learned. These individuals can usually function independently at home and may be able to drive, although some impairments in abstract reasoning, judgment, and stress tolerance may persist.

Individuals Who Have Had Strokes or Cerebrovascular Accidents

About 85 percent of strokes are ischemic, which occur when narrowed or blocked arteries reduce blood flow to the brain (Mayo Clinic 2015). If the brain vessel leaks or ruptures, it is a hemorrhagic stroke. Strokes are related to lifestyle, especially smoking, and genetic factors: "Smoking, or being the first degree relative of a stroke patient, is reported to independently almost double the risk of ischemic stroke" (Ross 2015, 1).

Patients who have had strokes or CVAs may have varied physical, cognitive, or socioemotional impairments, such as paralysis, memory problems, neglect of one side of the body, difficulty with new learning, emotional lability, inappropriate affect, distorted sensory input, and difficulties regulating and checking their own speech and behavior ("social judgment") (Brunk 1992; Fowler and Fordyce 1974; Prazich 1985; Sandness 1995; Thaut 1992c; Zamula 1986). These events are caused by an interruption of blood supply to the brain, which reduces the needed oxygen supply (Thaut, Thaut, and La Gasse 2008). Each individual will have different problems, depending on the particular part of the brain that was damaged. Those with left brain damage usually have a slow, cautious behavioral style and frequently have communication disorders, such as aphasia (impaired ability to understand or use language that may affect expressive or receptive language skills or both), apraxia (impaired speech ability due to loss of motor planning abilities involving the muscles used for articulating words), or dysarthria (slow, slurred, monotonous speech, often with disruptions in flow and phrasing and imperfect articulation, due to motor control disturbances caused by central or peripheral nervous system damage affecting muscles related to speech production). Patients who have severe speech disorders may need to learn to use an augmentive communication system to communicate with others.

Patients who lose the ability to speak or who lose normal speech quality often also lose their self-confidence. Their difficulties in communicating and interacting with others may lead to frustration, withdrawal, and/or decreased self-esteem. Some patients may become depressed. Many individuals need time to grieve the losses caused by their stroke, as well as emotional support to help them adjust to the changes in their abilities and roles (Bright 1986; Clair 1996b).

Individuals with Spinal Cord Injuries

Spinal cord injuries usually result in some degree of paralysis (i.e., loss of motor function). The site of the injury determines the extent of the damage; the farther up on the spinal cord the injury occurs, the more extensive the loss of function. Paralysis imposes many severe emotional, social, and occupational changes on a person's life. For example, quadriplegic individuals may need to learn to cope with changes in relationships (e.g., with spouse, children, parents, friends) as well as changes in body image and physical functioning abilities. They need much emotional support as they "adapt to being different, rather than remaining ill" (Bright 1986, 137).

Treatment plans for rehabilitating persons who have spinal cord injuries are based on interdisciplinary assessments that include a determination of motor impairments and functional limitations: "Functional assessment of the client includes all spheres of activity, such as home and family, recreation, employment, and independence in daily living skills" (Sandness 1995, 78). Clients may help set treatment goals by indicating which activities are most important for them to learn in order to function more independently or be more comfortable. In addition to helping patients increase upper extremity function, increase endurance and respiratory function, and learn to use adaptive devices, treatment programs also help clients with spinal cord injuries cope with psychological adjustment issues (e.g., loss of privacy, loss of control, loss of independence, changed physical abilities, and changed self-image), vocational and independent living skills, and leisure education (Brunk 1992).

SETTINGS FOR SERVICE DELIVERY

Individuals who need rehabilitation services because of traumatic brain injuries, strokes, or spinal cord injuries may receive special programs and services to help meet their specific needs in various settings, including general hospitals, special rehabilitation hospitals, centers, or clinics, nursing homes, long-term care facilities, speech clinics (e.g., for aphasia rehabilitation), or in-home services. In addition, school-aged individuals may receive services through special education programs in their local school districts. Sometimes, rehabilitation may begin in one setting (e.g., hospital) and then, after the individual is medically stable, continue in another setting that is geared more specifically to rehabilitation.

Music therapists may work with individuals of varying ages who have traumatic brain injuries, strokes, or spinal cord injuries. Music therapists usually work as part of an interdisciplinary team that may include physicians, nurses, psychologists, social workers, dietitians, physical therapists, occupational therapists, speech therapists, educators, vocational rehabilitation specialists, therapeutic recreation specialists, other creative arts therapists, chaplains, and family counselors (Brunk 1992; Thaut 1992c). Goodman (2007, 118) lists likely fellow team members: "1) Special education teacher; 2) Speech language pathologist; 3) Occupational therapist; 4) Physical therapist; 5) School psychologist or Learning Disabilities Teaching Consultant." Each team member will contribute to the child's IEP.

HOW MUSIC IS USED IN THERAPY

Unique Contributions to the Rehabilitation Process

As music therapists cooperate with other professionals in providing interventions that address the physical, cognitive, communication, and socioemotional needs of individuals in physical rehabilitation programs, they bring to the treatment program specialized sets of music-based activities and experiences that can address client needs in unique ways (Thaut 1992c). Music provides an additional entryway to the brain, thereby activating additional neurological pathways through which learning and skill development can occur (Hofmeister and Cole 1986). For example, music's rhythmic and temporal qualities can provide cues and structures that help patients structure and organize movement and sequence activities (Brunk 1992; Clair 1996b; Lathom-Radocy 2014; Lucia 1987; Radocy and Boyle 2012; Staum 1988, 1996; Taylor 1997; Thaut et al. 1991). However "in patient centered approaches, all disciplines work to support the same therapeutic goals from different angles, using as many collaborative and interdisciplinary techniques as possible" (Thaut 2008, 132). Music experiences also facilitate the development of a therapeutic relationship (Claeys et al. 1989), helping establish a common bond between therapist and client and reducing the barrier that tends to separate the helper and the helpee (Bright 1986).

Since music is a normal activity that is valued by society, music therapy interventions can help humanize and normalize the treatment setting, providing a nonthreatening environment that increases motivation, decreases tension and stress, and helps individuals feel comfortable expressing their inner feelings (Confrancesco 1985; Radocy and Boyle 2012). Music experiences can also be adapted to enable participation at different ability levels yet be individualized to include material that is meaningful to and motivational for a particular client (Lathom-Radocy 2014). In music therapy work with coma patients, Boyle (1987, 52) observed:

> It [music] seemed suited to the limitations of the patients while simultaneously tapping their potential to be controlled by conditioned reinforcers from their

own unique histories. . . . In addition, music is unobtrusive, easy to administer, unlikely to produce satiation, and unlikely to create resistance from caretakers, medical personnel, or members of patients' families.

Music therapy interventions can be structured as enjoyable leisure activities that help clients practice skills or as social experiences that family members can enjoy with the clients or help implement (Barker and Brunk 1991; Lathom-Radocy 2014). Because of the wide range of materials and methods of interaction available in music experiences, music therapy interventions can add interest and motivation to treatment programs, increasing patient participation and potential level of recovery (Thompson et al. 1990). In addition to targeting specific skill development areas, music therapy experiences can provide the setting for a holistic integration of physical, cognitive, and socioemotional skills (Brunk 1992).

General Music Therapy Goals and Treatment Techniques

Music therapy interventions for patients in rehabilitation programs utilize a variety of structured music experiences (e.g., listening to music, playing instruments, singing or vocalizing, moving to music, improvising or composing music, and discussing music) to motivate or assist patients in working toward the greatest degree of independence possible in functional motor, communication, cognitive, self-care, and socioemotional skills.

As with any population, music therapy treatment for individuals in physical rehabilitation programs begins with referral and assessment. The patient's physician should give medical approval for music therapy treatment, and the physician and/or other team members should provide specific recommendations regarding precautions, adaptations, or goals that are applicable to the music therapy setting (Brunk 1992). Working cooperativly with other treatment team members, music therapists can "develop a more comprehensive treatment program, ensuring maximal rehabilitation of the affected and residual functions, and providing quality of life at the highest level attainable" (Thompson et al. 1990, 29).

While assessments and reports from other disciplines may provide considerable information concerning a patient's general functioning level, music therapists also will wish to obtain information on the individual's musical history, interests, and preferences and observe the patient's responses to various types of music materials and experiences (Sandness 1995). Since music influences brain functions in unique ways (Taylor 1997; Thaut 2008), patients may exhibit responses to music experiences that are not present with other types of stimulation. Music therapy assessments for coma patients may include observation of patients' responses to a sequenced presentation of musical stimuli (vibrating string with various pitches, recorded music, tuning forks, autoharp) (Claeys et al. 1989). Music therapy activities also can be used to assess stroke patients' cognitive, motor, communication, social, and visual skills (Thompson et al. 1990).

Music therapy interventions can be structured to help individuals in physical rehabilitation programs improve their physical, cognitive, communication, and socioemotional skills (Adamek and Shiraishi 1996; Barker and Brunk 1991; Brunk 1992; Claeys et al. 1989; Gfeller and Davis 2008; Hofmeister and Cole 1986; Lucia 1987; Sandness 1995; Staum 1988, 1996; Thaut 1992c; Thompson et al. 1990). Potential applications of music therapy treatments are very broad. Boyle (1989, 144) observed that "music can be an integral part of treatment programming ranging from contingent auditory stimulation to the development of new lifetime leisure skills for the traumatic brain-injured patient." Brunk (1992) noted that patients in a rehabilitation center could participate in music therapy at all recovery levels, from coma stimulation (music for auditory stimulation and as a contingent stimulus) to active treatment (using goal-directed music experiences to work on speech, motor control and coordination, memory, or other concerns) to discharge (using music-based activities to facilitate discussion of discharge concerns or helping patients and their families find ways to continue using music activities to develop skills or to provide social integration after hospitalization).

Music Therapy Interventions to Improve Physical Functioning

Music therapy interventions can help patients in rehabilitation programs improve physical functioning by providing (a) motivation for movement (especially if the movements are difficult for the patient), (b) purpose and direction for movement, (c) structure or timing cues for movement or physical exercises, (d) feedback for movement (e.g., tactile/kinesthetic feedback from the feel of strumming the strings of an autoharp as well as auditory feedback when a sound is produced), and (e) practice in motor coordination and motor planning (Brunk 1992; Sandness 1995; Thaut 1992c). Restoring motor function following a stroke or traumatic brain injury often is a long, difficult, and frustrating task, involving such developmental steps as increasing the patient's ability to initiate movement, increasing range of motion necessary to assume desired postures or to move far enough to accomplish desired tasks, and improving fluidity of movement or increasing motor control and coordination (Clair 1996b). Research has shown that rhythmic auditory stimulation from music can facilitate this process as sound stimuli excite motor neurons and stimulate muscular responses and as rhythmic stimuli synchronize and organize motor activity (Clair 1996b; Staum 1988, 1996; Taylor 1997; Thaut 1992c; Thaut et al. 1991). Thaut, Mertel, and Leins (2008, 155), explain that "through the input of auditory rhythm, not only the movement is regulated, but the timing of the sequence of the muscle contractions that produce the movement is optimized."

Attention deficits are common in brain injury. Wood (1987, 121–122) lists four components of attention that may be affected by brain injury: decrease in alertness, failure of selective attention, forced responsiveness to irrelevant stimuli, and reduced attention span. Knox, Yokota-Adachi, Kershner, and Jutai (2003) conducted research on alternating attention in an 18-year-old subject who had a closed head injury resulting from a motorcycle accident. The investigation defined alternating attention as "the capacity of mental flexibility which allows for moving between tasks having different cognitive requirements" (99). They used the alternating attention component of the Musical Attention Training Program (Witt, Knox, Jutai, and Loveszy 1994; revised by Jutai 1997). One task was to recognize a melodic motive, and the other was to track a drum pattern. At first, the subject heard the music without the drum track, and when he heard the predetermined four-note pattern, he was to strike a key at the end of the motive. When the drum track was on, he was to strike a key on the downbeat of each measure. When the drum track was turned off, he was to return to the melodic motive and strike a key at the end of the four-note motive. Thus, he had to shift attention from the melodic component to the drum component and back again. A dichotic listening method was used to test his ability to alternate attention, and he scored within a normal range. His ability to shift attention was increased with treatment (Jutai 1997, 103).

Jeong and Lesiak (2011) developed an assessment instrument to provide initial information on auditory attention in TBI patients. A sample included 15 participants, with a mean age of 29.87 years, who had a traumatic brain injury an average of 20.87 months before the study. They used the following method: "Music-based Attention Assessment (MAA) for patients with TBI is a melodic contour identification test with three subtests consisting of sustained attention, selective attention, and divided attention" (557). The test was field tested to determine that it had acceptable item difficulty, related to musical characteristics, and maintained an acceptable internal consistency. This study needs to be followed by testing with larger samples. In 2013, Jeong published a revised version and discussed its use with patients with traumatic brain injury. The revised version used "various combinations of sounds (e.g., melodic contours presented with environmental noise, two melodic contours played by different instrument timbres) in order to mimic existing real-world auditory events" (68).

At a very basic level, music can reinforce and increase purposeful motor responses. Boyle (1987) found that 15 seconds of contingent music (using the patient's preferred music, as determined from conversations with the patient's family) effectively increased targeted behaviors such as lateral head movement, mouth movement, finger movement, eye focus, and eye blinks. Research suggests that vibroacoustic therapy, "a process in which vibrations are applied directly to the body in the form of low frequency sinus tones in combination with selected music" (Skille 1989, 62), can benefit stroke patients by decreasing muscle spasms, increasing responsiveness to range-of-motion exercises, and stimulating or facilitating independent movements. In addition, clinical studies in China have shown that music electro-acupuncture techniques, in which music is electrically added to the acupuncture stimulation by attaching electrodes from the sound source to the acupuncture needle by metal clips as the subjects listen to the same music through headphones, can stimulate muscle function and increase muscle strength in patients with cerebral hemiplegia (Shi-jing et al. 1991).

Many music therapy programs in physical rehabilitation settings use movement to music (e.g., exercises to music, music with gait training) or the movements used in playing instruments to help motivate movement and increase motor control and coordination (Brunk 1992; Hofmeister and Cole 1986; Lucia 1987; Sandness 1995; Staum 1988, 1996; Thaut 1992c). As Thaut (2008, 158) explains, "TIMP [Therapeutic Instrumental Music Performances] exercises can be purely instrumental as well, such as in keyboard exercises for finger, hand, arm, and postural control, or in tone bar exercises to practice shoulder adduction and abduction or elbow flexion and extention exercises." This is also a part of neurologic music therapy. Frequently, music and rhythmic stimulation are used as timing cues to organize and structure physical movements and exercise. According to Thaut (1992c), music is very useful as a timing cue for physical movement because of three factors: Music's rhythmic organization helps patients organize their movement in time; music activates the auditory sense, the sense in which timing develops earliest and most efficiently; and sound activates the motor neurons and puts the muscles in a state of readiness, while learning to move to rhythmically organized sounds (e.g., music) activates the muscles in synchrony with the auditory rhythm.

Dyrlund and Wininger (2008) studied the effect of preferred music compared with that of nonpreferred music in exercise. They concluded that "attending to music during exercise will result in more enjoyment of the activity when listening to preferred music compared to nonpreferred music" (126).

Neurophysiological research shows that music not only stimulates movement but also serves as a "neurological entrainment mechanism" for movement (Taylor 1997, 121). For example, music and auditory stimuli can be very beneficial in facilitating gait training for individuals who have had strokes or have Parkinson's disease (Clair 1996b; Staum 1988, 1996; Thaut 1992a):

> Rhythmic entrainment occurs when the frequency and pattern sequence of movement become locked to the frequency and pattern of an auditory rhythmic

stimulus, such as in metronome pulses or the metric and rhythm patterns in music. (Thaut, Thaut, and La Gasse 2008, 286)

Summarizing some of the research in this area, Clair (1996b, 213) concluded:

> Although the work of Thaut and colleagues is complex and involves sophisticated measurement protocols, the outcomes are clear: Rhythmic auditory cues presented during gait training cause walking to become more symmetrical, more efficient, and better balanced.

Music also may be used in conjunction with behavioral techniques to improve physical functioning. For example, Kearney and Fussey (1991) found that contingent music administered by a headband with a special switch that allowed the music to be played only when the subjects held their head in the correct upright position significantly increased correct head position during ambulation in adult males who had brain injuries. This study incidentally showed music's neurological entrainment power, for the researchers noted that rhythmic auditory stimulation also decreased the patients' stride deviation and improved their gait rhythmicity.

Reviewing the literature concerning music and physical rehabilitation, Staum (1996) observed that reinforcing music's rhythmic stimulation with sounds of one's own production (as in singing, chanting, playing instruments) seemed to increase the inherent drive to synchronize movement with music's rhythm. In her work with patients who had traumatic brain injuries, Lucia (1987) found that singing familiar songs (selected to match the time frame, tempo, and feel of the movement) during exercise routines developed by physical or occupational therapists motivated and facilitated patients' participation by helping them focus on the task and by providing diversion from the boredom of repeated exercises. The group practiced singing the songs before adding the movement. Lucia found that this technique was most beneficial to patients with right hemiplegia who had left frontal lobe damage or bilateral damage, where the singing centers of the right brain hemisphere were still relatively intact.

Research has shown that auditory rhythm can enhance performance of upper-extremity gross motor tasks, implying that using rhythmic techniques to teach and accompany movement in neuromuscular reeducation programs may lead to a quicker recovery of motor control and skill by improving the anticipation and timing of muscular efforts (Thaut 2008; Thaut et al. 1991). Organizing movements to a rhythmic accompaniment or practicing functional movements of upper extremities by playing musical instruments may help patients who have had strokes or TBIs sustain consistent muscular efforts (Thaut et al. 1991). For example, Confrancesco (1985) used musical instruments matched to the client's physical needs to increase hand grasp strength and functional arm and hand movements in stroke patients.

Lim, Miller, and Fabian (2011) studied the effects of therapeutic instrumental music performance (TIMP) on endurance level, self-perceived fatigue level, and self-perceived exertion of inpatients in physical rehabilitation. TIMP is a neurologic music therapy technique that "utilizes instrument playing to structure, coordinate and facilitate specific functional movement patterns in rehabilitation exercise" (127). They compared TIMP with traditional occupational therapy (TOT), using a single application of each treatment condition. They found no differences between TIMP and TOT in endurance measures. However, there were differences in patient perception of fatigue and exertion after exercises with TIMP. Apparently, "playing instruments with musical cueing provides a sensory stimulus that focuses one's attention away from the physical sensations of the exercise, resulting in perception of less exertion and fatigue" (144).

The use of appropriate musical instruments to exercise specific physical movement gives patients immediate feedback and reinforcement (via the production of a tone or a beat). When the movement is performed correctly, the music adds enjoyment to the exercise and motivation to practice the movements, which facilitate memory of the muscle movements that produce certain rhythmic and melodic patterns (Thaut 1992c). Various instruments, including simple rhythm instruments, autoharps, guitars, recorders, and keyboards, traditional band and orchestral instruments, and electronic or computerized instruments, can be used in movement retraining. The key is to match the instrument to the patient's physical needs, abilities, and interests (Elliott 1982; Thaut 1992c). For example, Erdonmez (1991) worked with a patient whose premorbid experience as a pianist motivated him to use the piano as an integral part of his rehabilitation following a left cerebral vascular accident. Sometimes, the music therapist will have to adapt instruments so patients can use them most effectively (Brunk 1992; Clark and Chadwick 1979; Elliott 1982; Rudenberg 1982). Other individuals, especially those who have severe physical limitations, may be able to use what limited movement they have to make music with electronic instruments, computers, and adaptive electronic equipment, such as special switches or input devices (Fegers et al. 1989; Howell et al. 1995; Krout 1992a, 1995; Nagler and Lee 1989; Swingler 1994).

Music therapy interventions can also help patients in rehabilitation cope with chronic pain that may be associated with their condition and improve their independence in activities of daily living (ADLs). Discussing music therapy in a medical setting, Kemper and Danhauer (2005, 286) said, "Carefully selected music can reduce stress, enhance a sense of comfort and relaxation, offer distraction from pain, and enhance clinical performance." They also noted that through entrainment to its rhythm, music can change neuronal activity in the left lateral temporal lobe and in the cortical areas devoted to movement.

Kim and Koh (2005) studied music's effects on pain perception of stroke patients during upper-extremity joint exercises. Following presentation of each of three conditions – song, song with karaoke accompaniment, and no music – patients rated their personal pain on a scale devised by the researchers. While patients made many positive comments, there were no statistical differences among the pain ratings across the three conditions. There were only 10 subjects, and the average time since their stroke was three years, which may have made it difficult for them to rate pain on the scale provided. Importantly their positive comments indicated a positive attitude toward upper-extremity exercises.

Kim (2010) developed a protocol to enhance swallowing training for dysphagic stroke patients. *Dysphagia*, difficulty in swallowing, is very common after a stroke. Most patients regain the ablility to swallow in a short period of time, but "at least 11% of dysphagic patients still have difficulties after 6 months" (102). Without improvement, food may enter the lungs, thereby causing aspiration pneumonia. Kim selected eight subjects, ranging in age from 50 to 70 years, who had stroke-involved oral and pharyngeal dysphagia, from a local hospital in South Korea. Each subject was scheduled for 12 individual music therapy sessions (three times per week for a four-week period). The Frenchay Dysarthria Assessment (Enderby 1983), a standardized test of speech neuromuscular activity, was given before the first session, after the sixth session, and following the last session. At the speech therapist's recommendation, three sections were used: reflex, respiration, and laryngeal categories. After a pilot test, Kim employed the following protocol: (1) a two-minute warmup of yawning and glissando slides; (2) three minutes of singing a song of the subject's choice; (3) a two-step breathing procedure of inhale and exhale for two minutes; (4) a three-step breathing procedure of breathing in, holding, and breathing out for 10 repetitions; (5) playing intervals (a major 2nd, major 3rd, perfect 5th, major 6th, and an octave) on the keyboard during which subjects vocalized the interval (on vowel sounds "aah," "ooh," and "eee," repeated 10 times), if possible, in a procedure meant to facilitate laryngeal elevation and throat muscle movement; and (6) three minutes of singing the same song used in the warmup. The results indicated "significant improvements across reflex, respiration, and laryngeal categories and indicate improved control" (117). Improvements in breathing and laryngeal elevation are important because they relate to swallowing.

Rider (1985) specifically explored music therapy techniques to reduce pain in patients with spinal cord injuries and found that "entrainment music," which began with much tension and dissonance to match the patients' pain and gradually shifted to more consonant, relaxed sounds, was most effective in reducing pain and muscular tension. Many of the other music-mediated pain reduction techniques discussed in Chapter Seventeen also may be beneficial for these patients.

In the area of activities of daily living (ADLs), cues provided by musical structure or song lyrics can assist in motor planning and facilitate the development of functional motor patterns that individuals can use in daily routines. For example, Gervin (1991) used song lyrics to train a patient recovering from a brain injury to dress independently. The external cues and pacing provided by the lyrics and music provided a structure for the activity that helped the patient overcome difficulties in initiation, sequencing, and motor planning and complete the task successfully.

Music Therapy Interventions to Improve Cognitive Functioning

Music therapy interventions can help patients in rehabilitation programs improve many areas of cognitive functioning, including alerting and orienting responses, awareness of self and others and the environment, reality orientation, attention span, memory, concentration and focus on tasks, ability to follow commands, problem-solving skills, and ability to learn and retain new information (Brunk 1992; Sandness 1995; Thaut 1992c). Thaut (2008, 75–76) reviewed the research and reported "that accessing musical memories provides a gateway for enhanced verbal nonmusical recall and knowledge, thus making musical memory training a tool in enhancing cognitive functions in patients." Rainey and Larsen (2002) had reached the same conclusion. Many types of music experiences can be structured to stimulate and reinforce orienting or attention responses and to focus attention and increase concentration. Music can assist in increasing reality orientation and awareness of self and others, as well as provide cues for memory and structure for learning or relearning information. It also can motivate individuals to participate in cognitive retraining programs, provide practice and reinforcement for following directions, and help individuals develop and practice problem-solving skills. Thus, therapeutic music interventions can facilitate cognitive response and skill development throughout the course of rehabilitation.

Music therapy often is included as part of a stimulation program for comatose patients (Boyle 1987, 1989; Brunk 1992; Claeys et al. 1989; Sandness 1995; Thaut 1992c). Other states of consciousness include a vegetative state (VS) and a minimally conscious state (MCS), as well as fully conscious state. Daveson (2010) reports that these patients require long-term care, although it is difficult to devise a treatment plan for clients who do not respond to most stimuli.

A primary treatment goal for patients in a low state of conciousness is to increase their awareness of stimuli and their ability to exhibit consistent, appropriate responses to stimuli (Claeys et al. 1989). To make the musical stimuli as meaningful as possible for the patient, music therapists may interview the patient's family to learn what types of music were meaningful to the patient prior to the injury. Music therapists then may present these selections in short, distinct segments "to provide a structure within which the client can process the musical experiences as being different from the random stimuli" (Claeys et al. 1989, 72). Other vibrational, rhythmic, harmonic (e.g., consonant and dissonant chords) and environmental sounds also may be used to elicit alertness or orienting responses or to signal times of the day or specific activities (Brunk 1992; Claeys et al. 1989). It is important that musical stimuli be intentional and played only for short periods so that they may be perceived as unique events and not just part of the background noise. As the therapist presents stimuli, she or he can first match them to the tempo of the patient's breathing, or to the rhythm of a patient's eye blinks or finger movements, and later vary the music's tempo or rhythm to see if the patient will show awareness of the change by matching his or her breathing or movement to the new tempo or rhythm (Brunk 1992). In addition to evoking responses, music or sounds that are meaningful to the patient can be used contingently to help reinforce purposeful responses and increase the patient's ability to exhibit consistent, appropriate responses (Boyle 1987, 1989).

Music is also useful in neurological assessments. Initially, as Giacino, Fins, Laureys, and Schiff (2014, 99) explain,

> in the clinical setting, neurologists and neurorehabilitation specialists are called on to discern the level of consciousness in patients who are unable to communicate, through word or gestures, and to project outcomes and recommend approaches to treatment.

As patients emerge from coma (levels II–III of the Rancho Los Amigos Scale), familiar music can be used to decrease agitation and anxiety (Thaut 1992c). Improvised songs about the patient's movements or vocalizations can help increase the patient's awareness of his or her behavior, while songs incorporating information about place, date, time, and season can be used to increase reality orientation (Claeys et al. 1989). Even with no observable response, patients still may hear and, at least to some degree, process the information. Therefore, all interactions should be encouraging and supportive, and persons conversing in the room should assume that the patient can hear and understand their conversations, even if she or he cannot respond (Bley 2015; Claeys et al. 1989; Clair 1996b).

As patients progress to levels IV–VI of the Rancho Los Amigos Scale, music therapists use music experiences to support treatment goals related to areas such as following directions, short-term memory, reality orientation, attention and concentration, etc. For example, song lyrics can present and structure information and help cue recall (Brunk 1992; Claeys et al. 1989; Sandness 1995; Thaut 1992c; Thaut 2008). Learning (or relearning) how to play musical instruments can also help patients increase cognitive skills such

as short-term memory, concentration, and perception of visual/spatial relationships (Erdonmez 1991; Hofmeister and Cole 1986; McMaster 1991;
Thaut 2008). As patients develop increased attention and concentration in
music therapy sessions, their general ability to concentrate also may improve.
For example, McMaster (1991) found that, as a 40-year-old woman recovering
from a stroke was able to attend to tasks in music therapy sessions for longer
periods of time, she also began to attend to subjects that interested her outside
of the session for up to one hour.

Music Therapy Interventions to Improve Communication Skills

Music therapy interventions often are very beneficial for patients who have
speech and language impairments resulting from strokes or traumatic brain
injuries (Adamek and Shiraishi 1996; Brunk 1992; Clair 1996b; N. Cohen
1988, 1992, 1994; Hofmeister and Cole 1986; Lucia 1987; Sandness 1995;
Taylor 1987b, 1989; Thaut 1992c, 2008). However, one must remember that
a particular individual's response to various types of music therapy strategies
will depend on many factors, including prior experience with music and the
exact site and extent of the brain damage (Cohen 1994; Taylor 1987b, 1989).
Music therapy interventions can address both receptive and expressive
language skills and may provide avenues for nonverbal as well as verbal
communication.

The benefits of singing for stimulating speech in neurologically impaired
individuals have been noted for many years. Cohen (1994) summarizes early
anecdotal records and research, all of which note how individuals with expressive aphasia, who have little or no speeech, maintain some singing ability.
More recently, special music therapy techniques have been developed to
assist in aphasia rehabilitation, techniques such as melodic intonation therapy
(Albert, Sparks, and Helms 1973; Baker 2000; Sparks, Helms, and Albert
1974; Sparks and Holland 1976), rhythm and melody in speech therapy
(Rogers and Fleming 1981), and the stimulation approach, in which familiar
song texts are used to trigger speech (Lucia 1987; Thaut 1992c). (See Chapter
Twelve for a more detailed explanation of these techniques.) Many music
therapy strategies used to facilitate or increase speech in persons who have
had strokes or TBIs "capitalize on preserved right brain functions for singing,
an automatic, non-propositional speech skill that generally precedes functional speech recovery" (Lucia 1987, 36). Propositional speech is specific to a
particular situation, as shown in sentences such as "Have you seen my
pencil?" or "I found my missing gloves." Nonpropositional speech is more
general, often a well-rehearsed sequence, such as reciting the day of the week
or months of the year, a traditional social sequence (such as "How are you?"),

or even profanity (King 2007, 15). In recovering aphasics, nonpropositional speech likely will precede propositional speech.

Baker and Tamplin (2005) examined themes within songs written by people with traumatic brain injury, with particular interest in gender differences in the lyrics. They found that both men and women used the songs to give messages to significant others:

> However, clinicians should be aware that males tend to simultaneously express fear [of lack of progress in therapy, and how they will cope with the future] but want to confront their future more than females . . . . females may need to reflect more on their relationships with others. (119–120)

Music was an important form of communication for both genders. The authors wrote a clinician's manual (2006) (listed in suggested readings).

In addition to stimulating speech production, music therapy techniques may improve the speech rate, vocal intensity, and verbal intelligibility of clients who have neurogenic communication disorders (N. Cohen 1988, 1992, 1994, 1995; Cohen and Masse 1993).

Music Therapy Interventions to Improve Social and Emotional Functioning

Since the social and emotional consequences of traumatic brain injuries, strokes, and spinal cord injuries often are as devastating as the physical and cognitive deficits, dealing with socioemotional concerns is an important part of the rehabilitation process. Music therapy interventions can help meet patients' emotional and social needs by reducing anxiety, serving as a means of nonverbal expression and an outlet for releasing tension or expressing frustration, motivating participation and interaction with others, decreasing depression, facilitating emotional expression, providing opportunities for creativity and success experiences, helping patients find ways to cope with or adapt/adjust to their limitations, and providing group experiences that facilitate supportive, positive interactions with others (Brunk 1992; Clair 1996b; Sandness 1995; Thaut 1992c; Thaut, Thaut, and LaGasse 2008).

As part of the rehabilitation process, individuals who have experienced losses of physical function, independence, etc., due to a stroke, TBI, or spinal cord injury need opportunities to express their grief and/or anger over these losses (Bright 1986; Clair 1996b; McMaster 1991). Since music is a language of feelings and emotions (Gaston 1968a; Whitwell 1993), it can facilitate this process, especially for those who have lost the ability to communicate verbally or who have limited insight and verbal processing capabilities. When individuals listen to, vocalize with, or play laments or other songs expressing grief and deep emotions, the songs may help them project their feelings and communicate emotions associated with their debilitation and express and work through their grief (Erdonmez 1991; McMaster 1991). The structured use of these songs within a therapeutic setting helps patients express their grief deeply and move from their grief "into a lighter state" (McMaster 1991, 555). Instrumental improvisations (McMaster 1991) or improvised songs (Amir 1990) also can help individuals express and work through feelings. In addition, Guided Imagery and Music (GIM) techniques may help some brain damaged patients work through feelings of depression, hopelessness, helplessness, and anger (Goldberg et al. 1988). Goldberg and her colleagues (1988) found that GIM techniques could be effective when more traditional psychotherapy techniques were not useful because of the patient's brain damage. However, they recommended that GIM be used only with "patients who are not psychotic, had good premorbid social, vocational, and psychological functioning, and evidence good current ego strength" (45).

Music can provide comfort and emotional support throughout the long and often frustrating process of rehabilitation. Precomposed, familiar songs that resonate with the patients' experience may provide tangible evidence that others understand their grief and feelings (Bright 1986; Erdonmez 1991; McMaster 1991). For example, one patient recovering from stroke found comfort and help in expressing and coping with his suffering from song cycles, such as Schubert's *Winterreise*, that he had known prior to his CVA (Erdonmez 1991). In another case, the song "Climb Every Mountain," together with a sketch depicting a climb from a dark valley to a sunny mountain ridge, encouraged patients to keep working toward their goals, even if the process seemed very slow:

> The image of slow but real progress from darkness into light, together with a familiar song which expresses much the same ideas and a sketch in the memory notebook, has provided comfort to a variety of people whose progress in therapy is slow, and the music has helped to keep the ideas in mind. (Bright 1986, 144)

Song writing, both individual and group, can be another important element in the therapeutic process for clients in physical rehabilitation programs by providing opportunities for creativity (Amir 1990; Barker and Brunk 1991; Brunk 1992; Claeys et al. 1989; Robb 1996). Amir (1990) used an "improvised song" technique to help a 20-year-old male, who had quadriplegia following a spinal cord injury from an automobile accident, express and work through his feelings of depression and despair over his lack of progress and his physical limitations. In this process, the therapist played an accompaniment as directed by the patient, who chose the instrument (e.g., guitar, keyboard), tempo, sounds, and general style of the music. As the patient listened to the music, he was asked to close his eyes and give words to his feelings:

> The music guides him to become attuned to his inner world and to feel his creative expressions. The therapist provides him with a musical framework in which he can free associate; the music serves as a constructive external support for expressing what might have otherwise gone unexpressed. (Amir 1990, 70)

When involved in the creative process of improvised songs and poetic expression supported by music, this patient was able to see himself as a whole human being, in spite of his physical limitations. Through these songs, he not only mourned the loss of his previous way of life, but also discovered new symbols and strengths that gave meaning to his current life situation.

In addition to providing outlets for creativity and expression of feelings, group song writing can help provide mutual support for patients by developing relationships and a sense of community (Claeys et al. 1989). For example, Robb (1996) used fill-in-the-blank scripts and improvisational song writing (instrumental and vocal improvisation or lyric narration to an improvised instrumental accompaniment) with adolescents who had traumatic brain or spinal cord injuries. These song writing experiences led to increased communication and self-esteem, facilitated adjustment to the rehabilitation process, helped patients recover repressed material, and improved coping and socialization skills. Robb (1996, 36) summarized: "Most patients came away from the experience having discovered something about themselves, wanting to share their experiences with others, and feeling a sense of pride in what they have accomplished." Sometimes, individual and group song writing processes are combined, as when individual verses about feelings or goals alternate with a group chant or chorus (Barker and Brunk 1991). Discharge songs may also help provide closure for the patients and help them integrate and synthesize their experiences (Robb 1996).

Music experiences lend themselves well to group activity, providing opportunities for patients to interact with others, verbally and nonverbally. For patients who are unable to speak but still able to sing, songs may provide a positive way of communicating and of socializing and interacting with others. Clair (1996b) described a case in which singing facilitated positive interactions between a stroke patient and her family. After the stroke, the patient was unable to speak and only responded to family visits by crying. When family members began to sing some well-known songs to her, the patient was able to join in singing, stopped crying, and began to laugh with delight that she could participate with her children in this way. However, the patient will face long hours of therapy to relearn skills:

> she was motivated to participate in rehabilitation because of the success she experienced in singing her much-loved music with her children. Her success also provided reassurance and joy to her children, who needed to feel that they were helping their mother rather than making her cry. (Clair 1996b, 215)

Hinman (2010) discussed using music to help married couples communicate. When one member of the couple is hospitalized, the other may experience role changes and many feelings that require discussion. However, they may be unable to do so, for fear of worrying their partner or causing increased stress. The hospitalized person also may hold back needed discussion, because that, too, may lead to feelings that may seem overwhelming. Hinman describes how to use "Our Song" as a tool to express many of these feelings. She includes four case examples illustrating ways to use music to support and encourage honest communication between partners.

Magee, Baker, Daveson, Hitchen, Kennelly, Leung, and Tamplin (2011) provided case material from six clients that shows how music therapy with brain injured children, adolescents, and adults can benefit from involving family members into the treatment program. They note that the music must be age appropriate and developmentally and socially relevant. When the frontal lobe control mechanisms are damaged, the client may be unable to regulate emotional impulses, which may lead to inappropriate behavior: "irritability, aggression, disinhibition, sexually-inappropriate behavior, reduced anger control, immature behavior in relation to age expectations, rigidity, social awkwardness, impaired social perception, and egocentrism" (5). Their goals were to facilitate emotional expression, improve communication, and increase appropriate social interaction.

Although not all patients will be able to respond by singing (the area and extent of brain damage may impact vocal responses), many will be comforted by well-known songs. It is also important to consult with the patient's physician to determine when sensory stimulation can safely begin (Clair 1996b).

Group singing also may provide a way for patients to begin to socialize with each other and encourage them to work on regaining communication skills (Cohen 1992; Lucia 1987). As Cohen (1992) observed in her work with singing instruction for speech rehabilitation of patients who had experienced TBIs or CVAs, group singing provided patients with important social and emotional benefits that are not present in individual sessions.

Thaut, Mertel, and Leins (2008, 158) note that "participating in functional music-centered exercises can generate feelings of accomplishment and collaboration, perhaps more so than doing other types of exercises such as bicep curls." Instrumental experiences also can be structured to provide emotional and social benefits for patients in physical rehabilitation programs (Barker and Brunk 1991; Brunk 1992; Claeys et al. 1989; Clair 1996b). For example, instrumental improvisation can provide opportunities for patients to express feelings and frustrations within the safe container of the musical structure. Group instrumental experiences provide opportunities for nonverbal relating experiences, where group members need to be aware of and depend on each other to produce a pleasing musical product (Barker and Brunk 1991). Participation in instrumental ensembles enables patients who are "isolated by illness or fear to become acquainted, to pool their strengths in mutually satisfying ways, and to develop skills and abilities that facilitate successful musical experiences" (Clair 1996b, 218). With appropriate adaptations of instruments (Clark and Chadwick 1979; Rudenberg 1982) and the use of technology such as adapted switches, electronic instruments, and computers (Adamek and Darrow 2010; Fegers et al. 1989; Krout 1992a, 1995; Nagler and Lee 1989), even patients who have severe physical limitations can independently create music and participate in ensemble experiences.

Impairments from TBIs, CVAs, or spinal cord injuries impact families, too, as roles and life styles change. Since family support is critical to recovery rehabilitation, programs must find ways to incorporate families in positive experiences as both patient and family adjust to the social and emotional effects of the injury (Barker and Brunk 1991).

Family participation can be incorporated easily into music therapy experiences, providing family members with a way to participate positively in the rehabilitation process and giving them opportunities to interact with their injured family member in experiences that are enjoyable and emotionally uplifting (Barker and Brunk 1991; Bright 1986; Brunk 1992; Claeys et al. 1989; Clair 1996b; Hinman 2010; Thaut 1992c). As Claeys et al. (1989) explain, "Unlike other disciplines, music therapy offers a setting in which the family can function as a group, thereby often improving family relationships." Many types of music activities, from simple hand-holding and singing, to partner activities, to instrumental groups, to song writing, to combined art and music experiences, can be structured to provide a setting where patients and their family members or friends can focus on expression of feelings, meaningful social interaction, re-establishing or learning new ways of relating to each other, and healthy creativity (Barker and Brunk 1991; Claeys et al. 1989). In addition, music and creative arts groups can help provide fun times in the midst of a serious, strenuous physical rehabilitation program, thus giving patients and families a necessary emotional outlet (Barker and Brunk 1991).

Finally, music therapy can play an important role in patients' leisure education. Music therapists can help patients (a) learn how to use adapted devices to participate in music activities they enjoyed before their injury, (b) find ways to use music as enjoyable structure to practice functional skills and support rehabilitation goals, or (c) learn new music skills to substitute for old music skills (e.g., using computers or synthesizers to compose or play music instead of playing a guitar) (Brunk 1992). Music therapy programs focusing on leisure skill development may include activities such as an introduction to adapted instruments and input devices (e.g., special switches), vocal or instrumental lessons, theory lessons or the development of composition skills, community outings, and the use of community resources.

Some patients may achieve a new interest in life and a purpose for living by learning to use previous musical skills or interests in new ways. For example, a young man who had played the bass guitar before a spinal cord injury from an automobile accident left him a quadriplegic was able to experience himself as a complete human being again through the creative process of improvising songs (Amir 1990). In another instance, a physician who also had been a talented classical pianist before a stroke left his right hand and arm paralyzed learned to play many of the right-handed piano parts with his left hand as part of his rehabilitation process (Erdonmez 1991). For this patient, "music became the focus of his life and gave him a purpose for his existence (Erdonmez 1991, 569).

SPECIAL CONSIDERATIONS AND TIPS FOR SUCCESS

Music therapists who work with patients in physical rehabilitation programs need to find optimal ways to structure and manage the environment (adaptive aids, minimize distractions, cues for responses, etc.) to maximize patients' performance and minimize the impact of their disabilities (Brunk 1992; Chance 1986). When therapists use musical instruments, "it is important to analyze the physical strengths and weaknesses of the patient and then match them with an instrument that requires positioning and motions appropriate to his or her physical ability" (Thaut 1992c, 268). Electronic instruments, adapted instruments, special switches, and computers may help persons with physical limitations be involved in actively making music (see Chapter Eleven). Therapists may also want to consult references, such as Edel (1994), that list resources for piano music of various difficulty levels that can be performed with one hand.

Tools like the Functional Independence Measure (FIM) can help provide a general idea of the patient's overall level of functional independence and his or her progress toward independence during treatment. Other assessment tools, such as the Glasgow Coma Scale and the Rancho Los Amigos Scale, are used to describe coma severity and describe cognitive functioning and behaviors typically exhibited by patients emerging from coma. Music therapists may make use of tools such as these to guide their planning. In addition, FIM scores may help demonstrate the effectiveness of some music therapy intervention strategies.

In work with comatose patients, it is important to remember that they may hear and understand ongoing conversations in the room, even though they may be unable to respond (Beil 2015). Therefore, interactions should be positive, concrete, encouraging and supportive, and persons in the room should remember to talk *to* the patients rather than *about* them (Claeys et al. 1989; Clair 1996b).

As research into music's direct effects on the human nervous system progresses, music therapists should consider approaching "movement objectives with stroke and traumatic brain injury patients from the viewpoint of using music as a neurological entrainment mechanism rather than simply as a way to stimulate movement" (Taylor 1997, 121). In addition, music therapists should consider the whole person when planning their treatment approaches, making use of music's ability to provide emotional support and positive experiences for both the patient and his/her family during the long rehabilitation process.

QUESTIONS FOR THOUGHT AND DISCUSSION

1. Relate the levels of the Rancho Los Amigos Scale to the three stages of recovery from TBI. Describe the way patients function at each level or stage and discuss the implications of these behaviors for music therapy programming
2. What are music's unique contributions to rehabilitation? How/why can these be important for patients and their families?
3. Describe several music therapy interventions that might be used to help improve (a) physical functioning, (b) cognitive functioning, (c) communication skills, and (d) social or emotional skills in patients who have had strokes, traumatic brain injuries, or spinal cord injuries. What unique benefits does music provide in each of these areas?
4. List several special considerations to remember when developing therapeutic intervention strategies for patients who have had a stroke, traumatic brain injuries, or spinal cord injuries. Why are these important? How might they impact the planning and implementation of music therapy programs?
5. For each of the situations listed below, (a) define the problem or areas of need for the client or group of clients, (b) describe one or more of the goals you might pursue in music therapy sessions with the client(s), (c) describe music activities you might use to help the client(s) meet those goals, (d) tell how the music activities you described relate to the goals and needs of the client(s), and (e) mention any special considerations you might take into account.

Situation 1:
    You have been asked to provide music therapy sessions for a small group of individuals between the ages of 25 and 40 years who are recovering from closed head injuries or strokes. These individuals are currently residents of a rehabilitation center. Some have limited movement and weakness on one side of their body. All can say at least a few words, but have varying degrees of difficulties with communication. Several have

difficulty with memory, concentration, and problem solving. Most need work on improving their ability to initiate tasks and carry them through to completion. All need to work on relearning appropriate social interaction and group cooperation skills. Individuals in the group are often irritable, quarrelsome, anxious, or easily depressed or excited. None of the group members were active musicians at the time of their injury, but a few had played in the band or had sung in the choir in high school. All used to enjoy listening to the radio or recorded music. Music interests ranged from rock to easy listening to country to gospel.

Situation 2:

A 25-year-old female who sustained severe head and back injuries in a diving accident has been referred to you for music therapy. She is paralyzed from the waist down and has limited use of her upper extremities at this time. She sometimes experiences severe back pain. She also has difficulties with short-term memory and sequencing skills. She has just entered a rehabilitation center, but is angry and depressed and has little interest in trying to regain any functional skills. Since she can no longer lead the type of active life to which she is accustomed, she has experienced some suicidal thoughts.

SUGGESTIONS FOR FURTHER READING

Adamek, M. S. & Shiraishi, I. M. (1996). Music therapy with traumatic brain injured patients: Speech rehabilitation, intervention models, and assessment procedures. In C. E. Furman (Ed.), *Effectiveness of music therapy procedures: Documentation of research and clinical practice* (2nd ed.) (267–278). Silver Spring, MD: National Association for Music Therapy.

Amir, D. (1990). A song is born: Discovering meaning in improvised songs through a phenomenological analysis of two music therapy sessions with a traumatic spinal-cord injured young adult. *Music Therapy, 9(1)*, 62–81.

Baker, F. & Tamplin, J. (2006). *Music therapy methods in neuro-rehabilitation: A clinician's manual.* Philadelphia: Jessica Kingsley.

Barker, V. L. & Brunk, B. (1991). The role of a creative arts group in the treatment of clients with traumatic brain injury. *Music Therapy Perspectives, 9*, 23–31.

Boyle, M. E. (1989). Comatose and head injured patients: Applications for music in treatment. In M. H. M. Lee (Ed.), *Rehabilitation, music and human well-being* (137–148). St. Louis: MMB Music.

Bruscia, K. E. (Ed.) (1991). *Case studies in music therapy.* Phoenixville, PA: Barcelona.

Claeys, M. S., Miller, A. C., Dalloul-Rampersad, R., & Kollar, M. (1989). The role of music and music therapy in the rehabilitation of traumatically brain injured clients. *Music Therapy Perspectives, 6*, 71–77.

Clair, A. A. (1996). Music in physical rehabilitation. In A. A. Clair (Ed.), *Therapeutic uses of music with older adults* (195–227). Baltimore, MD: Health Professional Press.

Clark, C. & Chadwick, D. (1979). *Clinically adapted instruments for the multiply handicapped.* Westford, MA: Modulations.

Cohen, N. S. (1988). The use of superimposed rhythm to decrease the rate of speech in a brain-damaged adolescent. *Journal of Music Therapy, 25*(2), 85–93.

Cohen, N. S. (1992). The effect of singing instruction on the speech production of neurologically impaired persons. *Journal of Music Therapy, 29*(2), 87–102.

Cohen, N. S. (1995). The effect of vocal instruction and Visi-Pitch™ feedback on the speech of persons with neurogenic communication disorders: Two case studies. *Music Therapy Perspectives, 13*(2), 70–75.

Cohen, N. S. & Ford, J. (1995). The effect of musical cues on the nonpurposive speech of persons with aphasia. *Journal of Music Therapy, 32*(1), 46–57.

Cohen, N. S. & Masse, R. (1993). The application of singing and rhythmic instruction as a therapeutic intervention for persons with neurogenic communication disorders. *Journal of Music Therapy, 30*(2), 81–99.

Confrancesco, E. M. (1985). The effect of music therapy on hand grasp strength and functional task performance in stroke patients. *Journal of Music Therapy, 22*(3), 129–145.

Elliott, B. (1982). *Guide to the selection of musical instruments with respect to physical ability and disability.* St. Louis: Magnamusic-Baton.

Lucia, C. M. (1987). Toward developing a model of music therapy intervention in the rehabilitation of head trauma patients. *Music Therapy Perspectives, 4*, 34–39.

Nagler, J. C. & Lee, M. H. M. (1989). Music therapy using computer music technology. In M. H. M. Lee (Ed.), *Rehabilitation, music and human well-being* (226–241). St. Louis: MMB Music.

Rudenberg, M. T. (1982). Orthopedically handicapped children. In W. B. Lathom and C. T. Eagle, Jr. (Eds.), *Music therapy for handicapped children*, Vol. 3, (37–116). Washington, DC: National Association for Music Therapy.

Sandness, M. I. (1995). The role of music therapy in physical rehabilitation programs. *Music Therapy Perspectives, 13*(2), 76–81.

Standley, J. (1991). *Music techniques in therapy, counseling, and special education.* St. Louis: MMB Music.

Staum, M. J. (1996). Music for physical rehabilitation: An analysis of literature from 1950–1993 and applications for rehabilitation settings. In C. E. Furman (Ed.), *Effectiveness of music therapy procedures: Documentation of research and clinical practice* (2nd ed.) (61–105). Silver Spring, MD: National Association for Music Therapy.

Thaut, M. H., Thaut, C., & LaGasse, B. (2008). Music therapy in neurologic rehabilitation. In W. B. Davis, K. E. Gfeller, & M. H. Thaut (Eds.) *An introduction to music therapy: Theory and practice* (3rd ed.) (261–304). Silver Spring, MD: American Music Therapy Association.

Thaut, M. H. (2008). *Rhythm, music, and the brain.* New York: Routledge.

Thompson, A. B., Arnold, C., & Murray, S. E. (1990). Music therapy assessment of the cerebrovascular accident patient. *Music Therapy Perspectives, 8*, 23–29.

Chapter Nineteen

MUSIC THERAPY WITH ELDERLY INDIVIDUALS

DEFINITION

lderly describes individuals who have reached a certain arbitrary, chronological age that society defines as being "old." Some sources classify people as "older" or "elderly" when they reach 55 years of age; others reserve this classification for those aged 60 years, 65 years, or older. Essentially, the only factor people in this population have in common is that they have lived past a certain chronological age (Prickett 1996). Other terms used to describe these individuals include *older adults, aged, aging, senior, senior citizens,* or *geriatric.* The field of scientific study that deals with aging and the problems of the aged is *gerontology. Geriatrics* is the branch of medicine that is concerned with the care of elderly persons and the treatment of problems associated with aging.

Due to many factors, the elderly population is one of the fastest growing segments of our society (Dychtwald 1993). These factors include improvements in lifestyle, nutrition, and medical services; the aging of the "baby boom" generation, those born between 1946 and 1964 (Hogan, Perez, and Bell 2008); the general decrease in the birth rate; and the increase in life expectancy. In 1900, about 4 percent of Americans were aged 65 years or older; by 1994, this percentage had tripled to 12.7 percent (Aging Statistics 1994; Richter 1996). Many of these people are in good health and are living active, independent lives (Hager 1983; Horn and Meer 1987; Jacobson 1987; Richter 1996). By 2030, more than 20 percent of the USA's population is expected to be over age 65 (Horn and Meer 1987; Richter 1996), compared with 13 percent in 2010 and 9.8 percent in 1970 (Ortman, Velkoff, and Hogan 2014).

People who are aged 85 years or older sometimes are called "old old" or the "oldest old" (Feil 1982; Horn and Meer 1987). From 1970 to 1987, this group increased by 165 percent to 2.5 million (Horn and Meer 1987). The baby boomers will be over the age of 85 years by 2050, when the population aged 65 years and over is projected to be 83.7 million, almost double the estimated 2012 population of 43.1 million. The total U. S. population is projected to increase from 314 million in 2012 to 400 million in 2050 (27 percent increase) (Ortman, Volkoff, and Hogan 2014; 2012 National Projection). Many individuals over the age of 85 years still lead healthy, active lives: more than half live in their own homes, and some still work for a living (Horn and Meer 1987; Jacobson 1987). Thirty percent live by themselves, while more than a third live with a spouse or children. Many socialize in various ways, by attending religious services or professional, social, church-related, or recreational groups. Only about one-fourth are in hospitals or long-term care facilities (e.g., nursing homes).

Ageism refers to the discriminatory treatment or prejudicial stereotyping of older people (Horn and Meer 1987; Purtilo 1978). Ageism is an attitude that old age means obsolescence, decline, deterioration, frailty, and uselessness, and that older people have nothing to do, no place to go, and nothing to become. Ageism assumes all people think, act, feel, and look pretty much the same. The reality, however, is that "there is no age group more varied in physical abilities; personal styles, tastes and desires; or financial capabilities than the older population" (Dychtwald 1993, 5).

COMMON CHARACTERISTICS, PROBLEMS, AND NEEDS OF CLIENTS

Elderly individuals are very diverse; in fact, "people grow less alike as they age" (Jacobson 1987, A19). Although certain physiological, psychological, and socioemotional changes often are associated with the aging process, these changes do not occur at the same rate or to the same degree in all individuals (Bright 1986; Purtilo 1978). Therefore, chronological age alone is a poor indicator of a person's physical, mental, or socioemotional abilities. Many other factors, such as general physical and mental health, economic status, access to family or close friends, and involvement in meaningful activities, greatly impact an individual's level of functioning in all of these areas (Erikson et al. 1986; Prickett 1996; Purtilo 1978).

For ease of discussion, this chapter groups elderly individuals into five general categories: (1) the well elderly, (2) those who are semi-independent, (3) those who are chronically ill or medically fragile and are being cared for in their own home or that of a caregiver, (4) those who are in nursing homes or long-term care facilities, and (5) those who have Alzheimer's disease (AD) or related neurocognitive disorders. (DSM-V (2013) now labels what formerly was "dementia" as "neurocognitive disorders.") Individuals who are terminally ill and receiving hospice care may be found in both categories 3 and 4, since some hospice programs are home-based and others are inpatient programs (Colligan 1987; Palmer 1989).

General Changes Associated with the Aging Process

Primary aging is a gradual, genetically determined process that affects the efficiency of all body systems and proceeds at different rates in different individuals. *Secondary aging* is the result of factors like disease, trauma, stress, abuse, and disuse. Many of these are lifestyle factors that, to some extent, the individual can control. In fact, some research suggests that many of the problems of old age are primarily due not to aging, but to the improper care of the body over an individual's lifetime (Dychtwald 1993). The overall rate at which an individual ages is determined by interaction of these primary and secondary factors (Horn and Meer 1987).

Elderly people have to contend with many biological, mental, and social changes (Purtilo 1978; Smith 1972). In some ways, the changes of old age are comparable to those experienced during adolescence. As Smith (1972, 3) observes:

> Just as adolescence is a process not only of growth but also of widespread change, so aging, from its start, is far from a process of mere decline. Instead it is in large measure a process of change in all aspects of the aging person's body, organs, senses, and mind, which in turn alters the aging person's conduct, emotions, self-control, personality and relations with others.

Common *biological* or *physiological changes* associated with aging are:

- loss of skin elasticity;
- a decrease in the body's ability to regulate temperature;
- a decrease in skin oils;
- more fragile blood vessels;
- reduced function of superficial nerve endings (resulting in a decreased sensitivity to pain or pressures that can lead to injury);
- decreased lung elasticity and lung capacity;
- decreased cardiac output and blood supply;
- an increase in the time needed to recover from injury;
- a generalized decrease in strength and stamina;
- loss of brain tissue (a gradual process that occurs throughout life since most neurons are not regenerated when they die);
- increased reaction or response time and decreased reflex strength due to changes in brain electrochemical activity;
- vision changes (*presbyopia*) such as decreased lens elasticity, decreased pupil size, and decreased speed of adjustment to light changes that may cause the need for more light or reading glasses and may make night driving difficult;
- decrease in hearing acuity (*presbycusis*) is a multifactorial disorder and

gradual loss of ability to hear high frequencies and occurs in both men and women;
- loss of calcium in the bones (*osteopenia*) is thinning of the bones due to loss of minerals and (*osteoporosis*) is fragile bones that break easily and is a more advanced form of bone thinning;
- a more compressed and less flexible spinal column;
- decreased muscle strength and endurance;
- increased time needed to recover between activities;
- changes in gait (e.g., shorter steps, less steady with more lateral movement);
- deterioration of the teeth and gums;
- reduced saliva output that may lead to difficulties chewing and swallowing;
- decline in the size and number of taste buds;
- deterioration in the sense of smell;
- decreased strength and elasticity in the bladder and muscles controlling urination (may result in more frequent urination or some degree of incontinence);
- decrease in hormonal secretions in both males and females. (Davis 1992a; Lazarus 1988; Lucchino 2015; Purtilo 1978; Smith 1972)

It is important to remember that these changes occur at different rates in different individuals and that not all changes happen to the same extent in every individual.

Some *medical problems* or diseases also become increasingly common among individuals over the age of 65 years. These include *arteriosclerosis* (hardening of the arteries caused by thickening and loss of elasticity of the arterial walls, often because of fatty deposits, resulting in decrease or cessation of blood flow to various parts of the body, with concomitant decrease or loss of function); *heart disease*; *hypertension*; *stroke* (see Chapter Eighteen); *cancer*, *Parkinson's disease* (a condition affecting the brain's basal ganglia characterized by mask-like facial expression, tremor of resting muscles, slowing of voluntary movements, a hurried and shuffling gait, muscular weakness, possible difficulties with speech flow, and mental capacity remaining intact); *hernia*; *enlargement of the prostrate* in men; *prolapse of the rectum or uterus*; *osteoporosis*; *arthritis*; *diabetes*; *glaucoma*; or *cataracts* (Davis 1992a; Lazarus 1988; Miller and Keane 1978; Tomaino 1992). Additional common conditions include *respiratory diseases* (e.g., COPD), *Alzheimer's disease, diabetes, influenza and pneumonia, falls and other injuries, substance abuse, obesity*, and *oral health problems*. These diseases are some-times not treated due to poverty, which affects about 9 percent of those over age 65 (Vann 2014). However, although older people may have an increasing number of chronic, controlled health problems as they age, many individuals are not necessarily limited or bothered by them (Dychtwald 1993).

Mental or psychological changes associated with aging may include changes in personality, intellectual functioning, and/or mental health (G. Cohen 1988; Davis 1992a; Lazarus 1988; Purtilo 1978; Smith 1972). *Personality changes* occurring with aging include increased withdrawal, decreased ability to compensate or adapt to changes, decreased attention to world or community events, or increased preoccupation with self or trivial things. These changes in behavior patterns often may result from physical or social factors (e.g., diminished hearing or vision, decreased ability to get around independently, and loss of friends and companions) or of a decreased self-concept. Changes in *intellectual functioning* include increased rigidity of thought patterns (possibly a means of coping with stress), decreased speed of perception and response time, and decreased awareness of environmental cues due to diminished sensory perceptions (Cevasco and Grant 2003). Other signs of cognitive decline appear as decreased immediate recall ability (especially if distracted), a need for longer rehearsal time to learn new material, a tendency to lose one's train of thought more easily, a decreased ability to spontaneously recall information, and increased memory difficulties or memory lapses. It is important to realize that aging, in and of itself, does *not* decrease a person's level of intelligence or ability to learn. Dychtward (1993, 5) notes that many declines in mental functioning occur in the mid-80s and beyond and relate to depression, drug interactions, lack of exercise, or other treatable conditions rather than physical age.

As older people continue to challenge themselves, they can learn new things, and their intelligence and understanding actually may increase with age. Also, many older people compensate for loss of speed by increased judgment, perspective, experience, insight, and decision-making and problem-solving abilities. In addition, research suggests that the brain can continue to create new neural connections, that it can "rewire" itself to compensate for losses, and that diminished skills can be relearned with training. Thaut (2008, 81) explains: "New learning inputs can strengthen positive coupling of neurons, resulting in formation of new cell ensembles. This is the process underlying what is frequently called brain plasticity."

Some *mental disorders* are also common among the elderly (G. Cohen 1988; Davis 1992a; Lazarus 1988; Tomaino 1992). The incidence of *depression* seems to increase with advancing age. Vann (2014, 4) notes: "About 16 percent of women over age 65 and 11 percent of men of that age report symptoms that suggest clinical depression, a threat to senior health." Depression in the elderly may have several forms and causes including clinical depression, drug-induced depression, depression in association with medical and neurological illnesses, and depression in association with cognitive impairments such as Alzheimer's disease (G. Cohen 1988). In the elderly, vague physical decline or multiple somatic complaints may mask depression, which, while often undiagnosed, is treatable (Bright 1986; Lazarus 1988). People aged 60 years or above are responsible for around a quarter of deaths from self-harm (World Health Organization 2015).

In addition to depression, elderly people may have other psychiatric disorders, such as *paranoid states* (for some, possibly resulting from isolation, illness, or sensory loss); *anxiety disorders* (often temporary, triggered by apprehension of traumatic events, decreased abilities, or illnesses); *substance abuse* (prescription or nonprescription medications, alcohol, or drugs, to which some may turn in an attempt to alleviate loneliness or depression); *schizophrenia*; or *sleep disorders*. Increasingly, organic mental disorders, such as *Alzheimer's disease, neurocognitive disorders, arteriosclerotic psychosis*, and *multi-infarction dementia*, also are prevalent with aging. These disorders affect brain processes and cause mental confusion and disorientation, personality changes, and physical problems. At any age, multiple social, psychological, and biological factors determine the level of mental health (World Health Organization 2015, 2).

In addition to physical and mental changes, most elderly individuals must cope with various *social changes* (Bright 1986; Purtilo 1978). In the United States, a loss of social status and a loss of opportunities for socialization frequently accompany aging. Many older people no longer seem to be needed by their children, their community, or their place of business. When they reach a certain chronological age, they are asked or forced to retire from their jobs. They also may be asked to resign from community boards to make way for younger people. These events may contribute to loss of income, loss of worth and respect, or loss of former self-image or identity. If older people are to maintain self-images as useful members of society, they must have opportunities to engage in some kind of ongoing activity that makes them feel needed.

According to Purtilo (1978), one of the greatest conscious fears of the elderly is the fear of losing their independence. As children or grandchildren move to other parts of the country and as their friends or spouses suffer debilitating illnesses or die, older people lose important social contacts and support systems. Their own physical deterioration may also lead to loss of mobility and opportunities for socialization. Elderly individuals who have severe physical and/or mental impairments may be forced to become more dependent on others. Increased dependency often leads to loss of self-esteem and, if alternate living arrangements are needed, to loss of home, possessions, and privacy.

The changes associated with aging affect people at different rates and in different ways. In addition, physical, mental, and social changes never have simple, isolated effects; changes in one area impact other areas. For example, decreased income may lead to poor nutrition which may cause changes in physical or mental health, or decreased sensory acuity may lead to decreased independence which may cause a diminished self-concept, withdrawal, and/or depression. Therefore, it is important to work with the elderly from an interdisciplinary, holistic perspective, considering all areas of each individual's life. While physical, mental, and social conditions all affect specific needs of elderly individuals in general, the essential needs of older people are the same as those of adults at any age: nourishing food, comfortable shelter, companionship, a sense of being useful and productive, intellectual stimulation, and spiritual refreshment (Otten and Shelley 1977).

The Well Elderly

The well elderly constitute the largest segment of the population of older individuals. Most older Americans are healthy, have adequate economic resources, and lead active lives (Dychtwald 1993; Hager 1983; Horn and Meer 1987; Palmer 1989; Richter 1996). They live independently and consider that being on their own is proof of their mental and physical vigor. Only about 45 percent have some chronic problem, such as arthritis or hearing impairment, that causes some kind of limitation (Hager 1983). More significant than chronological age is an often younger functional age, defined by Horn and Moor (1987, 77) as "a combination of physical, psychological and social factors that affect their attitudes toward life and the roles they play in the world."

The well elderly are a diverse group, whose members have very definite preferences. They are receiving increasing attention from businesses, especially the travel, housing, and health industries, because they represent a vast new market for goods and services. Because they represent a powerful voting block, the well elderly also receive considerable attention from politicians. The well elderly are individuals who now have plenty of leisure time to pursue new interests. They want experiences that provide opportunities for self-discovery and creativity (Whitwell 1993). Many seek quality, enriching experiences and are self-directed, highly motivated learners. They gather at senior centers not just to play cards but also to get information on retirement investments, exercise, travel, and wellness (Richter 1996). They may be active in clubs and associations, participate in park and recreation programs, care for grandchildren, travel, or take courses at universities that have special programs for older adults. Although the well elderly usually have fewer physical needs than institutionalized elderly persons, they may have similar emotional needs: a need for meaningful activity, a need to fill their time constructively, a need to feel useful and worthwhile, a need for a support system, a need to find ways to cope with the stresses of experiencing loss and grief with increasing frequencies, and a need to find ways to cope with social losses and physical changes associated with aging (Glassman 1983).

Semi-Independent Elderly Individuals

Semi-independent elderly individuals live in their own home or that of a caregiver but spend three or more days a week in an adult day care program for supportive or supervised care (Palmer 1989). Others may live in assisted living centers that provide meals, transportation, activities, and some personal care services. Some mental or physical impairment interferes with their ability to function independently. Many are physically frail and/or have memory impairments (Kay 1996; Smith and Knudson 1995). They need opportunities for socialization, programs that will increase and support their functional abilities, and opportunities to participate in meaningful activities that will give them a sense of accomplishment and self-esteem. Some may need assistance with activities of daily living, such as eating, bathing, or walking.

Adult day care centers have existed since the 1970s but did not begin to grow in popularity until the mid-1980s and 1990s. The number of adult day care centers in the United States more than doubled between 1985 and 1994, growing from 1,200 to 3,000 (Kay 1996). Currently, there are 4,800 adult day service centers, but many are in metropolitan areas and vary by geographical region. Adult day care centers help both elderly clients and their caregivers by providing (a) alternatives to premature or inappropriate institutionalization, (b) programs that maximize client's functional abilities, and (c) respite to caregivers while giving psychosocial support to their clients (Palmer 1989). Some adult day care centers work with specific groups of clients, such as individuals who have Alzheimer's disease. Most centers, however, serve clients with widely varying abilities and disabilities. Adult day care centers usually operate five days a week and provide meals, recreational services and programs, transportation, and other therapeutic programs.

Other facilities and programs that provide alternatives to institutionalization for persons who need assistance in some areas of daily living are increasing. For example, in the mid- to late-1990s, a number of assisted-living residences have opened in various areas of the country. These facilities provide in-home services such as meals, transportation, laundry and housekeeping, recreational programs, and medication supervision for residents.

Chronically Ill Elderly Individuals Receiving Home Care

Some chronically or terminally ill persons receive care in their own homes or a caregiver's home. Caregivers often receive support from a community home health agency or a hospital or hospice program. Insurers and the Federal government are finding that providing services to the chronically ill elderly in their homes through community-based agencies is a viable, less expensive alternative to traditional nursing home care (Palmer 1989).

A study by Brotons (2003) shows that both the elderly person and the caregiver have needs. All patients had a probable diagnosis of Alzheimer's disease, were mobile, and had a spouse as their caregiver. There were 14 patients and 14 caregivers. The patients had ten music therapy sessions, patients and caregivers usually received seven sessions, and the caregivers alone had four sessions. Sessions included music listening, singing, instrument playing, and movement/dance. Patient objectives were in the cognitive and social-emotional areas, and caregivers reported improvements in these areas; improvements were reflected in a battery of psychological tests. There also were positive gains for the caregivers: "It has provided the caregivers with the opportunity to share feelings and experiences with other caregivers that face the same problems and situations. At the same time, these caregivers have been introduced to different coping techniques, including music" (148).

Chronically ill individuals have various physical and medical needs which others must meet; however, they (and their caregivers) also have important social, psychological, emotional, and spiritual needs. These include (a) meaningful contact and communication with others, (b) mental stimulation, (c) ways to express feelings and emotions related to their situation, and (d) spiritual refreshment and fulfillment. It is important to keep in mind the needs of the *whole person*, not just his or her obvious medical needs, for all aspects of a person affect each other and are important to quality of life.

Elderly Individuals Who Are in Nursing Homes or Long-Term Care Facilities

According to the CDC (2015), "In 2012, about 58,000 paid regulated long-term care service providers served about 8 million people in the United States." Only about 8 percent of all persons aged 65–85 years live in nursing homes, while about 20 percent of those aged 85 years or older live in nursing homes (Aging Statistics 1994; Barna 1993). Over two-thirds of nursing home residents are women, most of whom are husbandless and in their late 70s or older. While some people enter nursing homes for short stays to recover from an acute medical condition and then return to the community or assisted-living facilities, the vast majority are there on a long-term basis. About 85 percent of nursing home residents are over 65 years old (CDC 2013, 30). There are 15,700 nursing homes, providing a total of 1,669,199 certified beds, with average homes having 106 beds (CDC Long-Term Care 2013, 11). Other services are from home health agencies, assisted-living facilities, hospices, and residential care communities. In 2011, these five types of agencies served 8,360,000 people annually (CDC Long-Term Care 2013, 26). With the population continuing to age, the need will be very great by 2050.

Most nursing home residents have multiple chronic illnesses, and many have some kind of mental disorder or organic brain syndrome. However, one must recognize that the population of elderly nursing home residents is very diverse. Nursing homes have residents who are very alert as well as residents who are very disoriented, residents who are middle-aged as well as residents who are very old, residents who have good family or community support systems as well as residents who are alone. Some residents are sociable; others prefer to keep to themselves. Physical abilities also vary greatly: some residents have good sight, while others are very visually impaired or blind; some have good hearing, while others are very hard-of-hearing or deaf; some are ambulatory, while others depend on wheelchairs or are bedridden; some can feed and dress themselves, while others are totally dependent in all areas of daily living. Thus, one must examine each individual carefully to determine his or her specific strengths and needs.

Factors leading to placement in a long-term care facility or nursing home include (1) some disturbance in thinking or feeling, (2) a physical illness that requires nursing care and supervision, (3) an individual becoming unmanageable at home because of potentially harmful behavior, (4) behavior that is harmful to one's self or others, and (5) environmental factors, such as having no other place to go when independent living becomes unfeasible or having no significant others (spouse, children, etc.) who can provide informal support. Most older people see moving to an institution as a prelude to death. Regardless of their situation, individuals often feel somewhat rejected. Therefore, feelings of fear, guilt, and resistance often accompany a move to a nursing home.

When moved to a nursing home, individuals lose much of their independence, their home, many of their personal possessions, privacy, familiar surroundings and routines, and at least some of their social contacts. These losses may affect negatively the person's self-image and self-esteem. In addition, people who live in long-term care facilities lose much of their freedom of choice: they must abide by the institution's rules, schedules, and routines. They have little control over their circumstances and few opportunities to make decisions. They generally depend on others for transportation and often are isolated from the general community.

Persons residing in nursing homes or other institutions for a long period of time may develop *institutional neurosis*, a pattern of behavior characterized by (1) overdependence on routines and other people, (2) lack of initiative, (3) apathy, (4) lack of interest in the future, and (5) deterioration of personal habits, such as grooming. It is important to remember that residents of nursing homes or long-term care facilities continue to need (a) meaningful activities that make them feel useful and productive, (b) intellectual stimulation, (c) ways to communicate and express their feelings, (d) opportunities for socialization with others, and (e) opportunities for creative expression and spiritual affirmation. Nursing home residents will enjoy and benefit from many of the same activities and experiences that other older adults enjoy if these experiences are structured and adapted to accommodate the special needs posed by individual physical and mental limitations.

O'Konski, Bane, Hettinga, and Krull (2010) compared Patterned Sensory Enhancement (PSE) (Thaut and McIntosh 1999) with background music for exercise with long-term care residents. PSE "uses the rhythmic, melodic, harmonic, and dynamic-acoustical patterns of music to provide temporal, spatial, and force cues to structure and regulate functional movements" (Thaut 2008, 139). They concluded that "PSE may not be more effective than big band music during exercise sessions for the frail elderly, although both types of music contribute to participant satisfaction" (130). The big band music had a strong beat and may have been a familiar style for many of the residents. These are variables that need further research. They did not have a no-music condition, so that comparison is not possible.

Elderly Individuals Who Have Neurocognitive Disorder Due to Alzheimer's Disease

When individuals have a *neurocognitive disorder* (NCD) (*dementia*), they have multiple cognitive deficits due to the direct physiological effects of a medical condition that are severe enough to interfere with their normal daily activities and social relationships (DSM-V 2013; Carruth 1997; McNeil 1995). Many types of NCD are related to a physiological disorder.

A *neurocognitive disorder due to Alzheimer's disease* is a progressive, age-related, degenerative brain disorder that is characterized by gradual onset and continuing, irreversible cognitive decline in areas such as memory, ability to perform routine tasks, orientation in time and space, language and communication skills, abstract thinking, and the ability to do mathematical calculations. A *major neurocognitive disorder* classified as *probable Alzheimer's disease* requires genetic testing to provide evidence of a mutation, or evidence of memory decline, gradual decline in cognition, and no evidence of other cerebrovascular disease. The term *mild neurocognitive disorder, probable Alzheimer's disease*, is used if there is evidence of genetic mutation from genetic testing or family history. Other symptoms may include personality and behavioral changes, impaired judgment, and decline in grooming and self-maintenance (Alzheimer's Association 2015; G. Cohen 1988; DSM-V 2013; Gwyther 1985; McNeil 1995; *Memory and Aging* 1987). Without evidence of a genetic mutation, the term *possible Alzheimer's disease* is used. Social cognition may be preserved until late in the progression of the disease (DSM-V 2013, 612). Alzheimer's disease is *not* a normal part of aging; it is a chronic, terminal brain disease marked by steady, progressive mental and physical deterioration that shortens one's expected life span. Vann (2014, 2) notes: "Alzheimer's disease accounts for about 184 deaths per 100,000 people over age 65 each year."

Alzheimer's disease was first described by a German physician, Alois Alzheimer, in 1907. It is characterized by two abnormal stuctures in the nerve cells of the brain: (a) *neurofibrillary tangles*, twisted threads of protein called tau; and (b) *neuritic plaques*, clumps of protein called amyloid-beta (Creagan 2006). Individuals with Alzheimer's disease also have much lower levels of some neurotransmitters as compared with people who are aging normally. In addition, the brain's thinking center (*cortex*) shrinks or atrophies in individuals with Alzheimer's disease, and the spaces in the ventricles become enlarged. These changes take place throughout the frontal and temporal lobes of the cerebral cortex and result in progressive loss of memory, thinking, judgment, and, finally, general functioning abilities. The average course of the disease is eight years, although it may progress as quickly as 2–4 years or last as long as 15–20 years (Alzheimer's Association 2015). The progression from onset of memory and cognitive disturbances to helplessness may take anywhere from a few months to several years (Chavin 1991; G. Cohen 1988; DSM-V 2013; Gwyther 1985; McNeil 1995).

In an attempt to measure progression of Alzheimer's disease (AD), researchers have devised various scales such as the five-stage Clinical Dementia Rating (CDR) and the seven-stage Global Dementia Scale (GDS) (Chavin 1991; Gwyther 1985; McNeil 1995). Most clinicians and family members, however, think of the progression of Alzheimer's disease in three stages: mild or early, moderate or middle, and severe or late (terminal) (Gwyther 1985; McNeil 1995).

In the *mild* or *early stage* of neurocognitive disorder due to Alzheimer's disease, symptoms include confusion and mild memory loss, disorientation, getting lost in familiar surroundings, trouble handling money or paying bills, difficulties with routine tasks, loss of spontaneity or initiative, mood or personality changes, and poor judgment. This stage may last as long as 2–4 years, leading up to and including diagnosis. The *moderate* or *middle stage* may last from several months to 10 years after diagnosis. Symptoms include increasing memory loss and confusion; shorter attention span; difficulty with activities of daily living (e.g., feeding, bathing); increased anxiety, suspiciousness, or agitation; sleep disturbances; late-afternoon or early-evening restlessness ("sundowning"); wandering or pacing; difficulty recognizing family and friends; repetitive statements or movements; increased difficulty organizing thoughts or thinking logically; confabulation; and problems with reading, writing, and numbers. Individuals in this stage usually need full-time supervision.

Individuals who are in the *severe* or *late (terminal) stage* of Alzheimer's disease lose their ability to speak, do not recognize family members or themselves in a mirror, lose weight even when given a good diet, lose bowel and bladder control, and sleep more. Individuals at this stage may try to put everything in their mouth or touch everything and may groan, scream, or make grunting sounds. They are totally dependent on their caregivers. This stage may last from a few months to two or three years. It is important to remember that these stages merely provide a framework to help understand Alzheimer's disease and prepare for changes that will occur in patients over time. In reality, stages often overlap and the appearance and progression of symptoms varies greatly from individual to individual.

Since the mid-1980s, international research into Alzheimer's disease and programs for persons with Alzheimer's disease and related disorders have received increasing attention (Bright 1988; Chavin 1991; G. Cohen 1988; Gwyther 1985; McNeil 1995). The Alzheimer's Association (2015, 5) states: "Ninety percent of what we know about Alzheimer's has been discovered in the last 15 years." Neurocognitive disease due to Alzheimer's disease is the leading cause of cognitive impairment in old age and the sixth leading cause of death in the United States (Alzheimer's Asssociation 2015). It "accounts for about 184 deaths per 100,000 people over age 65 each year" (Vann 2014, 2). About 60–80% of neurocognitive disorders are from this progressive, degenerative brain disorder. Although early onset of Alzheimer's disease (before age 65 years) occurs in up to 5 percent of people, most cases of Alzheimer's disease occur in elderly persons, affecting approximately 6 percent of those over age 65 years and 25–35 percent of those over age 85. Studies show that the incidence of Alzheimer's disease increases dramatically with age. Evidence indicates that after age 65 years, "the percentage of affected people approximately doubles with every decade of life" (McNeil 1995, 8).

At this writing, neurocognitive disorder due to Alzheimer's disease is neither preventable nor curable. A definite diagnosis still is possible only on autopsy, when the characteristic structural changes in the brain can be detected. However, using diagnostic tools such as a detailed patient history, brain scans and imaging, genetic testing, comprehensive physical examination and laboratory tests to eliminate other possible causes of neurocognitive disorders, and neuropsychological evaluation, clinicians now can diagnose probable Alzheimer's disease with 85–90 percent accuracy (Creagan 2006; McNeil 1995). Current research suggests that this disease may have many causes or a number of factors that combine over time to trigger the syndrome (Chavin 1991; McNeil 1995). Researchers are also testing drugs that may help control, delay, or possibly reverse the chemical changes that occur in the brains of individuals who have neurocognitive disorder due to Alzheimer's disease. Even though there presently is no cure or definitive treatment for Alzheimer's disease, there are ways to manage symptoms and improve the affected person's quality of life (Chavin 1991; Creagan 2006; Gwyther 1985; McNeil 1995; Whitcomb 1992).

Research and experience suggest that with the proper approach and facilitation, "the person with dementia can learn new skills, relearn old skills, and adjust to new situations" (Chavin 1995, 4). Although routine is important, new experiences also are needed to provide intellectual stimulation. There is some evidence that keeping people with neurocognitive disorders intellectually stimulated can help keep them mentally alert and perhaps even slow the progression of the disease (Chavin 1995). However, stimulation must be structured and adapted to the individual's level of functioning. For example, even small amounts of excitement may upset a confused person, but carefully structured activities within the limits of his/her abilities (e.g., a walk, a visit with an old friend) may add interest and meaning to life.

Individuals who have Alzheimer's disease still have a need for meaningful, purposeful activities that contribute to their self-esteem and quality of life. Cevasco (2010) studied the effects of the therapist's nonverbal behavior on participation and affect of individuals with Alzheimer's Disease during group music therapy sessions. Positive changes in the person's affect indicate improved quality of life. After studying the therapist's work on affect and proximity with the client during music therapy, she concludes that affect and proximity have an effect on participation.

Individuals with Alzheimer's disease also need opportunities to socialize and interact with others. Activities that draw on lifelong interests and are adapted to the individual's current level of functioning are generally most successful. To communicate effectively with individuals who have Alzheimer's disease, caregivers must remember to minimize outside distractions, secure the person's attention (a touch on the shoulder or holding hands may help secure and sustain attention), use short sentences, be consistent, use distraction rather than confrontation, demonstrate when possible, physically guide and reassure the person during movement, reassure the person of sustained care, show respect for the person's adult feelings, and respond to what the person appears to be feeling, so she or he will sense the caregiver's understanding. Using body language that demonstrates respect and caring also can facilitate effective interactions with individuals who have a neurocognitive disorder. As caregivers seek things the person still is able to do and focus on these, adapting activities and situations so the person can continue to be involved within the limits of his/her abilities, both caregiver and patient will benefit.

With each stage of neurocognitive disorder, there are issues, needs, and problems that affect caregivers as well as the affected person. Family members often experience a deep sense of loss as the disease progresses, as they gradually lose a person they love. In addition, as their burden of responsibility and caring for the physical needs of the individual increases, that individual's ability to respond to them decreases. For all these reasons, caring for persons with Alzheimer's disease or related neurocognitive disorders can be very stressful. Therefore, goals of care for individuals with Alzheimer's disease also usually include providing support for the caregivers, be they family members or facility staff (Clair 1996b; Gwyther 1985; Hanser et al. 2011; McNeil 1995; Special

Committee on Aging 1992). This support may take various forms, including (1) emotional and social support (e.g., support groups, individual and family counseling, home visits from professionals); (2) services, such as respite care that give family caregivers some temporary relief; and (3) knowledge and skills training that give caregivers information about Alzheimer's disease, including resources available to them that help caregivers learn behavior management techniques, skills for coping with the symptoms of Alzheimer's disease, and practical ways to resolve day-to-day problems.

Hanser, Butterfield-Whitcomb, and Kawata (2011) conducted a study to test a music program that caregivers administered to family members with neurocognitive disorders. The program was designed "to improve mood and psychological state, while attempting to reduce the caregivers' distress and enhance their satisfaction with caregiving" (6). Psychological state was measured with the Visual Analog Scale (VAS), and "both care recipients and caregivers experienced enhanced relaxation during the treatment period." There also was an increase in comfort level and happiness. The authors provided an account of the music used and the suggested music therapy intervention (10–12). This study is important because it exemplifies a music therapy program to be administered by caregivers in their own home.

Although Alzheimer's disease is the most common form of neurocognitive disorder in elderly persons, other conditions may cause cognitive deficits in the elderly (Carruth 1997; Chavin 1991; G. Cohen 1988; DSM 2013, 603–604; McNeil 1995). Some of the more frequently seen causes of cognitive decline include *vascular disease* (including strokes) and a number of other neurocognitive disorders. *Parkinson's disease*, named for James Parkinson, who observed and named it in the early 1800s, is a slowly progressive neurological condition characterized by tremor, rigidity, postural instability, slow movements with stooped gait and a blank, staring facial expression. It affects the neurotransmitter dopamine, and in late stages can lead to cognitive decline. *Huntington's disease*, a hereditary, progressive, degenerative disease of brain tissue affecting cognition, emotion, and movement, usually begins in midlife. It is characterized by involuntary, spasmodic, jerky, twisting movements of neck, trunk, and extremities; severe memory deficits, disorganized speech, and psychotic features are sometimes present as the disease progresses. *Prion disease* (once called *Creutzfeldt-Jakob disease*) is a central nervous system disease that manifests itself in neurocognitive disorder, twitching or spasmodic involuntary movements, and characteristic periodic sharp EEG readings. It most often develops in adults between the ages of 40 and 69 years and typically progresses very rapidly over several months. And finally, *HIV disease* and *alcohol abuse* can cause cognitive decline. All types of neurocognitive disorder feature memory loss, decline in language skills, personality changes, impaired judgment, disorientation, loss of motor function, and eventual decrease in ability to perform activities of daily living.

The severe deterioration and eventual incapacity that occur in persons with a neurocognitive disorder differ dramatically from the symptoms of *age-associated memory impairment* (AAMI) or *benign senescent forgetfulness*, a decline in short-term memory that sometimes accompanies aging (G. Cohen 1988; Gwyther 1985; McNeil 1995; Memory and Aging 1987). AAMI is neither progressive nor disabling; it is characterized only by brief short-term memory lapses and does not progress to other cognitive impairments, such as neuro-cognitive disorders. AAMI often is most noticeable when an individual is under stress or pressure; once the person relaxes, she or he is often able to recall the forgotten material. Persons with "normal" memory loss or AAMI usually are able to continue to follow written or spoken directions, develop compensatory strategies to deal with their memory loss (e.g., notes and re-minders), and continue to care for themselves. In contrast with the progressive losses of memory and cognitive functioning associated with neurocognitive disorders, the memory problems of AAMI do not interfere with the individual's ability to carry on daily activities.

Hirokawa (2004) studied the effects of music listening and relaxation instructions on arousal changes and the working memory task in older adults. Her subjects were 15 socially active, nonmusician adults, with a mean age 72.7 years and no neurocognitive disorder. Subjects participated in three conditions: music listening to subject-preferred music, relaxation instructions with music, and silence. The results showed a trend for subject-preferred music to increase energy levels. A feeling of tiredness increased after silence and relaxation instructions. Music reduced tension at the same time that it increased energy level. Hirokawa suggests that "subject-preferred music may be used to facilitate reminiscence and mood changes, and consequently to enhance their quality of life" (123). Wolfe, O'Connell, and Waldon (2002) compared musi-cians and nonmusicians on ratings of selected musical recordings that might be used for relaxations. The purpose of their study was to form a portfolio of music to be used in a relaxation program for parents of children in a pediatric hospital. They concluded: "Mean rankings for the experts and nonmusicians were nonsignificant for seven of the 10 musical selections" (46). They had subjects specify characteristics of music they found to be relaxing and music that was not relaxing. The content analysis placed responses into the follow-ing categories: dynamics, tempo, instrumentation, rhythm, harmony, melody, extra musical (other associations), and other. This list is supported by research of others on music and relaxation. A very wide variety of music was listed by subjects as music they used to relax. It includes the following categories (in hierarchical order): "classical, easy listening, alternative, country, soundtrack, jazz, rock, pop, and rhythm and blues" (51). The question of how music is used needs further exploration. Is it for purposeful relaxation or just as a background?

Examining the long-term effects of music therapy on the elderly with moderate/severe neurocognitive disorder, Takahashi and Matsushita (2006) conducted a music therapy group once weekly with elderly (mean age 83 years) people suffering from moderate or severe neurocognitive disorders. There were 24 persons in the music therapy group and 19 in the control group. For the music therapy group, a saliva sample and blood pressure measurement was taken before and after music therapy sessions for 6 months, as well as at one year and two years after the first session. The music therapy group sang a greeting song, followed by light exercises, vocalization, playing instruments, and singing familiar songs to elicit memories. Takahashi and Matsushita (2006) conclude that these activities led to socialization and emotional stability:

> It was believed that these sessions further led to the maintenance of their physiological functions such as normal systolic blood pressure and cortisol level in saliva and the maintenance of cognitive function. . . . In summary, the results suggest that music therapy, during which the elderly people with moderate or severe neurocognitive disorder can enjoy themselves, is effective in preventing cardiac and cerebral diseases. (331)

PSYCHOSOCIAL THEORIES OF AGING

As the elderly population continues to grow, many people have become interested in learning what helps individuals age successfully. Some have found that people age more successfully when they do not accept the myth that aging is a time of inevitable decline (Creagan 2006; Hager 1983). However, elderly individuals do need to adjust their ways of thinking, feeling, and coping to meet the demands of their changing internal and external circumstances (Muslin 1992). If they face problems and opportunities associated with aging thoughtfully and realistically, aging individuals can, as long as they have reasonably intact mental abilities, largely determine the course their aging will take (Smith 1972). Individuals also may increase their positive outlook, coping abilities, and general life satisfaction in later life by continuing in cognitive activities (G. Cohen 1988).

When individuals age successfully, they do not overreact to the external world and do not show symptoms of fragmentation or loss of self-worth. These individuals have not merely *adjusted* to aging, which may imply an acceptance of inadequacy, but have *adapted* successfully by achieving a cohesive "elderly self" (Muslin 1992). These individuals have made conscious adjustments and adaptations that enable them to be at peace with themselves and have a joyous, fulfilled life.

Whether they realize it or not, people who work with elderly individuals are influenced both directly or indirectly by their ideas about what constitutes successful aging. The attitudes, perspectives, assumptions, and beliefs people have about aging "influence the way in which the elderly are approached and treated and the way that their hopes and aspirations are either thwarted or realized to the fullest" (Watts 1980, 88). Often, people may draw some of their beliefs and attitudes from the various psychosocial theories that attempt to define successful aging. Two of the most common of these are the *disengagement theory* and the *activity theory* (G. Cohen 1988; Schooler and Estes 1979; Watts 1980).

According to the *disengagement theory* of aging, originating with the work of Cummings and Henry (1961), as people age, they gradually and voluntarily withdraw from various roles they have assumed in life and become increasingly introverted and interested in fulfilling personal needs while decreasing their involvement with others (G. Cohen 1988; Davis 1992a; Purtilo 1978; Schooler and Estes 1979; Watts 1980). In this view, high satisfaction in old age is found by accepting the inevitability of reduced personal and social interactions and voluntarily disengaging from them. Elderly people are seen as withdrawing from social and psychological involvement in their environment at the same time society is withdrawing its support from them. This mutual dissociation results in decreased interactions between the individual and society. Some see this process as occurring both as a response to a lower level of energy and as preparation for death.

In recent years, many gerontologists have questioned whether disengagement is universal and unavoidable (Davis 1992a). While some people will disengage with relative comfort as they age, others disengage with great discomfort and, in that process, show a great drop in life satisfaction (Schooler and Estes 1979). Others have been relatively disengaged for most of their lives and continue to be satisfied with that state as they age.

In some cases, however, disengagement may not be a normal part of aging but an indication of depression, one of the most unrecognized and undertreated illnesses in the elderly (Bright 1986; Davis 1992a). Depression results from imbalance in neurotransmitters (serotonin, norepinephrine, and dopamine), but there is no single cause of depression (Creagan 2006). As Davis (1992a, 149) states: "It is now generally accepted that not all elderly people reduce their societal roles and that those who do may suffer from depression."

Ashida (2000) studied the effect of reminiscence music therapy sessions on changes in depressive symptoms in elderly persons with neurocognitive disorders. The Cornell Scale for Depression in Dementa (Alexopoulos et al. 1988) was administered in the first week as a pretest period and at the end of the second week as a no-treatment phase. In the third week, daily music therapy sessions were held. All participants were greeted with a drumming activity and personal attention, then a consistent opening song was played, followed by reminiscence. The therapist sang a familiar song, repeated part of the lyrics, and asked relevant questions directed at each participant. The Cornell Scale was administered at the end of the third week. The researchers concluded: "The results of this study showed significant decrease in the depressive symptoms of participants after they received 5 days of reminiscence focused music therapy treatment" (178). Observation of the groups showed that active participation increased as the treatment week progressed.

The *activity theory* of aging originated with the work of Havighurst (1963). Used in many facilities and in much music therapy, activity theory focuses on engagement rather than disengagement. It contends that people age most successfully and maintain satisfaction, health, and self-esteem when they remain as active and involved as possible (G. Cohen 1988; Davis 1992a; Watts 1980). Thus, individuals have the most satisfaction in their older years when they are able to maintain the pursuit of activities that are congruent with their longstanding preferences and relationships. Because of this emphasis on continuing or maintaining activity, the activity theory of aging sometimes is called the *maintenance* or *continuity theory*.

Neither the disengagement theory nor the activity theory will be applicable to all elderly individuals. Davis (1992a, 149–150) contends that "some elderly individuals will choose to withdraw and reduce the number and quality of their social contacts, whereas others will maintain and seek an active life style." Although the assumption that there is a limited number of ways to grow old may be appealing, the reality is that there is a tremendous variety of behaviors and experiences and levels of development among elderly individuals, just as there is variety among people of all age levels (Kastenbaum 1979). Each person brings unique traits, strengths, and weaknesses to this stage of development, and successful aging will differ for each individual. The personality patterns that individuals had throughout their lives, rather than some preconceived notions about aging, may be among the best predictors of whether they will tend to disengage or to remain active as they age.

Developmental theories of aging recognize that old age, as any stage of life, has its own challenges, and that different individuals meet the challenges in different ways. Although movement to a new stage of psychological development may occur in later life, it is just one of several alternatives (Kastenbaum 1979). Some elderly individuals feel that relinquishing the values, activities, and orientations of their middle adult years would be a sign of regression. Others may experience decline due to multiple stresses but regain a higher level of functioning and life satisfaction when these stresses are identified and alleviated or modified. Still others will enter a new phase of development, orienting their life around a somewhat different set of tasks and values than those that had been of primary importance in earlier life. These individuals may develop a strategy of simplification or essentialization, voluntarily shedding some of their past activities and relationships as excess baggage. They have less energy, but it is under more efficient control. Without turning their backs on life, they begin to orient themselves toward death, although not in a morbid way (Kastenbaum 1979).

TREATMENT APPROACHES

Various treatment approaches and interventions have been developed to rehabilitate and/or improve the life quality of elderly individuals (Bright 1972; Davis 1992a; Feil 1982; Hackley 1973; Karras 1985, 1987; Purtilo 1978; Riegler 1980; Smith 1990). Creagan (2006, 42) notes: "Enjoying life means taking part in activities that are meaningful to you – those that engage your body, mind and soul, that motivate you to get up every morning." These include sensory stimulation (sensory training), reality orientation, remotivation, validation, reminiscence, and life review. While many interventions target impaired or institutionalized elderly persons, some approaches, like reminiscence or life review, can be used with most segments of the elderly population. Smith (1990) notes that gerontological studies increasingly are finding that behavioral interventions provide effective ways to deal with many problems of the elderly.

Many rehabilitation programs for institutionalized elderly individuals use different approaches and techniques, depending upon the individual's level of functioning. These programs often have three components: sensory stimulation (sensory training), reality orientation, and remotivation (Davis 1992a). *Sensory stimulation* or *sensory training* approaches usually are recommended for the most severely impaired individuals. These programs aim to restore or improve the individual's contact with his/her environment by providing short, simple, concrete, highly structured activities for multisensory stimulation. As individuals respond to this sensory input, they begin to interact with their surroundings, often nonverbally at first. Passive activities that require few independent physical or verbal responses from the client frequently are used in the program's initial stages. For example, the therapist may rub the client's arm with various textures, describing the feel of each, or present samples of various smells, describing what each is. Goals include improved awareness of and responsiveness to the environment, improved body awareness, increased attention span, improved motor function, and increased communication and interaction with others.

Reality orientation (RO), the next level up in a staged program, is used with people who are confused and disoriented but who are still able to participate in a group. This technique, pioneered in 1959 by the psychiatrist James C. Folsom in the Veterans Administration Hospital in Topeka, Kansas, uses consistent reminders of everyday facts as tools to decrease confusion, apathy, and isolation and to increase independence and improve awareness of self, others, and the environment (Hackley 1973). Consistency and repetition within a calm, structured environment are the keys to success. RO programs have two components: (1) daily classes that review basic facts; help orient the clients to person, place, and time; and encourage socialization and maximum independence and (2) constant, consistent reality based communication in the course of everyday conversation and activities by all people interacting with the clients that reminds clients of who they are and who is talking to them (person); where they are (place); time (day, year, time of day, time in se-quence of activities [e.g., just before lunch], season, etc.); why they are there; and what is expected of them. RO boards that list information such as the place, day of the week, date, next meal, next holiday, and weather are an in-tegral part of both aspects of the RO program. Other materials, such as clocks, calendars, pictures, color-coded hallways and doors, name plates, charts or pictures outlining the steps of a routine, and pictures of friends and family members are also used as cues to promote reality orientation. Research shows that consistent RO programs can arrest and, in many cases, reverse confusion and disorientation (Hackley 1973).

Remotivation is the final step of the three-tiered rehabilitation program. It tries to stimulate cognitive abilities, verbal interaction, and improved social skills among individuals who may be moderately confused or apathetic but who are aware of their immediate surroundings, have some verbal abilities, and have enough of an attention span to participate in a 30–60 minute group interaction. Remotivation programs use structured, small-group discussions to promote communication with and among the group members, trying to get them reinterested in simple, objective features of everyday life that are unrelated to any emotional difficulties they may have. The group leader uses pictures, slides, objects, recordings, or other concrete examples of the chosen topics to focus attention on the topic, and then encourages interaction and discussion through structured, objective questions. Goals include initiating a renewed interest in one's surroundings, increasing interaction with others, encouraging reality-based discussions, improving socialization, and increasing one's desire to take an active role in the society in which one lives.

Other treatment approaches are in use with various groups of elderly indi-viduals. For example, the technique of *validation,* also known as *validation/ fantasy therapy* or the *Feil method,* was developed in the mid-1960s by Naomi Feil in her work with severely disoriented individuals aged 80–100 plus years (the "old-old"). Feil (1982) discovered that these individuals often withdraw or become hostile when attempts are made to orient them to their present reality by using traditional RO techniques but that they do respond positively to experiences using music, movement, feeling exploration, and reminiscence.

She theorizes that reality orientation, although useful with younger people who might return to the community, does not relate to the lives of disoriented old-old individuals nor to the conflicts they were trying to resolve (e.g., justifying their lives in preparation for death). Many of these individuals that she studied had used denial as a coping mechanism throughout their lives. Because of permanent damage to their senses, mobility, memory, etc., that resulted from the normal processes of aging and a loss of familiar roles, they chose to retreat from their painful present reality and live at a subliminal level of awareness. These disoriented old-old people coped and survived by recreating or living in the past, when they were useful and rewarded, instead of acknowledging the unbearable present.

A person using validation techniques respects the unique differences in individuals and uses empathy to tune into the feelings of the disoriented old-old. By noticing the clients' cues and helping them put their feelings into words, the therapist acknowledges the legitimate feelings behind the clients' disoriented statements, thus validating the clients and restoring their dignity. Goals of validation include restoring self-worth, reducing stress, justifying life, resolving unfinished conflicts from the past, and increasing positive feelings. Universal feelings (e.g., missing one's parents, spouse, home, or job; fear of being alone; boredom; uselessness; anger at uselessness or rejection; need to belong and be loved) are explored through words, symbols, music, and movement in a nurturing environment, with the therapist acknowledging through words and actions that the person's feelings are true and valid. The technique of discovering and validating the feelings behind confused words or actions also can be very useful in relating to and calming individuals who have Alzheimer's disease or related neurocognitive disorders (Clair 1996b; Feil 1993; Whitcomb 1992).

Reminiscence techniques can be beneficial for almost all groups of elderly people (Ashida 2000; Bright 1972, 1981, 1986; Butler 1963; Davis 1992a; Merriam and Cross 1981; Purtilo 1978; Wylie 1990). Many elderly people naturally recall past events and think or talk about them. In fact, at least a periodic retreat into the past is a normal phenomenon for elderly individuals (Feil 1982; Purtilo 1978). Reminiscence may be a natural and important part of the lives of elderly individuals because it (1) serves as their way of *daydreaming* and (2) provides a means of *life review* (Butler 1963; Purtilo 1978).

Daydreams may carry people's hopes and help them see what they might become. As people become older and less oriented to the future, they often focus more on what they were rather than on what they may become. Thus, reminiscing about the past and about times of pleasure and self-worth becomes their way of expressing hope. As they reminisce, individuals also have an opportunity to put their life in order and perspective, to form a clear image of their legacy, and to determine their own significance in the present. As they

relate their reminiscing to the present, reminiscence also may assist in recon-
ciliation and resolution of conflicts individuals may have (Ashida 2000; Bright
1972, 1986; Butler 1963).

The haphazard flow of memories that sometimes occurs in reminiscence
may lead others to think the elderly person is confused and disoriented when
he or she may, in fact, merely be engaged in life review, where memories
from the past are so vivid they seem to actually be happening in the present
(Feil 1982; Purtilo 1978). For example, a 94-year-old woman described her
feelings and thoughts this way:

> To me, there is no past, present, or future; the 1960's or the 1900's are equally
> current for me. . . . Actually I am well aware of most situations but with things
> flashing through my mind the way they do, I'm likely to speak of my school
> days in the same breath as I talk about traffic outside my window. I know it's
> confusing to others but I can't help it. (Purtilo 1978, 219)

Reminiscence now is recognized as a healthy process that can provide
satisfaction, increase socialization and interpersonal interactions, facilitate
adaptation to change or stress, aid in the resolution of grief over various
losses, help validate and give meaning to one's life, strengthen self-esteem,
and provide access to prior personal strengths and resources (Ashida 2000;
Bright 1972, 1981, 1986; Butler 1963; Davis 1992a; Merriam and Cross 1981;
Purtilo 1978; Wylie 1990). Reminiscence can be effective in both individual
or group situations and can occur informally (e.g., casual conversations) or
formally (e.g., structured groups or individual sessions with therapeutic goals).
Various materials, such as photographs, scrapbooks, antique objects, clothing,
movies, magazines, posters, and music, often are used to stimulate reminiscence and focus discussion in structured groups. Many elderly people find
pleasure in sharing their recollections with others, especially with those who
experienced the same events and times.

Because reminiscence is so important to the life and mental health of elderly
people, many facilities that serve the elderly offer *structured reminiscence groups*
as part of their programs. A study conducted in the mid-1980s shows that
nursing home residents who meet weekly in small groups with a discussion
leader to tell stories about themselves and their families are happier with their
lives and rate themselves as healthier after only three months of meetings
(Meer 1985). Forty percent of the participants also show improved short-term
memory, leading the researchers to conclude that talking about past events and
their relationship to the present stimulates the participants cognitively as well
as emotionally. Reminiscence techniques also may stimulate memories of the
past for some individuals with Alzheimer's disease by providing connections
that give them back some awareness of a positive sense of self (Clair 1996b).

Recent research also shows that *behavioral approaches* can be very effective and efficient tools for enhancing self-control and self-management in elderly individuals (Smith 1990). Many behavioral techniques, such as positive reinforcement, systematic desensitization, assertiveness training, relaxation training, cognitive-behavioral approaches, and procedures based on social learning principles can help remediate many behavioral problems commonly seen among elderly persons, including "(a) wandering and disorientation, (b) dependence in aging, (c) age-related changes in social activities, (d) sleep disturbances, (e) urinary incontinence, and (f) family management of the elderly" (Smith 1990, 37). In behavioral approaches, music itself may be the most reinforcing tool available for the therapist to use. In a 2008 study conducted by Gfeller and Thaut, they note: "Because most everyone has some type of music they enjoy listening to, and because music activities can be gratifying, music listening or participation can be used as a reward to help change behavior in the desired direction" (226).

Smith (1990) provides many references and summaries of studies documenting the successful use of behavioral interventions with elderly individuals. These techniques seem to show much promise for alleviating specific behavioral problems in at least some elderly individuals, especially the institutionalized. However, for behavioral interventions to be most effective, it is also important for therapists to determine both the most effective cues and reinforcement schedules for elderly clients and the variables which are most likely to increase, maintain, and generalize positive treatment effects.

SETTINGS FOR SERVICE DELIVERY

Elderly individuals receive special programs and services in varied settings, depending on their individual needs and functioning levels. These settings include community senior centers, church groups, adult or senior learning programs at community colleges, adult day care settings, retirement communities, assisted living centers, private homes (home health care), private or public clinics or medical centers, nursing homes or long-term care facilities, general hospitals, rehabilitation facilities, psychiatric facilities, or hospice programs. Music therapists may work on a full-time or part-time basis in any of these settings, or they may provide contractual services to a number of different groups or agencies. In addition, music therapists may provide services to elderly clients through music stores, music studios, or in private practice settings. Depending on the situation and needs of the clients and the agencies, music therapists may provide direct and/or consultant services and work with clients as individuals and/or in groups.

The elderly population continues to be a growing area of employment for music therapists, both in the traditional areas of long-term care (nursing homes) and in the newer areas of home health, adult day care, community centers, assisted living centers, special programs for individuals with Alzheimer's disease and related neurocognitive disorders, programs for the well elderly, and the like (Clair 1996b; Palmer 1989; Prickett 1996; Special Committee on Aging 1992).

HOW MUSIC IS USED IN THERAPY

Music and Elderly Persons – Myths and Facts

People often have many false assumptions about elderly persons and their musical capacities and preferences (Davis 1992a; Gibbons 1988). Common misconceptions include:

1. Most elderly people are frail, malfunctioning individuals who lack any capacity for musical development.
2. The vocal ranges of most elderly people are so deteriorated that they cannot adequately sing most melodies.
3. Because auditory abilities decline with age, many elderly people are unable to aurally discriminate differences between familiar and unfamiliar melodies.
4. Most elderly people have no desire to learn or relearn musical skills.
5. Most elderly people prefer passive music activities requiring minimal skills and minimal involvement.
6. Most elderly people prefer religious music to all other types of music.
7. Elderly people who do not prefer religious music, prefer music of the late 1800s or early 1900s to all other time periods.
8. Elderly people prefer quiet, sedative music at all times.
9. Elderly persons cannot and do not strive for quality musical products.

Research and clinical examples, however, give quite a different picture of the musical interests and capabilities of elderly individuals (Bowles 1991; Clair 1996b; Clair and Davis 2008; Gibbons 1985, 1988; Jonas 1991; Moore, Staum, and Brotons 1992; Prickett 1988, 1996; Smith 1989). In reality, musical ability does not decrease significantly as people age (Gibbons 1982, 1985; Prickett 1988, 1996). For example, Gibbons (1982) has found that the composite Music Aptitude Profile (Gordon 1968) scores of subjects in three age groups (ages 65–70; 71–75; 76–93) do not differ significantly. Research and practical experience also show that the arts continue to be integral to development throughout life (Erikson, Erikson, and Kivnick 1986; Gibbons 1982; Weisberg and Wilder 1985). Research and clinical experience indicate that "as a group, elderly people have both the interest and ability to develop their music skills" (Clair and Davis 2008, 203). However, although *ability* for music and other arts experiences does not diminish with age, *opportunities* that society gives to participate in certain arts experiences or to learn or relearn skills often do decrease as people age (Gibbons 1985).

For most elderly people, the physical changes associated with normal aging seem to have little effect on musical enjoyment or aptitude. Solé, Mercadal-Brotons, Gallego, and Riera (2010), compared the effects of "three music programs (choir, music appreciation, and preventive music therapy sessions) on the quality of life of healthy older adults" (264). For these researchers, the concept of healthy aging includes opportunities for physical, cognitive, and social well-being which lead to increasing the life expectancy and quality of life. They found that all three activities produce positive perceptions of change after the program. There are some differences on individual items on the pre- and posttest questionnaire, but the overall effect is positive after each music program. They concluded that "being involved in music activities contributes positively to a more active and satisfactory aging process" (279).

Research shows that most elderly people are able to aurally discriminate melodies and rhythms (Cevasco and Grant 2003; Gibbons 1982, 1983b, 1988). In addition, one study shows that the functional vocal range of most elderly people is a minor seventh (A below middle C to G above middle C) (Green-wald and Salzberg 1979), and another indicates an octave and a fifth (F below middle C to C above middle C) (Moore, Staum, and Brotons, 1992), which is large enough to provide satisfying singing experiences of most melodies, especially if the melodies are transposed to lower keys so that most tones lie within the most comfortable singing range for most elderly people. Cevasco (2008) notes that music therapy students prefer a higher range, but elderly clients have greater ability in a lower range. Advanced assessment of a client's preferred singing range may facilitate the creation of a therapeutically successful experience. Those who assume that music played for older individuals should automatically be played louder to compensate for decreased hearing acuity also may be in error. Smith (1989) found that in music listening situations, older adults generally prefer *lower* loudness levels than younger adults. In addition, in his research, older adults did *not* compensate for decreased hearing capa-bilities by increasing the music's loudness level.

Gibbons (1977) found that many elderly people enjoy and sometimes even prefer lively, upbeat music to slow, sedative music. Thus, although elderly people do enjoy some sedative music, it is not their exclusive choice. Another study found that in the context of sing-alongs, many elderly clients prefer songs of moderate or slower tempos to those of faster tempos (Moore, Staum, and Brotons 1992). This may indicate that different types and tempos of music may be appropriate for elderly people in different situations (e.g., listening or

dancing/moving vs. singing). What music will be most useful and most preferred by particular clients in a given situation will depend on factors such as
the task associated with the music, activity goals, individual preferences, etc.
In a 2003 study, Cevasco and Grant investigated responses to vocal music
compared with those to instrumental music and found: "Data indicated participation in exercise to instrumental music was significantly greater than
exercise with instruments to vocal music, p < .05" (42). Other important variables were tempo, style, familiarity, and preference.

Elderly people enjoy a wide variety of music and musical experiences and
are able to discriminate and express definite preferences. Although factors
such as community size and location, living situation, state of health, educational level, and previous life experience may influence their initial expressed
preferences (Gilbert and Beal 1982; Jonas 1991), their interests may broaden
as they are exposed to and educated about music of various styles (Gibbons
1977). While religious music may be important to many (but certainly not *all*)
elderly people, it is not the only type of music most enjoy (Gibbons 1977,
1988; Gilbert and Beal 1982; Moore, Staum, and Brotons 1992).

Researchers also have found that while older people do enjoy music of
many styles and periods, most show a significant preference for songs that
were popular in their young adult years (approximately ages 18 to 30) (Bartlett
and Snelus 1980; Gibbons 1977; Jonas 1991; Lathom, Petersen, and Havilicek
1982; Prickett, 1988, 1996). Thus, the popular music preferences of a 65-year-
old person likely will be quite different from those of an 85-year-old. Other
studies suggest that many elderly people prefer patriotic, old popular, and
religious songs over folk songs (Moore, Staum, and Brotons 1992), and they
prefer country music, traditional jazz, or art music over current popular music
(Jonas 1991). However, when VanWeelden and Cevasco (2009) investigated
geriatric clients' preferences for specific popular songs to use during singing
activities, they found that music from the "young adult years" was not always
supported in the choice of their sample. It is, of course, only one factor to be
considered in song selection, and may not be the most important.

Elderly people frequently show a strong desire to gain musical skills and to
improve their skills in singing, playing, and general musical knowledge
(Bowles 1991; Gibbons 1977, 1985; Myers 1991, 1992). Elderly people also
show a strong commitment to quality musical performances and products and
are able to develop musically when given appropriate opportunities (Boswell
1992; Darrough 1992; Ernst and Emmons 1992; Gibbons 1977, 1985; Myer,
1991, 1992). Some research has shown that elderly persons are most likely to
develop new musical skills when they are able to observe other elderly persons succeeding at musical activities and when they receive peer support and
encouragement (Gibbons 1985).

Even elderly individuals who have Alzheimer's disease may retain some musical capabilities and enjoy participating in musical experiences (Bright 1988; Brotons, Koger, and Pickett-Cooper 1997; Brotons and Marti 2003; Cevasco and Grant 2003; Chavin 1991; Clair 1996b; Cordrey 1994; Gfeller and Hanson 1995; Prickett 1996). In some individuals with a severe neuro-cognitive disorder, musical behaviors are maintained while all other cognitive functions decline (York 1994). Many individuals with middle- to late-stage neurocognitive disorders retain rhythmic abilities even when singing ability is lost and overall cognitive functioning is severely compromised (Clair and Bernstein 1990; Clair, Bernstein, and Johnson 1995; Lipe 1995).

Groene (2001) worked with eight persons with moderately severe to severe neurocognitive disorder and living in a healthcare facility. Their average age was 81 years. He led sixteen sessions divided into four conditions: live music with complex guitar accompaniment, live music with simple guitar accompaniment, recorded music of simple guitar accompaniment, and recorded music of complex guitar accompaniment. There were no singing differences among the four conditions, but clients stayed in the singing area more frequently during the complex guitar accompaniments. The live complex condition produced more behaviors indicating attention and responsiveness (reading lyrics, compliments and applause after the session). Groene suggests that this may have been in response to the complex style's rhythmic characteristics, either live or recorded.

Why Music Is Useful with Elderly Individuals

Since music has been an enjoyable part of most people's lives, it can be a very effective tool for establishing communication with older adults, motivating them to participate in treatment programs, and helping them improve or maintain their level of physical, mental, social, and/or emotional functioning (Bright 1972, 1981; Brotons and Marti 2003; Clair 1996b; Gibbons 1988; Karras 1987; Palmer 1977, 1989; Prickett 1988, 1996; Smith and Lipe 1991; Tanner and O'Briant 1980).

Music is structured in time. As such, it can help structure many situations, interactions, and activities. Music's rhythms and melodies capture an individual's attention and evoke physical, intellectual, and emotional responses on many different levels. Memories and life experiences often are associated with music and emotions tied to certain pieces; thus, music can stimulate reminiscence and be an ideal tool for life review (Bright 1981, 1986). Music communicates at a feeling level, touching and serving as an expressive medium even for those unable to communicate with words. Music is also a very flexible modality through which improvisation can be changed to fit the tempos and responses of the moment. Because music experiences can be adapted to many levels of functioning and degrees of participation, most elderly people, from the healthiest, most independent to the most severely impaired, can participate successfully in some type of music experience (Clair 1996b; Palmer 1989; Special Committee on Aging 1992).

The Older Americans Act Amendments of 1992, Public Law 102–375, recognizes that musical or rhythmic interventions specifically selected and structured by a music therapist can help restore, maintain, or improve the social or emotional functioning, mental processing, or physical health and functioning of older individuals. This law added music therapy to a list of supportive and preventative services that are provided for older individuals. Provisions also were made for research and demonstration projects and education, training, and information dissemination projects regarding the use of music therapy with elderly individuals (*Congressional Record,* September 22, 1992, No. 130-Part II, H. 8969-H. 9007).

General Music Therapy Treatment Goals with Older Adults

Music experiences can be used therapeutically with older adults in many ways. Music therapists can structure music experiences involving listening, playing musical instruments, singing, moving to music, creating music, or discussing music to (a) evoke and stimulate desired physical responses, from relaxation to structured movements or various degrees and types of physical activity; (b) influence mood and affect and facilitate transitions to more desirable emotional states and reactions; (c) facilitate verbal and/or nonverbal communication; (d) improve social skills and facilitate social integration; (e) serve as an outlet for and a vehicle of emotional expression; (f) provide intellectual stimulation and improve mental functioning; (g) stimulate meaningful associations; or (h) provide purposeful, enjoyable activities that add meaning and quality to life and help improve and maintain self-esteem (Bright 1972, 1981, 1988; Cevasco and Grant 2003; Clair 1996b; Douglass 1985; Karras 1987; Palmer 1977; Special Committee on Aging 1992).

As with any population, music therapists design treatment goals and interventions for older adults based on an individual assessment of client needs, abilities, and preferences. A national survey (Smith and Lipe 1991) of music therapists working with older adults found that the most frequent goal areas in rank order were (1) socialization skills, (2) sensory stimulation, (3) cognitive skills, (4) expression of feelings, (5) physical functioning, (6) relaxation/anxiety reduction, (7) creative expression, (8) problem behaviors, and (9) spiritual affirmation (i.e., using the client's spiritual resources to help maintain overall well-being) (209). The next sections of this chapter provide more specific examples of music therapy goals and interventions with various subgroups of the elderly population.

Music Therapy Approaches with the Well Elderly

Therapeutically structured music experiences can have many benefits for elderly people who remain in the community and are relatively healthy and independent. For example, music experiences can provide (1) opportunities to find new roles, (2) meaningful and challenging activities, (3) mental and physical stimulation, (4) appropriate and enjoyable social experiences, and (5) new ways to contribute to society (Clair 1996b; Palmer 1985, 1989; Special Committee on Aging 1992).

Clair (2007) suggests that music therapy may be used in the community to promote wellness and prevent some of the illnesses or diseases that are common among elderly residents. Research on leisure activities finds that older adults show an overwhelming preference for music (Birkenshaw-Fleming 1993). Other research shows that involvement in music groups can enhance life satisfaction and that involvement in meaningful activities correlates strongly with both longevity and life satisfaction (Palmer 1989). Many older adults find that music can be a great motivator for exercise and that involvement with music (e.g., learning music skills, participating in ensembles and community music activities) can help them maintain physical, mental, and emotional well-being (Clair 1996b). Both music therapists and music merchants also are beginning to recognize the major contributions learning and participating in music can make to wellness and disease prevention in older adults (Bruhn et al. 1996; Farbman 1994).

VanWeelden and Whipple (2004) studied the effect of field experiences on music therapy students' perceptions of choral music for geriatric wellness programs. Fourteen undergraduate music therapy majors were enrolled in a choral conducting class that included two hours of on-campus instruction and one hour of field-based choral lab experience, working for a semester with a choir for senior citizens. The choir members showed significant gains in their willingness to start a choral group in the future, as well as in their comfort and preparedness in directing/conducting a senior citizens' choral ensemble. Having these kinds of groups in the community can add to quality of life for an aging population.

Some older people may find that they finally have the time to learn an instrument they have wanted to play all their lives; others may now have the time to participate in community or church choirs and ensembles (Birkenshaw-Fleming 1993; Clair 1996b; Erikson et al. 1986; Palmer 1985). Developing music skills and then using them in social situations (e.g., ensembles, sing-alongs) also facilitates positive interactions with others and provides a sense of belonging and being needed. As individuals develop new skills and make meaningful contributions to a music group, their self-esteem increases, and they have increased opportunities to receive positive recognition from others. Intergenerational music programs also can facilitate interactions and understanding between younger people (e.g., children, teens, college students) and older adults (Bowers 1998; Darrow et al. 1994; Frego 1995; Wilder 1985). Belgrave (2011) studied the effect of a music therapy intergenerational program on children and older adults' intergenerational interactions, attitudes, and older adults' psychosocial well-being. In the music therapy sessions, the therapist used singing, structured conversations, instrument playing, and moving to music to elicit participation. The 21 children and 26 older adults attended ten 30-minute sessions. Belgrave analyzed seven interaction behaviors during the four interventions and concluded: "The seven interaction behaviors were on-task participation, smiles, touches, looks, encourages, or assists partner, and initiates conversation with partner" (495). All interventions produced mostly on-task behavior from all participants. Belgrave stated: "The interventions that occurred in dyads, structured conversation and moving to music, were more effective than larger group interventions, singing and instrument playing, in eliciting participant interaction behaviors" (502). Those in the music therapy sessions had more positive attitudes towards each other at the end of the 10-week intergenerational program.

Older adults who develop or redevelop music skills have expanded opportunities for self-expression. In addition, music skills can provide enjoyable activities to fill time spent alone (Clair 1996b). Moreover, music offers opportunities for varying degrees of intellectual stimulation and challenges as older adults develop performance skills, learn more about music styles and music theory, or compose and create song lyrics and/or instrumental parts. Older people who prefer to be consumers (passive participants) rather than performers or composers also can receive intellectual, emotional, and social benefits from music as they attend school and community concerts, contribute to fund-raising efforts of arts organizations, or participate in music appreciation or music discussion groups (Clair 1996b; Palmer 1985, 1989).

Older adults can enjoy and participate successfully in many different types of music experiences, including singing, listening, learning about or discussing music, playing instruments, moving or exercising to music, and creating music. As Clair (1996b) notes: "At some level of participation, music is available and accessible to most individuals who have an interest in it" (58). Music experiences that have been used to help older adults improve or maintain their level of physical, mental, social or emotional functioning include

- vocal ensembles or choirs (Clair 1996b; Darrough 1992; Glassman 1983; Palmer 1985)
- sing-alongs (Glassman 1983)
- individual vocal or instrumental lessons to develop or relearn musical skills (Bowles 1991; Clair 1996b; Gibbons 1977; Glassman 1983; Gold 1982; Hoerning 1982)

- bell choirs (Palmer 1985)
- bands, orchestras, or small instrumental ensembles (Clair 1996b; Ernst and Emmons 1992; Gibbons 1985)
- intergenerational music programs, choirs, or instrumental ensembles (Belgrave 2011; Bowers 1998; Clair 1996b; Darrow et al. 1994; Frego 1995; Wilder, 1985)
- rhythm bands (Glassman 1983)
- talent shows (Glassman 1983)
- spontaneous, creative group experiences to produce sound collages and vocal and instrumental improvisations and compositions (Carle 1982)
- groups that attend and discuss concerts (Clair 1996b; Palmer 1985)
- music appreciation groups (Bowles 1991; Clair 1996b; Palmer 1985)
- reminiscence through music (Palmer 1989)
- musical journeys through time or life review through discussion of music associated with various periods of life (Bright 1981; Kellman 1986)
- music as an accompaniment to and motivation for exercise (Cevasco and Grant 2003; Clair 1996b; O'Konski et al. 2010)
- music-based or music-mediated relaxation, stress management, and pain control (Clair 1996b)
- song lyric analysis to facilitate discussion of issues associated with aging (Smith 1991)
- studying music in a societal context (Coates 1984)

The well elderly are vital, capable, alert adults who value and demand quality experiences and expect to achieve and learn (Erikson et al. 1986; Myers 1991, 1992). Many have great interest in music performance skills and perceptive listening/music appreciation activities (Bowles 1991). For music programs to be successful with this population, therapists must accurately define and assess capabilities and interests and gear programs to participants' strengths (Coates 1984; Davidson 1980; Gibbons 1985). Participants must not only know the benefits that involvement with music can have for their physical, mental, and emotional health but also have opportunities to participate in programs and activities having meaning for them and their life situation. To engage the healthy elderly and facilitate their use of music as a tool for continued growth and development, therapists must plan quality, challenging experiences using materials that are age-appropriate, interesting, and personally relevant to the participants (Boswell 1992; Coates 1984; Davidson 1980; Gibbons 1985; Myers 1991, 1992). As Smith (1991, 11–12) observes:

> The challenge for the future is to devise techniques and treatment strategies that not only accomplish specific treatment objectives but are sought out by the growing number of higher functioning older adults.

Music Therapy Approaches with Semi-Independent Elderly Individuals

The rapid growth of adult day care centers and assisted living residences offers a tremendous new potential area for music therapy services. Music therapy treatment techniques have been used effectively with frail elderly individuals in nursing homes and long-term care facilities for many years (Gibbons 1988; Karras 1987; Prickett 1988, 1996), and most, if not all, of these interventions also can be used successfully with elderly individuals who have physical or mental impairments that cause them to need some degree of supervised care in adult day care or assisted living situations (Palmer 1985, 1989; Smith and Knudson 1995; Special Committee on Aging 1995).

Because music experiences are flexible, adaptable, and accessible at many different levels of ability and participation, they can be important aspects of programming in day treatment centers that serve clients with a wide range of abilities and disabilities. Music therapists may structure experiences such as listening to music, playing instruments, singing or humming, creating or improvising music with voices or instruments, relaxing or stretching and exercising to music, creating movements to music, or discussing song lyrics to maximize elderly clients' opportunities to socialize appropriately, develop a sense of belonging as they draw together for a common cause and function successfully within a group, discover or rediscover talents, enhance self-esteem through new accomplishments and positive recognition by others, express feelings and emotions (nonverbally as well as verbally), and improve their physical and mental functioning (Smith and Knudson 1995). As the elderly clients participate successfully in music therapy experiences, they can enjoy and be appreciated for their *current* accomplishments, rather than being appreciated only for their life work in the distant past.

Smith and Knudson (1995) provide an excellent description of a model music therapy program for frail elderly and disabled adults in adult day care settings. Interventions include (a) instrumental and vocal improvisation (used to encourage expression of feelings, provide opportunities for verbal and nonverbal communication); (b) music-assisted reminiscence (to facilitate communication, interaction, life review); (c) music-meditated relaxation (to reduce physical and mental tension and to improve coping techniques and stress management); (d) music and rhythmic movement (to improve physical coordination and physical functioning and to encourage social interaction, creative expression, and cognitive awareness); (e) song writing (to express feelings and encourage creativity); (f) developing or redeveloping music skills by learning to play musical instruments (to improve physical and mental functioning, decrease depression, provide meaningful activities); and (g) solo or group musical performances in talent shows, bell choirs, singing groups, instrumental groups, choral readings, etc. (to enhance self-esteem, provide opportunities for praise by others, increase interaction with others and feelings of belongingness, and improve physical and mental functioning). Some interventions, such as vocal or instrumental performing groups and rhythm/movement groups, occur in large group situations (15–30 members), while others, such as music-based discussion or reminiscence groups, smaller performing groups (e.g., bell choir, drum circle), improvisation groups, creative arts groups, relaxation/guided imagery groups, or groups with a specific diagnosis (e.g., neurocognitive disorder-specific groups) are more effective in medium (8–15 members) or small groups (4–8 members). While participants sometimes are grouped according to similar needs and levels of functioning, other groups integrate clients with varied diagnoses, abilities, levels of physical and mental functioning, and ages. Individual sessions are used to help clients learn or relearn/maintain music skills, facilitate expression of feelings and concerns, decrease agitation, or work on other individual needs in a more intensive situation.

The music therapy program (Smith and Knudson 1995) also includes some experiences, such as sing-alongs, client talent shows, patriotic or seasonal programs, and melodramas, that involve whole group participation by 30 or more clients. These whole group activities emphasize general participant enjoyment and enhanced self-esteem. Smith and Knudson (1995) frequently included performance activities as part of the music therapy process, noting the great benefits these experiences had for both the performers/clients (e.g., increased self-esteem, sense of accomplishment, improved mental and physical functioning as they mastered new skills) and the audience:

> Whether the performance is done by one very frail individual, only in the presence of the music therapist and a family member, or by the large Bell Choir before a national conference audience of 400, laughter, tears, hugs, and standing ovations all attest to the fact that these elderly/disabled performers carry a message more powerful than words. (Smith and Knudson 1995, 77)

Music therapists who work at adult day care or assisted living centers may be full-time employees, part-time or contract employees, or consultants (Palmer 1989; Smith and Knudson 1995; Smith and Lipe 1991). For music experiences to be music *therapy*, rather than just generalized music *activity*, they must be based on individual assessment of clients' needs, strengths, and weaknesses and have specific, measurable individual *goals* within a treatment plan designed to help clients use the music experiences to gain skills or improve their functioning in *nonmusical* areas. In addition to conducting specific sessions for certain clients or groups in adult day care or assisted living settings, music therapists might supervise goal-directed music programming that is designed by the music therapist but implemented by other staff or volunteers. Some programs might include daily exercise to music, music listening or music and reminiscence groups, music and reality orientation groups, singing groups, ensembles using simple percussion or recreational instruments, or individual tapes for clients with special needs (Palmer 1989; Smith and Knudson 1995). To help ensure the quality and appropriateness of this programming in meeting client needs, music therapists should meet regularly with those implementing the programs to evaluate the program and make any necessary changes, either in the group structure as a whole or in particular approaches with individual clients.

Music Therapy Approaches with Chronically Ill Elderly Individuals Who Are Cared for at Home

As more and more chronically ill individuals are cared for at home or that of a caregiver with assistance from community or home health agencies, music therapists are developing innovative ways to help meet the social, psychological, emotional, physical, and spiritual needs of these individuals and their caregivers (Palmer 1989; Special Committee on Aging 1992). For example, music therapists may (a) contract with home health or community agencies to give an added dimension to their services, (b) work through outreach programs of hospitals or rehabilitation facilities or community agencies, (c) work for or contract with agencies that provide in-home hospice programs, or (d) contract privately with individuals or their families. In addition to providing direct services in the home, music therapists may assess the elderly client to determine his/her capabilities, needs, and interests and then train family members or other volunteers or caregivers to implement goal-directed music programming under the music therapist's supervision. When family members implement or participate in music therapy experiences, they can interact with the elderly individual in meaningful ways within the context of enjoyable activities that are within the individual's physical, social, and psychological capabilities. Some innovative programs have used teleconferencing to connect homebound senior citizens, thereby allowing them to participate in many different types of programs, including sing-alongs and discussion groups, via their telephones (Kadaba 1995). Being able to interact with others through teleconferencing gives these mentally alert but physically impaired, homebound elderly adults something to anticipate and increases their mental stimulation and feelings of connectedness while decreasing depression.

Specific benefits of music therapy services to homebound chronically ill elderly individuals include (1) decreasing stress, anxiety, and depression; (2) providing alternatives for pain relief and relaxation; (3) decreasing isolation and facilitating communication and interaction with others; (4) integrating family members; (5) providing additional avenues for communication and emotional expression; (6) facilitating reminiscence and life review; (7) helping individuals and family members deal with the emotional impact of the individual's illness or condition; and (8) facilitating the grieving process (Bright 1986; Clair 1996b; Hanser 1990; Special Committee on Aging 1992).

Music therapy interventions often utilize approaches that are low cost and easily accessible. For example, Hanser (1990) found that an eight-week music listening program facilitated by a music therapist helped clinically depressed, homebound older adults increase their ability to cope with stress and decrease symptoms of depression, anxiety, and physical complaints. Music listening selections specially selected by the music therapist after assessing the client also can be used to facilitate reminiscence and life review and help bring closure to life (Bright 1981, 1986; Palmer 1989). In addition, music listening and discussion, improvisation, song writing, and other techniques can be used to help clients and family members communicate with each other and share information, emotions, and feelings (Special Committee on Aging 1992). Many of the techniques for music-facilitated relaxation, stress reduction, and pain management or for music therapy and physical rehabilitation described elsewhere in this text (see especially Chapters Seventeen and Eighteen) also may be useful for homebound, elderly clients who have needs in these areas (Clair 1996b).

In addition to the interventions described above, many of the treatment techniques described elsewhere in this chapter can be adapted for use with elderly individuals in their private homes. Of course, the exact types of music therapy interventions and approaches used with any particular individual will depend on that individual's specific needs, interests, preferences, and abilities, as determined by the music therapist's assessment.

Norman (2012) provided an assessment tool to use with older adults in nursing homes. She indicates that "music therapists working with this population need an assessment protocol that can provide an holistic, musical, ability-based picture of the nursing home resident while indicating what kind of music therapy treatment, if any, is best suited for that resident" (8). This tool is intended to be used in music therapy to add to other assessment information gathered in the facility, e.g., from the Minimum Data Set (MDS) (Saliba and Buchanan 2008) or the Mini-Mental Status Examination (MMSE) (Folstein, Folstein, and McHugh 1975). These are widely used tools that give a good picture of the clients' cognitive and behavioral functioning, but they do not include musical behaviors. Norman (2012) notes: "Prescriptively, the music therapy assessment tool seeks to determine whether music – particularly the live music experience provided by a music therapist – is uniquely motivating for the resident and therefore whether he or she should be involved in music therapy sessions" (10). The assessment protocol itself is provided on pages 14–16.

One other tool described in the literature is the Residual Music Skills Test (RMST), useful with persons with Alzheimer's Disease (York 1994). Another is the Music-Based Evaluation of Cognitive Functioning (MBECF) (Lipe 1995). Lipe, York, and Jensen (2007) studied the correlation between these two measures and found good validity. Both correlate with the MMSE but also indicate musical cognition. They note that "there is uniqueness to the melodic, singing and rhythmic aspects of music cognition" (369).

Music Therapy Approaches with Elderly Individuals Residing in Nursing Homes or Long-Term Care Facilities

Music therapy interventions can be an integral part of comprehensive treatment and rehabilitation programs for elderly residents of long-term care facilities, both by providing a unique way of engaging residents and helping them improve or maintain physical, mental, and social/emotional skills (Bright 1972, 1981; Clair 1996b; Groene 2001; Karras 1987; Palmer 1977, 1985, 1989; Prickett 1988, 1996; Special Committee on Aging 1992; Weissman 1983), and by complementing and enhancing other rehabilitative approaches commonly used with geriatric residents, such as sensory stimulation/sensory training, reality orientation, remotivation, resocialization, validation, reminiscence, life review, and behavioral approaches (Bumanis and Yoder 1987; Davis 1992a; Karras 1985, 1987; Riegler 1980; Smith 1990; Wylie 1990).

Weissman (1983) divides music therapy treatment goals and objectives with institutionalized elderly clients into six areas: (1) *sensory* (includes sensory awareness and discrimination, identifying, locating, and recalling objects in the environment); (2) *perceptual-motor* (includes identifying body parts, maintaining balance, walking unassisted); (3) *cognitive* (includes comprehension, judgment, memory, reasoning, problem-solving); (4) *physical fitness* (includes breathing, circulation, ability to care for oneself); (5) *self-image* (includes maintaining self-identity, having realistic expectations, grieving appropriately for losses, expressing a perspective on one's life); and (6) *social* (includes giving and receiving concern and support, engaging in meaningful activity, sharing life experience). Comprehensive music therapy programs in nursing homes and long-term care facilities use a wide variety of music experiences (listening, moving, singing, playing, creating, discussing) to help clients reach goals in these areas (Bright 1972, 1981; Davis 1992a; Gibbons 1988; Hylton 1983; Karras 1987; Palmer 1977, 1985). Music activities commonly found in nursing homes include solo or small group singing, large group sing-alongs, resident choirs, music listening or appreciation groups, listening to performances of outside musical groups, recorded music or radios in rooms or lounges, musical games, music-assisted relaxation, music-mediated reminiscence programs, solo instrument playing, rhythm bands, bell choirs, resident bands or other instrumental ensembles, instrumental improvisation, dances, exercise to music, creative movement to music, song writing, and music discussion groups (Hylton 1983; Karras 1987; Palmer 1977). Because music experiences impact individuals physically, mentally, and socioemotionally, therapeutically directed music experiences can do much to help meet the total spectrum of needs of elderly individuals in extended care facilities (Clair 2007; Palmer 1977, 1985, 1989).

Many elderly individuals residing in extended-care facilities need help improving or maintaining their *physical functioning* abilities. Needs may include increasing or maintaining range of motion, identifying body parts, maintaining balance, improving locomotion, increasing tolerance for physical activity, improving breathing and circulation, increasing self-care abilities, rebuilding muscle strength and function after illness or stroke, decreasing muscle tension, decreasing pain perception, or improving sensory abilities (Bright 1972, 1981; Cevasco and Grant 2003; Clair 1996b; Hamburg and Clair 2003a, 2003b; Karras 1987; Palmer 1977, 1985, 1989; Weissman 1983). Therapeutically structured music experiences can provide individuals with enjoyable activities that also help them improve their functioning in these areas. For example, music used to accompany exercise routines may help distract clients from the pain often associated with physical exercise and provide the motivation and incentive to join in exercise and movement activities (Bright 1972, 1981; Clair 1996b; Palmer 1977, 1985). Lively, rhythmic music that is meaningful to the residents (e.g., something from their ethnic heritage) may motivate even those with arthritic fingers to open their hands and straighten their fingers to clap along (Palmer 1977, 1985; Tanner and O'Briant 1980). Even though some residents, at least initially, may require physical assistance from the therapist to participate actively in movement-to-music experiences, the music itself can motivate participation. For example, Palmer (1977) noted that "the sound of a polka or march was usually sufficient inducement to assure their cooperation even though it was painful" (194).

Movement-to-music experiences can both stimulate independent movement and help residents improve motor control and coordination. Activities such as marching, dancing, walking rhythmically to music, or moving creatively to music can give ambulatory residents increased confidence, grace, and security in independent movement. For nonambulatory residents, activities like kicking and stamping to music can provide flexion and extension in the lower extremities, improve circulation, and increase muscle strength and tolerance for activity. Scarves, hoops, ribbons, and other props can provide additional visual and tactile stimulation along with additional motivation to participate in creative movement-to-music experiences. Such props can help encourage movement in both ambulatory and nonambulatory residents. In addition, many dances and music movement exercises can be adapted for participation by nonambulatory as well as ambulatory residents (Bright 1972, 1981; Douglass 1985; Johnson, Otto, and Clair 2001; Karras 1987; O'Konski, Bane, Hettinga, and Krull 2010; Palmer 1977, 1985). Music and rhythmic stimuli also can help organize movement and facilitate gait training in residents who are recovering from strokes or who have Parkinson's disease (Clair 1996b; Staum 1988, 1996; Thaut 1992a; 2008).

Musical instruments also can be used to encourage physical movement, increase range of motion, improve motor control and coordination, and increase muscle strength (Confrancesco 1985; Karras 1987; O'Konski et al. 2010; Palmer 1977). Some residents may enjoy playing rhythm instruments or recreational instruments, while others may prefer the piano, more traditional band or orchestral instruments, or bell choirs. As the length of time residents play instruments gradually increases, residents develop increased physical endurance as well as improved motor skills (Palmer 1977). As music therapists carefully match instrumental characteristics to individual residents' physical movement needs, musical instruments also can be used to reinforce or help achieve physical therapy goals (Elliott 1982). For example, Confrancesco (1985) used rhythm instruments, piano playing, and autoharp playing to help increase hand grasp strength and functional hand and arm movements in individuals who were recovering from strokes. The hand and arm strength and control developed through playing musical instruments then can be used to perform some self-care activities (e.g., holding brush or comb to brush/comb hair, holding adaptive spoon and feeding self).

The act of musical conducting also can have important physical benefits. Residents may serve as client-conductors for vocal or instrumental ensembles, or they may conduct to recorded music. As they move their arms to conduct, individuals reactivate and revitalize large arm and shoulder muscles, release tension, and improve physical coordination and endurance. In addition, clients who act as conductors for the group reap the psychological and socioemotional benefits of increased self-confidence and improved leadership abilities (Tanner and O'Briant 1980).

Therapeutic music experiences can also improve the physical functioning of geriatric residents by helping to decrease pain, reduce tension, and facilitate relaxation (Clair 1996b; Karras 1987; Weissman 1983). With some adaptations, even Guided Imagery and Music (GIM) approaches may be beneficial (Summer 1981). Vocal improvisational/meditative exercises, where residents state the location of their pain, moan and groan to acknowledge the pain, and then create a pleasant, comforting vocal sound to send to the painful area to reduce tension, also may be useful in helping nursing home residents alleviate pain (Weissman 1983).

In addition to having numerous physical needs, many elderly residents of extended care facilities need help improving or maintaining their *mental functioning*. Therapeutic music activities can play important roles in stimulating cognitive functioning, in helping to maintain good mental health, and in improving or rehabilitating cognitive awareness for geriatric residents. For example, learning new skills in vocal or instrumental lessons may stimulate mental functioning (Gibbons 1985; Goll 1982; Hoerning 1982). Learning new songs (lyrics and melody), either from song sheets or through a "lining out" procedure (therapist sings line; clients repeat), also helps individuals redevelop or maintain memory skills (Palmer 1977, 1985). Procedures such as having residents supply missing phrases in songs or naming songs or tunes played by the therapist continue to develop residents' recall and memory skills. In addition, critical thinking skills, increased attention span, comprehension, judgment, memory, reasoning, problem solving, and spontaneous verbal interaction can be improved as residents discuss song lyrics or events associated with songs, participate in music appreciation classes, or write their own songs or parodies (Ahida 2000; Hirokawa 2004; Karras 1987; Palmer 1977, 1985; Scalenghe 1984; Weissman 1983).

Music therapy interventions also can be structured to promote and encourage active decision making by nursing home residents who seldom have opportunities to make choices or decisions. Opportunities for decision making may be as simple as choosing a song sheet folder or ribbon of a certain color or selecting a particular rhythm instrument to play from a choice of two or more (Palmer 1977). Increased independence in decision making often is approached through carefully structured successive steps of approximation. For example, Kemper (1982) gradually developed geriatric residents' abilities to select songs independently for the group to sing in a sing-along by first having group members pull slips of paper listing song titles from a bag and then, as group members gained confidence, having them select titles from a multiple-choice listing of titles.

Music experiences also can play an important role in promoting good mental health among nursing home residents. Shaw (1988) found that ragtime music was very useful in eliciting attention and stimulating responsiveness in depressed, apathetic nursing home residents. In addition to increasing attention and responsiveness, the ragtime music was comforting to the residents because it was performed on the piano, an instrument that was familiar and enjoyable to them and had lyric melodies as well as stimulating rhythms.

As residents participate in enjoyable music experiences, they are engaging in a form of adult play. According to Tanner and O'Briant (1980, 30), "'play' appears to be a necessary part of maintaining good mental health in adulthood." Some who subscribe to Gardner's (1983) theory of multiple intelligences have observed that in certain aging individuals, some intelligences (e.g., verbal/linguistic, logical/mathematical) may fade while others (e.g., musical/rhythmic, bodily/ kinesthetic) may become more prominent (Kay 1998). Because music can address and integrate all of these intelligences, it can engage people at many levels and help them develop and exercise whatever aspect of intelligence is strongest for them (Kay 1998).

Therapeutic music experiences can be particularly beneficial for residents who have problems with memory loss and mental confusion. For residents who are very disoriented and nonresponsive, music therapy interventions can be effective components of *sensory stimulation* or *sensory training programs* (Belgrave 2009; Davis 1992a; Olson 1984; Weissman 1983; Wolfe 1983). Because music is a multisensory stimulus and something that has been an enjoyable part of many residents' past life experiences, music often stimulates attention responses or physical movement in even the most severely regressed individuals. By studying the resident's social history and speaking with family members, the music therapist can find clues about what types of music or instruments are meaningful to a particular resident and are most likely to elicit a response. For example, Palmer (1985) used the song "Take Me out to the Ball Game" to increase attention and responsiveness in a nonverbal, withdrawn resident who had always loved baseball. At first, this resident merely opened her eyes and looked toward the therapist when she heard the singing. With individual attention and gentle encouragement, the resident gradually joined the music group, eventually singing along, joining in conversation, and even playing instruments and participating in movement activities to the best of her ability. In another situation, Olson (1984) found that listening to player piano music increased physical activity, rhythmic participation, and feelings of well-being in severely regressed geriatric patients.

Music therapy activities used in sensory training or sensory stimulation programs are usually short, predictable, and highly structured experiences designed to elicit responses, improve awareness and responsiveness to simple directions and people and objects in the environment, and increase body awareness, motor function, and attention to activities (Davis 1992a; Weissman 1983). Passive activities (e.g., therapist physically assisting the individual in moving to music or in playing musical instruments) may be used initially to help develop awareness and responsiveness. Activities often are paired with short phrases, sometimes in the form of improvised song lyrics, describing the action or giving concise directions (e.g., "move your arm up; move your arm down"). Physical guidance gradually is faded as the individual's independent responses increase.

At the next level of cognitive rehabilitation, music therapy interventions can both encourage participation in *reality orientation programs* and increase elderly individuals' abilities to learn and recall important information about person, place, and time (Bright 1972; Bumanis and Yoder 1987; Clair and Davis 2008; Davis 1992a; Riegler 1980). For example, Riegler (1980) found that geriatric patients who participate in a music-based, reality orientation program show marked improvement in reality orientation and behavior functioning, while those who participate in a reality orientation program without music show no improvement over the same period of time. The music-based reality orientation program includes activities such as "listening to and discussing music written about a particular place or time" and "singing and playing rhythm instruments to accompany songs and jingles dealing with names, numbers, day, date, and year" (Riegler 1980, 30). Clair and Davis (2008) discuss reality orientation as one of the objectives of an activity-oriented music therapy program. Music/dance-based reality orientation programs, using hello songs incorporating group member's names, multisensory creative movement-to-music and dance activities, hand dancing and mirroring exercises, songs with added gestures, seasonal songs, songs that incorporate names or weather or place, and rhythm instrument activities, can also be effective with geriatric nursing home residents (Bumanis and Yoder 1987). Other research has shown that singing can improve face-name recognition in nursing home residents with memory loss (Carruth 1997).

Johnson, Otto, and Clair (2001) studied the effect of instrumental and vocal music on adherence to a physical rehabilitation exercise program for elderly residents of a care center. The mean age of study participants was 84.3 years, and they all either were referred for physical therapy or were already in a program. Researchers conducted six sessions: two with instrumental music, two with vocal music, and two with no music. They paired familiar music with the exercise. The instrumental music served as a cue for fluid, full-range movements, while the subjects stopped exercising during most songs and sang along during the majority of the vocal conditions: vocal music apparently was a distraction. In the no music condition, movements were less fluid and more varied. The authors concluded: "Unfamiliar music, suitable to the speed and range of specific movements, will likely cause the least distraction, and consequently provide the best engagement and adherence" (93).

Cevasco and Grant (2003) compared different methods for eliciting exercise to music for clients with Alzheimer's disease. In one experiment, they compared two conditions to facilitate exercise: verbalizing the movement followed by visual cueing, and verbally and visually cueing each rhythmic change. They recorded the participation at 30-second intervals. Level of participation was noted. Clients were more responsive with continuous verbal cueing. The level of participation recorded as "approximation/precise response (easy)" led to greater response.

In the third step or level of cognitive rehabilitation, music can motivate residents of long-term care facilities to participate in *remotivation programs* and set moods or introduce topics and stimulate discussion for remotivation sessions (Bright 1972; Davis 1992a; Gibbons 1988). For example, an opening welcome song may be used to encourage residents to join in the group and help set a climate of acceptance. Songs about particular topics (e.g., springtime, laughing, World War II) then can be used to focus attention and act as a starting point for sharing memories and opinions. Related songs, pictures, props, and instrumental or songwriting activities then might be used to help develop the topic and expand the discussion. Music also may be very helpful in refocusing the group at the end of the session. For example, one or more of the songs used might be sung with the group to help summarize the discussion. A concluding song (perhaps composed by the therapist to fit the group's specific activities and dynamics) can help establish closure and be used to express appreciation to the group members for their contributions to the session.

Music therapy interventions can be an important component of *validation approaches* with disoriented "old-old" nursing home residents (Bumanis and Yoder 1987; Feil 1982). Songs, listening experiences, instrument play, and movement to music experiences can be structured to validate and explore universal feelings that the confused residents may be experiencing. Experiences that acknowledge and validate their feelings make these individuals feel they are understood and give them a reason to participate actively and begin to interact more positively with others.

In addition, music is an ideal stimulus for *reminiscence and life review* (Ashida 2000; Bright 1972, 1981, 1986; Davis 1992a; Feil 1982; Karras 1985, 1987; Wylie 1990). Music can be used in reminiscence groups in several ways (Karras 1987): (1) as a background when residents are gathering, to set the mood for the discussion to come (e.g., dance music from the 1940s if discussing that period); (2) as a topic for discussion (e.g., favorite movie musicals, singing stars of the 1930s); (3) as a method using songs to introduce particular topics of discussion (e.g., songs mentioning items of clothing for a discussion of fashions; songs mentioning places for a discussion of travel or vacations; songs about animals for a discussion of pets or farm animals); (4) as a method using song lyrics that focus discussions of other topics or memories of certain times or activities (e.g., writing on slates in "School Days"; "My Merry Oldsmobile" as lead-in to discussion of early cars); (5) to start and end groups (focus and summarize discussion); (6) as a basis for talking about the past with occasional use of more recent songs (e.g., "Those Were the Days" or "Sunrise, Sunset" from *Fiddler on the Roof*; (7) as a bridge to discussions of more serious topics (e.g., life and death, the Great Depression, war times); (8) as a method for sharpening thinking through identifying singers and theme songs; (9) as a means of engaging attention through songs of historical significance (e.g., World War I: "Over There"); or (10) the use of old sheet music to stimulate discussion. Songs of residents' teen and adult years are usually most useful for eliciting memories of adulthood activities (e.g., dances, when they first heard songs) (Karras 1987; Wylie 1990). Activities such as taking musical journeys through time or discussing songs associated with a certain period in an individual's life also can facilitate the life review process (Bright 1981, 1986; Kellman 1986).

Like any group of people, geriatric residents of long-term care facilities have *social* and *emotional needs* that impact their overall level of functioning. Many residents have lost not only their home, their role in society, and some significant others in their lives but also some of their mental or physical abilities; consequently, they often have a poor self-image and may try to withdraw into a private world (Palmer 1985; Purtilo 1978). Because music has been an enjoyable part of the past experience of most residents and can be structured for successful participation at many different levels, music therapy interventions can be an excellent tool for increasing self-esteem in geriatric nursing home residents and for drawing them back into contact with others. Interpersonal contact may be established initially through individual interactions with the music therapist and then gradually expanded to include small and large group experiences. For example, Redinbaugh (1988) described a slow, 15-month process in which music therapy interventions (shaping attention responses to songs that interested the resident, clapping and foot-tapping, instrument play, ball and parachute activities, sing-alongs, and opportunities to choose instruments, props or songs) increased nonverbal and verbal communication and social interaction for a depressed, 91-year-old nursing home resident. As her communication and interaction skills redeveloped in music activities, the resident eventually increased her participation in other social activity groups as well, which gave her an increased system of social support.

Music experiences provide residents with many opportunities for both verbal and nonverbal interaction through sharing the experience of listening to a particular piece of music, singing or playing instruments together, moving or dancing to music, creating or composing songs, or discussing music. As they participate successfully in these activities, learn new skills, and have the opportunity to make choices and decisions, their dignity is enhanced and their self-esteem increased (Kemper 1982; Palmer 1977). In a study of the effect of the therapist's nonverbal behavior, Cevasco (2010, 295) found that "when the music therapists utilized both affect and proximity combined, participants with ADRD [Alzheimer's disease and other neurocognitive disorders] evinced the greatest amount of positive affect compared to the other treatment conditions." Vanderark and colleagues (1983) found that nursing home residents who participated in structured 45-minute music sessions twice a week showed significantly improved life satisfaction and self-concept, along with some increases in socialization and self-confidence. To achieve these goals, music activities may include singing familiar songs, learning simple chordal accompaniments on autoharp or tone bells, playing rhythm instruments, and performing motions to songs. Residents who perform as soloists or as members of musical ensembles also have increased opportunities for positive recognition by others, another means of enhancing self-esteem (Cevasco 2010; Glassman 1983; Gold 1982; Hoerning 1982; Palmer 1977).

Music therapy interventions also may be useful in helping residents develop realistic expectations, grieve appropriately for losses, and place their lives in perspective (Bright 1986; Weissman 1983). The simple activity of a therapist singing a song about loss and inviting residents to hum along if they have lost something can help residents begin to express grief nonverbally (Weissman 1983). More complex activities like song writing can help residents who are mentally alert but physically disabled learn to accept their new limitations. Palmer (1977) found that writing ballads initiates communication and facilitates more positive perspectives among hostile, withdrawn residents by providing a structure that allows them "to air complaints and interact with each other while working on a meaningful project" (196). Adaptations of Guided Imagery and Music (GIM) techniques also can help nursing home residents who have physical disabilities address and deal with many past, current, and future issues, including disability, grieving, sexuality, and the aging process (Short 1992). In addition, using GIM techniques in a group setting increases residents' participation and encourages sharing and support among residents. Summer (1981) also found that GIM can increase self-esteem, help residents recall strengths and assets from their past and find ways to use these in their current setting, break the cycle of rumination over certain thoughts and memories by bringing different thoughts to conscious awareness, and give residents new experiences (e.g., an imaginary GIM trip to Hawaii) without leaving the nursing home. The group support developed during discussions of GIM experiences "can help to increase self-awareness and self-acceptance, an internal change that fosters interpersonal relationships at the nursing home" (41).

Music therapy interventions can be important *behavior management* tools by helping nursing home residents to increase active participation in appropriate, meaningful social activities and to eliminate undesirable behaviors (Clair 1990, 1996b; Mercado and Mercado 2006; Smith 1990). The music therapist can use music to provide structure to control the behavior of elderly nursing home residents by intentionally modifying tempo, pitch, loudness, timbre, harmony, rhythmic activity, or accompaniment to elicit the desired responses. As Clair (1990, 74) notes: "Active participation in carefully designed and structured musical activities can ease the need for other types of behavior management, at least for a time."

Music therapy interventions can help manage or alleviate many behavioral problems of elderly nursing home residents, including depression, insomnia, agitation, eating problems, problems during activities of daily living (ADLs) (e.g., bathing, dressing, toileting), and catastrophic reactions (Clair 1996b; Thomas et al. 1997). Music-based relaxation may help alleviate depression or insomnia. Because music provides structure and predictability through rhythm, form, and familiarity, participation in music activities such as singing, dancing/moving, or playing rhythm instruments can decrease agitation and promote appropriate social interactions in disoriented as well as alert nursing home residents (Clair 1990, 1996b). Background music that establishes a positive mood, focuses attention, and masks distracting sounds may reduce eating problems. According to Clair (1996b, 106), "upbeat music with moderate, danceable tempos and familiar, singable melodies is most appropriate." After studying music's effect on agitated nursing home residents with psychiatric disorders, Mercado and Mercado (2006, 36) conclude that "positive music therapy interventions for agitated residents can significantly enhance quality of life by providing musical structure, masking environmental noise, and providing unique and creative means by which residents can interact with caregivers." It is important to find nonpharmaceutical interventions to calm agitated persons, and music therapy appears to be one possible way to do this.

Hearing familiar songs sung by caregivers during ADLs also may help establish a secure environment and decrease confused residents' agitation during these activities. Clair (1990) observed that many caregivers find that singing to elderly residents during ADLs helps them gradually become more physically relaxed. For these residents, "singing may provide access to feelings of comfort that are associated with times when they were nurtured . . . and with feelings of belonging" (107). Familiar, preferred music also may help diffuse emotional stress and decrease catastrophic reactions. In addition, contingent music can be used with nursing home residents to reinforce desired behaviors and eliminate negative behaviors, such as chronic screaming (Smith, 1990). Because research has shown behavioral interventions can ameliorate many of the more common problems of elderly nursing home residents effectively, Smith (1990, 39) suggests that music therapists strongly consider an "increased use of behavioral techniques within music therapy treatment programs for the elderly."

Music Therapy Approaches with Elderly Individuals Who Have Alzheimer's Disease or Related Disorders

Music therapy interventions can be important components of treatment during the early, middle, and late stages of neurocognitive disorder (Bright 1988; Brotons et al. 1997; Chavin 1991; Clair 1996b; Gfeller and Hanson 1995; Hanson et al. 1996; Prickett 1996; Special Committee on Aging 1992). An analysis of the literature by Brotons and colleagues (1997, 204–205) indicates that "in general, music/music therapy is an effective intervention to maintain and improve active involvement, social, emotional and cognitive skills, and to decrease behavior problems of individuals with dementia."

Most individuals with neurocognitive disorder respond positively to music, as its rhythm, form, and familiarity provide them with a sense of security and structure. Some research suggests that individuals with Alzheimer's disease use alternative cognitive, memory, and neural mechanisms to process and respond to auditory stimuli, thereby allowing some individuals with severe neurocognitive disorder to maintain musical behaviors after other cognitive functions have declined (York 1994). In many cases, music that holds significance and meaning for individuals with neurocognitive disorder can help them regain access to lost memories and restore, at least for a time, some of their 'lost' personality (Brotons et al. 1997; Sacks and Tomaino 1991). In addition, music tasks can be very useful in assessing cognitive functioning in older adults with neurocognitive disorders (Lipe 1995; York 1994). Thus, music has great potential for providing individuals with neurocognitive disorder the important tools for relating positively to themselves, their caregivers, and others around them.

However, not all music or types of music experience are suitable for all individuals with neurocognitive disorders. To be effective, music and music interventions must (1) have meaning for the individual (relate in some way to his/her preferences or life experiences); (2) be suited to the individual's current needs and functional abilities in the verbal, cognitive, and physical skills that the music experience requires; and (3) be implemented by a sensitive music therapist who can adapt the activity to the individual's responses and needs at a particular moment (Bright 1988; Brotons et al. 1997; Cevasco and Grant 2003; Chavin 1991; Clair 1996b; Cordrey 1994; Gfeller and Hanson 1995; Sacks and Tomaino 1991).

Agitation has been defined as "a general term which refers to a range of behavioral disturbances, including aggression, combativeness, shouting, hyperactivity and disinhibition" (Ziv, Granot, Hai, Dassa, and Haimov 2007, 331). After studying agitation and social behavior in music therapy in a group of 28 persons with Alzheimer's of medium-advanced stage, Ziv et al. (2007) concluded that there was improved social behavior and a reduction of agitated behavior as well as other negative or aggressive behaviors.

Experiences in singing, moving (folk or ballroom dances, scarf dances, exercises or creative movement to music), and playing instruments (rhythm activities, bell choirs, accompaniment instruments such as the autoharp) all can be structured at high or low levels of demand to meet the needs of individuals at various stages of neurocognitive disorder. Singing is effective in persons with Alzheimer's disease who are hypoaroused (sleepy, depressed, nonresponsive), and it seems to provide regulatory function (McHugh et al. 2012). Some individuals also can participate successfully in structured composition/improvisation experiences or musical games (e.g., musical bingo, Name that Tune) (Brotons 1994b; Chavin 1991). Generally, individuals are able to continue to participate more purposefully in movement and rhythm activities than in singing activities through their stages of decline (Brotons 1994b; Clair 1996b; Gfeller and Hanson 1995; Hanson et al. 1996). As the neurocognitive disorder progresses, music therapy interventions that have lower demands (simpler, nonverbal, requiring less precise responses, or requiring fewer active responses) continue to offer successful, purposeful experiences for individuals who have Alzheimer's disease or related disorders (Gfeller and Hanson 1995; Hanson et al. 1996). Books by Chavin (1991), Cordrey (1994), and Gfeller and Hanson (1995) specifically describe several music therapy activities and session plans suitable for individuals at various stages of Alzheimer's disease.

Cevasco and Grant (2006) investigated the therapist's use of musical instruments used to elicit responses from individuals in various stages of Alzheimer's disease. Their first experiment observed 15 persons, with a mean age of 80 years, in early- to mid-stage Alzheimer's; the second experiment observed 10 persons, with an approximate average age of 85 years, in the middle to later stages. The second group showed more cognitive decline. In the first experiment, the most accurate rhythmic response occurred when the therapist presented the pattern on a djembe, followed by paddle drum, maraca, and claves. A pattern of eight eighth notes was performed most accurately. The goal of the second experiment was to provide an optimal sensory environment and successful group experiences. Here, a cappella singing produced the greatest overall participation. When moving and singing were combined, more people participated. From the evidence, Cevasco and Grant (243) conclude: "Seemingly, there is something about popular music that makes people want to clap their hands or tap their fingers or feet, and according to the data herein, persons in the middle to later stages of AD are no exception."

Music Therapy Interventions for Early Stages of Neurocognitive Disorder

Music therapy interventions can give persons with early stages of neurocognitive disorder many opportunities for successful experiences, meaningful and purposeful activities to structure time, and feelings of accomplishment, thus adding to life quality, facilitating positive moods, and helping to relieve some symptoms of fear, anxiety, and depression (Clair 1996b). Bruer, Spitznagel, and Cloninger (2007) found that improved cognitive functioning in a group of patients with neurocognitive disorders could be maintained until the next day, but not the next week. They explain that "the observed rise and fall in cognition over a week is congruent with theory to suggest that music therapy acts primarily by way of short-term anxiety reduction" (324). They suggest that many persons with neurocognitive disorders might benefit from music therapy the day before maximum cognitive abilities are required (e.g., legal appointments).

Participation in goal-directed music activities also can increase overall cognitive functioning significantly, as indicated by scores on the Mini Mental

Status Questionnaire (Smith 1986), while singing can help some individuals retain memory functions (Prickett and Moore 1991). Cevasco (2008) identifies many benefits of singing for people of all ages. Individuals with early-stage neurocognitive disorder are most likely to participate in music experiences that (a) utilize skills that have been practiced over many years (e.g., singing for people who have always enjoyed singing, prompting a person to play a favorite song on an instrument he/she has played most of his/her life, doing familiar dances or creative movement using actions from well-known activities like sweeping the floor); (b) use songs, dances, movements, instruments, or activities that have personal significance and meaning for the individual; and (c) draw on cognitive, physical, or verbal skills that are still accessible to the individual at an appropriate level of challenge and demand (Brotons et al. 1997; Chavin 1991; Clair 1996b; Gfeller and Hanson 1995; Hanson et al. 1996; Vanweelden and Cevasco 2007).

Vanweelden and Cevasco (2007) conducted a survey to determine which songs, from which decade, music therapists use with geriatric clients. They list the "top ten" in the categories of (1) popular, (2) patriotic, (3) hymns, (4) folk, and (5) musicals (10). They note that while these may be songs that were popular when the clients were young adults, the list needs to be updated, because clients age and have different preferences. Popular music was the category with the most songs recommended by the music therapists in the survey. In 2008, Vanweelden, Juchniewicz, and Cevasco conducted a follow-up study by investigating music therapy students' recognition of a popular song repertoire for geriatric clients. They asked if the students "(a) had heard the songs before, (b) could 'name the tune' of each song, and (c) list the decade each song was composed" (446). Although the students had heard many of the songs, they had difficulty providing a title or telling in which decade it was composed. These are important skills if a music therapist is to retrieve appropriate songs to use in music therapy groups. Graduate music therapy majors score higher than undergraduate, which may reflect more clinical experience or more course work in the field.

After studying the preferred vocal ranges of young and older adults, Cevasco (2008) reported that older adults tend to prefer lower singing ranges than young adults. When songs are pitched uncomfortably high, geriatric clients may refuse to sing. Regardless of young music therapists' personal preferences regarding range and tonality, they must develop the skill to transpose song material to the key that will be most comfortable for the clients, not necessarily for the therapist, or what is found in the song book or most comfortable on the guitar.

Many different types of structured music interventions can be used therapeutically with individuals in the early stages of neurocognitive disorder, either individually or in groups. For example, group sing-alongs or adapted choir experiences can facilitate successful interactions with others, help maintain socialization, increase awareness of self and others, increase self-esteem through successful participation and positive recognition by others, help individuals release tension and frustration, and provide opportunities for choice (e.g., choosing songs) and creative expression (Bright 1988; Brotons et al. 1997; Chavin 1991; Clair 1996b), while one-to-one singing experiences can distract individuals from depression and facilitate positive mood changes, promote communication and emotional closeness between family members or caregivers and the individual, and serve as an auditory cue to help individuals retain language and memory functions (Brotons et al. 1997; Clair 1996b; Prickett and Moore 1991). Music-based reminiscence groups (Chavin 1991; Smith and Knudson 1995; Takahashi and Matsushita 2006), music groups using songs and activities centered around a certain theme (Bright 1988; Cordrey 1994), and music games (e.g., finishing a lyric line, playing Name that Tune or music trivia) (Bright 1988; Chavin 1991) promote verbal interaction and socialization, decrease loneliness and isolation, provide opportunities to discuss/express feelings and voice opinions, provide opportunities for choice and decision making, stimulate cognitive and memory functions, maintain attending skills, and enhance self-esteem and self-concept through successful participation with others and recollections of past accomplishments, significant life events, and significant others. Props and prompts from the group leader (e.g., multiple-choice or yes-no questions rather than open-ended questions) can greatly facilitate individuals' responsiveness to reminiscence and song-related discussion activities (Chavin 1991).

Structured song-writing experiences (e.g., lyric substitution, lyrics on a theme given by therapist) also can help increase communication, socialization, cognitive function, creative expression, and self-esteem (Chavin 1991; Silber and Hes 1995). Because it utilizes the "feelingful" parts of the brain that may remain intact when other cognitive functions have declined, song writing can help individuals with early-stage neurocognitive disorder temporarily to overcome memory and language deficits and give emotionally withdrawn individuals a way to express feelings that they are unable to express in speech (Silber and Hes 1995). Individual "lessons" on previously learned instruments can help individuals retain music skills, enhance self-expression and feelings of self-worth, decrease agitation and depression, facilitate positive affect, and stimulate cognitive and physical functioning (Clair 1996b; Smith and Knudson 1995; Ziv et al. 2007), while group instrumental ensembles, such as bell choirs (Chavin 1995; Smith and Knudson 1995) or rhythm groups (Bright 1988; Gfeller and Hanson 1995; Smith and Knudson 1995), can promote active participation and interaction with others, decrease withdrawal and isolation, increase cognitive awareness and help maintain cognitive functioning, improve/maintain motor functioning and eye-hand coordination, provide opportunities for creative self-expression, provide ways to nonverbally express feelings, and increase self-esteem and feelings of belonging.

Many individuals in the early stages of neurocognitive disorder also enjoy dancing (especially ballroom dancing or square dancing, if these are in their past experience) or music-movement experiences (e.g., exercise to music, actions to songs, scarf dancing, creative movement to music, massage to music) (Bright 1988; Brotons et al. 1997; Brotons and Marti 2003; Clair 1996b; Gfeller and Hanson 1995; Hamburg and Clair 2003a, 2003b, 2008; Hanson et al. 1996; Johnson, Otto, and Clair 2001; Shively and Henkin 1986; Smith and Knudson 1995). Therapeutically structured music and movement sessions using familiar, enjoyable music can provide a nonthreatening environment that increases feelings of comfort and security while decreasing anxiety and agitation (Shively and Henkin 1986). Music/movement experiences also increase socialization and interaction with others, promote creativity and nonverbal expression of feelings, help increase or maintain physical functioning, and increase awareness of self and others. Bright (1988), Chavin (1991), Cordrey (1994), Gfeller and Hanson (1995), and Smith and Knudson (1995) provide many examples of plans for specific interventions using singing, song writing, reminiscence, instrumental, and music/movement experiences.

Hamburg and Clair (2008) studied the effects of Laban/Bartenieff-based movement on physical function measures in older adults. The movement program observed 20 healthy older adults (aged 66–84 years). The Laban dance movement involves a program for older adults, called "Motivating Moves®: Movement with Music to Promote the Health of Older Adults." Clients first completed the Reuben Physical Performance Test (RPPT) (Reuben and Siu 1990) as a measure of physical function. The Motivating Moves program then was offered for a five-week period (the time had been determined in earlier studies, Hamburg and Clair 2003a, 2003b), with time extended for clients to refine their movements and learn new movements. The RPPT was repeated after the fifth week. The study found significant changes in walking and ability to put on and remove a jacket, which are important for independent living. Its results "show that the Motivating Music® program potentially can assist participants in developing the gross motor skills, coordination, flexibility, and balance that are integral to faster walking speeds and upper body flexibility" (36).

Music Therapy Interventions for Middle Stages of Neurocognitive Disorder

Although the mental and physical abilities of individuals in the middle stage of neurocognitive disorder are steadily declining, they still need appropriately challenging activities that can help them maintain their highest level of functioning for as long as possible (Chavin 1995; Gfeller and Hanson 1995;

Hanson et al. 1996). Given appropriate structure and adaptations, they still can participate successfully in ensembles like bell choirs (Chavin 1995; Smith and Knudson 1995) or fairly demanding dances and music/movement experiences (Clair 1996b; Gfeller and Hanson 1995; Hanson et al. 1996). These experiences provide interaction with others and help reduce isolation and maintain physical and cognitive functioning. Some individuals also still may be able to sing familiar songs, especially ones that were learned early in life. In addition to providing socialization, enjoyment, and emotional expression, singing may positively influence other behaviors. For example, Millard and Smith (1989) found that during sing-alongs, individuals in the middle stage of Alzheimer's disease vocalize and verbalize more than during discussion sessions, increase sitting or walking with others both during and after the sessions, show more awareness of and concern for others, and show pleasure by smiling more often. During sing-alongs, clients also show more attention to task and less wandering than they do in the discussion activity.

Clients who are unable to sing still may derive benefits and pleasure from singing experiences as they interact by vocalizing with the melodies and showing attention or affective reactions to the songs (Clair 1996b; Lipe 1991). In addition, songs can help individuals communicate feelings and emotions they no longer can express verbally. Kaser (1993) describes an elderly man in the middle stage of Alzheimer's disease who selected songs to express feelings he was experiencing and eventually began to verbalize and interact more through this process. The songs enabled the man to form a supportive, meaningful relationship and gave him a unique way to "converse" and discuss his feelings. In addition, his positive experiences in music therapy sessions led to less agitation, more relaxation, and decreased hostile and inappropriate behaviors outside the sessions as well.

Familiar music can give meaning and order to the environment at a time when so many experiences are becoming confused and meaningless, thus adding pleasure and quality of life and helping restore some sense of mental and emotional well-being (Clair 1996b). Music that has been part of the individuals' past life experiences "carries with it a full range of well-integrated associations, emotions, and memories" (74), enabling it to provide the individuals with pleasant, satisfying experiences that "are immediate and do not require cognitive processing for success" (74).

Recorded selections of familiar music can be very useful in establishing rapport with clients, facilitating positive mood shifts, and evoking initial responses. Some clients may show excitement at hearing familiar selections and spontaneously may begin to hum or sing along (Lipe 1991). After establishing trust and a common bond through listening to tapes of the clients' preferred music, therapists can add more active goals and activities such as singing on cue, playing instruments with songs, manipulating objects associated with songs, following directions to start and stop, increasing attention span and amount of on-task behavior, or participating in music activities away from the client's room (Prange 1990). Eventually, clients may begin to fill in titles or even talk about the songs and associated memories (Lipe 1991).

Structured rhythmic activities also are very successful for engaging these clients in purposeful, enjoyable activities that encourage interaction with others. Even severely regressed individuals can participate successfully with others in rhythmic activities such as playing drums (Clair 1996b; Clair and Bernstein 1990; Clair et al. 1995). Rhythm activities can be done one-to-one (Pollack and Namazi 1992) or in small groups of four to six (Clair et al. 1995; Gfeller and Hanson 1995). Research suggests that vibrotactile stimulation, such as that obtained from larger drums that emit strong vibrations, promotes longer, more active participation in severely regressed persons in the middle or later stages of Alzheimer's disease (Clair 1996b; Clair and Bernstein 1990). Often, some participation will occur spontaneously. However, the music therapist's structure and guidance are necessary to help the clients sustain participation and develop awareness of others in the group (Clair et al. 1995). Modeling by the therapist (Clair 1996b) or higher performing peers (Christie 1995) also can positively influence group members' participation level.

Over time, group members can significantly improve their ability to successfully strike the drum and to imitate simple rhythm patterns (Clair et al. 1995). Nonverbal interaction in music activities also can help offset the void in interaction caused by the loss of expressive language skills and foster social interaction of severely regressed individuals with Alzheimer's disease both during and after the music therapy sessions (Pollack and Namazi 1992). As successful as rhythm activities are for many individuals with Alzheimer's disease, it is important to realize that not all clients will respond positively. Some may react with pain or increased agitation to the loud noise, while others simply may not be interested in playing (Clair 1996b). For these individuals, singing or movement activities may offer better avenues of expression and interaction.

Research and clinical experience indicate that a structured, predictable session format is most successful as a group music therapy treatment protocol for individuals in the middle stages of neurocognitive disorder (Clair 1991, 2007; Gfeller and Hanson 1995; Mercado and Mercado 2006; Smith and Knudson 1995). Groups are usually small (4–6 members), about 30 minutes in length, and begin and end with a greeting song that stays the same from week to week. The body of the session (treatment portion) usually includes two to four activities involving familiar songs, rhythmic activities, and/or music/movement activities. These activities focus on encouraging active involvement and increasing social interaction, awareness of self and others, self-expression, attention span, communication (verbal and nonverbal), and self-esteem. Clair (2007) describes the musical behavior of persons with middle- to late-stage neurocognitive disorder:

> Musical characteristics remain intact. Persons with neurocognitive disorder can vocalize after they can no longer sing songs, they can move to music after they can no longer stand to dance, and they continue to entrain their movements to rhythm until voluntary movements are no longer possible. These persons can play rhythmic instruments in ensemble and can participate musically when they can no longer verbally communicate.

Clair's (1991) protocol included (1) a greeting song, using each group member's name; (2) singing familiar songs (e.g., those from group member's young adult years, patriotic songs) led by the music therapist with guitar accompaniment; (3) individual rhythm instrument play in which clients select an instrument from a choice of two and imitate the music therapist's two- and three-beat patterns; (4) rhythm ensemble work, unaccompanied and with singing/acoustic guitar; and (5) a good-bye song, using each group member's name. Smith and Knudson (1995) recommended a five-part session structure: (1) greeting song using clients' names; (2) warm-up songs; (3) rhythm instrument playing (clients choose instrument and play with songs); (4) singing familiar songs/individual performances; (5) closure with good-bye song using clients' names and thanking them for their contributions to group. Gfeller and Hanson (1995) utilized a three-part session structure: (1) an opening, introductory activity to greet group members and signal the beginning of the session; (2) a 20-minute treatment portion, using two activities, with each activity representing one of the three categories of singing, movement, or rhythm at an appropriate complexity level for the group; (3) a short closing activity to thank the group members and say good-bye.

Class participation is usually enhanced when activities use music materials and instruments corresponding to the group members' preferences and drawing on lifelong music skills or interests (Gfeller and Hanson 1995; Smith and Knudson 1995). The therapist's ability to guide and lead participation and adjust the demands of the task to the participant's responses and functional abilities helps optimize on-task behavior while reducing agitation and disruptive behaviors (Clair 1996b; Clair et al. 1995; Gfeller and Hanson 1995; Ziv et al. 2007). In addition, some research suggests that including a peer with a high level of performance/participation in music therapy groups helps motivate and increase the active participation of lower-functioning persons with middle-stage Alzheimer's type neurocognitive disorder (Christie 1995).

Music therapy interventions also can help manage many of the behavior problems that may occur in middle-stage neurocognitive disorders. For many such individuals, music therapy can facilitate sleep and reduce agitation and disruptive behaviors effectively, particularly if their preferences are taken into account (Brotons et al. 1997). Both live and taped music, as well as participation in singing, playing instruments, music games, music/movement experiences, or composition/improvisation activities can be used to decrease agitation (Brotons et al. 1997). Some studies have found that individualized taped music programs, tailored to the patients' preferences, can help soothe patients prior to and during bathing by reducing agitation and aggressive behaviors (Thomas et al. 1997). Developing taped music programs to decrease agitation requires identifying the precise music that traditionally has satisfied or comforted the individual so that the taped program will have meaning and relevance.

For many individuals with middle-stage neurocognitive disorder, participation in music activities also decreases wandering and promotes attention to and positive interactions with others (Brotons and Pickett-Cooper 1996; Fitzgerald-Cloutier 1993; Groene 1993, 2001; Millard and Smith 1989). Fitzgerald-Cloutier (1993) found that unaccompanied singing was particularly effective in maintaining the attention of a wandering, agitated 81-year-old female resident with middle-stage Alzheimer's neurocognitive disorder; she remained seated in one place for as long as twenty minutes. Brotons and Pickett-Cooper (1996) found that music therapy sessions using singing, instrument playing, dance/movement, musical games, and simple composition/improvisation activities (e.g., playing name or feelings on instruments) decreased the agitation and wandering of individuals with Alzheimer's disease both during and for at least twenty minutes following the session. Ninety-eight percent of these subjects stayed for the entire session, and 88 percent stayed for the entire postsession observation period.

Because music therapy experiences like singing, dancing, or playing rhythm instruments can be done easily while standing or moving, they can be adapted for use in a "Walker's Club" and used to provide constructive, meaningful activities for individuals who need to pace (Chavin 1991). Generally, music that is not too loud and movements that are not too fast help hold attention and prevent overstimulation.

Music Therapy Interventions for Late Stages of Neurocognitive Disorders

Although persons with late-stage neurocognitive disorder have lost all verbal articulation and physical ambulation abilities, are incontinent of bowel and bladder, and may sleep for long periods of time and be unresponsive to most stimuli, they still need programs and activities that contribute to their dignity and quality of life. Listening to music is one experience that remains accessible to most of these individuals, but taped music programs and radios must be used with care if they are to be most beneficial:

> Although this music can provide needed stimulation, it can be harmful if it does not match the musical taste of the individuals who must listen to it or if it plays

incessantly. . . . Music preferred by staff, especially if the resident responds to it with cries, tensed muscles, and pained facial affect, must never be used in the resident's room unless it can be established that the resident also likes it. (Clair 1996b, 82)

When working with individuals in the late stage of neurocognitive disorder, music therapists must be alert for small changes in facial expression or tension, short increases in eye contact or a slight turning toward the sound, or a slightly more alert posture, as well as more obvious observable responses such as a change in vocal activity or movement of arms/fingers or legs/feet. Movement responses may be very small, such as slight foot or finger movement (Belgrave 2009). Goals for these individuals include sensory stimulation; increased awareness of self and others; increased interaction with others; increased opportunities for creative self-expression and nonverbal communication; increased participation in positive, meaningful experiences; and increased self-esteem through successful participation in structured, nonthreatening, enjoyable activities (Chavin 1991; Clair 1996b). Belgrave (2009) investigated the effect of expressive and instrumental touch on the behavior state of individuals with late-stage neurocognitive disorder and the music therapist's perceived rapport. Expressive touch is the kind of touch one might use to indicate support or comfort, while instrumental touch is the kind that occurs when a client is assisted to participate in music therapy. She found that instrumental touch leads to more alert states than expressive touch, and the effect is maintained longer. However, expressive touch is more effective than baseline of no touch. There is much variability in the alert state behavior of persons with late-stage neurocognitive disorder.

Most interventions with these individuals will take place in one-to-one interactions, in the individual's room or at his or her bedside. Persons also may be gathered in groups around a table or in a circle, but interactions still will be on an individual basis, with the therapist going from person to person and repeating the same activity with each one (Chavin 1991).

Some research has shown that persons with late-stage neurocognitive disorder have the most frequent alertness and attention responses during live, unaccompanied singing (Clair 1996a). Singing provides a point of contact with another human being on an emotional and sensory level, making no cognitive demands (Clair 1996b). At some level of awareness, individuals may perceive that they are receiving heightened attention when a person takes the time to sing with them (Clair 1996a). Many individuals' alerting and attention responses to singing increase over time; persons who are relatively nonresponsive in initial sessions may begin to show some responsiveness in the fourth or fifth session (Clair 1996a). Different music will evoke alerting responses in different individuals. Some will respond best to familiar songs of youth, while others may respond more to lullabies. Adding touch (e.g., holding hands; rocking or swaying; sitting in close proximity; stroking the shoulder, arm, or face; massaging with creams or oils) to the singing may provide an additional level of contact (Clair 1996b).

During the final stages of neurocognitive disorder, music therapy interventions often take on a palliative form, helping to provide physical and psychological comfort (Lipe 1991). In addition to the comfort derived from being sung to, persons may benefit from individualized recorded music programs that provide them with a sense of security and familiarity. Whitcomb (1992) gives the example of an 86-year-old French priest with late-stage neurocognitive disorder whose agitation and screaming were replaced with relaxation and peace when a tape of Gregorian chants was played at his bedside. This familiar music touched him on some level of awareness and helped bring him back to a place of serenity and comfort.

To be most effective, recorded music must not be played continuously but at specific times or for specific purposes. Clair (1996b) recommended managing the music on a schedule determined by individual responses to music and individual sleep patterns. For some people, this may be 15 to 20 minutes of music an hour, while for others it may be an hour of music followed by an hour of quiet. Recorded music programs appropriately may be used any time the person is awake, during the day or night.

Caregivers and Music Therapy

Shared music experiences can be an important means of increasing communication (verbal and nonverbal), facilitating meaningful interactions, enhancing emotional closeness, triggering positive memories, and deepening relationships between caregivers and care recipients, especially when the recipients are in the middle and late stages of neurocognitive disorder where they have lost the physical, cognitive, verbal, and social abilities to interact independently and meaningfully with others (Clair 1996b; Clair and Ebberts 1997; Clair et al. 1993; Hanser, Butterfield-Whitcomb, and Kawata 2011; Lipe 1991; Prickett and Moore 1991; Special Committee on Aging 1992; Whitcomb 1992). Even in the early stages of neurocognitive disorder, music therapy interventions can help caregivers and care recipients nonverbally express the feelings associated with knowing the care recipient has a progressive, incurable disease. As music making taps some of the still intact skills and abilities of the care recipient, music experiences also can provide opportunities for pleasant, meaningful interactions between caregiver and care recipient. This positive interactive experience can evoke feelings of success and satisfaction for both caregiver and care recipient. In addition, music experiences help caregivers focus on their loved one's strengths and residual abilities, rather than on all the disease is taking away (Clair 1996b).

Many music experiences can enhance the interactions of caregivers and care recipients. Those who have played instruments together may continue to interact in this way (Clair 1996b), while others may prefer to sing favorite songs (Clair 1996b; Prickett and Moore 1991) or listen to music together (Clair 1996b; Lipe 1991). Favorite songs also can evoke reminiscences that caregiver and care recipient can share (Chavi 1991; Clair 1996b; Palmer 1989). Many of these experiences can continue to give satisfaction to both caregiver and care recipient into the middle and late stages of neurocognitive disorder. For example, dancing together or sitting next to each other while singing or while one plays the piano or guitar and both hum or sing can provide caregivers and care recipients with moments of emotional closeness and intimacy (Clair 1996b; Clair et al. 1993; Special Committee on Aging 1992). As the structure of these musical experiences provides the focus and encouragement for care recipients to reach out to their caregivers with loving, physical gestures, they also allow the caregivers to receive something back from the recipients and contribute to fulfilling the caregivers' needs for emotional closeness with their loved ones.

Other benefits of music therapy interventions for caregivers dealing with care recipients in the middle and late stages include providing a (1) means of decreasing agitation or boredom of care recipients and (2) structure for positive, meaningful interactions between caregivers and care recipients. Caregivers may sing care recipients' favorite songs or use tapes of their favorites songs to help focus care recipients' attention on positive experiences and decrease their agitation, boredom, or restlessness (Clair 1996b; Lipe 1991). Songs and singing also may be vehicles for providing satisfying interpersonal interactions between caregivers and care recipients when fluent speech no longer can (Prickett and Moore 1991). Even care recipients in the late stage of neurocognitive disorder frequently will respond to their loved ones' singing by making eye contact, having a more relaxed or more alert facial expression, or vocalizing at certain points of the song (Clair 1996b). In addition, hearing caregivers sing familiar, comforting songs or hearing recordings of familiar, comforting music may help decrease recipients' agitation and combativeness during assisted personal care activities (e.g., bathing, changing soiled clothing), thus making the caregiver's job easier and less stressful (Clair 1996b; Thomas et al. 1997; Whitcomb 1992).

Music therapy interventions also can help give structure and meaning to visits among family members and their loved ones in the middle and late stages of neurocognitive disorder, thus making the experience less frustrating and more pleasant for both parties (Clair 1996b, 2007; Clair and Ebberts 1997; Lipe 1991). Using music that is familiar and well liked by both family members and their loved ones with neurocognitive disorder, be it live singing by the family member, recordings of preferred songs or dance music that can be listened to, sung with, or moved to, or taped performances by children or grandchildren, can help alleviate much of the anxiety and frustration family members often feel at visits. As the music structures and enhances the time they have together, "caregivers can let go of the responsibility they feel to maintain their loved one's comfort by allowing the music to take over" (Clair 1996b, 271). A recent model music therapy program used structured, 10-minute singing, dancing, and drum playing experiences to enhance interactions between family members and their loved ones who had late-stage neurocognitive disorder (Clair and Ebberts 1997). By eliciting active responses from both caregivers (family members) and care recipients, the experience gave purpose and direction to their interactions. Family members participating in the study showed a statistically significant increase in satisfaction with the visits using music therapy, as compared with previous visits without music therapy. Music therapy interventions also may be used with caregivers alone to help alleviate stress (Brotons and Marti 2003; Clair 1996b; McCarthy 1992; Palmer 1989) or to facilitate the process of dealing with their own grief, anger, and disappointment as they gradually lose their loved one to neurocognitive disorder (Bright 1988; Clair 1996b). For example, music-mediated relaxation techniques can help release tension, manage stress, and gain temporary respite from worry and fear (Clair 1996b; Palmer 1989). These techniques can be useful to individual caregivers in the home or to staff members in residential facilities. McCarthy (1992) designed a music therapy program to decrease stress and reduce burnout among staff members in a nursing home unit for patients with Alzheimer's disease. Techniques taught to staff members include deep breathing and progressive muscle relaxation to music, simple yoga and gentle stretching to music, imagery with music, and massage therapy with music.

Repeating positive, self-affirming statements rhythmically to appropriate accompaniment music may help other caregivers (Clair 1996b). In addition, songs, groaning vocalizations, and instrumental improvisations can provide a safe container for caregivers to express their grief, anger, fear, pain, or other emotions (Bright 1988; Clair 1996b). Structured song writing experiences (e.g., filling in the blanks about things they miss about the person, things the disease is taking from them, things they hate about the care process but still love about the care recipient, etc.) also may help some caregivers safely express strong emotions.

SPECIAL CONSIDERATIONS AND TIPS FOR SUCCESS

Careful individual assessment of client needs, interests, previous experiences, strengths, and preferences, as well as ongoing assessment and evaluation of treatment interventions and client responses are key ingredients to effective music therapy programming with any elderly population. Generally, activities will be most successful when they (a) use materials that are interesting and personally relevant to the participants or that incorporate their previous life experience; (b) provide appropriate levels of challenge; (c) recognize the participants' physical and mental capabilities and make any necessary adaptations; (d) are age-appropriate (geared to characteristics, needs, interests of older adults); (e) use high-quality equipment and materials; (f) focus on using participants' strengths; (g) are designed for sequential skill-building, using preferred methods and materials; (h) emphasize the personal meaning each individual gains from the experience; and (i) promote success and enhance the participants' self-concept and self-esteem (Chavin 1991; Clair 1996b; Clair and Davis 2008; Coates 1984; Cordrey 1994; Davidson 1980; Douglass 1985; Gfeller and Hanson 1995; Gibbons, 1977, 1985, 1988; Hanser, Butterfield-Whitcomb, and Kawata 2011; Karras 1987; Myers 1991, 1992; Smith and Knudson 1995; Weissman 1983). While enthusiastic, confident leadership enhances participation and success (Davidson 1980), group leaders must remember they are not performing for the clients but structuring the music to elicit certain responses and help the clients reach specific goals.

It is important to realize that music may have negative as well as positive effects (Chavin 1991; Clair 1996b; Karras 1987). What is comforting and relaxing or enjoyable to one person may be distressing and even painful to another; music or instruments that one prefers may be hated by another; experiences that are just right for one may be over-stimulating for another. Therefore, music therapists always must observe individual reactions carefully and be ready to change or adapt materials and experiences to meet individual needs.

Purtilo (1978) observed that a therapist's success in working with geriatric clients will be enhanced if the therapist recognizes that most older people fear dependence and is aware of differences in sensory or motor acuity that may affect the client's responses. Because of motor and sensory limitations, many geriatric clients may have difficulty performing music with small intervals or complex rhythm patterns; however, they can have successful musical experiences if the therapist chooses music that has marked changes in pitch and duration and employs simple rhythm patterns (Gibbons 1983a). Large-print song sheets may be needed to compensate for deteriorating vision. Adequate lighting and good acoustics also will enhance the music experience for geriatric clients (Nowicki and Trevisan 1978). In addition, because the functional vocal range of most geriatric clients is rather limited, many songs will require transposition for successful use with geriatric clients (Greenwald and Salzberg 1979; Moore, Staum, and Brotons 1992). In addition, providing musical cues or prompts for songs (rather than just announcing titles) may increase lyric recall and facilitate participation (Bartlett and Snelus 1980; York 1994). A list by Cevasco and Vanweelden (2010 42–75), classified by decade, includes 1,896 songs from the 1900s to 1960s. This is an important time range, since much literature indicates that the elderly respond best to music from their youth. Songs in the list are from four songbooks, and the sources are provided (38).

Acknowledging clients by name and thanking them for their contributions to the group, along with some physical contact (e.g., handshakes, hugs), are also important aspects of establishing therapeutic relationships with geriatric clients, for those actions help rebuild a sense of dignity and self-esteem in the clients (Palmer 1977).

Remembering that geriatric clients, like any group of people, have a wide range of musical interests is important (Gibbons 1985). Elderly people are not interested exclusively in religious music or popular music from the turn of the century. The type of popular music people prefer tends to vary with their age. Usually, older people tend to prefer music that was popular during their early adult years (Gibbons 1977). There also are indications that older people prefer stimulative to sedative music and place a high premium on quality musical experiences (Gibbons 1977, 1985). Finally, it is important to remember that musical aptitude does not necessarily deteriorate just because an individual reaches the age of sixty-five. Both older people in the community and many geriatric clients in residential settings maintain the capacity to develop musically as they age (Gibbons 1983b, 1985; Kellmann 1986).

QUESTIONS FOR THOUGHT AND DISCUSSION

1. Discuss some of the special characteristics and needs of (1) the well elderly, (2) those elderly individuals who are semi-independent, (3) those who are chronically ill or medically fragile and are being cared for in their own home or that of a caregiver, (4) those who are in nursing homes or long-term care facilities, and (5) those who have Alzheimer's disease or related disorders. What implications do these have for music therapy programming?
2. Briefly describe the disengagement, activity, developmental and aging subculture theories of aging. What are some implications of each for programming for elderly individuals? Which do you feel are most applicable to music therapy interventions with the elderly? Why?
3. Describe some of the major treatment approaches (e.g., sensory stimulation/sensory training, reality orientation, remotivation, validation, reminiscence, life review, behavioral approaches) used with individuals who are elderly. For which groups of clients might each be most useful? How might music experiences be incorporated into each of these approaches?
4. Discuss some of the myths and realities about elderly persons and music. What are the implications of these for music therapy programming?
5. Why are music experiences useful for individuals who are elderly? Are some types of experiences and activities more useful than others for par-

ticular types of clients? Which ones? Why?

6. Describe some specific music therapy experiences that might be used to help (1) the well elderly, (2) those elderly individuals who are semi-independent, (3) those who are chronically ill or medically fragile and are being cared for in their own home or that of a caregiver, (4) those who are in nursing homes or long-term care facilities, (5) those in the early, middle, and late stages of neurocognitive disorder, and (6) caregivers. What unique benefits does music provide for each of these groups?

7. List several special considerations that may be important to remember when developing therapeutic intervention strategies for persons are elderly. Why are these important? What are their implications for the structure of music therapy intervention strategies?

8. For each of the situations listed below, (a) define the problem or areas of need for the client or group of clients, (b) describe one or more of the goals you might pursue in music therapy sessions with the client(s), (c) describe music activities you might use to help the client(s) meet those goals, (d) tell how the music activities you describe relate to the goals and needs of the client(s), and (e) mention any special considerations you might want to take into account when working with the client(s).

Situation 1:

Mr. H. is a 65-year-old man who recently retired and is looking for constructive ways to fill his time. He just started attending a senior center with his wife. One day he mentioned that although he and his wife have always enjoyed music (in fact, they still go to concerts and love to sing and listen to music), he never learned to play an instrument, because he never had enough time. Now that he has the time, he wonders if he might be too old to learn. Mr. and Mrs. H. have a piano that their children or grandchildren play when they come to visit. Mr. H. also enjoys country music and has thought about learning to play the guitar.

Situation 2:

Mrs. C. is a 75-year-old widow who has been in a nursing home for about three months. She is slightly confused and uses a walker to help her get around. She rarely goes out of her room because she is afraid she will get lost. She has few visitors and often seems to be very nervous. Occasionally, she has been observed to be silently crying, but she will not discuss what is wrong. She rarely initiates conversation with staff or other residents and hardly even talks to her roommate. Mrs. C. keeps herself busy by reading her Bible, napping, listening to religious music, or watching TV. Her social history indicates that her husband played the violin and that she used to play the piano and sing in the church choir.

Situation 3:

You have been contracted to provide music therapy sessions for a small group of residents on the newly formed Alzheimer's care unit of a local nursing home. There are three women and two men in the group. All are ambulatory. Their neurocognitive disorders have progressed to the point where they now have trouble recognizing close friends and family members. Most still speak, but they frequently have problems finding the words they need to express their thoughts and feelings. These residents often engage in repetitive motions like pacing and tapping; a few also repeat certain phrases like "help me" or "Where's my mother?" Their restlessness and agitation tend to increase in the late afternoon and early evening. The activity director has scheduled your music therapy group for a late afternoon time in the hope that you can decrease their agitation and get them to engage in some purposeful activities.

SUGGESTIONS FOR FURTHER READING

Bright, R (1981). *Practical planning in music therapy for the aged.* Lynbrook, NY: Music-graphics.

Bright, R. (1986). *Grieving: A handbook for those who care.* St. Louis: MMB Music.

Bright, R. (1988). *Music therapy and the dementias: Improving the quality of life.* St. Louis: MMB Music.

Brotons, M., Koger, S., & Pickett-Cooper, P. (1997). Music and dementias: A review of literature. *Journal of Music Therapy, 34(4),* 204–245.

Bruscia, K. E. (Ed.) (1991). *Case studies in music therapy.* Phoenixville, PA: Barcelona.

Cevasco, A. M. & Vanweelden, K. (2010). An analysis of songbook series for older adult populations. *Music Therapy Perspectives, 28(1),* 37–78.

Chavin, M. (1991). *The lost chord: Reaching the person with dementia through the power of music.* Mt. Airy, MD: ElderSong Publications.

Clair, A. A. (1996). *Therapeutic uses of music with older adults.* Baltimore, MD: Health Professions Press.

Clair, A. A. & Davis, W. B. (2008). Music therapy and elderly populations. In W. B. Davis, K. E. Gfeller, & M. H. Thaut (Eds)., *An introduction to music therapy theory and practice* (3rd ed.) (181–207). Silver Spring, MD: American Music Therapy Association.

Cordrey, C. (1994). *Hidden treasures: Music and memory activities for people with Alzheimer's.* Mt. Airy, MD: Eldersong.

Erikson, E. H., Erikson, J. M., & Kivnick, H. Q. (1986). *Vital involvement in old age.* New York: W. W. Norton & Co.

Feil, N. (1982). *Validation – the Feil method: How to help the disoriented old-old.* Cleveland, OH: Edward Feil.

Feil, N. (1993). *The validation breakthrough: Simple techniques for communicating with people with "Alzheimer's-type dementia."* Baltimore, MD: Health Professions Press.

Gfeller, K. & Hanson, N. (Eds.). (1995). *Music therapy programming for individuals with*

Alzheimer's disease and related disorders. St. Louis: MMB Music.

Gibbons, A. C. (1988). A review of literature for music development/education and music therapy with the elderly. *Music Therapy Perspectives, 5*, 33–40.

Hanser, S. B., Butterfield-Whitcomb, J., & Kawata, M. (2011). Home-based music strategies with individuals who have dementia and their family caregivers. *Journal of Music Therapy, 48(1)*, 2–27.

Hanson, N., Gfeller, K., Woodworth, G., Swanson, E., & Garand, L. (1996). A comparison of the effectiveness of differing types and difficulty of music activities in programming for older adults with Alzheimer's disease and related disorders. *Journal of Music Therapy, 33(2)*, 93–123.

Karras, B. (1985). *Down memory lane: Topics and ideas for reminiscence groups.* Wheaton, MD: Circle Press.

Karras, B. (Ed.) (1987). *"You bring out the music in me": Music in nursing homes.* Binghamton, NY: Haworth Press.

Kellman, R. H. (1986). Developing music programs for older adults. *Music Educators Journal, 72(5)*, 30–33.

Palmer, M. (1989). Music therapy in gerontology: A rewind and projection. *Music Therapy Perspectives, 6*, 52–56.

Prickett, C. A. (1988). Music therapy for the aged. In C. E. Furman (Ed.), *Effectiveness of music therapy procedures: Documentation of research and clinical practice* (285–299). Washington, DC: National Association for Music Therapy.

Prickett, C. A. (1996). Music therapy as a part of older people's lives. In C. E. Furman (Ed.), *Effectiveness of music therapy procedures: Documentation of research and clinical practice* (2nd ed.) (144–166). Silver Spring, MD: National Association for Music Therapy.

Schulberg, C. H. (1981). *The music therapy sourcebook: A collection of activities categorized and analyzed.* New York: Human Sciences Press.

Short, A. E. (1992). Music and imagery with physically disabled elderly residents: A GIM adaptation. *Music Therapy, 11(1)*, 65–98.

Smith, D. S. & Lipe, A. W. (1991). Music therapy practices in gerontology. *Journal of Music Therapy, 28(4)*, 193–210.

Standley, J. (1991). *Music techniques in therapy, counseling, and special education.* St. Louis: MMB Music.

Summer, L. (1981). Guided imagery and music with the elderly. *Music Therapy, 1(1)*, 39–42.

Vanweelden, K. & Cevasco, A. (2007). Repertoire recommendations by music therapists for geriatric clients during singing activities. *Music Therapy Perspectives, 25(1)*, 4–12.

Weisberg, N. & Wilder, R. (1985). *Creative arts with older adults.* New York: Human Sciences Press.

Weissman, J. A. (1983). Planning music activities to meet needs and treatment goals of aged individuals in long-term care facilities. *Music Therapy, 3(1)*, 63–70.

Chapter Twenty

MUSIC THERAPY FOR TERMINALLY ILL INDIVIDUALS

DEFINITION

Individuals are considered *terminally ill* after diagnosis with some fatal, incurable disease or condition. Many terminally ill patients have incurable diseases such as certain types of cancer (especially metastasized cancer) or AIDS. Others are in the advanced stages of degenerative neurological diseases such as amyotrophic lateral sclerosis (ALS, or Lou Gehrig's disease), Alzheimer's disease, Huntington's disease, multiple sclerosis, muscular dystrophy, or Parkinson's disease. As Purtilo (1978) observes, one main difficulty with this term is its generality: Both individuals who may live for years before dying from a malignant or degenerative condition and those who almost certainly will die within a few days or weeks are labeled "terminally ill."

Terminally ill people usually receive palliative care rather than active, aggressive medical treatment. *Palliative care* serves to alleviate the distressful symptoms of the disease or condition (e.g., reduces pain as much as possible) but does not strive for a cure. The terms *hospice, palliative care*, and *end-of-life care* sometimes are used interchangeably. However, while end-of-life care may be a part of either hospice or palliative care, they have separate definitions. According to the American College of Surgeons (2005):

> Palliative care aims to relieve physical pain and psychological, social, spiritual suffering while supporting the patient's treatment goals and respecting the patient's racial, ethnic, religious, and cultural values. Like all good patient care, palliative care is based on the fundamental ethical priniciples of autonomy, beneficence, nonmaleficence, justice, and duty.

> Although palliative care includes hospice care and care near the time of death, it also embraces the management of pain and suffering in medical and surgical conditions throughout life.

Palliative care is used to control suffering as needed and is considered as important as curing disease. Thus, it is used with patients whose disease is terminal but also with patients who are expected to recover, but who have pain and suffering during treatment and recovery.

The principles of palliative care and hospice are very similar. In 1998, the American College of Surgeons published a Statement of Principles Guiding Care at the End of Life, which extended palliative care to many patients receiving surgical care, not just those who were terminal. The following is a statement of principles of palliative care provided by the American College of Surgeons (2005):

1. Respect the dignity and autonomy of patients, patients' surrogates, and caregivers.
2. Honor the right of the competent patient or surrogate to choose among treatments, including those that may or may not prolong life.
3. Communicate effectively and empathically with patients, their families, and caregivers.
4. Identify the primary goals of care from the patient's perspective, and address how the surgeon's care can achieve the patient's objectives.
5. Strive to alleviate pain and other burdensome physical and nonphysical symptoms.
6. Recognize, access, discuss, and offer access to services for psychological, social, and spiritual issues.
7. Provide access to therapeutic support, encompassing the spectrum from life-prolonging treatments through hospice care, when they can realistically be expected to improve the quality of life as perceived by the patient.
8. Recognize the physician's responsibility to discourage treatments that are unlikely to achieve the patient's goals, and encourage patients and families to consider hospice care when the prognosis for survival is likely to be less than a half-year.
9. Arrange for continuity of care by the patient's primary and/or specialist physician, alleviating the sense of abandonment patients may feel when "curative" therapies are no longer useful.
10. Maintain a collegial and supportive attitude toward others entrusted with care of the patient.

Palliative care focuses on providing individualized, supportive care that improves quality of life and preserves dignity. *Hospice programs* coordinate supportive and palliative services from a variety of professionals and disciplines to help meet the total needs (physical, psychological, social, emotional, and spiritual) of terminally ill individuals and their families. Agencies providing hospice include independent facilities, hospitals, and nursing homes. However, most hospice care is provided at home. The National Hospice and Palliative

Care Organization (NHPCO) reported that in 2012, 77.4 percent of hospices had fewer than 500 total admissions in that year. The mean census was 148.5 patients. Some hospices are primarily volunteer organizations and serve few patients, and some are large corporations that care for thousands each day (NHPCO 2013, 8). Hospice care is covered under Medicare, Medicaid, and many private insurance plans. In the United States, an increase in nursing home residents accompanies an increase in progressive chronic disease as the lifespan lengthens. Consequently, nursing home residents are comprising an increasing proportion of hospice patients (NHPCO 2013, 6):

> As the average life span in the United States has increased, so has the number of individuals who die of chronic progressive diseases that require longer and more sustained care. An increasing number of these individuals reside in nursing homes prior to their death. This rise has been mirrored by growth in the number of hospice patients who reside in nursing homes.

While hospice serves clients with many types of disease, cancer accounts for over a third of hospice patients. Hospice programs aim to keep the integrity and personal choices of the patient and the family intact by providing individualized, supportive, interdisciplinary care that encourages each patient to live as fully as possible and then allows them to die in peace and with dignity (NHPCO 2014), surrounded by their loved ones. In hospice programs, health care workers "view death not as a medical failure, but as a part of life" (Life's Work 1987, 55).

The term *hospice* (from the same linguistic root as "hospitality") can be traced back to medieval times, when it referred to a place of shelter and rest for weary or ill travelers on a long journey. The name was first applied to specialized care for dying patients by physician Dame Cicely Saunders, who began her work with the terminally ill in 1948 in England and eventually created the first modern hospice – St. Christopher's Hospice – in a residential suburb of London:

> Saunders introduced the idea of specialized care for the dying to the United States during a 1963 visit with Yale University. Her lecture, given to medical students, nurses, social workers, and chaplains about the concept of holistic hospice care, included photos of terminally ill cancer patients and their families, showing the dramatic differences before and after the symptom control care. This lecture launched the . . . chain of events, which resulted in the development of hospice care as we know it today. (NHPCO 2014)

Dame Cicely Saunders died in 2006, and there was a celebration of her life in Westminster Abbey.

The first modern hospice programs in Canada and the United States were established in the mid-1970s, and the National Hospice Organization was founded in 1978. Speaking at a symposium in 1989, Patrice O'Connor,

Coordinator of the Palliative Care Program at St Luke's/Roosevelt Hospital Center in New York City, observed:

> The growth and the development of Hospice in the United States from three programs in 1975 to over 1800 programs in 1988 shows the interest and concern of people in taking control of this aspect of their lives in a highly technical health-care system. (Martin 1989, 79)

For 40 years, the NHPCO and its affiliates have worked for legislation and medical practice acceptance of hospice and palliative care. By 2004, more than one million patients had received services from hospice: "In 2012, an estimated 1.5 to 1.6 million patients received services from hospices" (NHPCO 2013, 4). By 2005, there were 4,000 hospice provider organizations throughout the United States (NHPCO 2014). That number grew to 5,560 by 2012 (NHPCO 2013, 8). In 2006, the *World Day* was held to focus attention on programs in 70 countries.

Services have expanded to include additional patients. Veterans Affairs (VA) hospitals increased access to services and educational programs for clinicians in 2002. In 2003, the White House Conference of Palliative Care for HIV/AIDS Global Pandemic included a guide to "Supportive and Palliative Care for HIV/AIDS." In 2005, The American Heart Association and the American College of Cardiology included recommendations for hospice care education in the treatment of patients with heart failure. In 2009, the NHPCO Standards of Practice for Pediatric Palliative Care and Hospice along with the companion publication, Facts and Figures on Pediatric Palliative and Hospice Care in America were released (NHPCO 2013). The Standards of Practice received "Affirmation of Value" from the American Academy of Pediatrics in 2010. In 2010, there was a "provision in the Patient Protection and Affordable Care Act [to] require state Medicaid programs to allow children with a life threatening illness to receive both hospice care and curative treatment" (NHPCO 2014).

Hospice and palliative care may be used together when relief from pain and suffering is a primary goal. Whereas palliative care may be offered either with curative care or independently, hospice clients, by definition, must be medically certified to have a life expectancy of six months or less, unless the disease goes into remission or changes course. If a hospice client needs more than six month's care, the physician must recertify that care is needed.

COMMON CHARACTERISTICS, PROBLEMS, AND NEEDS OF CLIENTS

As with any population, terminally ill individuals are a very heterogeneous group. Factors such as the type and severity of the illness or condition, the expected time left before death, the existence of associated conditions or impairments, the reactions of family and friends, and the degree and type of support services available all will have varying effects on the individual's level of functioning, needs, and treatment program. In addition, each terminally ill individual has a unique combinations of abilities, needs, personality traits, strengths, and weaknesses that will impact his or her particular responses and functional abilities.

According to Kubler-Ross (1969), most terminally ill people go through five stages in confronting death: (1) denial and isolation, (2) anger, (3) bargaining, (4) depression, and (5) acceptance. Because individuals move through these stages in different ways and some patients may revisit any or all of them (often at different levels) before death, it may be more accurate to think of these stages as a range of responses that terminally ill individuals likely will exhibit, rather than as a sequence through which they will pass (Purtilo 1978; West 1994).

Others view the progression from life to death as consisting of four phases, each of which presents new tasks, challenges, and emotions (West 1994). The length of each phase can vary greatly from patient to patient. In phase one, *early phase*, the patient is adjusting to the reality of a terminal diagnosis, deciding to shift from aggressive to palliative treatment and learning to adapt to various role and body image changes. During phase two, *stabilization*, the acute crisis of the diagnosis has subsided and there may be few significant changes in health or lifestyle. The patient's focus moves between tasks of living and tasks of dying as she or he processes any "unfinished business," attends to such things as will preparation, funeral plans, and care for family members after his or her death, engages in life review or values clarification, and finds ways to continue living fully while she or he remains alive. This lingering stage, between diagnosis and disease progression/imminent death, may be one of the hardest stages for many family members (Bright 1986; Purtilo 1978). The third phase, *disease progression*, may occur only once or several times before death. Some patients cycle between disease progression and stabilization many times before approaching imminent death. Disease progression is a crisis phase, during which the patient experiences many physical, psychological, and spiritual challenges as she or he adjusts to more losses, decreased functioning, and diminished energy. During this phase, patients may be placed in hospitals or care facilities, resulting in additional losses and changes in quality of life. In phase four, *end stage and death*, the patient's death is imminent. During this phase, the patient becomes detached and disengaged, adjusts to changes in sensory awareness, and physically, psychologically, and spiritually shifts from living to dying. Patients in this phase often become increasingly isolated and unresponsive. Others may get confused or anxious. Some may show a decrease in affective expression and experience a decrease in tolerance for light, sound, or other stimuli.

Throughout the course of their terminal illness, individuals will have many physical, psychological, social, and spiritual needs (Bright 1986; Colligan 1987; "Hospice Web" 1999; "Life's Work" 1987; Martin 1989; Munro 1984; Munro and Mount 1978; Purtilo 1978; Visiting Nurses Association of Dallas 1981). *Physical needs* may include relief of acute or chronic pain and physical distress, muscle relaxation, appropriate medication and medical care procedures to manage medical conditions and symptoms, nutritional counseling, or assistance with activities of daily living (bathing, toileting, grooming, eating, etc.). Terminally ill individuals also may need programs or strategies that help facilitate their participation in physical activities for the greatest extent possible. *Psychological needs* may include help in increasing or maintaining a healthy self-concept and high self-esteem, decreasing depression or anxiety, finding ways to continue living to the fullest until death, facilitating expression of a broad range of conscious and unconscious feelings, having time and space to grieve or express anger, discussing and finding ways to manage or work through present concerns, continuing involvement in decision making about one's own life or care to the fullest possible extent, reviewing part or all of one's past life, finding outlets for fantasy and creativity, and finding ways to tap and express those parts of the individual that are still vital and healthy. The patient needs to become aware of feelings and emotions, to own them, and to express them to the group, therapist, or family members.

Many terminally ill individuals also need support and guidance in dealing with fears often associated with the dying process, such as fear of isolation, increasing pain, increased dependence on others (loss of independence and control), indignity or rejection because of one's condition, mounting medical costs, the unknown (what comes after death), and grief and sadness over the impending loss of relationships (Bright 1986; Maranto 1988; Purtilo 1978). When a terminally ill individual has a condition that has some societal stigma attached to it (e.g., AIDS), fears of rejection or isolation and feelings of shock, guilt, panic, and worry over what others will think may be compounded, giving rise to additional needs for psychological counseling and support (Maranto 1988).

The physical changes and psychological concerns associated with terminal illnesses also may impact an individual's ability to relate to and communicate with others. *Social needs* of terminally ill individuals include physical touch, companionship, private times with family and friends, ways to stay involved with others in meaningful activities, links to the individual's life before the terminal diagnosis, entertainment or diversion from dealing with the painful reality of terminal illness, and ways to facilitate conversations between themselves and their family members, including discussion of difficult, emotional, or intimate issues. Several music therapists have prescribed entrainment as used in music therapy (Dileo 1997a; Dileo and Bradt 1999; Dimaio 2010; Thaut 2008). For some individuals, religion or exploration of spiritual issues becomes increasingly important as they face death. *Spiritual needs* may include pastoral counseling, grief counseling, finding ways to express and discuss spiritual feelings and questions, finding comfort and reassurance in religious or spiritual beliefs and/or rituals, obtaining support for one's beliefs, confronting questions about the meaning of life and what comes after death, and facilitating the transition from life to death ("Hospice Web" 1999; Munro and Mount 1978; West 1994).

Healthcare for terminally ill individuals emphasizes (1) managing pain and related symptoms to decrease suffering and maximize comfort; (2) helping individuals maintain independent physical function and encouraging them to live life as fully as possible; (3) providing patients and family members with information on the patient's illness and care (including what to expect as the illness progresses), along with the reassurance that everything possible is being done; and (4) attending to the emotional and spiritual needs of patients and family members, by supporting them rather than abandoning them (Krout 2000; Purtilo 1978; Visiting Nurses Association of Dallas 1981). The overall treatment goal is to enhance and maintain the individual's quality of life until the moment of death, thus facilitating the adaptation of the individual's family (Purtilo 1978; Schwankovsky and Guthrie 1982).

COMMON NEEDS OF FAMILY MEMBERS

Most hospice or palliative care programs are concerned not only with the patient's needs but also with the needs of the patient's family members (Bright 1981, 1986; "Hospice Web" 1999; "Life's Work" 1987; Martin 1989; Purtilo 1978; Schwankovsky and Guthrie 1982; Visiting Nurses Association of Dallas 1981; West 1994). Since family members, too, are unique individuals, each responds differently to their loved one's illness; therefore, it is unwise to attempt to predict a particular person's needs or responses based on broad generalizations.

The terminal illness of one family member, be it spouse, parent, or child, impacts all other family members, for their roles in the family will change, at least to some extent, as they care for and continue to live and interact with the ill family member while preparing for life without them. Krout (2003) noted that "the work of hospice is best realized when we allow families to come together and share meaningful moments during the end-of-life transition" (112). He provided five case examples to illustrate this point. Family members, too, need much support in all areas of their lives. They may need to be reminded to take time for their own physical or nutritional needs. Some need help in finding workable stress management, relaxation, tension release, or anxiety reduction techniques. Family members, especially primary caregivers, need to have breaks or diversions from dealing with the pain and realities of their loved one's terminal illness. In many cases, respite care arrangements or helpful friends or neighbors can provide needed relief. Some families also may need practical assistance in dealing with financial or legal matters in arranging for in-home care or in making funeral arrangements.

Family members need time to be with their loved one, to share fun and diversional activities as well as quiet companionship, life review, and discussion of emotional and difficult topics. They need acceptance and permission both to recall the past and enjoy what time they have left together. They need to find ways to stimulate and celebrate those parts of the patient that remain intact and healthy, so that they can have enjoyable, meaningful interactions together. Family members also need time by themselves, both to solve practical and emotional difficulties and to continue their lives. They need information (in words they can understand) about the patient's condition, treatment, and what to expect as the illness progresses. In addition, they need freedom to express all kinds of emotions, along with psychological and spiritual support, as they deal with fears and questions throughout the patient's illness and after the patient's death.

Family members continue to need support and follow-up care during the bereavement period (Bright 1981, 1986; "Hospice Web" 1999; Munro 1984; Visiting Nurses Association of Dallas 1981). Bereavement support, provided by hospice for a minimum of one year, includes follow-up phone calls, visits, and various community programs (Hospice Net 2014, 4). During this time of grieving, family members are (a) learning to accept the reality of the loss, (b) experiencing the pain of the loss, (c) adapting to life without the loved one, and (d) withdrawing emotional energy from the former relationship with the loved one (Worden 1982). Feelings may include shock, bewilderment, intense emptiness, sadness, despair, depression, restless anxiety, or fatigue and lethargy. Over time, most will experience a kind of "recovery," when they finally can remember their deceased loved one without overwhelming sadness. As grief and sorrow give way to treasured memories, family members will begin to invest energy in other thoughts and activities and create new or revised identities and social roles for themselves. A good social, emotional, and spiritual support network can do much to help bereaved individuals maintain good physical and psychological health as they work through their grief.

SETTINGS FOR SERVICE DELIVERY

Terminally ill individuals may receive care in varied settings, including nursing homes, hospitals, clinics, private homes, and inpatient free-standing hospice programs. Music therapists may provide direct or consultive services to individuals or agencies. While much work with terminally ill clients is done individually, music therapy services also can be provided to groups of patients or to patients and family members. In a recent survey of populations served by music therapists in which respondents were permitted to list as many categories as appropriate (AMTA 2010), 183 music therapists responded that they work with terminally ill clients. Others reported working with individuals who had cancer and those who had AIDS.

HOW MUSIC IS USED IN THERAPY

Music, with its ability to affect all aspects of a person's being, to enhance emotional expression, and to facilitate interactions between and among people (see Chapter Five), can be a very powerful and beneficial tool for helping patients and their families deal with the physical, psychological, social, and spiritual effects and challenges of the various phases of terminal illnesses. In addition to accomplishing clinical goals (e.g., pain or anxiety reduction, strengthening self-concept, facilitating emotional expression), "music can be a source of deep, meaningful interaction – between patients and families, patients and patients, and patients and [music therapist]" (Martin 1991, 630). Songs and music experiences also have the power to reawaken vitality and "build intimate relationships between human beings and life" (Bailey 1984, 16). Cevasco and Vanweelden (2010, 37), directly quoting the substantiation of the "therapeutic importance of singing" by American Music Therapy Association (AMTA) Professional Competencies (2004, 19), point out that "music therapists are expected to utilize vocal, piano, and guitar skills to perform a variety of music genres; acquisition of these skills is considered essential during undergraduate training." Since hearing is the last sense to leave the body, music can even provide comfort and support in the final stages of death (Froehlich 1996). Of course, each individual patient's reaction to a particular intervention or musical selection will be unique; therefore, music therapists constantly assess and evaluate patient responses and adjust music experiences accordingly (Bright 1986; Froehlich 1996; Martin 1989; Munro 1984; Munro and Mount 1978; Schwankovsky and Guthrie 1982; West 1994). A particular patient's type of pain, phase of dying, cognitive style, functional defenses, spiritual and cultural background, and readiness to connect with or express feelings also will influence the type of music therapy interventions selected. In hospice work, music therapists are generally concerned less with facilitating change and more with supporting the patient, enabling the patient and family to make choices, and have experiences that will "enhance the quality of life in the face of death" (West 1994, 120).

Many music therapy techniques have been used effectively to help meet the physical, psychological, social, and spiritual needs of both children and adults who have terminal illnesses, as well as those of their friends and families – techniques such as music listening, guided imagery and music (GIM), music-mediated relaxation, music and massage, discussion of music or music experiences, song choice, lyric interpretation and discussion, song writing, lyric substitution, singing or instrumental performance, music improvisation, use of music vibrations (from instruments, tuning forks, or mattresses/chairs that provide a kinesthetic experience of music vibrations), selecting/writing songs or taping musical performance as a lasting gift or legacy to friends/family members, and music-facilitated life review (Bright 1986; Froehlich 1996; Krout 2000; Martin 1989; Munro 1984; Munro and Mount 1978; Schwankovsky and Guthrie 1982; West 1994). Under the skillful direction of a sensitive music therapist, these techniques can enhance in several ways the quality of life of patients in palliative or hospice care.

Music therapy interventions for terminally ill individuals include many benefits such as decreasing pain, facilitating relaxation, diminishing stress and anxiety, providing enjoyment and recreation, providing an increased sense of control over one's life, decreasing depression, facilitating emotional expression and providing a safe container to hold and organize all kinds of feelings, providing psychological and/or spiritual support, increasing interaction and communication with family members, identifying and eliciting strengths and coping resources, stimulating reminiscence and life review, reinforcing identity and strengthening self-concept, providing outlets for creativity and self-expression, renewing interest in life, increasing self-esteem, and easing the transition from life to death (Bailey 1984; Bright 1986; Clair 1996b; Colligan 1987; Froehlich 1996; Maranto 1988; Martin 1989, 1991; Munro 1984; Munro and Mount 1978; O'Callaghan 1996; Schwankovsky and Guthrie 1982; Standley 1996b; West 1994). In addition, music therapy interventions can provide stress relief and emotional or spiritual support to family members, enhance or facilitate their interactions with the patient, assist them in understanding and accepting their loved one's illness, and support them during the period of bereavement (Bailey 1984; Bright 1986; Edwards 1976; Froehlich 1996; Maranto 1988; Martin 1989, 1991; O'Callaghan 1996; Schwankovsky and Guthrie 1982; West 1994). The next sections of this chapter provide more specific examples of music therapy interventions that can be used effectively to help meet various needs of terminally ill patients and their families.

Therapeutic Music Experiences to Help Meet Physical Needs

One of the important uses of music therapy in palliative care is pain relief (Bright 1981, 1986; Hepburn and Krout 2004; Magill 2001; Maranto 1996;

Martin 1989; McCaffry 2009; Munro 1984; Munro and Mount 1978; Schwankovsky and Guthrie 1982; Spintge 1989; Taylor 1997). Dimaio (2010, 108) states that: "A person's physical, psychological, social, and spiritual health can influence his or her perception and experience of pain." Music therapy can address all these aspects. According to Achterberg (1985), as sound travels through the brain stem's reticular activating system, it can activate the entire brain and hold the individual's entire cognitive awareness, thus blocking or diminishing the perception of other sensory stimuli such as pain or nausea. The "reticular formation stimulates cortical activity, without which there is no conscious awareness" (Carter, Aldridge, Page, and Parker 2009, 178). Although music therapy interventions cannot change the cause of the pain, they can "help patients alter their perception of and responses to the pain" (Froehlich 1996, 229). Froehlich (1996) developed a music therapy model for pain management with terminally ill individuals that uses live or taped music for (1) pain distraction, (2) relaxation, (3) mood alteration, (4) focusing attention or concentration in a relaxed state, and (5) dissociation, especially near the end stages of the illness (requires advanced clinical training). Music with guided imagery sometimes can ease pain. Carter, Aldridge, Page and Parker (2009, 107) state that: "people can affect pain consciously by directing attention away from it, or imagining that they are pain-free." When Froehlich speaks of using music for distraction, she is using what neurologists know about the anterior cingulate cortex, a section of the brain that can divert attention from pain" (Carter, Aldridge, Page, and Parker 2009, 107).

Some patients find that listening to recordings of favorite, preferred music can decrease pain perception and help them to relax and become more comfortable (Bright 1981, 1986; Curtis 1986; Munro 1984; Standley 1996). According to Krout (2000, 369), "the actual function of music for listening can be foreground for active listening and possible related experiences such as reminiscence, lyric analysis, and verbal discussion/processing, or background for contribution to a pleasant sensory environment." Often, songs that have slower tempos and calmer rhythms are most effective in facilitating relaxation and decreasing pain. Individual patients, however, may be comforted also by music of other styles or tempos that hold particular meaning for them. For example, Bright (1986) tells of a man who received pleasure, peace, and comfort from a tape of Bach's organ "Toccata and Fugue in D Minor." Recorded music choices effective for pain reduction and relaxation are unique to each individual (Curtis 1986); what works for one may be totally ineffectual for another. Thaut (2005, 138) noted:

> Music can bring back memories associated with certain experiences (the "honey they're playing our song" phenomenon). This associative mechanism in music . . . accounts for a good deal of our experiences of emotional meaning in music.

When recorded music is used as a specifically prescribed treatment to facilitate relaxation and pain relief, patients often are given individual tapes or CD players and headphones "so that the music can be played at any time of the day or night as the patient feels the need" (Bright 1981, 38). Krout (2000, 370) reports using music in patient rooms in a hospice inpatient unit, where each room had controls above the patient's head tuned to one of six music channels. Since background *noise* usually increases discomfort and tension (Curtis 1986), background *music* that masks unpleasant environment sounds also may help decrease pain and discomfort.

Many patients find that relaxation and pain relief are facilitated when they do relaxation exercises to music (Froehlich 1996; Maranto 1993; Martin 1989; Mave-Johnson and Tanguay 2006; Munro 1984; Munro and Mount 1978), or they are massaged in time to music (Clair 1996b). After studying music's effect on falling asleep, Iwaki, Tanake, and Hori (2003, 25) concluded that "music does promote falling asleep for those that are used to listening to music during bedtime." Others achieve optimum relaxation, comfort, and pain relief through imagery coupled with music (Rider 1985; West 1994) or through the specific techniques of the Bonny method of Guided Imagery and Music (GIM) (Bonny 1978b; Colligan 1987; Froehlich 1996; Munro 1984; Skaggs 1997c; Wylie and Blom 1986). GIM techniques facilitate deep relaxation and may help individuals "journey" to places of peace and comfort. Imagery emerging from the individual through the guidance of the therapist and the music also can help patients exercise control over their pain (Skaggs 1997c). Many patients then are able to learn to apply these techniques on their own to help them manage their pain at times when the therapist is not present (Colligan 1987; Skaggs 1997c; Wylie and Blom 1986). Follow-up discussion of GIM experiences also helps individuals achieve insights into their feelings and needs (Colligan 1987). Music therapists who use GIM techniques need specific advanced clinical training.

Live music, too, can be very effective in reducing pain and comforting terminally ill individuals (Bailey 1983; Froehlich 1996; Martin 1991; Taylor 1997). In fact, Bailey (1983) found that listening to live performances decreased tension and anxiety and increased vigor in hospitalized cancer patients significantly more than listening to recordings of the same music. As therapists perform live music with individual patients, they can use gradual changes readily in mood and tempo and lengthen musical phrases gradually to help calm and soothe rapid breathing, thus facilitating peace and relaxation (Forinash and Gonzalez 1989; Martin 1991). Dileo (1999, 183) also listed ways music therapy may be used in pain reduction:

1. As a distraction from the pain
2. As a stimulus for comfort and relaxation

3. As a conditioned stimulus
4. As a provider of sensory stimulation (according to the Gate Control Theory)
5. As a means for mood-enhancement
6. As a mechanism for providing choice and control
7. As a means for perceived time-compression
8. As an outlet for self-expression
9. As a method for cognitive reframing
10. As a vehicle for social support

Other individuals are distracted from their pain and have increased feelings of comfort and decreased feelings of anxiety when they *actively participate* in live music experiences by singing or playing instruments (Froehlich 1996; Levine-Gross and Swartz 1982; Martin 1989; Schwankovsky and Guthrie 1982; Taylor 1997; Tims 1981). For example, one woman with chronic pain from terminal pancreatic and liver cancer experienced her first pain-free, full night of sleep in many months after singing Christmas songs for about ninety minutes (Taylor 1997, 61). Dimaio (2010, 106) provides four case studies of patients experiencing pain: "The perception of pain is the reality for the client and the therapist must enter into the reality of that person for the perception to be changed."

In addition to being an important tool for pain management, music therapy interventions can help alleviate some of the unpleasant side effects of chemotherapy. Studies show that listening to preferred music during chemotherapy can help decrease nausea, delay the onset of nausea, reduce the length of vomiting, and/or reduce anxiety (Maranto 1996; Standley 1992; Taylor 1997). Standley (1992) found that music of many different styles could achieve these effects for various patients; the effectiveness depended not so much on the musical selection itself, but on the individual's associations with the music.

Music experiences can also be structured therapeutically to motivate and facilitate people's participation in physical activities to the fullest extent possible (Bright 1981; Froehlich 1996; Munro and Mount 1978; Schwankovsky and Guthrie 1982). Because music can lessen pain perception and gently persuade clients to be part of the group (Gaston 1968a), putting exercise routines to music may motivate clients to participate in physical exercises (Bright 1977; Munro and Mount 1978). Therapists should remember the SAID (Specific Adaptation to Imposed Demands) principle, as suggested by Hamburg and Clair (2008). This states "that to achieve improved physical performance, it is necessary to impose specific demands through exercise programming that are similar to the desired physical outcomes (Escamilla, 2005). In some cases, instruments may motivate physical activity and a renewed interest in life. For example, reviving an 86-year-old terminally ill man's interest in playing the violin increased his interest in doing things for himself and taking part in some physical activities (Beggs 1991). In another instance, guitar lessons helped increase a terminally ill 15-year-old boy's level of physical activity and participation (Standley 1996b). Music therapy activities also can be structured to help terminally ill children reach developmental goals and milestones (Froehlich 1996).

Therapeutic Music Experiences to Help Meet Psychological Needs

Since music may express a wide range of emotions while providing structure, grounding, and presence, it can help support both children and adults with terminal illnesses in times of joy, anger, doubt, and sorrow, through all the challenges of the various phases of terminal illness (Bailey 1984; Bright 1986; Edwards 1976; Fagen 1982; Froehlich 1996; Gilbert 1977; Hamilton and Bailey 1981; Martin 1989; Munro 1984; Munro and Mount 1978; Schwankovsky and Guthrie 1982; West 1994). Krout (2005a, 120) discusses using lyric metaphors "to help facilitate the participants' feelings of connectedness and group identity, as well as to enable the participants' identification, reflection, normalizing, sharing, and exploration of feelings." In the face of the many role and body image changes that accompany terminal illnesses, music experiences can be structured to help reinforce identity and self-concept, increase self-esteem, and restore or maintain feelings of usefulness. For example, song lyrics can help reinforce identity and self-concept and provide a springboard for discussion of present concerns (Bailey 1984; Edwards 1976; Fagen 1982; Munro 1984; Munro and Mount 1978; Schwankovsky and Guthrie 1982). Renewing interest in previously played instruments or learning to play new instruments also can help increase self-esteem, interest in life, and feelings of being worthwhile and useful (Beggs 1991; Bright 1986; Bunt and Marston-Wyld 1995; Standley 1996b). Bright (1986, 130) tells of a patient who played the harmonica to entertain fellow patients and staff during his many hospital admissions for inoperable cancer. Through this contribution, the patient gained much self-esteem and feelings of usefulness that "helped to defuse much of the anger which he had experienced when his diagnosis first became clear." Performing songs on instruments also can help decrease depression, motivate cooperation, and increase interest in life for both terminally ill adolescents (Standley 1996b) and adults (Beggs 1991). Other terminally ill individuals increase their self-esteem through the pride they get from creating lyrics or musical settings (O'Callaghan 1997).

Other music therapy experiences bolster patients' self-concept and self-esteem by giving them opportunities to make decisions and positively influence outcomes. People choose to participate in music therapy. From their choice, action (or activity) occurs, which can then elicit feelings. One cannot go directly from choice to feeling; e.g., one cannot simply decide to not be depressed. However, one can decide to participate in therapy, including music therapy, that can gradually lead to less depressed mood:

Human choice → Action → Feeling

The simple act of selecting songs to sing or play, instruments to use, music to hear, or music-mediated options to control pain can provide patients with welcome opportunities for choice and control in a situation that is so often beyond their control (Bailey 1984; Bright 1986; Dunn 1995; Fagen 1982; Froehlich 1996; Gilbert 1977; Hamilton and Bailey 1981; Martin 1989, 1991; Munro 1984; Munro and Mount 1978; Schwankovsky and Guthrie 1982; Standley 1996b; West 1994). Krout (2005b, 215) explained that lyrics can lead to discussion with teenage patients: "It was hoped that the teenagers would experience some choice and control, as well as ownership of the lyrics and messages. Choice and control have been related to the concept of empowerment in music therapy with children."

GIM techniques also can provide terminally ill patients with opportunities to control some aspect of their lives (e.g., images, thoughts, feelings) and to be creative (Colligan 1987; Skaggs 1997c; Wylie and Blom 1986). Other patients find creative outlets in song writing, lyric substitution, or composing musical settings for poems or pictures (Fagen 1982; Froehlich 1996; Hamilton and Bailey 1981; Martin 1989; O'Callaghan 1996, 1997; Schwankovsky and Guthrie 1982). Through these creative acts, terminally ill patients also control the elements of their creation (e.g., words, musical sounds) and form them into things of beauty.

Adults as well as children need fun and recreational activities, even when they are terminally ill. One challenge of being diagnosed with a terminal illness is finding ways to enjoy life and keep living fully until the time of death. Having opportunities for appropriately structured diversional and creative music experiences can help. By adapting singing, listening, instrumental performance, improvisation, or dance/movement-to-music experiences to fit the functioning levels of individual patients, music therapists can devise unique experiences that give terminally ill patients and their families much-needed opportunities for enjoyment and diversion, creativity, and connection with health and life (Bright 1986; Bunt and Marston-Wyld 1995; Clair 1996b; Edwards 1976; Froehlich 1996; Martin 1989, 1991; Munro 1984; Munro and Mount 1978; Schwankovsky and Guthrie 1982). In addition, passive or active participation in enjoyable music experiences can give both terminally ill children and adults a new focus for interest and stimulation that helps relieve boredom, renews their interest in life, and increases positive interactions with other people. Other patients (and family members) may enjoy being transported in their minds and imaginations to more pleasant times and places through songs or imagery associated with music (Bright 1981, 1986; Colligan 1987; Dunn 1995; Fagen 1982; Froehlich 1996; Hamilton and Bailey 1981; Martin 1989; Schwankovsky and Guthrie 1982; Skaggs 1997c; Wylie and Blom 1986).

Teahan (2000) explained his goals for music therapy with the VINE concept, a useful acronym he devised to describe four important considerations in the treatment of the bereaved:

Validation. Feelings are real and true for them. Every patient experiences unique feelings and should be given validation for these emotions.

Identification. Feelings may be confused in a general sense of anxiety. Music therapy can assist in identifying and expressing particular feelings.

Normalization. Clients need to be reassured that their feelings and expectations are normal.

Expression Feelings, thoughts, and emotions may be shared with others in a safe environment.

Krout (2005c, 129) presented lyric metaphors related to VINE. He based his work on the assumption that "music expresses that which cannot be stated verbally, and it can provide the means for words to be voiced and given new life as song. Song may then be used as part of the therapeutic process with patients and their loved ones." He used lyric metaphors in one-session music therapy, but he explained that these one-time programs could not take the place of on-going grief or bereavement programs. However, the VINE concept could be extended for longer music therapy sessions. His article includes examples of songs he composed for these one-time sessions.

Since most individuals have enjoyed music throughout their lives, music can be an important tool for stimulating reminiscence and life review with terminally ill clients. Sato (2011, 31) states that "music therapists play a unique role in guiding life review because music evokes memories and feelings." Some of the ways clients participate in session to evoke life review include singing, playing instruments, listening, and discussion (Forest 2001; Hilliard 2001b; Sato 2011). In life review, memories are brought into conscious awareness to allow re-evaluation and possible resolution of conflict or troubling memories. Sato (2011, 34) gives eight outcomes of life review with hospice patients, based on the literature: "1) integrating, . . . 2) sustained hope, . . . 3) positive changes in mood, . . . 4) increased understanding of life's meaning, . . . 5) emotional intimacy between patients and families, . . . 6) working through emotions, . . . 7) awareness of what to do with the time left, . . . 8) increased rapport between therapist and patient."

Hearing songs and music from different time periods of an individual's life can facilitate recall of events, experiences, and feelings associated with those times (Bright 1981, 1986; Clair 1996b; Hepburn and Krout 2004; Krout 2005c; Martin 1989; Munro 1984; Munro and Mount 1978; West 1994). Kirkland (1999) notes that song lyrics may evoke memories of life experiences. Songs can be suggested by the therapist, requested by patients, or chosen by patients from a list provided by the therapist. The act of recording a life review with music and reminiscence may help individuals recall strengths and increase feelings of self-worth, thus helping to reawaken their interest in life (Beggs 1991; Bright 1986). For individuals who play instruments, performing songs they learned in years past may facilitate reminiscence and life review (Beggs 1991). Other palliative care patients may enjoy writing songs that express themes significant to their life experiences (O'Callaghan 1996, 1997). GIM techniques also can help stimulate reminiscence and life review in terminally ill clients (Bruscia 1991b; Colligan 1987; Skaggs 1997c; Wylie and Blom 1986). In addition, video or audio recordings of musical life review sessions can be a significant gift to family members that will give them pleasant memories after the patient has died (Beggs 1991; Bright 1986; Clair 1996b). Collections of songs chosen or written by the patient can provide family members with lasting gifts of love or musical legacies from the patient (Froehlich 1996; Standley 1996b; Whittall 1991).

Because music can access and express feelings directly and immediately, music therapy experiences can play a unique and important role when individual clients or their families have feelings to communicate but no words to name or express them (Bunt and Marston-Wyld 1995). According to Kubler-Ross (1974, 43), "Music is a much-neglected form of language and can be used with these patients in a very effective way." Various music experiences can be structured therapeutically to provide terminally ill clients and their family members with many ways to express a wide range of emotions, both verbally and nonverbally. Often, action-based, nonverbal experiences, such as instrumental improvisation, help individuals express feelings they are unable to verbalize (Froehlich 1996; Hamilton and Bailey 1981; Martin 1989; Schwankovsky and Guthrie 1982). Learning to access and express these feelings nonverbally helps many individuals gain the insight, awareness, security, and confidence to then articulate these feelings verbally as they feel the need (Bunt and Marston-Wyld 1995). Other individuals are more comfortable choosing song lyrics to give symbolic, structured expression to feelings they have difficulty verbalizing (Bailey 1984; Bright 1986; Martin 1989, 1991; Whittall 1991):

> Often patients express, through the lyrics of the songs, that which they are either unable or unwilling to state verbally and directly. . . . Songs provide an element of safety . . . it is the therapist, who, when singing the lyrics chosen by the patient, gives voice to the thought or feelings. Songs seem to provide the support and distance necessary to broach frightening or otherwise difficult topics. (Martin 1989, iv)

Verbal discussion may follow song selection if the patient appears ready to verbalize exploration of the topics and feelings arising in the songs. Some patients will be ready to talk, while others will just want to let the song lyrics do the talking for them, at least for a time. The therapist must be sensitive to cues from the patient about whether or not to encourage additional verbal exploration of the material described by the song lyrics (Martin 1989, 1991; West 1994).

Familiar songs also can provide emotional comfort and support and help decrease anxiety (Clair 1996b; West 1994) or help stimulate verbalization about fears and feelings associated with hospitalization or terminal illness (Brodsky 1989; Fagen 1982; Froehlich 1996; Hamilton and Bailey 1981; Martin 1989; Munro 1984; Schwankovsky and Guthrie 1982). In some cases, repeated listening to selected songs can help patients work through the pain associated with leaving loved ones (Whittall 1991). Dalton and Krout (2006, 96–97) identify and describe five progressive grief process areas: "understanding, feeling, remembering, integrating, and growing." They explain the music therapy protocol used with adolescent clients and give examples of music created during the group process. They also provide the ten steps they followed in the Grief Song-Writing Process (GSWP).

Other music therapy approaches used in facilitating expressions of fears and emotions include drawing or painting to music, creating collages to background music, orchestrating poems or pictures or stories, lyric substitution, and song writing (Fagen 1982; Froehlich 1996; Hamilton and Bailey 1981; Martin 1989; Munro 1984; Munro and Mount 1978; O'Callaghan 1996, 1997; Schwankovsky and Guthrie 1982). Structured song writing experiences "offer creative non-intrusive opportunities for patients to connect with and process feelings at their own pace" (O'Callaghan 1997, 32), while giving both verbal and musical validation to the individual's emotional expression.

Finally, music therapy experiences can provide support and release in the last moments of life, thus easing the transition to death (Clair 1996b; Forinash and Gonzalez 1989; Skaggs 1997c; West 1994). Some patients may benefit from using GIM procedures to mentally rehearse their death (Skaggs 1997c). For many, familiar music can help provide an environment of love, support, and comfort during the last hours of life (Clair 1996b; West 1994). Music therapists may use various techniques, including singing and playing of precomposed songs (e.g., familiar songs that are meaningful to the patient and hymns), improvised songs, and vocal and guitar improvisation, to help relax patients who are near death and support them as they let go of life. Live performance allows the therapist to match rhythms and tempos to the patient's breathing, thus providing additional nonverbal support and connection.

Hepburn and Krout (2004, 64) note that "the non-verbal quality of the music can help the music therapist relate with the healthy side of the patient." Forinash and Gonzalez (1989, 40) described one experience of using music to connect with and support a patient just prior to and through death. This patient, who could no longer communicate verbally and whose death was imminent, was referred to music therapy because "the staff sensed she might need support to let go of life." The music therapists began with a simple guitar progression, gradually adding improvised "oo" and "ah" vocal sounds. During this time, the patient's breathing was deep and jerky. As they moved to structured songs with soothing melodies and lyrics focusing on love being a shelter and leaving troubles behind, the patient's breathing became softer and gentler. This continued during a transition to improvised lyrics and vocal sounds over guitar chord progressions matched to the patient's breathing. The session ended with a soft, gentle instrumental guitar improvisation, during which the patient died. Through nonverbal (changes in chord progressions, tempos, styles) and verbal (words or lyrics and improvised songs, images associated with them) means, music had supported and facilitated this patient's transition from life to death.

Therapeutic Music Experiences to Help Meet Social Needs

Songs and shared musical experiences can be very helpful in decreasing feelings of isolation and loneliness that often occur in terminally ill clients (Bright 1986; Clair 1996b; Edwards 1976; Froehlich 1996; Martin 1989, 1991; Munro 1984; Munro and Mount 1978; Schwankovsky and Guthrie 1982). Krout (2005c, 130) provides an example of therapist-composed songs to create a community "to serve in gathering, connecting, and providing a common focus for participants coming into a new experience." As they passively or actively participate in music experiences with one or more other individuals (e.g., therapist, other patients, friends, family members), patients can interact and communicate verbally or nonverbally with others in a nonthreatening, supportive, and pleasurable atmosphere. The acts of singing or sharing familiar songs (Bailey 1984; Hamilton and Bailey 1981), writing songs together (Cordobes 1997; Froehlich 1996; O'Callaghan 1996, 1997), playing or improvising on instruments together (Brodsky 1989; Bunt and Marston-Wyld 1995; Froehlich 1996; Martin 1989; Schwankovsky and Guthrie 1982), choosing songs and/or discussing song lyrics or memories associated with songs (Bailey 1984; Bright 1981, 1986; Clair 1996b; Froehlich, 1996; Martin 1989, 1991), and/or dancing/moving to music (Bright 1981; Clair 1986; Froehlich 1996; Martin 1989; Schwankovsky and Guthrie 1982) can help establish a bond of trust among group members, increase group cohesion, and facilitate communication (verbal and nonverbal). Shared music experiences also can help bridge cultural differences (Munro 1984; Munro and Mount 1978), facilitate sharing of memories (Beggs 1991; Bright 1981, 1986; Clair 1996b; Martin 1989; West 1994), and provide a socially appropriate context for touching and tactile stimulation (Clair 1996b). In addition, group music projects like song writing or improvisations allow patients to support each other, work with others on meaningful projects, and transcend their illness, at least for a time, through creative aesthetic expression (Bunt and Marston-Wyld 1995; Cordobes 1997; O'Callaghan 1996, 1997). Krout (2005a) gives examples of rituals used in grief work. He includes examples of music used with the rituals. With appropriate precautions and adaptations, shared music therapy experiences, including instrument playing, singing, song selection, song writing, lyric substitution, relaxation, imagery, and improvisation, can even be used with patients in isolation rooms (Brodsky 1989; Froehlich 1996). For example, Brodsky (1989) describes how small portable electronic instruments (e.g., keyboard, Omnichord) can be played inside a plastic bag, thus adhering to the sanitary requirements of isolation while still allowing the patient to have a "hands-on" musical experience. This "hands-on" participation in music-making helps decrease the patient's feelings of isolation and facilitates the development of positive coping mechanisms. In addition, the act of making music provides an appropriate vehicle for emotional expression that helps increase motivation, socialization, and ego strength.

Therapeutic Music Experiences to Help Meet Spiritual Needs

Spiritual support is an important part of hospice care. Given that "music and religion are integrally related" (Gaston 1968a, 22) and "hospice patients frequently make associations between music and spirituality" (West 1994, 119), music experiences can be an important source of spiritual support for many terminally ill clients. Religious music of the patient's particular heritage and culture or inspirational music and lyrics may comfort and reassure some patients (Bailey 1984; Bright 1981, 1986; Clair 1996b; Gilbert 1977; Kubler-Ross 1974; Martin 1989; Munro 1984; Munro and Mount 1978; West 1994). Some music therapists have found that music from religious rituals can trigger awareness responses (e.g., opening eyes, turning head, speaking, smiling, becoming more relaxed), even in patients who no longer seem to be aware of or responsive to their surroundings (Clair 1996b). Relaxing music combined with scripture readings also can provide comfort to patients with religious faith and help reinforce the idea of a spiritual self that will continue after death (Colligan 1987). In other cases, using spiritual readings with GIM techniques may help patients come to terms with their spiritual identity (Colligan 1987). Music therapists who work with terminally ill clients must be prepared to provide music from diverse religions and cultures so that they can use music to help meet the spiritual needs of clients from all cultural and religious backgrounds (Bright 1986; West 1994).

Some terminally ill clients may have a need for spiritual and existential exploration, expressing doubts, anger, fears, and questioning the meaning of life. Music can also provide a safe structure or container for the exploration and expression of these types of feelings and questions (Bailey 1984; Bright 1986; Edwards 1976; Maranto 1988; Martin 1989, 1991; Munro 1984; Munro and Mount 1978; West 1994). Some patients may approach these feelings and questions from the lyrics of precomposed songs (Bailey 1984; Edwards 1976; Martin 1991), while others may explore them through instrumental improvisation or by writing original songs (O'Callaghan 1996). GIM techniques also may help some patients explore the meaning of their lives, address spiritual questions, and/or prepare for death (Bruscia 1991b; Colligan 1987; Skaggs 1997c).

Music Therapy with Family Members

Dimaio (2010, 113) states that "the needs and goals in hospice care are not limited to the client alone, but include his or her caregivers and family." Martin (1989) lists five ways music therapy interventions may be used with families of terminally ill patients between the time of the diagnosis of terminal illness and the time of death. *First*, music activities like singing, playing instruments, or creating music can give family members "something to do" (24) with or for the patients. Beggs (1991) tells of a terminally ill patient who played the violin while his family members sang and the music therapist played the piano. This activity was very pleasurable and emotionally fulfilling for both the patient and his family members. Clair (1996b) and Martin (1991) also note that music activities can play important roles in helping structure family members' visits with palliative care patients, thus making the visits more positive experiences for both family members and patients. Songs chosen by family members can have the added benefit of giving them meaningful emotional and cognitive connections to past pleasurable experiences with the patient or to sources of spiritual support and comfort. When music experiences help fill and enhance the time family members have with their loved ones, family members "can let go of the responsibility they feel to maintain their loved one's comfort by allowing the music to take over" (Clair 1996b, 271).

Other music-based activities that family members might use to interact with their loved one include massaging or moving rhythmically with the patient to familiar music, listening to familiar music or recordings of family members playing instruments, or using songs to stimulate reminiscence and life review. Family members can also help inform the music therapist of the patient's preferences and musical background. Song choice can be a very beneficial activity for patients and family members (Bailey 1984; Martin 1989, 1991), helping them to broach difficult or emotional topics and enhancing their communication. For example, Bailey (1984) found that music therapy sessions in which family members and cancer patients chose songs about hope, pleasure, the world, reminiscence, needs and desires, feelings, loss and death, and peace helped patients and family members (a) establish trust and a working relationship; (b) express feelings, needs, and desires; and (c) process issues, thoughts, and feelings. In other cases, combined music therapy and social work approaches can help children and adults learn more about the illness and one another's needs while creating a relaxed environment in which they can explore and express deep thoughts and emotions, share intimate feelings, and increase their coping skills (Slivka and Magill 1986).

Second, music therapists can record sessions that include the patient and the family members and give the recordings to the family (Martin 1989). Recordings can be very meaningful to family members after the patient's death by providing positive memories (Beggs 1991; Bright 1986; Clair 1996b; Martin 1989; Whittall 1991). *Third*, music therapists can help family members use music in rituals (Krout 2005a; Martin 1989). For example, songs and music might be used as a way of saying good-bye to family members (Froehlich 1996; Whittall 1991) or to support religious rituals and beliefs (Bright 1986; Clair 1996b; Colligan 1987; West 1994). Hearing or singing along with favorite or religious songs also can help family members share emotional closeness and connect with their loved one in a special way in the final moments of his or her life. These songs may evoke movement or speech responses in patients who have been unresponsive for days or weeks, which "indicate a level of consciousness that families yearn to experience while they wait at the bedside of loved ones who are no longer responsive to their touch or voices" (Clair 1996b, 189). *Fourth*, Martin (1989) suggests that music can offer a way for families to connect and interact with neuropsychologically impaired patients. *Finally*, music therapists can help family members and patients plan music for the patient's funeral (Martin 1989).

In addition to facilitating family members' interactions with their loved ones, music therapy interventions can be important *self-care tools* for the family members themselves, especially for the primary caregivers. For example, music-mediated relaxation exercises can help family members deal with and manage the stress associated with caring for and being with the dying patient (Clair 1996b). After the patient's death, music therapy interventions also can help family members through the grief process by facilitating their acceptance of the reality of the loss and their expression of the emotions of grief as well as serving as a source of support and comfort (Bright 1986; Munro 1984; Ridgway 1983; West 1994). Some family members "detach" from feelings that may otherwise seem overshelming. Floyd (2005) gives an example: "I've been struggling with religion. I try to go to church, but I feel nothing. I bow my head in prayer like the rest of the congregation, but I don't feel a thing." Music therapy can provide assurance that this is one step of this person's grief journey. Using the nonverbal access to emotions, the music can elicit feelings and decrease detachment. Audio or video recordings of the patient's work or collections of songs written or chosen by the patient can be important tools in providing grieving family members with positive, soothing memories of their loved one (Beggs 1991; Bright 1986; Clair 1996b; Martin 1989; Whittall 1991). These articles might serve as transitional objects during the bereavement process, for they give grieving family members something comforting that is a real presence of the person from whom they are now separated (Krout 2005a; Whittall 1991). Songs can be a very important tool for facilitating the expression of unresolved grief and reducing associated physical and emotional distress during times of bereavement. In fact, songs seem to be a cross-cultural means of supporting and facilitating the grieving process (Wexler, 1989). Dalton and Krout (2006) explain the song-writing process with bereaved adolescents.

Hilliard (2005) provides a protocol for use in hospice care. Written from a base of personal experience in hospice and palliative care, he includes techniques and examples of "care plans." Of great importance, he explains how to write and present a protocol for a new music therapy program.

Other music therapy techniques used in bereavement follow-up include providing family members with copies of recordings they used with the patient for relaxation or reminiscence, assisting with music for funerals or memorial services, song writing to express feelings associated with grieving or missing the loved one, and listening to songs and music that affirm the positive and triumphant aspects of life and death or that affirm spiritual beliefs. Dalton and Krout (2006) are a good source for use of the song-writing process with bereaved adolescents. Other techniques include lyric analysis and discussion to help survivors identify feelings and actualize their loss, music-based support groups to facilitate stress management or release of emotions, songs and music to facilitate reminiscence about the loved one, music-mediated relaxation techniques to decrease stress and/or facilitate normal sleep patterns, and attendance of music programs or music performance groups (e.g., church or community choirs) as a way of maintaining social contacts and/or developing new interests (Martin 1989; Munro 1984; Ridgway 1983). Techniques such as nonverbal instrumental improvisations, music play, music/movement techniques, improvised songs or stories, and music-mediated relaxation exercises can be particularly helpful in bereavement follow-up or grief counseling sessions with children (Froehlich 1996). In addition, music combined with grief-counseling techniques and guided imagery may be used to help survivors revisit the relationship and work through issues left unresolved at the time of the patient's death (Bright 1986). Music associated with the relationship may elicit unresolved and conflicting feelings and bring them to conscious awareness where they can be dealt with under the guidance of a trained therapist. Music therapists who use music in in-depth grief counseling should have advanced training in psychotherapeutic techniques.

Music Therapy with Children in Hospice

Lane (1996a; 1996b) and McDonnell (1983) discuss using songs to establish a nonthreatening and familiar atmosphere for children to build trust and begin to express feelings about dying. Hynson and Sawyer (2001) reported that children with neurogenerative, genetic, and metabolic disorders frequently receive hospice services. It is important to assess the child's understanding of his or her illness and concept of death, which may be very different from that of adults. Some have a clear understanding of their prognosis, while others are concerned only with the immediate concerns of fear, anxiety, and missing their home and family if they are hospitalized. With hospitalization, a child may show developmental regression by behaving like a younger child. The team must be in solid agreement on what the child should and should not be told.

Turry (1999, 15) discusses circumstances that affect children with cancer:

- Extended stays in the hospital
- Separations from friends and family members
- Loss of control and feelings of powerlessness
- Painful and intrusive medical procedures
- Noxious side effects from medical treatment (i.e., nausea, pain, fatigue, etc.)
- Misunderstanding of the nature of illness and cause of disease
- Confrontation with multiple losses on different levels
- Potential exacerbation of pre-morbid conflicts or psychopathology
- Potential changes in appearance or disfigurement
- Fear of death/annihilation

McFerran and Shanahan (2011) worked in two settings. One worked in a hospice for children; the other worked in special education. Both used improvisation and familiar songs with profoundly disabled, preadolescent boys diagnosed with cerebral palsy. The two therapists found that they conducted very similar sessions: "the therapeutic focus was on listening rather than guiding" (107). Instruments were positioned carefully and altered, as needed, to allow participation. Sometimes they were made accessible by switches or buttons. Participation was "expressed through vocal or instrumental play, relying on facial expression, eye gaze, and body movements" (110). Both therapists agree that choice and control opportunities were valuable in both settings.

Choice is always important in pediatric hospice. It is related to quality of life (QOL), which is often the main goal in children's hospice (even more so than pain control). McFerran and Shanahan (2011, 104) wrote that "within music therapy, choices promote a sense of feeling understood and heard"

(Davis, 2005; Levetown, 1996).

When a child dies, the whole family may need therapy. A child's death is one of the greatest losses a family can experience. Siblings may have an especially difficult time processing this event, which is disruptive and difficult for their whole family. The loss can be especially difficult for children, who may have a limited means of expressing strong emotions. Krout (2006, 6) notes: "Few families know what to expect or do when their child dies. Parents are often at a loss as to how to help themselves or their surviving children." Bereavement music therapy may be offered to family members who are experiencing grief and loss following the death of a loved one. Dalton and Krout (2006, 94) describe a bereavement model for children and teens that includes five progressive and integrative grief process areas: understanding, feeling, remembering, integrating, and growing. This model can be used with therapist-composed songs, lyric discussion, client-composed songs (with help from the therapist), or songs the clients may choose. If the whole family can be involved, it can be a very therapeutic experience in which all of them can face their feelings, discussing them so other members of the family know what they are feeling, and discover that they are not alone with these strong feelings, thus strengthening the bond of the family unit. Helping them find a "new reality" and begin to move forward without the child is a primary goal in bereavement work with families who have lost a child.

SPECIAL CONSIDERATIONS AND TIPS FOR SUCCESS

Working with terminally ill clients is stressful and painful. Flexibility is essential to management of the patient's constantly changing condition (Fagen 1982). Those who work with terminally ill people also need "initial and ongoing support in order to adjust to the daily confrontation with death" (Schwankovsky and Guthrie 1982, 19). Because of the constant exposure to pain, suffering, sadness, and grief, therapists may at times experience emotional overload. When this happens, "it is important to seek staff support or, if necessary, to request a short respite period" (Munro 1984, 83). It is also essential that those who work with terminally ill clients come to terms with their own fears of death (Bright 1986; Kubler-Ross 1969; Martin 1989; Munro 1984; Schwankovsky and Guthrie 1982; West 1994). We are all vulnerable to feelings of disappointment and rejection, and to the cruelty and tragedy reported on the news each day. For the music therapist, knowing one's own history is the best way to understand and cope with stressful reminders. This self-knowledge is essential in working with terminally ill patients. Fitzgerald (2014) notes that only by being aware of your own history and emotional reactions can you understand feelings triggered by current events:

To work with the dying patients requires a certain maturity which only comes from experience. We have to take a good hard look at our own attitudes toward death and dying before we can sit quietly and without anxiety next to a terminally ill patient. (Kubler-Ross 1969, 269)

Music therapists also must realize that although music therapy may diminish the impact of the crises associated with death and dying and thus facilitate the client's continuing adjustment to dealing with terminal illness and impending death, music therapy will not necessarily resolve all these crises (Munro 1984). Thus, while music therapists must take risks in order to motivate and challenge terminally ill clients, they must also "be wary of delving into patient and family issues which cannot be resolved" (Munro 1984, 79). It may be beneficial for music therapists to remember that creative life need not be dismissed as secondary in times of severe illness, but that it can share equal importance with other physical and intellectual needs (Bright 1986; Fagen 1982; Froehlich 1996; Martin 1989; Munro 1984; O'Callaghan 1996, 1997; Schwankovsky and Guthrie 1982; Skaggs 1997c; Wylie and Blom 1986). Music therapy can help build up the client's sense of personhood by speaking to these creative needs and dealing with that creative part of the client's life that still may be a symbol of health and vitality. As Munro (1984, 33) writes, "Music reflects the depth of experience of humanity and is accessible to the uniqueness in each person. The challenge for the music therapist in terminal care lies in searching for ways to link the uniqueness of music with the uniqueness of the dying patient."

Music therapy work with terminally ill patients may present many negative situations. Morom (2008) found that patients may display apathy, depression, anger, and frustration. Family members may become overly protective. Therapists must be aware of their own reactions to these feelings: "Working with people who are dying presents a host of possible counter-transference challenges" (Marom 2008, 14). This is why supervision, as well as the opportunity to explore their own feelings, is highly advised for therapists working in this area. Regarding working with patients who touch the therapist's personal feeling, Dileo (2000, 8) indicates that "the most difficult client is one who not only presents a clinical challenge, but whose issues also provoke strong emotional reactions from the therapist."

Music therapists who work with terminally ill patients focus on supporting and encouraging the patients, offering them choices that will give them some degree of control over their situation, and providing experiences that will help them to live to the fullest until death (Bright 1986; Bruscia 1991; Froehlich 1996; Martin 1989, 1991; Munro 1994; Schwankovsky and Guthrie 1982; West 1994; Whittall 1991). Music therapists continually must assess the patient to determine which particular tasks of living or dying are most important to him or her at that particular point in time (West 1994). Whittall (1991, 610) states: "It is important to give the person space, and to take cues from him or her as to the content and depth of music therapy sessions." Music therapists also must be sensitive to the individual's perceptions, defenses, receptiveness to music therapy, cultural background, and religious or spiritual beliefs, so they can provide appropriate support through music (Bright 1986; Munro 1984; Schwankovsky and Guthrie 1982; West 1994).

Moreover, music therapists will be able to plan more effective support and intervention strategies if they have technical knowledge about the patient's illness and treatment procedures (including isolation or infection control procedures, if applicable), as well as what the illness means to the patient and the family (in physical, psychological, social, spiritual, and financial terms) (Bright 1986; Maranto 1988; Martin 1989; West 1994). In addition, since the family, not just the patient, is the unit of care in hospice settings, music therapists may be concerned with providing support and comfort to family members as well, by helping them accept and adjust to the patient's deteriorating condition, facilitating communication and interaction with their loved one, and assisting them during the period of bereavement as necessary (Bailey 1984; Bright 1986; Martin 1991; Munro 1984; West 1994).

QUESTIONS FOR THOUGHT AND DISCUSSION

1. What is meant by palliative care? Briefly describe the main features of hospice programs. What are the implications for music therapy programming in these settings?
2. Discuss some of the special characteristics and needs of terminally ill individuals. What are the primary emphases of health care for terminally ill children or adults? What implications do these characteristics/needs and emphases have for music therapy programming?
3. Discuss some of the special characteristics and needs of the family members of terminally ill individuals. What implications do these have for music therapy programming?
4. Why and how are music experiences useful in making contact with terminally ill individuals? Are some types of experiences and activities more useful than others? Which ones? Why?
5. Describe some specific music therapy experiences that might be used to help meet (a) physical needs, (b) psychological needs, (c) social needs, or (d) spiritual needs of terminally ill individuals. What unique benefits does music provide in each of these areas?
6. Describe some ways music therapy experiences might be used with family members of terminally ill patients before and after the patient's death. What unique benefits does music provide in each of these areas?

7. List several special considerations that may be important to remember when working with terminally ill persons. Why are these important? What are their implications for the structure of music therapy intervention strategies?

8. For each of the situations listed below, (a) define the problem or areas of need for the client or group of clients, (b) describe one or more of the goals you might pursue in music therapy sessions with the client(s), (c) describe music activities you might use to help the client(s) meet those goals, (d) tell how the music activities you describe relate to the goals and needs of the client(s), and (e) mention any special considerations you might want to take into account when working with the client(s).

Situation 1:

Mrs. Keith is a 73-year-old woman with terminal cancer. Her cancer is inoperable, and radiation and chemotherapy treatments have been ineffective. She is in great pain, very weak, and bedridden. She often asks why God just doesn't let her die, as she's lived a long life and is now in so much pain. Mrs. Keith has few visitors. When her family comes, they stay only a few minutes, stand nervously at the foot of her bed, and try to cheer her up with small talk. One time, just after the family had left, a nurse came in and found Mrs. Keith sobbing softly to herself. When the nurse asked what was wrong, Mrs. Keith just put her lips tightly together and turned toward the wall. Her social history shows that Mrs. Keith has enjoyed music throughout her life, so her doctor prescribed music therapy sessions to try to help Mrs. Keith communicate with her family, facilitate her emotional expression, and provide her with support and comfort.

Situation 2:

Mr. Jones is 46 years old and has terminal cancer. He has been discharged from the hospital and is now receiving home hospice care services. Mr. Jones is married and has three children, aged 15, 12, and 7 years. He feels sad and guilty about no longer being able to take care of his wife and children and about leaving them without a husband and father. He is searching for ways to stay involved in their lives as much as he can while preparing them for life without him. He would like to leave them some sort of legacy and/or happy memory of their times with him. Mr. Jones is also in a lot of physical pain. He does not like the way the pain medication makes him feel groggy and drowsy, so he is interested in finding alternate means of pain management.

Situation 3:

You have been asked to provide music therapy services for a group of terminally ill patients who are not imminently dying but who must be hospitalized for short periods to receive various treatments. They have needs for diversional or enjoyable activities, so they do not have to focus constantly on their illness during their hospital stay. They also need programs that will help decrease their anxiety about treatment procedures. In addition, many of these individuals are looking for creative, meaningful activities to make life still seem worthwhile and help them put the time they have left to good use.

Situation 4:

A social worker from a local hospice program has just started a support group for family members of terminally ill patients. The group will meet twice a month to discuss issues related to living with and caring for a terminally ill family member. The social worker has heard that music can facilitate discussion of emotionally laden, difficult issues, and has asked you to help lead this group.

SUGGESTIONS FOR FURTHER READING

Bruscia, K. E. (Ed.) (1991). *Case studies in music therapy.* Phoenixville, PA: Barcelona.

Bunt, L. & Marston-Wyld, J. (1995). Where words fail music takes over: A collaborative study by a music therapist and a counselor in the context of cancer care. *Music Therapy Perspectives, 13(1),* 46–50.

Colligan, K. G. (1987). Music therapy and hospice care. In B. Karras (Ed.), *"You bring out the music in me": Music in nursing homes* (103–122). Binghamton, NY: Haworth Press.

Cordobes, T. K. (1997). Group song writing as a method for developing group cohesion for HIV-seropositive adult patients with depression. *Journal of Music Therapy, 34(1),* 46–67.

Curtis, S. L. (1986). The effect of music on pain relief and relaxation of the terminally ill. *Journal of Music Therapy, 23(1),* 10–24.

Dalton, T. A. & Krout, R. E. (2006). The grief song-writing process with bereaved adolescents: An integrated grief model and music therapy protocol. *Music Therapy Perspectives, 24(2),* 94–107.

Davis, G. (2005). Living community: Music therapy with children and adults in a hospice setting. In M. Pavlicek (Ed.), *Music therapy in children's hospices* (124–38). London: Jessica Kingsley.

Dimaio, L. (2010). Music therapy entrainment: A humanistic music therapist's perspective of using music therapy entrainment with hospice clients experiencing pain. *Music Therapy Perspectives, 28(2),* 106–115.

Forinash, M. & Gonzalez, D. (1989). A phenomenological perspective of music therapy. *Music Therapy, 8(1),* 35–36.

Froehlich, M. A. R. (1996). Terminal illness. In M. A. R. Froehlich (Ed.), *Music therapy with hospitalized children: A creative arts child life approach* (207–242). Cherry Hill, NJ: Jeffrey Books.

Gilbert, J. P. (1977). Music therapy perspectives on death and dying. *Journal of Music Therapy, 14*(*4*), 165–171.

Hilliard, R. E. (2001). The use of music therapy in meeting the multidimensional needs of hospice patients and families. *Journal of Palliative Care, 12*(*3*), 161–166.

Hilliard, R. E. (2005). *Hospice and palliative care music therapy: A guide to program development and clinical care.* Cherry Hill, NJ: Jeffrey Books.

Krout, R. (2000). Hospice and palliative care music therapy: A continuum of creative caring. In *Effectiveness of music therapy procedures: Documentation of research and clinical practice,* (3rd ed.) (323–411). Silver Spring, MD: The American Music Therapy Association.

Krout, R. E. (2005). Applications of music therapist-composed songs in creating participant connections and facilitating goals and rituals during one-time bereavement support groups and programs. *Music Therapy Perspectives, 23*(*2*), 118–128.

Marom, M. K. (2008). "Patient declined": Contemplating the psychodynamics of hospice music therapy. *Music Therapy Perspectives, 26*(*1*), 13–22.

Mave-Johnson, E. L. & Tanguay, C. L. (2006). Assessing the unique needs of hospice patients: A tool for music therapists. *Music Therapy Perspectives, 24*(*1*), 13–21.

Munro, S. (1984). *Music therapy in palliative/hospice care.* St. Louis: Magnamusic Baton.

O'Callaghan, C. C. (1996). Lyrical themes in songs written by palliative care patients. *Journal of Music Therapy, 33*(*2*), 74–92.

O'Callaghan, C. C. (1997). Therapeutic opportunities associated with the music when using song writing in palliative care. *Music Therapy Perspectives, 15*(*1*), 32–38.

Sato, Y. (2011). Musical life review in hospice. *Music Therapy Perspectives, 29*(*1*), 31–37.

Standley, J. M. (1992). Clinical applications of music and chemotherapy: The effects on nausea and emesis. *Music Therapy Perspectives, 10*(*1*), 27–35.

West, T. M. (1994). Psychological issues in hospice music therapy. *Music Therapy Perspectives, 12*(*2*), 117–124.

Chapter Twenty-One

MUSIC THERAPY TO PROMOTE HEALTH AND WELL-BEING IN THE GENERAL POPULATION

DEFINITION

In a narrow sense, *health* often is defined as the absence of disease, infirmity, or abnormality. However, in recent decades, the concept of health has expanded so that mere absence of disease alone does not necessarily constitute health. Creagan (2006, 14) observes that good health encompasses mental and emotional as well as physical attributes; an optimistic attitude and continued connections with family, friends, and community are especially important. In the broad sense, then, one may define health or wellness as a state of optimal functioning and complete mental, physical, spiritual, and social well-being (Ghetti, Hama, and Woolrich 2008; Lipe 2002; Purtilo 1978; World Health Organization 1964). Others view health not as an all-or-nothing state of wellness or illness, but as something that exists on a continuum from optimum health to suboptimal health to overt illness or disability to approaching death to death (Itoh and Lee 1989). Most people move back and forth along this continuum throughout their lives, although they are always striving to maintain optimum health. In general, the task of medical professionals, then, is to help individuals maintain good health, provide information and procedures related to preventing disease, and cure those who become ill as quickly as possible (Creagan 2006; Itoh and Lee 1989).

The increased emphasis on health and wellness in recent years has led members of the medical community to focus more on *preventative medicine*, which strives to help individuals maintain optimum health. From the preventative point of view, "good medical care acts on a person's health rather than reacting to a person's health problems" (Itoh and Lee 1989, 27). *Follow-up care* provided to an individual after acute medical treatment also may be considered part of wellness or preventative services, for this follow-up care aims to help an individual achieve and maintain the highest possible degree of health and independent functioning (Creagan 2006; Purtilo 1978). Follow-up care may involve problems with following a prescribed regimen and adapting to new constraints (Gfeller 2008, 329).

In recent decades, increased awareness of and interest in holistic medicine and alternative healing practices also have helped focus the public's attention not just on curing disease but on striving for and maintaining optimum wellness by "adopting a life style that focuses on health" (Scovel 1990, 105). In 1926, Jon Christian Smuts, a South African philosopher, introduced the concept of "holism." Medical science had become increasingly concerned with understanding disease from analytic studies of smaller physiological components. Gordon (1980, 3) states that "holistic (sometimes spelled wholistic) medicine has come to denote both an approach to the whole person in his or her total environment and a variety of healing and health promoting practices." Music therapy is one of the health-promoting practices that can lead to wellness. The *holistic* (or wholistic) view proposes an integrated approach to health and wellness in which body, mind, and spirit are seen as integrated parts of the whole system. Holistic medicine treats the whole person (body, mind, and spirit), not just the symptoms or disease (Robb 2000b; Scovel 1990; Trevisan 1978). It encourages individuals to take responsibility for their own health and stresses self-care, self-help, prevention, and striving for optimum wellness and balance in all areas of life (Adelman 1985; Scovel 1990; Trevisan 1978). Holistic practices focus on the individual and encourage furthering one's potential, self-awareness, and growth through finding answers within one's self (Bonny 1986; Scovel 1990; Summer and Summer 1996). As Robb (2000b, 3) explains, "With the resurgence of a holistic approach to health care, studies now use multiple measures that take into account both physical and psychological responses to stress."

COMMON CHARACTERISTICS, PROBLEMS, AND NEEDS OF CLIENTS

Basically healthy people in the general population may need to find lifestyles that will help them maintain optimum health and independent functioning. General needs often include maintaining healthy diet and exercise regimens; having adequate social, emotional, and spiritual support systems; developing coping strategies and creative problem-solving techniques to weather difficult times; finding ways to manage stress and relieve frustration; and having outlets for creative or emotional expression. According to Maslow (1968), when more basic needs (e.g., food and shelter, safety, love and belongingness, self-esteem) are met, individuals strive for self-actualization and the full realization of all their potentialities. Some individuals in the general population, therefore, seek tools for personal growth and increased self-awareness and personal fulfillment.

Many individuals also desire experiences that add meaning, joy, or beauty to their lives. Montello (2002) discusses music and sound and presents techniques of relaxation to lead to personal growth and wellness. This book provides clinical examples and specific exercises for relaxation.

SETTINGS FOR SERVICE DELIVERY

Health and wellness programs and services for the general public exist in various settings, including hospital-sponsored programs, community health fairs, park and recreation programs, workshops and seminars, fitness centers, wellness centers, stress reduction clinics, schools or community colleges, corporate wellness programs, churches, and community centers. Individual service providers working in private practice may contract their services to individuals or groups. Music therapists could work in any of these settings by providing direct or consultant services and by working with clients as individuals or in groups (Peters, 1989). In addition, music therapists may provide services through music stores or studios or in private practice settings.

HOW MUSIC IS USED IN THERAPY

One of the pioneers of music therapy, Willem van de Wall, advocated using music for wellness as early as the 1930s. Van de Wall believed that music not only could provide aesthetic satisfaction for adults in the general population but also enhance "muscle relaxation, emotional expression, and relief from routine, which could lead to increased efficiency when responsibilities were resumed" (Clair and Heller 1989, 173). In recent years, music therapists have given increasing attention to ways they can expand their services beyond the institutional setting and clients with disabilities to also promote health and wellness in the general population (Broucek 1987; Clair 1996b; Clark and Ficken 1988; Peters 1989; Reuer 2007). According to Ghetti, Hama, and Woolrich (2009, 136), "Wellness components of social integration, emotional health and spirituality are also meaningfully addressed through music therapy."

The use of music as preventative medicine and as a strengthener of health and character made a resurgence in the United States in the latter part of the twentieth century. The holistic health movement, focusing on interdependence of body, mind, and spirit for maintaining health and well-being, generated interest in ancient healing practices using music and in contemporary ways to use music to facilitate healing, relaxation, centering, stress reduction, emotional release, consciousness expansion, and the highest possible state of well-being (Bonny 1986; Bonny and Savary 1973, 1990; Campbell 1988,

1991a, 1991b; Crowe 1991; Feder and Feder 1981; Ghetti, Hama, and Woolrich 2008; Goldman 1988; Halpern 1978, 1989; Hamel 1976/1979; Harvey 1987, 1991; Kenny 1982; Trevisan 1978). The therapeutic use of music has moved into board rooms and wellness programs of businesses, hospitals, and major corporations as employers recognize the need to reduce stress, alleviate staff burnout, promote wellness, and inspire innovative and effective ways to encourage team work and enhance creativity (Clark and Ficken 1988; Gfeller 2008; Mandel 1996; McCarthy 1992; Weitz 1993). The medical community also is beginning to recognize the important role music and the arts can play in preventative care and health maintenance (Guzzetta 1991; Itoh and Lee 1989; Spencer 1978). For example, medical doctors Itoh and Lee (1989, 28) observe:

> If food is a nutrient for the body, music is for the mind. . . . As music is closely related to human well-being, it does have therapeutic value. In the total concept of health care, music therapy should be recognized as another modality for Prevention and Health Promotion.

Music educators, too, are beginning to recognize music's lifelong health benefits and are finding ways to help people enjoy music throughout their lives (Boswell 1992; Bowles 1991; Clair 1996b; Coates 1984; Darrough 1992; Davidson 1980; Ernst and Emmons 1992; Gibbons 1985, 1988; Kellman 1986; Loga, 1996; Myers 1992). Ghetti, Hama, and Woolrich (2008, 139) point out: "Children should be made aware of the long-term impact their health-related decisions have on their lives and the importance of maintaining a healthy lifestyle in order to avoid health problems later in life."

With its ability to structure order out of chaos and be a transcendent event (Crowe 1991; Spencer 1978), music can "match an individual's level of functioning whatever it may be and help the person move toward the wholeness of healing" (Crowe 1991, 119). Music is also a natural vehicle for addressing the whole person (body, mind, and spirit). Since "people can enjoy participating in music at every stage of life" (Logan 1996, 42), music can be an important tool for promoting wellness and channeling creativity productively in the general population with individuals of all ages. Furthermore, Kenny (1982, 79–80) has argued that "even though music may not be the natural vehicle for everyone's creativity, it can be an experimental ground in which to try out creative processes and apply them through a powerful medium."

Music experiences can help individuals in the general population maintain health and well-being in many ways. Sometimes, individuals may use music in therapeutic or beneficial ways for themselves, as when they listen to certain types of music to relax or lift their spirits, when they listen to music while exercising, or when they play musical instruments to relieve tension. While beneficial, this is not true music therapy, because it does not have the interaction among therapist, client, and music (Priestley 1985; see also Chapter

One). At other times, music experiences will be more beneficial if they are structured by and performed under the direction or supervision of a trained music therapist, who bases interventions on an assessment of the unique needs of the particular individual or individuals and adapts programs to their specific responses.

People who wish to use music to increase their total health must realize that sound and music can have both positive and negative effects (Harvey 1987). In addition, certain experiences, like Guided Imagery and Music (GIM), may arouse painful issues that are best addressed under the guidance of a trained therapist (Bonny 1989, 1994). The next sections of this chapter provide some examples of music experiences that can facilitate relaxation, reduce stress, decrease isolation, facilitate cooperative interactions, improve coping and problem-solving abilities, promote healthy habits and behaviors, humanize the environment, expand consciousness, and increase personal transcendent event awareness (Crowe 1991; Spencer 1978). All these experiences can play a role in helping people in the general population reach a state of optimal functioning and complete mental, physical, and social well-being.

Music Experiences for Relaxation and Stress Reduction

The "most widely accepted application of music as a therapeutic agent" throughout history has been "its use as a calming agent to combat anxiety, tension, and stress." (Taylor, 1997, 102). Based on work by Bernar and Krupat (1994), Burns et al. (2004, 101–102) report that stress is based on three main elements: "the external stimuli, the internal response, and the interaction between the two." When the goal is to promote relaxation, the music therapist faces complex choices about the best music for an individual client. After investigating the characteristics of relaxing music used for anxiety control, Elliott, Polman, and McGregor (2011) list the most desirable characteristics of music for relaxation. The components they consider, in descending order of importance, are "tempo, melody, beat, harmony, rhythm, complexity, key, scale, articulation, interval, melodic range, voice, instrumentation, dynamics, and character" (276–277). For each of these, they describe relaxing and nonrelaxing characteristics. Many of these same music-mediated relaxation and stress reduction techniques will work very well for most people in the general population.

One aspect of relaxing music that has received attention from several researchers is its complexity. According to Walker's 1980 "hedgehog" theory ("so named because the theory has one explanation for many situations, just as the spiny little European animal rolls into a ball in response to many stimuli" [Radocy and Boyle 2012, 419]) – the closer a musical stimulus is to the optimal complexity level, the greater is the preference for that structure. Preferred music usually is related to greater response in music therapy research. For example, Heyduk (1975) rates preference of musical compositions as it relates to complexity and exposure frequency. Radocy and Boyle (2012, 419) discuss the relationship between preference and complexity: "Although optimal complexity levels vary among and within individuals, each individual has an optimal complexity level for a stimulus class at any particular time." Crowe (2004) wrote the book *Music and Soulmaking: Toward a New Theory of Music Therapy* from the perspective of complexity science, which provides a more inclusive paradigm that allows her to go beyond the traditional, research-based perspective and discuss music's effect on the total person in the therapeutic setting. She says, "The theory of music and soulmaking is based on the contention that music is a fundamental, holistic experience that impacts functioning in all areas – body, mind, emotion and spirit" (xvi). She writes of music therapy as a process which leads to achievement of higher potential.

Tan, Yowler, Super, and Fratianne (2012) examine the relationship of preference, familiarity and psychophysical properties that define relaxing music. The musical properties that they find related to relaxation are "tempo, mode, harmonic, rhythmic, instrumental, and melodic complexities, timbre, vocalization/lyrics, pitch range, dynamic variations, and contour" (151). Both preference and familiarity are important in eliciting the relaxation response. However, Pelletier (2004, 208), after carefully examining the research literature on music and relaxation, suggests that "it may be that subject preferred music is too distracting and therefore stimulates the subject rather than increasing relaxation." There is no substitution for careful observation of the client and subsequently using music that the music therapist judges most effective. Not all people respond the same way to the music, and not every person will respond the same way at different times. Sensitivity is required. Pelletier (2004) summarizes her meta-analysis of the music and relaxation literature:

> music selections based on research are most effective; . . . musicians, females, and those under 18 years of age will respond more to music assisted relaxation techniques when under stress; and . . . verbal suggestions and vibrotactile stimulation with music are the most effective music assisted relaxation techniques.

Kopacz (2005) studied the relationship of personality traits to preferences regarding musical elements. Her subjects were 85 women and 60 men, between the ages of 19–26 years, from Polish universities. The personality traits that seemed related to preference were liveliness, social boldness, vigilance, openness to change, and extraversion:

> Important in the subjects' musical preferences were . . . those musical elements having stimulative value and the ability to regulate the need for stimulation. These are: tempo, rhythm in relation to metrical basis, number of melodic themes, sound voluminosity, and meter. (216)

Is listening to music more relaxing than simply sitting in a quiet place? Gadberry (2011) investigated this question by studying the effect of a steady beat compared to silence in a group of 36 healthy volunteers between the ages 20–50 years. Anxiety was induced by using a modified Stroop color-word test in which cards are presented to the subjects who say the color of the printed text on the card, although the word itself may indicate a different color (e.g., the word red may be printed in green ink, so the subject should say "green.") Following the Stroop test, the experimental group sat and listened to a steady beat produced by a low-pitched tone bar, and the control group sat in silence. Gadberry (2011, 350) found that "subjects who listened to the steady beat . . . reported less anxiety than subjects who sat in silence." This study design should be repeated for different elements of music, as well as for intact musical examples.

Listening to specially chosen music (e.g., familiar music that has pleasant, calming, or uplifting associations) by itself may help improve emotional states and allay anxiety in some situations (Giles et al. 1991). Clayton (2009) discusses music's functions such as regulation of an individual's emotional, cognitive, or physiological state. The ability to recognize stress and have techniques to self-regulate are important to maintain optimum wellness. To investigate the cognitive component of stress, Burns et al. (2002) divided 60 undergraduate students into four groups: hard rock music group, control group, self-selected music group, and classical music group and measured the cognitive effects of stress using a State-Trait Anxiety Inventory (STAI), self-reports, and various physiological responses measured using biofeedback equipment. The state anxiety scores decreased for all groups. As might be expected, those who listened to hard rock reported that they did not feel more relaxed after the music listening session. Those who listened to classical music reported feeling more relaxed, and both the control group and the self-selected music group showed the greatest changes in measured relaxation. Results from the study "partially support the main hypothesis of the research, which is that different types of music have different effects on stress" (Burns et al. 2002, 113). It is interesting that sitting in silence (control group) produced changes in relaxation and anxiety, which may indicate that just stopping and being quiet is an important way to control stress reactions. The research design of Burns et al. (2002) differs from the Gadberry (2011) design, which has one group listen to a repeated tone bar, while the other group sits in silence.

Biomedical research (Knight and Rickard 2001; Taylor 1997, 103) has shown that "music has a direct effect on physiological processes whose functional variations are indicators of anxiety, tension, or stress." However, not all music categorized as relaxing will have the same effect on all listeners (Guzzetta 1991; Hadsell 1989; Hanser 1985; Logan and Roberts 1984; Pelletier 2004; Stratton and Zalanowski 1984; Taylor 1973, 1997); and "depending on the individual's psychophysiology, mind state, and mood, music can produce different feelings at different times" (Guzetta 1991, 161). According to Ghetti, Hama, and Woolrich (2008, 141), "Music may be paired with relaxation techniques to facilitate stress management." Music therapists, therefore, can play an important role in helping individuals learn how to select the most effective music for relaxation and stress management at various times in their lives. After studying neurophysiological responses to music, Krout (2007) provided an overview of how music can affect human physiology when it is used as part of a wellness program. Since research indicates that music specifically composed or marketed for relaxation is no more effective in reducing tension than music personally selected by the individual (Thaut and Davis 1993) and that music preferred by the individual generally best facilitates his or her relaxation (Hadsell 1989; Hanser 1985; Tan et al. 2012; Taylor 1973), music therapists often can help individuals find appropriate selections from their preferred type of music. In addition, music therapists can help individuals experience a variety of musical genres that may help them relax effectively. Music therapists also may help individuals learn more about ways music can affect moods and attitudes (Ghetti, Hama, and Woolrich 2008; Giles et al. 1991; Harvey 1991) and facilitate their exploration of additional techniques, such as imagery, biofeedback, or progressive muscle relaxation that can be combined with music listening to facilitate relaxation and decrease tension (Burns et al. 2002; Gfeller 2008; Scartelli 1989).

Music listening can be combined with many specific group or individual relaxation training techniques, including: (1) *music with progressive muscle relaxation training* (appropriate relaxing music is paired with progressive muscle relaxation techniques, and music becomes a conditioned stimulus for relaxation); (2) *music for surface relaxation* (individuals learn to select music with characteristics that will help them relax and provide temporary relief from anxiety or stress); (3) *music imagery* (listening to music in a relaxed state with therapist-suggested, open-ended scenarios to promote imagery or aid concentration or relaxation); and (4) *music-centered relaxation* (music is used as a stimulus or focus to divert individuals' attention from unpleasant thoughts and to block out feelings of anxiety, fear, or tension) (Unkefer 1990). In these approaches, individuals usually learn relaxation exercises through repetition with guidance from the therapist and then are encouraged to include the exercises in their daily lives for self-maintenance.

Robb (2000a, 2) compares relaxation results with progressive muscle relaxation, progressive muscle relaxation with music, music listening, and silence. In her study, 60 university students, 15 in each condition, comprised the subject pool. While each group's scores on the State Trait Anxiety Inventory (STAI) and the Visual Analog Scale (VAS) indicated that "each treatment condition was equally effective in producing significant changes in anxiety and perceived relaxation from the pre- to posttest period," the music plus progressive muscle relaxation condition elicited the greatest change.

Music also can facilitate relaxation responses to biofeedback relaxation techniques (Scartelli 1989; Scartelli and Borling 1986; Wagner 1975). For example, Scartelli and Borling (1986) found that when sedative music is used with biofeedback, both subject reports and microvolt readings show that the music "maintained and in many cases fostered an enhanced state of relaxation" (163). Subjects reported that music helped keep their minds from wandering, facilitated relaxation, and was a positive part of the procedure. Knight and Rickard (2001) had subjects listen to Pachelbel's *Canon in D Major*. They found that listening was "capable of preventing the significant increases in subjective anxiety, systolic blood pressure, and heart rate caused by a cognitive stressor" (265). They acknowledge that their findings cannot be generalized, because they used only one piece of music and one control condition. However, they provide a good overview of the physiological response to anxiety and stress.

Music therapists who have appropriate special training may use the Bonny Method of Guided Imagery and Music (GIM) to help individuals decrease anxiety, facilitate relaxation, and increase feelings of well-being (Bonny 1978b, 1986, 1989; Bonny and Savary 1990; Gregoire et al. 1989; Hammer 1996). Hammer (1996) finds that state anxiety, or perceived situational stress, decreases significantly in subjects in a GIM group, indicating GIM can be an effective intervention for persons dealing with acute or chronic stress. In addition, Hammer's research indicates that GIM programs "may have an overall effect on improving one's ability to react to stress, improving concentration and general contentment, and improving one's ability to relax in general" (67). However, Pelletier (2004, 207) finds from her analysis of research concerning music and stress that "GIM had the smallest effect on subjects' relaxation and as a result it may not be an effective technique for therapists to use when the goal is to decrease stress." Although relaxation is used in the induction phase of GIM, relaxation is not GIM's primary purpose. Bonny (1980, 279) states: "New insights may allow greater differentiation and control of purposeless noise that pollutes body and mind and may promote the sensitive and healing use of sounds that we call music." Insight, rather than relaxation, is GIM's primary goal.

Active participation in singing or playing instruments, dancing or creative movement, or writing songs also can provide important forms of emotional release by helping reduce stress and discharging tension. For example, Priestley (1985) suggests that individuals use improvisational drumming as a means of releasing physical tension. Creative improvisation and composition activities based on the Orff-Schulwerk approach also can help relieve stress and tension (Gregoire et al. 1989). In addition, the pleasant social interaction involved in music experiences, such as playing or singing in ensembles and the cathartic effect of releasing repressed emotions through singing or playing instruments, may help people "de-stress" (Clynes 1991, 135). Lyric discussion, song writing, and instrumental improvisation exercises also can help individuals identify stressors and stress reactions, explore emotions, and develop positive coping and stress management techniques.

Pelletier (2004) conducted a meta-analysis of 22 quantitative studies involving the use of music to decrease arousal due to stress where the researcher measures stress or anxiety prior to treatment. Six factors were considered: "(a) terminal diagnosis, (b) surgery, (c) other medical procedures, (d) labor, (e) preparation for labor, (f) researcher-induced stress or arousal condition with a self-report test indicating levels of stress and anxiety" (195). Her meta-analysis led her to conclude that "music combined with relaxation techniques does have a significant impact on decreasing arousal due to stress" (202).

Music Experiences to Decrease Isolation and Facilitate Cooperative Interactions

Since prehistoric times, people have gathered in groups to create and share music as together they experience its energy and spirit (Goldman 1998). Group music experiences that are prevalent in society today can decrease isolation by giving people reasons for assembling in groups: to listen, to attend concerts, to practice or perform, to dance, to learn, and to discuss (e.g., in music appreciation or theory classes). Throughout life, music experiences can offer people many opportunities for positive interactions with others and for volunteer opportunities (e.g., mentoring younger students, involvement in church or community choirs and instrumental ensembles, helping with paperwork or publicity for school or community groups) that research shows are vital components of good health (Logan 1996). Especially as they actively make music together, people find they "are not singular, isolated units, but rather an interrelated web of unified beings whose purpose is to work together as one" (Goldman 1988, 32). Thus, interesting and meaningful non-threatening group music experiences can turn indifference and isolation into interest and involvement. One study (Gregoire et al. 1989) demonstrates how gifted students, who were isolated, vulnerable, and interacted poorly with others, learn to work together cooperatively, share ideas and feelings, and improve their self-concept through music therapy experiences using GIM and Orff-Schulwerk techniques. Another study (Anshel and Kipper 1988) showed that group singing increased trust and cooperation among group members significantly more than music listening, games, or film viewing.

In ancient cultures, music and dance were part of communal ceremonies and rituals that helped the group maintain the health, well-being, and identity of their community (Kenny 1982). Today, some people take an interest in finding ways to use music for the health and good of society in general. For example, the organization Music Therapists for Peace, founded in 1988, sponsors various projects and activities with the aim of "making more conscious use of the possibilities of music to promote healing and unite people" (Moreno 1992, 87). Perhaps, "if the nations of our world were willing to play a new kind of music together that allows for the beauty of each unique player to remain while creating a unified and harmonious piece that has room for all" (Hesser 1995, 49), they could also learn to live and work together in peace.

Music Experiences to Improve Coping Strategies and Problem-Solving Skills

In the mid-1930s, Willem van de Wall, one of music therapy's early pioneers in the United States, "spoke of music as a means for adults to be physically, mentally, and culturally developed despite the ever-increasing burdens of life" (Clair and Heller 1989, 173). Throughout history, people have used songs and music to help lift their spirits and cope with difficult life situations (Kenny 1982; Peters 1989). Even today, involvement in various kinds of music experiences (singing, playing, listening, moving, and creating) can help people experience beauty, joy, personal satisfaction, and meaning that lifts them, at least for a time, above and beyond their not-so-pleasant life situations (Taylor et al. 1997; Whitwell 1993). Studies show that "at-risk" children and adolescents often respond more positively to music experiences than to verbal interventions or traditional teaching methods (Staum 1993; Taylor et al. 1997). For all people, participation in structured singing, instrumental, listening, movement-to-music, or improvisation/composition experiences can stimulate creativity; help sustain a sense of wonder and curiosity (something people often lose after childhood); lead people to see problems in new ways and find innovative solutions; and give people courage to improvise, experiment, explore alternatives, and try different things (Kenny 1982; Taylor et al. 1997; Whitwell 1993). Even major corporations now use music experiences such as drum circles to help increase creative problem solving, break preexisting molds and barriers, and facilitate innovative thinking (Weitz 1993).

Music therapists have found that music therapy experiences can be effective crisis intervention and prevention techniques. For example, having individuals improvise music that expresses feelings or conflicts about an anticipated or recently experienced traumatic event may help them maintain or regain an accurate reality perspective, while shared group music experiences (e.g., active listening and discussion, singing, group improvisations) can provide needed support from others (Luetje 1989). In addition, structured experiences involving lyric analysis, song writing, improvisation, and music-assisted guided imagery may (a) assist with cognitive and emotional processing of the crisis event, (b) lead individuals to discover alternative solutions or responses, (c) help individuals find new ways of coping, (d) increase identification and awareness of inner strengths, and (e) facilitate internalizing affirmative messages (Luetje 1989; Scheve 2004).

Governments, too, are recognizing music's power to help people cope with difficult situations. For example, during the 1991 Persian Gulf War, the Israeli Broadcasting Authority intentionally used music to help its citizens cope with the crisis by playing songs stressing strength and national unity, using parodies of popular tunes to give specific instructions for safety and defense preparations, and broadcasting soothing, nostalgic music during attacks to help reduce fear and anxiety (Brodsky 1991). During the war, only Hebrew songs were broadcast, and special children's music was played in the evening to help the children cope with the stress and trauma of the situation. In these ways, "through mass communication, the power of music was used to assist the entire population in developing more adaptive coping methods, which included instilling feelings of national unity and establishing support systems" (Brodsky 1991, 99).

Music Experiences to Promote Healthy Habits and Behaviors

As many people strive for improved health and well-being, they know the things they should do but have difficulty making these things a regular part of their lives. Exercise, for example, often is perceived as boring and tedious. Adding music, however, may make exercise more enjoyable and provide the needed motivation for people to participate in and sustain exercise (Beckett 1990; Brody 1988; Ghetti, Hama, and Woolrich 2008; Gfeller 1988, 2008). Wininger and Pargman (2003) studied factors associated with exercise enjoyment among 282 female aerobic dance students with a mean age of 21.06 years: "Satisfaction with the music was the best predictor of exercise enjoyment accounting for 21% of the variance" (69). Other factors considered were satisfaction with the instructor and role identity. Tempo/beat and intensity/loudness were found to be the most important musical characteristics in the exercise class. Because exercise enjoyment relates to frequency and regularity in participation in exercise classes, it is an important consideration in a wellness program. According to NASA, music can promote compliance with exercise routines, decrease the tedium of repeated movements, and help individuals attain the desired level of intensity (Brody 1988). Gfeller (1988) found that music helped young adults increase their motivation, pacing, strength, and endurance during aerobic activities. Beckett (1990) reported that individuals who listened to music walk farther and with less effort than when they exercised without music. Other research concludes that people who listen to music during exercise perceive the exercise as less stressful (Brody 1988).

Moreover, music with phrases and tempos that correspond to those of the physical movement can facilitate muscle coordination and rhythmic movement. As Thaut (2008, 89) remarks, "The tempo of the music is adjusted to accommodate the subject's baseline gait capabilities and then incrementally increased as gait performance improves." In fact, many cultures historically have used marching songs and work songs to decrease fatigue, increase rhythmicity and fluidity of movement, and help lessen injury (Itoh and Lee 1989). The music best facilitates exercise when it (a) matches the exercising person's individual preferences, (b) provides appropriate rhythmic and structural support for the movement, and (c) evokes pleasant associations (Gfeller 1988).

Many music activities, such as singing, playing instruments, conducting, and dancing/creative movement-to-music also, in and of themselves, are enjoyable forms of physical activity that can exercise the circulatory and respiratory systems and various muscle groups. These activities, as well as music therapy interventions involving listening and discussion or improvisation and discussion, also can be used to help individuals identify healthy lifestyle patterns and coping techniques and increase compliance with exercise routines (Beckett 1990; Mandel 1996). Wininger and Pargman (2003, 57) report, "A collection of quantitative and qualitative studies has shown enjoyment of exercise to be an important factor in determining adherence to exercise." In addition, some research indicates that involvement in music listening, music and imagery, and music therapy interventions that provide patients with active coping strategies and promote self-expression can enhance immune system responses (Bartlett et al. 1993; Brennan and Charnetski 2000; Krout 2007; Kuhn 2002; Lane 1991, 1994; Rider 1985; Robb 1996; Taylor 1997; Tsao et al. 1991). Halpern (1989) even speculated that as the emphasis in health care shifts to individuals taking a more conscious and active role in their own healing and growth, health specialists may begin "prescribing a proven therapeutic listening program for home or institutional follow-up" (80).

Carefully chosen background music also may assist people trying to control their eating habits. Some research has shown that relaxing music can help decrease the number of bites per minute, thereby causing people to eat more slowly and consume less food, while fast music makes them chew faster and eat more ("Eating" 1991). Even though they may eat less food, individuals who dine to slower music report feeling fuller and more satisfied than when dining to no music or fast music. The positive outcomes of this type of music therapy can be far reaching: "Control is the . . . primary issue in treating eating disorders. . . . Providing opportunities for choice and acceptance of their choice can enlarge the feeling of control to more than food" (Lathom-Radocy 2014, 136).

Finally, structured music therapy interventions can precipitate the development of more healthy behavior patterns in individuals who are "at risk" for various reasons, by increasing their self-esteem and motivation, providing a form of emotional support and emotional or creative expression, and decreasing depression and isolation (Lathom-Radocy 2014; Shiraishi 1997; Spencer 1978; Taylor et al. 1997; Whitwell 1993). For example, Shiraishi (1997) developed a home-based music therapy program for multi-risk mothers who were experiencing high levels of distress, low self-esteem, and depression. Clients consulted with a music therapist to choose and be instructed in the use of one or more taped music programs, which they then implemented at home. The music therapist contacted clients weekly by phone or a visit to discuss progress and determine whether any changes or additions were necessary. General formats of available music programs included (1) familiar, upbeat music for gentle exercise to decrease muscle tension; (2) pleasant, calming familiar vocal or instrumental music for use with gentle facial massage to decrease face and neck tension; (3) slow instrumental music for progressive muscle relaxation and full body relaxation; (4) preferred calming music for deeper relaxation after programs 1, 2, or 3, to facilitate sleep; and (5) energetic, rhythmic music for more vigorous exercise. The majority of the participants enjoyed the music protocol and found the techniques helpful in decreasing stress, decreasing depression, and increasing self-esteem: "Participants reported a sense of pride that they were able to do something positive and enjoyable for themselves" (21). In addition, some of these multi-risk mothers found that "the music was able to help them interact more positively with their children, a skill that all the mothers acknowledged was important" (21).

Music Experiences to Humanize the Environment

In an increasingly computerized and mechanized world, human beings still need and long for experiences that speak to the imaginative, creative, "feelingful" side of life (Leonhard 1982; Whitwell 1993). Throughout history, societies and cultures have recognized music as an important vehicle for expressing feelings and imagination and connecting human beings to each other (Gaston 1968a; Kenny 1982; Merriam 1964; Radocy and Boyle 2012). Music both evokes aesthetic responses and provides a vehicle for creative expression of beauty, meaning, and order (Gaston 1968a; Radocy and Boyle 2012). Therefore, music programs that stimulate imagination, creativity, feelingful thought, and thoughtful feeling can do much to restore humanness and "counter the sterility, the depersonalization, the retreat into isolation that pervade contemporary society" (Leonhard, 1982, 24).

Music can help "humanize" sterile medical environments by providing experiences that speak to patients' psychoemotional needs and by masking stress-producing sounds of medical machinery (Krout 2007; Radocy and Boyle 2012). Music experiences can provide necessary diversion from the more stressful or painful aspects of treatment or therapy, help patients relate to aspects of their lives outside of the treatment setting, and provide expression for those parts of the patient that are still intact and healthy. Music listening may be used to induce a relaxed state of mind, resulting in fewer pain impulses reaching conscious awareness (Crowe 2004). Besides managing the patient's stress, music therapists can address parental stress as well: "Because sleep deprivartion, worry, and noise can create significant stress, music therapists may attempt to develop coping interventions that can be of therapeutic value to parents" (Wolfe and Waldon 2009, 108).

In the general population, too, appropriate background music can help mask stressful and annoying environmental noises, help aid concentration and improve work capacity, and positively influence moods and behaviors (Clearwater 1985; Prueter and Mezzano 1973; Radocy and Boyle 2012). Recognizing music's powerful physical, mental, and emotional effects, scientists have used music as a stimulus to provide sensory variety and set the proper moods for various work and rest activities aboard space stations (Clearwater 1985). In addition, people are becoming more aware that high noise levels can increase stress and damage hearing (Brody 1982; Harrison 2008; Lathom-Radocy 2014; Jaret 1991; Ponte 1989) and are learning to structure their "sonic environment" in ways that promote rather than detract from health (Harvey 1987; Ponte 1989). As people utilize aesthetic and creative processes through active participation in music experiences, they also develop a better capacity to cope with and find meaning in life (Aigen 1995a; Edelman 1978; *The Healing Role of the Arts* 1978; May 1975; Spencer 1978; Taylor et al. 1997). Thus, music experiences can play a vital role in helping individuals connect with the "feelingful" side of their being and realize their full human potential (Leonhard 1982; Whitwell 1993).

Music Experiences to Expand Consciousness and Increase Personal Awareness

With the holistic health movement's emphasis on taking responsibility for one's own health, striving for optimum wellness and balance in all areas of life, and furthering of one's potential, self-awareness, and growth through finding answers within one's self (Adelman 1985; Bonny 1986; Scovel 1990; Summer and Summer 1996; Trevisan 1978), many people are looking for ways to increase their personal awareness and add more meaning and fulfillment to their lives. Clearly, wellness includes self-responsibility, good nutritional choices, adequate exercise to maintain physical fitness, management of stress and awareness of environmental and social triggers of stress (Creagan 2006; Gfeller 2008; Ghetti, Hama, and Woolrich 2004; Reuer 2007). Reuer (2007) lists wellness programs as a trend that music therapy consultants should acknowledge in offering their services. She also notes that aging baby boomers are looking for ways to stay healthy, which impacts the health and spa industries. Music therapists may work as consultants in organizations where they can work on "team building and stress management" (113).

Occupations that require creative problem solving, as opposed to simple pattern recognition skills, may lead to stress. Lesiuk (2010) studied the effect of preferred music on mood and performance in a high-cognitive demand occupation. Her subjects were designing computer information systems, which requires creative problem-solving skills and knowledge of systems design. Lesiuk argues that music therapists can contribute to performance in stressful professions:

> In the role of consultant to high-cognitive demand occupations, music therapists may help facilitate employee awareness and identification of daily mood states, and assist with individualized music choices that help alter mood states or meet a desired psychological state. (150)

Her data and subjects' comments support the conclusion that music can relieve anxiety and stress.

In 2005, The American Music Therapy Association defined the use of music therapy in wellness as "the specialized use of music to enhance quality of life, maximize well-being and potential, and increase self-awareness in individuals seeking music therapy services" (AMTA 2005). Music experiences may be both curative and preventative, both enjoyable and rehabilitative, both artistic and therapeutic (Aigen 1995a; Edelman 1978; Kenny 1982; Spencer 1978). Therefore, music therapy experiences aimed at tapping and productively channeling an individual's emotional energy for growth, nondestructive self-expression, personal satisfaction, and increased self-awareness can do much to increase the average person's total health and quality of life. As Broucek (1987, 54–55) observes:

> For average people, the satisfaction, affirmation, identification, and exploration offered in music therapy may mean the difference between sickness and full health. . . . Music therapy becomes an affirmation of the risky but rewarding growth choice toward health, rather than a sanction for the stagnation of safety.

Many music therapy techniques and approaches can be used with individuals or groups to help enhance cognitive functioning, expand consciousness, increase creativity and self-expression, improve life satisfaction, facilitate self-awareness, and promote personal growth and optimum health. For example, some individuals may find that improvisation or composition exercises help stimulate creative problem solving, encourage creative exploration of different possibilities and provide a safe structure for experimenting and taking risks, and lead to increased boldness in personal exploration (Broucek 1987; Kenny 1982;

Priestley 1985). Others may find that song lyric discussion and personal or group song writing can stimulate increased personal awareness and help them see other points of view or other possible solutions.

Many music therapists also utilize various music and imagery techniques to help individuals expand consciousness, explore alternatives, facilitate access to and expression of emotions, enhance self-awareness, and increase life satisfaction (Bonny 1978b, 1986, 1989, 1994; Bonny and Savary 1973, 1990; Campbell 1991a; Crowe 1991; Ventre 1994a). One of the most widely used methods is the Bonny Method of Guided Imagery and Music (GIM) (Bonny 1978b, 1986, 1989, 1994; Bonny and Savary 1990). According to its founder, Helen Bonny, GIM is a process to promote personal growth:

> [It is] a process that focuses on the conscious use of imagery which arises in re-sponse to a formalized program of relaxation and music to effect self-under-standing and personal growth processes in the person. Used one-to-one with a trained guide, GIM may be a powerful uncovering process in exploring levels of consciousness not usually available to normal awareness. (Bonny 1989, 7)

GIM helps individuals in their "quest for individuation, for creative life living, for healing and health" (Ventre 1994a, 35) and "may be used as an ongoing process by anyone who is a seeker after that truth which lies within each of us" (Bonny and Savary 1990, 9). Research into the GIM process has demonstrated that GIM is usually most effective as a tool for personal trans-formation, growth, and self-discovery when it is carried out in dyads (i.e., one-to-one sessions with therapist and client) with a planned series of sessions (usually five) under a competent, specially trained GIM therapist/guide (Bonny 1989, 1994; Bonny and Savary 1990). Since the GIM process transcends word and thought, helps individuals tap into and gain strength from their creative forces, breaks through denial, facilitates new insight and understand-ing, and leads to a new level of acceptance and integration of all facets of an individual (Ventre 1994a), it can be a potent tool in the quest for increased self-awareness, wholeness, and optimum health and well-being.

POTENTIAL HARMFUL EFFECTS OF SOUND OR MUSIC

Priestley (1985, 257) argues: "Not all uses of music are therapeutic." There-fore, individuals must be aware of both the positive and negative effects of sound and music, if they are to use music most effectively as a source of indi-vidual and group health (Harvey 1987). Some song lyrics or types of music may reinforce unhealthy thought or behavior patterns in certain individuals. Some types of music or music experiences also have the potential to over-stimulate the nervous system, even causing musiogenic seizures in some individuals (Priestley 1985). In addition, the same piece of music or the same type of instrument or experience will not have the same effect on every person. What is helpful, relaxing, or uplifting to one person may have no effect or the opposite effect on another (Clair 1996b). Therefore, it is important to monitor individual reactions and adjust music and experiences accordingly. Certain music therapy techniques may be contraindicated for some individuals. For example, among the poor candidates for GIM are individuals who have poor ego strength, are incapable of symbolic thinking, have difficulty distinguishing between symbolic thinking and reality, or are unable to relate their experiences to the therapist (Bonny 1986; Summer 1988).

Since prolonged exposure to loud music or sounds from powerful speakers at concerts, personal stereo headphones, customized car stereos, and television sets can lead to noise-induced hearing damage (Brody 1982; Jaret 1991; Lathom-Radocy 2014; Lovejoy and Estridge 1987; Ponte 1989), therapists and clients should always carefully monitor the loudness level of music used in music experiences. In addition to damaging hearing acuity, noisy environments can increase stress levels, irritability, and fatigue, and possibly contribute to increased blood pressure, cardiovascular injury, ulcers, accidents, and reduced work efficiency (Jaret 1991). High environmental noise levels may also disrupt sensory and motor skill development in infants and toddlers (Jaret 1991). Thus, by alerting people to the dangers associated with prolonged exposure to loud sounds or noisy environments, music therapists might do much to improve the general health and well-being of the population at large as well as help to prevent noise-induced hearing losses.

MUSIC THERAPY VERSUS NEW AGE MUSIC HEALING AND SOUND HEALING TECHNIQUES

During the last two to three decades of the twentieth century, the new age movement brought with it an increased interest in both the healing practices of non-Western cultures and the possible direct healing effects of certain types of music or sounds (Campbell 1991a, 1991b; Crowe and Scovel 1996; Halpern 1978; Hamel 1976/1979). Usually, these techniques focus on the direct impact of physical, acoustical vibrations on body structures and functions and on neural activity (Bruscia 1989a; Crowe and Scovel 1996; Summer and Summer 1996). In order to be most effective, music used for healing purposes, like medicine, must be *individually prescribed and applied*, taking into account the unique physical, psychological, emotional, and spiritual make-up of the individual. In addition, the personal relationship and interaction between therapist and client can add much to the healing potential of music and sound. Krout (2007) provides a useful overview of ways in which music listening can positively affect human physiology within a wellness model. His report is supported by research in music therapy.

Krout (2007) notes that a positive attitude toward one's own health is an important component in a wellness program. Individuals may want to use MP3 players (e.g., iPod) or portable CD players to provide a relaxation break when needed. These can be used with headphones to mask environmental noise. It is important that individuals learn methods for self-relaxation to maintain wellness (Krout, 2007).

SPECIAL CONSIDERATIONS AND TIPS FOR SUCCESS

Individuals who wish to use music for health and well-being must remember that each individual responds in unique ways to particular sounds, compositions, or musical instruments. In addition, any individual's responses to a certain musical stimulus may vary from time to time, depending on his/her emotional, physical, and mental state. Therefore, it is always important for the therapist to monitor individual reactions and adjust music materials or techniques accordingly. In addition, "anyone who uses music for healing, either for their own benefit or for others, should be aware that unsuspected effects may occur" (Campbell 1991a, 251). Therefore, it is often beneficial to work with or consult a trained therapist who can deal effectively with any problems that may arise. This is especially true with techniques that involve altered states of consciousness (e.g., GIM) and that work on self-discovery and increased personal awareness. The skills of trained music therapists also can be helpful in initial selections and eventual monitoring of the most effective music or musical techniques for individual self-help programs, such as music to motivate and accompany exercise.

One may think of using music to promote health and well-being in the general population as a continuum, with self-prescribed activities at one end (e.g., listening to music to relax or become happier) and individualized treatment programs implemented by a music therapist on the other. This continuum is comparable to the range of general medicine services available, from self-prescribed, over-the-counter medications and home remedies to individualized, prescribed medications or treatment implemented by a physician. Just as consumers or clients self-medicate for common colds or take vitamins to promote health, so they can "self-musicate" as they find certain types of music or musical activities that effectively relieve their stress, increase their mental alertness, help them exercise, elevate their mood, etc. And, just as physicians sometimes use nonprescription medications in treatment for specific purposes in dosages matched to the individual patient, so music therapists sometimes may use commercially available recordings and materials (e.g., prepackaged relaxation tapes or exercise tapes) in treatment interventions matched to individual client's needs and interests, or they may instruct clients on ways to use these materials for health maintenance. A book by Hanser and Mandel (2010), based on music therapy research and wellness programs, includes a section on wellness and a helpful CD. This book is well informed about the research in music therapy and wellness programs.

However, just as consumers/clients seek the help of trained physicians for more severe problems, for guidance in using over-the-counter medications and remedies, or for help when nonprescription medications or home remedies are not effective, they must also learn to seek the help of trained music therapists when commercially available music materials or self-prescribed music programs or activities no longer have the desired effects. As they seek to move into the mainstream of wellness services, music therapists must take the lead in educating consumers about the entire spectrum of music and wellness treatments and help individuals identify which treatments may be most beneficial for their personal use at particular times or for particular purposes. Music therapists also must help the general public develop guidelines for when they can safely "self-musicate," when they might need to consult with a professional music therapist, and when they might need the direct services of a professional music therapist to help them reach their desired goals for improving their total health and quality of life. Finally, music therapists must be able to support their claims for music's preventative, health maintenance, and health enhancement effects with solid scientific research. Then music therapy will be able to find a place as an important part of wellness/preventative medicine services, as well as rehabilitative services, and as a vital service for the general population as well as for disabled individuals. Krout (2007, 139) hopes that "consumers, creative arts therapists, and other allied health professionals may be better educated as to the physiological effects of music listening as they relate to facilitating relaxation as part of an ongoing wellness initiative and lifestyle."

QUESTIONS FOR THOUGHT AND DISCUSSION

1. What implications do the expanded concept of health, the increased focus on wellness and preventative medicine, and the growing interest in holistic medicine have for the expansion of music therapy services?
2. Discuss some of the characteristics and needs of individuals in the general population who are interested in obtaining, maintaining, or regaining optimal health and well-being. What implications do these have for music therapy programming?
3. Why and how are music experiences useful in promoting health and well-being in the general population? Are some types of experiences and activities

more useful than other? Which ones? Why?

4. Describe some specific music therapy experiences that might be used to help individuals (a) facilitate relaxation and reduce stress, (b) decrease isolation and facilitate cooperative interactions, (c) improve coping and problem-solving abilities, (d) promote healthy habits and behaviors, (e) humanize the environment, and (f) expand consciousness and increase personal awareness. What unique benefits does music provide in each of these areas?

5. Discuss some potential harmful side effects of sound or music. What implications might these have for music therapy services?

6. Describe some new age music healing and sound healing techniques. How do these differ from music therapy? Are there any ways some of these techniques might be included as part of music therapy intervention strategies? If so, how?

7. List several special considerations that may be important to remember when using music to promote health and well-being in the general population. Why are these important? What are the implications for the structure of music therapy intervention strategies?

8. For each of the situations listed below, (a) define the problem or areas of need for the client or group of clients, (b) describe one or more of the goals you might pursue in music therapy sessions with the client(s), (c) describe music activities you might use to help the client(s) meet those goals, (d) tell how the music activities you describe relate to the goals and needs of the client(s), and (e) mention any special considerations you should take into account when working with the client(s).

Situation 1:

A local hospital is starting community outreach wellness programs. The hospital staff is looking for ways to make these programs as enjoyable and appealing as possible, and they want your ideas on ways music therapy interventions could be a part of this effort. Initially, these community outreach programs will focus on stress reduction, coping skills, and developing good exercise habits.

Situation 2:

Ms. F. is a 49-year-old, successful business woman. She is divorced and has two grown children. Even though she is successful, her life seems void and empty at times. She is seeking experiences that will expand her self-awareness and add more meaning, fulfillment, balance, and wholeness to her life. In addition, she is interested in activities that will help her maintain optimal physical, mental, and emotional health as she grows older.

SUGGESTIONS FOR FURTHER READING

Bonny, H. L. (1989). Sound as symbol: Guided imagery and music in clinical practice. *Music Therapy Perspectives, 6,* 7–10.

Bonny, H. L. (1994). Twenty-one years later: A GIM update. *Music Therapy Perspectives, 12(2),* 70–74.

Bonny, H. L. & Savary, L. M. (1990). *Music and your mind: Listening with a new consciousness* (rev. ed.). Barrytown, NY: Station Hill Press.

Boyce-Tillman, J. (2000). *Constructing musical healing: The wounds that sing.* London: Jessica Kingsley.

Brain Injury.com (2015). Retrieved April 16, 2015 from http://www.braininjury.com/injured.shtml.

Braswell, C. (1961). Education and research in music therapy. Music Therapy 1960, Proceedings of the National Association for Music Therapy, Vol. 10. Lawrence, KS: The Allen Press.

Broucek, M. (1987). Beyond healing to "whole-ing": A voice for the deinstitutionalization of music therapy. *Music Therapy, 6(2),* 50–58.

Broucek, M. (1987). Beyond healing to music therapy, medicine, and well-being. In W. B. Davis, K. E. Gfeller, & M. H. Thaut (Eds). *An introduction to music therapy: Theory and practice* (3rd ed.) (305–341). Silver Spring, MD: American Music Therapy Association.

Ghetti, C. M., Hama, M., & Woolrich, J. (2008). Music therapy in wellness. In A-A. Darrow (Ed.), *Introduction to approaches in music therapy* (2nd ed.) (131–151). Silver Spring, MD: American Music Therapy Association.

Hanser, S. B. & Mandel, S. E. (2010). *Manage your stress and pain through music.* Berkeley, CA: Berkley Press.

Harvey, A. W. (Compiler) (1988). *Music and health: Sourcebook of readings.* Richmond, KY: Music for Health Services Foundation.

Itoh, M. & Lee, M. H. M. (1989). Epidemology of disability and music. In M. H. M. Lee (Ed.), *Rehabilitation, music, and human well-being* (13–31). St. Louis: MMB Music.

Kenny, C. B. (Ed.) (1995). *Listening, playing, creating: Essays on the power of sound.* Albany, NY: State University of New York Press.

Krout, R. E. (2007). Music listening to facilitate relaxation and promote wellness: Integrated aspects of our neurophysiological responces to music. *The Arts in Psychotherapy, 34,* 134–141.

Logan, K. (1996). Music is key to lifelong wellness. *Teaching Music, 3(4),* 42–43.

Montello, L. (2002). *Essential musical intelligence: Using music as your path to healing, creativity, and radiant wholeness.* Wheaton, IL: Quest Books Theosophical Publishing House.

Scartelli, J. P. (1989). *Music and self-management methods.* St. Louis: MMB Music.

Standley, J. (1991). *Music techniques in therapy, counseling, and special education.* St. Louis: MMB Music.

Staum, M. J. & Brotons, M. (1992). The influence of auditory subliminals on behavior: A series of investigations. *Journal of Music Therapy, 29(3),* 130–185.

Summer, L. & Summer, J. (1996). *Music: The new age elixir.* Amherst, NY: Prometheus.

Chapter Twenty-Two

OVERVIEW OF SELECTED APPROACHES TO MUSIC THERAPY

The clinical examples of music therapy practice presented in Chapters Seven to Twenty-one reveal that using music in therapy involves many different procedures, approaches, and techniques. As the music therapy profession developed during the last half of the twentieth century, certain models of music therapy practice evolved. Some are based on particular music techniques, such as improvisation, music and imagery, or vibroacoustic techniques. Others draw from music education approaches, adapting Orff, Kodály, Dalcroze, or Suzuki methods for clinical use. Developmental music therapy also grew from a child development approach. Still others center on specific educational, psychotherapeutic, or medical models and theories. However, although they may emphasize different types of music experiences or use different language, terminology, and frameworks to process, explain, and evaluate client responses, all these approaches to music therapy have one basic principle in common: they seek to "enhance the quality of life of individuals with various types of or potential clinical problems through the use of music and the therapeutic relationship" (Maranto 1993a, 706).

This chapter overviews some of the more common current approaches to music therapy practice in the United States. Certainly, this listing is by no means exhaustive, and other groupings or classifications are indeed possible (e.g., see Bruscia 1989a, 1991a; Darrow 2008; Davis, Gfeller, and Thaut 2008; Maranto 1993b; Taylor 1997; Unkefer 1990). In addition, as the music therapy profession continues to develop and as new medical, psychotherapeutic and educational treatment theories emerge, models or approaches to music therapy treatment likely will continue to evolve. Hopefully, the overview presented in this chapter will give the reader a basic understanding of some of the more common approaches to music therapy treatment currently in use in the United States.

NORDOFF-ROBBINS CREATIVE MUSIC THERAPY (NRMT)

In their work with handicapped children, Nordoff and Robbins developed an approach to music therapy which centers on piano improvisation. Nordoff and Robbins (1968, 1971a, 1971b, 1977) found that improvisational music therapy techniques were very effective in eliciting responses from profoundly handicapped, seemingly unresponsive children. Improvisational music therapy techniques have become so important that an entire issue of *Music Therapy Perspectives* (2014, *32:1*) was devoted to providing greater understanding of the basic principles of this model.

Turry and Marcus (2005, 54–56) provide a history of the development of Creative Music Therapy in which working as a therapist/co-therapist team is critical: "Nordoff-Robbins practitioners are currently either 'primary therapists' – playing their primary instruments – or 'cotherapists' – 'on the floor' (56)." All clients are viewed as inherently musical. Nordoff and Robbins (1977) call this innate musical ability the "music child":

> The *music child* is therefore the individualized musicality inborn in every child: the term has reference to the universality of human musical sensitivity – the heritage of complex and subtle sensitivity to the ordering and relationship of tonal and rhythmic movement – and to the uniquely personal significance of each child's musical responsiveness. (Nordoff and Robbins 2007, 1)

The music child is reached by the sensitive use of improvisation: "This reliance on music transcends any predefined sense of role definition. Such openness to creative possibility has been and remains an essential quality of the Nordoff-Robbins approach" (Turry and Marcus 2005, 68).

In the Nordoff-Robbins clinical improvisation technique, the music therapist's primary aim is to develop contact with the client within the context of a musical experience. Initially, the therapist works supportively, by creating a musical-emotional environment that accepts and enhances the client's responses (Nordoff and Robbins 1977). The client's behavior directs the improvisation. For example, the therapist might base an improvisation on some rhythm found in the client's movement or on drum-beating, or he or she might try to relate the tonal content of the improvisation to a tonal pattern found in the client's cries or vocalizations. In addition, Gfeller and Davis (2008, 466) explain that "this form of communication is an important concept in active music therapy, with the therapist accepting whatever the client presents musically." Once contact and rapport have been established, musical interaction between the music therapist and client becomes the focus of the sessions. Throughout the course of therapy, the music therapist works progressively with the client, building on the responses elicited and skills developed in previous sessions. In Nordoff-Robbins therapy, the goals and direction come from sensitive observation and response to the client's musical behavior. In much music therapy, the client completes an assessment, and the therapist (or treatment/education team) defines the goals. Music therapy, then, is designed to work on the goals and objectives as stated in the clients' treatment/educational plan. Each Nordoff-Robbins session is recorded and analyzed (Ansdell and Pavlicevic 2010). As Aigen (2009, 242) suggests, "All aspects of melody, harmony, rhythm and meter, and texture that constitute one's clinical-musical interventions should have an underlying rationale." The review of the recordings, with careful "indexing" of responses, leads to documentation (Ansdell and Pavlicevic 2010). Thus, the musical intervention is explained retrospectively, rather than prescribed to elicit predetermined behavior. Sometimes, the resulting goal achievement is similar: "After all, it is the way in which the direct *experience of* music facilitates the achievement of motor, cognitive, and emotional goals that is the focus of music therapy theory" (Aigen 2009, 263). Goals in Nordoff-Robbins Music Therapy differ. Aigen (2001, 33) explains:

> In contrast to some other forms of music therapy practice, clinical goals are usually framed within musical parameters, such as establishing a basic beat, developing flexibility in tempo and dynamics, or increasing vocal range. This choice stems from the overriding concern in this work which is to expand the client's capacity for human experience and thereby foster self-actualization.

Creative music therapy uses improvisation (usually piano and/or vocal) to musically reflect the client; evoke movement, vocal, or instrumental responses from the client; develop the client's musical skills and expressive freedom; and develop communication and interresponsiveness between therapist and client (Bruscia 1987, 1989c; Nordoff and Robbins 1971a, 1971b, 1977; Robbins and Robbins 1980).

Soshensky (2005, 117) provided an interesting approach to using guitar in Nordoff-Robbins Music Therapy. Through a case study, he explains how one can use the guitar to produce "tension, dissonance, modal influences, diverse harmonies, and flexible rhythms that served as contexts" for the client's artistic collaboration. Improvisations used in creative music therapy make free use of dissonances and employ many different meters, modes, scales, structures, and styles. Through these improvisations, the therapist creates music situations and sequences that engage the client in active music making to enhance cognitive, motor, behavioral, and affective growth and development (Aigen 1995b; Bruscia 1987; Nordoff and Robbins 1977). Verbal instructions and interventions are minimal; musical expression is "both the stimulus and response medium for therapeutic growth" (Bruscia 1987, 67). Nordoff and Robbins (1977) also have developed evaluation scales to show how a client's responses to musical improvisation reflect various degrees of participation, resistiveness, and communicativeness.

Nordoff-Robbins creative music therapy focuses on working with those behaviors and emotional responses of the client that are functional and non-exceptional. There is a great emphasis on music's power to awaken emotional responses and to act as an ego-organizing or self-actualizing force:

> In the Nordoff-Robbins approach, it is believed that music bypasses areas of pathology or dysfunction to access an individual's healthy core. . . . Cognitive and affective processes not otherwise detected are activated in and through music. (Aigen 1995b, 24)

Creative music therapy is perhaps one of the most well-known systems of improvisational music therapy. It is useful in both individual and group sessions with clients who have a wide range of disabilities and functioning levels, including those with autism or emotional disturbances, developmental disabilities, physical or neurological impairments, hearing or visual impairments, or severe multiple disabilities (Aigen 1995b, 2001; Nordoff and Robbins, 1968, 1971a, 1971b, 1977; Pfeifer 1982; Robbins and Robbins 1980; Salas and Gonzalez 1991; Shoemark 1991). Although it was developed for children, the approach also has been used effectively with adolescent and adult populations (Aigen et al. 2008; Bruscia 1987, 1991a; Clarkson 1991; Pavlicevic et al. 1994; Ritholz and Turry 1994). Clients need not have any preexistent musical or verbal skills to benefit from creative music therapy; however, music therapists who use the approach need to be highly competent, skilled, expressive, and sensitive musicians who have a broad range of skills, particularly in piano and vocal improvisation, as well as a high degree of clinical awareness (Bruscia 1987; Forinash 1992). Training programs in the Nordoff-Robbins creative music therapy approach are located in England, Germany, the United States, and Australia. In the United States, the Nordoff-Robbins approach is taught at New York University in the Nordoff-Robbins Center. Taught at the graduate level, it includes a 38-week internship, with 25 hours of clinical and course work each week. Aigen, et al. (2008, 66–67) explain the training program in greater detail.

PSYCHODYNAMIC MUSIC THERAPY

There are many ways to access the unconscious material. In verbal therapy, free association is often used. Based on Freudian theory, the client says anything that comes to mind while the therapist maintains a nonjudgemental attitude and listens for themes or patterns of thought, information on relationships, and any traumatic events the client may have experienced. In music therapy, unconscious material may be revealed nonverbally through improvisation or verbally while in a relaxed state as in guided imagery and music.

According to Isenberg, Goldberg, and Dvorkin (2008, 99), "Psychodynamic music therapy, simply stated, is based on the concept that events in the past have an impact on the present and that unconscious material drives current behavior." Various psychoanalytic approaches exist to allow the client to access the unconscious material, express it and come to some resolution, and thus have greater self-realization. Approaches in this model are based on the theories of Freud, Adler, Jung, Fromm, and Erickson (Scovel 1990).

Psychodynamic music therapy approaches can be used effectively with clients of all ages who are seeking relief from various mental, emotional, or behavioral conditions, including autism spectrum disorders (Alvin 1978; Alvin and Warwick 1991; Bruscia 1991a), mood disorders (Bruscia 1991a; Priestley 1985; Warja 1994), eating disorders (Nolan 1989), personality disorders (Bruscia 1991a; Dvorkin 1991), anxiety disorders (Priestley 1985; Tyson 1966, 1981, 1987), or schizophrenia (Bruscia 1991a; Priestley 1985; Warja 1994). Music can be a very effective tool of psychodynamic therapy because it may bypass verbal censorship and reach emotions and the deeper parts of an individual's psyche (Wheeler 1981). In addition, it is a powerful nonverbal form of expression and communication that can be used to access and explore unconscious materials at a nonverbal, feeling level before clients are ready or able to verbalize them (Ruud 1980; Wheeler 1981). Music activities also can give clients an outlet for expressing anger or other urges or feelings in nondestructive ways, thus providing a form of sublimation (Ruud 1980). Finally, as clients successfully participate in music experiences, they can gain a sense of mastery, control, and confidence that will build ego strength and increase feelings of self-worth (Ruud 1980; Wheeler 1981).

Juliette Alvin

Several other music therapy models also rely on musical improvisation as their primary tool for assessment, treatment, and/or evaluation. For example, in her work with children who had autism and various other handicaps, Alvin (1978; Alvin and Warwick 1991) developed an approach that gives the client complete freedom to improvise on a variety of musical instruments and find his or her own way to order sounds. Alvin was an exceptionally fine musician who received the First Excellence Prize and Gold Medal from the Conservatory of Paris. Her major instrument was cello; she was a soloist with leading European orchestras. She published cello instruction books and *Musical Theory and Instrumental Technique* (1953), as well as several books on music therapy. One of the founders of the British Society for Music Therapy, she directed a music therapy course begun at the Guildhall School of Music and Drama (Haneishi 2005). She also was important in establishing music therapy in Japan (Haneishi 2005). Excellent musicianship was an essential part of her approach.

Haneishi stresses the importance of excellent musicianship in Alvin's approach: "According to Alvin, a music therapist should be a trained musician who can express his or her innermost feelings through live music as a prerequisite for nonverbal communication" (Haneishi 2005, 286). As sessions progress, the therapist guides the client in developing appropriate relationships with objects, self, and others through improvisations that form a dynamic part of the therapist-client interaction and relationship. In Alvin's method, improvisation is used in conjunction with other active and receptive music experiences, and music therapy is seen as "a developmental process which must be planned and implemented in sequential stages of intellectual, physical, and social-emotional growth" (Bruscia 1987, 108).

Other factors noted by Alvin include "musical skills, structuring the environment, controlling stimuli for concentration, respecting individual differences in responses to music, musical function as nonverbal communication, [and] knowledge of related areas" (Haneishi 2005, 292). Her use of music, or even single sounds, to elicit responses is somewhat like the Nordoff-Robbins approach. Both are nonverbal in their first interactions with children. She also used a variety of musical sounds, composed music, pentatonic scales, folk songs, and improvised music to make a musical connection with each person.

Bruscia (1987, 1989c) calls this model *Free Improvisation Therapy*. This approach has been used successfully in individual, family, and group therapy sessions, as well as with children who have autism or other developmental or psychiatric disabilities. It also has been used to a limited extent with adults.

Mary Priestley

Another improvisational model, *Analytical Music Therapy*, was developed by Priestley (1975, 1985, 1994; Priestley and Eschen 2002). Based on the theories of Jung and Freud, this model uses words and symbolic improvisations to explore the client's inner life and facilitate growth. In this approach, after issues for emotional investigation are identified, improvisation often is based on programmatic titles. Clients choose from a wide variety of instruments, and the therapist usually accompanies their improvisations. Client and therapist roles in improvisation are defined according to the issue at hand. Verbal discussion and processing are used throughout the session. To use this model effectively, therapists must be trained and experienced in both analytical psychotherapy and analytical music therapy.

Transference and countertransference are important concepts in Priestly's model. Everyone has feelings, thoughts, and desires that lie within the unconscious parts of the mind. When the client transfers these emotions to the therapist, unconscious material may be revealed. The client reacts to the therapist emotionally by transferring feelings representative of other figures.

The therapist may take the role of mother, father, teacher, or child. What was repressed becomes available to the conscious mind (Rosenhan and Seligman 1986). When the therapist transfers unconscious material to the client, it is called countertransference: "An ability to use musical and verbal countertransference is dependent upon the music therapist's awareness of the personal needs that he or she brings to the session" (Scheiby 2005, 10).

A music therapist working in a psychotherapeutic context requires supervision. Supervisory issues include boundary issues, process management problems, control issues, dissociation (losing interest during the session), and "the rescuer" (overinvolvement in the client, even out of the session) (Scheiby 2005, 11). Advanced training in analytical music therapy is required to work in this model. The training model includes personal therapy for the therapist (Isenberg, Goldberg, and Dvorkin 2008). The Priestley model has been used with normal adults, adults who have psychiatric or anxiety problems, couples, prisoners, therapy students, and, occasionally, with children (Bruscia 1987, 1991a; Priestley 1975, 1985).

Silverman (2007, 388) surveyed music therapists to determine the "philosophies, interventions and clinical objectives" of music therapists working in psychiatric institutions. Analyzing 176 surveys, he found that "most participants reported they used a behavioral [83.1%] or psychodynamic approach [49.2%]" (Silverman 2007, 406). Obviously, some music therapists choose both approaches: "For example, one session may focus on increasing insight (a psychodynamic approach) while the next session may focus on practicing healthy coping skills through role-playing (a behavioral approach)" (Silverman 2007, 406). Choi's (2008, 103) survey also revealed a wide choice of models used in therapy: "Many music therapists naturally would try to employ all necessary techniques and methods to make their therapy a success."

OTHER METHODS BASED ON IMPROVISATION

Boxill (1985, 1989) developed a method of clinical improvisation she called the *Continuum of Awareness.* This approach, specifically designed for use with developmentally disabled individuals, uses improvisation in conjunction with specially structured and adapted experiences in singing/chanting, instrument playing, and moving to music to build relationships with clients and increase their levels of awareness and adaptive functioning. The three primary strategies used to awaken and expand awareness and develop relationships are (1) *reflection* (mirroring; imitating; or synchronizing with client's actions, movements, or sounds, while simultaneously structuring the improvisation to reflect and support underlying moods and feelings); (2) *identification* (providing instantaneous feedback to the client in improvised songs and chants of who the client is, who the therapist is, what measures the activities that the client and therapist are doing together, and what measures those that the client is doing independently, thereby heightening awareness of experiences); and (3) *our contact song* (developed through strategies 1 and 2, the first vehicle, either composed or improvised, through which the client initiates musical communication toward the therapist; provides a base that may be adapted in various ways to affirm or reaffirm client-therapist relationship). These three primary strategies have been used effectively in both individual and group settings with all age groups of developmentally disabled clients.

Bruscia (1987, 211) developed another improvisational music therapy model, the *Experimental Improvisation Therapy*, as an adaptation of Riordan's method of using improvised dance or movement to help disabled individuals "develop creativity, self-expression, and interpersonal skills." Bruscia's model may use group improvisations in dance, music, or both. The therapist provides themes or "givens" to direct the group's attention to a limited area of music and/or dance. The group then experiments with possibilities within that area. Throughout the session, improvisation and discussion alternate to help the group refine and connect themes. This approach has been used successfully with disabled adults and children, normal adults, and therapy students. The model emphasizes "the development of personal self-expression, interpersonal freedom and responsibility, and creativity, all within a group situation" (Bruscia 1987, 211).

Bruscia (1987, 1989b, 1989c, 1998a, 1998d) has identified and provided a comprehensive description of several other improvisational music therapy models, including *Orff Improvisation Models, Paraverbal Therapy, Metaphoric Improvisation, Adult Improvisational Therapy, Integrative Improvisation Therapy, Developmental Therapeutic Process, Psychodrama Music,* and *Vocal Improvisation Therapy.* While improvisational models differ in emphases, aspects of musical or improvisation experience, theoretical orientations, and intended client populations, all use musical stimulation or verbal direction to engage the client in some sort of musical improvisation through various expressive modes (e.g., playing instruments, singing/chanting, moving/dancing, drama/mime) that will evoke increased nonverbal communication and self-expression. By reviewing the improvisation, either musically or verbally, through active or receptive techniques, the therapist helps the client identify emerging skills, clarify or concretize elicited ideas, or connect new insights and behaviors to their lives (Bruscia 1989c).

Through extensive study of and clinical practice with improvisational models of music therapy, Bruscia (1987) also developed the *Improvisation Assessment Profiles* (IAPs), which "provide a model of client assessment based upon clinical observations, musical analysis, and psychological interpretation of the client's improvisation." The IAPs focus on both the client's experience of the improvisation process and the resulting musical product in an attempt to discover general tendencies the client exhibits and how the client responds under various combinations of conditions (e.g., solo, dyad, or group; movement, different instruments, vocal). Each musical element or improvisational component (rhythm, melody, harmony, texture, phrasing, volume, timbre, body-motor, program/lyrics, interpersonal) is rated on six profiles: integration, variability, tension, congruence, salience (which elements receive more control or prominence), and autonomy (role relationships in dyadic or group improvisations). The IAPs can be used effectively with normal or disabled children or adults who have a developmental age of at least 18 months. Tasks can be adapted for clients with severe motor or hearing impairments. IAPs are used mainly to gather information about the client, which then can be interpreted according to any relevant psychological theory (Bruscia 1987, 1989c).

THE BONNY METHOD OF GUIDED IMAGERY AND MUSIC

Helen Bonny first developed the technique that eventually became known as the Bonny Method of Guided Imagery and Music (BMGIM or GIM) in the early 1970s. GIM evolved from work with music in LSD therapy (controlled, clinical use of lysergic acid diethylamide, a potent psychotogenic drug to increase self-awareness and expand consciousness) and the subsequent search for alternate ways to achieve altered states of consciousness that would enhance self-awareness, induce deep relaxation, and facilitate personal transformation or peak experiences without mind-altering chemicals (Bonny 1975, 1978b, 1986, 1989, 1994; Bonny and Savary 1973, 1990; Burns and Woolrich 2008; Summer 1988). Because "the multidimensional qualities of musical sound allow it to touch many levels of consciousness both simultaneously or in sequence" (Bonny 1975, 130), it became evident that listening to music in a state of deep relaxation could give a person access to altered states of consciousness and increased awareness without using drugs. Since the 1970s, research into the GIM process has refined methods of practice and procedures steadily. GIM now is recognized as a powerful form of music psychotherapy that can reach deep intrapsychic material and help individuals go beyond ordinary levels of consciousness to reach emotional material normally hidden from conscious awareness as well as higher states of expanded awareness (Bonny 1994; Burns and Woolrich 2008; Goldberg 1989; Jarvis 1988; Unkefer 1990). As such, GIM should be used only by specially trained practitioners. In 2002, Bonny (271) defined qualities of a successful GIM guide as "open-minded, open-ended, receptive, allowing and caring." Discussing the therapist's roles, Grocke (2005, 48) explains that common goals in GIM include "health issues and the management of pain, relationship problems, decision-making, and transitions through phases of life." The music acts as a stimulus for imagery, which allows unconscious material to surface for examination and resolution. Personal and spiritual growth may occur through this process.

According to its founder, GIM focuses on the conscious use of imagery that arises in response to a formalized program of relaxation and music to effect self-understanding and personal growth processes in the individual. Used one-to-one with a trained guide, GIM may be a powerful uncovering process in exploring levels of consciousness not usually available to normal awareness (Bonny 1989, 7).

GIM sessions have four basic phases: prelude, induction, music program, and postlude (Bonny 1978a, 1989, 1994; Summer 1988). Burns and Woolrich (2008, 54–55) explain this four-step process in greater detail. During the *prelude*, the GIM process is explained and goals are set for the session. In the *induction*, the therapist leads the client through a relaxation and focus procedure to facilitate deep relaxation and new levels of consciousness. During the *music program*, the therapist plays a GIM tape program suited to the client's needs and goals. GIM taped music programs are 20 to 40 minutes in length and consist of specially selected pieces of classical music designed to facilitate the client's moods and visualization themes. As the music plays, the therapist verbally guides or interacts with the client as the client relates personal images that are elicited by the music. The exchange and interaction may prompt the therapist to change music tapes "to facilitate the fast movement which is taking place in inner dynamics" (Bonny 1989, 8). Sessions conclude with the *postlude*, an integration and processing phase during which the therapist guides the client in returning to a normal state of consciousness, discusses images or experiences from the music program with the client, and helps the client process the images or experiences and relate them to personal goals or session goals. Integration and processing are essential to the GIM process, for "the validity of GIM as a therapeutic technique rests on its capacity for giving insights for the solution of problems in the real world" (Summer 1988, 41).

GIM is based on a humanistic, transpersonal orientation (Burns and Woolrich 2008) using client-centered interpretation of the images generated by the music that "with the guide, serves as therapist and healer" (Bonny 1994, 70). Music is central to the GIM process because the music evokes changes that occur in perception and helps create and elicit movement through and into various states of consciousness (Bonny 1989, 1994). As noted above, GIM almost exclusively uses classical music (i.e., art music of the Western culture). Burns and Woolrich (2008, 51) explain that "Bonny (1972) developed a series of listening programs that contained emotional characteristics based on the melodic contour, dynamic range, harmonic structure, rhythm, and orchestration of the music." While popular music usually has fixed meanings and specific agendas or referents and directs attention to itself, classical music seldom has fixed meanings and is perceived anew by each listener with each hearing (Summer 1988; Whitwell 1993). Classical music can be experienced on many levels and in many ways, is able to provide depth of experience and variety of musical color and form or melodic and harmonic complexity, can stimulate imagery that is not bound to specific words or situations, and may elicit archetypal images (Bonny 1994; Summer 1988; Ventre 1994a). Thus, classical music is particularly well-suited to the deep, intrapsychic work associated with GIM. Music designed only to create a state of relaxation (e.g., new age or minimalist music with much repetition, lack of dissonance, and a very simple structure) is not useful for GIM (Summer 1988), because GIM's goal is not relaxation but active exploration of the psyche. Thus, GIM requires music that includes contrasts, tensions, dissonances, variations, and complex structures to facilitate the movement through various states of consciousness.

Music programs for GIM sessions are chosen not by the clients but by the therapist, who is specially trained in selecting and preparing music-listening programs to evoke imagery and facilitate psychic exploration (Bonny 1978b, 1989). By definition, "the Bonny Method of Guided Imagery and Music (GIM) is an indepth music psychotherapy that utilizes specially sequenced Western Art music to elicit imagery and emotional expression" (Burns 2001, 55). In contrast to many other music therapy approaches, research into the GIM process has found that music choices based on the client's preferences usually are not helpful for in-depth GIM work (Bonny 1986). While the therapist may wish to note client preferences for diagnostic purposes or use with other music therapy techniques,

> the use of client preferred music in GIM creates problems similar to those found with the use of popular music, that is, specific and rigid associations that draw the client out of an altered state and into an alert state of consciousness associated with his listening habits. (Summer 1988, 6)

GIM is usually most powerful and effective when employed in dyads (i.e., one-to-one sessions with therapist and client) utilizing a planned series of sessions (usually five) under a competent, specially trained GIM therapist/ guide (Bonny 1978a, 1989, 1994). Therefore, intensive GIM work usually occurs in individual sessions, in private practice or other clinical settings, often as a primary psychotherapeutic approach (Bonny 1994; Goldberg 1989; Jarvis 1988). However, GIM techniques have been adapted for group use (Blake and Bishop 1994; Peach 1984; Short 1992; Skaggs 1997a, 1997b; Summer 1981, 1988). Generally, group GIM is less intense and therefore may be more useful in hospital or acute inpatient settings (Bonny 1994). The music program in group sessions is usually shorter, often consisting of a single selection of music, and may, especially in sessions designed to be less intrusive, use appropriate instrumental popular music as well as classical music. In group GIM sessions, guidance occurs not during the music program but during the postlude, when the guide, aiming to apply the GIM experience to individual and group goals, asks for a report of each member's imagery and then facilitates a discussion of that imagery with each client and the group as a whole (Bonny 1994; Summer 1988).

GIM can benefit many different client populations, including normal clients who desire to increase personal awareness and personal growth (Bonny and Savary 1990; Goldberg 1989; Ventre 1994a); those with relationship problems (Bonny 1989); individuals with depression or other affective disorders (Bonny 1989; Goldberg 1989; Summer 1988); those with anxiety, phobias, obsessive-compulsive disorders, borderline personality disorders, or sexual identity or dysfunction problems (Bonny 1978a, 1989); short-term psychiatric inpatients who are dealing with specific situations or traumatic events (Blake and Bishop 1994; Goldberg 1989; Short 1991; Ventre 1994b); prison populations (Nolan 1983; Skaggs 1997b); alcoholics and substance abusers who are in treatment and abstinent (Skaggs 1997a; Summer 1988); individuals with physical disabilities (Short 1992) or traumatic brain damage (Goldberg et al. 1988); elderly individuals (Summer 1981); individuals who have AIDS (Bruscia 1991b; Jarvis 1988); terminally ill individuals (Skaggs 1997c; Wylie and Blom 1986); adult children of alcoholics (Jarvis 1988); children and adolescents with emotional disturbances (Summer 1988); and normal children who wish to increase creativity and problem-solving abilities (Summer 1988). Short (1991) found that GIM can be useful in helping to diagnose physical illness or trauma.

Burns (2001) completed a study using GIM to affect the mood and life quality of cancer patients. Eight people who had previously experienced cancer were randomly assigned to GIM sessions or a wait-list control. Two tests, the Profile of Mood States (POMS) (McNair, Lorr, and Droppleman 1971) and Quality of Life – Cancer (QOL-CA) (Padilla, Grant, Presant, and Ferrell 1996) were given before and after GIM (10 weekly sessions) and at a six-week follow-up. According to the results, "GIM was effective in improving mood and quality of life in these cancer patients" (Burns 2001, 51).

Generally, in order to benefit from GIM therapy, individuals must be able to think symbolically and differentiate symbolic thinking from reality, as well as be able and willing to report their experiences to the therapist (Bonny 1989, 1994; Summer 1988). GIM is usually contraindicated for patients with active psychoses, for the GIM experience, with its lack of reality referents, may be assimilated into and reinforce psychotic thinking and fantasies (Bonny 1994; Burns and Woolrich 2008; Summer 1988). GIM also is contraindicated for those who are actively abusing drugs or alcohol (Summer 1988). In addition, patients who have insufficient ego strength or certain types of neurological impairments (e.g., those that make communication difficult or impossible) are less likely to benefit from GIM (Bonny 1989). However, some individuals with affective disorders who do not have the necessary ego strength to benefit from *individual* GIM sessions can be treated effectively in *group* GIM sessions (Summer 1988).

Therapists who use GIM techniques require additional special training, including "tutelage with a trained GIM practitioner" (Summer 1988, v). The various texts and monographs describing GIM practice provide material for theoretical study and information on additional applications, but simply reading about GIM does not qualify one to be a GIM practitioner. GIM training takes place at the postgraduate level and encompasses both didactic and experiential in-depth learning experiences in the processes of music and psychotherapy over a period of at least three years. The intermediate and advanced levels of training include personal and supervised GIM sessions with a trained GIM facilitator, as well as readings, and instruction in and practice of advanced clinical applications for both individual and group GIM work. The Association for Music and Imagery (AMI) endorses and regulates GIM training programs, and those who satisfactorily complete the total GIM training regimen become Fellows of the Association for Music and Imagery (FAMI) (Bonny 1994). GIM training programs and institutes are offered at various locations in the United States and in England, New Zealand, Australia, Denmark, Sweden, Switzerland, and Germany.

The AMI serves to create a professional network, resource, and authority on GIM; to provide conferences for sharing, nurturing, and continuing education; and to stimulate research and publication on GIM theory and practice. AMI has published its own journal since 1992 (Maranto 1993b). Individuals who have completed at least one level of approved GIM training are eligible for membership in the AMI.

Other Music and Imagery Techniques

The use of music and imagery in music therapy practice is not limited to the Bonny Method of GIM. For example, Summer (1988, 37–38) describes three "GIM-like music listening exercises" that can be used by therapists who have not had formal training in GIM to focus on specific goals with groups of clients. In these exercises, after a brief relaxation exercise and short focusing statement by the therapist, clients draw, write stories, or create movements in reaction to classical music. After the music, the therapist facilitates group discussion of the clients' work or experiences, possibly comparing an individual's work to real life feelings or situations. Music and imagery techniques also can be used to take clients on imaginary vacations or help them experience places outside their current situation (Summer 1981).

Other techniques combine music and imagery solely for the purposes of relaxation and/or pain reduction (Campbell 1991a; Rider 1985; Summer 1988; Unkefer 1990). After doing a general progressive muscle relaxation exercise, with or without music, clients are asked to concentrate on peaceful and relaxing images suggested by the therapist while listening to music that helps to support and sustain a relaxed feeling. Such music and imagery techniques have been effective in diverse situations, including labor and delivery (Clark et al. 1981; McKinney 1990), stress reduction programs (Hanser 1985; Hanser and Mandel 2010), pain management programs for persons with chronic pain from spinal cord injuries (Rider 1985), preoperative situations (Robb et al. 1995), acute care mental health settings (Wolfe 1996), pain clinics (Godley 1987), and palliative/hospice care (Munro 1984). In addition, some research suggests that music and imagery can enhance immune system responses (Bartlett et al. 1993; Lane 1991, 1994; Rider 1985; Taylor 1997; Tsao et al. 1991).

When music is used with imagery for relaxation purposes, music that the client prefers may be most effective (Clark et al. 1981; Hanser 1985; Munro 1984). However, environmental sounds (Munro 1984), new age music (Campbell 1991a; Summer 1988), entrainment music (Rider 1985), or sedative classical music (Summer 1988) also may induce relaxed states when combined with imagery. Since clients can also move into altered states of consciousness as they listen to music in states of deep relaxation during vibroacoustic treatment techniques, therapists must be aware that some clients may need support in dealing with or working through images or feelings resulting from this experience, while others may need time to recover from or emerge from their deep state of relaxation/altered state of consciousness (Crowe and Scovel 1996; Wigram 1995).

OTHER TECHIQUES AND MODELS USED IN MUSIC THERAPY

Clinical Orff-Schulwerk

Clinical Orff-Schulwerk, or Orff music therapy, stems from and relates closely to Orff-Schulwerk, an approach to music education developed in Germany by Carl Orff (1895–1992) (Barclay 1987; Bitcon 1976; Colwell, Pehotsky, Gillmeister, and Woolrich 2008; Froehlich 1996; Orff 1980; Schulberg 1981). (Orff is perhaps best remembered as a composer; his *Carmina Burana* often is performed. The main theme is even played at football games!) A multisensory approach, Orff-Schulwerk integrates music, movement, speech, and drama, guiding participants through several phases of musical development, including exploration, imitation, improvisation, and creation. Orff and a dancer, Dorothee

Gunther, combined their work to begin the Guntherschule in Munich, Germany (Colwell et al. 2008).

Rhythm marks the starting point and basis for most music making. The rhythms and sounds of the words in songs and chants provide rhythmic and melodic fragments for accompaniment figures, introductions, and codas. Creativity and exploration (through speech, sound, rhythm, song, movement, and instruments) are important components of Orff-Schulwerk, and materials for songs and chants ideally come from the participants themselves and their immediate world and experience (Froehlich 1996; Landis and Carder 1972).

As clients participate in dances and musical clapping games, they learn to increase their tolerance for physical closeness (Clarkson 1991). Orff-Schulwerk uses a special instrumentarium that "is easily accessible to children's abilities and offers a variety of timbres and textures" (Froehlich 1996, 25). The instrumentarium includes xylophones, metallophones, glockenspiels of different sizes, tunable drums, cymbals, and recorders. Orff-Schulwerk experiences also use many "body percussion" sounds, such as snapping, clapping, *patschen* (tapping the upper legs), and stomping. Beginning Orff-Schulwerk activities use many simple musical elements or forms, such as pentatonic scales, ostinato patterns (repeating rhythmic, harmonic, melodic, or speech patterns), repetition and exploration/development of simple motives, rondos, canons, chants, call-response, folk songs, children's songs, and musical games. Advanced activities gradually incorporate more complex scales and modes, harmonies, textures, meters, instruments, musical forms, musical dramas, and dance forms. Although originally developed for elementary school-age children, Orff-Schulwerk has been widely adapted to other populations and age levels. When experiences match the group's interests and capabilities, Orff-Schulwerk can be an enjoyable learning process for all age groups, preschoolers through senior citizens (Bitcon 1976; Shamrock 1986).

In Orff music therapy, or clinical Orff-Schulwerk, the music therapist uses the Orff-Schulwerk materials (instrumentarium, speech, movement, supplementary props), processes, and forms to stimulate participation and create situations that allow the clients to express themselves musically; experience themselves as a person through music; make music with others; and use the music experiences to develop needed motor, social, behavioral, communication, cognitive, or emotional skills or deal with current issues (Froehlich 1996; Hilliard 2007; Hollander and Juhrs 1974; Orff 1980; Ponath and Bitcon 1972; Tonchick 1981). According to Gertrud Orff (1980), the Orff-Schulwerk instrumentarium can have three important therapeutic applications: (1) allowing for acoustic-active participation, (2) linking therapist and client while serving both as a distancer and a binding force, and (3) giving the client a means of communication and social practice. Furthermore, as the Orff-Schulwerk materials are applied therapeutically, they enable a "threefold non-verbal communication"

(Orff 1980, 13): from client to material, from client to therapist via the material, and from client to client.

Many Orff-Schulwerk components offer numerous possibilities for clinical applications (Bitcon 1976; Colwell et al. 2008; Froehlich 1996; Hilliard 2007; Orff 1980; Ponath and Bitcon 1972; Tonchick 1981). "The Orff-Schulwerk pedagogy focuses on leading children through four areas of musical development: exploration, imitation, improvisation, and creativity" (Colwell et al. 2008, 17).For example, the emphasis on rhythm and the integration of speech, body, and musical rhythms can facilitate motor skill development. The emphasis on body movement and playing instruments also helps develop motor skills in addition to facilitating development of concepts such as body image, directionality, laterality, and spatial orientation. Chanting and singing, which are important parts of many Orff-Schulwerk activities, can stimulate vocalization and help develop speech and language skills. The content of chants and songs also can help clients learn information, develop coping skills, and explore and verbalize feelings (Bitcon 1976, 2000; Froehlich 1996; Ponath and Bitcon 1972). Nonverbal clients still can participate freely in many aspects of chants and rondos through movement, body percussion, or use of instruments. McRae (1982) gives several suggestions for adapting traditional Orff-Schulwerk activities to the needs of special populations. Colwell et al. (2008, 18) expands this information to include an overview of clinical applications and authors who have contributed information on their use of this method.

The musical forms used in Orff-Schulwerk activities can have important uses in therapy. For example, the rondo form (alternation of group chant and individual responses) can structure routines, such as turn-taking and group versus individual participation, while allowing individuals to give creative contributions within a nonthreatening atmosphere and receive immediate reinforcement from the group (Bitcon 1976, 2000; Froehlich 1996; Ponath and Bitcon 1972). Small, repetitious forms also work well with clients who have limited attention spans; in addition, they can be expanded or lengthened easily as the clients' attention spans increase (Tonchick 1981). Improvisation (using instruments, movement, speech, rhythm, etc.) and creativity, integral parts of Orff-Schulwerk, also can be important therapeutic tools (Bruscia 1987, 1989c; Froehlich 1996; Orff 1980). Since Orff-Schulwerk activities are usually group experiences, they also can help clients develop important socialization and group cooperation skills.

Orff-Schulwerk techniques have been used clinically with a wide variety of populations, including individuals who are intellectually disabled (Bitcon 1976, 2000; Dervan 1982; McRae 1982; Orff 1980; Ponath and Bitcon 1976), autistic (Hollander and Juhrs 1974), behaviorally disturbed (Orff 1980), learning disabled (Rink 1989), hearing impaired (Bitcon 1976, 2000; Darrow 1985; Darrow and Gfeller 1991; McRae 1982; Orff 1980), visually impaired (Bitcon 1976;

McRae 1982; Orff 1980), speech impaired (McRae 1982; Orff 1980), orthopedically impaired (McRae 1982; Orff 1980), hospitalized children (Froehlich, 1996), and elderly (Bitcon 1976, 2000). In addition, since the Orff-Schulwerk instrumentarium is so readily accessible to clients with little musical experience or training, music therapists often use Orff instruments in other improvisational activities and techniques (e.g., Goldberg 1989). Of course, Orff-Schulwerk activities and experiences by themselves will not facilitate therapeutic changes in clients; they are only a framework for therapeutic work and direction. The therapist always must keep individual goals in mind and consciously direct, structure, and adapt the experiences based on individual client responses to help the clients reach their therapeutic goals (Orff 1980; Ponath and Bitcon 1972).

Hilliard (2007) studied the effects of Orff-based music therapy and social work groups on two conditions: (1) childhood grief symptoms and (2) behavioral distress. His subjects were 26 children, mean age = 8 years, selected from three schools. All had experienced the death of a loved one within the last two years. They were assigned to three groups: music therapy, social work, and wait-list control. He found that children in both the social work and music therapy groups showed "significant improvement in the behavioral distress" (134) compared with children in the control group, as measured by the Behavior Rating Index for Children (BRIC) (Stiffinan, Oime, Evans, Feldman, and Keeney 1984). Grief symptoms did not improve in the social work or control group; however,

> participants who engaged in the music therapy groups . . . showed significant improvement from the pre- to the posttest scores on the BP [Bereavement Group Questionnaire for Parents and Guardians (Tonkins and Lambert 1999)] indicating a reduction in grief symptoms. . . . This study supports the use of Orff-based music therapy in treating childhood bereavement needs. (135)

Clinical Applications of Kodály Concepts

Zoltan Kodály (1882–1967) believed that everyone in his native Hungary, not just the musically gifted, "should receive training in the reading and writing of music just as he received training in the reading and writing of his native language" (Landis and Carder 1972, 41). To this end, Kodály devised a carefully planned, sequential music curriculum using native Hungarian folk songs to teach basic musical concepts to young children. The Kodály approach emphasizes relative solmization, rote learning, and "inner hearing" (i.e., mental rehearsal). Techniques include "signs, games, clapping, reading musical notes, rhythmic notation, and, most centrally, singing" (Hurwitz et al. 1975, 45). Intellectual concepts are addressed only after performance skills have been thoroughly acquired.

The Education through Music (ETM) approach of Mary Helen Richards, first developed for music education in the late 1950s and early 1960s, adapts Kodály methods to American children and American folk songs (Bennett 1987). In developing ETM, Richards met with Kodály and incorporated his suggestions. ETM utilizes characteristic rhythms and melodic patterns of American folk songs (which are somewhat different than those of Hungarian folk songs) to reach children *through* music, using active involvement in making music (especially singing) to focus and organize responses and gradually develop more refined levels of musical knowledge. The method gives priority to the development of social and communication skills through cooperative group music activities involving "singing, playing, problem solving and studying" (Bennett 1987, 41) and uses children's responses to shape subsequent teaching strategies and lesson plans (Bennett 1987).

Some music therapists and music educators who work with disabled students have found that Kodály methods, techniques, and approaches can be very useful for working with individuals with varied disabilities, such as intellectual disabilities (Lathom 1974), hearing impairments (Darrow and Cohen 1991; Darrow and Gfeller 1991), learning disabilities (Hurwitz et al. 1975; Lathom 1974), or emotional disturbances (Lathom 1974). Froehlich (1996) and Schulberg (1981) observed that several aspects of the Kodály philosophy, such as the belief that every individual should be able to participate in and enjoy music, the careful attention given to the structure and presentation of music and musical learning, the use of music indigenous to the culture as a basis for learning, and the emphasis on experiential involvement rather than note reading, are used in many music therapy approaches.

Lathom (1974) noted several ways to use Kodály methods in music therapy contexts. In the Kodály approach, carefully selected and sequenced materials provide for thorough learning and repetition at each step, thereby giving the clients security in the learning situation and providing them with the skills to progress successfully. Learning is first accomplished through imitation, not by following complex verbal instructions. Musical performance skills are learned thoroughly by rote before being connected with symbols or intellectual concepts. Thus, difficulty with symbols or concepts does not prevent a client from developing and deriving pleasure from musical performance skills. The visual aids provided by the solmization hand signals (a trademark of the Kodály approach) provide an additional form of sensory input that may facilitate the learning process. In addition, hand signals can provide important visual and kinesthetic pitch references for hearing-impaired individuals (Darrow and Cohen 1991; Darrow and Gfeller 1991) or provide wrist rotation and finger flexion/extension exercises for those with motor difficulties (Zinar 1987). Arm signal variations have been developed for those who are unable to use hand signals (Bennett 1987), so individuals with fine motor difficulties also may benefit from the additional sensory input of this method.

Other researchers have found that many components of the Kodály method, such as its emphasis on sensorimotor involvement to develop rhythmic skills, its strong connection between music and language, its structured, sequential approach to singing, and its emphasis on building listening skills and auditory memory, can help learning-disabled individuals improve rhythmic, attention, spatial, and sequencing skills that are important for reading and academic achievement (Hurwitz et al. 1975). Moreover, since the Kodály approach tries to promote close and secure relationships by emphasizing eye contact and individual attention and by incorporating various degrees of physical closeness or touching in musical games, it also can be helpful in developing social skills. However, those who work with emotionally disturbed individuals must be careful to note that any necessary contact required is within the individual's tolerance (Lathom 1974).

Clinical Applications of Dalcroze Eurhythmics

While singing is predominant in the Kodály approach, the Dalcroze method focuses on natural movement responses to rhythm as the vehicle for learning and internalizing music skills (Bachman 1991; Frego, Liston, Hama, and Gillmeister 2008; Froehlich 1996; Landis and Carder 1972; Mead 1986; Schulberg 1981). Frego et al. (2008, 25) point out that "Jaques-Dalcroze believed that the goal of every musician is to be sensitive and expressive, and to express music through movement, sound, thought, feeling, and creation." Emile Jaques-Dalcroze (1865–1950) used the term *eurhythmics* to describe his system of rhythmic movement exercises that used body motion to help individuals develop an internal feel for musical rhythm, flow, and phrasing by linking experiential movement with cognitive processing. Eurhythmics mobilizes both mind and body as individuals act, react, and adapt to the rhythmic/musical environment (Bachman 1991). In addition to eurhythmics, the Dalcroze method also includes ear training and solfege singing to develop inner hearing, as well as improvisation through movement, speech, song, and instruments to encourage spontaneity, creativity, and freedom in music making to move students beyond mere mechanical reproduction of notes. As students work on developing both inner hearing and their kinesthetic or muscle sense, rhythmic body movement links with cognitive awareness (Froehlich 1996) and individuals experience with their "whole being the elements of time, space, and energy as they happen in music" (Mead 1986, 46). As they help individuals learn to mobilize their mind and body in response to music, Dalcroze programs can enhance any person's ability "to act, react, and adapt to the surrounding world in order to cope with it to best advantage" (Bachman 1991, 21). In addition, since it requires no preexistent musical talent on the part of the participant and can be adapted to enhance the functioning of individuals of many different age and ability levels, Dalcroze techniques can be very useful for music therapy as well as music education programs. It even has been used in college solfege and ear training classes. As Frego et al. (2008, 28) remark, "Musicians should be able to hear what they write and write what they hear."

Since the early twentieth century, some Dalcroze teachers have used eurhythmics programs therapeutically to help individuals who were blind or deaf or had mental or physical impairments or serious maladjustment problems (Bachman 1991). Dalcroze himself taught music to blind students in Barcelona (Bachman 1991; Frego et al. 2008; Landis and Carder 1972). He devised special eurhythmics exercises to help blind people develop spatial awareness and spatial concepts, tactile sensibility, muscular sense and consciousness, and increased auditory skills. Dalcroze felt that the interaction between teacher and class through music helped compensate for the loss of the usual nonverbal cues of teacher approval (e.g., smiles). Kersten (1981) also found that Dalcroze rhythmic movement exercises were very useful in helping visually impaired individuals gain confidence in exploring space.

Because the movement to music activities of eurhythmics programs can reach the level of unconscious emotional response, eurhythmics exercises can serve as tools for educating and expressing feelings, something that may be an important aspect of therapy for individuals who have emotional disturbances, behavior disorders, developmental disabilities, or mental illnesses. As music therapists accompany an individual's movement with improvised music, thus placing the movement in a musical context, they also can nurture the individual's physical self-expression, facilitate purposeful interactions with music and others, and guide individuals in exploring feelings and ideas as they move to different types of music (Hibben 1984). Frego (2007) used Dalcroze eurythmics in working with music teachers in Bosnia and Herzegovina. All had been diagnosed with post-traumatic stress disorder (reported in Frego et al. 2008, 32).

Clinically, eurhythmics programs have been used to benefit individuals who have behavioral and learning disabilities (Hibben 1984), serious maladjustment problems (Bachman 1991), visual impairments (Bachman 1991; Kersten 1981), hearing impairments (Bachman 1991; Brick 1973; Darrow 1985; Swaiko 1974), intellectual disabilities (Bachman 1991; Hibben 1984), physical disabilities (Bachman 1991), mental illness (Benenzon 1981; Schneider 1961), autism (Bachman 1991), or who are elderly (Heidenreich n.d.). Eurhythmics programs may be particularly helpful in improving speech rhythms and auditory perception and awareness in hearing-impaired individuals (Brick 1973; Darrow 1985); increasing freedom of movement and spatial awareness in visually impaired individuals (Kersten 1981); improving motor planning and coordination in intellectually disabled individuals (Hibben 1984);

strengthening body image/awareness, improving awareness of physical and emotional boundaries, and increasing motor control and coordination in individuals who have behavior and learning disabilities (Hibben 1984); increasing rhythmic awareness and awareness of self and others in mentally ill individuals (Benenzon 1981); and improving physical, mental, and spiritual health in elderly individuals (Heidenreich n.d.). Schneider (1961) also found that eurhythmics programs improved reaction time in patients who had schizophrenia.

Other Techniques Sometimes Used in Music Therapy

Less has been written or researched on the Suzuki method or vibroacoustic techniques. However, they deserve mention because some music therapists have had success with these techniques. They do not have sufficient literature to call them models of music therapy, but there are some reports.

Sukuki Method

The Suzuki method is based on the mother tongue concept, the idea that just as children learn their native language by being immersed in its sounds from birth, so they also can develop exceptional musical abilities if they are immersed in rich musical environments (Froehlich 1996; Kendall 1986; Suzuki 1969). Shinichi Suzuki (1898–1998) believed all people are born with musical ability that can be developed if given a proper environment and sufficient repetition of stimuli. His talent education approach begins with a listening program at birth and introduces children to playing musical instruments (e.g., violin, cello, piano, harp) at age two and a half or three years. Early learning is based on imitation, using exercises and games as well as instrument playing, with constant repetition leading to mastery and intimate knowledge of material. Parents, teachers, and children are cooperative partners in the learning process, with parents being actively involved in home teaching and practice. Note reading is postponed until the child is technically well-established on the instrument (Kendall 1986).

Some music therapists, noting similarities between Suzuki's philosophy of and approach to music education and music therapy principles and practices, are beginning to explore the clinical application of Suzuki methods (Froehlich 1996; Metzler 1982). Suzuki (1969) himself related how his method of violin instruction, with patient and persistent application, could help physically disabled students improve muscle strength and motor control (27–29) and make violin playing accessible to blind students (58–60). The Suzuki method has been used effectively with individuals who have developmental disabilities, visual impairments, learning disabilities, cerebral palsy, or chronic illnesses, as well as with elderly individuals (Froehlich 1996; Suzuki 1969). His approach is all-inclusive:

> Suzuki's life approach to developing a music making ability in any individual, regardless of age or ability, gives evidence that he would not conceive of music therapy and music education of the exceptional as separate fields, but rather view them as extensions of one another. (Froehlich, 1996, 334)

Vibroacoustic Techniques

Vibroacoustic techniques use special equipment to provide both auditory input and vibrotactile stimulation to the entire body by applying both music's auditory and tactile aspects for clinical purposes. According to Skille (1989, 62), who originated vibroacoustic treatment techniques in Norway in 1968,

> VibroAcoustic therapy is the therapeutic use of VibroAcoustic (VA) equipment and software that emit low frequency sound signals [range of 30 Hz to 120 Hz] mixed with special audio cassettes. It is a process in which vibrations are applied directly to the body in the form of low frequency sinus [sic] tones in combination with selected music.

Skille requires potential users to receive instruction in the proper use of the equipment before purchasing it. When the VA equipment is used for therapy, music and low tone frequencies are selected and calibrated to each patient's individual needs. Thus, the music therapist plays an important role in matching the music and vibrational components to the client's unique needs and responses of the client, in monitoring responses and adapting treatment accordingly, and in supporting the client before, during, and after the treatment (Wigram 1995). VibroAcoustic Therapy has been used in Norway, Denmark, Finland, England, Germany, and Estonia. In the United States, Chesky and Michel (1991, 34) have applied vibroacoustic techniques clinically through their specially designed piece of equipment, the Music Vibration Table (MVT)™, which "consists of a base table, a sound system, a vibrating membrane (tabletop), and a computerized vibration feedback system that measures and controls the transmission of vibrations as they affect a subject's body." Studies and clinical work using VibroAcoustic Therapy (MVT) suggest that combining music and low-frequency sound vibrations can have a number of beneficial effects, such as pain reduction, alleviation of bronchospasm in asthmatic conditions, increased contact allowed by children on the autistic spectrum, reduced muscle tone and increased range of motion in individuals with spastic conditions, reduction of heart rate and blood pressure, and decreased anxiety (Chesky and Michel 1991; Skille 1989; Wigram 1995).

DEVELOPMENTAL MUSIC THERAPY

Developmental Music Therapy (DMT) is a particular system of music therapy techniques based on the Developmental Therapy model which originated at the Rutland Center for emotionally disturbed children in Athens, Georgia. It is "a psychoeducational approach to therapeutic intervention with young children who have serious emotional and behavioral disorders" (Wood et al. 1974, 2). DMT draws its theoretical orientation from child development, child psychology, special education, and learning theory, and uses the changes and sequences of normal child development to sequence goals and facilitate therapeutic development (Sandness 1991). The process is primarily geared to children aged two through eight years, but it has been used successfully with children as old as fourteen years.

Music therapists working in childhood education settings with children who have emotional disturbances or behavior disorders face the additional challenge of translating traditional music therapy activities and practices into an approach that incorporates sequential patterns of growth and development. The DMT system was developed to help meet this challenge. Since music skills develop sequentially just as skills in other areas, music therapists using the DMT approach must also "consider the musical capabilities at various ages, in order to design therapeutic experiences appropriate to each child's level of functioning" (Wood et al. 1974, 6). For a more detailed explanation of the developmental sequence of learning music skills see Lathom-Radocy (2014, 33–34) and Radocy and Boyle (2012), as well as Deliege and Sloboda (1996).

The DMT program provides a series of sequential music therapy experiences designed to complement the Developmental Therapy curriculum. There are five DMT stages: (1) responding to the musical environment with pleasure, (2) responding to the musical environment with success, (3) learning music skills for successful group participation, (4) investing in group music processes, and (5) applying individual and group music skills in new situations. In each stage, the therapist uses various types of music activities to pursue goals in four basic curricular areas: behavior, communication, socialization, and academics. In stage one, children learn to respond to the sound environment with pleasure and to trust the music therapist and themselves. In stage two, children learn specific musical skills while learning to participate successfully in routines, use words to affect others in constructive ways, interact appropriately with others, and perform activities incorporating concepts of same/different, labels, colors, and numbers. In stage three, children learn to apply their individual music, behavior, communication, academic, and motor skills in group situations. Activities used during stage three require cooperation and sharing among group members to produce a group product. In stage four, the focus of music therapy shifts to group commitment as children learn to value the group and function in a less clinically oriented environment. In stage five, children learn to generalize their skills to nonclinical settings. During this stage, the music therapist may function as a consultant to help children become involved in music situations common to their everyday environment (Wood et al. 1974). As children progress through the DMT stages, they become increasingly well-adjusted. The music therapist's role, the amount and type of intervention required, and the type of musical environment and musical experiences needed by the children vary with each stage (Graham 1975; Purvis and Samet 1976; Wood et al. 1974):

> In assessment, the therapist should have recorded the child's level of listening, moving, instrument playing, and singing skills. These then can be used to develop activities that will allow the child to identify and express feelings. Later, this may be the basis for understanding the feelings of others and responding in adaptive, culturally appropriate ways. (Lathom-Radocy 2014, 34)

BEHAVIORAL MUSIC THERAPY

Behavioral models focus on observable behaviors, not underlying processes. These approaches are based on the theories and work of behavioral psychologists such as Pavlov, Guthrie, Hull, Watson, Thorndike, Skinner, and Wolpe (Atterbury 1990; Kaplan and Sadock 1991; Scovel 1990; Standley, Johnson, Robb, Brownell, and Kim 2008). Therapists who work from a behavioral orientation carefully observe a client's behaviors and target specific undesirable behaviors for change. They then strive to create an environment that rewards positive, desirable behaviors and does not reward negative, undesirable behaviors. Treatment uses operant or classical conditioning techniques, employing various types of reinforcers to increase more appropriate or adaptive behaviors and responses (Gfeller and Davis 2008). Therapists also may establish contingencies to help increase desired behaviors. Other techniques include token economies, modeling methods, systematic desensitization, self-management programs, and assertion training. In behavioral approaches, the therapist assumes an active and directive role, structuring the environment and providing rewards and consequences to help the client achieve the desired changes (Scovel 1990). Throughout the history of music therapy in the United States since the formation of the National Association for Music Therapy in 1950, there has been an emphasis on music therapy using behavioral approaches. This is evident in the research literature (Gfeller and Davis 2008; Standley et al. 2008).

Music is a powerful contingency and motivator for appropriate behaviors that can be used effectively in both group and individual settings, and applications of behavioral principles and techniques to music therapy treatment approaches have been investigated extensively and widely documented (Hanser 1987, 1995; Madsen 1981; Standley 1996a; Standley et al. 2008). A survey conducted in the mid-1980s found that music therapists used behaviorism more than any other single treatment strategy or approach (Choi 2008; Taylor 1987a). Research has shown that many different types of music experiences (e.g., music listening, instrumental lessons, preferred creative experiences or group music activities) can serve as positive reinforcement to help increase or maintain desired behaviors (Hanser 1987; Madsen 1981). In her meta-analysis of 98 studies employing music as a contingency for therapeutic or educational objectives, Standley (1996a) found that contingent music was a more effective reinforcer than either contingent nonmusic stimuli or continuous music. Gfeller and Davis (2008, 469) observed that "one of the special and powerful tools that music therapists have to offer is *music itself*." While the contingent presentation of music can effectively increase behaviors, the contingent withdrawal or interruption of music (e.g., stopping or interrupting music listening, removing instruments, or taking away participation in music group when undesirable behaviors occur) can effectively decrease behaviors.

Behavioral music therapy techniques have been used successfully with many different age groups and client populations in varied clinical settings (Hanser 1987; Michel 1985). (For a brief history of behaviorism in music therapy, see Standley et al. 2008, 107–109.) For example, several studies mentioned in previous chapters show the effectiveness of behavioral music therapy approaches with individuals with intellectual disabilities (Bellamy and Sontag 1973; Dileo 1975; Dorow 1976; Edison 1989; Garwood 1988; Johnson and Phillips 1971; Madsen 1981; Metzler 1974; Saperston et al. 1980; Underhill and Harris 1974; Walker 1972), are electively mute (Castellano and Wilson 1970), have autism (Mahlberg 1973; Staum and Flowers 1984; Watson 1979), are disadvantaged or at-risk (Michel 1971), are hyperactive (Reid et al. 1975; Scott 1970), have behavior problems or behavioral disorders (Presti 1984; Steele 1968; Wilson 1976), are receiving acute care mental health services (Wolfe 1996), have cerebral palsy (Wolfe 1980), are comatose (Boyle 1987, 1989), or have Alzheimer's disease or related dementias (Fitzgerald-Cloutier 1993). Many music-based relaxation training approaches or self-management techniques also employ behavioral techniques (Scartelli 1989; Scovel 1990). Silverman (2007) found that cognitive-behavioral approaches are selected most frequently by music therapists working with clients who have behavioral emotional disturbances.

COGNITIVE MUSIC THERAPY

Cognitive therapy was an outgrowth of learning theory and social psychology, e.g., Bandura's Social Learning Theory (SLT) (Bandura and Adams 1977). In approaches, treatment focuses on helping clients become aware of negative or irrational thought patterns or beliefs that create stress or cause feelings of inadequacy. Confronting these maladaptive thought patterns and identifying life experiences in which they operate allow reality testing. Finding ways to reverse the negative or irrational thinking leads to altered behavior (Gfeller and Davis 2008). Cognitive therapy has roots in a potpourri of theories and therapeutic approaches (Meagher, Jr. 1982, 501). Examples of cognitive approaches include Beck's cognitive therapy (1976, updated by Clark and Beck 1999); Ellis's rational emotive therapy (RET) (1998); Glasser's reality therapy (1965); Maultsby's rational behavior therapy (RBT) (1977); and Meichenbaum's cognitive behavior modification (1977, discussed by Kaplan and Sadoc 1991; Scovel 1990; Thaut and Gfeller, 1992). Music therapy interventions have been combined with several of these approaches, including transactional analysis (Arnold 1975; Schulberg 1981; Shreffler 1976; Williams 1979), rational behavior therapy (Maultsby 1977), and rational emotive therapy (Bryant 1987; Parente 1989). Some music therapists also structure music experiences within a cognitive behavioral framework as part of their treatment interventions (Brodsky and Sloboda 1997; Cassity and Theobold 1990; Justice 1994; Murphy 1992; Parente 1989; Slotoroff 1994).

Music Therapy and Rational Emotive Therapy

Ellis's (1998) rational emotive therapy (RET) conceives behavioral events as occurring in three steps: (a) an activating event or situation to which the person responds, (b) the person's beliefs about or perceptions and interpretations of the situation, and (c) the emotional and behavioral consequences. RET aims to help clients detect irrational beliefs (step b) that result in unhealthy emotional and behavioral consequences (step c). Intervention is based on debating and refuting irrational beliefs, especially by examining "musts" and "shoulds" that often are evidence of unrealistic or irrational thinking and self-imposed demands. After identifying and disputing these irrational beliefs or self-defeating ideas, clients learn to replace them with new, healthier ways of thinking and reacting. The therapist acts as a guide, helping clients detect irrational beliefs and facilitating their efforts to express and resolve conflicts and adopt healthier thought patterns (Bryant 1987; Scovel 1990). Music therapists who have used RET with song writing include Maultsby (1977) and Parente (1989).

According to Bryant (1987, 31), clients perceive and approach music therapy experiences in the same way they approach all life experiences: "Values, attitudes, and beliefs, both rational and irrational, are brought to bear in all experiences, and are therefore subsequently projected upon the client's approach to the music therapy setting." Consequently, by superimposing cognitive frameworks on music-related behaviors, music therapists can use music experiences to help clients examine the behavioral or emotional consequences of irrational or unrealistic beliefs, define and challenge these beliefs, develop new attitudes, and relate these to other life situations, thus ameliorating emotional disorders. Useful music therapy techniques in this process include discussing song lyrics to explore beliefs and emotional reactions and exploring beliefs about emotional/ behavioral reactions to music performance situations (Bryant 1987; Scovel 1990; Thaut and Gfeller 1992). Once irrational beliefs are identified, challenged, and replaced with healthier attitudes and thought patterns in the context of music experiences, the therapist can help clients see how these attitudes also may relate to their approach to other life situations (Bryant 1987).

Hilliard (2001, 111) used cognitive and behavioral approaches in treating women with eating disorders:

> Because cognitive issues are important in treating eating disordes, a small (maximum of 10 patients) music therapy group met weekly and addressed more insight-oriented aspects of the eating disorder through the use of music therapy. . . . Interventions focused on increasing self-esteem, embodying a sense of empowerment, and challenging negative and self-defeating body distortions.

Music therapy interventions used within a cognitive/behavioral framework can effectively help clients with eating disorders (a) increase self-awareness and self-esteem, (b) increase awareness of irrational or destructive feelings and behaviors, (c) decrease anxiety that may be experienced as they try to discontinue their eating disorder behaviors, and (d) find new ways of taking control and coping with emotions. Helpful music therapy interventions in this context include (1) music-reinforced relaxation, using music to complement, support, and ground muscle stretching, deep breathing, progressive muscle relaxation, and directed imagery techniques; (2) structured music therapy groups, using music and movement, hand bells and choir chimes, group singing, or instrumental improvisation; (3) insight-oriented music/creative arts and imagery techniques, using group adaptations of the Bonny method of Guided Imagery and Music (GIM) or drawing or writing in response to stories or poems read to music; and (4) musical theater productions utilizing songs expressing personal affirmation or relating to treatment issues (Justice 1994; Parente 1989).

Music Therapy and Rational Behavior Therapy

Maultsby's (1977, 1984) rational behavior therapy (RBT) is derived from RET and based on a logical synthesis of several learning theories that apply only to human beings. RBT's comprehensive methodology deals with cognitive, emotional, and physical behaviors and aims to help people solve problems by teaching them practical, rational techniques for emotional self-help. According to RBT theory, people's thoughts and perceptions create, maintain, or eliminate their emotions. Therefore, if they wish to change emotive feelings without drugs, people must change their thoughts or perceptions. RBT also recognizes that emotive feelings are only a small fraction of total emotion, which includes perceptions and thoughts that give logical support to feelings.

RBT helps individuals assess how emotionally healthy or unhealthy their behaviors are by providing five rules or criteria for healthy or rational behaviors (Maultsby 1977, 1984). According to RBT, rational or healthy cognitive, emotive, and physical behaviors (1) are based on obvious fact or objective reality, not subjective opinions; (2) help individuals protect themselves; (3) help individuals achieve their short- and long-term goals in the best or most efficient way possible; (4) help individuals avoid significant undesirable conflict with others; and (5) help individuals feel the emotions they want to feel.

Because music can both stimulate and powerfully reinforce new learning, therapeutically structured music experiences can be a valuable tool for RBT (Maultsby 1977). For example, song lyrics (often specially composed or adapted by the therapist to express rational ideas) can help individuals learn and practice new thought patterns. Positive emotive reactions can be reinforced through repetition of the lyrics; and, eventually, the lyrics can become cues for rational, logical emotive, cognitive, and physical behaviors. With the therapist's aid, clients might also use song writing or lyric discussion activities to identify motivations of behaviors or discuss solutions to personal problems. In addition, singing or listening to recordings of song lyrics that restate insights or ideas gained in RBT sessions could provide clients with "an excellent emotional self-defense against unhealthy, negative emotions between therapy sessions" (Maultsby 1984, 105). Music therapists also might structure song writing, listening/discussion, or instrumental improvisation activities that could guide clients through RBT techniques like rational self-analysis or facilitate their practicing rational emotive imagery to establish new, healthy patterns or habits of thought, perception, and behavior.

Music Therapy and Cognitive Behavioral Approaches

In recent years, more music therapists have been using music therapy techniques within a cognitive behavioral framework as they strive to develop approaches and interventions that help clients achieve lasting, positive results within only a few sessions (Murphy 1992). "There is a definite need for short-term, efficacious treatment in mental and physical health" (Luce 2001, 101). Luce wrote about cognitive therapy and music therapy as ways to meet this need. Some approaches are based on Yalom's (1983) model of group psychotherapy. Music therapy interventions following cognitive behavioral models such as this have two important facets: (1) the musical experience that provides the activating event in which the clients are involved and to which they respond and (2) the verbal discussion (processing and feedback) of the clients' experience in and responses to the musical event.

A typical music therapy session structure in this orientation may include (a) an introduction by the therapist that focuses the clients on the task; (b) a music warm-up with the therapist modeling a response; (c) a music experience (e.g., improvisation, creating a group song); (d) therapist-facilitated verbal processing and discussion of the musical experience and how clients' responses/ experiences/reactions relate to their own specific emotional or behavioral issues; and (e) closure, led by the therapist (Murphy 1992). Music activities are often very effective in quickly illuminating the clients' maladaptive thought processes and/or modes of interaction, for they reach clients on an immediate, emotional level that bypasses verbal rationalizations and defenses: "While words can accomplish the same end results, for some patients it is the nonverbal experience that may best bring to conscious awareness recurrent, self-defeating patterns" (Murphy 1992, 105).

Music therapists can use various techniques and music-based interventions, such as singing, song lyric discussion or creating, music listening/discussion, music performance, music improvisation, or music/movement techniques (Luce 2001), within a cognitive behavioral framework to help clients change disordered ways of thinking and build healthier, more adaptive ways of thinking and relating to the world and others around them. For example, Slotoroff (1994) found that structured and improvisational drumming techniques and cognitive behavioral processing approaches could help adolescents with conduct disorders increase awareness of their thoughts and feelings and practice ways of controlling their anger and impulsive behavior. These same techniques also were very effective in helping abused female adolescents increase awareness of their thoughts and feelings and practice ways of changing their behavior, so that they felt more empowered and more assertive. These changes occurred very quickly in music therapy treatment, with positive responses often seen in only one or two sessions. In another study, Brodsky and Sloboda (1997) found that, for some clients who have extreme stress and anxiety over certain situations, the use of music plus vibrotactile stimulation or music-based relaxation and imagery training within a cognitive behavioral framework can be just as effective as traditional psychotherapeutic counseling in reducing symptoms of anxiety.

HUMANISTIC MUSIC THERAPY

Humanistic therapy models include Rollo May's existential therapy (1961), and Fritz Perls's Gestalt therapy (1973). Gestalt refers to the "whole, configuration, integration, pattern, or form" (Patterson 1986, 344). Humanistic approaches emphasize each individual's uniqueness, value, and worth and believe all individuals have the capacity to control their own lives and make good decisions; individuals are responsible for their choices. Therapists who follow a humanistic approach give unconditional acceptance to the client and focus on the here-and-now of the therapeutic relationship. They develop a supportive relationship so that the client can feel secure enough to confront basic questions about the meaning of life and achieve insights about his/her own life, moving beyond the basics of existence to a state of "self-actualization" (Maslow 1968), a life filled with meaning and a sense of well-being and completeness: "Whether one feels free to choose and control and how one uses that freedom play a significant and central role in humanistic and existential approaches to abnormality" (Rosenhan and Seligman 1984, 115).

Music therapists who work within a humanistic framework use various types of music experiences (e.g., music listening or discussion, music improvisation, GIM) for building and developing a supportive relationship with clients and a means through which clients can achieve insight and increase their life quality and sense of meaning and fulfillment (Thaut and Gfeller 1992). Music therapy techniques described earlier in this chapter that have a humanistic orientation include the improvisational models of Nordoff-Robbins (*Creative Music Therapy*) and Boxill (*Continuum of Awareness*) and the Bonny Method of Guided Imagery and Music. In addition to various clinical improvisation and GIM techniques, music therapists working from within a humanistic framework also may use interventions employing techniques and experiences such as song selection, fantasy and lyric improvisation, music listening, song writing, and music-facilitated life review (Bruscia 1991a; Krout 2005c). Humanistic music therapy approaches can be used successfully with almost every client population, including both those who have various disabilities and those in the general population who are seeking greater meaning or quality in their lives.

BIOMEDICAL MUSIC THERAPY

A biomedical treatment model focuses on the biological factors (e.g., biochemical imbalances, genetic problems, physical abnormalities or illnesses) that underlie emotional, physical, cognitive, or behavioral disorders. Once a diagnosis is made, treatments that address the biological abnormalities or problems are prescribed (Scovel 1990; Thaut and Gfeller 1992). These may include medications, special procedures (e.g., surgeries), changes in diet or lifestyle, or changes in environment. In disorders where stress is a factor, treatments also may focus on changing behavioral responses to stressors, including such things as structured relaxation training.

As medical research technology has developed to the point where one may observe and precisely measure music's actual effects on physical processes, biomedical explanations for the effectiveness of music therapy procedures have increased. Gfeller and Davis (2008, 474) provide some core aspects of a biomedical perspective:

1. The focus on the neurobiological foundations of the human nervous system,
2. A strong emphasis on music perception and active music participation as a form of stimulation that activates physiological and neurophysiological processes in the body (which include affect and cognition as part of neural behavior), and
3. The belief that the unique structural and cultural properties of music can be harnessed to access brain and behavior functions to facilitate and to promote healing and rehabilitation.

Drawing on decades of research related to the physiological effects of music and music therapy procedures, Taylor (1997) proposed a biomedical theory that focuses on establishing a medical basis for music therapy treatment procedures, independent of other psychological theories or intervention strategies. The key to Taylor's approach is the research in neuroscience indicating that the brain generates all human behavior (Gaston, 1968). Therefore, investigations into the influence of music and participation in music experiences on brain functioning will provide an objective framework for explaining the effectiveness of *all* types of music therapy applications and procedures. Krout (2007, 135) lists many authors who have referred to physiological functioning as a part of wellness.

According to Taylor (1997, 121), biomedical music therapy is "the enhancement of human capabilities through the planned use of musical influences on human brain functioning." This definition is based on his Biomedical Theory of Music Therapy, which, in summary, states that

> music influences human behavior by affecting the brain and subsequently other bodily structures in ways that are observable, identifiable, measurable, and predictable, thereby providing the necessary foundation for its use in treatment procedures. (Taylor 1997, 52)

In biomedical music therapy, then, the brain and investigations of music's direct effects on the brain and the human nervous system are essential components for defining music therapy and for guiding music therapy practice. The four hypotheses included in Taylor's Biomedical Theory of Music Therapy deal with the specific brain and nervous system processes involved in music's effect on (1) pain perception, (2) emotional behavior, (3) motor activity (includes both physical functioning and interpersonal communication skills), and (4) the physiological processes that indicate anxiety, stress, and tension. These processes cover all areas of human functioning commonly addressed by music therapy interventions, thus making interventions based on biomedical music therapy approaches applicable to almost any client population.

In citing clinical examples to support his theory, Taylor (1997) provides biomedical explanations for the positive influence of music and music-based experiences on (a) pain management in surgery, childbirth, cancer treatment, coronary treatment, burn treatment, and pain rehabilitation; (b) emotional control in physical medicine situations (organ transplants, oncology, pediatrics, hemodialysis) and the biomedical determinants of eating disorders and behavior disorders; (c) the recovery of physical and communication skills; and (d) anxiety and stress management for infants and children, individuals undergoing dental procedures, patients with psychotic disorders, and suicidal individuals. Biomedical music therapy procedures include all the types of music experiences commonly used in other approaches: singing, playing instruments, listening to music, discussing music, moving or relaxing to music, and creating or improvising music. The difference lies not in the techniques themselves but in the music therapist's explanation of the techniques' effectiveness, especially regarding their direct effects on the human nervous system. Taylor (1997, 121) believes that the biomedical theory of music therapy, grounded as it is in extensive and expanding amounts of empirical, scientifically verifiable data, can both elevate the status of the music therapy profession in medical and health care circles and "provide a unifying conceptual framework for many of the various theoretical positions and clinical modalities existing within music therapy."

NEUROLOGIC MUSIC THERAPY

Neurologic Music Therapy (NMT) is another biomedical approach to research and practice of music therapy. Based on the sizeable body of research on music and brain function, NMT has provided standardization of supplication and terminology (Gfeller and Davis 2008). The NMT model is based on neuroscience and perceptual models, which "are based on how music perception and music production engage the brain in ways that can be meaningfully translated and generalized to nonmusical therapeutic learning and training" (Thaut 2008, 61–62).

NMT Techniques include:

1. *Rhythmic auditory stimulation (RAS)*, "a technique of rhythmic motor cueing to facilitate training of movements that is intrinsically and biologically rhythmical" (Thaut, 2008, 138).
2. *Patterned Sensory Enhancement (PSE)*, which "utilizes all musical elements in a multidimensional framework to use sound patterns to cue movement patterns" (150).
3. *Therapeutic Instrumental Music Performance (TIMP)*, which "uses playing of musical instruments to exercise and simulate functional movement patterns in motor therapy . . . to train appropriate ranges of motion, endurance, strength, limb coordination, and functional movements entailing finger dexterity, grasp, flexion/extension, adduction/abduction, rotation, supination/pronation, and so on" (139).

Becoming qualified to use NMT techniques requires extensive graduate level training and supervised practice.

THE PROS AND CONS OF FOLLOWING ONE APPROACH OR ORIENTATION

According to Wheeler (1983), integrating music therapy techniques into a specific psychotherapeutic theory or system can have two important benefits for music therapists: (1) predicting client responses in music therapy and serving as a basis for making predictions about client responses, evaluating treatment, and finding ways to improve results and (2) increasing music therapists' credibility and professional stature, particularly in psychiatric settings. Taylor (1997) also suggested that explaining the effects of music therapy treatment procedures in biomedical terms could elevate music therapy to levels of professional respect and credibility equivalent to those accorded other medical professions and disciplines that have treatment techniques and approaches firmly grounded in verifiable, scientific data. Others have noted the importance of integrating music therapy interventions into specific treatment models and approaches used by other professionals in special education settings in order to minimize client confusion and to assure that all interventions complement and reinforce one another (F. Johnson 1981; Wood et al. 1974).

As important as it is to coordinate therapeutic efforts with other professionals, music therapists also must remember to heed the warning of Gaston (1968b), who cautioned against ceasing to observe and report behavior because of adopting a specific theory or treatment model "so emotionally that the adoption has all the earmarks of a religious conversion" (230). No one theory or treatment model can possibly have all the answers for all clients in all situations. Choi (2008, 108) notes that many believe that good therapists are eclectic: "Whatever the experience, a therapist is responsible for knowing any theoretical bases that influence music's role in their practice, as well as having forethought of how they will direct their practice." While particular therapists or clinics may favor a certain treatment model or approach, therapy teams often find that an eclectic approach, drawing from many models and combining the best features of several approaches, is most helpful in meeting the unique needs of a particular client (Thaut and Gfeller 1992). After thoroughly studying music therapy's relationship to various treatment theories, Ruud (1980, 71) observed that adopting one model to the exclusion of all others would decrease human beings' potential views of themselves and argued that music therapy "ought to be an open field where different models of understanding are given the possibilities to collaborate with each other." The therapist should use whichever models will work best:

> It is important for the therapist to consider which theories provide the best basis for understanding cognitive, emotional, behavioral, and biophysical dimensions, and then reflect on therapeutic approaches that are the best fit for the client's presenting problems, cultural background, and individual personality. (478)

In addition to subscribing exclusively to a particular theory or treatment model, music therapists may be tempted to adopt one particular musical technique (e.g., piano improvisation) to the exclusion of all other techniques and approaches. As this text has noted repeatedly, music therapy interventions are usually most effective when they incorporate, at least initially, instruments, music, and modes of musical experience and expression in accordance with client preferences. While some specific musical techniques, instruments, or types of experiences will be helpful in working with most individuals of given client populations on certain goals, there always will be those individuals for whom those techniques are not particularly effective or for whom they are even contraindicated. Music therapists must *always* carefully assess *individual* client preferences, needs, strengths, and weaknesses and continually observe and evaluate *individual* client responses and behaviors to structure music therapy intervention strategies most effectively. In addition, over the course of their careers, music therapists are very likely to work with individuals of many different age groups with widely varying needs and disabilities (Lathom 1982; Lathom-Radocy 2002, 2014). Therefore, music therapists should be informed about and relatively proficient in numerous musical techniques and approaches for effective use with widely varying client populations. Recognizing that no one existing treatment model or musical technique will be effective for every client in every situation, most music therapists in the United States have adopted an eclectic approach to treatment (Choi 2008; Maranto 1993b; Taylor 1987a).

Music therapists are responsible for being aware of current trends in music, music therapy, psychotherapy, special education, and medicine; for judging the value of these trends; and for putting into practice those procedures they believe are best-suited to their clients (Gfeller and Davis 2008). Integrating music therapy techniques into the psychotherapeutic or educational model used by other professionals on the treatment team certainly will benefit the client, since all will be working toward a common goal in a common way. However, fanatically adopting one theory, model, approach, or technique to the exclusion of all others serves neither clients nor therapist, for no single theory, model, approach, or technique can be most beneficial for all clients in all situations.

Music therapists also should remember that their skills and abilities to assess individual client needs; to relate to clients in and through music experiences; and to structure music experiences to facilitate clients' movement toward positive growth and change, as well as their personal attributes and qualities (e.g., musical creativity, insight, empathy, confidence) are in many ways *more* important to implementing successful music therapy interventions than is adopting any particular technique, approach, or theoretical perspective. As Aigen (1993, 23) observed:

> There is no evidence that the adoption of any one theoretical perspective leads to more efficacious therapy than any other perspective. This is not to say that music therapists do not subscribe to and use elements of a particular theoretical approach, but rather to emphasize that the *person* who makes the interventions is more important than the actual technique or method.

QUESTIONS FOR THOUGHT AND DISCUSSION

1. List and briefly describe some approaches to music therapy practice centered on *particular music techniques*. What special skills or types of training does the music therapist need to use these models of practice? Are there any particular groups of clients who are most likely to benefit from these approaches? Which ones? Why?

2. List and briefly describe some approaches to music therapy practice centered on *particular music education approaches*. What special skills or types of training does the music therapist need to use these models of practice? Are there any particular groups of clients who are most likely to benefit from these approaches? Which ones? Why?

3. List and briefly describe some approaches to music therapy practice based on specific *educational, psychotherapeutic,* or *medical models and theories*. What special skills or types of training does the music therapist need to use these models of practice? Are there any particular groups of clients who are

most likely to benefit from these approaches? Which ones? Why?
4. What one basic principle unites all these schools of practice? Why is this important?
5. What are some advantages and disadvantages of adopting a particular theory or approach to treatment? What must music therapists, working primarily from one technical approach or theoretical orientation, always consider? Why?
6. Is it important for music therapists to be skilled in and aware of a number of different treatment techniques and approaches? Why or why not?

SUGGESTIONS FOR FURTHER READING

Aigen, K. (1998). *Paths of development in Nordoff-Robbins music therapy.* Gilsum, NH: Barcelona.

Bachman, M. L. (1991). *Dalcroze today: An education through and into music.* New York: Oxford University Press.

Bitcon, C. H. (1976; 2000). *Alike and different: The clinical and educational use of Orff-Schulwerk.* Santa Ana, CA: Rosha Press.

Bonny, H. L. (1994). Twenty-one years later: A GIM update. *Music Therapy Perspectives, 12*(2), 70–74.

Bonny, H. L. (2002). Music consciousness: The evolution of Guided Imagery and Music. In L. Summer, (Ed.). Gilsum, NH: Barcelona.

Bonny, H. L., & Savary, L. M. (1990). *Music and your mind: Listening with a new consciousness* (rev. ed.). Barrytown, NY: Station Hill Press.

Bruscia, K. E. (1987). *Improvisational models of music therapy.* Springfield, IL: Charles C Thomas.

Bruscia, K. E. (1989). The practical side of improvisational music therapy. *Music Therapy Perspectives, 6,* 11–15.

Darrow, A-A. (Ed.). (2008). *Introduction to approaches in music therapy* (2nd ed.). Silver Spring, MD: American Music Therapy Association.

Froehlich, M. A. R. (1996). Orff-Schulwerk music therapy in crisis intervention with hospitalized children. In M. A. R. Froehlich (Ed.), *Music therapy with hospitalized children: A creative arts child life approach* (25–36). Cherry Hill, NJ: Jeffrey Books.

Froehlich, M. A. R. (1996). Introduction to current music education methods applicable to music therapy. In M. A. R. Froehlich (Ed.), *Music therapy with hospitalized children: A creative arts child life approach* (330–340). Cherry Hill, NJ: Jeffrey Books.

Hadley, S. (Ed.), (2003). *Psychodynamic music therapy: Case studies.* Gilsum, NH: Barcelona.

Hibben, J. (1984). Movement as musical expression in a music therapy setting. *Music Therapy, 4*(1), 91–97.

Lathom, W. (1974). Application of Kodály concepts in music therapy. *Journal of Music Therapy, 11*(1), 13–20.

McRae, S. W. (1982), The Orff connection . . . reaching the special child. *Music Educators*

Journal, 68(*8*), 32–34.

Music Therapy Perspectives (2014), *32*(*1*). [The entire issues is on Nordoff Robbins Music Therapy.]

Nordoff, P. & Robbins, C. (1977; 2007). *Creative music therapy.* New York: John Day.

Orff, C. (1980). *The Orff music therapy.* London: Schott & Co.

Ponath, L. H. & Bitcon, C. H. (1972). A behavioral analysis of Orff-Schulwerk. *Journal of Music Therapy, 9*(*2*), 56–63.

Priestley, M. (1985). *Music therapy in action* (2nd ed.). St. Louis: MMB Music.

Purvis, J. & Samet, S. (1976). *Music in developmental therapy: A curriculum guide.* Baltimore, MD: University Park Press.

Robbins, C. (2005). A journey into creative music therapy. *Nordoff-Robbins Music Therapy Monograph Series,* Vol. 3. St. Louis: MMB Music.

Ruud, E. (1980). *Music therapy and its relationship to current treatment theories* (rev. Eng. ed.). St. Louis: Magnamusic-Baton.

Schulberg, C. H. (1981). *The music therapy sourcebook: A collection of activities categorized and analyzed.* New York: Human Sciences Press.

Scovel, M. A. (1990). Music therapy within the context of psychotherapeutic models. In R. F. Unkefer (Ed.), *Music therapy in the treatment of adults with mental disorders* (96–108). New York: Schirmer.

Skille, O. (1989). VibroAcoustic therapy. *Music Therapy, 8*(*1*), 61–66.

Standley, J. M. (1996). A meta-analysis on the effects of music as reinforcement for education/therapy objectives. *Journal of Research in Music Education, 44*(*2*), 105–133.

Summer, L. (1988). *Guided imagery and music in the institutional setting.* St. Louis: MMB Music.

Taylor, D. B. (1997). *Biomedical foundations of music as therapy.* St. Louis: MMB Music.

Thaut, M. H. (2000). *A scientific model of music in therapy and medicine.* San Antonio, TX: IMR Press.

Wheeler, B. (1981). The relationship between music therapy and theories of psychotherapy. *Music Therapy, 1*(*1*), 9–16.

Wigram, T., Pedersen, I. N., & Bonde, L. O. (2002). *A comprehensive guide to music therapy theory, clinical practice, research and training.* London: Jessica Kingsley.

Wood, M. M., Graham, R. M., Swan, W. W., Purvis, J., Gigliotti, C., & Samet, S. (1974). *Developmental music therapy.* Lawrence, KS: National Association for Music Therapy.

Chapter Twenty-Three

CLINICIANS AND RESEARCH

THE IMPORTANCE OF RESEARCH

Since the earliest days of the modern music therapy profession, leaders in the profession have viewed research as an essential element in establishing the therapeutic use of music as a viable treatment approach. The father of modern music therapy, E. Thayer Gaston (1968b, 408), strongly emphasized that research, along with theory and practice, is vital to the continuing existence and viability of the discipline of music therapy:

> Without practice and research, theory is impotent and unproven; without theory and research, practice is blind; and without theory and practice, research is inapplicable. To fail to have some understanding of research is to remove one leg of the tripod supporting music therapy.

Although research and clinical practice may at times seem to have little in common, research can be very important to practicing music therapy clinicians in several ways. Research can help clinicians (1) understand normal or usual reactions to musical stimuli that will guide them in initial selections of music to accomplish certain effects, (2) determine and select music therapy methods and intervention strategies that are most likely to be most effective and efficient in accomplishing certain goals with particular client populations, (3) refine and create theories and conceptual models to guide practice, (4) confirm and substantiate methods of practice, or (5) reflect on and improve methods of practice (Davis, Gfeller, and Thaut 2008; Kenny 1998; Shuler 1990; Siegel et al. 1986). Thus, an understanding of research techniques and methods is important to music therapy clinicians as well as music therapy researchers, for clinicians must be able to judge effectively the quality of the research on which they base their practice and theories (Colwell 1990; Prickett 1989).

As Duerksen (1968, 409) noted, "The advancement of knowledge and practice in music therapy depends on the quality of the research performed and used by its practitioners." De l'Etoile (2000, 66) noted that basic research skills and understanding were advocated as early as 1960 by Charles Braswell

(1961) who "suggested students learn basic research principles as well as techniques of scientific writing, and the ability to apply research to problem solving in the clinical setting."

There is considerable emphasis on robust research as music therapists are asked to present evidence that music therapy is a viable treatment. Evidence presented in research studies allows clinicians to make informed healthcare and treatment decisions (Hanson-Abromeit and Moore 2014). After conducting a content analysis of *Journal of Music Therapy* articles from 1964 (when publication of the *Journal* began) to 1999, Gregory (2002, 56) found that "of the 607 articles published . . . 96 or 15.8% included a behavioral research design." She also provided a useful history of behavioral studies utilizing music (2002, 57–59).

During the 1920s, 1930s, and 1940s, music therapy pioneers like Willem van de Wall were stressing the need for "scientific research that could establish the validity and practical efficiency of music in institutions" (Clair and Heller 1989, 171). When the National Association for Music Therapy was established in 1950, the Research Committee became its first standing committee (Boxberger 1963; Smith 1998). Since then, professional music therapy organizations have continued to emphasize the importance of research for the growth and acceptance of the music therapy profession. In fact, NAMT, AAMT, and AMTA all have listed encouraging, developing, or promoting research in music therapy as part of their goal or purpose statements (AAMT 1993; AMTA 1998; NAMT 1980).

A survey by Nicholas and Gilbert (1980) found that music therapists hold a generally positive attitude toward research. Over 95 percent of the respondents agreed with the need for both undergraduate and graduate research classes for music therapy students, and over 96 percent cited the need for more research in music therapy. Moreover, "81.3 percent felt that increasing accountability regulations and budget restrictions would force music therapists to become more aware of research results in the next five years" (209). In the late 1980s and 1990s, there was an increasing emphasis on documenting (and researching) the cost effectiveness as well as the treatment effectiveness of music therapy procedures (Clark and Ficken 1988; Furman 1988, 1996). Recently established music therapy research grants and funds also demonstrate that research continues to be perceived as a key component of the future development of music therapy (Smith 1998). In 2005, the American Music Therapy Association adopted the Strategic Priority on Research, a plan to integrate research, clinical practice, and advocacy efforts (http://www.musictherapy.org/research/strategic_priority_on_research/overview/). AMTA anticipates that this coordinated effort may lead to more robust studies that can be used in defining Evidence Based Practice (EBP). Hanson-Abromeit and Moore (2014, 34) point out that "evidence based practice has best been summarized as a means to translate ambiguity into accountability by systematically gathering the most relevant and best evidence available to answer a clinical question." Burns (2014, 208) states:

> To attempt a comprehensive understanding of the 'best practices' within music therapy, we must consider the elements involved within a clinical encounter, including the decisions that a music therapist makes preparing for sessions, the influence that music has on the therapeutic relationship, and the influence of the music itself.

Abrams (2010, 351) explains that the AMTA action plan, *Research Strategic Priority* (AMTA 2005), has as one of its central purposes "to advance the music therapy field through research promoting the *Evidence Based Practice* (EBP) of music therapy."

TYPES OF RESEARCH

Research, or systematic inquiry, in music therapy and related disciplines (e.g., music education, special education, education, psychology) can take many forms and can be grouped or classified by purpose, degree of formality, topic, method, or general orientation/perspective (Elder, Ghrayeb, Machura, McNulty, and Meadows 2012; Gay 1981; Hanson-Abromeit and Moore 2014; Isaac and Michael 1971; Madsen and Madsen 1978; Merrion 1990; Wheeler 1995). Each of these divisions or classifications "serves a different purpose and may contribute in a different way to our understanding" (Wheeler 1995, 8). Elder et al. (2012) summarize the music therapy literature published in 2011. Their classifications may be useful to those who are learning to read research and extract the most important information.

Jones (2006) studied clinical and nonclinical populations used in the research published in the *Journal of Music Therapy* from 1964 through 2004. She found 94 studies that met the criteria, which were "music or music therapy as an independent variable applied to one or more groups and at least one control group that did not receive a music treatment" (334). Within these studies, the most common design was the pretest-posttest, with a treatment-as-usual control group compared to a music therapy treatment. From these studies she found that "experimental music groups significantly improved over control groups in the vast majority of studies identified. Undoubtedly, the foundation for evidence-based clinical practice is firm" (334). Often, designs include more than a treatment and control group. For example, Kuhn (2002) randomly assigned each of a sample of 33 undergraduate volunteers to one of three groups: active, passive, or control; and she observed the effect of participation in music activity on the immune system. Her data suggest "that the musical activity can increase immune system function within the mouth which is the first line of defense against pathogens of the upper respiratory tract" (36).

When research is classified *by purpose*, it often is grouped into the two broad divisions of *basic* or *applied* research (Merrion 1990; Wheeler 1995). *Basic research*, also known as *pure research* or *fundamental research* is done to increase fundamental knowledge about phenomena or to provide explanations for observed events. It is not concerned with practical applications. However, the knowledge gained from basic research (e.g., information regarding auditory processing or basic acoustics or how the brain responds to music) may lead to changes in practice or refinements of theories. Therefore, basic research frequently "provides the building blocks for applied research" (Merrion 1990, 23). In a discussion of basic versus applied research, De l'Etoile, Dachinger, Fairfield, and Lathroum (2012, 130) note: "The ultimate purpose of research in music therapy . . . is to provide clear and effective paradigms for patient care."

Applied research focuses on practical problems, devising ways to test hypotheses or models of practice to solve concerns in real life situations. Jones (2006, 335) notes "the value of research, whether basic or applied, is that it contributes to evidence-based clinical practice and best-practices models for education and clinical training."

Gay (1981) also includes evaluation research, research and development, and action research in his classification of research by purpose. *Evaluation research* systematically collects and analyzes data to guide individuals in selecting alternatives and making decisions. When research evidence is summarized with clearly stated questions, it may be called a *Systematic Review* (Hanson-Abromeit and Moore 2014, 6) including "meta-analyses, Cochrane reviews, narrative syntheses, meta-syntheses, and mixed methods systematic reviews." These same authors (2014, 7–10) present a table with examples of each type of systematic review research. *Research and development* is concerned with developing and testing products that will be most effective for specific purposes. *Action research* applies the scientific method to devise solutions for a specific problem in a specific setting. Its goal is a local solution, not a contribution to science or general knowledge.

Research sometimes is classified by *degree of formality* as formal educational, or therapeutic research, action research, or casual research (Isaac and Michael 1971; Rutkowski 1996). *Casual* or *"common sense"* research is frequently used by teachers and therapists as an approach to identifying problems and finding solutions that will improve teaching/therapy methods and increase student/client learning or adaptive functioning. Observation is casual, and methods do not involve rigorous procedures or require any special training. The focus is on making changes in current procedures that seem likely to improve the situation. Individuals who conduct *formal research* need extensive training in research methods, statistics, and measurement procedures. Formal research tries to find knowledge or solutions that will be generalizable to broad populations. It also is used to develop and test theories of practice. While less rigorous than formal research, *action research* provides a framework for problem solving that is more orderly and directed than casual inquiry. Individuals who conduct action research need some training in measurement techniques, research methods, and possibly statistics. Rigorous designs and complex statistics are usually unnecessary in action research; the research simply tries to show some numbers that demonstrate change. The goal of action research is obtaining knowledge or developing new skills and approaches that can be applied directly to solve problems in classroom or therapy situations. Action research takes a flexible, adaptive approach to problem solving, "sacrificing control in favor of responsiveness and on-the-spot experimentation and innovation" (Isaac and Michael 1971, 27). Subjects are students, clients, or staff with whom the researcher works. Since the sample is restricted and unrepresentative of the general population, findings are useful within the practical dimensions of the specific situation but usually not generalizable to broader populations.

In discussing the boundaries of music therapy research, Bruscia (1995a) classified research in still another way, *by topic*, as discipline, profession, or foundational research. *Discipline research* is concerned with how music therapists interact with clients and use music to help clients improve their health or level of functioning. It may include *assessment studies* that show how clients use or respond to various musical materials, musical experiences, or types/styles of music under a variety of conditions and then relate these data to their treatment needs, as well as *treatment studies* that focus on specific methods of intervention used in music therapy and evaluation studies that measure the outcomes or effects of music therapy treatment. *Profession research* focuses on music therapists and socioeconomic, educational, or political concerns that affect the profession. Topics may include employment practices, characteristics or opinions of music therapists, professional education and training, professional standards, legislative and public relations issues that impact the profession and its relationship to other disciplines, the history of music therapy (organizational, cultural, or individual), and meta-analyses or compilations of research and clinical literature. *Foundational research*, though not itself directly about music therapy, provides knowledge, evidence, or support for concepts that relate to music therapy and may impact music therapy practice. Examples include studies on music psychology, music physiology, sociology or anthropology of music; acoustics; psychoacoustics; music education; general needs and characteristics of client populations; other therapeutic methods, theories, or approaches; or characteristics of and issues in other health professions.

One of the most common ways to classify research is *by method*. Traditionally, research methods have been grouped into four main types: philosophical, historical, descriptive, and experimental (Davis, Gfeller, and Thaut 2008;

Madsen and Madsen 1978; Merrion 1990; Wheeler 1995). *Philosophical research* asks why and is concerned with analyzing and synthesizing ideas to discern truths or principles that are foundational to music therapy or certain music therapy methods. It involves speculation based on logical thinking, analysis, and criticism and uses argument as its primary mode of inquiry and presentation (Aigen 1995d; Davis, Gfeller, and Thaut 2008; Madsen and Madsen 1978; Wheeler 1995). Philosophical methods clarify terms, expose and evaluate underlying assumptions, and relate ideas as systematic theories. Philosophical research is useful for (a) developing theories and value systems for practice, training, and research; (b) evaluating current theories and paradigms; (c) increasing the integration of the field of music therapy; (d) comparing concepts and theories from different disciplines; (e) drawing implications of music therapy practice to related areas; (f) suggesting conceptual solutions to alleviate practical problems in music therapy; and (g) discussing the scientific and artistic aspects of music and music therapy (Aigen 1995d).

Historical research describes what was, systematically studying the evidence of the past to gain knowledge about the past and understand it in relation to the present (Davis, Gfeller, and Thaut 2008; Gay 1981; Madsen and Madsen 1978; Solomon 1995; Solomon and Heller 1982; Wheeler 1995). Historical researchers may study people; places (e.g., geographic regions, institutions, organizations); or events and ideas and may use evidence from pictorial records, official records, personal correspondence, interviews, published books or articles, artifacts, or handwritten materials. Researchers must take care to analyze any historical evidence for authenticity and credibility. Authentic evidence is what it purports to be (e.g., a letter from music therapist XYZ discussing a first job, indeed was written by XYZ; the minutes of an AMTA committee meeting were written by someone who attended the actual meeting). Credible evidence is an accurate representation (e.g., XYZ's letter accurately describes aspects of initial job conditions; the minutes accurately portray the committee's discussions and decisions). Historical research can help educate and inform music therapists about past practices, problems, and trends; increase their collective sense of purpose and identity; and help them use and draw on the accumulated wisdom of the past (Solomon 1995; Solomon and Heller 1982).

Descriptive research is concerned with what is and uses systematic methods to observe people, places, settings, or things; gather information about a current situation and identify themes and patterns; or examine the relationship between certain observed phenomena (Aigen 1995c; Davis, Gfeller, and Thaut 2008; Gay 1981; Lathom-Radocy and Radocy 1995; Madsen and Madsen 1978; Merrion 1990; Wheeler 1995). Although descriptive research often uses numbers to help quantify observations or describe probabilities or correlations (Lathom-Radocy and Radocy 1995; Merrion 1990; Wheeler 1995), it may also focus on identifying themes and constructs suggested and supported by detailed descriptions of human experiences (Aigen 1995c; Wheeler 1995). While descriptive research may be concerned with the relationships among variables, it does not manipulate the variables in question, but simply describes their current relationship. Types of descriptive studies include *surveys*, *ex post facto research*, which includes *correlational* and *causal-comparative studies*; *case studies*; *developmental studies*, which include *longitudinal studies*, *activity analyses* (i.e., tasks and procedures needed to do a certain job), *trend studies*, and *cross-sectional studies*; *ethnographic studies*; and *interpretational research* (Aigen 1995c; Lathom-Radocy and Radocy 1995; Merrion 1990; Wheeler 1995).

Silverman (2006) identifies and analyzes 123 case studies published in the *Journal of Music Therapy*, *Music Therapy*, or *Music Therapy Perspectives* between 1964 and 2003. He suggests that clinicians form a catalog of case studies that relate to their professional area of practice. This then can be used to review procedures and techniques that others, working in similar areas, carefully have studied and reported. A number of music therapists have noted the case study's value (Elder, Ghrayeb, Machura, McNulty, and Meadows 2012; Hanser 1999; Lathom-Radocy and Radocy 1995; Silverman 2006). It allows an in-depth study of one subject or one group. If measurement is desired, varying designs are available (see Silverman 2006, 5). Silverman (2006b) also provides a useful summary of case study publications on pages six through nine.

Experimental research carefully selects groups and systematically manipulates a variable or variables to determine effects of certain factors, parameters, and conditions (Davis, Gfeller, and Thaut 2008; Gay 1981; Hanser and Wheeler 1995; Madsen and Madsen 1978; Wheeler 1995). Experimental research is the *only* research method that can precisely establish cause-and-effect relationships. It does this "by isolating the experimental variable and manipulating certain other factors under highly controlled conditions to ascertain how and why a particular event occurs" (Madsen and Madsen 1978, 17). Procedures in experimental research are characterized by exactness and rigor. Variables are isolated by precise definition and/or design structure, and extreme care is taken to insure validity and reliability in measurement. Data usually are subjected to statistical analysis. Experimental research may use one-sample, two-sample, or multiple-sample designs. A single subject design known as *applied behavior analysis*, which systematically examines "the functional relationship between music therapy or other treatments and the particular behavior(s) of interest" (Hanser 1995, 151), can be very useful in examining or testing the effectiveness of music therapy treatment procedures.

In recent years, research frequently has been classified not so much by method as *by the researcher's general orientation or perspective* and has been divided into the two major categories of quantitative or qualitative research (Rutkowski 1996; Wheeler 1995). These methods differ significantly in philosophy, research focus or interest, and methodology (Bruscia 1995b).

Quantitative research strives to quantify events or observations, focusing on things that can be measured or counted and using numbers to describe data and report outcomes (Aigen 1995e; Bruscia 1995b; Prickett 1995; Rutkowski 1996; Wheeler 1995). It is an objective approach to investigation based on the empirical method. Quantitative researchers focus on objectivity and the discovery of time- and context-free generalizations that may transfer from one setting to another in a value-free manner. Quantitative research looks at specific variables and uses operational definitions and deductive reasoning in a directed search for truth. This type of study always proceeds from a basic research question that serves to focus the investigation (Bruscia 1995d). Through careful methodology and rigorous research design, the researcher tries to maintain the position of an impartial observer.

Silverman (2008) presents a quantitative comparison of cognitive behavioral therapy and music therapy research. He notes the need for high-quality research studies concerning the use of music therapy with adult psychiatric clients, although that is one of AMTA's primary client groups. There is often a gap between research and clinical practice, and he explains some of the barriers to the establishment of newer treatments. He includes a table analyzing randomized and controlled studies in music therapy concerned with persons with mental illness (462–469).

Randomized controlled trials (RCTs) are conducted to establish the effectiveness of music therapy treatments. Robb (2013, 3) states that RCTs are "efficacy or effectiveness trials that are designed to examine questions about whether an intervention had a statistically significant effect on specified outcomes." They are the "gold standard" when establishing evidence-based practices (EBP). However, she warns that pilot studies should be conducted before rushing into RCTs. She explains that "investigators can examine whether their procedures for identifying, recruiting, and enrolling eligible study participants will work – refining their procedures as they move through the study" (Robb 2013, 3).

Qualitative research has produced a sizeable body of literature, especially in the late twentieth century that "was prompted by dissatisfaction with the positivist approach in health care research, which has produced methods such as the randomized controlled trial (RCT). Critical voices asserted that such methods could not capture the voices of healthcare participants" (Edwards 2012, 375). Some qualitative methods have been adopted from sociology. Terms describing qualitative research include "descriptive, evaluative, and exploratory" (Edwards 2012, 377). One example of qualitative research is "grounded theory," described and explained by O'Callaghan (2012, 237–238). Her literature search found thirty music therapy research projects from 1993 to 2012 (in press at the time of her publication).

An emerging method called *mixed methods research* is defined by Bradt, Burns, and Creswell (2013, 125): "A core assumption of mixed methods research is that it combines the strengths of both quantitative and qualitative research and that quantitative or qualitative research, each by itself, is often insufficient to understand research problems." Currently, because music therapists are not well trained in both qualitative and quantitative research, they are not prepared to combine the best of both traditions. The authors (Bradt et al. 2013, 138–145) discuss three examples of mixed methods research in music therapy. Mixed methods research usually is not taught, although there are text books on the subject. It offers useful methodology in music therapy.

Until recently, most music therapy research utilized quantitative methods, such as quantitative descriptive research (Lathom-Radocy and Radocy 1995; Prickett 1995), experimental research (Hanser and Wheeler 1995; Prickett 1995), or applied behavior analysis (Hanser 1995; Prickett 1995). Quantitative methods usually yield reliable results and measurements that professionals in other disciplines easily may understand and employ and research designs, methodology, and analysis procedures that others can replicate (Prickett 1995; Taylor 1997). Some music therapists believe that quantitative research methods are essential "in order to establish music therapy firmly within the community of medical and scientifically based disciplines" (Taylor 1997, 123). However, some research situations, such as preliminary investigations to identify basic variables, holistic comparisons of therapeutic processes, or complex issues regarding deeply held values or fluctuating emotional responses, do not lend themselves well to quantitative methods and may be better approached in other ways (Prickett 1995).

Qualitative research takes a more subjective, humanistic, and holistic view and relies more on detailed verbal descriptions than on measurements or numbers (Aigen 1993, 1995e, 1998; Bruscia 1995b; Forinash 1995; Forinash and Lee 1998; Kenny 1998; Rutkowski 1996; Ruud 1998; Wheeler 1995). Instead of trying to reduce experience to isolated, quantifiable variables, qualitative researchers strive to describe and interpret the entire process or experience using sounds, music, words, and pictures. Qualitative research takes place in natural settings, has a broad focus, and uses inductive reasoning and analysis to draw hypotheses and conclusions from events and descriptions emerging from the research process. Qualitative researchers believe that there are multiple levels of knowing (affective, intellectual, sensory, intuitional) and multiple truths and realities dependent on individual perspectives and perceptions. They believe that all research is value-bound and that findings are context-specific. Therefore, they seek not to uncover universal truths but to discover the meanings, patterns, and essences of specific acts.

Qualitative studies may focus on (a) holistic description, identifying all facets of an experience; (b) definition of essence, identifying aspects of an experience that defines it; (c) analysis, looking at how an experience is organized; (d) theory building, striving to find how things work; (e) interpretation, trying to identify the meaning of an experience; (f) re-creation, reproducing behaviors, phenomena, or interactions to try to understand them from the participants' points of view and verify meaning with the participants; (g) critique, determining value according to a particular system of beliefs or standards; or (h) self-exploration, analyzing and interpreting the researcher's own personal understanding and experience (Bruscia 1995e). In qualitative methods, interactions between the researcher and participant(s) are essential to the process. The researcher assumes the role of participant-observer, and the researcher and participant(s) often work together in gathering data and interpreting phenomena. Instead of trying to eliminate their own values and beliefs, qualitative researchers delineate them and use them as tools in the research process.

Rather than choosing a method or design beforehand, qualitative researchers allow the method to evolve during the course of the investigation. Qualitative methods also have standards that are very different from those of quantitative methods yet still assure research value and integrity (Bruscia 1998). Qualitative research methods include (1) *grounded theory*, which focuses on generating and testing theory; (2) *naturalistic inquiry*, which studies events and interactions in natural contexts or settings and uses the researcher's whole self as a tool for data collection and analysis; (3) *phenomenology*, which studies participants' holistic experience of a given phenomenon or situation; and (4) *hermeneutics*, an interpretive-descriptive approach that studies, describes, and interprets human actions and practices (Aigen 1995c, 1995e, 1998; Forinash 1995). These methods have been used increasingly in music therapy research since the late 1980s as music therapists look for methods that can provide insights into the entire music therapy experience, including its subjective, creative, and aesthetic aspects (Aigen 1993, 1995e, 1998; Bruscia 1995b; Forinash 1995; Kenny 1998; Taylor 1997; Wheeler 1995). Forinash and Lee (1998) provide a comprehensive bibliography of books and articles addressing qualitative music therapy research approaches.

The preceding paragraphs provide abundant evidence that many different research types, philosophies, and methods exist. However, one must realize that no research method or philosophy is inherently better than or superior to any other, and all methods or approaches have their own strengths and weaknesses in given situations (Bruscia 1995b; Davis, Gfeller, and Thaut 2008; Ruud 1998). The question, therefore, becomes not so much which approach or method is better but which is best suited to (a) the nature of the particular phenomenon to be studied, (b) the nature of the research question or problem, (c) the research setting, (d) the type of researcher-subject relationship needed to achieve the objective, and (e) the study's purpose and the type of information needed by the researcher and his or her audience (Bruscia 1995b; Isaac and Michael 1971). For example, music therapists who are interested in focusing on *behaviors* changed by music therapy interventions or on evaluating *outcomes* of music therapy treatment will be more likely to utilize *quantitative* approaches, while those who wish to focus more on the *process* of therapy, including unconscious issues and subjective *experiences* that occur *during* therapeutic treatment may find *qualitative* methods more appropriate (Wheeler 1995). In order to project as complete a picture of their discipline as possible, music therapists need to develop a "comprehensive research culture" (Kenny 1998, 215) that values and utilizes all forms and methods of research and has "the intellectual flexibility to envision more than one path to knowledge" (Prickett 1995, 99). As Bruscia (1995b, 71) concluded after surveying, comparing, and contrasting quantitative and qualitative research paradigms, "Music therapy is too broad and complex to be defined, contained, or limited by one approach to research. . . . Both quantitative and qualitative research are needed to enhance our mission."

THE RESEARCH ATTITUDE

The research attitude is a certain way of thinking, a way of systematically investigating and studying phenomena to learn more about the world. According to Madsen and Madsen (1978, 5), the research attitude has three primary components: "(1) an objective state of mind, (2) a structured mode of action, and (3) an evaluation for future action." A research attitude enables individuals "to analyze, critique, make transfers, and choose alternatives in light of all possible evidence" (Madsen 1986, 51).

When individuals approach problems with an objective state of mind, they gather information or data without any preconceived notions about what this information means. This attitude is important both to quantitative researchers, who try to eliminate personal biases and values and examine situations as objectively as possible, and to qualitative researchers, who focus on letting meaning and research design evolve from the data. For example, phenomenological researchers strive to describe indigenous phenomena as completely as possible and then question, analyze, and critique their descriptions. The information gained from this process then guides further inquiry (Forinash 1995). All researchers, then, start objectively by gathering information and analyzing or critiquing this information to determine patterns and themes, make implications, and/or choose alternatives. This type of thinking is not limited to researchers; it also is used regularly in decision-making processes in everyday life.

The next characteristic of the research attitude is a structured plan for action, which may be a predetermined design or methodology (quantitative approaches) or a more flexible, fluid process that evolves as the information gathered in one step of the process, along with the interactions between researcher and participants, impacts the process and procedures in the next step (qualitative approaches). The structured mode of action and thoughtful observation and inquiry allow individuals both to organize their activities and investigations in a way that is consistent with their thoughts, ideas, values, and interests, and to test the worth or value of their ideas and actions. Finally, a research attitude prompts individuals to use the results of their investigations in planning future actions and transferring and applying these results to other situations (Geist and Hitchcock 2014; Madsen 1986). While research does not establish absolutes, it does enable one to suggest explanations and predictions that may help future investigations yield more information.

APPLYING THE RESEARCH ATTITUDE IN CLINICAL PRACTICE

The Research Attitude

According to Michel (1976, 113), developing the research attitude is perhaps the most important aspect of music therapy education: "Not only must students be able to continue to learn and grow in their field once formal education has been completed, but they must also know how to objectively evaluate their daily work with patients." The research attitude, then, with its characteristic objective state of mind and structured plan of action that enables individuals to gather, analyze, critique, and evaluate information so they can use it in planning future actions, should not be foreign to music therapy clinicians. Rather, the characteristics of the research attitude are essential to effective clinical practice. This point can be illustrated further by comparing the steps taken in conducting an experimental research study with the procedures followed in developing, implementing, and evaluating the effectiveness of music therapy treatment plans.

The Research Process

The first step in the research process involves stating the problem to be investigated. This is a natural step, for researchers must have something they wish to investigate, a purpose for the study, before they can conduct research. Likewise, before clinicians can design treatment plans, they must determine that their clients have certain problems or needs that music therapy interventions may treat successfully.

The second step in the research process entails discovering more about the problem by learning what others have had to say about the same or similar problems. In experimental research, this information usually is obtained through a bibliographic search and is reported formally in the "Related Literature" section of the research paper. To plan effective intervention strategies, music therapy clinicians also need to learn more about the problem they have defined as the target of therapy. This knowledge may be gained by continuing to observe the client, by reading reports in the client's records, and by talking with others who have observed or worked with the client. Clinicians also may consult colleagues who have had extensive experience working with the particular client population in question or search the literature of music therapy and related fields to learn what types of approaches and treatment techniques others have used effectively with clients who have similar needs or problems. Many bibliographic sources (Eagle 1976, 1978, 1982; Eagle and Miniter 1984) and databases are now available to assist clinicians in searching for information through the internet. Dileo (2005) suggests the following databases: MEDLINE, PsychInfo, PubMed, CINAHL, ERIC, and Social Sciences Abstracts. Another useful source is an academic library (see listing of examples in "Passion for Research" 1998, 39).

The third step consists in narrowing down the general problem to something more specific that one can test and evaluate. The information gained in the second step helps one determine more precisely what questions need to be asked or what answers must be sought. In experimental research, this third step involves formulating hypotheses that state exactly what is to be investigated. In clinical practice, this third step involves specifying what particular therapeutic goals and/or objectives the music therapy treatment procedures should help the client reach. Shoemark (2013) suggests conducting feasibility research to determine if the project is acceptable and possible within the confines of the social and environmental limitations. Following this step, it usually is advisable to conduct a pilot study. As a small-scale exploratory study, a pilot study usually will indicate the need for design changes and even may suggest different questions to be answered. It is an important step before initiating costly and time-consuming research (LaGasse 2013): "Essentially, the pilot study allows investigators to develop a procedurally sound methodology, garner important information about intervention content, and ultimately determine whether it is feasible to proceed to the main study" (Robb 2013, 3). Another reason to conduct a pilot study is to determine "intervention fidelity." Can the examiner conduct the steps of the protocol each time it is repeated? Would another music therapist be able to conduct the study with the same protocol? Intervention fidelity can be established through monitoring:

> The fidelity of the intervention and the occurrence of unplanned or intervention modifications can be monitored using pre-planned audits, where reviewers compare the videotaped intervention(s) to a checklist of protocol expectations/steps. (LaGasse 2013, 313)

Magee and Davidson (2002) provide a useful example of a pilot study concerning mood states in neurological patients.

The next step in the research process involves determining ways to find answers to the questions posed in the third step. Obviously, the more controlled one can make a situation, the more likely it will be that the answers one finds are the correct ones for the questions asked. In experimental research, this step regards determining the research design, including components such as number and manner of selection of subjects, setting, materials and equipment, procedure, and evaluation techniques. Jones (2006, 339–340) found that the mean size of subject group was 38.1 in the 94 studies she evaluated. She also explained the parameters of four types of control group: "alternative treatment, placebo, no contact, or treatment as usual."

Assignment of subjects to the experimental group(s) or control group(s) is important for using parametric statistics. Jones (2006, 346) found: "Random assignment of subjects to groups was documented in 53% of the nonclinical articles, while only 32% of the clinical articles reported true random assignment to treatment and control conditions." The purpose of randomization is to ensure that all participants have an equal chance of being assigned to the treatment or control group (Bradt 2012; Porter, McConnell, Lynn, McLaughlin, Cardwell, and Holmes 2014, 358). There are several types of randomization, such as simple randomization, block randomization, and stratified randomization. Bradt (2012, 125–128) explains each type and suggests software for use with various randomization methods (e.g., www.randomizer.org). This step is sometimes eliminated in music therapy research because of the lack of large groups from which to draw the sample. However, randomization is important to reduce bias and the influence of unrelated factors. Porter et al. (2014) discuss reasons for inadequate recruitment of samples large enough for randomization. Beck, Hansen, and Gold (2015, 323) report on a slightly different type of control group in another research project: "Twenty Danish workers on sick leave were randomized to music therapy versus wait-list control." A "wait-list control" group is a group that acts as a control group during the study but will receive the music therapy treatment later (Jones 2006, 347 and 351). Bradt (2012, 138–141) discusses additional types of control groups.

Geist and Hitchcock (2014) discuss single case design (SCD) studies in music therapy. They explain that the "case" may be one subject or some group, such as a classroom or client group. Several designs are appropriate for such groups: "the ABAB (also called *Withdrawal* and/or *Reversal*), Multiple Baseline, Alternating Treatment, Multiple Probe, and Changing Criterion designs" (297). Krout (2001) investigated the effectiveness of 90 single music sessions with 80 subjects. Data consisted of behavioral observations and the subjects' self-reports concerning level of pain control, physical comfort, and relaxation before and after each session. There were significant differences for both observed and self-reported data collections. Krout (2001, 383) concluded that "single-session music therapy interventions appear to be effective in increasing subject pain control, physical comfort, and relaxation during both data collection scenarios." He reported inter-observer reliability with a coefficient of $r = 0.85$, which is high agreement between an independent observer and the primary observer. In this study, the case was a single subject, but the study was repeated for 90 sessions, with data collected before and after each session. With this amount of data, Krout could have confidence in this clinical application of music therapy. The evaluation indicated effectiveness of the intervention. Geist and Hitchcock (2014, 307) note that "it is important that clinicians and researchers in music therapy promote and conduct SCD studies that examine the effectiveness of interventions." In another pre/posttest single-session study, Hogan and Silverman (2015, 420) studied a medical music therapy protocol for hospitalized organ transplant patients with 25 subjects randomly assigned to the treatment and wait-list control group. They found differences in "positive affect, negative affect, and pain, with experimental participants having more favorable posttest scores than control participants."

In clinical practice, this step involves the process of determining what music therapy intervention strategies will be used to help the client meet the therapeutic goals, including consideration of components such as setting (group or individual treatment, specific way room is set up), materials and equipment to be used, specific implementation procedures, and method for determining whether or not the client has reached the goal.

The final steps in the research process involve reporting results and drawing conclusions, generalizations, and/or implications from the results. Researchers do this by reporting the findings of their observations and statistical evaluations, accepting or retaining their hypotheses based on the results, and proposing implications or generalizations from their findings. Music therapy clinicians go through a similar process when they report their observations of the client's behavior in music therapy sessions and, based on the client's responses and behavior, determine whether or not the client has reached the therapeutic goals or objective. Clinical results lead to conclusions about the effectiveness of the treatment procedures and decisions about whether the treatment plan should be continued, discontinued, or revised. The results also may provide implications for revisions in the treatment technique or for intervention strategies that may be useful in future sessions with clients having the same or similar problems and needs.

Although the preceding paragraphs focus on comparing the clinician's approach to developing, implementing, and evaluating music therapy with other intervention strategies utilizing the steps of experimental research studies, one may draw similar parallels between music therapy clinical practice and other methods of quantitative or qualitative research. The point is that the same attitude that is important for conducting good research is also essential for effective clinical practice. Thus, the clinician already possesses some of the attitudes, skills, and knowledge necessary for doing quality research. The next section of this chapter focuses on ways clinicians can use the research of others as well as conduct their own research in clinical settings.

USING AND DOING RESEARCH IN CLINICAL SETTINGS

If the music therapy profession is to advance, develop, and be accepted as an important health and rehabilitation service, music therapists must learn to integrate research and research findings into everything they do (Smith 1998). Research is essential both as a guide to practice and as a tool to develop and support theory (Gaston 1968b). Thus, research is vital both to increasing knowledge about music therapy and to advancing music therapy clinical practice. It is essential, then, that clinicians (1) know how to *use* quality research, making appropriate applications and transfers to their particular clinical situation as they base their approaches on interventions, theories, and techniques that are supported by research; and (2) know how to *do* quality research that demonstrates the effectiveness and efficiency of unique or innovative strategies and applications that they discover in their clinical work.

Music therapy clinicians *use* research when they read research reports and make transfers and applications to their clinical practice. Waldon (2015, 171) conducted a survey to determine "the extent to which AMTA members engage in the following research-related activities: reading journals, attending research conference sessions, consulting with knowledgeable colleagues, and conducting research." Respondents (974 AMTA members) reported that reading the journal is the most frequent activity and conducting research is the least frequent. This finding seems to reflect educational preparation since most research classes (statistics, design, etc.) are at the graduate level. Many studies are completed to fulfill the requirement for a research thesis or dissertation. Thus, music therapists with an undergraduate degree may not feel qualified to conduct and report research. Of great concern, many reported that they did not understand the research reports. This may implicate the writing style of many researchers who may fail to explain terms, clearly define the methodology, and report findings in clear language that all can understand.

If research in music education is seen as the means to better teaching and more successful learning (Colwell 1990), research in music therapy might be seen as a means to improve clinical practices and find ways to help clients reach their therapeutic goals more efficiently and effectively. By reading published research, clinicians can learn about solutions to clinical problems that formal research methods already have tested (Prickett 1989; Shuler 1990). By learning to make conscious use of research in their clinical practices, music therapists can grow professionally and discover ways to help their clients more effectively. As music therapy clinicians cultivate some knowledge of research terminology, analysis, and applications and learn to find ways of transferring research findings to their own situations and interests, they will find that much research will have important clinical applications (Madsen 1986; Taylor 1987a).

Not only the researcher but also the clinician must be able to evaluate research, be aware of its limitations, and make potential appropriate parallels and applications (e.g., what techniques might be used and which should be avoided in a particular situation, what procedures might make therapy more efficient and effective, what directions it suggests for the future). As Shuler (1990, 38) notes: "A research study only provides information, and it is the reader – not the author – who draws the really important conclusions" as he/she considers the implications of the study for his/her particular clinical situation. The user (as well as the researcher) must evaluate, clarify, and interpret data before accepting a study's results, applying them to practice, and using them as a basis for clinical decisions (Colwell 1990). The discussion sections of research reports may give clinicians ideas for potential applications, but ultimately it is the independent clinician's responsibility to make transfers and draw implications so that research will have greater meaning in his/her particular situation (Madsen 1986; "Passion for Research" 1998).

Keeping abreast of current research and developments in the field through reading and attending convention sessions about cutting-edge research and innovative practice is an important part of professional behavior, something professionals in many fields do (Merrion 1990, 24). Music therapists, too, will benefit from learning to become stronger and better-informed consumers of research and willing participants in the use and development of research within their area of practice. In addition to assisting clinicians in finding the most effective, efficient clinical strategies for helping their clients reach particular goals, intelligent and informed use of research can give music therapists added credibility as they explain their clinical practices to other professionals, clients, administrators, and reimbursers (Prickett 1995; Taylor 1997):

> The degree to which music therapists can look other professionals, our clients, and our reimbursers straight in the eye when we talk about the viability of our clinical practices is directly related to the level of objective, documented research that we can cite. Research may be difficult, but the effort is worthwhile. (Prickett 1995, 114)

As well as learning to use and apply the research of others, music therapy clinicians also can find ways to do research (i.e., to conduct their own research in clinical settings). Discussing the value of team science, Burns (2014, 207) writes: "Effective research teams include individuals from different disciplines who can share and value diverse perspectives and address research questions about complex problems with multiple causes and potentially, multiple solutions." She also notes (2014, 207): "Approximately 97% of scientific disciplines have shifted from individual to team science." It is not necessary for music therapy researchers to work alone. A team approach, either with other music therapists or people from other disciplines, is very effective.

Clinical and research papers published by clinicians, as well as educators and graduate students, are vital to continued development of systematic knowledge regarding music therapy clinical techniques and approaches (Braswell, Maranto, and Decuir 1979b). Clinicians commonly develop clear, objective, and appropriate measures to test the effectiveness of clinical intervention strategies in the course of their clinical work in music therapy. When they take the time to (a) reflect on these data in relationship to other situations or other knowledge in the field of music therapy; (b) draw general or broader implications, applications, or conclusions; and (c) share these with others, they move from a *clinical process*, which involves action and reflection in relation to a particular client or situation, to a *research process*, which includes "an added perspective or meta reflection" (Bruscia 1995a, 22) and seeks to apply, generalize, or transfer the findings to similar clients and contexts, thus increasing or modifying the general knowledge base in music therapy. As Aigen (1995e) notes, there is a type of natural progression from session notes to treatment summaries, to in-depth case studies, to research projects that analyze and compare the responses of many individual clients, to music therapy procedures. By doing research in clinical settings, music therapy clinicians can improve their professional and clinical skills, determine which methods and procedures are most effective and efficient, and share their results (both positive and negative) "as sources of information and inspiration for others" (Rutkowski 1996, 62).

Some forms of research – such as action research (Rutkowski 1996), applied behavior analysis (Hanser 1995), certain types of descriptive research (e.g., case studies, developmental studies, or interpretational research [Aigen 1995c; Lathom-Radocy and Radocy 1995; Merrion 1990; Wheeler 1995]), and some types of quantitative research (Aigen 1995e; Forinash 1995) – may more easily coexist with the natural, day-to-day activities of music therapy clinicians than some of the more formal, experimental methods. However, experimental studies also can occur in clinical settings, usually with some modifications that help balance clinical and research concerns and make *a priori* decisions to place clinical benefits above experimental concerns (Standley 1992):

> Clinicians should not be discouraged from conducting research by the necessity to accommodate methodology to clinical priorities. . . . The impact of any new information on a developing field of study can be of great value since a body of research requires time to accumulate and is stimulated by a variety of factors. (Standley 1992, 27)

Therefore, clinicians should be encouraged to perform all kinds of research. Those who wish to do more formal studies may find it useful to collaborate or form partnerships with university professors (Shuler 1990). The American Music Therapy Association's Research Committee also offers clinicians assistance and expertise in designing and reporting research studies.

IMPORTANCE OF REPORTING FINDINGS

Research may lead to new insights or discoveries for the individual researcher, but contributing to or modifying existing knowledge or practice requires adequate documentation and dissemination (Bruscia 1995a). The body of knowledge in music therapy, like that of any profession, is contained within and dependent upon its literature (Braswell, Decuir, and Maranto 1980). Therefore, music therapy clinicians who have first-hand knowledge of the effectiveness or ineffectiveness of music therapy interventions with various populations must take the time and make the effort to document and report the knowledge and insights they gain from their clinical work and research if the knowledge base of music therapy is to be expanded.

As noted earlier, many research methods and approaches are available. Both descriptive and experimental methods, quantitative and qualitative approaches, increase music therapy's knowledge base. Moreover, "nothing is more scientific than to observe well and report accurately" (Gaston 1968b, 230).

In addition to increasing the knowledge base, published reports of clinical research findings may help generate new ideas for theories or more formal research studies that will lead to improved or innovative clinical techniques and practices. Standley (1992, 27) maintains that "sometimes the most stringent empirical research is derived from clinical innovation or exploratory endeavor." However, if these innovations or explorations are not shared with others through publications or conference presentations, they will have little impact on music therapy knowledge, research, or practice. Published articles and research also provide an accessible, widely available database to help document the contributions of music therapy interventions and determine the cost effectiveness of music therapy treatment procedures (Furman 1988, 1996). Thus, taking the time to report or publish clinical findings is essential to the growth and development of the profession.

QUESTIONS FOR THOUGHT AND DISCUSSION

1. List several ways research is important or helpful to music therapy clinicians.
2. List five different ways music therapy research can be classified and briefly

describe the divisions in each classification. Which of these do you think would be most useful to music therapy clinicians? Why?

3. What are the three general characteristics of the research attitude? How is this attitude important to the practicing music therapy clinician as well as to the active researcher?

4. Describe some ways music therapy clinicians might *use* the research of others. How/why are these important?

5. Describe ways music therapy clinicians might *do* research in clinical settings. Of what value is this to the profession?

6. Why is it vital to report and disseminate research and clinical findings? What are some ways this can be done?

SUGGESTIONS FOR FURTHER READING

Aigen, K. (1993). The music therapist as qualitative researcher. *Music Therapy, 12(1)*, 16–39.

Aigen, K. (1998). Creativity in qualitative music therapy research. *Journal of Music Therapy, 35(3)*, 150–175.

Bradt, J. (2012). Randomized controlled trials in music therapy: Guidelines for design and implementation. *Journal of Music Therapy, 49(2)*, 120–149.

Bruscia, K. E. (1998). Standards of integrity for qualitative music therapy research. *Journal of Music Therapy, 35(3)*, 176–200.

Cargill, M. & O'Connor, P. (2013). *Writing scientific research articles: Strategy and steps* (2nd ed.). Chichester, UK: Wiley-Blackwell. [Reviewed by Alaine E. Reschke-Hernandez (2014). *Journal of Music Therapy, 51(4)*, 396–399.]

Colwell, R. (1990). Research findings: Shake well before using. *Music Educators Journal, 77(3)*, 29–34.

Gfeller, K. E., Davis, W. B., Thaut, M. H., Forinash, M. (2008). The role of research in music therapy. In W. B. Davis, K. E. Gfeller, & M. H. Thaut (Eds), *An introduction to music therapy: Theory and practice* (3rd ed.) (487–537). Silver Spring, MD: American Music Therapy Association.

Gilbertson, S. & Aldridge, D. (2008). *Music therapy and traumatic brain injury: A light on a dark night.* London: Jessica Kingsley. [This book uses a style of qualitative research called the Therapeutic Narrative Analysis method. It provides good examples of case studies.]

Kenny, C. B. (1998). Embracing complexity: The creation of a comprehensive research culture in music therapy. *Journal of Music Therapy, 35(3)*, 201–217.

Madsen, C. K. (1986). Research and music therapy: The necessity for transfer. *Journal of Music Therapy, 23(2)*, 50–55.

Madsen, C. K. & Madsen, C. H., Jr. (1978). *Experimental research in music.* Raleigh, NC: Contemporary Publishing.

Phillips, K. H. (2008). *Exploring research in music education and music therapy.* New York: Oxford University Press.

Ruud, E. (1998). Science as metacritique. *Journal of Music Therapy, 35*(3), 218–224.

Shuler, S. C. (1990). Solving instructional problems through research. *Music Educators Journal, 77*(3), 35–40.

Solomon, A. L. & Heller, G. N. (1982). Historical research in music therapy: An important avenue for studying the profession. *Journal of Music Therapy, 19*(3), 161–178.

Thaut, M. H. (2000). *A scientific model of music in therapy and medicine.* San Antonio, TX: IMR Press.

Wheeler, B. L. (Ed.). (1995). *Music therapy research: Quantitative and qualitative perspectives.* Phoenixville, PA: Barcelona.

REFERENCES

Abeles, H. F. (1980). Responses to music. In D. A. Hodges (Ed.), *Handbook of music psychology* (105–140). Lawrence, KS: National Association for Music Therapy.

Abeles, H. F. & Chung, J. W. (1996). Responses to music. In D. A. Hodges (Ed.), *Handbook of music psychology* (2nd ed.) (285–342). San Antonio, TX: Institute for Music Research Press, The University of Texas at San Antonio.

Abrams, B. (2010). Evidence-based music therapy practice: An integral understanding. *Journal of Music Therapy, 47*(4), 351–379.

Accardo, P. J. (Ed.) (2008). *Capute and Accardo's neurodevelopmental disabilities in infancy and childhood* (3rd ed.). Baltimore, MD: Paul H. Brookes.

Adamek, M. S. (1996). In the beginning: A review of early special education services and legislative/regulatory activity affecting the teaching and placement of special learners. In B. L. Wilson (Ed.), *Models of music therapy interventions in school settings: From institution to inclusion* (3–12). Silver Spring, MD: National Association for Music Therapy.

Adamek, M. & Darrow, A-A. (2008). Music therapy in special education. In W. B. Davis, K. E. Gfeller, & M. H. Thaut (Eds.). *An introduction to music therapy theory and practice.* (405–426). Silver Spring, MD: American Music Therapy Association.

Adamek, M. S. & Darrow, A-A. (2010). *Music in special education* (2nd ed.). Silver Spring: MD: The American Music Therapy Association.

Adamek, M. S. & Shiraishi, I. M. (1996). Music therapy with traumatic brain injured patients: Speech rehabilitation, intervention models, and assessment procedures. In C. E. Furman (Ed.), *Effectiveness of music therapy procedures: Documentation of research and clinical practice* (2nd ed.) (267–278). Silver Spring, MD: National Association for Music Therapy.

Adelman, E. J. (1985). Multimodal therapy and music therapy: Assessing and treating the whole person. *Music Therapy, 5*(1), 12–21.

Adler, R. F. (2006). Goals and treatment objectives, settings, and service delivery models for the school age years. In M. E. Humpal & C. Colwell (Eds.). *Early childhood and school age educational settings.* Silver Spring, MD: American Music Therapy Association.

Adreon, D. A. (1994, November). Understanding autism: Implications for music therapy. Paper presented at the 45th Annual Conference of the National Association for Music Therapy, Orlando: FL.

Aging Statistics. (1994). ElderSong. *The Music and Gerontology Newsletter, 8*(1), 1.

Aigen, K. (1990). Echoes of silence. *Music Therapy, 9*(1), 44–61.

Aigen, K. (1991). The voice of the forest: A conception of music for music therapy.

Music Therapy, 10(1), 77–98.

Aigen, K. (1993). The music therapist as qualitative researcher. *Music Therapy, 12(1)*, 16–39.

Aigen, K. (1994). "One voice" – The unification of AAMT and NAMT. *Tuning In: The Newsletter of the American Association for Music Therapy*, Fall 1, 4–5.

Aigen, K. (1995a). An aesthetic foundation of clinical theory: An underlying basis of creative music therapy. In C. B. Kenny (Ed.), *Listening, playing, creating: Essays on the power of sound* (235–257). Albany, NY: State University of New York Press.

Aigen, K. (1995b). Cognitive and affective processes in music therapy with individuals with developmental delays: A preliminary model for contemporary Nordoff-Robbins practice. *Music Therapy, 13(1)*, 13–46.

Aigen, K. (1995c). Interpretational research. In B. L. Wheeler (Ed.), *Music therapy research: Quantitative and qualitative perspectives* (329–364). Phoenixville, PA: Barcelona.

Aigen, K. (1995d). Philosophical inquiry. In B. L. Wheeler (Ed.), *Music therapy research: Quantitative and qualitative perspectives* (447–484). Phoenixville, PA: Barcelona.

Aigen, K. (1995e). Principles of qualitative research. In B. L. Wheeler (Ed.), *Music therapy research: Quantitative and qualitative perspectives* (283–311). Phoenixville, PA: Barcelona.

Aigen, K. (1998). Creativity in qualitative music therapy research. *Journal of Music Therapy, 35(3)*, 150–175.

Aigen, K. (1998). *Paths of development in Nordoff-Robbins music therapy*. Gilsum, NH: Barcelone.

Aigen, K. S. (2001). Popular musical styles in Nordoff-Robbins clinical improvisation. *Music Therapy Perspectives, 19(1)*, 31–44.

Aigen, K. (2009). Verticality and containment in song and improvisation: An application of schema theory to Nordoff-Robbins music therapy. *Journal of Music Therapy, 46*, 238–267.

Aigen, K., Miller, C. K., Kim, Y., Pasiali, V., Kwak, E-M., & Tague, D. B. (2008). Nordoff-Robbins music therapy. In A-A. Darrow (Ed.), *Introduction to approaches in music therapy* (2nd ed.) (61–77). Silver Spring, MD: American Music Therapy Association.

Albert, M. L., Sparks, R. W., & Helms, N. A. (1973). Melodic intonation therapy for aphasia. *Archives of Neurology, 29*, 130–131.

Alexopoulos, G. S., Abrams, R. C., Young, R. C., & Shamoran, C. A. (1998). Cornell Scale for Depression in Dementia. *Biological Psychiatry, 23*, 271–284.

Alley, C. F. (1977). The effect of relaxation training to music on heart rate and verbal reports. *Dissertation Abstracts International, 37(12-B)*, 6391.

Altrows, I. F. & Bryden, M. P. (1977). Temporal factors in the effects of masking noise on fluency of stutterers. *Journal of Communication Disorders, 10*, 315–329.

Altshuler, I. M. (1940). Rational music therapy of the mentally ill. In T. M. Finney (Ed.), *Volume of Proceedings, MTNA* (153–157). Pittsburgh: Arthur Rippl.

Altshuler, I. M. (1948). A psychiatrist's experience with music as a therapeutic agent. In D. Schullian & M. Schoen (Eds.), *Music and medicine* (266–281). New York: Henry Schuman.

Alvin, J. (1953). *Musical theory and instrumental technique*. London: Augener.

Alvin, J. (1975). *Music therapy.* New York: Basic Books.

Alvin, J. (1978). *Music therapy for the autistic child.* London: Oxford University Press.

Alvin, J. & Warwick, A. (1991). *Music therapy for the autistic child* (2nd ed.). New York: Oxford University Press.

Alzheimer's Association (2015). What is Alzheimer's? Retrieved September 28, 2015 from http://www.alz.org/alzheimers_disease_whatisalzheimers.asp.

American Association for Music Therapy (AAMT). (1994). *Membership directory 1994.* Valley Forge, PA: Author.

American Association of Neuromuscular and Electrodiagnostic Medicine (AANEM) (2015). Arthrogryposis multiplex congenita. Retrieved April 14, 2015 from www.aanem. org/Education/Patient-Resources/Disorders/Arthrogryposis-Multiplex-Congenita. aspx.

American Association on Intellectual and Developmental Disabilities (AAIDD) (2011). *Intellectual disability: Definition, classification, and systems of support* (11th ed.). Washington, DC: Author.

American Association on Mental Retardation (AAMR). (1992). *Mental retardation: Definition, classification, and systems of support* (9th ed.). Washington, DC: Author.

American Association on Mental Retardation (AAMR) (2002). *Mental retardation: Definition, classification, and systems of support* (10th ed.). Washington, DC: Author.

American College of Surgeons (2005). Statement of principles of palliative care. *Bulletin of the American College of Surgeons, 92(8).*

American Music Therapy Association (AMTA). (1998). *AMTA member sourcebook 1998.* Silver Spring, MD: Author.

American Music Therapy Association (AMTA) (n.d.). *Music therapy as a career* (brochure). Silver Spring, MD: Author.

American Music Therapy Association (AMTA) (n.d.). Website. Downloaded June 5, 2014 from http://www.musictherapy.org/faq/#40.

American Music Therapy Association (2007). A career in music therapy. Retrieved from http://www.musictherapy.org/handbook/career.html.

American Music Therapy Association (2010). Code of ethics. AMTA member source-book. Silver Spring, MD: Author.

American Music Therapy Association (2013). Profile of the 2012 AMTA member-ship. http://www.musictherapy.org/profile.html.

American Music Therapy Association (2014). Standards of clinical practice. Down-loaded August 2, 2014 from http://www.musictherapy.org/about/standards/?print=y.

American Psychiatric Association (APA) (1994). *Diagnostic and statistical manual of mental disorders* (4th ed.) (DSM-IV). Washington, DC: Author.

American Psychiatric Association (2013). *Diagnostic and statistical manual of mental disorders* (5th ed.) (DSM-V). Washington, DC: Author.

American Speech and Hearing Association (ASHA) (1980). *Speech and language disorders and the speech and language pathologist.* Washington, DC: Author.

American Speech-Language-Hearing Association. Childhood fluency disorders. Clinical topics. Retrieved May 26, 2015 from www.asha.org/PRPSpecificTopic.aspx?folc.

American Speech-Language-Hearing Association (1993). Definition of communication disorders and variations. Retrieved May 26, 2015 from www.asha.org/policy.

American Speech-Language-Hearing Association (ASHA). Late blooming or language problem? Retrieved May 26, 2015 from www. Asha.org/public/speech/disorders/Late Blooming.htm.

Amir, D. (1990). A song is born: Discovering meaning in improvised songs through a phenomenological analysis of two music therapy sessions with a traumatic spinal-cord injured young adult. *Music Therapy, 9(1),* 62–81.

Ansdell, G. & Pavlicevic, M. (2010). Practicing "Gentle Empiricism" – The Nordoff-Robbins research heritage. *Music Therapy Perspectives, 28(2),* 131–139.

Anshel, A. & Kipper, D. A. (1988). The influence of group singing on trust and cooperation. *Journal of Music Therapy, 25(3),* 145–155.

Anthony, W. A. (1993). Recovery from mental illness: The guiding vision of the mental health service system in the 1990s. *Psychosocial Rehabilitation Journal, 16,* 11–23.

Apel, W. (1972). *Harvard dictionary of music* (2nd ed.). Cambridge, MA: Harvard University Press.

Arnold, M. (1975). Music therapy in a transactional analysis setting. *Journal of Music Therapy, 12(3),* 104–120.

Arthritis Foundation (1987). *Programs and services of the arthritis foundation.* Atlanta, GA: Author.

Arthritis Foundation (2015). Arthritis facts. Retrieved April 14, 2015 from www.arthritis.org/arthritis-facts.

Ashida, S. (2000). The effect of reminiscence music therapy sessions on changes in depressive symptoms in elderly persons with dementia. *Journal of Music Therapy, 37,* 170–182.

Atterbury, B. W. (1983a). A comparison of rhythm pattern perception and performance in normal and learning-disabled readers, age seven and eight. *Journal of Research in Music Education, 31(4),* 259–270.

Atterbury, B. W. (1983b). Success strategies for learning disabled students. *Music Educators Journal, 69(8),* 29–31.

Atterbury, B. W. (1986). Success in the mainstream of general music. *Music Educators Journal, 72(7),* 34–36.

Atterbury, B. W. (1990). *Mainstreaming exceptional learners in music.* Englewood Cliffs, NJ: Prentice-Hall.

Auchter, M. & LePrall, L. G. (2014). Hearing loss prevention education using Adopt-a-Band: Changes in self-reported earplug use in two high school marching bands. *American Journal of Audiology, 23,* 211–226.

Autism Society of America. (1995). *What is autism?* (Brochure). Bethesda, MD: Author.

Ayres, B. R. (1987). The effects of a music stimulus environment versus regular cafeteria environment during therapeutic feeding. *Journal of Music Therapy, 24(1),* 14–26.

Azeredo, M. (2007). Real-time composition of image and sound in the (re)habilitation of children with special needs: A case study of a child with cerebral palsy. *Digital Creativity, 18(2),* 115–120.

Bachman, M. L. (1991). *Dalcroze today: An education through and into music.* New York:

Oxford University Press.

Bailey, L. M. (1983). The effects of live music versus tape recorded music on hospitalized cancer patients. *Music Therapy, 3(1)*, 17–28.

Bailey, L. M. (1984). The use of songs in music therapy with cancer patients and their families. *Music Therapy, 4(1)*, 5–17.

Bain, L. J. (1991). *A parent's guide to attention deficit disorders*. New York: Delta.

Baker, F. A. (2000). Modifying the melodic intonation program for adults with severe non-afluent aphasia. *Music Therapy Perspectives, 18(2)*, 110–114.

Baker, F. & Tamplin, J. (2005). Themes within songs written by people with traumatic brain injury: Gender differences. *Journal of Music Therapy, 42*, 111–122.

Baker, F. & Tamplin, J. (2005). *Music therapy methods in neuro-rehabilitation: A clinician's manual*. Philadelphia: Jessica Kingsley.

Baker, F. & Wigram, T. (2005). *Songwriting: Methods, techniques and clinical applications for music therapy clinicians, educators, and students*. London: Jessica Kingsley.

Bandura, A. & Adams, M. E. (1977). Analysis of self-efficacy theory of behavioral change. *Cognitive Therapy and Research, 1(4)*, 287–310.

Bang, C. (1980). A world of sound and music: Music therapy and musical speech therapy with hearing impaired and multiply handicapped children. *Journal of the British Association of Teachers of the Deaf, 4(4)*.

Barclay, M. W. (1987). A contribution to a theory of music therapy: Additional phenomenological perspectives on GestaltQualitat and transitional phenomena. *Journal of Music Therapy, 24(4)*, 224–238.

Barker, L. W. (1991). The use of music and relaxation techniques to reduce pain of burn patients during daily debridement. In C. D. Maranto (Ed.), *Applications of music in medicine* (123–140). Washington, DC: National Association for Music Therapy.

Barker, V. L. & Brunk, B. (1991). The role of a creative arts group in the treatment of clients with traumatic brain injury. *Music Therapy Perspectives, 9*, 23–31.

Barna, V. (1993). Twilight years. *The Mesquite News* (March 11, 1993), *110(32)*, 1A, 8A.

Barnard, R. I. (1953). The philosophy and theory of music therapy as an adjuvant therapy. In E. G. Gilliland (Ed.), *Music therapy 1952* (45–49). Lawrence, KS: Allen Press.

Barrickman, J. (1989). A developmental music therapy approach for preschool hospitalized children. *Music Therapy Perspectives, 7*, 10–16.

Bartlett, D. L. (1996). Physiological responses to music and sound stimuli. In D. A. Hodges (Ed.), *Handbook of music psychology* (2nd ed.) (343–385). San Antonio, TX: Institute for Music Research Press.

Bartlett, D., Kaufman, D., & Smeltekop, R. (1993). The effects of music listening and perceived sensory experiences on the immune system as measured by interleukin-1 and control. *Journal of Music Therapy, 30(4)*, 194–209.

Bartlett, J. C. & Snelus, P. (1980). Lifespan memory for popular songs. *American Journal of Psychology, 93(3)*, 551–560.

Bartov, T. & Most, T. (2014). Song recognition by young children with cochlear implants: Comparison between unilateral, bilateral, and bimodal users. *Journal of Speech, Language, and Hearing Research, 57*, 1929–1939.

Basso, A. (1999). The neuropsychology of music. In G. Denes & L. Pizzamiglio (Eds.),

Handbook of clinical and experimental neuropsychology (409–418). Hove, UK: Psychology Press/Erlbaum.

Bauch, C. D. (2014). *Mayo clinic on better hearing and balance.* Rochester, MN: Mayo Clinic.

Beck, A. T. (1976). *Cognitive therapy and the emotional disorders.* New York: International Universities Press.

Beck, B. D., Hansen, A. M., & Gold, C. (2015). Coping with work-related stress through guided imagery and music (GIM): Randomized controlled trial. *Journal of Music Therapy, 52*(3), 323–352.

Beckett, A. (1990). The effects of music on exercises as determined by physiological recovery heart rates and distance. *Journal of Music Therapy, 27*(3), 126–136.

Bednarz, L. F. & Nikkel, B. (1992). The role of music therapy in the treatment of young adults diagnosed with mental illness and substance abuse. *Music Therapy Perspectives, 10*(1), 21–26.

Beggs, C. (1991). Life review with a palliative care patient. In K. E. Bruscia (Ed.), *Case studies in music therapy* (611–616). Phoenixville, PA: Barcelona.

Behrens, G. A. (1988). An objective approach to the expression of feelings. *Music Therapy Perspectives, 5*, 16–22.

Beil, L. (2015). Locked inside. *Science News Magazine, 188*(3), 18–21.

Belgrave, M. (2009). The effect of expressive and instrumental touch on the behavior states of older adults with late-stage dementia of the Alzheimer's type and on music therapist's perceived rapport. *Journal of Music therapy, 46*(2), 132–146.

Belgrave, M. (2011). The effect of a music therapy intergenerational program on children and older adults' intergenerational interactions, cross-age attitudes, and elder adults' psychosocial well-being. *Journal of Music Therapy, 43*(4), 486–508.

Belgrave, M., Darrow, A-A., Walworth, D., & Wolodarczyk, N. (2011). *Music therapy in geriatric populations.* Silver Spring, MD: American Music Therapy Association.

Bellamy, T. & Sontag, E. (1973). Use of group contingent music to increase assembly line production rates of retarded students in a simulated sheltered workshop. *Journal of Music Therapy, 10*(3), 125–136.

Benenzon, R. O. (1981). *Music therapy manual.* Springfield, IL: Charles C Thomas.

Benenzon, R. O. (1982). *Music therapy in child psychosis.* Springfield, IL: Charles C Thomas.

Bennett, P. (1987). From Hungary to America: The evolution of education through music. *Music Educators Journal, 74*(1), 36–45, 60.

Berger, D. S. (2002). *Music therapy and sensory integration and the autistic child.* London/Philadelphia: Jessica Kingsley.

Berman, C. (1982, September). Dyslexia – Adults can have it too. *Good Housekeeping,* 231.

Bernar, L. C. & Krupet, E. (1994). *Health psychology: Biopsychosocial factors in health and illness.* Ft. Worth, TX: Harcourt Brace.

Bernstorf, E. D. & Welsbacher, B. T. (1996). Helping students in the inclusive classroom. *Music Educators Journal, 82*(5), 21–29.

Berry, P. & Kirk, S. A. (1980). Issues in specific learning disabilities: Towards a data base for decision making. *The Exceptional Child, 27*(2), 115–125.

Bhogal, S. K., Teasell, R., Foley, N. C., et al. (2003). Rehabilitation of aphasia: More is better. *Topics in Stroke Rehabilitation, 10*(2), 66–76.

Binger, C. & Light, J. (2006). Demographics of preschoolers who require AAC. *Language, Speech, and Hearing Services in the Schools, 37,* 200–208.

Birkenshaw-Fleming, L. (1993). *Music for all: Teaching music to people with special needs.* Toronto: Gordon V. Thompson.

Bitcon, C. H. (1976). *Alike and different: The clinical and educational use of Orff-Schulwerk.* Santa Ana, CA: Rosha Press.

Bitcon, C. H. (2000). *Alike and different: The clinical and educational use of Orff-Schulwerk* (2nd ed.). Gilsum, NH: Barcelona.

Blacking, J. (1973). *How musical is man?* Seattle: University of Washington Press.

Blacking, J. (1995). *Music, culture, and experience.* Chicago: University of Chicago Press.

Blake, R. L. & Bishop, S. R. (1994). The Bonny method of Guided Imagery and Music (GIM) in the treatment of post-traumatic stress disorder (PTSD) with adults in the psychiatric setting. *Music Therapy Perspectives, 12*(2), 125–129.

Blissymbolics Communication Foundation. (1978). *Handbook of blissymbolics.* Toronto: Author.

Bloch, B., Reshef, A., Vadas, L., Haliba, Y., Ziv, N., Kremer, I., & Haimov, I. (2010). The effects of music relaxation on sleep quality and emotional measures in people living with schizophrenia. *Journal of Music Therapy, 47,* 27–52.

Boldt, S. (1996). The effects of music therapy on motivation, psychological well-being, physical comfort, and exercise endurance of bone marrow transplant patients. *Journal of Music Therapy, 33*(3), 164–188.

Bolger, E. P. & Judson, M. A. (1984). The therapeutic value of singing. *New England Journal of Medicine, 311,* 1704.

Bonny, H. L. (1975). Music and consciousness. *Journal of Music Therapy, 12*(3), 121–135.

Bonny, H. L. (1978a). *Facilitating guided imagery and music sessions.* Baltimore, MD: ICM.

Bonny, H. L. (1978b). *Guided imagery and music therapy: Past, present and future implications.* Baltimore, MD: ICM.

Bonny, H. L. (1980). Music and sound in health. In A. C. Hastings, J. Fadiman, & J. S. Gordon (Eds.), *Health for the whole person* (277–281). Boulder, CO: Westview Press.

Bonny, H. L. (1983). Music listening for intensive coronary care units: A pilot project. *Music Therapy, 3*(1), 4–16.

Bonny, H. L. (1986). Music and healing. *Music Therapy, 6A*(1), 3–12.

Bonny, H. L. (1989). Sound as symbol: Guided imagery and music in clinical practice. *Music Therapy Perspectives, 6,* 7–10.

Bonny, H. L. (1994). Twenty-one years later: A GIM update. *Music Therapy Perspectives, 12*(2), 70–74.

Bonny, H. L. & McCarron, N. (1984). Music as an adjunct to anesthesia in operative procedures. *Journal of the American Association of Nurse Anesthesiologists, 52,* 55–57.

Bonny, H. L. & Savary, L. M. (1973). *Music and your mind: Listening with a new consciousness.* New York: Harper & Row.

Bonny, H. L. & Savary, L. M. (1990). *Music and your mind: Listening with a new consciousness* (rev. ed.). Barrytown, NY: Station Hill Press.

Bonny, H. (2001). Music and spirituality. *Music Therapy Perspectives, 19*(*1*), 59–67.

Bonny, H. (2002). Music consciousness: The evolution of Guided Imagery and Music. In L. Summer, (Ed.). Gilsum, NH: Barcelona.

Boothroyd, A. (1980). Audiological considerations in music with the deaf. In C. Robbins & C. Robbins, *Music for the hearing impaired and other special groups: A resource manual and curriculum guide* (1–23). St. Louis: Magnamusic Baton.

Borczon, R. M. (1995). Remembering Oklahoma City. *NAMT Notes*, Summer, 1995, 1, 13–15.

Borczon, R. M. (1997). *Music therapy: Group vignettes.* Gilsum, NH: Barcelona.

Borczon, R. (2004). Attributes of a music therapist. In R. Borczon (Ed.), *Music therapy: A fieldwork primer* (1–19). Gilsum, NH: Barcelona.

Borczon, R. M. (2004). *Music therapy: A fieldwork primer.* Gilsum, NH: Barcelona.

Bosco, F. (1997). Sensing and resonating with pain: A process-oriented approach to focusing the body/mind using music therapy. In J. Loeoy (Ed.), *Music therapy and pediatric pain* (12–14). Cherry Hill, NJ: Jeffrey Books.

Boswell, B. & Vidret, M. (1993). Rhythmic movement and music for adolescents with severe and profound disabilities. *Music Therapy Perspectives, 11*(*1*), 37–41.

Boswell, J. (1992). Human potential and lifelong learning. *Music Educators Journal, 79*(*4*), 38–40.

Botting, N. (2005). Non-verbal cognitive development and language impairment. *Journal of Child Psychology and Psychiatry, 46*, 317–326.

Bouhuys, A. (1964). Lung volumes and breathing patterns in wind-instrument players. *Journal of Applied Physiology, 19*(*5*), 967–975.

Bowers, J. (1998). Effects of an intergenerational choir for community-based seniors and college students on age-related attitudes. *Journal of Music Therapy, 35*(*1*), 2–18.

Bowles, C. L. (1991). Self-expressed adult music education interests and music experiences. *Journal of Research in Music Education, 39*(*3*), 191–205.

Boxberger, R. (1962). Historical bases for the use of music in therapy. In E. H. Schneider (Ed.), *Music therapy 1961* (125–166). Lawrence, KS: Allen Press.

Boxberger, R. (1963). A historical study of the National Association for Music Therapy. In E. H. Schneider (Ed.), *Music therapy 1962* (133–197). Lawrence, KS: Allen Press.

Boxill, E. H. (1985). *Music therapy for the developmentally disabled.* Rockville, MD: Aspen Systems.

Boxill, E. H. (1989). *Music therapy for living: The principle of normalization embodied in music therapy.* St. Louis: MMB Music.

Boyce-Tillman, J. (2000). *Constructing musical healing: The wounds that sing.* London: Jessica Kingsley.

Boyd, J. (1989). Problems and concerns with a diverse population. *Music Therapy Perspectives, 6*, 34–36.

Boyle, M. E. (1987). Music in operant procedures for the comatose patient. In R. R. Pratt (Ed.), *The fourth international symposium on music: Rehabilitation and human well-being* (49–60). New York: University Press of America.

Boyle, M. E. (1989). Comatose and head injured patients: Applications for music in treatment. In M. H. M. Lee (Ed.), *Rehabilitation, music and human well-being* (137–148). St. Louis: MMB Music.

Braddock, D., Hemp, R., & Rizzolo, M. C. (2004). The state of the states in developmental disabilities 2004. *Mental Retardation, 42*(5), 356–370.

Bradt, J. (2012). Randomized controlled trials in music therapy: Guidelines for design and implementation. *Journal of Music Therapy, 49*(2), 120–149.

Bradt, J., Burns, D. S., & Creswell, J. W. (2013). Mixed methods research in music therapy research. *Journal of Music Therapy, 50*(2), 123–148.

Brain Injury.com (2015). Retrieved April 16, 2015 from http://www.braininjury.com/injured.shtml.

Braswell, C. (1961). Education and research in music therapy. *Music Therapy 1960, 10th Book of Proceedings of the National Association for Music Therapy, 10,* Lawrence, KS: Allen Press.

Braswell, C. (1968). Part IX. Development of music therapy in the community. In E. T. Gaston (Ed.), *Music in therapy* (345–406). New York: Macmillan.

Braswell, C., Decuir, A., & Jacobs, K. (1989). Job satisfaction among music therapists. *Journal of Music Therapy, 26*(1), 2–17.

Braswell, C., Decuir, A., & Maranto, C. D. (1980). Rating of entry level skills by music therapy clinicians, educators, and interns. *Journal of Music Therapy, 17*(3), 133–147.

Braswell, C., Moranto, C. D., & Decuir, A. (1979a). A survey of clinical practice in music therapy, part I: The institutions in which music therapists work and personal data. *Journal of Music Therapy, 16*(1), 2–16.

Braswell, C., Maranto, C. D., & Decuir, A. (1979b). A survey of clinical practice in music therapy, part II: Clinical practice, educational and clinical training. *Journal of Music Therapy. 16*(2), 50–69.

Brayton, E. R. & Conture, E. G. (1978). Effects of noise and rhythmic stimulation on the speech of stutters. *Journal of Speech and Hearing Research, 21*(2), 285–294.

Brennan, F. X. & Charretski, C. J. (2000). Stress and immune system function in a newspaper's newsroom. *Psychological Reports, 87*(1), 218–222.

Brewer, J. E. (1955). Music therapy for the mentally deficient. In E. T. Gaston (Ed.), *Music Therapy 1954* (113–116). Lawrence, KS: Allen Press.

Brick, Sr., R. M. (1973). Eurhythmics: One aspect of audition. *Volta Review, 75*(3), 155–160.

Briggs, C. A. (1991). A model for understanding musical development. *Music Therapy, 10*(1), 1–21.

Bright, R. (1972). *Music in geriatric care.* New York: St. Martin's Press.

Bright, R. (1981). *Practical planning in music therapy for the aged.* Lynbrook, NY: Music-graphics.

Bright, R. (1986). *Grieving: A handbook for those who care.* St. Louis: MMB Books.

Bright, R. (1988). *Music therapy and the dementias: Improving the quality of life.* St. Louis: MMB Music.

Brodsky, K. W. (1991). A personal perspective of the power of music and mass communication, prior to and during the Gulf War crisis in Israel: Implications for music therapy. *Music Therapy, 10*(1), 99–113.

Brodsky, W. (1989). Music therapy as an intervention for children with cancer in isolation rooms. *Music Therapy, 8(1)*, 17–34.

Brodsky, W. & Sloboda, J. A. (1997). Clinical trial of a music generated vibrotactile therapeutic environment for musicians: Main effect and outcome differences between therapy subgroups. *Journal of Music Therapy, 34(1)*, 2–32.

Brody, J. E. (1982). Rock music fans suffer hearing loss, studies say. *Dallas Morning News* (November 21), 33AA, 40AA.

Brody, R. (1988). Tune and tone: Music can keep you upbeat about exercise. *Dallas Times Herald* (January 29), E-1, E-10.

Brooks, D. M. (1989). Music therapy enhances treatment with adolescents. *Music Therapy Perspectives, 6*, 37–39.

Brookshire, R. H. (2003). *Introduction to neurogenic communication disorders* (6th ed.). St. Louis: Mosby.

Brotons, M. (1994a). Effects of performing conditions on music performance anxiety and performance quality. *Journal of Music Therapy, 31(1)*, 63–81.

Brotons, M. (1994b). Preferences of Alzheimer's disease patients for music activities: Singing, instrumenta, dance/movement, games, and composition improvisation. *Journal of Music Therapy, 31(3)*, 220–233.

Brotons, M., Koger, S., & Pickett-Cooper, P. (1997). Music and dementias: A review of literature. *Journal of Music Therapy, 34(4)*, 204–245.

Brotons, M. & Marti, P. (2003). Music therapy with Alzheimer's patients and their family caregivers: A pilot project. *Journal of Music Therapy, 40(2)*, 138–150.

Brotons, M. & Pickett-Cooper, P. (1996). The effects of music therapy intervention on agitation behaviors of Alzheimer's disease patients. *Journal of Music Therapy, 33(1)*, 2–18.

Broucek, M. (1987). Beyond healing to "whole-ing." A voice for the deinstitutionalization of music therapy. *Music Therapy, 6(2)*, 50–58.

Brown, C. J., Chen, A. C. N., & Dworkin, S. F. (1989). Music in the control of human pain. *Music Therapy, 8(1)*, 47–60.

Brown, L. S. & Jellison, J. A. (2012). Music research with children and youth with disabilities and typically developing peers: A systematic review. *Journal of Music Therapy, 49(3)*, 335–364.

Brownell, M. D. (2002). Musically adapted social stories to modify behaviors in students with autism: Four case studies. *Journal of Music Therapy, 34*, 117–144.

Brownell, M. D., Frego, R. J. D., Kwak, B-M., & Rayburn, A. M. (2008). The Kodály approach to music therapy. In A-A. Darrow (Ed.), *Introduction to approaches to music therapy* (2nd ed.) (37–46). Silver Spring, MD: American Music Therapy Association.

Browning, L. A. (2001). Music therapy in childbirth: Research in practice. *Music Therapy Perspectives, 19(2)*, 74–81.

Bruer, R. A., Spitznagel, E., & Cloninger, C. R. (2007). The temporal limits of cognitive change from music therapy in elderly persons with dementia or dementia-like cognitive impairment: A randomized controlled trial. *Journal of Music Therapy, 44(4)*, 308–328.

Bruhn, K., Cohen, D., Fletcher, R., McKinney, C., Smith, D. S., & Tims, F. C. (1996, November). Music making and wellness: Strategic alliances between music therapists and the music products industry. Paper presented at the 1996 Joint Conference of the National Association for Music Therapy and the American

Association for Music Therapy, Nashville, TN.

Brunk, B. K. (1992, February). Music therapy in physical medicine rehabilitation. Seminar presented as part of the continuing education program of the Southwestern Region, National Association for Music Therapy, Dallas, TX.

Bruscia, K. E. (1986). Advanced competencies in music therapy. *Music Therapy, 6A(1)*, 57–67.

Bruscia, K. E. (1987). *Improvisational models of music therapy.* Springfield, IL: Charles C Thomas.

Bruscia, K. E. (1988). Standards for clinical assessment in the arts therapies. *The Arts in Psychotherapy, 15(1)*, 5–10.

Bruscia, K. E. (1988b). *Defining music therapy*, (2nd ed.). Spring City, PA: Spring House Books.

Bruscia, K. E. (1989b). The content of music therapy education at undergraduate and graduate levels. *Music Therapy Perspectives, 7*, 83–87.

Bruscia, K. E. (1989c). The practical side of improvisational music therapy. *Music Therapy Perspectives, 6*, 11–15.

Bruscia, K. E. (Ed.) (1991a). *Case studies in music therapy.* Phoenixville, PA: Barcelona.

Bruscia, K. E. (1991b). Embracing life with AIDS: Psychotherapy through guided imagery and music (GIM). In K. E. Bruscia (Ed.), *Case studies in music therapy* (581–602). Phoenixville, PA: Barcelona.

Bruscia, K. E. (1995a). The boundaries of music therapy research. In B. L. Wheeler (Ed.), *Music therapy research: Quantitative and qualitative perspectives* (17–27). Phoenixville, PA: Barcelona.

Bruscia, K. E. (1995b). Differences between quantitative and qualitative research paradigms: Implications for music therapy. In B. L. Wheeler (Ed.), *Music therapy research: Quantitative and qualitative perspectives* (65–76). Phoenixville, PA: Barcelona.

Bruscia, K. E. (1995c). Modes of consciousness in guided imagery and music (GIM): A therapist's experience of the guiding process. In C. B. Kenny (Ed.), *Listening playing, creating: Essays on the power of sound* (165–197). Albany, NY: State University of New York Press.

Bruscia, K. E. (1995d). Topics and questions in quantitative research. In B. L. Wheeler (Ed.), *Music therapy research: Quantitative and qualitative perspectives* (119–127). Phoenixville, PA: Barcelona.

Bruscia, K. E. (1995e). Topics, phenomena, and purposes in qualitative research. In B. L. Wheeler (Ed.), *Music therapy research: Quantitative and qualitative perspectives* (313–327). Phoenixville, PA: Barcelona.

Bruscia, K. E. (1998). Standards of integrity for qualitative music therapy research. *Journal of Music Therapy, 35(3)*, 176–200.

Bruscia, K. E. (Ed.) (1998c). *The dynamics of music psychotherapy.* Gilsum, NH: Barcelona.

Bruscia, K. E. (1998d). An introduction to music psychotherapy. In K. Brucia (Ed.), *The dynamics of music psychotherapy* (1–15). Gilsum, NH: Barcelona.

Bruscia, K. (2001). Special feature: A qualitative approach to analyzing client improvisations. *Music Therapy Perspectives, 19(1)*, 7–21.

Bruscia, K. E. (2005). Developing theory. In B. Wheeler (Ed.), *Music therapy research* (2nd ed.). Gilsum, NH: Barcelona.

Bruscia, K., Clair, A. A., Crowe, B., Farnan, L. A., Forinash, M., Hesser, B., Hughes, J. E., Selesky, E. C., Thomas, C. B., & Wright-Bower, L. M. (1998, November). Plenary session: Envisioning music therapy education and training for the next millennium: The process of unification. Paper presented at the Inaugural Conference of the American Music Therapy Association, Cleveland, OH.

Bruscia, K. E., Hesser, B., & Boxill, E. H. (1981). Essential competencies for the practice of music therapy. *Music Therapy, 1(1)*, 43–49.

Bryant, D. R. (1987). A cognitive approach to therapy through music. *Journal of Music Therapy, 24(1)*, 27–34.

Buday, E. M. (1995). The effects of signed and spoken words taught with music on sign and speech imitation by children with autism. *Journal of Music Therapy, 32(3)*, 189–202.

Buechler, J. (1982). Music therapy for handicapped children: Hearing impaired. Washington, DC: National Association for Music Therapy.

Bulletin of NAMT (1961). Central office for NAMT established. *10(4)*, 26.

Bumanis, A. & Yoder, J. W. (1987). Music and dance: Tools or reality orientation. In B. Karras (Ed.), *"You bring out the music in me": Music in nursing homes* (23–35). Binghamton, NY: Haworth Press.

Bunt, L. & Hoskyns, L. (Eds.), (2002). *The handbook of music therapy.* New York: Brunner/Routledge.

Bunt, L. & Marston-Wyld, J. (1995). Where words fail music takes over: A collaborative study by a music therapist and a counselor in the context of cancer care. *Music Therapy Perspectives, 13(1)*, 46–50.

Burge, R., Dawson-Hughes, B., Solemon, D. H., Wong, J. B., King, A., & Tosteson, A. (2007). Incidence and economic burden of osteogenetic-related fractures in the United States, 2005–2025. *Journal of Bone and Mineral Research, 22(3)*, 465–475.

Burleson, S. J., Center, D. B., & Reeves, H. (1989). The effect of background music on task performance in psychotic children. *Journal of Music Therapy, 26(4)*, 198–205.

Burns, D. (2001). The effect of the Bonny method of Guided Imagery and Music on the mood and life quality of cancer patients. *Journal of Music Therapy, 38(1)*, 51–66.

Burns, D. W. (2012). Theoretical rationale for music selection in oncology intervention research. An integrative review. *Journal of Music Therapy, 49*, 7–22.

Burns, D. S. (2014). Guest editorial. Gaining perspectives and momentum: The value of team science. *Journal of Music Therapy, 51(2)*, 207–210.

Burns, D. S., Sledge, R. B., Fuller, L. A., Dagzy, J. K., & Monahan, P. O. (2005). Cancer patients' interest and preferences for music therapy. *Journal of Music Therapy, 42*, 185–199.

Burns, D. & Woolrich, J. (2004). The Bonny method of Guided Imagery and Music. In A-A. Darrow (Ed.), *Introduction to approaches in music therapy.* (53–62). Silver Spring, MD: American Music Therapy Association.

Burns, D. & Woolrich, J. (2008). The Bonny method of Guided Imagery and Music. In A-A. Darrow (Ed.), *Introduction to approaches in music therapy* (2nd ed.) (49–59). Silver Spring, MD: American Music Therapy Association.

Burns, J. L., Labbe, E., Arke, B., Capeless, K., Cooksey, B., Steadman, A., & Gonzales,

C. (2002). The effects of different types of music on perceived and physiological measures of stress. *Journal of Music Therapy, 39*(2), 101–116.

Burt, J. W. (1995). Distant thunder: Drumming with Vietnam veterans. *Music Therapy Perspectives, 13*(2), 110–113.

Bushong, D. L. (2002). Good music/bad music: Extant literature on popular music media and antisocial behavior. *Music Therapy Perspectives, 20*(2), 69–79,

Butler, R. N. (1963). The life review: An interpretation of reminiscence in the aged. *Psychiatry, 26*, 65–76.

Caine, J. (1991). The effects of music on the selected stress behaviors, weight, caloric and formula intake, and length of hospital stay of premature and low birth weight infants in a newborn intensive care unit. *Journal of Music Therapy, 28*(4), 180–192.

Campbell, D. G. (1988). The cutting edge: Personal transformation with music. *Music Therapy, 7*(1), 38–50.

Campbell, D. G. (1991a). Imagery and the physiology of music. In D. Campbell (Ed.), *Music: Physician for times to come* (243–254). Wheaton, IL: Quest Books.

Campbell, D. G. (Ed.) (1991b). *Music: Physician for times to come.* Wheaton, IL: Quest Books.

Campbell, P. H., Milbourne, S., Dugen, L. M., & Wilco, M. I. (2006). A review of evidence on practices for teaching young children to use assistive technology devices. *Topics in Early Childhood Special Education, 26*(1), 3–13.

Cargill, M. & O'Connor, P. (2013). *Writing scientific research articles: Strategy and steps* (2nd ed.). Chichester, UK: Wiley-Blackwell.

Carle, I. L. (1982). Music therapy in a different key. *Music Therapy, 2*(1), 63–71.

Carruth, E. K. (1997). The effects of singing and the speed retrieval technique on improving face-name recognition in nursing home residents with memory loss. *Journal of Music Therapy, 34*(3), 165–186.

Carter, R., Aldridge, S., Page, M., & Parker, S. (2001). *The human brain.* New York: DK Publishing.

Carter, S. A. (1982). Mentally retarded. In W. B. Lathom & C. T. Eagle (Eds.), *Music therapy for handicapped children*, (vol. 2) (63–114). Washington, DC: National Association for Music Therapy.

Cassidy, J. W. (1992). Communication disorders: Effect on children's ability to label music characteristics. *Journal of Music Therapy, 29*(2), 113–124.

Cassidy, J. W. & Ditty, K. M. (2001). Gender differences among newborns on a transient otoacoustic emission test for hearing. *Journal of Music Therapy, 37*, 25–35.

Cassidy, J. W. & Standley, J. M. (1995). The effect of music listening on physiological responses of premature infants. *Journal of Music Therapy, 32*(4), 208–227.

Cassity, M. D. (1976). The influence of a music therapy activity upon peer acceptance, group cohesiveness, and interpersonal relationships of adult psychiatric patients. *Journal of Music Therapy, 13*(2), 66–76.

Cassity, M. D. (1977). Nontraditional guitar techniques for the educable and trainable mentally retarded residents in music therapy activities. *Journal of Music Therapy, 14*(1), 39–42.

Cassity, M. D. (2007). Psychiatric music therapy in 2016: A Delphi Poll of the future.

Music Therapy Perspectives, 25(2), 86–93.

Cassity, M. D. & Cassity, J. E. (1991). *Psychiatric music therapy assessments and treatment employed in NAMT approved clinical training facilities with adults, adolescents and children.* Weatherford, OK: Authors.

Cassity, M. D. & Cassity, J. E. (1994a). *Multimodal psychiatric music therapy for adults, adolescents, and children.* St. Louis: MMB Music.

Cassity, M. D. & Cassity, J. E. (1994b). Psychiatric music therapy assessment and treatment in clinical training facilities with adults, adolescents and children. *Journal of Music Therapy, 31(1)*, 2–30.

Cassity, M. & Cassity, J. (2006). *Multimodal psychiatric music therapy for adults, adolescents, and children: A clinical manual* (3rd ed.). Philadelphia: Jessica Kingsley.

Cassity, M. D. & Theobold, K. A. K. (1990). Domestic violence: Assessments and treatments employed by music therapists. *Journal of Music Therapy, 27(4)*, 179–194.

Castellano, A. & Wilson, B. L. (1970). The generalization of institute therapy to classroom behavior of an electively mute adolescent. *Journal of Music Therapy, 7(4)*, 139–143.

Centers for Disease Control (CDC) (2007). Prevalence of Duchenne/Becker muscular dystrophy among males aged 5–24 years – Four states, 2007. Retrieved April 14, 2015 from www.cdc.gov.

Centers for Disease Control (CDC) (2010). Cerebral palsy. Retrieved March 6, 2015 from cdcinfo/www.cdc.gov.

Centers for Disease Control (CDC) (2013). Long-term care services in the United States: 2013 Retrieved April 16, 2015 from http://www.cdc.gov/nchs/data/nsltcp/long_term_care_services_2013 pdf.

Centers for Disease Control (CDC) (2015). Muscular dystrophy facts. Accessed April 9, 2015 from www.cdc.gov/ncbdd/md/causes.html.

Centers for Disease Control (CDC) (2015). Facts about cerebral palsy. Retrieved April 14, 2015 from http://www.cdc.gov/ncbdd/cp/facts.html.

Centers for Medicare and Medicaid Services (2013). CMS Product No. 02154. Baltimore, MD: Author. Retrieved August 27, 2014 from www.Medicare.gov.

Center to Advance Palliative Care (2012). What is palliative care? Retrieved from http://getpalliativecare.org?what is/.

Certification Board for Music Therapists (CBMT) (1983, September–October). Music therapy certification information sheet. *NAMT Notes*, 6, 8.

Certification Board for Music Therapists (CBMT). Frequently asked questions. Retrieved July 18, 2014 from http://www.cbmt.org/frequently-asked-questions/.

Certification Board for Music Therapists (CBMT) (1991). *Recertification manual.* Tucson, AZ: Author.

Certification Board for Music Therapists (CBMT) (1992). *Commonly asked questions about board certification and recertification.* Tucson, AZ: Author.

Certification Board for Music Therapists (CBMT) (1997). CBMT: The certification board for music therapists (brochure). Richmond, VA: Author.

Certification Board for Music Therapists (CBMT) (1998a). Certification board for music therapists code of professional practice (brochure). Richmond, VA: Author.

Certification Board for Music Therapists (CBMT) (1998b). Your music therapist is certified by the certification board for music therapists (brochure). Richmond, VA: Author.

Cevasco, A. M. (2008). Preferred vocal range of young and older adults: Implications for music therapy majors' clinical training experience. *Music Therapy Perspectives, 26(1),* 4–12.

Cevasco, A. M. (2010). Effects of the therapist's nonverbal behavior on participation and effort of individual's with Alzheimer's Disease during group music therapy sessions. *Journal of Music Therapy, 47(3),* 282–299.

Cevasco, A. M. & Grant, R. (2003). Comparison of different methods for eliciting exercise-to-music for clients with Alzheimer's disease. *Journal of Music Therapy, 40(1),* 41–56.

Cevasco, A. M. & Grant, R. E. (2006). Value of musical instruments used by the therapist to elicit responses from individuals in various stages of Alzheimer's disease. *Journal of Music Therapy, 49(3),* 226–246.

Cevasco, A., Kennedy, R., & Generally, N. (2005). Comparison of movement-to-music, rhythm activities, and competitive games on depression, stress, anxiety, and anger of females in substance abuse rehabilitation. *Journal of Music Therapy, 42,* 64–80.

Cevasco, A. M. & Vanweelden, K. (2010). An analysis of songbook series for older adult populations. *Music Therapy Perspectives, 29(1),* 37–78.

Chance, P. (1986). Life after head injury. *Psychology Today, 20(10),* 62–69.

Chance, P. (1987). Music hath charms to soothe a throbbing head. *Psychology Today, 21(2),* 14.

Chang-Miller, A. (Medical Ed.) (2013). *Mayo Clinic on arthritis.* Rochester, MN: Mayo Clinic.

Chapman, J. S. (1975). The relation between auditory stimulation of short gestation infants and their gross motor limb activity (Doctoral dissertation, New York University, 1974). *Dissertation Abstracts International, 36,* 1654B–1655B. (University Microfilms No. 75-21, 138).

Chase, K. M. (2002). *The music therapy assessment handbook.* Columbia, MS: Southern Pen Publishing.

Chase, K. M. (2004). Music therapy assessment for children with developmental disabilities: A survey study. *Journal of Music Therapy, 41(1),* 28–54.

Chavin, M. (1991). *The lost chord: Reaching the person with dementia through the power of music.* Mt. Airy, MD: ElderSong Publications.

Chavin, M. (1995). Can people with dementia learn? *ElderSong, 8(4),* 4–5.

Chesky, K. (2008). Hearing conservation and music education. *Seminar in Hearing, 29,* 90–93.

Chesky, K. & Amlani, A. M. (2014/2015). Playing healthy staying healthy: Hearing conservation in music requires new testing standards. *American Music Teacher,* (December–January), 16–18.

Chesky, K. S. & Michel, D. E. (1991). The Music Vibration Table (MVT™): Developing a technology and conceptual model for pain relief. *Music Therapy Perspectives, 9,* 32–38.

Chetta, H. D. (1981). The effect of music and desensitization on preoperative anxiety in children. *Journal of Music Therapy, 18*(2), 74–87.

Children and Adults with Attention Deficit Disorders (CH.A.D.D) (1995). *The disability named ADD: An overview of attention deficit disorders.* Plantation, FL: Author.

Chlan, L. & Heiderscheit (2009). A tool for music preference assessment in critically ill patients receiving mechanical ventilator support. *Music Therapy Perspectives, 27*(2), 42–47.

Choi, B. C. (1997). Professional and patient attitudes about the relevance of music therapy as a treatment modality in NAMT-approved psychiatric hospitals. *Journal of Music Therapy, 34*(4), 277–292.

Choi, B. C. (2008). Awareness of music therapy practices and factors influencing specific theoretical approaches. *Journal of Music Therapy, 45*(1), 83–108.

Christenberry, E. B. (1979). The use of music therapy with burn patients. *Journal of Music Therapy, 16*(3), 138–148.

Christie, M. E. (1995). The influence of a highly participatory peer on motivating group behaviors of lower functioning persons who have probable Alzheimer's type dementia: A feasibility study. *Music Therapy Perspectives, 13*(2), 87–90.

Christopher and Dana Reeve Foundation (2015). Retrieved April 15, 2015 from www.christopherreeve.org.

Claeys, M. S., Miller, A. C., Dalloul-Rampersad, R., & Kollar, M. (1989). The role of music and music therapy in the rehabilitation of traumatically brain injured clients. *Music Therapy Perspectives, 6*, 71–77.

Clair, A. A. (1990). The need for supervision to manage behavior in the elderly care home resident and the implications for music therapy practice. *Music Therapy Perspectives, 8*, 72–75.

Clair, A. A. (1991). Music therapy for a severely regressed person with a probable diagnosis of Alzheimer's disease. In K. Bruscia (Ed.), *Case studies in music therapy* (571–580). Phoenixville, PA: Barcelona.

Clair, A. A. (1996a). The effect of singing on alert responses in persons with late stage dementia. *Journal of Music Therapy, 33*(4), 234–247.

Clair, A. A. (1996b). *Therapeutic uses of music with older adults.* Baltimore: Health Professions Press.

Clair, A. A. (2007). Prognosis grim/situation hopeless: Making a difference with music therapy. *Music Therapy Perspectives, 25*(2), 76–79.

Clair, A. A. & Bernstein, B. (1990). A comparison of singing, vibrotactile and nonvibrotactile instrumental playing responses in severely regressed persons with dementia of the Alzheimer's type. *Journal of Music Therapy, 27*(3), 119–125.

Clair, A. A., Bernstein, B., & Johnson, G. (1995). Rhythmic playing characteristics in persons with severe dementia, including those with probable Alzheimer's type. *Journal of Music Therapy, 32*(2), 113–131.

Clair, A. A. & Davis, W. B. (2008). Music therapy and elderly populations. In W. B. Davis, K. E. Gfeller, & M. H. Thaut (Eds.), *An introduction to music therapy theory and practice* (3rd ed.) (181–207). Silver Spring, MD: American Music Therapy Association.

Clair, A. A. & Ebberts, A. G. (1997). The effects of music therapy on interactions between family caregivers and their care receivers with late stage dementia. *Journal of Music Therapy, 34*(*3*), 148–164.

Clair, A. A. & Heller, G. N. (1989). Willem Van de Wall (1887–1953): Organizer and innovator in music education and music therapy. *Journal of Research in Music Education, 37*(*3*), 165–178.

Clair, A. A. & Memmett, J. (2008). *Therapeutic uses of music with older adults.* Silver Spring, MD: American Music Therapy Association.

Clair, A. A., Tebb, S., & Bernstein, B. (1993). The effects of a socialization and music therapy intervention on self-esteem and loneliness in spouse caregivers of those diagnosed with dementia of the Alzheimer's type: A pilot study. *The American Journal of Alzheimer's Care and Related Disorders and Research,* (Jan/Feb), 24–32.

Clark, C. & Chadwick, D. (1979). *Clinically adapted instruments for the multiply handicapped.* Westford, MA: Modulations.

Clark, D. A. & Beck, A. T. (1999). *Scientific foundations of cognitive theory and therapy of depression.* New York: John Wiley & Sons.

Clark, M. E. (1986). Music therapy-assisted childbirth: A practical guide. *Music Therapy Perspectives, 5,* 23–27.

Clark, M. E. & Ficken, C. T. (1988). Music therapy in the new health care environment. *Music Therapy Perspectives, 5,* 23–27.

Clark, M., Gosnell, M., & Young, J. (1982). The bizarre riddle of MS. *Newsweek* September 6, 50–51.

Clark, M. E., McCorkle, R. R., & Williams, S. B. (1981). Music therapy-assisted labor and delivery. *Journal of Music Therapy, 18*(*2*), 88–100.

Clarkson, A. L. & Robey, K. L. (2000). The use of identity structure modeling to examine the central role of musical experiences within the self-concept of a young woman with physical disabilities. *Music Therapy Perspectives, 18*(*2*), 115–121.

Clarkson, G. (1991). Music therapy for a nonverbal autistic adult. In K. E. Bruscia (Ed.), *Case studies in music therapy* (373–385). Phoenixville, PA: Barcelona.

Clayton, L. & Morrison, J. (1992). *Coping with a learning disability.* New York: Rosen.

Clayton, M. (2009). The social and personal functions of music in cross-cultural perspective. In S. Hallam, I. Cross, & M. Thaut (Eds.), *The Oxford handbook of music psychology* (35–44). New York: Oxford University Press.

Clearwater, Y. (1985). A human place in outer space. *Psychology Today, 19*(*7*), 34–43.

Clendenon-Wallen, J. (1991). The use of music therapy to influence the self-confidence and self-esteem of adolescents who are sexually abused. *Music Therapy Perspectives, 9,* 73–81.

Cleveland Music School Settlement Music Therapy Department (1985). *The music therapy levels system: A manual of principles and applications.* Cleveland, OH: The Cleveland Music School Settlement.

Clynes, M. (1977). *Sentics: The touch of emotions.* New York: Doubleday Anchor.

Clynes, M. (Ed.) (1982). *Music, mind and brain: The neuropsychology of music.* New York: Plenum Press.

Clynes, M. (1991). On music and healing In D. Campbell (Ed.), *Music: Physician for times to come* (121–145). Wheaton, IL: Quest Books.

Coates, P. (1984). Sixty and still growing. *Music Educators Journal, 70*(*9*), 34–35.

Coates, P. (1987). "Is it functional?" A question for music therapists who work with the institutionalized mentally retarded. *Journal of Music Therapy, 24*(*3*), 170–175.

Coates, R. (2010). Noisemakers to music makers: Developing a school band for students who are visually impaired. *Journal of Visual Impairment and Blindness, 104*(*1*), 8–11.

Coates, R. L. (2012). Accommodating band students with visual impairments. *Music Educators Journal, 99*(*1*), 60–66.

Codding, P. (1982). *Music therapy for handicapped children: Visually impaired.* Washington, DC: National Association for Music Therapy.

Codding, P. A. (1988). Music in the education/rehabilitation of visually disabled and multiply handicapped persons: A review of literature from 1946–1987. In C. E. Furman (Ed.), *Effectiveness of music therapy procedures: Documentation of research and clinical practice* (107–136). Washington, DC: National Association for Music Therapy.

Codding, P. A. (2002). A comprehensive survey of music therapists practicing in correctional psychiatry: Demographics, conditions of employment, service provision, assessment, therapeutic objectives, and related values of the therapist. *Music Therapy Perspectives, 23*(*2*), 56–68.

Cohen, G. D. (1988). *The brain in human aging.* New York: Springer.

Cohen, J. M. (1986). Rhythm and tempo in mania. *Music Therapy, 6A*(*1*), 13–29.

Cohen, N. S. (1988). The use of superimposed rhythm to decrease the rate of speech in a brain-damaged adolescent. *Journal of Music Therapy, 25*(*2*), 85–93.

Cohen, N. S. (1992). The effect of singing instruction on the speech production of neurologically impaired persons. *Journal of Music Therapy, 29*(*2*), 87–102.

Cohen, N. S. (1994). Speech and song: Implications for therapy. *Music Therapy Perspectives, 12*(*1*), 8–14.

Cohen, N. S. (1995). The effect of vocal instruction and Visi-Pitch™ feedback on the speech of persons with neurogenic communication disorders: Two case studies. *Music Therapy Perspectives, 13*(*2*), 70–75.

Cohen, N. S. & Ford, J. (1995). The effect of musical cues on the nonpurposive speech of persons with aphasia. *Journal of Music Therapy, 32*(*1*), 46–57.

Cohen, N. S., Hadsell, N. A., & Williams, S. L. (1997). The perceived applicability of applied music requirements in the vocational practices of professional music therapists. *Music Therapy Perspectives, 15*(*2*), 67–72.

Cohen, N. S. & Masse, R. (1993). The application of singing and rhythmic instruction as a therapeutic intervention for persons with neurogenic communication disorders. *Journal of Music Therapy, 30*(*2*), 81–99.

Coleman, K. A. (1996). Music therapy for learners with severe disabilities in a public school setting. In B. L. Wilson (Ed.), *Models of music therapy interventions in school settings: From institution to inclusion* (142–155). Silver Spring, MD: National Association for Music Therapy.

Coleman, K., McNairn, P., & Shioleno, C. (1995). *Quick tech magic: Music-based literacy activities.* Solana Beach, CA: Mayer-Johnson.

Colligan, K. G. (1987). Music therapy and hospice care. In B. Karras (Ed.), *"You bring out the music in me": Music in nursing homes* (103–122). Binghamton, NY: Haworth Press.

Collins, C. I. (1982, November). The life and work of Ira M Altshuler: Pioneer in music therapy. Paper presented at the 33rd Annual Conference of the National Association for Music Therapy, Baltimore, MD.

Colwell, C. M. (1994). Therapeutic applications of music in the whole language kindergarten. *Journal of Music Therapy, 31*(*4*), 238–247.

Colwell, C. M. (1997). Music as a distraction and relaxation to reduce chronic pain and narcotic ingestion: A case study. *Music Therapy Perspectives, 15*(*1*), 24–31.

Colwell, C. M., Davis, K., & Schroeder, L. K. (2005). The effect of composition (art or music) on the self-comcept of hospitalized children. *Journal of Music Therapy, 42*, 49–63.

Colwell, C. M. & Murliess, K. D. (2002). Music activities (singing vs. chanting) as a vehicle for reading accuracy of children with learning disabilities: A pilot study. *Music Therapy Perspectives, 20*(*1*), 13–19.

Colwell, C. M., Pahotsky, C. A., Gillmeister, G., & Woolrich, J. (2008). The Orff approach to music therapy. In A-A. Darrow (Ed.), *Approaches in music therapy* (2nd ed.) (11–24). Silver Spring, MD: American Music Therapy Association.

Colwell, R. (1990). Research findings: Shake well before using. *Music Educators Journal, 77*(*3*), 29–34.

Confrancesco, E. M. (1985). The effect of music therapy on hand grasp strength and functional task performance in stroke patients. *Journal of Music Therapy, 22*(*3*), 129–145.

Conti-Ramsden, G., St. Clair, M. C., Pickles, A., Durkin, K., Oetting, J., & Hadley, P. (2012). Developmental trajectories of verbal and nonverbal skills in individuals with a history of specific language impairement: From childhood to adolescence. *Journal of Speech, Language and Hearing Research, 55*(*6*), 1716–1735.

Cooke, R. M. (1969). The use of music in play therapy. *Journal of Music Therapy, 6*(*3*), 66–75.

Cooper, N. (1985). Adult psychiatric patients. Concentration and communication skills: General hospital, psychiatric unit. In *The music therapy levels system: A manual of principles and applications* (37–43). Cleveland, OH: The Cleveland Music School Settlement.

Cordobes, T. K. (1997). Group songwriting as a method for developing group cohesion for HIV-seropositive adult patients with depression. *Journal of Music Therapy, 34*(*1*), 46–67.

Cordrey, C. (1994). *Hidden treasures: Music and memory activities for people with Alzheimer's.* Mt. Airy, MD: ElderSong.

Cormier, L., Sr. (1982). Music therapy for deaf-blind children (97-120). In W. B. Lathom & C. T. Eagle, Jr. (Eds.) *Music therapy for handicapped children Vol. I.* Washington, DC: National Association for Music Therapy.

Corning, J. L. (1899). The use of musical vibration before and during sleep – supplementary employment of chromatoscopic figures. *The Medical Record: A Weekly Journal of Medicine and Surgery, 14*, 79–86.

Cowan, D. S. (1991). Music therapy in the surgical arena. *Music Therapy Perspectives, 9*, 42–45.

Creagan, E. (2006). *The Mayo Clinic plan for healthy aging.* Rochester, MN: Mayo Clinic Health Information.

Cripe, F. F. (1986). Rock music as therapy for children with attention deficit disorder: An exploratory study. *Journal of Music Therapy, 23*(*1*), 30–37.

Cross, I. (2009a). Music, cognition, cultures and evolution. In J. Peretz & R. J. Zatorre (Eds). *The cognitive neuroscience of music* (42–56). New York: Oxford University Press.

Cross, I. (2009b). The nature of music and its evolution. In S. Hallam, I. Cross, & M. Thaut (Eds.), *The Oxford handbook of music psychology* (3–13). New York: Oxford University Press.

Crowe, B. (1985). Music therapy and physical medicine – expanding opportunities for employment. *Music Therapy Perspectives, 5*(*1*), 44–51.

Crowe, B. (1991). Music – the ultimate physician. In D. Campbell (Ed.), *Music: Physician for times to come* (111–120). Wheaton, IL: Quest Books.

Crowe, B. (2004). *Music and soul making: Toward a new theory of music therapy.* Lanham, MD: Scarecrow Press.

Crowe, B. J. (2007a). Assessment. In B. J. Crowe & C. Colwell (Eds.). *Music therapy for children, adolescents and adults with mental disorders* (14–23). Silver Spring, MD: American Music Therapy Association.

Crowe, B. J. (2007b). Music therapy for adolescents with emotional/behavioral characteristics. In B. J. Crowe & C. Colwell (Eds.), *Music therapy for children, adolescents and adults with mental disorders* (224–230). Silver Spring, MD: American Music Therapy Association.

Crowe, B. J. (2007c). History of mental disorders and music therapy. In B. J. Crowe & C. Colwell (Eds.), *Music therapy for children, adolescents, and adults with mental disorders* (3–13). Silver Spring, MD: American Music Therapy Association.

Crowe, B. J. (2007d). Insight music therapy with re-educative goals: An overview. In B. J. Crowe & C. Colwell (Eds.). *Music therapy for children, adolescents and adults with mental illness* (41–49). Silver Spring, MD: American Music Therapy Association.

Crowe, B. J. (2007e). Supportive, activity-oriented music therapy: An overview. In B. J. Crowe & C. Colwell (Eds.). *Music therapy for children, adolescents, and adults with mental disorders* (31–33). Silver Spring, MD: American Music Therapy Association.

Crowe, B. & Bruscia, K. (1999). Draft report of recommendations of the AMTA commission on education and clinical training. *Music Therapy Matters, 2*(*1*), 8–9.

Crowe, B. J. & Rio, R. (2004). Implications of technology in music therapy practice and research for music therapy education: A review of literature. *Journal of Music Therapy, 41*, 282–320.

Crowe, B. & Scovel, M. (1996). An overview of sound healing practices: Implications for the profession of music therapy. *Music Therapy Perspectives, 14*(*1*), 21–29.

Cummings, E. & Henry, W. E. (1961). *Growing old: The process of disengagement.* New York: Basic Books.

Cunningham, T. D., Jr. (1986). The effect of music volume on the frequency of vocalizations of institutionalized mentally retarded persons. *Journal of Music Therapy, 23*(*4*), 208–218.

Curtis, S. L. (1986). The effect of music on pain relief and relaxation of the terminally ill. *Journal of Music Therapy, 23*(*1*), 10–24.

Dalton, T. A. & Krout, R. E. (2006). The grief-song-writing process with bereaved adolescents: An integrated grief model and music therapy protocol. *Music Therapy*

Perspectives, 24(2), 94–107.

Darrough, G. P. (1992). The effect of music on pain relief and relaxation of the terminally ill. *Music Educators Journal, 79*(4), 27–29.

Darrow, A-A. (1985). Music for the deaf. *Music Educators Journal, 71*(6), 33–35.

Darrow, A-A. (1987a). Exploring the arts of sign and song. *Music Educators Journal, 74*(1), 32–35.

Darrow, A-A. (1987b). An investigative study: The effect of hearing impairment on musical aptitude. *Journal of Music Therapy, 24*(2), 88–96.

Darrow, A-A. (1989). Music therapy in the treatment of the hearing impaired. *Music Therapy Perspectives, 6*, 61–70.

Darrow, A-A. (1990). The effect of frequency adjustment on the vocal reproduction accuracy of hearing impaired children. *Journal of Music Therapy, 27*(1), 24–33.

Darrow, A-A. (1991). An assessment and comparison of hearing impaired children's preference for timbre and musical instruments. *Journal of Music Therapy, 28*(1), 48–59.

Darrow, A-A. (1992). The effect of vibrotactile stimuli via the SOMATRON™ on the identification of pitch change by hearing impaired children. *Journal of Music Therapy, 29*(2), 103–112.

Darrow, A-A. (1993). The role of music in deaf culture: Implications for music educators. *Journal of Research in Music Education, 41*(2), 93–110.

Darrow, A-A. (2006). The role of music in deaf culture: Deaf students' perception of emotion in music. *Journal of Music Therapy, 43*, 2–15.

Darrow, A-A. (Ed.), *Introduction to approaches in music therapy.* Silver Spring, MD: American Music Therapy Association.

Darrow, A-A. & Cohen, N. (1991). The effect of programmed pitch practice and private instruction on the vocal reproduction accuracy of children with hearing impairments: Two case studies. *Music Therapy Perspectives, 9*, 61–65.

Darrow, A-A. & Gfeller, K. E. (1988). Music therapy with hearing-impaired children. In C. E. Furman (Ed.), *Effectiveness of music therapy procedures: Documentation of research and clinical practice* (137–174). Washington, DC: National Association for Music Therapy.

Darrow, A-A. & Gfeller, K. E. (1991). A study of public school music programs mainstreaming hearing impaired students. *Journal of Music Therapy, 28*(1), 23–39.

Darrow, A-A. & Gfeller, K. E. (1996). Music therapy with children who are deaf and hard-of-hearing. In C. E. Furman (Ed.), *Effectiveness of music therapy procedures: Documentation of research and clinical practice* (2nd ed.) (230–266). Silver Spring, MD: National Association for Music Therapy.

Darrow, A-A. & Goll, H. (1989). The effect of vibrotactile stimuli via the SOMATRON™ on the identification of rhythmic concepts by hearing impaired children. *Journal of Music Therapy, 26*(3), 115–124.

Darrow, A-A. & Heller, G. N. (1985). Early advocates of music education for the hearing impaired: William Wolcott Turner and David Ely Bartlett. *Journal of Research in Music Education, 33*(4), 269–279.

Darrow, A-A., Johnson, C. M., & Ellenberger, T. (1994). The effect of participation in an intergenerational choir on teens' and older persons' cross-age attitudes. *Journal of Music Therapy, 31*(2), 119–134.

Darrow, A-A. & Novak, J. (2007). The effect of vision and hearing loss on listeners' perception of referential meaning in music. *Journal of Music Therapy, 44,* 57–73.

Darrow, A-A. & Schunk, H. A. (1996). Music therapy for learners who are deaf/hard-of-hearing. In B. L. Wilson (Ed.), *Models of music therapy interventions in school settings: From institution to inclusion* (200–223). Silver Spring, MD: National Association for Music Therapy.

Darrow, A-A. & Starmer, G. W. (1986). The effect of vocal training on the intonation and rate of hearing impaired children's speech: A pilot study. *Journal of Music Therapy, 23(4),* 194–201.

Data Accountability Center (2010). Individuals with disabilities education act (IDEA) data. Retrieved from http://www.ideadata.org/Part-BReport.asp.

Daveson, B. A. (2001). Music therapy and childhood cancer: Goals, methods, patient choice and control during diagnosis, intensive treatment, transplant and palliative care. *Music Therapy Perspectives, 19(2),* 114–120.

Daveson, B. (2010). An audit about music therapy assessments and recommendations for adult patients suspected to be in a low awareness state. *Journal of Music Therapy, 47,* 408–422.

Davidson, J. B. (1980). Music and gerontology: A young endeavor. *Music Educators Journal, 66(9),* 27–31.

Davis, C. A. (1992). The effects of music and basic relaxation instruction on pain and anxiety of women undergoing in-office gynecological procedures. *Journal of Music Therapy, 29(4),* 202–216.

Davis, G. (2005). Living community: Music therapy with children and adults in a hospice setting. In M. Pavlicek (Ed.), *Music therapy in children's hospices* (124–128). London: Jessica Kingsley.

Davis, W. B. (1987). Music therapy in 19th century America. *Journal of Music Therapy, 24(2),* 76–87.

Davis, W. B. (1989). Music therapy in Victorian England: Frederick Kill Harford and the guild of St. Cecilia. *Music Therapy Perspectives, 7,* 17–22.

Davis, W. B. (1992a). Music therapy and elderly populations. In W. B. Davis, K. E. Gfeller, & M. H. Thaut (Eds.), *An introduction to music therapy: Theory and practice* (133–163). Dubuque, IA: Wm. C. Brown.

Davis, W. B. (1992b). Music therapy for mentally retarded children and adults. In W. B. Davis, K. E. Gfeller, & M. H. Thaut (Eds.), *An introduction to music therapy: Theory and practice* (67–92). Dubuque, IA: Wm. C. Brown.

Davis, W. B. (1992c). The music therapy treatment process. In W. B. Davis, K. E. Gfeller, & M. H. Thaut (Eds.), *An introduction to music therapy: Theory and practice* (287–301). Dubuque, IA: Wm. C. Brown.

Davis, W. B. (1993). Keeping the dream alive: Profiles of three early twentieth century music therapists. *Journal of Music Therapy, 30(1),* 34–45.

Davis, W. B. (1996). An instruction course in the use and practice of musical therapy: The first handbook of music therapy clinical practice. *Journal of Music Therapy, 33(1),* 34–49.

Davis, W. B. (1997). Music therapy practice in New York city: A report from a panel of experts, March 17, 1937. *Journal of Music Therapy, 34,* 68–81.

Davis, W. B. (2003). Ira Maximilian Altshuter: Psychiatrist and pioneer music therapist. *Journal of Music Therapy, 40,* 247–263.

Davis, W. B. (2012). The first systematic experimentation in music therapy: The genius of James Leonard Corning. *Journal of Music Therapy, 49(1),* 102–117.

Davis, W. B. & Farnan, L. A. (2008). Music therapy with children and adults with intellectual disabling conditions. In W. B. Davis, K. E. Gfeller, & M. H. Thaut (Eds.), *An introduction to music therapy: Theory and practice* (79–115). Silver Spring, MD: American Music Therapy Association.

Davis, W. B. & Gfeller, K. E. (Eds.) (1992). *An introduction to music therapy: Theory and practice.* Silver Spring, MD: The American Music Therapy Association.

Davis, W. B. & Gfeller, K. E. (1992). Music therapy: An historical perspective. In W. B. Davis, K. E. Gfeller, & M. H. Thaut (Eds.), *An introduction to music therapy: Theory and practice* (16–37). Dubuque, IA: Wm. C. Brown.

Davis, W. B., Gfeller, K. E., & Thaut, M. H. (Eds.) (2008). *An introduction to music therapy: Theory and practice* (3rd ed.). Silver Spring, MD: American Music Therapy Association.

Dawson, W. J. (2006). Playing without pain: Strategies for the developing instrumentalist. *Music Educators Journal, 93(2),* 38–41.

De Bary, E. O. (Ed.) (2001). *Education for ministry year three, church history.* Sewanee, TN: University of the South.

Dehaene, S. (2009). *Reading in the brain.* London: Viking Penguin.

de l'Etoile, S. (2000). The history of the undergraduate curriculum in music therapy. *Journal of Music Therapy, 37,* 51–71.

de l'Etoile, S. K. (2002). The effect of a musical mood induction procedure on mood state dependent word retrieval. *Journal of Music Therapy, 39,* 145–160.

de l'Etoile, S. K. (2008). The effect of rhythm auditory stimulation on the gait parameters of patients with incomplete spinal cord injury. An exploratory study. *International Journal of Rehabilitation Research, 31(2),* 155.

de l'Etoile, S. K., Dachinger, C., Fairfield, J., & Lathroum, L. (2012). The rational-scientific mediating model (R. SMM). A framework for scientific research in music therapy. *Music Therapy Perspectives, 30(2),* 130–140.

Deliege, I. & Sloboda, J. (Eds.) (1996). *Musical beginnings: Origins and development of musical competence.* Oxford, UK: Oxford University Press.

Del Olmo, F. (1998). Biomedicine brings hope for autism. *The Dallas Morning News* (January 3), 25A.

DeMyer, M. K. (1974). *Parents and children in autism.* Washington, DC: V. H. Winston.

Denckla, M. B. (1990). The paradox of the gifted/impaired child. In F. R. Wilson & F. L. Roehmann (Eds.), *Music and child development: Biology of music making.* Proceedings of the 1987 Denver Conference (227–240). St. Louis: MMB Music.

Denenholz, B. (1959). Music as a tool of physical medicine. In E. H. Schneider (Ed.), *Music Therapy 1958* (67–84). Lawrence, KS: Allen Press.

Denton, C. A. & Vaughn, S. (2008). Reading and writing intervention for older students with disabilities. Possibilities and challenges. *Learning Disabilities Research and Practice, 32,* 61–62.

Department of Health and Human Services. (1986). Hocus-pocus as applied to arthritis (HHS Publication No. (FDA) 85-1080). Rockville, MD: Author.

Dervan, N. (1982). Building Orff ensemble skills with mentally handicapped adolescents. *Music Educators Journal, 68(8),* 35–36.

Deschenes, B. (1990). Music therapy and the composer. *Music Therapy Perspectives, 8,* 85–87.

Dickens, G. & Sharpe, M. (1970). Music therapy in the setting of a psychotherapeutic centre. *British Journal of Medical Psychology, 43(1),* 83–94.

DiGiammarino, M. (1990). Functional music skills of persons with mental retardation. *Journal of Music Therapy, 27(4),* 209–220.

DiGiammarino, M. (1994). Functional music leisure skills for individuals with mental retardation. *Music Therapy Perspectives, 12(1),* 15–19.

Dileo, C. (1975). The use of a token economy program with mentally retarded persons in a music therapy setting. *Journal of Music Therapy, 12(3),* 155–160.

Dileo, C. (1997). Reflections on medical music therapy: Biopsychosocial perspectives of the treatment process. In J. Loewy (Ed.), *Music therapy and pediatric pain* (125–143). Cherry Hill, NJ: Jeffery Books.

Dileo, C. (1999). Definitions, theoretical orientations and levels of practice. In C. Dileo (Ed.), *Music therapy and medicine: Theoretical and clinical applications* (3–10). Silver Spring, MD: American Music Therapy Association.

Dileo, C. (2000). *Ethical thinking in music therapy.* Cherry Hill, NJ: Jeffrey Books.

Dileo, C. & Bradt, J. (1999). Entrainment, resonance, and pain-related suffering. In C. Dileo (Ed.), *Music therapy and medicine: Theoretical and clinical applications* (181–188). Silver Spring, MD: American Music Therapy Association.

Dimaio, L. (2010). Music therapy entrainment: A humanistic music therapist's perspective of using music therapy entrainment with hospice clients experiencing pain. *Music Therapy Perspectives, 28(2),* 106–115.

DiPaoloa, M. & Franko, O. I. (2012). Classification apps allow users to carry knowledge in their pockets. *Orthopedics Today,* (April). Retrieved April 8, 2015 from www.healio.com/orthopedics.

Ditson, R. (1961). A study of the effects of moderate background music on the behavior of cerebral palsied children. *Bulletin of the National Association for Music Therapy, 10,* 6.

Doak, B.A. (2003). Relationships between adolescent psychiatric diagnoses, music preferences, and drug preferences. *Music Therapy Perspectives,* 21(2), 69-76.

Donnelly, M. (1991). Feeling the beat: Class helps deaf students make music. *Dallas Times Herald* (April 13), A-21.

Dorow, L. (1976). Televised music lessons as educational reinforcement for correct mathematical responses with the educable mentally retarded. *Journal of Music Therapy, 13(2),* 77–86.

Dote-Kwan, J. & Chen, D. (1995). Learners with visual impairment and blindness. In M. C. Wong, M. C. Reynolds, & H. J. Walberg (Eds.), *Handbook of special and remedial education research and practice* (2nd ed.) (205–228). Tarrytown, NY: Elsevier Science.

Douglass, D. (1985). *Accent on rhythm: Music activities for the aged* (3rd ed.). St. Louis: MMB Music.

Douglass, E. T. (2006). The development of a music therapy assessment tool for hospitalized children. *Music Therapy Perspectives, 24(2),* 73–79.

Dowling, W. J. & Harwood, D. L. (1986). *Music cognition.* Orlando, FL: Academic Press.

Downing, J. P. (2004). Related services for students with disabilities. *Intervention in School and Clinic, 39(4)*, 195–208.

Duerksen, G. (1968). The research process. In E. T. Gaston (Ed.), *Music in therapy* (409–424). New York: Macmillan.

Duerksen, G. (1978). Music therapy: Using music to help others. Unpublished paper. Lawrence, KS: University of Kansas.

Dunn, B. (1995). A different beat: Music therapy in children's cardiac care. *Music Therapy Perspectives, 13(1)*, 35–39.

Dvorkin, J. M. (1991). Individual music therapy for an adolescent with borderline personality disorder: An object relations approach. In K. E. Bruscia (Ed.), *Case studies in music therapy* (251–268). Phoenixville, PA: Barcelona.

Dworkis, J. L. (1994). Adult distractors: Attention deficit disorder affects grownups, too. *Dallas Morning News* (April 19), 1C–2C.

Dychtwald, K. (1993). The age wave. *The Lutheran Witness, 112(1)*, 2–5.

Dykman, R. A. (1979). In step with 94-142, two by two. *Music Educators Journal, 65(5)*, 58–63.

Dyrlund, A. K. & Wininger, S. R. (2008). The effects of music preference and exercise intensity on psychological variables. *Journal of Music Therapy, 45*, 114–134.

Eagle, C. T., Jr. (Ed.) (1976). *Music therapy index* (Vol. 1). Lawrence, KS: National Association for Music Therapy.

Eagle, C. T., Jr. (Ed.) (1978). *Music psychology index* (Vol. 2). Denton, TX: Institute for Therapeutics Research.

Eagle, C. T., Jr. (Ed.) (1982). *Music therapy for handicapped individuals: An annotated and indexed bibliography.* Washington, DC: National Association for Music Therapy.

Eagle, C. T. (1991). Steps to a theory of quantum therapy. *Music Therapy Perspectives, 9*, 56–60.

Eagle, C. T. & Harsh, J. M. (1988). Elements of pain and music: The aio connection. *Music Therapy, 7(1)*, 15–27.

Eagle, C. T., Jr. & Miniter, J. J. (Eds.) (1984). *Music psychology index* (Vol. 3). Phoenix, AZ: Oryx Press.

Early Childhood Intervention Council [ECIC]. (1992). *Policy and procedures manual.* Austin, TX: Author.

Edel, T. (1994). *Piano music for one hand.* Bloomington, IN: Indiana University Press.

Edelman, P. B. (1978). Juvenile corrections and the arts. In Working papers – The Rockefeller Foundation. *The healing role of the arts* (42–49). New York: The Rockefeller Foundation.

Edelstein, J. E. (1987). Musical options for upper limb amputees. In R. R. Pratt (Ed.), *The fourth international symposium on music: Rehabilitation and human well-being* (102–107). New York: University Press of America.

Edelstein, J. E. (1989). Musical options for upper limb amputees. In M. H. M. Lee (Ed.), *Rehabilitation, music and human well-being* (213–225). St. Louis: MMB Music.

Edgerton, C. D. (1990). Creative group songwriting. *Music Therapy Perspectives, 8*,

15–19.

Edgerton, C. L. (1994). The effect of improvisational music therapy on the communicative behaviors of autistic children. *Journal of Music Therapy, 31(1)*, 31–62.

Edison, C. E., Jr. (1989). The effect of behavioral music therapy on the generalization of interpersonal skills from sessions to the classroom by emotionally handicapped middle school students. *Journal of Music Therapy, 26(4)*, 206–221.

Edwards, D. (1976). *Peacebird.* Los Angeles: Franciscan Communications Center.

Edwards, J. (2005). A reflection on the music therapist's role in developing a program in a children's hospital. *Music Therapy Perspectives, 23(1)*, 36–44.

Edwards, J. (2012). We need to talk about epistemology: Orientations, meaning, and interpretation within music therapy research. *Journal of Music Therapy, 49(4)*, 372–394.

Edwards, M. C., Eagle, C. T., Pennebaker, J. W., & Tunks, T. W. (1991). Relationships among elements of music and physiological responses. In C. D. Maranto (Ed.), *Applications of music in medicine* (41–57). Washington, DC: National Association for Music Therapy.

Elder, M. J., Ghrayeb, A., Machura, P., McNulty, M. K., & Meadows, A. (2012). A year in review: Summarizing published literature in music therapy in 2011. *Music Therapy Perspectives, 30(2)*, 117–129.

Elliot, T. G. & McGahan, C. (1987). The power of music in prison. In R. R. Pratt (Ed.), *The fourth international symposium on music: Rehabilitation and human well-being* (170–175). New York: University Press of America.

Elliott, B. (1982). *Guide to the selection of musical instruments with respect to physical ability and disability.* St. Louis: Magnamusic-Baton.

Elliott, D., Polman, R., & McGregor, R. (2011). Relaxing music for anxiety control. *Journal of Music Therapy, 48(3)*, 264–288.

Ellis, A. & MacLaren, C. (1995). *Rational emotive behavioral therapy: A therapist's guide.* Atascadero, CA: Impact.

Engen, R. L. (2005). The singer's breath: Implications for treatment of persons with emphysema. *Journal of Music Therapy, 42*, 20–48.

Epstein, L., Hersen, M., & Hemphill, D. P. (1974). Music feedback in the treatment of tension headache: An experiment case study. *Journal of Behavior Therapy and Experimental Psychiatry, 5(9)*, 59–63.

Epstern, M., Marozeau, J., & Cleveland, S. (2010). Listening habits of iPod users. *Journal of Speech, Language, and Hearing Research, 53*, 1472–1477.

Erdonmez, D. (1991). Rehabilitation of piano performance skills following a left cerebral vascular accident. In K. E. Bruscia (Ed.), *Case studies in music therapy* (561–570). Phoenixville, PA: Barcelona.

Erikson, E. H. (1963). *Childhood and society.* New York: Norton.

Erikson, E. H. (1968). *Identity: Youth and crisis.* New York: Norton.

Erikson, E. H., Erikson, J. M., & Kivnick, H. Q (1986). *Vital involvement in old age.* New York: Norton.

Ernst, R. E. & Emmons, S. (1992). New horizons for senior adults. *Music Educators Journal, 79(4)*, 30–34.

Escamilla, R. F. (2005). Exercise testing and prescription. In K. P. Speer, (Ed.), *Injury prevention and rehabilitation for older adults.* (30). Champaign, IL: Human Kinetics.

Euper, J. A. (1968). Early infantile autism. In E. T. Gaston (Ed.), *Music in therapy* (181–190). New York: Macmillan.

Eustis, E. (1952). Volunteer music service in hospitals. *Bulletin of the National Association for Music Therapy, 1(1)*, 5.

Eustis, E. (1953). Personality qualifications of the volunteer music therapist. *Music Therapy, 2*, 210–211.

Eyre, L. (2011). Therapeutic chorale for persons with chronic mental illness: A descriptive survey of participant experiences. *Journal of Music Therapy, 48*, 149–168.

Fachner, J. (2010). 25th anniversary of the World Federation of Music Therapy: Looking forward. Voices resources. Retrieved July 17, 2014 from http://testvoices.uib.no/community/?qzcountry-of-the-month/2010-25th-anniversary-world-federation-music-therapy-looking-forward

Fagen, T. S. (1982). Music therapy in the treatment of anxiety and fear in terminal pediatric patients. *Music Therapy, 2(1)*, 13–23.

Farbman, A. (1994). Opportunities for the music products industry in the 21st century: The emerging markets of people with disabilities and elderly persons. *Music Therapy Perspectives, 12(2)*, 35–38.

Farnan, L. (1993). FracTunes – The 21st century light organ. *Music Therapy Perspectives, 11(2)*, 50–51.

Farnan, L. (1996). Music therapy for learners with severe disabilities in a residential setting. In B. L. Wilson (Ed.), *Models of music therapy interventions in school settings: From institution to inclusion* (113–126). Silver Spring, MD: National Association for Music Therapy.

Farnan, L. A. (2007). Music therapy and developmental disabilities: A glance back and a look forward. *Music Therapy Perspectives, 25(2)*, 80–85.

Farnan, L. & Johnson, F. (1988a). *Everyone can move: Music and activities that promote movement and motor development.* New Berlin, WI: Jenson.

Farnan, L. & Johnson, F. (1988b). *Music is for everyone: A handbook for providing music to people with special needs.* New Berlin, WI: Jenson.

Feder, E. & Feder, B. (1981). *The expressive arts therapies.* Englewood Cliffs, NJ: Prentice-Hall.

Federal Register. (1977, Tuesday, August 23) *42*(163).

Federman, J. & Picou, E. (2009). Music and hearing protection: A call to action. *Perspectives in Audiology, 38*, 2777–2780.

Fegers, B., Fricke, J. P., Minkenberg, H., & Moog, H. (1989). The use of the Fricke synthesizer in music education programs for severely physically handicapped students. In R. R. Pratt & H. Moog (Eds.), *First research seminar of the ISME commission on music therapy and music in special education: Proceedings of 1986* (69–84). St. Louis: MMB Music.

Feil, N. (1982). *Validation – The Feil method: How to help the disoriented old-old.* Cleveland, OH: Edward Feil.

Feil, N. (1993). *The validation breakthrough: Simple techniques for communicating with people with Alzheimer's-type dementia.* Baltimore: Health Professions Press.

Ficken, T. (1976). The use of songwriting in a psychiatric setting. *Journal of Music Therapy,*

13(*4*), 163–172.

Fitzgerald, H. (2014). Finding links to the past. American Hospice Foundation. Retrieved August 16, 2014 from http://american hospice.org/working-through-grief/in-times-of-stres-finding-links-to-the-past/.

Fitzgerald, M. (2006). "I send my Best Matthew to school every day": Music educators collaborating with parents. *Music Educators Journal, 92*(*4*), 40–45.

Fitzgerald-Cloutier, M. L. (1993). The use of music therapy to decrease wandering: An alternative to restraints. *Music Therapy Perspectives, 11*(*1*), 32–38.

Fles, M. (1995). Sound wave mirror. In C. B. Kenny (Ed.), *Listening, playing, creating: Essays on the power of sound* (87–90). Albany, NY: State University of New York Press.

Floyd, J. (2005). Grieving moms offer help to those facing child cancer. Retrieved September 8, 2014, from http://www.do=allosnews.com/shared- contact/dws/dn/local news/columnists/html

Folstern, M. F., Foistein, S. E., & McHugh, P. R. (1975). Mini-Mental state: A practical method for grading the cognitive state of patients for the clinician. *Journal of Psychiatric Research, 12*, 189–198.

Ford, S. C. (1984). Music therapy for cerebral palsied children. *Music Therapy Perspectives, 1*(*3*), 8–13.

Ford, T. A. (1988). The effect of musical experiences and age on the ability of deaf children to discriminate pitch. *Journal of Music Therapy, 25*(*1*), 2–16.

Forest, L. C. (2001). Addressing issues of ethnicity and identity in palliative care through music therapy practice. *Voices: A World Forum for Music Therapy, 1*(*2*). Retrieved from http://www.voices.no/mainissues/voices1(2)Forest.html.

Forinash, M. (1992). A phenomenological analysis of Nordoff-Robbins' approach to music therapy: The lived experience of clinical improvisation. *Music Therapy, 11*(*1*), 120–141.

Forinash, M. (1995). Phenomenological research. In B. L. Wheeler (Ed.), *Music therapy research: Quantitative and qualitative perspectives* (367–387). Phoenixville, PA: Barcelona.

Forinash, M. & Gonzalez, D. (1989). A phenomenological perspective of music therapy. *Music Therapy, 8*(*1*), 35–36.

Forinash, M. & Lee, C. (1998). Guest editorial. *Journal of Music Therapy, 35*(*3*), 142–149.

Fowler, K. L. (2006). The relations between personality characteristics, work environment, and the professional well-being of music therapists. *Journal of Music Therapy, 43*, 174–197.

Fowler, R. S., Jr. & Fordyce, W. E. (1974). *Stroke: Why do they behave that way?* Seattle: Washington State Heart Association.

Freed, B. S. (1987). Songwriting with the chemically dependent. *Music Therapy Perspectives, 4*, 13–18.

Frego, R. J. D. (1995). Uniting the generations with music programs. *Music Educators Journal, 81*(*6*), 12–19, 55.

Frego, R. J. D., Listen, R. E., Hama, M., & Gillmeister, G. (2008). The Dalcroze approach to music therapy. In A-A. Darrow (Ed.), *Introduction to approaches in music therapy*, (2nd ed.) (25–36). Silver Spring, MD: American Music Therapy Association.

Friedlander, L. H. (1994). Group music psychotherapy in an inpatient psychiatric setting for children: A developmental approach. *Music Therapy Perspectives*, *12*(*2*), 92–97.

Frisch, A. (1990). Symbol and structure: Music therapy for the adolescent psychiatric inpatient. *Music Therapy*, *9*(*1*), 16–34.

Froehlich, M. A. R. (1984). A comparison of the effect of music therapy and medical play therapy on the verbalization behavior of pediatric patients. *Journal of Music Therapy*, *21*(*1*), 2–15.

Froehlich, M. A. R. (Ed.) (1996). *Music therapy with hospitalized children: A creative arts child life approach.* Cherry Hill, NJ: Jeffrey Books.

Fulford, M. (2002). Overview of a music therapy program at a maximum security unit of a state psychiatric facility. *Music Therapy Perspectives*, *20*(*2*), 112–116.

Furman, A. G. & Humpal, M. E. (2006). Goals and treatment objectives, settings, and service delivery models in early childhood and early intervention setting. In M. E. Humpal & C. Colwell (Eds.), *Early childhood and school age educational settings* (82–96). Silver Spring, MD: American Music Therapy Association.

Furman, C. E. (Ed.) (1988). *Effectiveness of music therapy procedures: Documentation of research and clinical practice.* Washington, DC: National Association for Music Therapy.

Furman, C. E. (Ed.) (1996). *Effectiveness of music therapy procedures: Documentation of research and clinical practice* (2nd ed.). Silver Spring, MD: National Association for Music Therapy.

Furman, C. E., Adamek, M. S., & Furman, A. G. (1991). Eminence of music therapy among music professions. *Music Therapy Perspectives*, *9*, 39–41.

Furman, C. E. & Furman, A. G. (1988). Music therapy research with mental retardation: Analysis and clinical implications. In C. E. Furman (Ed.), *Effectiveness of music therapy procedures: Documentation of research and clinical practice* (285–299). Washington, DC: National Association for Music Therapy.

Furman, C. E., & Furman, A. G. (1996). Uses of music therapy with people having mental retardation: An update of a previous analysis. In C. E. Furman (Ed.), *Effectiveness of music therapy procedures: Documentation of research and clinical practice* (2nd ed.) (279–296). Silver Spring, MD: National Association for Music Therapy.

Gadberry, A. L. (2011a). A survey of the use of aided augmentative and alternative communication during music therapy sessions with persons with autism spectrum disorders. *Journal of Music Therapy*, *48*, 74–89.

Gadberry, A. L. (2011b). Steady beat and state anxiety. *Journal of Music Therapy*, *48*(*3*), 346–356.

Gadberry, A. L. (2012). Client communication acts and therapist prompts with and without aided augmentative and alternatie communication systems. *Music Therapy Perspectives*, *30*(*2*), 151–157.

Gallagher, A. G., Dinan, T. B., & Baker, A. J. V. (1994). The effects of varying auditory input on schizophrenic hallucinations: A replication. *British Journal of Medical Psychiatry*, *67*, 67–75.

Gallagher, L. M. & Steele, A. L. (2012). Music therapy with offenders in a substance abuse mental illness treatment program. *Music Therapy Perspectives, 20(2),* 117–122.

Galloway, H. F., Jr. (1974). Stuttering and the myth of therapeutic singing. *Journal of Music Therapy, 11(4),* 202–207.

Galloway, H. F., Jr. & Bean, M. F. (1974). The effect of action songs on the development of body-image and body-part identification in hearing impaired preschool children. *Journal of Music Therapy, 11(3),* 125–134.

Gardner, H. (1993). *Frames of mind: The theory of multiple intelligences.* New York: Basic Books.

Gardner, H. (1999). *Intelligence reframed: Multiple intelligences for the 21st century.* New York: Basic Books.

Gardner, W., Licklider, J. C. R., & Weisz, A. Z. (1960). Suppression of pain by sound. *Science, 132,* 32–33.

Gardstrom, S. C. (1987). Positive peer culture: A working definition for the music therapist. *Music Therapy Perspectives, 4,* 19–23.

Gardstrom, S. C. (1996). Music therapy for juvenile offenders in a residential setting. In B. L. Wilson (Ed.), *Models of music therapy interventions in school settings: From institution to inclusion* (127–141). Silver Spring, MD: National Association for Music Therapy.

Gardstrom, S. & Hiller, J. (2010). Song discussion as music psychotherapy. *Music Therapy Perspectives, 28(2),* 149–156.

Gardstrom, S. C. & Jackson, N. A. (2011). Personal therapy for undergraduate music therapy students: A survey of AMTA program coordinators. *Journal of Music Therapy, 48(2),* 226–255.

Garwood, E. C. (1988). The effect of contingent music in combination with bell pad on enuresis of a mentally retarded adult. *Journal of Music Therapy, 25(2),* 103–109.

Gaston, E. T. (1947). Functional aspects of music in hospitals. In H. N. Morgan (Ed.), *Music education source book* (205–207). Chicago: Music Educators National Conference.

Gaston, E. T. (1964). The aesthetic experience and biological man. *Journal of Music Therapy, 1(1),* p. 1–7.

Gaston, E. T. (1968a). Man and music. In E. T. Gaston (Ed.), *Music in therapy* (7–29). New York: Macmillan.

Gaston, E. T. (Ed.) (1968b). *Music in therapy.* New York: Macmillan.

Gay, L. R. (1981). *Educational research: Competencies for analysis and application* (2nd ed.). Columbus, OH: Charles E. Merrill.

Geist, K. & Hitchcook, J. H. (2014). Single case design studies in music therapy: Resurrecting experimental evidence in small group and individual music therapy clinical settings. *Journal of Music Therapy, 51(4),* 293–309.

Geist, K., McCarthy, J., Rodgers-Smith, A., & Porter, J. (2008). Integrating music therapy services and speech-language therapy services for children with severe communication impairments: A co-treatment model. *Journal of Instructional Psychology, 34(4),* 311–316.

Gervin, A. P. (1991). Music therapy compensatory techniques utilizing song lyrics during dressing to promote independence in the patient with a brain injury. *Music Therapy Perspectives, 9,* 87–90.

Gfeller, K. E. (1983). Musical mnemonics as an aid to retention with normal and learning disabled students. *Journal of Music Therapy, 20*(*4*), 179–189.

Gfeller, K. E. (1984). Prominent theories in learning disabilities and implications for music therapy methodology. *Music Therapy Perspectives, 2*(*1*), 9–13.

Gfeller, K. (1987a). Music therapy theory and practice as reflected in research literature. *Journal of Music Therapy, 25*(*1*), 28–43.

Gfeller, K. (1987b). Songwriting as a tool for reading and language remediation. *Music Therapy, 6*(*2*), 28–38.

Gfeller, K. (1988). Musical components and styles preferred by young adults for aerobic fitness activities. *Journal of Music Therapy, 25*(*1*), 28–43.

Gfeller, K. (1990). A cognitive-linguistic approach to language development for the preschool child with hearing impairment: Implications for music therapy practice. *Music Therapy Perspectives, 8*, 47–51.

Gfeller, K. (1992a). Music: A human phenomenon. In W. B. Davis, K. E. Gfeller, & M. H. Thaut (Eds.), *An introduction to music therapy: Theory and practice* (38–64). Dubuque, IA: Wm. C. Brown.

Gfeller, K. (1992b). Music therapy in the treatment of learning disabilities. In W. B. Davis, K. E. Gfeller, & M. H. Thaut (Eds.), *An introduction to music therapy: Theory and practice* (197–208). Dubuque, IA: Wm. C. Brown.

Gfeller, K. (1992c). Music therapy in the treatment of medical conditions. In W. B. Davis, K. E. Gfeller, & M. H. Thaut (Eds.), *An introduction to music therapy: Theory and practice* (234–250). Dubuque, IA: Wm. C. Brown.

Gfeller, K. (1992d). Music therapy in the treatment of sensory disorders. In W. B. Davis, K. E. Gfeller, & M. H. Thaut (Eds.), *An introduction to music therapy: Theory and practice* (209–233). Dubuque, IA: Wm. C. Brown.

Gfeller, K. (1992e). The profession in a larger context. In W. B. Davis, K. E. Gfeller, & M. H. Thaut (Eds.), *An introduction to music therapy: Theory and practice* (352–360). Dubuque, IA: Wm. C. Brown.

Gfeller, K. E. (1998). Music therapy in the treatment of sensory disorder. In W. B. Davis, K. E. Gfeller, & M. H. Thaut (Eds.), *Introduction to music therapy: Theory and practice*, (179–194). Boston: McGraw-Hill.

Gfeller, K. (2000). Accommodating children who use cochlear implants in music therapy or educational settings. *Music Therapy Perspectives, 18*(*2*), 122–130.

Gfeller, K. (2001). Aural rehabilitation of music listening for adult cochlear implant recipients: Addressing learner characteristics. *Music Therapy Perspectives, 19*(*2*), 88–95.

Gfeller, K. (2007). Music therapy and hearing loss: A 30-year retrospective. *Music Therapy Perspectives, 25*(*2*), 100–107.

Gfeller, K. (2007). Music therapy, medicine, and well-being. In W. B. Davis, K. E. Gfeller, & M. H. Thaut (Eds.), *An introduction to music therapy: Theory and practice* (3rd ed.) (305–341). Silver Spring, MD: American Music Therapy Association.

Gfeller, K. & Bauman, A. A. (1988). Assessment procedures for music therapy with hearing impaired children: Language development. *Journal of Music Therapy, 25*(*4*), 192–205.

Gfeller, K. E. & Darrow, A-A. (2008). Music therapy in the treatment of sensory disorders. In W. B. Davis, K. E. Gfeller, & M. H. Thaut (Eds.), *An introduction to music therapy: Theory and practice* (3rd ed.) (365–404). Silver Spring, MD: American Music Therapy Association.

Gfeller, K. & Davis, W. B. (1992). The role of research in music therapy. In W. B. Davis, K. E. Gfeller, & M. H. Thaut (Eds.), *An introduction to music therapy: Theory and practice* (302–351). Dubuque, IA: Wm. C. Brown.

Gfeller, K. E. & Davis, W. B. (2008). The music therapy treatment process. In W. B. Davis, K. E. Gfeller, & M. H. Thaut (Eds.), *An introduction to music therapy: Theory and practice* (3rd ed.) (429–486). Silver Spring, MD: American Music Therapy Association.

Gfeller, K., Driscoll, V., Kenworthy, M., & VanVoorst, T. (2011). Music therapy for preschool cochlear implant recipients. *Music Therapy Perspectives, 29*(*1*), 30–49.

Gfeller, K. & Hanson, N. (Eds.) (1995). *Music therapy programming for individuals with Alzheimer's disease and related disorders.* St. Louis: MMB Music.

Gfeller, K., Jiang, D., Oleson, J. J., Driscoll, V., Olszewski, C., Knutson, J. F., Turner, C., & Gantz, B. (2012). The effects of musical and linguistic components in recognition of real-world musical excerpts by cochlear implant recepients and normal-hearing adults. *Journal of Music Therapy, 49*, 68–101.

Gfeller, K., Logan, H., & Walker, J. (1990). The effect of auditory distraction and suggestion on tolerance for dental restorations in adolescents and young adults. *Journal of Music Therapy, 27*(*1*), 13–23.

Gfeller, K. E. & Thaut, M. H. (2008). Music therapy in the treatmentof behavioral-emotional disorders. In W. B. Davis, K. E. Gfeller, & M. H. Thaut (Eds.), *An introduction to music therapy: Theory and practice* (3rd ed.) (209–246). Silver Spring, MD: American Music Therapy Association.

Gfeller, K., Turner, C., Oleson, J., Kliethermes, M. S., & Driscoll, V. (2012). Accuracy of cochlear implant recipients in speech reception in the presence of background music. *Annals of Otology, Rhinelogy, & Laryngology, 121*(*12*), 782–791.

Gfeller, K., Witt, S. A., Spencer, L. J., Stordahl, J., & Tomblin, B. (1998). Musical involvement and enjoyment of children who use cochlear implants. *Volta Review, 100*, 213–233.

Ghetti, C. M. (2002). Comparison of the effectiveness of three music therapy conditions to modulate behavior states in students with profound disabilities: A pilot study. *Music Therapy Perspectives, 20*(*1*), 20–30.

Ghetti, C. M., Hama, M., & Woolrich, J. (2008). Music therapy in wellness. In A-A. Darrow (Ed.), *Introduction to approaches in music therapy* (2nd ed.) (131–151). Silver Spring, MD: American Music Therapy Association.

Giacino, J. T., Fins, J. J., Koureys, S., & Schiff, N. D. (2014). Disorders of consciousness after acquired brain injury: The state of the science. *Nature Reviews Neurology, 10*, 99–114.

Gibbons, A. C. (1977). Popular music preferences of elderly people. *Journal of Music Therapy, 14*(*4*), 180–189.

Gibbons, A. C. (1982). Music aptitude profile scores in a noninstitutionalized, elderly population. *Journal of Research in Music Education, 30*(*1*), 23–29.

Gibbons, A. C. (1983a). Item analysis of the primary measures of music audiation in elderly care home residents. *Journal of Music Therapy, 20*(*4*), 201–210.

Gibbons, A. C. (1983b). Primary measures of music audiation scores in an institution-alized elderly population. *Journal of Music Therapy, 20*(*1*), 21–29.

Gibbons, A. C. (1985). Stop babying the elderly. *Music Educators Journal, 71*(*7*), 48–51.

Gibbons, A. C. (1988). A review of literature for music development/education and music therapy with the elderly. *Music Therapy Perspectives, 5*, 33–40.

Gibbons, A. C. (1989). Music therapy education/training at the University of Kansas. In R. R. Pratt & B. Hesser (Eds.), *Music therapy and music in special education: The international state of the art*. I. (ISME Edition Number Three) (101–128). St. Louis: MMB Music.

Gibbons, A. C. & McDougal, D. L. (1987). Music therapy in medical technology: Organ transplants. In R. R. Pratt (Ed.), *The fourth international symposium on music: Rehabilitation and human well-being* (61–72). New York: University Press of America.

Gilbert, J. P. (1977). Music therapy perspectives on death and dying. *Journal of Music Therapy, 14*(*4*), 165–171.

Gilbert, J. P. (1983). A comparison of motor music skills in non-handicapped and learning disabled children. *Journal of Research in Music Education, 31*(*2*), 147–155.

Gilbert, J. P. & Beal, M. R. (1982). Preferences of elderly individuals for selected music education experiences. *Journal of Research in Music Education, 30*(*4*), 247–253.

Gilbertson, S. & Aldridge, D. (2008). *Music therapy and traumatic brain injury: A light on a dark night*. London: Jessica Kingsley.

Giles, M. M., Cogan, D., & Cox, C. (1991). A music and art program to promote emotional health in elementary school children. *Journal of Music Therapy, 28*(*3*), 135–148.

Gillespie, J. (1968). *The music experience*. Belmont, CA: Wadsworth.

Gilliland, E. G. (1952). Highlights of the second annual conference. *Bulletin of the National Association for Music Therapy, 1*(*1*), 1.

Gilliland, E. G. (1952). The development of music therapy as a profession. Preface to *Music therapy 1951* (Vol. 1). Proceeding of the National Association for Music Therapy. Lawrence, KS: Allen Press.

Gilliland, E. G. (1959). The mentally retarded. In E. H. Schneider (Ed.), *Music therapy 1958* (153-154). Lawrence, KS: Allen Press.

Gladfelter, N. D. (1996). Music therapy for learners with learning disabilities in a private day school. In B. L. Wilson (Ed.), *Models of music therapy interventions in school settings: From institution to inclusion* (184–199). Silver Spring, MD: National Association for Music Therapy.

Glasser, W. (1965). *Reality therapy*. New York: Harper and Row.

Glassman, L. R. (1983). The talent show: Meeting the needs of the healthy elderly. *Music Therapy, 3*(*1*), 82–93.

Glassman, L. R. (2004). *Here comes the music lady: Memoirs of a music therapist*. Bloom-ington, IN: AuthorHouse.

Godley, C. A. S. (1987). The use of music in pain clinics. *Music Therapy Perspectives, 4*, 24–28.

Goetinck, S. (1996a). Arsenal of treatments presents tough choices. *The Dallas Morning News* (April 29), IF, 3F.

Goetinck, S. (1996b). Genes, environment both play major role. *The Dallas Morning News* (April 29), 1F, 3F.

Gold, M. (1982). Voice class without note reading: Training voices of students 55 and older. *National Association for Music Therapy, 26(1)*, 31.

Goldbeck, L. (2012). A randomizer control trial of multimodal music therapy for children with anxiety disorders. *Journal of Music Therapy, 49*, 395–413.

Goldberg, F. S. (1989). Music psychotherapy in acute psychiatric inpatient and private practice settings. *Music Therapy Perspectives, 6*, 40–43.

Goldberg, F. S. (1994). Guest editorial: Introduction to the special issue on psychiatric music therapy. *Music Therapy Perspectives, 12(2)*, 67–69.

Goldberg, F. S., Hoss, T. M., & Chesna, T. (1988). Music and imagery as psychotherapy with a brain damaged patient: A case study. *Music Therapy Perspectives, 5*, 41–45.

Goldman, J. S. (1988). Toward a new consciousness of the sonic healing arts: The therapeutic use of sound for personal and planetary health and transformation. *Music Therapy, 7(1)*, 28–33.

Gonzales, A. (1981, April). Music therapy techniques to promote and enhance verbal and vocal responses in severe and profound developmentally handicapped clients. Paper presented at the 1981 Conference of the Great Lakes Regional Chapter of the National Association for Music Therapy. Cleveland, OH.

Good, M., Stanton-Hicks, M., Grass, J. H., Anderson, G. C., Lai, H., Roykulcharen, V., et al. (2001). Relaxation and music to reduce postsurgical pain. *Journal of Advanced Nursing, 33*, 208–215.

Gooding, L. (2011). The effect of a music therapy social skills training program on improving social competence in children and adolescents with social skills deficits. *Journal of Music Therapy, 48*, 440–462.

Goodglass, H. (1963). Musical capacity after brain surgery. In E. H. Schneider (Ed.), *Music therapy 1962* (101–107). Lawrence, KS: Allen Press.

Goodman, K. D. (2007). *Music therapy groupwork with special needs children*. Springfield, IL: Charles C Thomas.

Goodman, K. D. (2011). *Music therapy education and training*. Springfield, IL: Charles C Thomas.

Goolsby, T. M., Jr., Frary, R. B., & Rogers, M. M. (1974). Observation techniques in determination of the effects of background music upon verbalization of disadvantaged kindergarten children. *Journal of Music Therapy, 11(1)*, 21–32.

Gordon, E. C. (1968). *Musical aptitude profile*. Boston: Houghton Mifflin.

Gordon, J. S. (1980). The paradigm of holistic medicine. In A. C. Hastings, J. Fadiman, and J. S. Gordon (Eds.), *Health for the whole person* (3–27). Boulder, CO: Westview Press.

Graham, R. M. (1974). The education of the music therapist. *College Music Symposium, 14*, 50–59.

Graham, R. M. (1975). Music education of emotionally disturbed children. In R. M. Graham (Compiler), *Music for the exceptional child* (111–129). Reston, VA: Music Educators National Conference.

Grandin, T. (1995). *Thinking in pictures*. New York: Doubleday.

Grandin, T. & Scarino, M. M. (1986). *Emergence: Labeled autistic.* Novato, CA: Arena Press.

Grant, R. E. (1989). Music therapy guidelines for developmentally disabled children. *Music Therapy Perspectives, 6,* 18–22.

Gray, C. A. & Garrand, J. (1993). Social stories: Improving responses of individuals with autism with accurate social information. *Focus onAutistic Behavior, 8,* 1–10.

Greespan, S. & Wieder, S. (1998). *The child with special needs.* Reading, MA: Addison-Wesley.

Greenspan, S. & Wieder, S. (2000). The infancy and early childhood training course. Reported by Wheeler and Stultz (2008) from material presented in a training course (April), Arlington, VA.

Greenwald, M. A. & Salzberg, R. S. (1979). Vocal range assessment of geriatric clients. *Journal of Music Therapy, 16(4),* 172–177.

Gregoire, M. A., Hughes, J. E., Robbins, B. J., & Voorneveld, R. B. (1989). Music therapy with the gifted: A trial program. *Music Therapy Perspectives, 7,* 23–27.

Gregory, D. (2001). Four decades of music therapy behavioral research designs: A content analysis of the *Journal of Music Therapy* articles. *Journal of Music Therapy, 39(1),* 56–71.

Gresham, F. M. & Reschly, D. J. (1986). Social skill deficits and low peer acceptance of mainstreamed learning disabled children. *Learning Disability Quarterly, 9,* 23–32.

Griffiths, T. D. (2009). The neural processing of complex sounds. In I. Peretz & R. J. Zatorre (Eds.), *The cognitive neuroscience of music* (168–177). New York: Oxford University Press.

Griggs-Drane, E. R. & Wheeler, J. J. (1997). The use of functional assessment procedures and individualized schedules in the treatment of autism: Recommendations for music therapists. *Music Therapy Perspectives, 15(2),* 87–93.

Grigorenko, E. L., Macombre, D., Hart, L., Naples, A., Chapman, J., Geib, C. F., Chart, H., Tan, M., Wolherdler, B., & Wagner, R. (2010). Academic achievement among juvenile detainees. *Journal of Learning Disabilities, 48(4),* 359–368.

Grocke, D. (2005). The role of the therapist in the Bonny Method of Guided Imagery and Music (BMGIM). *Music Therapy Perspectives, 23(1),* 45–52.

Grocke, D., Bloch, S., & Castle, D. (2009). The effect of group music therapy on quality of life for participants living with a severe and enduring mental illness. *Journal of Music Therapy, 46,* 90–104.

Grocke, D. & Wigram, T. (2007). *Receptive methods in music therapy: Techniques and clinical applications for music therapy clinicians, educators, and students.* London: Jessica Kingsley.

Groene, R. W. (1993). Effectiveness of music therapy 1:1 interventions with individuals having senile dementia of the Alzheimer's type. *Journal of Music Therapy, 30(3),* 138–157.

Groene, R. (2001). The effect of presentation and accompaniment styles on attention and responsive behaviors of participants with dementia diagnosis. *Journal of Music Therapy, 38(1),* 36–50.

Groene, R. (2003). Wanted: Music therapists. A study of the need for music therapists in the coming decade. *Music Therapy Perspectives, 21*(*1*), 4–13.

Groene, R. W. & Pembrook, R. E. (2000). Curricula issues in music therapy: A survey of collegiate facaulty. *Music Therapy Perspectives, 18*(*2*), 92–102.

Groeneweg, G., Stan, E. A., Celser, A., MacBeth, L., & Vrbancic, M. I. (1988). The effect of background music on the vocational behavior of mentally handicapped adults. *Journal of Music Therapy, 25*(*3*), 118–134.

Gromko, J. E. & Cohen, M. L. (2011). Choir in prison: The relationship of psychological needs to perceptions of meaning in music. In P. M. Ward-Steinman, (Ed.), *Advances in social-psychology and music education research* (107–114). Burlington, VT: Ashgate.

Guerrero, N. & Turry, A. (2013). Nordoff-Robbins music therapy: An expressive and dynamic approach for young children on the autism spectrum. In P. Kern & M. Humpal (Eds.), *Early childhood music therapy and autism spectrum disorders* (130–144). London: Jessica Kingsley.

Grout, D. J. (1973). *A history of western music* (2nd ed.). New York: Norton.

Gunsberg, A. (1988). Improvised musical play: A strategy for fostering social play between developmentally delayed and nondelayed preschool children. *Journal of Music Therapy, 25*(*4*), 178–191.

Gunsberg, A. (1991). A method for conducting improvised musical play with children both with and without developmental delays in preschool classrooms. *Music Therapy Perspectives, 9*, 46–51.

Guzzetta, C. E. (1991). Music therapy: Nursing the music of the soul. In D. Campbell (Ed.), *Music: Physician for times to come* (146–166). Wheaton, IL: Quest Books.

Gwyther, L. P. (1985). *Care of Alzheimer's patients: A manual for nursing home staff.* Chicago, IL: American Health Care Association and Alzheimer's Disease and Related Disorders Association.

Haas, F., Pineda, H., & Axen, K. (1989). Music and respiration. In M. H. M. Lee (Ed.), *Rehabilitation, music and human well-being* (188–205). St. Louis: MMB Music.

Habboushe, F. & Maranto, C. D. (1991). Medical and psychological problems of musicians: An overview. In C. D. Maranto (Ed.), *Applications of music in medicine* (201–221). Washington, DC: National Association for Music Therapy.

Hackley, J. A. (1973). Reality orientation brings patients back from confusion and apathy. *Modern Nursing Home.*

Hadsell, N. (1974). A sociological theory and approach to music therapy with adult psychiatric patients. *Journal of Music Therapy, 11*(*3*), 113–124.

Hadsell, N. A. (1989). Multivariate analyses of musicians' and nonmusicians' ratings of pre-categorized stimulative and sedative music. *Journal of Music Therapy, 26*(*3*), 106–114.

Hadsell, N. A. (1993). Levels of external structure in music therapy. *Music Therapy Perspectives, 11*(*2*), 61–65.

Hadsell, N. A. & Coleman, K. A. (1988). Rett syndrome: A challenge for music therapists. *Music Therapy Perspectives, 5*, 52–56.

Hager, M. (1983). Aging: Growing old actively. *Consumers Digest* (January/February), 21–23, 34.

Haines, J. H. (1989). The effects of music therapy on the self-esteem of emotionally disturbed adolescents. *Music Therapy, 8*(*1*), 78–91.

Hakvoort, L. (2002). A music therapy anger management program for forensic offenders. *Music Therapy Perspectives, 20*(2), 123–132.

Hall, M. J., Levant, S., DeFrances, C. J. (2012). Hospitalization for stroke in U. S. hospitals, 1989–2009. NCHS data brief, no. 95. Hyattsville, MD: National Center for Health Statistics.

Halpern, S. (1978). *Tuning the human instrument.* Belmont, CA: Helpern Sounds.

Halpern, S. (1989). A new age of music in medicine. In M. H. M. Lee (Ed.), *Rehabilitation, music and human wellbeing* (82–100). St. Louis: MMB Music.

Hamburg, J. & Clair, A. A. (2003a). The effects of a Laban-based movement program with music on measuresof balance and gait in older adults. *Activities, Adaptation, and Aging, 28,* 17–33.

Hamburg, J. & Clair, A. A. (2003b). The effects of a movement with music program on measures of balance and gait speed in healthy older adults. *Journal of Music Therapy, 40,* 212–216.

Hamburg, J. & Clair, A. A. (2008). The effects of a Laban/Bartenieff-based movement program with music on physical function measures in older adults. *Music Therapy Perspectives, 26*(1), 30–37.

Hamel, P. M. (1979). *Through music to the self* (P. Lemesurier, Trans.). Boulder, CO: Shambala.

Hamill, D. D., Leigh, J. E., McNutt, G., & Larson, S. C. (1981). A new definition of learning disabilities. *Learning Disability Quarterly, A,* 336–342.

Hamilton, P. & Bailey, L. (1981, November). The role of the healing arts in the care of the person with cancer. Paper presented at the 32nd Annual Conference of the National Association for Music Therapy, Denver, CO.

Hammer, S. E. (1996). The effects of guided imagery through music on state and trait anxiety. *Journal of Music Therapy, 33*(1), 47–70.

Haneishi, E. (2001). Effects of a music therapy voice protocol on speech intelligibility, vocal acoustic measures, and mood of individuals with Parkinson's disease. *Journal of Music Therapy, 38,* 273–290.

Haneishi, E. (2005). Juliette Alvin: Her legacy for music therapy in Japan. *Journal of Music Therapy, 42*(4), 273–295.

Hannon, A. (2008). General pediatric medical/surgical. In D. Hanson-Abromeit & C. Colwell, (Eds.), *Medical music therapy for pediatrics in hospital settings* (107–146). Silver Spring, MD: American Music Therapy Association.

Hanser, S. B. (1984). Music group psychotherapy: An evaluation model. *Music Therapy Perspectives, 1*(4), 14–16.

Hanser, S. B. (1985). Music therapy and stress reduction research. *Journal of Music Therapy, 22*(4), 193–206.

Hanser, S. B. (1987). *Music therapist's handbook.* St. Louis: Warren H. Green.

Hanser, S. B. (1990). A music therapy strategy for depressed older adults in the community. *Journal of Applied Gerontology, 9,* 283–298.

Hanser, S. B. (1995). Applied behavior analysis. In B. L. Wheeler (Ed.), *Music therapy research: Quantitative and qualitative perspectives* (149–163). Phoenixville, PA: Barcelona.

Hanser, S. B. (1999). *The new music therapist's handbook* (2nd ed.). Boston: Berklee Press.

Hanser, S. B., Butterfield-Whitcomb, J., & Kawata, M. (2011). Home-based music strategies with individuals who have dementia and their family caregivers. *Journal of Music Therapy, 48*(*1*), 2–27.

Hanser, S. B., Larson, S. C., & O'Connell, A. S. (1983). The effect of music on relaxation of expectant mothers during labor. *Journal of Music Therapy, 20*(*2*), 50–58.

Hanser, S. B. & Mandel, S. E. (2010). *Manage your stress and pain through music.* Berklee, CA: Berklee Press.

Hanser, S. B. & Wheeler, B. L. (1995). Experimental research. In B. L. Wheeler (Ed.), *Music therapy research: Quantitative and qualitative perspectives* (129–146). Phoenixville, PA: Barcelona.

Hanson-Abromeit, D. (2008). Introduction to pediatric medical music therapy. In D. Hanson-Abromeit & C. Colwell (Eds.), *Medical music therapy for pediatrics in hospital settings* (3–11). Silver Spring, MD: American Music Therapy Association.

Hanson-Abromeit, D. & Colwell, C. (Eds.) (2008). *Medical music therapy for pediatrics in hospital settings.* Silver Spring, MD: The American Music Therapy Association.

Hanson-Abromeit, D. & Moore, K. G. (2014). The systematic review as a research process in music therapy. *Journal of Music Therapy, 51*(*1*), 4–38.

Hanson, N., Gfeller, K., Woodworth, G., Swanson, E., & Garand, L. (1996). A comparison of the effectiveness of differing types and difficulty of music activities in programming for older adults with Alzheimer's disease and related disorders. *Journal of Music Therapy, 33*(*2*), 93–123.

Hardman, M. L., Drew, C. L., & Egan, M. W. (2008). *Human exceptionality. School, community and family* (9th ed.). Boston: Houghton Mifflin.

Hargreaves, D. J. & North, A. C. (1999). The function of music in everyday life: Redefining the social in music psychology. *Psychology of Music, 27*, 71–83.

Harris, C. S., Bradley, R. J., & Titus, S. K. (1992). A comparison of the effects of hard rock and easy listening on the frequency of observed inappropriate behaviors: Control of environmental antecedents in a large public area. *Journal of Music Therapy, 29*(*1*), 6–17.

Harrison, R. (2008). Noise-induced hearing loss in children: A "less than silent" environmental danger. *Pediatric Child Health,* 13, 372-382.

Harvey, A. W. (1987). Utilizing music as a tool for healing. In R. R. Pratt (Ed.), *The fourth international symposium on music: Rehabilitation and human well-being* (73–87). New York: University Press of America.

Harvey, A. W. (1991). Music in attitudinal medicine. In D. Campbell (Ed.), *Music: Physician for times to come* (186–196). Wheaton, IL: Quest Books.

Havighurst, R. J. (1963). Successful aging. In R. H. Williams, C. Tibbitts, & W. Donahue (Eds.), *Processes of aging.* New York: Atherton Press.

The healing role of the arts (Working papers – The Rockefeller Foundation) (1978). New York: The Rockefeller Foundation.

Health insurance portability and accountability act of 1996, Public Law No. 104-191 (1996).

Healthline (2015). Brittle bone disease (osteogenesis imperfecta). Retrieved April 16, 2016 from www.healthline.com/health/osteogenesis-imperfecta#Overview/.

Healthline (2015). Burns: Types, treatments, and more. Retrieved April 15, 2015 from www.healthline.com.

Heaney, C. J. (1992). Evaluation of music therapy and other treatment modalities by adult psychiatric inpatients. *Journal of Music Therapy, 29*(2), 70–86.

Heaton, P., Hermelin, B., & Pring, L. (1999). Can children with autistic spectrum disorders perceive affect in music? An experimental investigation. *Psychology of Medicine, 29,* 1405–1410.

Hedden, S. K. (1980a). The physical basis of music. In D. A. Hodges (Ed.), *Handbook of music psychology* (37–41). Lawrence, KS: National Association for Music Therapy.

Hedden, S. K. (1980b). Psychoacoustical parameters of music. In D. A. Hodges (Ed.), *Handbook of music psychology* (63–85). Lawrence, KS: National Association for Music Therapy.

Heidenreich, L. (n.d.). Be active! Comprehensive eurhythmics: A video program of movement to music (brochure). Milwaukee, WI: School Sisters of Notre Dame.

Heller, G. N. (1987). Ideas, initiatives, and implementations: Music therapy in America, 1789–1848. *Journal of Music Therapy, 24*(1), 35–46.

Heller, G. N. (2000). History, celebrations, and the transmission of hope: The American Music Therapy Association, 1950–2000. *Journal of Music Therapy, 37,* 238–249.

Henderson, S. M. (1983). Effects of a music therapy program upon awareness of mood in music, group cohesion, and self-esteem among hospitalized adolescent patients. *Journal of Music Therapy, 20*(1), 14–20.

Henry, D., Knoll, C. D., & Anderson, S. E. (1982). *Music works . . . A handbook for music therapists.* Stephenville, TX: Music Works.

Hepburn, M. & Krout, R. E. (2004). Meaning, purpose, transcendence and hope – Music therapy and spirituality in end of life hospice care. *New Zealand Journal of Music Therapy, 2,* 58–82.

Herlein, D. G. (1975). Music reading for the sightless: Braille notation. *Music Educators Journal, 62*(1), 42–45.

Herman, F. (1981, November), "Hey! Look at me!" Presentation at the 32nd Annual Conference of the National Association for Music Therapy, Denver, CO.

Herman, F. (1985). Music therapy for the young child with cerebral palsy who uses Blissymbols. *Music Therapy, 5*(1), 28–36.

Herman, F. (1991). The boy that nobody wanted: Creative experiences for a boy with severe emotional problems. In K. E. Bruscia (Ed.), *Case studies in music therapy* (99–108). Phoenixville, PA: Barcelona.

Hesser, B. (1995). The power of sound and music in therapy. In C. B. Kenny (Ed.), *Listening, playing, creating: Essays on the power of sound* (43–50). Albany, NY: State University of New York Press.

Hesser, B. (2001). Special feature: The transformative power of music in our lives: A personal perspective. *Music Therapy Perspectives, 19*(1), 53–58.

Hewett, F. M. & Forness, S. R. (1974). *Education of exceptional learners.* Boston: Allyn and Bacon.

Heyduk, R. G. (1975). Rated preference of musical compositions as it related to complexity and exposure frequency. *Perception and Psychophysics, 17,* 84–91.

Heyer, J. L., Downs, D. W., Kalloy, V., & Magdinec, M. (1986). Music conditioning before pure-tone screening of severely and profoundly mentally retarded adults.

Journal of Music Therapy, 23(*3*), 142–156.

Hibben, J. (1984). Movement as musical expression in a music therapy setting. *Music Therapy, 4*(*1*), 91–97.

Hibben, J. (1991a). Group music therapy with a classroom of 6–8 year old hyperactive-learning disabled children. In K. E. Bruscia (Ed.), *Case studies in music therapy* (175–189). Phoenixville, PA: Barcelona.

Hibben, J. (1991b). Identifying dimensions of music therapy activities appropriate for children at different stages of group development. *Arts in Psychotherapy, 18*, 301–310.

Hibben, J. (1992). Music therapy in the treatment of families with young children. *Music Therapy, 11*(*1*), 28–44.

Hilliard, R. E. (2001a). The use of cognitive-behavioral music therapy in the treatment of women with eating disorders. *Music Therapy Perspectives, 19*(*2*), 109–113.

Hilliard, R. E. (2001). The use of music therapy in meeting the multidimensional needs of hospice patients and families. *Journal of Palliative Care, 17*(*3*), 161–166.

Hilliard, R. E. (2005). *Hospice and palliative care music therapy: A guide to program development and clinical care.* Cherry Hill, NJ: Jeffrey Books.

Hilliard, R. E. (2007). The effects of Orff-based music therapy and social work groups on childhood grief symptoms and behaviors. *Journal of Music Therapy, 46*(*2*), 123–138.

Hines, S. J. (2010). Name that word. Using song lyrics to improve the decoding skills of adolescents with learning disabilities. *Teaching Exceptional Children, 43*(*1*), 16–21.

Hinman, M. L. (2010). Our song: Music therapy with couples when one partner is medically hospitalized. *Music Therapy Perspectives, 28*(*1*), 29–36.

Hirokawa, E. (2004). Effects of music listening and relaxation instructions on arousal changes and the working memory task in older adults. *Journal of Music Therapy, 41*(*2*), 107–127.

Hobson, M. R. (2006). The collaboration of music therapy and speech-language pathology in the treatment of neurogenic communication disorders: Part II – collaborative strategies and scope of practice. *Music Therapy Perspectives, 24*(*2*), 60–72.

Hock, M. F., Brasseur, I. F., Deshler, D. D., Cotts, H. W., Marquis, J. G., Mark, C. A., & Stribling, J. W. (2009). What is the reading component skill profile of adolescent struggling readers in urban schools? *Learning Disability Quarterly, 32*, 21–38.

Hodges, D. A. (1980). Neurophysiology and musical behavior. In D. A. Hodges (Ed.), *Handbook of music psychology* (195–223). Lawrence, KS: National Association for Music Therapy.

Hodges, D. A. (1996). Neuromusical research: A review of the literature. In D. A. Hodges (Ed.), *Handbook of music psychology* (2nd ed.) (197–284). San Antonio, TX: Institute for Music Research Press.

Hodges, D. A. & Haack, P. A. (1996). The influence of music on human behavior. In D. A. Hodges (Ed.), *Handbook of music psychology* (2nd ed.) (469–555). San Antonio, TX: Institute for Music Research Press.

Hoelzley, P. D. (1991). Reciprocal inhibition in music therapy: A case study involving wind instrument usage to attenuate fear, anxiety, and avoidance reactivity in a child with pervasive developmental disorder. *Music Therapy, 10(1)*, 58–76.

Hoerning, K. (1982). A joyful sound. Voice of the lakes. *National Association for Music Therapy, 26(1)*, 32–33.

Hoffman, N. E. (1974). *Hear the music! A new approach to mental health.* Boynton Beach, FL: Star Publishing.

Hofmeister, G. L. & Cole, C. F. (1986, November). The use of music in neuropsychological rehabilitation. Paper presented at the 37th Annual Conference of the National Association for Music Therapy, Chicago, IL.

Hogan, H., Perez, D., & Bell, W. R. (2008). Who (really) are the first baby boomers? (1000–1067). In Joint Statistical Meetings Proceedings, Social Statistics Section, Alexandria, VA: American Statistical Association.

Hogan, T. J. & Silverman, M. J. (2015). Coping-infused dialogue through patient-preferred live music: A medical music therapy protocol and randomized pilot study for hospitalized organ transplant patients. *Journal of Music Therapy, 52(3)*, 420–436.

Hollander, F. M. & Juhrs, P. D. (1974). Orff-Schulwerk, an effective treatment tool with autistic children. *Journal of Music Therapy, 11(1)*, 1–12.

Holloway, M. S. (1980). A comparison of passive and active music reinforcement to increase preacademic and motor skills in severely retarded children and adolescents. *Journal of Music Therapy, 17(2)*, 58–69.

Hooper, J. (2001). Overcoming the problems of deinstitutionalization using music activities to encourage interaction between four adults with a developmental disability. *Music Therapy Perspecives, 19(2)*, 121–127.

Horn, J. C. & Meer, J. (1987). The vintage years. *Psychology Today, 21(5)*, 76–84, 88–90.

Hoskins, C. (1988). Use of music to increase verbal response and improve expressive language abilities of preschool language delayed children. *Journal of Music Therapy, 25(2)*, 73–84.

Hospice Net. Hospice, frequently asked questions. Retrieved August 16, 2014 from http://www.hospicenet.org/html/faq.html.

Hospice web: A special kind of caring. (1999). Online, April 16, 1999. (Available at http://teleport.com/hospice/index.html).

Howell, R. D., Flowers, P. J., & Wheaton, J. E. (1995). The effects of keyboard experiences on rhythmic responses on elementary school children with physical disabilities. *Journal of Music Therapy, 32(2)*, 91–112.

Hsiao, F. (2008). Mandarin melody recognition by pediatric cochlear implant recipients. *Journal of Music Therapy, 45*, 390–404.

Hsiao, F. (2011). From the ideal to the real world: A phenomenological inquiry into student sojourners' re-entry adaptation. *Journal of Music Therapy, 48(4)*, 420–439.

Hughes, J. E., Robbins, B. J., McKenzie, B. A., & Robb, S. S. (1990). Integrating exceptional and nonexceptional young children through music play: A pilot program. *Music Therapy Perspectives, 8*, 52–56.

Humpal, M. E. (1990). Early intervention: The implications for music therapy. *Music Therapy Perspectives, 8*, 30–35.

Humpal, M. E. (1991). The effects of an integrated early childhood music program on social interaction among children with handicaps and their typical peers. *Journal of Music Therapy, 28*(*3*), 161–177.

Humpal, M. E. & Dimmick, J. A. (1995). Special learners in the music classroom *Music Educators Journal, 81*(*5*), 21–23.

Humpal, M. & Kern, P. (2013a). Evidence-based practice for young children with autism spectrum disorders. In P. Kern & M. Humpel (Eds.), *Childhood music therapy and autism spectrum disorder* (39–57). London: Jessica Kingsley.

Humpal, M. & Kern, P. (2013b). Strategies and techniques. In P. Kern & M. Humpal (Eds.), *Early childhood music therapy and autism spectrum disorder* (162–182). London: Jessica Kingsley.

Hunder, G. (Ed.) (2006). *Mayo clinic guide to managing arthritis.* Rochester, MN: Mayo Clinic.

Hunter, B. C. (1994). Presidential perspectives: Reaching out. *NAMT Notes,* July–September, 1, 3.

Hurley, D. (1987). A sound mind in an unsound body. *Psychology Today, 21*(*8*), 34–43.

Hurwitz, I., Wolff, P. H., Bortnick, B. D., & Kokas, K. (1975). Nonmusical effects of the Kodály music curriculum in primary grade children. *Journal of Learning Disabilities, 8*(*3*), 167–174.

Hylton, J. (1983). Music programs for the institutionalized elderly in a midwestern metropolitan area. *Journal of Music Therapy, 20*(*4*), 211–223.

Hynson, J. L. & Sawyer, S. M. (2001). Paediatric palliative care: Distinctive need and emerging issues. *Journal of Paediatrics and Child Health, 37*(*4*), 323–328.

Iliya, Y. A. (2011). Singing for healing and hope: Music therapy methods that use the voice with individuals who are homeless and mentally ill. *Music Therapy Perspectives, 29*(*1*), 14–22.

Ingbar, J. (2003). Using MIDI with adults who have developmental disabilities. *Music Therapy Perspectives, 21*(*1*), 46–50.

Innes-Brown, H., Marozeau, J. P., Storey, C. M., Blamey, P. J. (2013). Tone, rhythm, and timber perception in school-age children using cochlear implants and hearing aids. *Journal of the American Academy of Audiology, 24*(*9*), 789–806.

International Rett Syndrome Association (1987). What is Rett Syndrome? Fort Washington, MD: Author.

Introducing the American Music Therapy Association (1998). *Music Therapy Matters, 1*(*1*), 4.

Isaac, S. & Michael, W. B. (1971). *Handbook in research and evaluation.* San Diego: EdITS.

Isenberg, C., Goldberg, F. S., & Dvorkin, J. M. (2008). Psychodynamic approach to music therapy. In A-A. Darrow (Ed.), *Introduction to approaches in music therapy* (2nd ed.) (79–104). Silver Spring, MD: American Music Therapy Association.

Isenberg-Grzeda, C. (1988). Music therapy assessment: A reflection of professional identity. *Journal of Music Therapy, 25*(*3*), 156–169.

Isenberg-Grzeda, C. (1995). The sound image: Music therapy in the treatment of the abused child. In C. B. Kenny (Ed.), *Listening, playing, creating: Essays on the power of sound* (137–149). Albany, NY: State University of New York Press.

Itoh, M. & Lee, M. H. M. (1989). Epidemiology of disability and music. In M. H. M.

Lee (Ed.), *Rehabilitation, music, and human well-being* (13–31). St. Louis: MMB Music.

Iwaki, T., Tanaka, H., & Hori, T. (2003). The effects of preferred familiar music on falling asleep. *Journal of Music Therapy, 40*, 15–26.

Jacko, V. A., Cobo, H., Cobo, A., Fleming, R., & Moore, J. E. (2010). Mainstream employment in music production for individuals who are visually impaired: Development of a model training program. *Journal of Visual Impairment and Blindness, 104*(9), 519–522.

Jackson, N. A. (2003). A survey of music therapy methods and their role in the treatment of early elementary school children with ADHD. *Journal of Music Therapy, 40*(4), 302–323.

Jacobowitz, R. M. (1992). Music therapy in the short-term pediatric setting: Practical guideline for a limited time frame. *Music Therapy, 11*(1), 45–64.

Jacobson, S. (1987). All elderly people are not alike. *Dallas Times Herald* (March 19), A-19.

James, M. R. (1986). Neurophysiological treatment of cerebral palsy: A case study. *Music Therapy Perspectives, 3*, 5–8.

James, M. R. (1987). Implications of selected social psychological theories on life-long skill generalization: Considerations for the music therapist. *Music Therapy Perspectives, 4*, 29–33.

James, M. R. (1988a). Music therapy and alcoholism: Part II. Treatment/services. *Music Therapy Perspectives, 5*, 65–68.

James, M. R. (1988b). Music therapy values clarification: A positive influence on perceived locus of control. *Journal of Music Therapy, 25*(4), 206–215.

James, M. R. & Freed, B. S. (1989). A sequential model for developing group cohesion in music therapy. *Music Therapy Perspectives, 7*, 28–34.

Jaret, P. (1991). Turn down the racket. *Readers Digest*, November, 153–156.

Jarvis, J. (1988). Guided imagery and music (GIM) as a primary psychotherapeutic approach. *Music Therapy Perspectives, 5*, 69–72.

Jellison, J. A. (1975). The effect of music on autonomic stress responses and verbal reports. In C. K. Madsen, R. D. Greer, & C. H. Madsen, Jr. (Eds.), *Research in music behavior: Modifying music behavior in the classroom* (206–219). New York: Teachers College Press.

Jellison, J. A. & Draper, E. A. (2015). Music research in inclusive school settings: 1975 to 2013. *Journal of Research in Music Education, 62*(4), 325–331.

Jellison, J. A. & Duke, R. A. (1994). The mental retardation label: Music teachers' expectations for children's social and music behaviors. *Journal of Music Therapy, 31*(3), 166–185.

Jellison, J. A. & Flowers, P. J. (1991). Talking about music: Interviews with disabled and nondisabled children. *Journal of Research in Music Education, 39*(4), 322–333.

Jensen, E. (2005). *Top tunes for teaching 977 song titles and practical tools for choosing the right music every time.* Thousand Oaks, CA: Corwin.

Jeong, E. (2013). Psychometric validation of a music-based attention assessment: Revised for patients with traumatic brain injury. *Journal of Music Therapy, 50*, 66–72.

Jeong, E. & Lesiak, T. L. (2011). Development and preliminary evaluation of a music-based attention assessment for patients with traumatic brain injury. *Journal of Music Therapy, 48*(*4*), 551–572.

Jin, S. H., Nelson, P. B., Schlauch, R. S., & Carney, E. (2013). Hearing conservation program for marching band members: A risk for noise-induced hearing loss? *American Journal of Audiology, 22*, 26–39.

Johnson, E. R. (1981). The role of objective and concrete feedback in self-concept treatment of juvenile delinquents in music therapy. *Journal of Music Therapy, 18*(*3*), 137–147.

Johnson, F. L. (1981). Music therapy for the multiply handicapped: A guide to references and resources. *National Association for Music Therapy, 25*(*2*), 20–22.

Johnson, F. L. (1996). Models of service delivery. In B. L. Wilson (Ed.), *Models of music therapy interventions in school settings: From institution to inclusion* (48–77). Silver Spring, MD: National Association for Music Therapy.

Johnson, G. (2007). Clinical practices in music therapy with the chronic adult psychiatric inpatient population. In B. J. Crowe & C. Colwell (Eds.), *Music therapy for children, adolescents, and adults with mental disorders* (119–124). Silver Spring, MD: American Music Therapy Association.

Johnson, G., Otto, D., & Clair, A-A. (2001). The effect of instrumental and vocal music on adherence to a physical rehabilitation exercise program with persons who are elderly. *Journal of Music Therapy, 38*(*2*), 82–96.

Johnson, J. M. & Phillips, L. L. (1971). Affecting the behavior of retarded children with music. *Music Educators Journal, 57*(*7*), 45–46.

Johnson, J. M. & Zinner, C. C. (1974). Stimulus fading and schedule learning in generalizing and maintaining behaviors. *Journal of Music Therapy, 11*(*2*), 84–96.

Johnson, R. E. (1981). E. Thayer Gaston: Leader in scientific thought on music in therapy and education. *Journal of Research in Music Education, 29*(*4*), 279–285.

Jonas, J. L. (1991). Preference of elderly music listeners residing in nursing homes for art music, traditional jazz, popular music of today, and country music. *Journal of Music Therapy, 28*(*3*), 149–160.

Jones, J. (1996, March). Attention deficit disorder: A professional and personal perspective. Paper presented at the Conference of the Southwestern Region of the National Association for Music Therapy, San Antonio, TX.

Jones, J. D. (2006). The use of control groups in music therapy research: A control analysis of articles in the *Journal of Music Therapy. Journal of Music Therapy, 43*(*4*), 334–355.

Jones, R. E. (1986). Assessing developmental levels of mentally retarded students with the musical perception assessment of cognitive development. *Journal of Music Therapy, 23*(*3*), 166–173.

Jorgenson, H. (1974). The use of a contingent music activity to modify behaviors which interfere with learning. *Journal of Music Therapy, 11*(*1*), 41–46.

Josepha, M., Sr. (1964). Therapeutic value of instrumental performance for severely handicapped children. *Journal of Music Therapy, 1*(*3*), 73–79.

Josepha, M., Sr. (1968). Part III. Music therapy for physically disabled children and adults. In E. T. Gaston (Ed.), *Music in therapy* (97–171). New York: Macmillan.

Jung, C. (1956). *Symbols of transformation.* Princeton, NJ: Princeton University Press.

Justice, R. W. (1994). Music therapy interventions for people with eating disorders in an inpatient setting. *Music Therapy Perspectives, 12(2),* 104–110.

Justice, R. W. (2007). Relaxation techniques. In B. J. Crowe & C. Colwell (Eds.), *Music therapy for children, adolescents, and adults with mental disorders* (36–39). Silver Spring, MD: American Music Therapy Association.

Justice, R. W. & Crowe, B. J. (2007). Adults with mental disorders in community settings. In B. J. Crowe & C. Colwell (Eds.), *Music therapy for children, adolescents, and adults with mental disorders* (133–146). Silver Spring, MD: American Music Therapy Association.

Kadaba, L. S. (1995). Shut in but not shut out: Senior citizens connect through teleconferencing. *The Dallas Morning News* (June 16), 1C–2C.

Kaiser, K. A. & Johnson, K. E. (2000). The effect of an interactive experience on music majors' perception of music for deaf students. *Journal of Music Therapy, 37,* 222–234.

Kalas, A. (2012). Joint attention responses of children with autism spectrum disorder to simple versus complex music. *Journal of Music Therapy, 49,* 430–452.

Kanner, L. (1943). Autistic disturbances of affective contact. *Nervous Child, 2,* 217–250.

Kaplan, H. I. & Sadock, B. J. (1991). *Comprehensive glossary of psychiatry and psychology.* Baltimore, MD: Williams & Wilkins.

Kaplan, R. (2011). Music Therapy: Global perspectives. Downloaded July 17, 2014 from http://www.huffingtonpost.com/2Fronna-kaplan-ma%2Fmusic-therapy-world congress.

Kaplan, R. S. & Steele, A. L. (2005). An analysis of music therapy program goals and outcomes for clients with diagnoses on the autism spectrum. *Journal of Music Therapy, 42,* 2–19.

Karras, B. (1985). *Down memory lane: Topics and ideas for reminiscence groups.* Wheaton, MD: Circle Press.

Karras, B. (Ed.) (1987). *"You bring out the music in me": Music in nursing homes.* Binghamton, NY: Haworth Press.

Kaser, V. A. (1993). Musical expression of subconscious feelings: A clinical perspective. *Music Therapy Perspectives, 11(1),* 16–23.

Kaser, V. & Bullard, E. (2007). The forensic mental health institution. In B. J. Crowe & C. Colwell (Eds.), *Music therapy for children, adolescents, and adults with mental disorders* (175–198). Silver Spring, MD: American Music Therapy Association.

Kastenbaum, R. (1979). A developmental-field approach to aging and its implications for practice. In D. P. Kent, R. Kastenbaum, & S. Sherwood (Eds.), *Research planning and action for the elderly: The power and potential of social science* (37–49). New York: Human Sciences Press.

Katagiri, J. (2009). The effect of background music and song texts on the emotional understanding of children with autism. *Journal of Music Therapy, 46,* 15–31.

Kauffman, J. M. (1977). *Characteristics of children's behavior disorders.* Columbus, OH: Charles E. Merrill.

Kay, L. (1996). Adult day care. *Correspondent, 94,* 22–23.

Kay, L. D. (1981). Music therapy activities for the severely and profoundly multiply handicapped child or adult. *National Association for Music Therapy, 25*(2), 26–30.

Kay, L. D. (1998, November). A beginner's guide to Gardner's multiple intelligences. Paper presented at the Inaugural Conference of the American Music Therapy Association , Cleveland, OH.

Kearney, S. & Fussey, I. (1991). The use of adapted leisure materials to reinforce correct head positioning in a brain-injured adult. *Brain Injury, 5*(3), 295–302.

Kellmann, R. H. (1986). Developing music programs for older adults. *Music Educators Journal, 72*(5), 30–33.

Kemper, K. J. & Danhauer, S. C. (2005). Music as therapy. *Southern Medical Journal, 98*(3), 282–288.

Kemper, M. B. (1982). The use of music therapy to promote decision-making behavior among geriatric clients in nursing care facilities. *National Association for Music Therapy, 26*(1), 18–25.

Kendall, J. (1986). Suzuki's mother tongue method. *Music Educators Journal, 72*(6), 47–50.

Kennedy, R. & Kua-Walker (2006). Movement, singing, and instrument playing strategies for a chld with myotonic dystrophy. *Music Therapy Perspectives, 24*(1), 39–51.

Kennelly, J. (2001). Music therapy in the bone marrow transplant unit: Providing emotional support during adolescence. *Music Therapy Perspectives, 19*(2), 104–108.

Kenny, C. B. (1982). *The mythic artery: The magic of music therapy.* Atascadero, CA: Ridgeview.

Kenny, C. B. (1998). Embracing complexity: The creation of a comprehensive research culture in music therapy. *Journal of Music Therapy, 35*(3), 201–217.

Kern, P. (2013). Autism spectrum disorders primer: Characteristics, causes, prevalence, and intervention. In P. Kern & M. Humpal (Eds.), *Early childhood music therapy and autism spectrum disorders* (23–38). London: Jessica Kingsley.

Kern, P. & Aldridge, D. (2006). Using imbedded music therapy interventions to support outdoor play of young children with autism in an inclusive community-based child care program. *Journal of Music Therapy, 43,* 270–294.

Kern, P., Rivera, N. R., Chandler, A., & Humpel, M. (2013). Music therapy services for individuals with autism spectrum disorder: A survey of clinical practices and training needs. *Journal of Music Therapy, 50,* 274–303.

Kern, P., Wakeford, L., & Aldridge, D. (2007). Improving the performance of a young child with autism during self-care tasks using embedded song interventions: A case study. *Music Therapy Perspectives, 25*(1), 43–51.

Kern, P. & Wolery, M. (2001). Participation of a preschooler with visual impairments on the playground: Effects of musical adaptations and staff development. *Journal of Music Therapy, 38,* 142–164.

Kersten, F. (1981). Music as therapy for the visually impaired. *Music Educators Journal, 67*(7), 63–65.

Kersten, F. (1987). Human well-being of visually impaired students through accommodation in music classes for the sighted. In R. R. Pratt (Ed.), *The fourth international symposium on music: Rehabilitation and human well-being* (132–150). New York: University Press of America.

Kim, S. J. (2010). Music therapy protocol development to enhance swallowing training for stroke patients with dysphagia. *Journal of Music Therapy, 47*, 102–119.

Kim, S. J. & Koh, I. (2005). The effects of music on pain perception of stroke patients during upper extremity joint exercises. *Journal of Music Therapy, 42*, 81–90.

Kimbo Educational (1995). Kimbo Educational 1995 catalog. Long Branch, NJ: Author.

King, B. (2007). Language and speech: Distinguishing between aphasia, apraxia, and dysarthria in music therapy research and practice. *Music Therapy Perspectives, 25(1)*, 13–18.

Kirkland, K. (1999). Sound and silence: Music therapy in palliative care. In S. L. Bertman (Ed.), *Grief and the healing arts: Creativity as therapy* (145-149). Amityville, NY: Baywood.

Kivland, M. J. (1986). The use of music to increase self-esteem in a conduct-disordered adolescent. *Journal of Music Therapy, 23(1)*, 25–29.

Knapp, R. A. (1980). A choir for total communication. *Music Educators Journal, 66(6)*, 54–55.

Knight, A. J. (2008). Music therapy internship supervisors and preinternship students: A comparative analysis of qustionnaires. *Journal of Music Therapy, 15(1)*, 75–92.

Knight, W. E. J. & Rickard, N. S. (2001). Relaxing music prevents stress-induced increases in subjective anxiety, systolic blood pressure, and heart rate in healthy males and females. *Journal of Music Therapy, 38(4)*, 254–272.

Knox, R., Yokota-Adachi, H., Kershner, J., & Jutai, J. (2003). Musical attention training program and alternating attention in brain injury: An initial report. *Music Therapy Perspectives*, 99–104.

Kok, L. M., Vlieland, T., Fiocco, M., & Nelissen, R. (2013). A comparative study on the prevalence of musculoskeletal complaints among musicians and non-musicians. *BMC Musculoskeletal Disorders, 14(9)*. Retrieved April 2, 2015 from www.biomedcentral.com/1471-2474/14/9.

Kolb, S. M. & Hanley-Maxwell, C. (2003). Critical social skills for adolescents with high incidence disabilities: Parental perspectives. *Exceptional Children, 68*, 168–179.

Kopecz, M. (2005). Personality and music preferences: The influence of personality traits on preferences regarding musical elements. *Journal of Music Therapy, 42(3)*, 216–239.

Korduba, O. M. (1975). Duplicated rhythm patterns between deaf and normal hearing children. *Journal of Music Therapy, 12(3)*, 136–146.

Kovach, A. M. S. (1985). Shamanism and guided imagery and music: A comparison. *Journal of Music Therapy, 22(3)*, 154–165.

Koza, J. E. (1990). Music instruction in the nineteenth century: Views from Godey's Lady's Book, 1830–1877. *Journal of Research in Music Education, 38(4)*, 245–257.

Kramer, S. A. (1978). The effects of music as a cue in maintaining handwashing in preschool children. *Journal of Music Therapy, 15(3)*, 136–144.

Kraus, T. & Galloway, H. (1982). Melodic intonation therapy with language delayed apraxic children. *Journal of Music Therapy, 19(2)*, 102–133.

Krout, R. (1986a). *Music therapy in special education: Developing and maintaining social skills necessary for mainstreaming.* St. Louis: MMB Music.

Krout, R. (1986b). Use of a group token contingency with school-aged special education students to improve a music listening skill. *Music Therapy Perspectives, 3*, 13–16.

Krout, R. (1987). Music therapy with multi-handicapped students: Individualizing treatment within a group setting. *Journal of Music Therapy, 24*(*1*), 2–13.

Krout, R. (1992a). Integrating technology. *Music Therapy Perspectives, 10*(*1*), 8–9.

Krout, R. (1992b). Integrating technology, version 5.1. *Music Therapy Perspectives, 70*(*2*), 84–86.

Krout, R. (1995). Integrating technology. *Music Therapy Perspectives, 13*(*1*), 5–6.

Krout, R. (2000). Hospice and palliative care music therapy: A continuum of creative caring. In AMTA (Ed.), *Effectiveness of music therapy procedures: Documentation of research and clinical practice* (3rd ed.) (333–411). Silver Spring, MD: American Music Therapy Association.

Krout, R. E. (2001). The effect of single-session music therapy interventions on the observed and self-reported levels of pain control, physical comfort, and relaxation of hospice patients. *American Journal of Hospice and Palliative Care, 18*(*6*), 383–390.

Krout, R. E. (2003). Music therapy with imminently dying hospice patients and their families: Facilitating release near the time of death. *American Journal of Hospice and Palliative Care, 20*(*2*), 129–134.

Krout, R. E. (2005a). Applications of music therapist-composed songs in creating participant connections and facilitating goals and rituals during one-time bereavement support groups and programs. *Music Therapy Perspectives, 23*(*2*), 118–128.

Krout, R. E. (2005b). The music therapist as singer-songwriter: Applications with bereaved teens. In F. Baker & T. Wigram (Eds.), *Song writing methods, techniques and clinical applications for music therapy clinicians, educators, and students* (206–223). London: Jessica Kingsley.

Krout, R. E. (2005c). The use of therapist-composed song in end of life music therapy care. In C. Dileo & J. V. Loewy (Eds.), *Music therapy at the end of life* (129–140). Cherry Hill, NJ: Jeffrey Books.

Krout, R. E. (2006). Following the death of a child: Music therapy helping to heal the family heart. *New Zealand Journal of Music Therapy, 4*, 6–22.

Krout, R. E. (2007). Music listening to facilitate relaxation and promote wellness: Integrated aspecs of our neurophysiological responses to music. *Arts in Psychotherapy, 34*, 134–141.

Krout, R., Burnham, A., & Moorman, S. (1993). Computer and electronic music applications with students in special education: From program proposal to progress evaluation. *Music Therapy Perspectives, 10*(*1*), 8–9.

Krout, R. E. & Mason, M. (1988). Using computer and electronic music resources in clinical music therapy with behaviorally disordered students, 12 to 18 years old. *Music Therapy Perspectives, 5*, 114–118.

Kubler-Ross, E. (1969). *On death and dying.* New York: Macmillan.

Kubler-Ross, E. (1974). *Questions and answers on death and dying.* New York: Macmillan.

Kuhn, D. (2002). The effects of active and passive participation in musical activity on the immune system as measured by salivary immunoglobulin A (SigA). *Journal of Music Therapy, 39*(*1*), 30–39.

Kwak, E. E. (2007). Effect of rhythmic auditory stimulation on gait performance in children with spastic cerebral palsy. *Journal of Music Therapy, 44*, 198–216.

LaGasse, B. (2012). Evaluation of Melodic Intonation Therapy for developmental apraxia of speech. *Music Therapy Perspectives, 30*(*1*), 49–55.

LaGasse, K. A. B. (2013). Pilot and feasibility studies: Application in music therapy research. *Journal of Music Therapy, 50*(*4*), 304–320.

Lamont, A. (2009). Music in the school years. In S. Hallam, I. Cross, & M. Thaut (Eds.), *The Oxford handbook of music psychology* (235–243). New York: Oxford University Press.

Landis, B. & Carder, P. (1972). *The eclectic curriculum in American music education: Contributions of Dalcroze, Koddly, and Orff.* Reston, VA: Music Educators National Conference.

Lane, D. L. (1991). The effect of a single music therapy session on hospitalized children as measured by salivary immunoglobin A, speech pause time, and a patient option Likert scale. *Pediatric Research, 29*(*4*), 11A.

Lane, D. L. (1994). Effects of music therapy on immune function of hospitalized patients. *Quality of Life – A Nursing Challenge, 3*(*4*), 74–80.

Lane, D. (1996a). Music therapy interventions with pediatric oncology patients. In M. A. Froehlich (Ed.), *Music therapy with hospitalized children* (109–116). Cherry Hill, NJ: Jeffrey Books.

Lane, D. (1996b). Songs of love: Music therapy can make a difference in the care of dying children. *Hospice, 7*(*5*), 6–7.

Lang, P. H. (1941). *Music in western civilization.* New York: Norton.

Langdon, G. S., Pearson, J., Stastny, P., & Thorning, H. (1989). The integration of music therapy into a treatment approach in the transition of adult psychiatric patients from institution to community. *Music Therapy, 8*(*1*), 92–107.

Langer, S. K. (1966). The cultural importance of the arts. *The Journal of Aesthetic Education, Spring*, 5–12.

Larson, B. A. (1977). A comparison of singing ranges of mentally retarded and normal children with published songbooks used in singing activities. *Journal of Music Therapy, 14*(*3*), 139–143.

Lathom, W. (1961). The use of music with cerebral palsied children during activities involving physical control. *Bulletin of the National Association for Music Therapy, 10*, 10–16.

Lathom, W. (1968). The use of music therapy with retarded patients. In E. T. Gaston (Ed.), *Music in therapy* (66–77). New York: Macmillan.

Lathom, W. (1974). Application of Kodály concepts in music therapy. *Journal of Music Therapy, 11*(*1*), 13–20.

Lathom, W. (1980). An overview of music therapy. In *The use of the creative arts in therapy* (36–38). Washington, DC: American Psychiatric Association.

Lathom, W (Ed.) (1981a). *Music therapy in the education of handicapped children and youth: A manual to conduct inservice training workshops for music educators, administrators, parents, and special educators* (rev. ed.). Lawrence, KS: National Association for Music Therapy.

Lathom, W (1981b). *The role of the music therapist in the education of severely and profoundly handicapped children and youth.* Lawrence, KS: National Association for

Music Therapy.

Lathom, W. (1982). Report on the Office of Special Education grant. *Music Therapy Perspectives, 1(1)*, 27–29.

Lathom, W. (1982). Survey of current functions of a music therapist. *Journal of Music Therapy, 19(1)*, 2–27.

Lathom, W. & Eagle, C. T. (1982). Music for the severely handicapped. *Music Educators Journal, 68(8)*, 30–31.

Lathom, W. B., Peterson, M., & Havelicek, L. (1982). Musical preference of older people attending nutritional sites. *Educational Gerontology, 8*, 155–165.

Lathom-Radocy, W. B. (2002/2014). *Pediatric music therapy.* Springfield, IL: Charles C Thomas.

Lathom-Radocy, W. B. & Radocy, R. E. (1995). Descriptive quantitative research. In B. L. Wheeler (Ed.), *Music therapy research: Quantitative and qualitative perspectives* (165–181). Phoenixville, PA: Barcelona.

Laureys, S. & Schiff, N. D. (2012). Coma and consciousness: Paradigms (re)framed by neuroimaging. *Neuroimage, 61(2)*, 478–491.

Lavine, R., Bucksbaum, M., & Poncy, M. (1976). Auditory analgesia: Somatosensory evoked response and subjective pain rating. *Psychophysiology, 13(2)*,140–148.

Law, J., Boyle, J., Harris, F., Harkness, A., & Nye, C. (2000). Prevalence and natural history of primary speech and language delay: Findings from a systematic review of the literature. *International Journal of Language and Communication Disorders, 35(2)*, 165–188.

Layman, D. L., Hussey, D. L., & Laing, S. J. (2002). Music therapy assessment for severely emotionally disturbed children: A pilot study. *Journal of Music Therapy, 39*, 164–187.

Layman, D. L., Hussey, D. L., & Reed, A. M. (2013). The Beech Brook Groups Therapy Assessment Tool: A pilot study. *Journal of Music Therapy, 50(3)*, 155–175.

Lazarus, A. A. (1976). *Multimodal behavior therapy.* New York: Springer.

Lazarus, A. A. (1989). *The practice of multimodal therapy.* Baltimore: Johns Hopkins University Press.

Lazarus, L. W. (Ed.). (1988). *Essentials of geriatric psychiatry: A guide for health professionals.* New York: Springer.

Lazer, M. (2007). When is music therapy necessary? Determining eligibility through the I.E.P. Presented at the autism agenda: An evidence based approach to music therapy. The ninth AMTA conference, 14 November, Louisville, KY.

Learning Disabilities Association for America. Retrieved January 5, 2015 from http://www.ldaamerica.org.

LeBlanc, A. (1994). A theory of music performance anxiety. *Quarterly Journal of Music Teaching and Learning, 5(4)*, 60–68.

Lefebvre, C. (1991). All her "yesterdays": An adolescent's search for a better today through music. In K. E. Bruscia (Ed.), *Case studies in music therapy* (219–230). Phoenixville, PA: Barcelona.

Leite, T. (2007). Psychodynamic music therapy with nonpsychotic adults. In B. J. Crowe & C. Colwell (Eds.), *Music therapy for children, adolescents, and adults with mental disorders* (61–76). Silver Spring, MD: American Music Therapy Association.

Lenhoff, H. M. (1998). Insights into the musical potential of cognitively impaired people diagnosed with Williams syndrome. *Music Therapy Perspectives, 16*(1), 33–36.

Leonhard, C. (1982). Humanizing music in a mechanized society. *Music Educators Journal, 68*(9), 23–24.

Lesiuk, T. (2000). The effect of music listening on a computer programming task. *Journal of Computer Information Systems, 40*(3), 50–57.

Lesiuk, T. (2005). The effect of music on work performance. *Psychology of Music, 33*(20), 173–191.

Lesiuk, T. (2010). The effect of preferred music on mood and performance in a high-cognitive demand occupation. *Journal of Music Therapy, 47,* 137–154.

Levetown, M. (1996). Ethical aspects of pediatric palliative care. *Journal of Palliative Care, 12*(3), 35–39.

Levey, S., Levey, I., & Fligor, B. J. (2011). Noise exposure estimates of urban MPs player users. *Journal of Speech, Language, and Hearing Research, 54,* 263–277.

Levine-Gross, J. & Swartz, R. (1982). The effects of music therapy on anxiety in chronically ill patients. *Music Therapy, 2*(1), 43–52.

Levinson, S. & Bruscia, K. (1985). Putting blind students in touch with music. *Music Educators Journal, 72*(2), 49.

Levis, L. & Lininger, L. (1994). *Increase the peace: A focused approach.* Austin & Buda, TX: Authors.

Lewis, C. B. (1985). *Aging: The health care challenge.* Philadelphia: F. A. Davis.

Liebman, S. S. & MacLaren, A. (1991). The effect of music and relaxation on third trimester anxiety in adolescent pregnancy. *Journal of Music Therapy, 28*(2), 89–100.

Lienhard, M. E. (1981, November). Music therapy in a stress treatment program. Paper presented at the 32nd Annual Conference of the National Association for Music Therapy, Denver, CO.

Life's Work (1987). What a hospice nurse does with her life is help people die. *Hippocrates, 1*(3), 54–61.

Lim, H. A. (2009). Use of music to improve speech production in children with autism spectrum disorders: Theoretical orientation. *Music Therapy Perspectives, 27*(2), 103–114.

Lim, H. A. (2010a). Effect of developmental speech and language training through music on speech production in children with autism spectrum disorders. *Journal of Music Therapy, 47,* 2–26.

Lim, H. A. (2010b). Use of music in the applied behavior analysis verbal behavior approach for children with autism spectrum disorders. *Music Therapy Perspectives, 28*(2), 95–105.

Lim, H. A. & Draper, E. (2011). The effects of music therapy incorporated with applied behavior analysis verbal behavior approach for children with autism spectrum disorders. *Journal of Music Therapy, 48,* 537–550.

Lim, H. A., Miller, K., & Fabian, C. (2011). The effects of therapeutic instrumental music performance on endurance level, self-perceived fatigue level, and self-perceived exertion of inpatients in physical rehabilitation. *Journal of Music Therapy, 48,* 124–148.

Lindberg, K. A. (1995). Songs of healing: Songwriting with an abused adolescent. *Music Therapy, 13*(*1*), 93–108.

Linderman, J. & Fridley, B. (1981, November). Medical setting: Getting in and staying there. Paper presented at the 32nd Annual Conference of the National Association for Music Therapy, Denver, CO.

Lipe, A. (1995). The use of music performance tasks in the assessment of cognitive functioning among older adults with dementia. *Journal of Music Therapy, 32*(*3*), 137–151.

Lipe, A. W. (1991). Using music therapy to enhance the quality of life in a client with Alzheimer's dementia: A case study. *Music Therapy Perspectives, 9*, 102–105.

Lipe, A. W. (2002). Beyond therapy: Music, spirituality, and health in human experience: A review of literature. *Journal of Music Therapy, 39*(*3*), 209–240.

Lipe, A. W., York, E., & Jensen, E. (2007). Construct validation of two music-based assessments for people with dementia. *Journal of Music Therapy, 44*(*4*), 369–387.

Lister-Sink, B. (2015). Playing-related injuries. *American Music Teacher, Feb./March*, 16–17.

Locsin, R. (1981). The effect of music on the pain of selected post-operative patients. *Journal of Advanced Nursing, 6*, 19–25.

Loewy, J. (1995). The musical stages of speech: A developmental model of pre-verbal sound making. *Music Therapy, 13*(*1*), 47–73.

Logan, K. (1996). Music is key to lifelong wellness. *Teaching Music, 3*(*4*), 42–43.

Logan, T. G. & Roberts, A. R. (1984). The effects of different types of relaxation music on tension level. *Journal of Music Therapy, 21*(*4*), 177–183.

Loiacono, E. T., Djamasbi, S., & Kiryazov, T. (2013). Factors that affect visually impaired users' acceptance of audio and music websites. *International Journal of & Human-Computer Studies, 71*(*3*), 321–334.

Lorch, C. A., Lorch, V., Diefendorf, A.O., & Earl, P. W. (1994). Effect of stimulative and sedative music on systolic blood pressure, heart rate, and respiratory rate in premature infants. *Journal of Music Therapy, 31*(*2*), 105–118.

Lovejoy, F. H. & Estridge, D. (Eds.) (1987). *The new child health encyclopedia*. New York: Delacorte Press.

Lucchino, R. (2015). Normal aging. Retrieved Oct. 1, 2015, from ruluc@pop.net.

Luce, D. W. (2001). Cognitive therapy and music therapy. *Music Therapy Perspectives, 19*(*2*), 96–103.

Lucia, C. M. (1987). Toward developing a model of music therapy intervention in the rehabilitation of head trauma patients. *Music Therapy Perspectives, A*, 34–39.

Luetje, V. M. (1989). Music therapy in crisis intervention. *Music Therapy Perspectives, 7*, 35–39.

Lukas, L. K. (2004). Orthopedic outpatient's perception of perioperative music listening as therapy. *The Journal of Theory Construction and Testing, 8*(*3*), 7–12.

Lunt, H. (2002). The journey through a barren landscape to practicing music therapist. *British Journal of Music Therapy, 16*, 71–82.

MacNay, S. K. (1995). The influence of preferred music on the perceived exertion, mood, and time estimation scores of patients participating in a cardiac rehabilitation exercise program. *Music Therapy Perspectives, 73*(*2*), 91–96.

Madsen, C. K. (1981). *Music therapy: A behavioral guide for the mentally retarded*. Lawrence, KS: National Association for Music Therapy.

Madsen, C. K. (1986). Research and music therapy: The necessity for transfer. *Journal of Music Therapy, 23*(*2*), 50–55.

Madsen, C. K. & Alley, J. M. (1979). The effect of reinforcement on attentiveness: A comparison of behaviorally trained music therapists and other professionals with implications for competency-based academic preparation. *Journal of Music Therapy, 16*, 70–82.

Madsen, C. K., Byrnes, S. R., Capperalla-Sheldon, D. A., & Brittin, R. V. (1993). Aesthetic response to music: Musicians versus nonmusicians. *Journal of Music Therapy, 30*(*3*), 174–191.

Madsen, C. K. & Madsen, C. H., Jr. (1978). *Experimental research in music.* Raleigh, NC: Contemporary Publishing.

Madsen, N. (2004). Diversity in music education. *Illinois Music Educator, Winter,* 50–51.

Madsen, S. A. (1991). The effect of music paired with and without gestures on the learning and transfer of new vocabulary: Experimenter-derived nonsense words. *Journal of Music Therapy, 28*(*4*), 222–230.

Magee, W. L. (2006). Electronic technologies in clinical music therapy: A survey of practice and attitudes. *Technology and Disability, 18*, 139–146.

Magee, W. L., Baker, F., Daveson, B., Hitchen, H., Kennelly, J., Leung, M., & Tamplin, J. (2011). Music therapy methods with children, adolescents, and adults, *Music Therapy Perspectives, 29*(*1*), 5–13.

Magee, W. L. & Bowen, C. (2008). Using music in leisure to enhance social relationships with patients with complex disabilities. *Neuro Rehabilitation, 23*, 305–311.

Magee, W. L. & Davidson, J. W. (2002). The effect of music therapy on mood states in neurological patients: A pilot study. *Journal of Music Therapy, 39*(*1*), 20–29.

Magee, W. L. & Davidson, J. W. (2004). Music therapy in multiple sclerosis: Results of a systematic qualitative analysis. *Music Therapy Perspectives, 22*(*1*), 39–51.

Magill, L. (2001). The use of music therapy to address the suffering in advanced cancer pain. *Journal of Palliative Care, 17*(*3*), 167–172.

Mahlberg, M. (1973). Music therapy in the treatment of an autistic boy. *Journal of Music Therapy, 10*(*4*), 89–193.

Malone, A. B. (1996). The effects of live music on the distress of pediatric patients receiving intravenous starts, venipunctures, injections, and heal sticks. *Journal of Music Therapy, 33*(*1*), 19–33.

Mandel, S. E. (1988). Music therapy: A personal peri-surgical experience. *Music Therapy Perspectives, 5*, 109–110.

Mandel, S. E. (1991). Music therapy: A repeated personal peri-surgical experience. *Music Therapy Perspectives, 9*, 111–112.

Mandel, S. E. (1996). Music for wellness: Music therapy for stress management in a rehabilitation program. *Music Therapy Perspectives, 14*(*1*), 38–43.

Mansson, H. (2007). Complexity, and diversity in early childhood stuttering. In J. Au-Yeung & M. Leahy (Eds.), *Proceedings of the fifth world congress on fluency disorders* (98–101). Dublin, Ireland: The International Fluency Association.

Maranto, C. D. (1988). AIDS: Information and issues for music therapists. *Music Therapy Perspectives, 5*, 78–81.

Maranto, C. D. (Ed.) (1991). *Applications of music in medicine.* Washington, DC: National Association for Music Therapy.

Maranto, C. D. (Ed.) (1993a). *Music therapy: International perspectives.* Pipersville, PA: Jeffrey Books.

Maranto, C. D. (1993b). Music therapy in the United States of America. In C. D. Maranto (Ed.), *Music therapy: International perspectives* (605–662). Pipersville, PA: Jeffrey Books.

Maranto, C. (1993). Applications of music in medicine. In M. Heal & T. Wigram (Eds.), *Music therapy in health and education* (153–174). London: Jessica Kingsley.

Maranto, C. D. (1996). Research in music and medicine: The state of the art. In M. A. R. Froehlich (Ed.), *Music therapy with hospitalized children: A creative arts child life approach* (39–66). Cherry Hill, NJ: Jeffrey Books.

Maranto, C. D. & Bruscia, K. E. (Eds.) (1987). *Perspectives on music therapy education and training.* Philadelphia: Temple University.

Maranto, C. D. & Bruscia, K. E. (1988). *Methods of teaching and training the music therapist.* Philadelphia: Temple University.

Marcus, D. (1995). Entering the world of tones. In C. B. Kenny (Ed.), *Listening, playing, creating: Essays on the power of sound* (19–41). Albany, NY: State University of New York Press.

Margo, A., Hemsley, D. R., & Slade, P. D. (1981). The effects of varying auditory input on schizophrenic hallucinations. *British Journal of Psychiatry, 139,* 122–127.

Market space. (1987). *Music Educators Journal, 73(4),* 11–12.

Marley, L. S. (1984). The use of music with hospitalized infants and toddlers: A descriptive study. *Journal of Music Therapy, 21(3),* 126–132.

Marom, M. K. (2008). "Patient declined": Contemplating the psychodynamics of hospice music therapy. *Music Therapy Perspectives, 26(1),* 13–22.

Martin, J. A. (Ed.) (1989). *The next step forward: Music therapy with the terminally ill.* NY: Calvary Hospital.

Martin, J. A. (1991). Music therapy at the end of a life. In K. E. Bruscia (Ed.), *Case studies in music therapy* (617–632). Phoenixville, PA: Barcelona.

Martin, L., Snell, A. M., Wolworth, D., & Humpal, M. (2013). Assessment and goals: Determining eligibility, gathering information, and operating treatment goals for music therapy services. In P. Kern & M. Humpal (Eds.), *Early childhood music therapy and autism spectrum disorders* (79–98). London: Jessica Kingsley.

Maslow, A. H. (1968). *Toward a psychology of being* (2nd ed.). New York: Van Nostrand.

Maslow, A. H. (1971). *The further reaches of human nature.* New York: Viking Press.

Matthias, B. (1989). Breaking the sound barrier: Deaf use many methods to join hearing world. *Dallas Times Herald* (August 28), B-1, B-3.

Maultsby, M. C. (1977). Combining music therapy and rational behavior therapy. *Journal of Music Therapy, 14(2),* 89–97.

Maultsby, M. C. (1984). *Rational behavior therapy.* Englewood Cliffs, NJ: Prentice-Hall.

Mauritz, K. H. (2002). Gait training in hemiplegia. *European Journal of Neurology, 9* (suppl. 1), 23–29, 53–61.

Mave-Johnson, E. L. & Tanguay, C. L. (2006). Assessing the unique needs of hospice patients: A tool for music therapists. *Music Therapy Perspectives, 24*(*1*), 13–21.

Mawhood, L., Howlin, P., & Rutter, M. (2000). Autism and developmental receptive language disorder – A comparative follow-up in early adult life, 1: Cognitive and language outcomes. *Journal of Child Psychology and Psychiatry, 41*, 547–559.

May, R. (1975). *The courage to create.* New York: W. W. Norton.

McCarthy, J., Geist, K., Zojwala, R., & Schock, M. Z, (2918). A survey of music therapists' work with speech-language pathologists and experiences with augmentative and alternative communication. *Journal of Music Therapy, 45*, 405–426.

McCarthy, K. M. (1992). Stress management in the health care field: A pilot program for staff in a nursing home unit for patients with Alzheimer's disease. *Music Therapy Perspectives, 10*(*2*), 110–113.

McCord, K. & Fitzgerald, M. (2006). Children with disabilities playing musical instruments. *Music Educator's Journal, 92*(*4*), 46–52.

McDonald, R., Kreutz, G., & Mitchell, L. (Eds.) (2012). *Music, health and wellbeing.* Oxford: Oxford University Press.

McDonnell, L. (1984). Music therapy with trauma patients and their families on a pediatric service. *Music Therapy, 4*(*1*), 55–63.

McDonnell, L. (1983). Music therapy: Meeting the psychological needs of hospitalized children. *Children's Health Care, 12*(*1*), 29–33.

McFerran, K. & Shanhan, E. (2011). Music therapy practice in special education and children's hospice: A systematic comparison of two music therapists' strategies with three preadolescent boys. *Music Therapy Perspectives, 28*(*2*), 103–111.

McGinty, J. K. (1980). Survey of duties and responsibilities of current music therapy positions. *Journal of Music Therapy, 17*(*3*), 148–166.

McGuire, M. G. & Smeltekop, R. A. (1994a). The termination process in music therapy: Part I – Theory and clinical implications. *Music Therapy Perspectives, 12*(*1*), 20–27.

McGuire, M. G. & Smeltekop, R. A. (1994b). The termination process in music therapy: Part II – A model and clinical implications. *Music Therapy Perspectives, 12*(*1*), 28–34.

McHugh, L., Gardstrom, S., Hiller, J., Brewer, M., & Diestelkamp, W. S. (2012). The effect of pre-meal, vocal re-creative music therapy on nutritional intake of residents with Alzheimer's Disease and related dementias: A pilot study. *Music Therapy Perspectives, 30*(*1*), 32–42.

McKinney, C. H. (1990). Music therapy in obstetrics: A review. *Music Therapy Perspectives, 8*, 57–60.

McMaster, N. (1991). Reclaiming a positive identity: Music therapy in the aftermath of a stroke. In K. E. Bruscia (Ed.), *Case studies in music therapy* (547–559). Phoenixville, PA: Barcelona.

McNair, D., Lorr, M., & Droppleman, L. (1971). EITS manual for the profile of mood states (POMS). San Diego: EITS.

McNeil, C. (1995). *Alzheimer's disease: Unraveling the mystery.* Bethesda, MD: National Institute on Aging.

McPherson, G. & Dunbar-Hall (2001). In D. J. Hargreaves & A. C. North, (Eds.), *Musical development and learning.* New York: Continuum.

McRae, S. W. (1982). The Orff connection: Reaching the special child. *Music Educators*

Journal, 68(*8*), 32–34.

McReynolds, J. C. (1988). Helping visually impaired students succeed in band. *Music Educators Journal, 75*(*1*), 36–38.

Mead, V. H. (1986). More than mere movement: Dalcroze eurhythmics. *Music Educators Journal, 72*(*6*), 42–46.

Meagher, R. B. Jr. (1982). Cognitive behavior therapy in health psychology. In T. Millon, C. Green, & R. Meagher (Eds.), *Handbook of clinical health psychology* (499–520). New York: Plenum Press.

Medline Plus (2015). Head injuries. Retrieved April 15, 2015 from http://www.nim.mih.gov/medlineplus/headinjuries.html.

Meer, J. (1985). Mental alertness and the good old days. *Psychology Today, 19*(*3*), 8.

Meichenbaum, D. (1979). Cognitive-behavior modification: The need for a fairer assessment. *Cognitive Therapy and Research, 3*(*2*), 127–132.

Melzack, R. & Wall, P. D. (1965). Pain mechanisms: A new theory. *Science, 150,* 971–979.

Melzack, R., Weisz, A. Z., & Sprague, I. T. (1963). Strategems for controlling pain: Contributions of auditory stimulation and suggestion. *Experimental Neurology, 8,* 239–247.

Memory and aging [brochure]. (1987). Chicago, IL: Alzheimer's Disease and Related Disorders Association.

Mercado, C. & Mercado, E. (2006). A program using environmental manipulation, music therapy activities, and the Somatron™ Vibroacoustic Chair to reduce agitation behaviors of nursing home residents with psychiatric disorders. *Music Therapy Perspectives, 24*(*1*), 30–38.

Mercer, C. D. (1987). *Students with learning disabilities* (3rd ed.). Columbus, OH: Merill Publishing.

Merriam, A. P. (1964). *The anthropology of music.* Evanston, IL: Northwestern University Press.

Merriam, S. & Cross, L. H. (1981). Aging, reminiscence, and life satisfaction. *Activities, Adaptation & Aging, 2,* 39–50.

Merrion, M. (1990). R & D for better teaching. *Music Educators Journal, 77*(*3*), 22–25.

Metzger, L. K. (1986). The selection of music for therapeutic use with adolescents and young adults in a psychiatric facility. *Music Therapy Perspectives, 3,* 20–24.

Metzger, L. K. (2004). Assessment of use of music by patients participating in cardiac rehabilitation. *Journal of Music Therapy, 41,* 55–69.

Metzler, R. K. (1974). The use of music as a reinforcer to increase imitative behavior in severely and profoundly retarded female residents. *Journal of Music Therapy, 11*(*2*), 97–110.

Metzler, R. K. (1982). Suzuki and therapy: Nurtured by love. *National Association for Music Therapy, 26*(*2*), 14–19.

Metzler, R. K. & Berman, T. (1991). Selected effects of sedative music on the anxiety of bronchoscopy patients. In C. D. Maranto (Ed.), *Applications of music in medicine* (163–178). Washington, DC: National Association for Music Therapy.

Miami Lighthouse for the Blind (2015). Better Chance Music Production Program. Retrieved March 6, 2015 from www.miamilighthouse.com/Music_Programasp.

Michel, D. E. (1963). Music therapy in the southeastern United States. In E. H. Schneider (Ed.), *Music therapy 1962* (201–204). Lawrence, KS: Allen Press.

Michel, D. E. (1968). Music therapy in speech habilitation of cleft-palate children. In E. T. Gaston (Ed.), *Music in therapy* (162–166). New York: Macmillan.

Michel, D. E. (1971). Self-esteem and academic achievement in black junior high school students: Effects of automated guitar instruction. *Council for Research in Music Education Bulletin, 24,* 15–23.

Michel, D. E. (1976). *Music therapy: An introduction to therapy and special education through music.* Springfield, IL: Charles C Thomas.

Michel, D. E. (1981, November). Music therapist role changes in the U.S.A. since 1946. Paper presented at the 32nd Annual Conference of the National Association for Music Therapy, Denver, CO.

Michel, D. E. (1985). *Music therapy: An introduction, including music in special education* (2nd ed.). Springfield, IL: Charles C Thomas.

Michel, D. E. & Farrell, D. M. (1973). Music and self-esteem: Disadvantaged problem boys in an all-black elementary school. *Journal of Research in Music Education, 21(1),* 80–84.

Michel, D. E. & Jones, L. (1991). *Music for developing speech and language skills in children: A guide for parents and therapists.* St. Louis: MMB Music.

Michel, D. E. & May, N. H. (1974). The development of music therapy procedures with speech and language disorders. *Journal of Music Therapy, 11(2),* 74–80.

Millard, E. (2007). Learning with personal media players. Downloaded January 10, 2015 from www.DistrictAdministration.com.

Millard, K. A. O. & Smith, J. M. (1989). The influence of group singing therapy on the behavior of Alzheimer's disease patients. *Journal of Music Therapy, 26(2),* 58–70.

Miller, A. M. (2005). *Baby sing and sign* (2nd ed.). Olathe, KS: Love Lnguage.

Miller, B. F. & Keane, C. B. (1978). *Encyclopedia and dictionary of medicine, nursing, and allied health* (2nd ed.). Philadelphia: W. B. Saunders.

Miller, E. B. (1994). Musical intervention in family therapy. *Music Therapy, 12(2),* 39–57.

Miller, K. J. (1979). *Treatment with music: A manual for allied health professionals.* Kalamazoo, MI: Western Michigan University.

Miller, L. K. & Schyb, M. (1989). Facilitation and interference by background music. *Journal of Music Therapy, 26(1),* 42–54.

Miller, S. G. (1982). *Music therapy for handicapped children: Speech impaired.* Washington, DC: National Association for Music Therapy.

Miller, W. E. (1983). Research and family factors in aural rehabilitation of the elderly. *Activities, Adaptation, and Aging, 3(4),* 17–29.

Miluk-kolasa, B., Matejek, M., & Stupnicki, R. (1996). The effects of music listening on changes in selected physiological parameters in adult pre-surgical patients. *Journal of Music Therapy, 33(3),* 208–218.

Miorin, A. C. & Covault, M. L. (1979, April). Nurturance therapy. Paper presented at the 1979 Conference of the Great Lakes Regional Chapter of the National Association for Music Therapy, Kalamazoo, MI.

Miranda, P. C., Sampaio, A. L. L., Lopes, R. A. F., Venosa, A. R., & deOliveira, C. A.

(2014). Hearing preservation in cochlear implant surgery. *International Journal of Otolaryngology*, 2014, Article ID468515, 1–6.

Mitani, C., Nakata, T., Trehub, S. E., Kanda, Y., Kumagami, H., Takasaki, K., Miramoto, I., & Takahashi, H. (2007). Music recognition, music listening, and word recognition by deaf children with cochlear implants. *Ear and Hearing, 28* (Suppl. *2*), 29S–33S.

Mitchell, G. C. (1966). Bedtime music for psychotic children. *Nursing Mirror and Midwives Journal, 122(20)*, 452.

Mitchell, L. A. & MacDonald, R. A. R. (2006). An experimental investigation of the effects of preferred and relaxing music listening on pain perception. *Journal of Music Therapy, 43*, 295–316.

Mitchell, R. L. (1978). Arts in the prisons. In *The healing role of the arts* (Working papers – the Rockefeller Foundation) (38–41). New York: The Rockefeller Foundation.

Mondanero, J. F. (2008). Music therapy in the psychosocial care of pediatric patients with epilepsy. *Music Therapy Perspectives, 26(2)*, 102–109.

Montello, L. (2002). *Essential musical intelligence: Using music as your path to healing, creativity, and radiant wholeness.* Wheaton, IL: Quest Books.

Montello, L. & Coons, E. E. (1998). Effects of active versus passive group music therapy on preadolescents with emotional, learning, and behavioral disorders. *Journal of Music Therapy, 35(1)*, 49–67.

Montgomery, J. & Martinson, A. (2006). Partnering with music therapists: A model for addressing students' musical and extramusical goals. *Music Educators Journal, 92(4)*, 34–39.

Monti, R. (1985). Music therapy in a therapeutic nursery. *Music Therapy, 5(1)*, 22–27.

Moog, H. (1987). Playing instruments with the blind and severely visually handicapped. In R. R. Pratt (Ed.), *The fourth international symposium on music: Rehabilitation and human well-being* (151–156). New York: University Press of America.

Moore, K. S. (2013). A systematic review on the neural effects of music on emotion regulation: Implications for music therapy practice. *Journal of Music therapy, 50*, 198–242.

Moore, R. S., Staum, M. J., & Brotons, M. (1992). Music preferences of the elderly: Repertoire, vocal ranges, tempos, and accompaniments for singing. *Journal of Music Therapy, 29(4)*, 236–252.

Moreno, J. (1988). Multicultural music therapy: The world music connection. *Journal of Music Therapy, 25(1)*, 17–27.

Moreno, J. (1992). International perspectives. *Music Therapy Perspectives, 10(2)*, 87–88.

Moreno, J. (1993). International perspectives. *Music Therapy Perspectives, 11(2)*, 53–54.

Moreno, J. (1996). International perspectives. *Music Therapy Perspectives, 14(2)*, 74–76.

Moreno, J., Brotons, M., Hairston, M., Hawley, T., Kiel, H., Michel, D., & Rohrbacher, M. (1990). International music therapy: A global perspective. *Music Therapy Perspectives, 8*, 41–46.

Morgan, E. (1975). Music – a weapon against anxiety: How music builds self-esteem in a psychiatric ward. *Music Educators Journal, 61(5)*, 38–40, 87.

Munro, S. (1984). *Music therapy in palliative/hospice care.* St. Louis: Magnamusic-Baton.

Munro, S. & Mount, B. (1978). Music therapy in palliative care. *Canadian Medical Association Journal, 119*, 1029–1034.

Murooka, H. (1975). *Lullaby from the womb.* Hollywood, CA: Capitol Records.

Murphy, M. E. (1992). Coping in the short term: The impact of acute care on music therapy practice. *Music Therapy, 11*(*1*), 99–119.

Muscular Dystrophy Association (MCA) (2015). Duchenne muscular dystrophy (DMD). Retrieved April 14, 2015 from www.mda.org.

Muskatevc, L. C. (1967). The compleat therapist. *Journal of Music Therapy, 4*(*4*), 137–139.

Muslin, H. L. (1992). *The psychotherapy of the elderly self.* New York: Brunner/Mazel.

Myers, D. E. (1991). Older adult learning: How important is achievement? *General Music Today, 4*(*3*), 30–31.

Myers, D. E. (1992). Teaching learners of all ages. *Music Educators Journal, 79*(*4*), 23–26.

Myers-Briggs, I., McCaulley, M. H., Quenk, N. L., & Hammer, A. I. (2003). *MBTI Manual: A guide to the development and use of the Myers-Briggs Type Indicator* (3rd ed.). Mountain View, CA: Cpp.

Nagler, J. C. (1995). Toward the aesthetic lifeworld. *Music Therapy, 13*(*1*), 75–91.

Nagler, J. C. & Lee, M. H. M. (1989). Music therapy using computer music technology. In M. H. M. Lee (Ed.), *Rehabilitation, music and human well-being* (226–241). St. Louis: MMB Music.

Nakata, T., Trehub, S. W., Mitani, C., & Kanda, Y. (2016). Pitch and timing in the songs of deaf children with cochlear implants. *Music Perception, 24*(*2*), 147–154.

Nakata, T., Trehub, S. E., Mitani, C., Kanda, Y., Shibusaki, A., & Sehellenberg, E. G. (2005). Music recognition by Japanese children with cochlear implants. *Journal of Physiological Anthropology and Applied Human Science, 24,* 29–32.

National Alliance on Mental Illness (NAMI) (2015a). Depression. Downloaded July 24, 2015 from http://www.nami.org/Learn-more/mental-Health-Conditions/depression.

National Alliance on Mental Illness (NAMI) (2015b). dual diagnosis. Retrieved July 24, 2015 from http://www.nami.org/Learn-More/Mental-Health-Conditions/Related-conditions/Dual Diagnosis.

National Association for Music Education (2014). Acceptance of hearing protection aids in members. Health in Music Education (position statement). Retrieved Dec. 12, 2014 from http://musiced.nafme.org/about/position--statements/health-in-music-education.

National Association for Music Therapy (NAMT) (1994a). *NAMT member sourcebook 1994.* Silver Spring, MD: Author.

National Association for Music Therapy (NAMT) (1994b). Standards and procedures for academic program approval. *Music Therapy Perspectives, 12*(*1*), 39–50.

National Association of Schools of Music (NASM) *Handbook 2013–2014.* Reston, VA: http://nasm.arts-accredit.org/index.jsp?page-standards-Handbook.

National Hospice and Pallative Care Organization (NHPCO) (2013). NHCPO'S Facts and figures. *Hospice Care in America.* Retrieved August 17, 2014 from www.hhpco.org/research.

National Hospice and Palliative Care Organization (NHPCO) (2013). *History of hospice care.* Alexandria, VA: Downloaded August 17, 2014 from www.nhpco.org/history-hospice-care.

National Hospice and Palliative Care Organization (NHPCO) (2014). *Palliative care.* Retrieved August 27, 2014 from http://www.nhpco.org/about/palliative-care.

National Information Center for Children and Youth with Disabilities (2001). Related services (2nd ed.). *News Digest*, ND16. Retrieved August 1, 2015 from www.nichcy. org.

National Institute of Health (NIH). (2015). Osteoporosis and related bone diseases. National Resource Center. Retrieved April 16, 2015 from http://www.niams.nih. gov/Health_Info/Bone/Osteoporosis/bon_mass.asp.

National Institute of Health (NIH) (2013). Spinal cord injury (SCI): Condition information. Retrieved April 15, 2015 from www.nichd.gov.

National Institute of Health (NIH) (2015). Osteoporosis in aging. Retrieved April 16, 2015 from http://www.news in health.nih.gov/issue/Jan2015/Feature/.

National Institute of Mental Health (NIMH) (1993). *Learning disabilities.* Washington, DC: U.S. Government Printing Office.

National Institute of Neurological Disorders and Stroke (NINDS) (2015). Cerebral palsy: Hope through research. Retrieved April 14, 2015 from www.NINDS.nih. gov.

National Institute of Neurological Disorders and Stroke (NINDS) (2011). Spinal cord injury: Emerging concepts. Retrieved September 11, 2015 from http://www.ninds. nih.gov/news-Spinal Cord Injury.

National Institute for Occupational Safety and Health (1998). *Criteria for a recommended standard-occupational noise exposure, revised criteria.* (DHHS Publication 98-126). Cincinnati, OH: U. S. Department of Health and Human Services.

National Joint Committee on Learning Disabilities (2008). Adolescent literacy and older students with learning disabilities: A report from the National Joint Committee on Learning disabilities. *Learning Disabilities Quarterly, 31,* 211–218.

National MS Society (2015). Symptoms and diagnosis. Retrieved April 14, 2015 from www.nationalmssociety.org.

National Osteoporosis Foundation (1995). Stand up to osteoporosis: *Your guide to staying healthy and independent through prevention and treatment.* Washington, DC: Author.

National Projections (2012). Available from www.census.gov/population/projections/ date/national/2012.html.

National Paralysis Foundation. (n.d.). *Spinal victory.* Dallas, TX: Author.

National Stroke Association (2015). Myths vs. facts. Retrieved April 15, 2015 from www.stroke.org.

Nelson, D. L., Anderson, V. G., & Gonzales, A. D. (1984). Music activities as therapy for children with autism and other pervasive developmental disorders. *Journal of Music Therapy, 21(3),* 100–116.

Nemeth, J. M. (2006). Methods, techniques, and effective clinical practice in school age settings. In M. E. Humpal & C. Colwell (Eds.), *Early childhood and school age educational settings* (120–143). Silver Spring, MD: American Music Therapy Association.

Nettl, B. (1956). *Music in primitive cultures.* Cambridge, MA: Harvard University Press.

Neugebauer, C. T. (2008). Pediatric burn recovery: Acute care, rehabilitation and reconstruction. In D. Hanson-Abromeit & C. Colwell (Eds.) *Medical music therapy for pediatrics in hospital settings.* (195–227). Silver Spring, MD: American Music Therapy Association.

Newcomer, P. L. (1980). *Understanding and teaching emotionally disturbed children.* Boston: Allyn & Bacon.

Newton, J. & Redmond, A. (1995, April). A song in the night: Music in the spiritual/emotional care of hospitalized children and their families. Paper presented at the Conference of the Southwestern Region of the National Association for Music Therapy, Irving, TX.

Nicholas, M. J. & Gilbert, J. P. (1980). Research in music therapy: A survey of music therapists' attitudes and knowledges. *Journal of Music Therapy, 17*(4), 207–213.

Nocera, S. D. (1979). *Reaching the special learner through music.* Morristown, NJ: Silver Burdett.

Nolan, P. (1983). Insight therapy: GIM in a forensic psychiatric setting. *Music Therapy, 3,* 43–51.

Nolan, P. (1989). Music as a transitional object in the treatment of bulimia. *Music Therapy Perspectives, 6,* 49–51.

Nolan, P. (1994). The therapeutic response in improvisational music therapy: What goes on inside? *Music Therapy Perspectives, 12*(2), 84–91.

Nolan, P. & Ierardi, F. (2007). Music therapy improvisation for adult psychiatric settings. In B. J. Crowe & C. Colwell (Eds.), *Music therapy for children, adolescents, and adults with mental illness* (45–56). Silver Spring, MD: American Music Therapy Association.

Nordoff, P. & Robbins, C. (1968). Improvised music as therapy for autistic children. In E. T. Gaston (Ed.), *Music in therapy* (191–195). New York: Macmillan.

Nordoff, P. & Robbins, C. (1971a). *Music therapy in special education.* New York: John Day.

Nordoff, P. & Robbins, C. (1971b). *Therapy in music for handicapped children.* London: Victor Gollancz.

Nordoff, P. & Robbins, C. (1977). *Creative music therapy.* New York: John Day.

Nordoff, P. & Robbins, C. (2007). *Creative music therapy: A guide to fostering clinical musicianship* (2nd ed.). Gilsum, NH: Barcelona.

Norman, R. (2012). Music therapy assessment of older adults in nursing homes. *Music Therapy Perspectives, 30*(1), 8–16.

Nowicki, A. L. & Trevisan, L. A. (1978). *Beyond the sound: A technical and philosophical approach to music therapy* (rev. ed.). Santa Barbara, CA: Nowicki/Trevisan.

O'Brien, I., Driscoll, T., & Ackermann, B. (2012). Hearing conservation and noise management practices in professional orchestras. *Journal of Occupational and Environmental Hygiene, 9*(10), 603–604.

O'Brien, I., Driscoll, T., & Ackermann, B. (2013). Sound exposure of professional orchestral musicians during solitary practice. *Journal of the Acoustical Society of America, 134*(4), 2748–2754.

O'Brien, N. & Goldstein, A. J. (1985). A systematic approach to developing a private practice in music therapy. *Music Therapy, 5*(1), 37–43.

O'Callaghan, C. C. (1996). Lyrical themes in songs written by palliative care patients. *Journal of Music Therapy, 33*(2), 74–92.

O'Callaghan, C. C. (1997). Therapeutic opportunities associated with music when using songwriting in palliative care. *Music Therapy Perspectives, 15*(1), 32–38.

O'Callaghan, C. (2012). Grounded theory in music therapy research. *Journal of Music Therapy, 49*(3), 236–277.

Occupational Safety and Health Administration (1998). Occupational noise exposure (OSHA Report No. 1910.95). Washington, DC: Author.

Ockelford, A. (2013). *Music, language, and autism.* London: Jessica Kingsley.

Ockelford, A., Welch, G., & Zimmerman, S. (2002). Music education for pupils with severe or profound and multiple difficulties – current provision and future need. *British Journal of Special Education, 29(4),* 178–182.

O'Konski, M., Bane, C., Hettinga, J., & Krull, K. (2010). Comparative effectiveness of exercise with patterned sensory enhanced music and background music for long-term care residents. *Journal of Music Therapy, 47(2),* 120–130.

Oliver, S. (1989). Music therapy services of Arizona: An alternative approach to service provision. *Journal of Music Therapy, 26(2),* 95–99.

Olson, B. K. (1984). Player piano music as therapy for the elderly. *Journal of Music Therapy, 21(1),* 35–45.

Orff, C. (1980). *The Orff music therapy.* London: Schott & Co.

Ortman, J. M., Velkoff, V. A., & Hogan, H. (2014). An aging nation: The older population in the United States. Current population reports (25–1140). Washington, DC. Retrieved October 1, 2015 from www.census.gov.

Otten, J. & Shelley, F. D. (1977). *When your parents grow old.* New York: Signet.

Owens, L. D. (1979). The effects of music on the weight loss, crying, and physical movement newborns. *Journal of Music Therapy, 16(2),* 83–90.

Padilla, G., Grout, M., Presant, C., & Ferrell, B. (1996). *Quality of life – Cancer Scale.* Los Angeles: QOL-CA.

Palisca, C. V. (1968). *Baroque music.* Englewood Cliffs, NJ: Prentice-Hall.

Palmer, D. S., Fuller, K., Arora, T., & Nelson, M. (2001). Taking sides: Parent views on inclusion for their children with severe disabilities. *The Council for Exceptional Children, 67(4),* 476–484.

Palmer, M. D. (1977). Music therapy in a comprehensive program of treatment and rehabilitation for the geriatric resident. *Journal of Music Therapy, 14(4),* 190–197.

Palmer, M. (1985). Older adults are total people: Music therapy with the elderly. In N. Weisberg & R. Wilder (Eds.), *Creative arts with older adults: A sourcebook* (103–111). NY: Human Sciences Press.

Palmer, M. (1989). Music therapy in gerontology: A review and a projection. *Music Therapy Perspectives, 6,* 52–56.

Palmer, M. F. (1953). Musical stimuli in cerebral palsy, aphasia, and similar conditions. In E. G. Gilliland (Ed.), *Music therapy 1952* (162–168). Lawrence, KS: Allen Press.

Parente, A. B. (1989). Feeding the hungry soul: Music as therapeutic modality in the treatment of anorexia nervosa. *Music Therapy Perspectives, 6,* 44–48.

Pasiali, V. (2004). The use of prescriptive therapeutic songs in a home-based environment to promote social skills acquisition by children with autism: Three case studies. *Music Therapy Perspective, 22(1),* 11–20.

Pasiali, V., Lin, S-Y., & Noh, H-E. (2009). An analysis of the editorial committee of the *Journal of Music Therapy,* 1964–2007. *Journal of Music Therapy, 46,* 272–286.

A passion for research (1998). *Teaching Music, 6(2),* 38–39, 56.

Patel, A. D. (2008). *Music, language, and the brain.* Oxford: Oxford University Press.

Patterson, C. H. (1986). Gestalt therapy: Perls. In *Theories of counseling and psychotherapy* (4th ed.) (342–378). New York: Harper & Row.

Paul, D. W. (1982). *Music therapy for handicapped children: Emotionally disturbed.* Washington, DC: National Association for Music Therapy.

Pavlicek, M., O'Neil, N., Powell, H., Jones, O., & Sampathianaki, E. (2014). Making music, making friends: Long-term music therapy with young adults with severe learning disabilities. *Journal of Intellectual Disabilities, 15(1)*, 5–19.

Pavlicevic, M. (2000). Improvisation in music therapy: Human communication in sound. *Journal of Music Therapy, 37(4)*, 267–285.

Pavlicevic, M., Trevarthen, C., & Duncan, J. (1994). Improvisational music therapy and the rehabilitation of persons suffering from chronic schizophrenia. *Journal of Music Therapy, 31(2)*, 86–104.

Peach, S. C. (1984). Some implications for the clinical use of music facilitated imagery. *Journal of Music Therapy, 21(1)*, 27–34.

Pelletier, C. L. (2004). The effect of music on decreasing arousal due to stess: A meta-analysis. *Journal of Music Therapy, 41(3)*, 192–214.

Pelletier, K. R. (1980). The mind in health and disease. In A. C. Hastings, J. Fadiman, & J. S. Gordon (Eds.), *Health for the whole person* (107–109). Boulder, CO: Westview Press.

Perez, M. (1989). Music, emotions, and hospitalized children: Some theoretical considerations. In M. H. M. Lee (Ed.), *Rehabilitation, music and human well-being* (242–252). St. Louis: MMB Music.

Perls, F. S. (1973). *The Gestalt approach and eyewitness to therapy.* Palo Alto, CA: Science and Behavior Books.

Perry, M. M. R. (2003). Relating improvisational music therapy with severely and multiply disabled children to communication development. *Journal of Music Therapy, 40*, 227–246.

Peterson, K. A. (2007). Drumming group experiences. In B. J. Crowe & C. Colwell (Eds.), *Music therapy for children, adolescents, and adults with mental disorders* (33–36). Silver Spring, MD: American Music Therapy Association.

Pfeifer, M., Sr. (1982).Multihandicapped. In W. B. Lathom & C. T. Eagle (Eds.), *Music therapy for handicapped children* (vol. 3) (3–36). Washington, DC: National Association for Music Therapy.

Pfeifer, M., Sr. (1989). A step in the right direction: Suggested strategies for implementing music therapy with the multihandicapped child. *Music Therapy Perspectives, 6*, 57–60.

Pfeiffer, J. P. & Pinquart, M. (2011). Attainment of developmental tasks by adolescents with and without visual impairments. *Journal of Visual Impairment and Blindness, 105*, 96–107.

Pfeiffer, J. P. & Pinquart, M. (2013). Computer use of adolescents with and without visual impairment. *Technology and Disability, 25*, 99–106.

Phipps, M. F. (1975). Music education for learning disabilities. In R. M. Graham (Compiler), *Music for the exceptional child* (130–135). Reston, VA: Music Educators National Conference.

Picture communication symbols combination book. (1994). Solana Beach, CA: Mayer-Johnson.

Pollack, N. J. & Namazi, K. H. (1992). The effect of music participation on the social behavior of Alzheimer's disease patients. *Journal of Music Therapy, 29*(*1*), 54–67.

Ponath, L. H. & Bitcon, C. H. (1972). A behavioral analysis of Orff-Schulwerk. *Journal of Music Therapy, 9*(*2*), 56–63.

Ponte, L. (1989). How noise can harm you. *Readers Digest, March,* 121–125.

Porter, S., McConnell, T., Lynn, F., Mclaughlin, K., Cardwell, C., & Holmes, V. (2014). Recruiting participants for randomized controlled trials of music therapy: A practical illustration. *Journal of Music Therapy, 51*(*4*), 355–381.

Powers, M. D. (Ed.) (1989). *Children with autism.* Rockville, MD: Woodbine House.

Prange, P. (1990). Categories of music therapy at Judson retirement community. *Music Therapy Perspectives, 8,* 88–89.

Pratt, R. R. (1989). A brief history of music and medicine. In M. H. M. Lee (Ed.), *Rehabilitation, music and human well-being* (1–12). St. Louis: MMB Music.

Prazich, M. N. (1985). *A stroke patient's own story.* Danville, IL: Interstate.

Presti, G. M. (1984). A levels system approach to music therapy with severely behaviorally handicapped children in the public school system. *Journal of Music Therapy, 21*(*3*), 117–125.

Prickett, C. A. (1988). Music therapy for the aged. In C. E. Furman (Ed.), *Effectiveness of music therapy procedures: Documentation of research and clinical practice* (285–299). Washington, D C: National Association for Music Therapy.

Prickett, C. A. (1989). A philosophy for music therapy. In R. R. Pratt & B. Hesser (Eds.), *Music therapy and music in special education: The international state of the art I* (98–100). St. Louis: MMB Music.

Prickett, C. A. (1995). Principles of quantitative research. In B. L. Wheeler (Ed.), *Music therapy research: Quantitative and qualitative perspectives* (97–117). Phoenixville, PA: Barcelona.

Prickett, C. A. (1996). Music therapy as a part of older people's lives. In C. E. Furman (Ed.), *Effectiveness of music therapy procedures: Documentation of research and clinical practice* (2nd ed.) (144–166). Silver Spring, MD: National Association for Music Therapy.

Prickett, C. A. & Moore, R. S. (1991). The use of music to aid memory of Alzheimer's patients. *Journal of Music Therapy, 28*(*2*), 101–110.

Priestley, M. (1975). *Music therapy in action.* London: Constable.

Priestley, M. (1985). *Music therapy in action* (2nd ed.). St. Louis: MMB Music.

Priestley, M. (1994). *Essays on analytical music therapy.* Phoenixville, PA: Barcelona.

Priestley, M. & Eschen, J. Th. (2002). Analytical music therapy – origin and development. In J. Th. Eschen (Ed.), *Analytical music therapy,* (11–16). London: Jessica Kingsley.

Prizant, B. M. & Wetherby, A. M. (2005). Critical issues in enhancing communication abilities for persons with autism spectrum disorders. In F. Volkmer, R. Paul, A. Ktin, & D. Cohen (Eds.), *Handbook of autism and percussive developmental disorders* (925–945). New York: John Wiley and Sons.

Prizant, B. M., Wetherby, A. M., Rubin, E., & Laurent, A. C. (2003). The SCERTS Model: A transactional family-centered approach to enhancing communication and socioemotional abilities of children with autism spectrum disorder. *Infants and Young Children, 16,* 296–316.

Prueter, B. A. & Giles, M. M. (1981). The effect of music on acquisition of sign language by EMR children. *National Association for Music Therapy, 25(1),* 20–25.

Prueter, B. A. & Mezzano, J. (1973). Effects of background music upon initial counseling interactions. *Journal of Music Therapy, 10(4),* 205–212.

Pujol, K. K. (1994). The effect of vibrotactile stimulation, instrumentation, and precomposed melodies on physiological and behavioral responses of profoundly retarded children and adults. *Journal of Music Therapy, 31(3),* 186–205.

Purtilo, R. (1978). *Health professional/patient interaction* (2nd ed.). Philadelphia: W. B. Saunders.

Purvis, J. & Samet, S. (1976). *Music in developmental therapy: A curriculum guide.* Baltimore: University Park Press.

Radocy, R. E. & Boyle, J. D. (1988). *Psychological foundations of musical behavior* (2nd ed.). Springfield, IL: Charles C Thomas.

Radocy, R. E. & Boyle, J. D. (2003). *Psychological foundations of musical behavior* (4th ed.). Springfield, IL: Charles C Thomas.

Radocy, R. E. & Boyle, J. D. (2012). *Psychological foundations of musical behavior* (5th ed.). Springfield, IL: Charles C Thomas.

Radocy, R. E. & Lathom-Radocy, W. (1999). Music psychology and music therapy: Mutual support. In S. W. Yi (Ed.), *Music, mind, and science.* Seoul, Korea: Seoul National University Press.

Rainey, D. W. & Larsen, J. D. (2002). The effect of familiar melodies on initial learning and long-term memory for unconnected text. *Music Perception, 29,* 173–186.

Rainey Perry, M. M. (2003). Relating improvisational music therapy with severely and multiply disabled children to communication development. *Journal of Music Therapy, 40,* 227–246.

Ragland, Z. & Apprey, M. (1974). Community music therapy with adolescents. *Journal of Music Therapy, 11(3),* 147–155.

Rawool, V. W. & Colligan-Wayne, L. M. (2008). Auditory lifestyles and beliefs related to hearing loss among college students in the USA. *Noise and Health, 10(38),* 1–10.

Redinbaugh, E. M. (1988). The use of music therapy in developing a communication system in a withdrawn, depressed older adult resident: A case study. *Music Therapy Perspectives, 5,* 82–85.

Reed, K. J. (2002). Music therapy treatment groups for mentally disordered offenders (MDO) in a state hospital setting. *Music Therapy Perspectives, 20(2),* 98–104.

Register, D. (2004). The effects of live music groups versus an educational children's television program on the emergent literacy of young children. *Journal of Music Therapy, 41,* 2–27.

Register, D., Darrow, A-A., Standley, J., & Swedberg, O. (2007). The use of music to enhance reading skills of second grade students and students with reading disabilities. *Journal of Music Therapy, 44,* 23–37.

Reid, D. H., Hill, B. K., Rowers, R. J., & Montegar, C. A. (1975). The use of contingent music in teaching social skills to a nonverbal, hyperactive boy. *Journal of Music Therapy, 12(1),* 2–18.

Remington, R. E., Foxen, T., & Hogg, J. (1977). Auditory reinforcement in profoundly retarded multiply handicapped children. *American Journal of Mental Deficiency, 82(2)*, 299–304.

Reschke-Hernandez, A. E. (2011). History of music therapy treatment interventions for children with autism. *Journal of Music Therapy, 48*, 169–207.

Restak, R. M. (1984). *The brain.* Toronto: Basic Books.

Reuer, B. (1996). Posturing for a changing world: Consulting as a career option. *Music Therapy Perspectives, 14(1)*, 16–20.

Reuer, B. (2007). An entrepreneurial journey: A music theapist's story – personal reflections. *Music Therapy Perspectives, 25(2)*, 108–114.

Reynolds, B. J. (1982). Music therapy literature related to mental retardation. In W. B. Lathom & C. T. Eagle, Jr. (Eds.), *Music therapy for handicapped children* (Vol. 2) (34–48). Washington, DC: National Association for Music Therapy.

Richter, M. (1996). Savvy senior centers: Facilities for older people expand as boomers near retirement. *The Dallas Morning News* (January 6), C1–C2.

Rickson, D. J. & Watkins, W. G. (2003). Music therapy to promote prosocial behaviors in aggressive adolescent boys – a pilot study. *Journal of Music Therapy, 40*, 283–301.

Rider, M. S. (1978). The development of the Musical-Perception Assessment of Cognitive Development (MPACD). Unpublished master's thesis, Southern Methodist University, Dallas, TX.

Rider, M. S. (1981). The assessment of cognitive functioning level through musical perception. *Journal of Music Therapy, 18(3)*, 110–119.

Rider, M. S. (1985). Entrainment mechanisms are involved in pain reduction, muscle relaxation, and music-mediated imagery. *Journal of Music Therapy, 22(4)*, 183–192.

Rider, M. S. (1987). Music therapy: Therapy for debilitated musicians. *Music Therapy Perspectives, A*, 40–42.

Rider, M., Mickey, C., Weldin, C., & Hawkinson, R. (1991). The effects of toning, listening, and singing on psychophysiological responses. In C. D. Maranto (Ed.), *Applications of music in medicine* (73–84). Washington, DC: National Association for Music Therapy.

Ridgway, R. W. (1983). A story – and a question. *Music Therapy Perspectives, 1(2)*, 2–3.

Riegler, J. (1980). Comparison of a reality orientation program for geriatric patients with and without music. *Journal of Music Therapy, 17(1)*, 26–33.

Rink, M. (1989). Music as a therapeutic aid for learning-disabled children with motor control problems. In R. R. Pratt & H. Moog (Eds.), *First research seminar of the ISME Commission on music therapy and music in special education: Proceedings of 1986* (93–107). St. Louis: MMB Music.

Rio, R. E. & Tenney, K. S. (2002). Music therapy for juvenile offenders in residential treatment. *Music Therapy Perspectives, 20(2)*, 89–97.

Ritholz, M. S. & Turry, A. (1994). The journey by train: Creative music therapy with a 17-year-old boy. *Music Therapy, 12(2)*, 58–81.

Robb, S. L. (1996). Techniques in song writing: Restoring emotional and physical well-being in adolescents who have been traumatically injured. *Music Therapy Perspectives, 14(1)*, 30–37.

Robb, S. L. (1999). Marian Erdman: Contributions of an American Red Cross hospital recreation worker. *Journal of Music Therapy, 34*(*4*), 314–329.

Robb, S. (2000a). Music assisted progressive muscle relaxation, progressive muscle relaxation, music listening, and silence: A comparison of relaxation techniques. *Journal of Music Therapy, 37*(*1*), 2–21.

Robb, S. L. (2000b), The effect of therapeutic music interventions on the behavior of hospitalized children in isolation: Developing a contextual support model of music therapy. *Journal of Music Therapy, 37*, 118–148.

Robb, S. L. (2003). Designing music therapy interventions for hospitalized children and adolescents using a contextual support model of music therapy. *Music Therapy Perspectives, 21*(*1*), 27–40.

Robb, S. L. (2003). Music interventions and group participation skills of preschoolers with visual impairments: Raising questions about music, arousal, and attention. *Journal of Music Therapy, 40*, 266–282.

Robb, S. L. (2013). Editorial: The power of the pilot. *Journal of Music Therapy, 50*(*1*), 3–5.

Robb, S. L., Nichols, R. J., Rutan, R. L., Bishop, B. L., & Parker, J. C. (1995). The Effects of music assisted relaxation on preoperative anxiety. *Journal of Music Therapy, 32*(*1*), 2–21.

Robbins, C. (2005). A journey into creative music therapy. In *Nordolff-Robbins music therapy monograph series* (Vol. 3). St. Louis: MMB Music.

Robbins, C. & Robbins, C. (1998). *Healing heritage: The tonal language of music.* Gilsum, NH: Barcelona.

Rogers, J. F. (1918). Music as medicine. *The Musical Quarterly, 4*(*3*), 365–375.

Rogers, L. (1968). Music therapy in a state hospital for crippled children. In E. T. Gaston (Ed.), *Music in therapy* (156–159). New York: Macmillan.

Rogers, A. & Fleming, P. L. (1981). Rhythm and melody in speech therapy for the neurologically impaired. *Music Therapy, 1*, 33–38.

Rorke, M. A. (1996). Music and the wounded of World War II. *Journal of Music Therapy, 33*(*3*), 189–207.

Rosenhan, D. L. & Saligman, M. E. P. (1984). *Humanistic and existential approaches.* New York: W. W. Norton.

Roskam, K. S. (1979). Music therapy as an aid for increasing auditory awareness and improving reading skill. *Journal of Music Therapy, 16*(*1*), 31–42.

Ross, O. A. (2015). Stroke and vascular disease. Jacksonville, FL: Dept. of Neuroscience, Mayo Clinic. Retrieved September 12, 2015 from http:www.mayo.edu/research/label/stroke-vascular-disease/overview?

Rubin, B. J. (1973). Music therapy in an outreach station of the Milwaukee County Mental Health Center. *Journal of Music Therapy, 10*(*4*), 201–204.

Rubin, B. J. (1975). Music therapy in a community mental health program. *Journal of Music Therapy, 12*(*2*), 59–66.

Rudd, E. (2010). Music therapy: *A perspective from the humanities.* Gilsum, NH: Barcelona.

Rudenberg, M. T. (1982). Music therapy for orthopedically handicapped children. In W. B. Lathom & C. T. Eagle, Jr. (Eds.), *Music therapy for handicapped children* (Vol. 3) (37–118). Washington, DC: National Association for Music Therapy.

Rudenberg, M. T. & Royka, A. M. (1989). Promoting psychological adjustment in pediatric burn patients through music therapy and child life therapy. *Music Therapy*

Perspectives, 7, 40–43.

Ruppenthal, W. W. (1957). Objectivity in clinical practice. *Music Therapy, 7*, 81–84.

Rutkowski, J. (1996). Conducting research in the music classroom. *Music Educators Journal, 82*(*5*), 42–44, 62.

Rutkowski, J., Thompson, K. P., & Huang, Y-T. (2011). Cited quantitative research articles in music education research journals, 1990–2005: A content analysis of selected studies. In *Advances in social-psychology and music education research* (169–183). Burlington, VT: Ashgate.

Ruud, E. (1980). *Music therapy and its relationship to current treatment theories* (rev. ed.). St. Louis: Magnamusic-Baton.

Ruud, E. (1995). Improvisation as a liminal experience: Jazz and music therapy as modern "rites de passage." In C. B. Kenny (Ed.), *Listening, playing, creating: Essays on the power of sound* (91–117). Albany, NY: State University of New York Press.

Ruud, E. (1998). Science as metacritique. *Journal of Music Therapy, 35*(*3*), 218–224.

Sachs, C. (1955). *Our musical heritage* (2nd ed.). Englewood Cliffs, NJ: Prentice-Hall.

Sacks, O. (1998). Music and the Brain. In C. M. Tomaino (Ed.), *Clinical applications of music in neurologic rehabilitation* (1–18). St. Louis: MMB Music.

Sacks. O. (2008). *Musicophilia.* New York: Vintage.

Sacks, O. & Tomaino, C. M. (1991). Music and neurological disorder. *The International Journal of Arts Medicine, 1*(*1*), 10–12.

Salas, J. (1990). Aesthetic experience in music therapy. *Music Therapy, 9*(*1*), 1–15.

Salas, J. & Gonzalez, D. (1991). Like singing with a bird: Improvisational music therapy with a blind four-year-old. In K. E. Bruscia (Ed.), *Case studies in music therapy* (17–28). Phoenixville, PA: Barcelona.

Saliba, D. & Buchanan, J. (2008). Development and validation of a revised nursing home assessment tool: MDS3.0. Retrieved from http://www.cms.gov/Nursing-HomeQuality/nits/downloads/MDS3.)Final Report-Appendices.zip.

Sandbank, G. (1989a). Music as a therapeutic resource for learning disabled children. In R. R. Pratt & H. Moog (Eds.), *First research seminar of the ISME Commission on music therapy and music in special education: Proceedings of 1986* (108–117). St. Louis: MMB Music.

Sandbank, G. (1989b). The right personality for the music therapist. In R. R. Pratt (Ed.), *Music therapy and music in special education: The international state of the art II* (87–93). St. Louis: MMB Music.

Sandness, M. I. (1991). Developmental sequence in music therapy groups: A review of theoretical models. *Music Therapy Perspectives, 9*, 66–72.

Sandness, M. I. (1995). The role of music therapy in physical rehabilitation programs. *Music Therapy Perspectives, 13*(*2*), 76–81.

Saperston, B. (1973). The use of music in establishing communication with an autistic mentally retarded child. *Journal of Music Therapy, 17*(*4*), 184–188.

Saperston, B. M. (1982). Case study: Timmy. In D. W. Paul (Ed.), *Music therapy for handicapped children: Emotionally disturbed* (42–57). Washington, DC: National Association for Music Therapy.

Saperston, B. M. (1989). Music-Based Individualized Relaxation Training (MBIRT): A stress-reduction approach for the behaviorally disturbed mentally retarded.

Music Therapy Perspectives, 6, 26–33.

Saperston, B., Chan, R., Morphew, C., & Carsrud, K. (1980). Music listening vs. juice as reinforcement for learning in profoundly mentally retarded individuals. *Journal of Music Therapy, 17(4),* 174–183.

Sapp, W. (2011). Somebody's jumping on the floor: Incorporating music into orientation and mobility for preschoolers with visual impairments. *Journal of Visual Impairment and Blindness, 105(10),* 715–719.

Sato, Y. (2011). Musical life review in hospice. *Music Therapy Perspectives, 29(1),* 31–37.

Scalenghe, R. (1984, November). Music therapy with geriatric clients on an in-patient psychiatric unit. Paper presented at the 35th Annual Conference of the National Association for Music Therapy, Albuquerque, NM.

Scartelli, J. P. (1982). The effect of sedative music on electromyographic biofeedback-assisted relaxation training of spastic cerebral palsied adults. *Journal of Music Therapy, 19(4),* 210–218.

Scartelli, J. P. (1984). The effect of EMG biofeedback and sedative music, EMG bio-feedback only, and sedative music only on frontalis muscle relaxation ability. *Journal of Music Therapy, 21(2),* 67–78.

Scartelli, J. P. (1989). *Music and self-management methods.* St. Louis: MMB Music.

Scartelli, J. P. (1991). A rationale for subcortical involvement in human response to music. In C. D. Maranto (Ed.), *Applications of music in medicine* (29–40). Washington, DC: National Association for Music Therapy.

Scartelli, J. P. & Borling, J. E. (1986). The effects of sequenced versus simultaneous EMG biofeedback and sedative music on frontalis relaxation training. *Journal of Music Therapy, 23(3),* 157–165.

Scheiby, B. B. (2005). An intersubjective approach to music therapy: Identification and processing of musical countertransference in a music psychotherapeutic context. *Music Therapy Perspectives, 23(1),* 8–17.

Scheve, A. (2004). Music therapy, wellness, and stress reduction. *Advances in Experimental Medicine and Biology, 546,* 253–263.

Schmid, W. & Aldridge, O. (2004). Active music therapy in the treatment of multiple sclerosis patients: A matched control study. *Journal of Music Therapy, 41,* 225–240.

Schmidt, J. A. (1981). A special challenge: The profoundly retarded multiply handi-capped. *National Association for Music Therapy, 25(2),* 23–25.

Schneider, C. W. (1961). The effects of Dalcroze eurhythmics upon the motor pro-cesses of schizophrenics. In E. H. Schneider (Ed.), *Music therapy 1960* (132–140). Lawrence, KS: Allen Press.

Schneider, E. H. (1954). The use of music with the brain damaged child. In M. Bing (Ed.), *Music therapy 1953* (95–98). Lawrence, KS: Allen Press.

Schneider, E. H. (1957). Relationships between musical experience and certain aspects of cerebral palsied children's performance on selected tasks. In E. T. Gaston (Ed.), *Music therapy 1956* (250–277). Lawrence, KS: Allen Press.

Schneider, E. H., Unkefer, R. F., & Gaston, E. T. (1968). Introduction. In E. T. Gaston (Ed.), *Music in therapy* (1–4). New York: Macmillan.

Scholl, S. & White, S. (1970). *Music and the culture of man.* New York: Holt, Rinehart and Winston.

Scholtz, D., Rhode, S., Grosbach, M., Rolinik, J., & Altenmuller, E. (2015). Moving with music for stroke rehabilitation: A sonification feasibility study. *Annals of the New York Academy of Sciences, 1337*, 69–76.

Schooler, K. K. & Estes, C. L. (1979). Differences between current gerontological theories: Implications for research methodology. In D. P. Kent, R. Kastenbaum, & S. Sherwood (Eds.), *Research planning and action for the elderly: The power and potential of social science* (107–116). New York: Human Sciences Press.

Schulberg, C. H. (1981). *The music therapy sourcebook: A collection of activities categorized and analyzed.* New York: Human Sciences Press.

Schullian, D. M. & Schoen, M. (Eds.) (1948). *Music and medicine.* New York: Henry Schuman.

Schulman, S. (1986). Facing the invisible handicap. *Psychology Today, 20(2)*, 58–64.

Schuster, B. L. (1985). The effect of music listening on blood pressure fluctuations in adult hemodialysis patients. *Journal of Music Therapy, 22(3)*, 146–153.

Schwankovsky, L. M. & Guthrie, P. T. (1982). Music therapy for other health impaired children. In W. B. Lathom & C. T. Eagle, (Eds.), *Music therapy for handicapped children* (Vol. 3). Washington, DC: National Association for Music Therapy.

Scott, C. (1958). *Music: Its secret influence throughout the ages.* New York: Samuel Weiser.

Scott, T. J. (1970). Use of music to reduce hyperactivity in children. *American Journal of Orthopsychiatry, 40(4)*, 677–680.

Scovel, M. A. (1990). Music therapy within the context of psychotherapeutic models. In R. F. Unkefer (Ed.), *Music therapy in the treatment of adults with mental disorders* (96–108). New York: Schirmer.

Sears, M. S. (Ed.) (2007). *Music: The therapeutic edge. Readings from William W. Sears.* Gilsum, NH: Barcelona.

Sears, W. W. (1963). Dynamic processes in music therapy. Paper presented at the National Association for Music Therapy Conference, Bloomington, IN.

Sears, W. W. (1968). Processes in music therapy. In E. T. Gaston (Ed.), *Music in therapy* (30–44). New York: Macmillan.

Sekeles, C. (1989). Sounds and music in the treatment of hypotonis Down's syndrome children. In R. R. Pratt & H. Moog (Eds.), *First research seminar of the ISME Commission on music therapy and music in special education: Proceedings of 1986* (22–38). St. Louis: MMB Music.

Selm, M. E. (1991). Chronic pain: Three issues in treatment and implications for music therapy. *Music Therapy Perspectives, 9*, 91–97.

Seymour, H. A. (1920). *What music can do for you.* New York: Harper and Brothers.

Seymour, H. A. & Garrett, E. E. (1944). *An instruction course in the use and practice of musical therapy.* New York: National Foundation of Music Therapy.

Shamrock, M. (1986). Orff Schulwerk: An integrated foundation. *Music Educators Journal, 72(6)*, 51–55.

Shargorodsky, J., Curhan, S., Curhan, G., & Eavey, R. (2010). Change in prevalence of hearing loss in U.S. adolescents. *Journal of the American Medical Association, 304*, 772–778.

Shaw, J. P. (1988). The application of ragtime in music therapy with older adults.

Music Therapy Perspectives, 5, 102–103.

Shaywitz, B. A., Shaywitz, S. E., Pugh, K. R., Mench, W. E., Fulbright, R. K., Skudlarski, P., Constable, R. T., Marchione, K. E., Fletcher, J. M., Lyon, G. R., & Gore, J. C. (2002). Disruption of posterior brain systems for reading in children with developmental dyslexia. *Biological Psychiatry, 52(2),* 101–110.

Sheedy, P. (1995). Juvenile offenders get wired. *WaveRider Mental Notes, Autumn,* 3, 5.

Shehan, P. K. (1981). A comparison of medication strategies in paired associate learning for children with learning disabilities. *Journal of Music Therapy, 18(3),* 120–127.

Sheldon, D. A. (1997). The Illinois school for the deaf band: A historical perspective. *Journal of Research in Music Education, 45(4),* 580–600.

Shi-jing, L., Hui-ju, S., Guo, W, & Maranto, C. D. (1991). Music and medicine in China: The effects of music electro-acupuncture on cerebral hemiplegia. In C. D. Maranto (Ed.), *Applications of music in medicine* (191–199). Washington, DC: National Association for Music Therapy.

Shiraishi, I. M. (1997). A home-based music therapy program for multi-risk others. *Music Therapy Perspectives, 15(1),* 16–23.

Shively, C. & Henkin, L. (1986). Music and movement therapy with Alzheimer's victims. *Music Therapy Perspectives, 3,* 56–58.

Shoemark, H. (1991). The use of piano improvisation in developing interaction and participation in a blind boy with behavioral disturbances. In K. E. Bruscia (Ed.), *Case studies in music therapy* (29–38). Phoenixville, PA: Barcelona.

Shoemark, H. (2013). Guest editorial: The pragmatic reality of clinical research. *Journal of Music Therapy, 50(3),* 150–154.

Short, A. E. (1991). The role of guided imagery and music in diagnosing physical illness or trauma. *Music Therapy, 10(1),* 22–45.

Short, A. E. (1992). Music and imagery with physically disabled elderly residents: A GIM adaptation. *Music Therapy, 17(1),* 65–98.

Shreffler, J. (1976). Music therapy and transactional analysis. *National Association for Music Therapy, 76(3),* 18–20.

Shuler, S. C. (1990). Solving instructional problems hrough research. *Music Educators Journal, 77(3),* 35–40.

Siegel, S. (2007). Music therapy practice for clients with eating disorders. In B. J. Crowe & C. Colwell (Eds.), *Music therapy for children, adolescents, and adults with mental disorders* (165–174). Silver Spring, MD: American Music Therapy Association.

Siegel, S. L., Cartwright, J. S., & Katy, E. (1986). Where's the research? *Journal of Music Therapy, 23(1),* 38–45.

Siegfried, T. (1997). Evidence from genes and brain reveals biology behind autism. *The Dallas Morning News* (December 15), 7D.

Siegfried, T. & Goetinck, S. (1996). Science gathers a growing body of physical clues to mental illness. *The Dallas Morning News* (April 29), IF, 6F, 8F.

Silber, F. & Hes, J. (1995). The use of songwriting with patients diagnosed with Alzheimer's disease. *Music Therapy Perspectives, 13(1),* 31–34.

Silcox, S. (2010). Audible warnings. *Occupational Health, 62(11),* 22.

Siligo, W. R. (2005). Enriching the ensemble experience for students with visual impairments. *Music Educators Journal, 91*(5), 31–36.

Silverman, F. H. (1976). Long term impact of a miniature metronome on stuttering: An interim report. *Perceptual and Motor Skills, 42,* 13–22.

Silverman, M. J. (2003a). Music therapy and clients who are clinically dependent: A review of literature and pilot study. *The Arts in Psychotherapy, 30,* 273–281.

Silverman, M. J. (2003b). The influence of music on the symptoms of psychosis: A meta-analysis. *Journal of Music Therapy, 40,* 27–40.

Silverman, M J. (2006a). Forty years of case studies: A history of clinical case studies in the *Journal of Music Therapy, Music Therapy,* and *Music Therapy Perspectives. Music Therapy Perspectives, 24*(1), 4–12.

Silverman, M. J. (2006b). Psychiatric patients' perception of music therapy and other psychoeducation programming. *Journal of Music Therapy, 43,* 111–122.

Silverman, M. J. (2007). Evaluating current trends in psychiatric music therapy: A descriptive analysis. *Journal of Music Therapy, 44,* 388–414.

Silverman, M. J. (2008). Quantitative comparison of cognitive behavioral therapy and music therapy research: A methodological best-practics analysis to guide future investigation for adult psychiatric patients. *Journal of Music Therapy, 45,* 457–506.

Silverman, M. J. (2009a). The effect of single-session psychoeducational music therapy on verbalizations and perceptions in psychiatric patients. *Journal of Music Therapy, 46,* 105–131.

Silverman, M. J. (2009b). The use of lyric analysis interentions in contemporary psychiatric music therapy: Descriptive results of songs and objectives for clinical practice. *Music Therapy Perspectives, 27*(1), 55–61.

Simpson, F. (2007). *Every note counts: The story of Nordoff-Robbins music therapy.* London: James and James.

Skaggs, R. (1997a). *Finishing strong: Treating chemical addictions with music and imagery.* St. Louis: MMB Music.

Skaggs, R. (1997b). Music-centered creative arts in a sex offender treatment program for male juveniles. *Music Therapy Perspectives, 15*(2), 73–78.

Skaggs, R. (1997c). The Bonny method of guided imagery and music in the Treatment of terminal illness: A private practice setting. *Music Therapy Perspectives, 15*(1), 39–44.

Skaggs, R. (2004). *Music: Keynote of the human spirit.* Baltimore, MD: PublishAmerica.

Skille, O. (1989). VibroAcoustic therapy. *Music Therapy, 8*(1), 61–66.

Skinner, B. F. (1953). *Science and human behavior.* New York: Macmillan.

Slivka, H. H. & Magill, L. (1986). The conjoint use of social work and music therapy in working with children of cancer patients. *Music Therapy, 6A*(1), 30–40.

Slotoroff, C. (1994). Drumming technique for assertiveness and anger management in the short-term psychiatric setting for adult and adolescent survivors of trauma. *Music Therapy Perspectives, 12*(2), 111–116.

Smaligo, M. A. (1998). Resources for helping blind music students. *Music Educators Journal, 85*(2), 23–26, 45.

Smeltekop, R. A. & Houghton, B. A. (1990). Music therapy and psychopharmacology. In R. F. Unkefer (Ed.), *Music therapy in the treatment of adults with mental disorders*

(109–125). New York: Schirmer.

Smith, B. B. & Knudson, L. A. (1995). *A song to set me free: A model for music therapy and music related activities for frail elderly and disabled adults.* Logan, UT: Sunshine Terrace Adult Day Center.

Smith, C. R., Katsiyannis, A., & Ryan, J. B. (2011). Challenges of serving students with emotional and behavioral disorders: Legal and policy consideration. *Behavior Disorders, 36(3)*, 185–194.

Smith, C. R. & Steinschneider, A. (1975). Differential effects of prenatal rhythmic stimulation on neonatal arousal states. *Child Development, 46,* 574–578.

Smith, D. S. (1989). Preferences for differentiated frequency loudness levels in older adult music listening. *Journal of Music Therapy, 26(1)*, 18–29.

Smith, D. S. (1990). Therapeutic treatment effectiveness as documented in the gerontology literature: Implications for music therapy. *Music Therapy Perspectives, 8,* 36–40.

Smith, D. S. (1991). A comparison of group performance and song familiarity on cued recall tasks with older adults. *Journal of Music Therapy, 28(1)*, 2–13.

Smith, D. S. (1998). Presidential perspectives: The family reunion. *Music Therapy Matters, 1(4)*, 2, 13.

Smith, D. S. & Lipe, A. W. (1991). Music therapy practices in gerontology. *Journal of Music Therapy, 28(4)*, 193–210.

Smith, E. D. (1972). *Handbook of aging.* New York: Barnes & Noble.

Smith, G. H. (1986). A comparison of the effects of three treatment interventions on cognitive functioning of Alzheimer's patients. *Music Therapy, 6A(1)*, 41–56.

Smith, L. (2012). Sparkling divas: Therapeutic music video groups with at-risk youth. *Music Therapy Perspectives, 30(1)*, 17–24.

Snell, A. M. (1996). Music therapy for learners with autism in a public school setting. In B. L. Wilson (Ed.), *Models of music therapy interventions in school settings: From institution to inclusion* (156–183). Silver Spring, MD: National Association for Music Therapy.

Snell, A. M. (2006). Definitions and characteristics of individuals served in early childhood and school age settings. In M. E. Humphill and C. Colwell, (Eds.) *Effective clinical practice in music therapy* (8–28). Silver Spring, MD: American Music Therapy Association.

Solé, C., Mercadel-Brotons, M., Gallego, S., & Riera, M. (2010). Contributions of music to aging adults' quality of life. *Journal of Music Therapy, 47(3)*, 264–281.

Solli, H. P., Rolvsjord, R., & Borg, M. (2013). Toward understanding music therapy as a recovery-oriented practice within mental health care: A meta-systhesis of service users' experiences. *Journal of Music Therapy, 50,* 244–273.

Solomon, A. L. (1980). Music in special education: Hearing and speech development. *Journal of Research in Music Education, 28(4)*, 236–242.

Solomon, A. L. (1995). Historical research. In B. L. Wheeler (Ed.), *Music therapy research: Quantitative and qualitative perspectives* (487–501). Phoenixville, PA: Barcelona.

Solomon, A. L. & Heller, N. (1982). Historical research in music therapy: An important avenue for studying the profession. *Journal of Music Therapy, 19(3)*, 161–178.

Soshensky, R. (2005). Developing a guitar-based approach in Nordoff-Robbins music therapy. *Music Therapy Perspectives, 23*(2), 111–117.

Soshensky, R. (2007a). Music therapy with children with emotional disturbance. In B. J. Crowe & C. Colwell (Eds.), *Music therapy for children, adolescents, and adults with mental disorders* (206–223). Silver Spring, MD: American Music Therapy Association.

Soshensky, R. (2007b). Music therapy for clients with substance abuse disorders. In B. J. Crowe & C. Colwell (Eds.), *Music therapy for children, adolescents, and adults with mental disorders* (149–164). Silver Spring, MD: American Music Therapy Association.

Sparks, R., Helms, N., & Albert, M. (1974). Aphasia rehabilitation resulting from melodic intonation therapy. *Cortex, 10*, 303–316.

Sparks, R. & Holland, A. (1976). Melodic intonation therapy for aphasia. *Journal of Speech and Hearing Disorders, 41*, 287–297.

Special Committee on Aging. (1992). Forever young: Music and aging. Hearing before the Special Committee on Aging, United States Senate, One hundred second Congress, first session, August 1, 1991 (Serial no. 102-9). Washington, DC: U.S. Government Printing Office.

Spencer, M. J. (1978). A case for the arts. In *The healing role of the arts* (Working papers – The Rockefeller Foundation) (1–9). NY: The Rockefeller Foundation.

Spencer, S. L. (1988). The efficiency of instrumental and movement activities in developing mentally retarded adolescents' ability to follow directions. *Journal of Music Therapy, 25*(1), 44–50.

Spina Bifida Association (SBA) (2015). Liptak, G. S. (Contributing Ed.). What is spina bifida? Retrieved April 14, 2014 from www.spinabifidaassociation.org.

Spintge, R. (1989). The anxiolytic effects of music. In M. H. M. Lee (Ed.), *Rehabilitation, music and human well-being* (82–100). St. Louis: MMB Music.

Spintge, R. (1991). The neurophysiology of emotion and its therapeutic applications in music therapy and music medicine. In C. D. Maranto (Ed.), *Applications of music in medicine* (59–72). Washington, DC: National Association for Music Therapy.

Spintge, R. & Droh, R. (1987). Effects of anxiolytic music on plasma levels of stress hormones in different medical specialties. In R. R. Pratt (Ed.), *The fourth international symposium on music: Rehabilitation and human well-being* (88–101). New York: University Press of America.

Spitzer, S. (1989). Computers and music therapy: An integrated approach. *Music Therapy Perspectives, 7*, 51–54.

Spraycar, M. (Ed.) (1995). *Stedman's Medical Distionary* (26th ed.). Baltimore, Williams & Wilkins.

Stambaugh, L. (1996). Special learners with special abilities. *Music Educators Journal, 83*(3), 19–23.

Standley, J. M. (1986). Music research in medical/dental treatment: Meta-analysis and clinical applications. *Journal of Music Therapy, 23*(2), 56–122.

Standley, J. M. (1991a). *Music techniques in therapy, counseling, and special education.* St. Louis: MMB Music.

Standley, J. M. (1991b). The role of music in pacification/stimulation of premature infants with low birthweights. *Music Therapy Perspectives, 9,* 19–25.

Standley, J. M. (1992). Clinical applications of music and chemotherapy: The effects on nausea and emesis. *Music Therapy Perspectives, 10(1),* 27–35.

Standley, J. M. (1996a). A meta-analysis on the effects of music as reinforcement for therapy objectives. *Journal of Research in Music Education, 44(2),* 105–133.

Standley, J. M. (1996b). Music research in medical/dental treatment: An update of a prior meta-analysis. In C. E. Furman (Ed.), *Effectiveness of music therapy procedures: Documentation of research and clinical practice* (2nd ed.) (1–60). Silver Spring, MD: National Association for Music Therapy.

Standley, J. M. & Hughes, J. E. (1997). Evaluation of an early intervention music curriculum for enhancing prereading/writing skills. *Music Therapy Perspectives, 15(2),* 79–86.

Standley, J. (1998). The effect of music and multimodal stimulation on physiologic and developmental responses of premature infants in neonatal intensive care. *Pediatric Nursing, 21(6),* 532–539.

Standley, J. M., Gregory, D., Whipple, J., Walsworth, D., Nguyen, J., Jarred, J., et al. (2005). *Medical music therapy: A model program for clinical practice, education, training, and research.* Silver Spring, MD: American Music Therapy Association.

Standley, J., Johnson, C. M., Robb, S. L., Brownell, M. D., & Kim, S. (2008). Behavioral approach to music therapy. In A-A. Darrow (Ed.), *Introduction to approaches in music therapy* (2nd ed.) (105–127). Silver Spring, MD: American Music Therapy Association.

Standley, J. M. & Walworth, D. (2010). *Music therapy with premature infants* (2nd ed.). Silver Spring, MD: American Music Therapy Association.

Staum, M. J. (1987). Music notation to improve the speech prosody of hearing impaired children. *Journal of Music Therapy, 24(3),* 146–159.

Staum, M. J. (1988). Music for physical rehabilitation: An analysis of literature from 1950–1986 and applications for rehabilitation settings. In C. E. Furman (Ed.), *Effectiveness of music therapy procedures: Documentation of research and clinical practice* (65–104). Washington, DC: National Association for Music Therapy.

Staum, M. J. (1989). Music as motivation for language learning. In R. R. Pratt & H. Moog (Eds.), *First research seminar of the ISME commission on music therapy and music in special education: Proceedings of 1986* (62–68). St. Louis: MMB Music.

Staum, M. J. (1993). A music/nonmusic intervention with homeless children. *Journal of Music Therapy, 30(4),* 236–262.

Staum, M. J. (1996). Music for physical rehabilitation: An analysis of literature from 1950–1993 and applications for rehabilitation settings. In C. E. Furman (Ed.), *Effectiveness of music therapy procedures: Documentation of research and clinical practice* (2nd ed.) (61–105). Silver Spring, MD: National Association for Music Therapy.

Staum, M. J. & Brotons, M. (1992). The influence of auditory subliminals on behavior: A series of investigations. *Journal of Music Therapy, 29(3),* 130–185.

Staum, M. J. & Brotons, M. (1995). Issues in music for children in a homeless shelter: Social objectives and choice of reinforcers. *Journal of Music Therapy, 32(4),* 248–264.

Staum, M. J. & Flowers, P. J. (1984). The use of simulated training and music lessons on teaching appropriate shopping skills to an autistic child. *Music Therapy Perspectives*, *1*(*3*), 14–17.

Steele, A. L. (1968). Programmed use of music to alter uncooperative problem behavior. *Journal of Music Therapy*, *5*(*4*), 103–107.

Steele, A. L. (1984). Music therapy for the learning disabled: Intervention and instruction. *Music Therapy Perspectives*, *1*(*3*), 2–7.

Steele, A. L. & Young, S. (2008). A comparison of music education and music therapy majors: Personality types as described by the Myers-Briggs type indicator and demographic profiles. *Journal of Music Therapy*, *45*(*1*), 2–20.

Steele, A. L. & Young, S. (2011). A descriptive study of Myers-Briggs Personality Types of professional music educators and music therapists with comparisons to undergraduate majors. *Journal of Music Therapy*, *48*(*1*), 55–73.

Steele, P. H. (1987). Musical personality therapy and wellbeing. In R. R. Pratt (Ed.), *The fourth international symposium on music: Rehabilitation and human well-being* (27–36). New York: University Press of America.

Stein, A. M. (1991). Music to reduce anxiety during cesarean births. In C. D. Maranto (Ed.), *Applications of music in medicine* (179–190). Washington, DC: National Association for Music Therapy.

Steinke, W. R. (1991). The use of music, relaxation, and imagery in the management of post-surgical pain for scoliosis. In C. D. Maranto (Ed.), *Applications of music in medicine* (141–162). Washington, DC: National Association for Music Therapy.

Stevens, E. & Clark, F. (1969). Music therapy in the treatment of autistic children. *Journal of Music Therapy*, *6*(*4*) , 98–104.

Stiffman, A. R., Orme, J. G., Evans, D. A., Feldman, R. A., & Keeney P. A. (1984). *Behavior Rating Index for Children* (BRIC). Minneapolis, MN: University of Minnesota.

Stordahl, J. (2002). Song recognition and appraisal: A comparison of children who use cochlear implants and normally hearing children. *Journal of Music Therapy*, *39*, 2–19.

Stothard, S. E., Snowling, M. J., Bishop, D. V. M., Chipchase, B., & Kaplan, C. (1998). Language-impaired preschoolers: A follow-up into adolescence. *Journal of Speech, Language, and Hearing Research*, *41*, 407–418.

Stratton, V. N. & Zalanowski, A. H. (1984). The relationship between music, degree of liking, and self-reported relaxation. *Journal of Music Therapy*, *21*(*4*), 184–192.

Sullivan, J. M. (2007). Music for the injured soldier: A contribution of American Women's Military Bands during World War II. *Journal of Music Therapy*, *44*(*3*), 282–305.

Summer, L. (1981). Guided imagery and music with the elderly. *Music Therapy*, *1*(*1*), 39–42.

Summer, L. (1988). *Guided imagery and music in the institutional setting*. St. Louis: MMB Music.

Summer, L. (1994). Considering classical music for use in psychiatric music therapy. *Music Therapy Perspectives*, *12*(*2*), 130–133.

Summer, L. (1995). Unsound medicine. In C. B. Kenny (Ed.), *Listening, playing, creating: Essays on the power of sound* (59–64). Albany, NY: State University of New

York Press.

Summer, L. & Nolan, P. (2001). Introduction to the music therapy perspectives special issue: The role of music in the music therapy process. *Music Therapy Perspectives, 19(1)*, 5–6.

Summer, L. & Summer, J. (1996). *Music: The new age elixir.* Amherst, NY: Prometheus Books.

Sussman, J. E. (2009). The effect of music on peer awareness in preschool age children with developmental disabilities. *Journal of Music Therapy, 46*, 53–68.

Sutton, J. (2002). Survival in the workplace. *British Journal of Music Therapy, 16(2)*, 62–64.

Suzuki, S. (1969). *Nurtured by love: A new approach to education.* New York: Exposition Press.

Swaiko, N. (1974). The role and value of a eurythmics program in a curriculum for deaf children. *American Annals of the Deaf, 119(3)*, 155–160.

Swingler, T. (1994). Unlocking musicality: Using soundbeam as a new key to eloquence. *Music Therapy Perspectives, 12(1)*, 4–5.

Takahashi, T. & Matsushita, H. (2006). Long-term effects of music therapy on elderly with moderate/severe dementia. *Journal of Music Therapy, 43(4)*, 317–333.

Talkington, L. W. & Hall, S. M. (1970). A musical application of Premack's hypothesis to low verbal retardates. *Journal of Music Therapy, 7(3)*, 95–99.

Tan, X., Yowler, C. J., Super, D. M., & Fratianne, R. B. (2012). The interplay of preference, familiarity, and psychophysical properties in defining relaxation music. *Journal of Music Therapy, 49(2)*, 150–179.

Tanner, D. R. & O'Briant, R. M. (1980). Music can color a graying America. *Music Educators Journal, 67(4)*, 28–30.

Taylor, D. B. (1969). Expressive emphasis in the treatment of intropunitive behavior. *Journal of Music Therapy, 6(2)*, 41–43.

Taylor, D. B. (1973). Subject responses to precatagorized stimulative and sedative music. *Journal of Music Therapy, 10(2)*, 86–92.

Taylor, D. B. (1981). Music in general hospital treatment from 1900 to 1950. *Journal of Music Therapy, 18(2)*, 62–73.

Taylor, D. B. (1987a). A survey of professional music therapists concerning entry level competencies. *Journal of Music Therapy, 24(3)*, 114–145.

Taylor, D. B. (1987b). The theoretical basis for the use of music with aphasic patients. In R. R. Pratt (Ed.), *The fourth international symposium on music: Rehabilitation and human well-being* (165–169). New York: University Press of America.

Taylor, D. B. (1988). Therapeutic musicians or musical physicians: The future is at stake. *Music Therapy Perspectives, 5*, 86–93.

Taylor, D. B. (1989). A neuroanatomical model for the use of music in the remediation of aphasic disorders. In M. H. M. Lee (Ed.), *Rehabilitation, music and human well being* (168–178). St. Louis: MMB Music.

Taylor, D. B. (1990). Childhood sequential development of rhythm, melody and pitch. In F. R. Wilson and F. L. Roehmann (Eds.), *Music and child development: Biology of music making: Proceedings of the 1987 Denver Conference* (241–253). St. Louis: MMB Music.

Taylor, D. B. (1997). *Biomedical foundations of music as therapy.* St. Louis: MMB Music.

Taylor, J. A., Barry, N. H., & Walls, K. C. (1997). *Music and students at risk: Creative solutions for a national dilemma.* Reston, VA: Music Educators National Conference.

Teahan, M. (2000). Grief interventions. In M. Teahan & T. Dalton (Eds.). *Helping children and adolescents cope with grief and bereavement.* Symposium conducted at the alumni conference of the Barry University School of Social work, Miami, FL.

Teasell, R. W., Bhagal, S. K., Foley, N. C., et al. (2003). Gait retraining post-stroke. *Topics in Stroke Rehabilitation, 19(2),* 34–65.

Thaut, M. H. (1984). A music therapy treatment model for autistic children. *Music Therapy Perspectives, 1(4),* 7–13.

Thaut, M. H. (1987). A new challenge for music therapy: The correctional setting. *Music Therapy Perspectives, 4,* 44–50.

Thaut, M. H. (1989a). Music therapy, affect modification, and therapeutic change: Toward an integrative model. *Music Therapy Perspectives, 7,* 55–62.

Thaut, M. H. (1989b). The influence of music therapy interventions on self-rated changes in relaxation, affect, and thought in psychiatric prisoner-patients. *Journal of Music Therapy, 26(3),* 155–166.

Thaut, M. H. (1992a). Music therapy for the physically disabled child. In W. B. Davis, K. E. Gfeller, & M. H. Thaut (Eds.), *An introduction to music therapy: Theory and practice* (164–179). Dubuque, IA: Wm. C. Brown.

Thaut, M. H. (1992b). Music therapy in correctional psychiatry. In W. B. Davis, K. E. Gfeller, & M. H. Thaut (Eds.), *An introduction to music therapy: Theory and practice* (273–284). Dubuque, IA: Wm. C. Brown.

Thaut, M. H. (1992c). Music therapy in the rehabilitation of stroke and traumatic-brain-injured clients. In W. B. Davis, K. E. Gfeller, & M. H. Thaut (Eds.), *An introduction to music therapy: Theory and practice* (251–272). Dubuque, IA: Wm. C. Brown.

Thaut, M. H. (1992d). Music therapy with autistic children. In W. B. Davis, K. E. Gfeller, & M. H. Thaut (Eds.), *An introduction to music therapy: Theory and practice* (180–196). Dubuque, IA: Wm. C. Brown.

Thaut, M. H. (2000). *A scientific model of music in therapy and medicine.* San Antonio, TX: IMR Press.

Thaut, M. H. (2008a). Group music psychotherapy in correctional psychiatry. In W. B. Davis, K. E. Gfeller, & M. H. Thaut (Eds.), *An introduction to music therapy: Theory and practice* (3rd ed.) (247–259). Silver Spring, MD: American Music Therapy Association.

Thaut, M. H. & Davis, W. B. (1993). The influence of subject-selected versus experimenter-chosen music on affect, anxiety, and relaxation. *Journal of Music Therapy, 30(4),* 210–223.

Thaut, M. H. & Gfeller, K. E. (1992). Music therapy in the treatment of mental disorders. In W. B. Davis, K. E. Gfeller, & M. H. Thaut (Eds.), *An introduction to music therapy: Theory and practice* (93–132). Dubuque, IA: Wm. C. Brown.

Thaut, M. H., McIntosh, G. C., & Rice, R. R. (1997). Rhythmic facilitation of gait training in hemiparetic stroke rehabilitation. *Journal of Neurological Sciences, 151,*

207–212.

Thaut, M. H., Mertel, K., & Leins, A. K. (2008). Music therapy for children and adults with physical disabilities. In W. B. Davis, K. E. Gfeller, & M. H. Thaut (Eds.), *An introduction to music therapy: Theory and practice* (3rd ed.). Silver Spring, MD: American Music Therapy Association.

Thaut, M. H., Peterson, D. A., Sena, K. M., & McIntosh, G. C. (2008). Musical structure facilitates verbal learning in mulitiple schlerosis. *Music Perception, 25(4)*, 325–330.

Thaut, M., Schleiffers, S., & Davis, W. (1991). Analysis of EMG activity in biceps and triceps muscle in an upper extremity gross motor task under the influence of auditory rhythm. *Journal of Music Therapy, 28(2)*, 64–88.

Thaut, M. H. & Smeltekop, R. A. (1990). Psychosocial and neurophysiological aspects of music therapy interventions. In R. F. Unkefer (Ed.), *Music therapy in the treatment of adults with mental disorders* (85–87). New York: Schirmer.

Thaut, M. H., Thaut, C., & La Gasse, B. (2008). Music therapy in neurologic rehabilitation. In W. B. Davis, K. E. Gfeller, & M. H. Thaut (Eds.) *An introduction to music therapy: Theory and practice* (3rd ed.) (261–304). Silver Spring, MD: American Music Therapy Association.

Thomas, C. (2007). Music therapy and acute care psychiatric treatment. In B. J. Crowe & C. Colwell (Eds.), *Music therapy for children, adolescents, and adults with mental disorders* (125–132). Silver Spring, MD: American Music Therapy Association.

Thomas, D. W., Heitman, R. J., & Alexander, T. (1997). The effects of music on bathing cooperation for residents with dementia. *Journal of Music Therapy, 34(4)*, 246–259.

Thomas, L. (1974). *The lives of a cell: Notes of a biology watcher.* New York: Viking Press.

Thompson, A. B., Arnold, J. C., & Murray, S. E. (1990). Music therapy assessment of the cerebrovascular accident patient. *Music Therapy Perspectives, 8,* 23–29.

Thompson, G. (2012). Family-centered music therapy in the home environment: Promoting interpersonal engagement between children with autism spectrum disorder and their parents. *Music Therapy Perspectives, 30(2)*, 109–116.

Thompson, S. (2007). Themes and metaphors in songwriting with clients participating in a psychiatric rehabilitation program. *Music Therapy Perspectives, 27(1)*, 4–10.

Timler, G. (2008). Social Communication: A framework for assessment and intervention. *The ASHA Leader.* Retrieved May 26, 2015 from www.asha.org/publications/leaded/2008/081104/Fo81104a.htm.

Tims, F. (1981, November). An American's experiences and music therapy work in a German hospital. Paper presented at the 32nd Annual Conference of the National Association for Music Therapy, Denver, CO.

Tims, F. (1989). Experiential learning in the music therapy curriculum. *Music Therapy Perspectives, 7,* 91–92.

Toigo, D. A. (1992). Autism: Integrating a personal perspective with music therapy practice. *Music Therapy Perspectives, 10(1)*, 13–20.

Tomaino, C. (1992). Medical problems of the elderly: Implications for music therapy assessment and intervention. In American Association for Music Therapy Procedings booklet: "Body, mind, spirit: AAMT coming of age" (220–227). American Association for Music Therapy.

Tonchick, K. A. (1981). An introduction to Orff-Schulwerk: A philosophy and process of music for children. *National Association for Music Therapy, 25(3)*, 30–35.

Tonkins, S. A. & Lambert, M. J. (1996). A treatment outcome study of bereavement groups for children. *Child and Adolescent Social Work Journal, 13*, 3–21.

Treder-Wolff, J. (1990). Affecting attitudes: Music therapy in addictions treatment. *Music Therapy Perspectives, 8*, 67–71.

Trehub, S. E. (2009). Musical predispositions in infancy: An update. In I. Peretz & R. J. Zatorre (Eds.). *The cognitive neuroscience of music.* New York: Oxford University Press.

Trehub, S. E., Mitani, C., Kanda, Y., & Nakata, T. (2006). Pitch and timing in the songs of deaf children with cochlear implants. *Music Perception, 24(2)*, 147–154.

Trevisan, L. A. (1978). A comparative study of scientific and spiritualistic perspectives of wholistic healing (via music and massage). In A. L. Nowicki & L. A. Trevisan (Eds.), *Beyond the sound: A technical and philosophical approach to music therapy* (rev. ed.) (vii–xxii). Santa Barbara, CA: Nowicki/Trevisan.

Tsao, C. C., Gordon, T. F., Maranto, C. D., Lerman, C., & Murasko, D. (1991). The effects of music and biological imagery on immune response (S-IgA). In C. D. Maranto (Ed.), *Applications of music in medicine* (85–121). Washington, DC: National Association for Music Therapy.

Tung, C-Y. & Chao, K-P. (2013). Effects of recreational noise exposure on hearing impairment among teenage students. *Research in Developmental Disabilities, 34(1)*, 126–132.

Turnbull, A., Turnbull, R., & Wenineyer, M. (2010). *Exceptional lives: Special education in today's schools* (6th ed.). Upper Saddle River, NJ: Merrill.

Turnbull, J., Muckle, W., & Masters, C. (2007). Homelessness and health. *Canadian Medical Association Journal, 177(9)*, 1065–1067.

Turry, A. (1999). A song of life: Improvised songs with children with cancer and serious blood disorders. In T. Wigram & J. DeBacker (Eds.), *Clinical applications of music therapy in developmental disability, pediatrics, and neurology* (13–31). London: Jessica Kingsley.

Turry, A. & Marcus, D. (2005). Teamwork: Therapist and cotherapist in the Nordoff-Robbins approach to music therapy. *Music Therapy Perspectives, 23(1)*, 53–69.

Tyson, F. (1959). The development of an out-patient music therapy referral service. In E. H. Schneider (Ed.), *Music therapy 1958* (129–134). Lawrence, KS: Allen Press.

Tyson, F. (1966). Music therapy in private practice: Three case histories. *Journal of Music Therapy, 3(1)*, 8–18.

Tyson, F. (1981). *Psychiatric music therapy: Origins and development.* New York: Fred Weidner and Sons.

Tyson, F. (1987). Analytically-oriented music therapy in a case of generalized anxiety disorder. *Music Therapy Perspectives, 4*, 51–55.

Underhill, K. K. & Harris, L. M. (1974). The effect of contingent music on establishing imitation in behaviorally disturbed retarded children. *Journal of Music Therapy, 11(3)*, 156–166.

United Cerbral Palsy (UCP) (2013). Cerebral palsy facts. Retrieved April 10, 2015 from http://ucp.org/wp-content/uploads/2013/02/ce-fact-sheet.Pdf.

United States Census Bureau. Current population survey (cps) – Definitions and explanations. Population Division fertility and family statistics branch. Retrieved July 1, 2015 from www.census.gov/population/www/cps/cpsdef.html.

Unkefer, R. F. (1961). The music therapist. In E. H. Schneider (Ed.), *Music therapy 1960* (27–31). Lawrence, KS: Allen Press.

Unkefer, R. F. (Ed.) (1990). *Music therapy in the treatment of adults with mental disorders.* New York: Schirmer.

Unkefer, R. & Thaut, M. (2002). *Music therapy in the treatment of adults with mental disorders.* St. Louis: MMB.

Van Besouw, R. M., Nicholls, D. R., Oliver, B. B., Hodkinson, S. M., & Grasmeder, M. L. (2014). Aural rehabilitation through music workshops for cochlear implant users. *Journal of the American Academy of Audiology, 25(4),* 311–323.

Vanderark, S., Newman, I., & Bell, S. (1983). The effects of music participation on quality of life of the elderly. *Music Therapy, 3(1),* 71–81.

Van de Wall, W. (1936). *Music in institutions.* New York: Russell Sage.

Van de Wall, W. (1944). Report on the survey. *National Music Council Bulletin, 5,* 9–13.

Van de Wall, W. (1946). *Music in hospitals.* New York: Russell Sage.

Vann, M. R. (2014). The 14 most common health concerns for seniors. *Everyday Health,* March. Retrieved from http://www.everydayhealth.com/news/most-common -health-concerns-seriors/.

Van Riper, C. (1984). *Speech correction: An introduction to speech pathology and audiology.* Englewood Cliffs, NJ: Prentice-Hall.

VanWeelden, K. & Cevasco, A. (2007). Repertoire recommendations by music therapists for geriatric clients during singing activities. *Music Therapy Perspectives, 25(1),* 4–12.

VanWeelden, K. & Cevasco, A. M. (2009). Geriatric clients' preferences for specific popular songs to use during singing activities. *Journal of Music Therapy, 46(2),* 147–159.

VanWeelden, K., Juchniewicz, J., & Cevasco, A. M. (2008). Music therapy students' recognition of popular song repertoire for geriatric clients. *Journal of Music Therapy, 45(4),* 443–456.

VanWeelden, K. & Whipple, J. (2009). Effect of field experiences on music therapy students' perception of choral music for geriatric wellness programs. *Journal of Music Therapy, 41(4),* 340–352.

Vega, V. R. (2010). Personality, burnout, and longevity among professional music therapists. *Journal of Music Therapy, 47,* 155–179.

Velasquez, V. (1991). Beginning experience in piano performance for a girl with Down syndrome: A case study. *Music Therapy Perspectives, 9,* 82–86.

Ventre, M. E. (1994a). Guided Imagery and Music in process: The interweaving of the archetype of the mother, mandala, and music. *Music Therapy, 12(2),* 19–38.

Ventre, M. E. (1994b). Healing the wounds of childhood abuse: A Guided Imagery and Music case study. *Music Therapy Perspectives, 12(2),* 98–103.

Vescelius, E. A. (1913). Music in its relation to life. *Music and Health, 1,* 5–10.

Vescelius, E. A. (1918). Music and health. *The Musical Quarterly, 4(3),* 376–401.

Visiting Nurses Association of Dallas (1981). Home hospice (brochure). Dallas, TX: Author.

Vongpaisal, T., Trehub, S. E., & Schellenberg, E. B. (2006). Song recognition by children and adolescents with cochlear implants. *Journal of Speech, Language and Hearing Research, 49*, 1091–1103.

Vongpaisal, T., Trehub, S. E., & Schellenberg, E. G. (2009). Identification of TV tunes by children with cochlear implants. *Music Perception, 27*, 17–24.

Vongpaisal, T., Trehub, S. E., Schellenberg, E. G., & Papsin, B. (2004). Music recognition by children with cochlear implants. *International Congress Series, 1273*, 193–196.

Wade, L. M. (2002). A comparison of the effects of vocal exercises/singing versus music-assisted relaxation on peak expiratory flow rates of children with asthma. *Music Therapy Perspectives, 20*(*1*), 31–37.

Wager, K. M. (2000). The effects of music therapy upon an adult male with autism and mental retardation: A four-year case study. *Music Therapy Perspectives, 18*(*2*), 131–140.

Wagner, M. J. (1975). Effect of music and biofeedback on alpha brain wave rhythms and attentiveness of musicians and non-musicians. *Journal of Research in Music Education, 23*(*1*), 3–13.

Waldon, E. G. (2001). The effects of group music therapy on mood states and cohesiveness in adult oncology patients. *Journal of Music Therapy, 38*, 212–238.

Waldon, E. G. (2015). Music therapists' research activity and utilization barriers: A survey of the membership. *Journal of Music Therapy, 52*(*1*), 168–194.

Walker, E. L. (1980). *Psychological complexity and preference: A hedgehog theory of behavior.* Monterey, CA: Brooks/Cole Publishing.

Walker, J. B. (1972). The use of music as an aid in developing functional speech in the institutionalized mentally retarded. *Journal of Music Therapy, 9*(*1*), 1–12.

Walters, C. L. (1996). The psychological and physiological effects of vibrotactile stimulation, via a Somatron, on patients awaiting scheduled gynecological surgery. *Journal of Music Therapy, 33*(*4*), 261–287.

Walworth, D. D. (2003). The effect of preferred music genre selection versus preferred song selection on experimentally induced anxiety levels. *Journal of Music Therapy, 40*, 2–14.

Walworth, D. D. (2007). The use of music therapy within the SCERTS model for children with autism spectrum disorder. *Journal of Music Therapy, 44*, 2–22.

Walworth, D. (2013). Family-centered practice: Integrating music into home routines. In P. Kern & M. Humpal (Eds.), *Early childhood music therapy and autism spectrum disorders* (233–249). London: Jessica Kingsley.

Walworth, D. D., Register, D., & Engel, J. N. (2009). Using the SCERTS model assessment tool to identify music therapy goals for clients with autism spectrum disorder. *Journal of Music Therapy, 46*, 204–216.

Warja, M. (1994). Sounds of music through the spiraling path of individuation: A Jungian approach to music psychotherapy. *Music Therapy Perspectives, 12*(*2*), 75–83.

Warner, D. (1981). Song and sign: The use of music in teaching sign language. *National Association for Music Therapy, 25*(*1*), 26–33.

Wasserman, N. M. (1972). Music therapy for the emotionally disturbed in a private hospital. *Journal of Music Therapy, 9*(*2*), 99–104.

Watson, D. (1979). Music as reinforcement in increasing spontaneous speech among autistic children. *Missouri Journal of Research in Music Education, 4*(*3*), 8–20.

Watson, D. (2002). Drumming and improvisation with adult male sexual offenders. *Music Therapy Perspectives, 20*(*2*), 105–111.

Watts, T. D. (1980). Theories of aging: the difference in orientations. *Journal of Music Therapy, 17*(*2*), 84–89.

Weisberg, N. & Wilder, R. (1985). *Creative arts with older adults: A sourcebook.* New York: Human Sciences Press.

Weissman, J. A. (1983). Planned music activities to meet needs and treatment goals of aged individuals in longterm care facilities. *Music Therapy, 3*(*1*), 63–70.

Weitz, M. (1993). Beats of different drummers. *The Dallas Morning News* (September 5), IF, 4F.

Weldin, C. & Eagle, C. T. (1991). An historical overview of music medicine. In C. D. Maranto (Ed.), *Applications of music in medicine* (7–27). Washington, DC: National Association for Music Therapy.

Wells, K. E. & Helmus, N. (1968). Music therapy for severe speech disorders. In E. T. Gaston (Ed.), *Music in therapy* (159–162). New York: Macmillan.

Welsbacher, B. (1975). Music for the learning disabled. In R. M. Graham (Compiler), *Music for the exceptional child* (136–147). Reston, VA: Music Educators National Conference.

Wentworth, R. (1991). The effects of music an distracting noise on the productivity of workers with mental retardation. *Journal of Music Therapy, 28*(*1*), 40–47.

Werbner, N. (1966). The practice of music therapy with psychotic children. *Journal of Music Therapy 3*(*1*), 25–31.

Werner, P. D., Swope, A. J., & Heide, F. J. (2009). Ethnicity, music experience, and depression. *Journal of Music Therapy, 46*, 339–358.

Wesecky, A. (1986). Music therapy for children with Rett syndrome. *Journal of Medical Genetics, 24*, 253–257.

West, T. M. (1994). Psychological issues in hospice music therapy. *Music Therapy Perspectives, 12*(*2*), 117–124.

Wexler, M. M. D. (1989). The use of song in grief therapy with Cibecue White Mountain Apaches. *Music Therapy Perspectives, 7*, 63–66.

Wheeler, B. (1981). The relationship between music therapy and theories of psychotherapy. *Music Therapy, 1*(*1*), 9–16.

Wheeler, B. (1983). A psychotherapeutic classification of music therapy practices: A continuum of procedures. *Music Therapy Perspectives, 1*(*2*), 8–12.

Wheeler, B. L. (1985). The relationship between musical and activity elements of music therapy sessions and client responses: An exploratory study. *Music Therapy, 5*(*1*), 52–60.

Wheeler, B. L. (1987). Levels of therapy: The classification of music therapy goals. *Music Therapy, 6*(*2*), 39–49.

Wheeler, B. L. (Ed.) (1995). *Music therapy research: Quantitative and qualitative perspectives.* Phoenixville, PA: Barcelona.

Wheeler, B. L. & Golden, S. (1987). NAMT and its Mid-Atlantic region: Changing together. *Music Therapy Perspectives, A*, 56–63.

Wheeler, B. L., Shultis, C. L., & Polen, D. W. (2005). *Clinical training guide for the student music therapist.* Gilsum, NH: Barcelona.

Wheeler, B. L. & Stultz, S. (2008). Using typical infant development to inform music therapy with children with disabilities. *Early Childhood Education Journal, 35,* 585–595.

Whipple, C. M., Gfeller, K., Driscoll, V., Oleson, J., & McGregor, K. (2015). Do communication disorders extend to musical messages? An answer from children with hearing loss or autism spectrum disorders. *Journal of Music Therapy, 52,* 78–116.

Whipple, J. (2003). Surgery buddies: A music therapy program for pediatric surgical patients. *Music Therapy Perspectives, 21*(2), 77–83.

Whipple, J. (2004). Music in intervention for children and adolescents with autism: A meta-analysis. *Journal of Music Therapy, 41,* 90–106.

Whitcomb, J. B. (1992). Therapeutic interventions between dementia residents and their caregivers. In American Association for Music Therapy Proceedings booklet "Body, Mind, Spirit: AAMT coming of age" (147–150). American Association for Music Therapy.

Whittall, J. (1991). Songs in palliative care: A spouse's last gift. In K. E. Bruscia (Ed.), *Case studies in music therapy* (603–610). Phoenixville, PA: Barcelona.

Whitwell, D. (1993). *Music as language: A new philosophy of music education.* Northridge, CA: WINDS.

Wigram, T. (1995). The psychological and physiological effects of low frequency sound and music. *Music Therapy Perspectives, 13*(1), 16–23.

Wigram, T., Pedersen, I. N., & Bonde, L. O. (2002). *A comprehensive guide to music therapy: Theory, clinical practice, research and training.* London: Jessica Kingsley.

Wilder, B. G. (1985). Singing bridges the gap. *Music Educators Journal, 71*(7), 34–36.

Williams, J. (1979). Music therapy and transactional analysis: Helping mothers and fathers develop their inner child. *National Association for Music Therapy, 23*(3), 21–23.

Wilson, B. L. (1990a). Assessment of adult psychiatric clients: The role of music therapy. In R. F. Unkefer (Ed.), *Music therapy in the treatment of adults with mental disorders* (126–144). New York: Schirmer.

Wilson, B. L. (1990b). Music therapy in hospital and community programs. In R. F. Unkefer (Ed.), *Music therapy in the treatment of adults with mental disorders* (88–95). New York: Schirmer.

Wilson, B. L. (Ed.) (1996). *Models of music therapy interventions in school settings: From institution to inclusion.* Silver Spring, MD: National Association for Music Therapy.

Wilson, B. L. (2002). Assessment of adult psychiatric clients: The role of music therapy. In R. F. Unkefer (Ed.), *Music therapy in the treatment of adults with mental disorders* (155–180). St. Louis: MMB Music.

Wilson, C. V. (1976). The use of rock music as a reward in behavior therapy with children. *Journal of Music Therapy, 13*(1), 39–48.

Windwer, C. M. (1981). An ascending music stimulus program and hyperactive children. *Journal of Research in Music Education, 29*(3), 173–181.

Wininger, S. R. & Pargman, D. (2003). Assessment of factors associated with exercise enjoyment. *Journal of Music Therapy, 40(1)*, 57–73.

Winn, T., Crowe, B. J., & Moreno, J. J. (1989). Shamanism and music therapy: Ancient healing techniques in modern practice. *Music Therapy Perspectives, 7*, 67–71.

Winslow, G. A. (1986). Music therapy in the treatment of anxiety in hospitalized high-risk mothers. *Music Therapy Perspectives, 3*, 29–33.

Witt, A. E. & Steele, A. L. (1984). Music therapy for infant and parent: A case example. *Music Therapy Perspectives, 1(4)*, 17–19.

Witt, V., Knox, R., Jutai, J., & Loveszy, R. (1994). Music therapy and rehabilitation of attention in brain injury: A pilot study. *Canadian Journal of Music Therapy, 2(1)*, 72–89.

Wolfe, D. (1978). Pain rehabilitation and music therapy. *Journal of Music Therapy, 15(4)*, 162–178.

Wolfe, D. (1980). The effect of automated interrupted music on head posturing of cerebral palsied individuals. *Journal of Music Therapy, 17(4)*, 184–206.

Wolfe, D. E. (1996). Group music therapy in acute mental health care: Meeting the demands of effectiveness. In C. E. Furman (Ed.), *Effectiveness of music therapy procedures: Documentation of research and clinical practice* (2nd ed.) (106–143). Silver Spring, MD: National Association for Music Therapy.

Wolfe, D. E. & Horn, C. (1993). Use of melodies as structural prompts for learning and retention of sequential verbal information by preschool students. *Journal of Music Therapy, 30(2)*, 100–118.

Wolfe, D. E., O'Connell, A. S., & Waldon, E. G. (2002). Music for relaxation: A comparison of musicians and nonmusicians on ratings of selected musical recordings. *Journal of Music Therapy, 39(1)*, 40–55.

Wolfe, D. E. & Stambaugh, S. (1993). Music analysis of Sesame Street: Implications for music therapy practice and research. *Journal of Music Therapy, 30(4)*, 224–235.

Wolfe, D. E. & Waldon, E. G. (2009). *Music therapy and pediatric medicine.* Silver Spring, MD: American Music Therapy Association.

Wolfe, J. R. (1983). The use of music in a group sensory training program for regressed geriatric patients. *Activities, Adaptation, and Aging, 3*, 49–62.

Wolfgram, B. J. (1978). Music therapy for retarded adults with psychotic overlay: A day treatment approach. *Journal of Music Therapy, 15(4)*, 199–207.

Wolfgram, B. J. (1980). *Songs of life.* Sherman Oaks, CA: Alfred Publishing.

Wood, M. M., Graham, R. M., Swan, W. W., Purvis, J., Gigliotti, C., & Samet, S. (1974). *Developmental music therapy.* Lawrence, KS: National Association for Music Therapy.

Wood, R. L. (1987). *Brain injury rehabilitation: A neurobehavioral approach.* London: Croom Helm.

Wooten, M. A. (1992). The effects of heavy metal music on affect shifts of adolescents in an inpatient psychiatric setting. *Music Therapy Perspectives, 10(2)*, 93–98.

Worden, J. W. (1982). *Grief counseling and grief therapy: A handbook for the mental health practitioner.* New York: Springer.

World Health Organization (WHO) (1964). Constitution of the World Health Organization. Geneva: World Health Organization.

World Health Organization (WHO) (2015). Mental health and older adults. Retrieved Oct. 2, 2015 from http://www.who.int/mediacentre/factsheets/fs381/erl.

Wyatt, J. G. (2002). From the field: Clinical resources for music therapy with juvenile offenders. *Music Therapy Perspectives, 20*(2), 80–88.

Wyatt, J. G. & Furioso, M. (2000). Music therapy education and training: A survey of master's level music therapists. *Music Therapy Perspectives, 18*(2), 103–109.

Wylie, M. E. (1983). Eliciting vocal responses in severely and profoundly mentally handicapped subjects. *Journal of Music Therapy, 20*(4), 190–200.

Wylie, M. E. (1990). A comparison of the effects of old familiar songs, antique objects, historical summaries, and general questions on the reminiscence of nursing home residents. *Journal of Music Therapy, 27*(1), 2–12.

Wylie, M. E. (1996). A case study to promote hand use in children with Rett syndrome. *Music Therapy Perspectives, 14*(2), 83–86.

Wylie, M. E. & Blom, R. C. (1986). Guided imagery and music with hospice patients. *Music Therapy Perspectives, 3*, 25–28.

Yairi, E. (1976). Effects of binaural and monaural noise on stuttering. *Journal of Auditory Research, 16*, 114–119.

Yairi, E. & Ambrose, H. (2013). Epidemiology of stuttering: 21st century advances. *Journal of Fluency Disorders, 38*(2), 66–87.

Yalom, I. D. (1983). *Inpatient group psychotherapy.* New York: Basic Books.

York, E. (1994). The development of a quantitative music skills test for patients with Alzheimer's disease. *Journal of Music Therapy, 31*(4), 280–296.

Zamula, E. (1986). Stroke: Fighting back against America's no. 3 killer (HHS Publication No. (FDA) 86-1131). Rockville, MD: Department of Health and Human Services.

Zatorre, R. J. (2009). Neural specializations for tonal processing. In I. Peretz & R. J. Zatorre (Eds.), *The cognitive neuroscience of music* (231–246). NewYork: Oxford University Press, Inc.

Zhang, D., Barrett, D. E., Katsiyannis, A., & Yoon, M. (2011). Juvenile offenders with and without disabilities. Risks and patterns. *Learning and Individual Differences, 21*, 12–18.

Zinar, R. (1987). *Music activities for special children.* West Nyack, NY: Parker.

Ziv, N., Granet, A., Hai, S., Dassa, A., & Haimov, I. (2007). The effect of background stimulative music on behavior in Alzheimer patients. *Journal of Music Therapy, 44*(4), 329–343.

Zoller, M. (1991). Use of music activities in speech-language therapy. *Language, Speech, and Hearing Services in Schools, 22*, 272–276.

AUTHOR INDEX

SUBJECT INDEX

A

Abused children and adolescents, 320,
338-340
  And music therapy interventions,
  338-340
  Characteristics, 320
Activities of daily living, 233, 246
  Orthopedic, 233, 246
Acupuncture 48, 80, 373, 476
  And enhancing motor responses, 476
Acute or chronic conditions, Mental or
  Behavioral Disorders, 393, 315, 430-
  433, 440, 445, 458
  Acute phase 367, 369, 376, 379, 381, 388
  Adolescents, 440
  Adults 367, 433, 445
  Children 433, 440
  Expression of feelings, 336, 339, 367, 378,
  384-385, 400
  Self-esteem within, 320, 321, 323, 325,
  331, 332, 337, 338, 339, 344, 345-347,
  352, 354, 367, 374
  Socialization within, 335, 351, 367, 376,
  378-379, 384, 386
Adaptive behavior, 120, 125-125, 127, 371,
  408
  Conceptual, 124, 127, 408
  Developmental period, 120
  Practical domains, 124, 127, 408
  Self-help skills in adults, 371
  Social, 124, 127, 408
Adaptive functioning, autism, 297-299
  Functional life skills, 299
  Increasing independence, 299
  Organizing and sequencing, 297
  Structure and routine, 298
Aesthetic experience, 88-90, 215, 234,
  250-251
Affective responses, 81-82, 93, 134, 329, 363

Age-associated memory impairment
  (AAMI), 507
  Contrast with Alzheimer's, 507
  Symptoms, 507
Aging, 99, 175, 245, 457, 492, 494, 496-498,
  500, 502-503, 506-511, 513, 515-517,
  520, 523-524, 526-528, 531, 536-537,
  548-549
  Activity theory of, 510
  Developmental theories of, 510-511
  Disengagement theory of, 509-510
  Psychosocial theories of, 508-509
Ageism, 493
Alternative communication (ACC), autism,
  310
Alvin, Juliette, 612-613
  And improvisation, 613
  Importance of musicianship for, 613
Alzheimer's disease, 403, 493, 495-497, 499-
  500, 502-510, 514-516, 518, 525-527,
  533, 536-539, 542-544, 546, 548-550,
  554
  And agitation, 503, 525, 536-538, 542-
  544, 546, 548-549, 554
  And brain decrements, 503
  And contrasts with memory impairment,
  507
  And interaction with caregivers, 504-505,
  526, 537
  And music therapy, 505-506, 508-510,
  516, 526, 548
  And neural abnormalities, 503
  And probable Alzheimer's disease, 502
  And support for family and caregivers,
  506, 526
  And symptom management, 504, 506
  Definition of, 503
  Stages of, 503
  Symptoms of, 502-504
Amblyopia, 202

H